ANATOMY OF THE CHORDATES

Anatomy of the Chordates

CHARLES K. WEICHERT

Professor of Zoology
University of Cincinnati

SECOND EDITION

McGRAW-HILL BOOK COMPANY, INC.

New York   Toronto   London

1958

v

69004

PREFACE

The author has been most gratified with the reception accorded the first edition of "Anatomy of the Chordates." The numerous communications he has received from teachers and students in various parts of the world have indicated that the labor involved in gathering, organizing, and presenting the vast amount of material included in a volume such as this has been worth the effort. In preparing the new edition an attempt has been made to correct the disconcerting errors and inconsistencies that unfortunately seem to appear no matter how meticulously one tries to avoid them. Many of the pages have been completely rewritten in an attempt to present the material more clearly; portions which the author and some of his critics have found to be inadequate have been revised; new concepts and interpretations have been incorporated; several illustrations have been changed, and a number of new ones added. The general plan of the text, which is designed for use in introductory courses in comparative vertebrate anatomy, has not been changed.

Part I is primarily a review of the phylum Chordata. Much of this portion is presented in accordance with the recognized system of classification of chordates. Here evolutionary trends and nontechnical aspects of the animals concerned are discussed. Emphasis has been placed on familiar living species. References to fossil forms, however, have been included where desirable and feasible. The material is meant to parallel that with which the subject of vertebrate paleontology is concerned, rather than to include it. The general discussion of the phylum Chordata is followed by a chapter on development, since much of the subsequent information is presented from an embryological point of view. A knowledge of the significance of germ layers and tissues is basic, in many cases, to an understanding of the comparative anatomy of the organ systems of chordates.

The structure of the organ systems is discussed in Part II. Functional aspects of the various organs have been included throughout this section. At the end of each chapter is a summary of the main points emphasized in that chapter. Some critics have objected to the sequential arrangement of the chapters on organ systems. The subject matter, however, is in most cases presented in such a manner that the information discussed in one chapter does not presuppose a knowledge of that contained within a previous chapter. The instructor may therefore prefer to follow a sequence of his own choice.

Part III is concerned with the detailed anatomy of four representative chordates usually studied in laboratory courses in comparative anatomy: the marine lamprey, spiny dogfish, mud puppy, and cat. Supplemented by a few directions from the instructor, this section may be used as a laboratory manual. Anatomical terms have been printed in boldface type for emphasis. The illustrations of the various anatomical features of the representative chordates are included in order to help the student in identifying structures, not to serve in lieu of dissection. By far the greater number of persons who have communicated with the author have expressed approval of this type of presentation.

A summary chapter, giving characteristics and advances of members of the phylum, has been placed at the end of the book where it properly belongs. Although this chapter is organized in a manner similar to that of Chapter 2, there is little duplication of subject matter.

Thanks are due to the many interested persons who have offered suggestions for improvement of the second edition. The criticisms and recommendations offered, in particular, by Dr. Hazel E. Field of Occidental College and Dr. Roland Walker of Rensselaer Polytechnic Institute have been invaluable. The author gratefully acknowledges the help given him by his students Joanne Moore, Roswitha Schugt, Ralph Archer, James Dohm, Arthur Page, George Schwenk, and Ronald Speigle in the preparation of many of the text figures. The drawings of George Schwenk, now working in the field of medical illustration, are noteworthy. He also wishes to take this means of expressing his appreciation to his wife, Kathryn H. Weichert, for her forbearance during the many months when he was wholly occupied in the preparation of the manuscript. Her untiring aid in reading proofs and in arranging the index have been most helpful.

Every effort has been made to present accurately the factual information contained in this book. The author will greatly appreciate receiving comments concerning inaccuracies and inconsistencies which have escaped his attention.

Charles K. Weichert

CONTENTS

PART I. REVIEW OF THE PHYLUM CHORDATA

CHAPTER 1

INTRODUCTION

The science of biology is the study of living things in all their aspects. The scope of biology is so vast that no single person can hope to master all its ramifications. Since most living things come under two general groups, plants and animals, biology is conveniently subdivided into two great studies, *botany*, which deals with plants, and *zoology*, which treats of animals. Biology, chemistry, and physics are closely interrelated. Many biological phenomena can be most readily explained in chemical and physical terms. Without a knowledge of chemistry and physics the biologist cannot go far in his study of living things.

METHODS OF APPROACH TO THE STUDY OF ZOOLOGY

There are several general methods of approach to the study of zoology. The more important ones are listed as follows:

Study of the physical and chemical properties of protoplasm, the only known form of matter in which life is manifested. Such study is, for the most part, relegated to the biochemist and biophysicist.

Morphology, the science of form and structure of living things. It may be subdivided in turn into a number of more specialized fields of study which include:

Gross anatomy, dealing with structures which can be seen with the unaided eye without the aid of optical instruments. Dissection is the method of approach that is used in gross anatomy.

Histology, or microscopic anatomy, which is the study of the more minute details of the relations of normal tissues. Preparations which can be examined under the microscope are used in histological studies.

Cytology, or cellular anatomy, which involves study of the detailed structure of cells.

Embryology, or developmental anatomy, which treats of the structure of the developing embryo and which utilizes both gross and histological methods of approach.

Physiology, the branch of zoology which deals with the functions of the living organism and its parts. These activities are so complex and the various structures of the body are so closely interrelated that the functions of organs must always be studied in relation to those of other organs.

Ecology, the science of organisms as they are affected by their environment. Both morphological and physiological aspects of animals in relation to their environment are considered in the study of ecology.

1

The study of evolution, the theory that existing organisms are the result of descent, with modification, from those of past times. Evolution is a fundamental biological principle which advances the idea that, in relation to natural changes which have occurred on the earth, the higher forms of life as we know them have evolved from lower forms.

Taxonomy, or systematic zoology, the science which has to do with the classification of animals according to their natural relationships. It also includes the laws and principles of such classification. Although taxonomy is based primarily upon morphological data, changes which take place during embryonic development are also taken into consideration. Moreover, taxonomic affinities are often substantiated by certain physiological likenesses and differences. Serological studies, in which reactions of certain blood groups have been observed, have established the accuracy or inaccuracy of taxonomic relationships based on structural similarities and differences.

THE STUDY OF COMPARATIVE ANATOMY

The student of chordate anatomy should realize at the beginning that taxonomy, ecology, and the study of evolution are all based in part upon comparative anatomical relationships. Comparative anatomy may also be used to explain some of the phenomena that appear during embryonic development. A knowledge of structure alone, however, has very little meaning unless it is interpreted in terms of function. Morphology and physiology complement each other. So far as is possible, it is desirable that both structure and function be considered together in studying animals. Nevertheless, a preliminary knowledge of morphology is a great aid to the study of physiology. In the following pages some discussion of function is included whenever feasible but the emphasis is placed upon anatomical observation.

Method of approach to comparative anatomical study. When similarities and differences in structural organization of the bodies of different animals are made objects of study, and when the facts obtained are compared, then from the study of structure general principles are derived from which deductive conclusions may be drawn. This is the method of the comparative anatomist, who seeks to explain the variations in structure that are found in the bodies of animals with a view to tracing biological relationships.

Most students of biology are interested in man, but a study of man alone would lead to an extremely narrow conception of his place on the earth. In order properly to understand the position of man in the world of life, a knowledge of his relations to other living things is almost essential.

Man is classified as a member of a large group of animals called the *vertebrates.* They are forms which have a backbone, or vertebral column, and include such diverse creatures as snakes, fishes, birds, frogs, elephants, and mice. The ancestors of these animals are the ancestors of man; the story of their origin is similar to his. A thorough understanding of the body, mind, and activities of man involves a study of his vertebrate ancestry.

Although the method of comparative anatomy has been used in studying the relationships of almost all forms in the animal kingdom, the scope of the subject is too vast to be considered in a single volume. We shall confine our attention here to a comparative study of the vertebrates and a few of their closest relatives, all of which are included in the phylum Chordata.

The student, when in the laboratory, studies and dissects representative chordate animals and gains an intimate knowledge of the detailed structure of each. This knowledge does not constitute a science unless the facts learned are properly correlated and blended into a harmonious whole. It is the aim of this volume to effect such a correlation.

At the beginning of a course of study it is valuable for the student to have an idea of its objectives so that time may be most profitably utilized in putting the emphasis upon the facts of greatest importance. The comparative anatomist recognizes that the vertebrates and some of their close relatives are built upon the same fundamental plan and that there is often a close correspondence even in detail. Within the general vertebrate plan there may be many variations which are, for the most part, adaptive in nature. By this is meant that they are modifications which meet particular needs in relation to the environment in which the animal lives. The object of a course in comparative anatomy of vertebrates, therefore, is to acquaint the student with the plan of vertebrate structure. Such knowledge serves as a background for the better appreciation of the studies of embryology, human anatomy, and medicine.

Homology. The term *homology* refers to the correspondence in type of structure between parts or organs of different animals. Because of evolutional differentiation, these may have diverged considerably from the same or corresponding part or organ of some remote ancestral form, so that superficially they bear but little resemblance to one another. For example, observation of the skeleton of a cat shows that its forelimb is composed of a single bone in the upper leg, two in the lower leg, and a number of intermediate bones situated between the lower leg and the toes. The wing of a bird, which is utilized in so different a manner, would at first sight seem to be a thing apart and in no way like the forelimb of a cat. The skeletons, however, reveal basic similarities in structure. The arm of man, the flipper of the whale, the hoofed leg of the horse, and the wing of a bat are all built upon the same fundamental plan and are, therefore, homologous (Fig. 1.1). In some cases differences in structure are so great that their homologies might be unsuspected. Observation of a series of intermediate stages between the two extremes may often clearly indicate their basic similarities. The study of homology of parts in various forms is one of the most interesting features of comparative animal studies. Observations on the details of embryonic development have in many instances rendered great service to the comparative anatomist in revealing such homologies. An embryological approach to comparative studies will, so far as is possible, be utilized in this volume.

The biogenetic law. It has long been realized by biologists that early embryos of all vertebrates show remarkable similarities in many respects. During the development of higher forms, certain anatomical features, apparently of little significance, make their appearance. In most cases these become modified, or they may degenerate and disappear. Many specula-

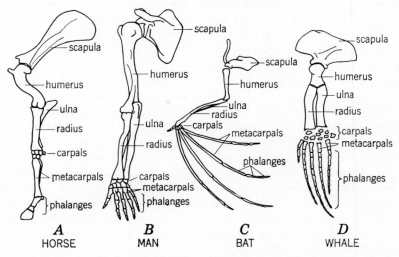

A   *B*   *C*   *D*
HORSE   MAN   BAT   WHALE

FIG. 1.1. Skeleton of forelimb, showing modifications of same fundamental type of structure. (*A, B, and C, after LeConte, "Evolution," Appleton-Century-Crofts, Inc. By permission.*)

tions have been made as to the significance of the presence of such structures. For example, at a certain stage of development in all vertebrates a series of pouches pushes out from the pharynx to establish connection with the outer covering of the body. In such lower forms as fishes perforations occur at the points of contact, becoming gill slits which persist throughout life. In the embryos of higher vertebrates, however, the pharyngeal pouches usually fail to open to the outside. They persist for a time but then become modified in various ways, retaining little or none of their original character. Why should pharyngeal pouches appear at all in higher forms? Another illustration of the principle under discussion is to be found in the appearance, in the region of the pharynx in all vertebrates during embryonic development, of certain blood vessels called *aortic arches*. The structural plan of the aortic arches in the *embryo* of a bird, for example, is somewhat similar to that found in the gill region of *adult* fishes. It is *almost identical* with that found in the *embryos* of such diverse forms as fishes, snakes, frogs, and man. In the bird, as well as in other higher forms, the aortic arches soon undergo considerable modification, ultimately forming an arrangement of vessels in the posterior part of the neck region or in the anterior part of the thoracic region which is characteristic of each particular group.

Several ideas have been advanced to explain why such structures as pharyngeal pouches and aortic arches should make their appearance in the embryos of higher vertebrates. Perhaps the best-known of these is the

FISH   TORTOISE   CHICK   PIG   CALF   MAN
SALAMANDER

Fig. 1.2. Three comparable stages in the development of embryos of several vertebrates. Such membranous structures as yolk sac, amnion, chorion, and allantois, which appear in some embryos but not in others, have been omitted in order to emphasize similarities and to minimize differences. (*After Haeckel, modified from Daugherty, "Principles of Economic Zoology," W. B. Saunders Company. By permission.*)

recapitulation theory, or *law of biogenesis*, which, when originally formulated, stated that during development an individual passes through certain ancestral stages through which the entire race passed in its evolution and that the embryos of higher forms in certain ways resemble the adults of lower forms. In other words, *ontogeny* (individual life history) recapitulates *phylogeny* (racial history). Although this concept has, in the past, furnished a good working hypothesis for embryologists in their attempts to work out homologies, there has been much debate as to its truth. Biologists today realize that ontogeny does *not* actually recapitulate phylogeny; that at no time does a mammalian embryo, for example, closely resemble an *adult* fish, amphibian, or any other lower vertebrate. The embryos of all vertebrates, however, show many remarkable similarities. Those of higher vertebrates undergo fundamental changes which are like those of lower forms and occur in the same sequence. From such basically similar embryonic stages, which are believed to be characteristic of ancestral forms, each group of vertebrates diverges in one direction or another, so that when fully developed they differ widely in structure and habits.

It is not to be assumed that during development an animal goes through *every* stage that its ancestors did. Some stages are omitted or are passed through so rapidly that they can scarcely be discerned. Some characteristics by which they differ have arisen as a result of genetic variation, so that the ancestral conditions do not always appear in a typical form. Other structures of significance in the adaptation of the embryo to its environment are obviously unrelated to ancestral conditions or resemblances. In addition, the principle fails in many cases to explain the appearance of new, or *cenogenetic*, structures in certain forms. The theory does, however, account for the fact that the early embryonic stages of all vertebrates are remarkably similar (Fig. 1.2) up to a point at which each group diverges in its own characteristic manner. Despite its shortcomings, the concept has been useful to biologists in establishing homologies, in making clear certain phylogenetic relationships, and in helping to give a picture of the probable structure and appearance of ancestral forms and stages in our evolutionary history.

CHARACTERISTICS OF CHORDATES

There are three characters of prime diagnostic importance which are possessed by all chordates, as follows.

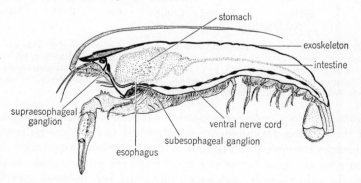

Fig. 1.3. Diagram showing exoskeleton, digestive tract, and position of ventral ganglionated nerve cord of crayfish.

A notochord is present sometime during life. A more or less typical invertebrate animal, such as a crayfish, possesses a hard, nonliving, external covering, the *exoskeleton*, which is deposited on the surface of the body by the secretory activity of the underlying cells. It protects the animal, serves for muscle attachment, and is provided with joints which permit movement and locomotion (Fig. 1.3). The vertebrate skeleton, on the other hand, is essentially a living *endoskeleton*, which provides protection for the delicate internal organs, gives support to the body, and is jointed so that movement is possible. Although all chordates have an endoskeleton, turtles, armadillos, and a few others possess exoskeletal structures as well, but the exoskeleton in these forms is primarily composed of living material and is not at all comparable to that of the invertebrate.

In all chordates a notochord, which is a primitive endoskeletal structure, is present during embryonic life. It is pliant, rodlike, and made up of vesicular connective tissue (Fig. 1.4). The notochord is located along the mid-dorsal line, where it forms the axis of support

Fig. 1.4. Vesicular connective tissue of which notochord is composed, as seen under the microscope.

for the body. In some animals it persists as such throughout life, but in most chordates it serves as a foundation about which the vertebral column, or backbone, is built. A salamander larva or a frog tadpole, for example, at first possesses a notochord (Figs. 1.5 and 1.6), but it is gradually replaced, first by a cartilaginous and then by a bony vertebral column. By the time

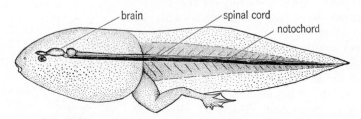

Fig. 1.5. Diagram showing position of notochord in relation to brain and spinal cord in frog tadpole.

a tadpole has metamorphosed into an adult frog, the notochord has for the most part disappeared.

A hollow, dorsal nerve tube is present sometime during life. The type of central nervous system found in arthropods, as well as in some lower phyla, is located on the ventral side of the body except for a dorsal ganglionic mass, known as the *brain*, which connects to the ventral portion by esophageal connectives (Fig. 1.3). This type of nervous system is sometimes called the "ladder type" because it is made up of a double chain of enlargements, called *ganglia*, united by nervous connections in both longitudinal and transverse directions and so has a ladderlike appearance. In the crayfish there is a considerable degree of fusion between right and left halves. The ventrally located nerve cord is solid and lies in the coelom.

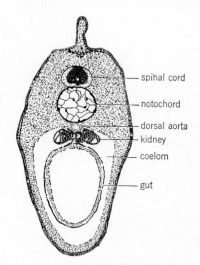

FIG. 1.6. Cross section of salamander larva, showing notochord lying beneath spinal cord.

The central nervous system of chordates, on the other hand, is located in a dorsal position. It lies just above the notochord and entirely outside the coelom (Figs. 1.5 and 1.6). Moreover, it is a tubular structure, having a small, hollow canal running from one end to the other. The dorsal hollow nerve tube persists throughout adult life in almost all chordates, but in a few it degenerates before maturity is attained.

Gill slits connecting to the pharynx or traces of them are present sometime during life. Many types of respiratory organs are found among animals belonging to phyla below the chordates in the evolutionary scale. Some respire through moist integuments, some have tracheal tubes, others have book lungs, and still others have gills of various kinds (Fig. 1.7). In none of these types, however, do the respiratory organs have any connection with the digestive tract.

A great many aquatic chordates respire by means of gills made up of vascular lamellae or filaments lining the borders of gill slits which connect to the pharynx and open directly or indirectly to the outside (Fig. 1.8). Even terrestrial chordates, which never breathe by means of gills, nevertheless have traces of gill slits present as transient structures during early development. There are no vascular lamellae lining these temporary structures, nor do they open to the outside. However, the fact that they are present in all chordates is of primary importance in denoting close relationship.

The three characteristics listed above are possessed only by members of the phylum Chordata. In addition, chordates have cer-

FIG. 1.7. Damsel fly larva with caudal tracheal gills used in respiration.

tain features which are common to members of other phyla as well.

Bilateral symmetry. All chordates are bilaterally symmetrical, at least in the embryonic stage. Bilateral symmetry is the symmetry of the right and left sides of an organism in which any structure on one side of the median plane is a mirror image of the corresponding organ on the other side.

Cephalization. In bilaterally symmetrical animals there is a concentration of nervous tissue and sense organs in or toward the head. This is known as *cephalization*.

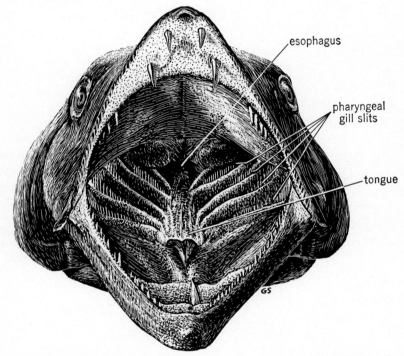

FIG. 1.8. The open mouth of a fish, the barracuda, showing the typical relation of gill slits to the pharynx.

Metamerism. When certain structures, primarily like each other, are repeated one after another, they are said to be metameric. Among metameric structures are included certain nerves and blood vessels as well as vertebrae, ribs, muscles, etc.

A true body cavity, or coelom, is present. Such animals as ascarid worms have a body cavity separating the alimentary tract from the muscles of the body wall. This cavity is not lined completely with tissue derived from mesoderm (one of the primitive embryonic germ layers). It is therefore not considered to be a true coelom. All chordates, as well as annelids and some others, have a true coelom lined entirely with mesoderm.

Direction of blood flow. In typical invertebrates a pulsating organ, or heart, is situated on the *dorsal* side of the body. In general, blood is forced anteriorly, then ventrally and posteriorly, returning finally to the dorsal heart. The chordate heart, on the other hand, is located on the *ventral* side of the body. Blood is pumped anteriorly and forced to the dorsal side. It then courses posteriorly and returns to the heart by veins. The larger veins are ventral in position.

CHAPTER 2

CLASSIFICATION AND EVOLUTION OF THE CHORDATES

Before undertaking a study of the anatomy of the chordates it is desirable to have a working knowledge of the animals included in the phylum. Zoologists have grouped these animals in an orderly fashion according to their natural and anatomical affinities. This grouping serves as a basis for classifying all members of the phylum. It is important that the student of comparative anatomy have some knowledge of the classification of the chordates; otherwise a study of their anatomy from a comparative viewpoint will have little meaning. In a book of this kind it is not feasible, nor is it necessary, to discuss all the animals concerned. In the following pages, therefore, emphasis has been placed on those forms of which some knowledge is almost essential to an understanding of the principles underlying the subject of comparative anatomy.

The chief principle used in classifying animals involves the division of larger groups into smaller groups according to certain distinctive traits which they possess in common. Thus phyla are divided into classes, classes into orders, orders into families, families into genera, and genera into species. The characteristics which separate the lower divisions are of lesser taxonomic importance than those used as a basis for separating the higher, or larger, groups. Often intermediate groupings are used, particularly when the number of animals included in a certain category is large. Thus there may be subphyla, superclasses, subclasses, superorders, etc.

The scientific name of an animal is made up of its generic and specific names, the genus always being written with a capital letter and the species with a small letter. This system was first devised by the great Swedish naturalist Linnaeus and is known as the system of binomial nomenclature.

PHYLUM CHORDATA

The phylum *Chordata* is divided into two main *groups*. The first of these, the *Acrania*, includes a few relatively simple animals which lack a brain and a cranium. The second group, the *Craniata*, or *Vertebrata*, is much larger and embraces those chordates having a brain, cranium, and vertebral column.

Group A. Acrania

The group *Acrania* is usually divided into three subphyla. The animals included in this category are believed to show similarities to the ancestors of the chordates and for this reason are sometimes referred to as the *protochordates*.

SUBPHYLUM I. HEMICHORDATA

Many zoologists consider the hemichordates to be the lowest form of chordate life, although there is some dispute about their classification. They are of special interest because they furnish a clue to the link which bridges the gap between chordates and some of the lower phyla. A free-swimming larva, the *tornaria*, occurs in the development of certain members of the subphylum. The tornaria is similar in appearance to the larval stages of some echinoderms.

A typical example is *Dolichoglossus (Saccoglossus) kowalevskii* (Fig. 2.1), a fragile, burrowing, wormlike, marine animal. Three body regions are

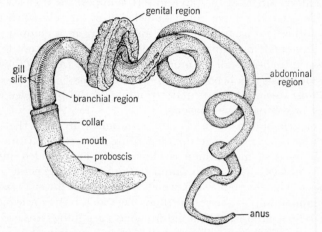

FIG. 2.1. Lateral view of *Dolichoglossus kowalevskii*.

present: (1) a proboscis, (2) a collar, (3) an elongated trunk. The trunk, in turn, is composed of an anterior branchial region with a row of transverse gill slits on either side, a genital region of irregular outline, and a posterior, abdominal region. The only obvious chordate character possessed by this animal is its pharyngeal gill slits. A peculiar forward extension of the gut into the proboscis has in the past been homologized with the notochord of higher forms. Most zoologists today doubt whether such a homology exists. *Dolichoglossus* possesses both dorsal and ventral nerve strands. The dorsal strand, which is the larger, is tubular only in the collar region. Nevertheless it is possibly homologous with the dorsal hollow nerve tube of higher forms.

SUBPHYLUM II. TUNICATA

The *tunicates* include a peculiar group of widely distributed marine animals commonly known as sea squirts, or ascidians. They are of no

FIG. 2.2.   *A*, internal organs of *Molgula manhattensis* as viewed from the left side; *B*, internal organs of *Molgula manhattensis* as viewed from the right side.

economic importance.   Many of them become sessile after a free-swimming larval period and attach themselves to a wharf pile, rock, or similar object. *Molgula manhattensis* (Fig. 2.2) is a fairly typical example of the sub-phylum.   In its adult state *Molgula* bears little resemblance to a typical chordate.   It lacks a notochord, and its nervous system has been reduced to a small ganglionic mass. Only the pharynx with its numerous gill slits gives evidence of its chordate relationships. An adult specimen is about an inch long, round or oval in shape, with two openings, or *siphons*, at its free end. A stream of water enters the larger *incurrent siphon* and leaves through the smaller *excurrent siphon*. The animal is invested by a rather

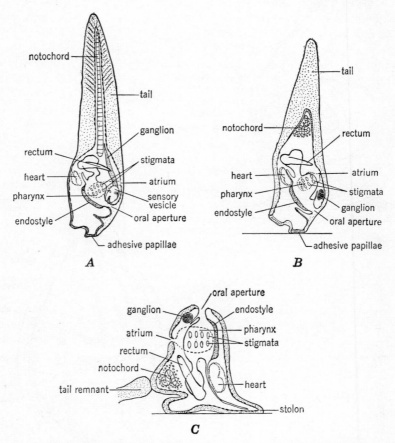

Fig. 2.3. Diagrams illustrating metamorphosis of free-swimming ascidian larva to the sessile form: *A*, free-swimming larva; *B*, larva soon after attachment; *C*, later attached stage but before disappearance of notochord. (*After Seeliger from Korschelt and Heider.*)

tough capsule, or *tunic*. This is composed of a substance called *tunicin* secreted by the cells of the *mantle* beneath. Tunicin has the same chemical formula as cellulose, which makes up the walls of plant cells. The greater part of the cavity enclosed by the mantle is occupied by the pharynx. The nerve ganglion lies embedded in the mantle in the region between the siphons. This is the dorsal side of the animal. Almost completely surrounding the ganglion is an *adneural gland* which opens by means of a duct into the pharynx. Some zoologists have homologized the adneural gland with the pituitary gland of vertebrates, but there is a difference of opinion concerning this. A ciliated groove, the *endostyle*, extends along the midventral line of the pharynx to the esophagus. Food particles that enter the pharynx with the incurrent stream of water are gathered by the endostyle and swept down to the esophagus. Some biologists believe that the endostyle may be the forerunner of the thyroid gland of higher forms. Certain other structures of *Molgula* are indicated in Fig. 2.2.

Sea squirts were formerly classified as mollusks because of their peculiar structure in the adult stage. It was not until 1866 that the proper classification was determined when Kowalevski, a Russian biologist, found that the ascidian larva possesses typical chordate characteristics. During its larval existence a sea squirt somewhat resembles a tadpole in appearance. It has a notochord which is confined to the tail, a hollow dorsal nerve cord, and a pharynx perforated with gill slits. After a free-swimming period it finally attaches itself to some object and becomes sessile. The animal then undergoes a metamorphosis during which the notochord disappears and the nerve cord is reduced to a simple ganglion (Fig. 2.3). The only one of the three essential chordate characters which persists is the pharynx with its numerous gill slits communicating indirectly with the exterior.

Sessile tunicates may be either solitary or colonial. Not all tunicates are sessile, however, for some are free-swimming, transparent pelagic forms throughout life.

Subphylum III. Cephalochordata

There are but two genera and about 20 species of animals included in the subphylum *Cephalochordata*. The common name, *amphioxus*, is applied to the more abundant genus, *Branchiostoma*. The primitive structure of amphioxus is of special interest to the zoologist. Furthermore, its early de-

Fig. 2.4. Lateral view of amphioxus.

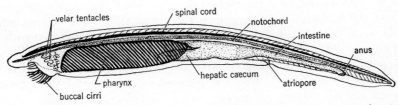

Fig. 2.5. Semidiagrammatic view of amphioxus, showing parts of digestive tract.

velopment illustrates with almost diagrammatic simplicity certain features which occur during embryonic stages of higher chordates.

Amphioxus (Figs. 2.4 and 2.5) is a small marine animal about 2 in. long and pointed at either end. At the anterior end an integumentary fold, the *oral hood,* surrounds a cavity, or *vestibule,* which leads to the mouth. The hood is encircled by 22 papillalike projections, the *buccal cirri.*

A median *dorsal fin* extends almost the entire length of the body and is continuous with the caudal fin posteriorly. On the ventral side the caudal fin continues anteriorly as far as an opening, the *atriopore,* and then divides, extending forward as a pair of *metapleural folds* (Fig. 2.6). These were at one time believed to represent the beginning of the paired appendages of vertebrates, a theory which is no longer tenable. The notochord extends practically the entire length of the body, projecting farther forward than the anterior end of the dorsal hollow nerve cord. The latter lies directly above the notochord. A slight enlargement, the *cerebral vesicle,* at the anterior end can scarcely be referred to as a brain. Metamerism is clearly indicated by the arrangement of the <-shaped muscle segments, or myotomes, which make up the greater part of the body wall.

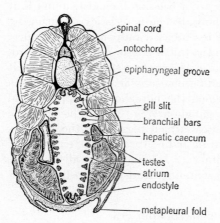

FIG. 2.6. Cross section through posterior pharyngeal region of amphioxus (anterior view.)

The digestive system is simple in structure. The vestibule leads to the mouth opening located in a membranous *velum* and encircled by 12 short *velar tentacles.* The mouth leads to a large pharynx with numerous gill slits. A system of ciliated and glandular grooves directs food particles to the intestine. A pouch, the *hepatic caecum,* projects forward from the ventral side of the intestine on the right side of the pharynx. The intestine terminates at the anus located on the left side at some distance back of the atriopore.

Each of the numerous gill slits is secondarily divided by a *tongue bar.* The gill slits of the adult do not lead directly to the outside but communicate with an *atrium,* or *peribranchial chamber,* which surrounds the greater part of the digestive tract except on the dorsal side. The atrium, which opens to the outside through the atriopore, should not be confused with the coelom.

A pulsating tube, homologous with the hearts of higher chordates, lies ventral to the pharynx. Blood is pumped anteriorly and then dorsally through the gill region.

The anatomy of amphioxus indicates in every way that the animal is truly a chordate. Further details concerning its anatomy are discussed under appropriate headings in the following pages.

Group B. Vertebrata (Craniata)

All chordates, with the exception of the protochordates, are included among the vertebrates. In these the anterior end of the dorsal hollow nerve cord is enlarged to form a brain, and a protective and supporting endoskeleton is present.

With the appearance of the brain a skeletal structure called the *neurocranium*, or simply the *cranium*, makes its appearance, serving to protect that delicate organ. The cranium forms part of the skull. Openings, or *foramina*, are present for the passage of cranial nerves, blood vessels, and the spinal cord. The latter is likewise protected by a series of metamerically arranged skeletal elements, the *vertebrae*, associated with the notochord in their development. Openings for the passage of spinal nerves are present between adjacent vertebrae.

The group *Vertebrata* is usually divided into two subphyla: *Agnatha* and *Gnathostomata*.

SUBPHYLUM IV. AGNATHA

Agnathans lack jaws and paired appendages, even in the embryo. There is but a single median nostril. The mouth in living species is round.

Class I. Ostracodermi. There are no living ostracoderms. Fossil remains indicate that these were probably the earliest vertebrates on record. Some forms possessed lateral body lobes which have been interpreted as possible forerunners of paired pectoral appendages. One genus, *Pterichthys* (Fig. 2.7), even had paddlelike flippers, but not true pectoral fins. Unlike living agnathans, the bodies of ostracoderms were covered with a heavy armor of dermal bone. It was formerly believed that the earliest vertebrates possessed cartilaginous skeletons much like those of the lowest vertebrates living today and that the appearance of bone was a later development. The presence of bony plates (and even of a bony endoskeleton, of a sort, in a few forms) in the fossil remains of the oldest vertebrates has changed the ideas of zoologists and paleontologists in this regard. The modern concept is that the presence of bone was a primitive character and that living cyclostomes and elasmobranch fishes with cartilaginous skeletons represent degraded descendants of bony ancestors which have lost their bony skeletal elements and armor secondarily.

Class II. Cyclostomata. Living agnathans, which include lampreys and hagfishes, are included in this class. Although primitive in many respects, they are believed to be modified and degenerate offshoots of the primitive vertebrate stock. In some respects they are so highly specialized that homologies with other vertebrates are difficult to ascertain.

Cyclostomes have rounded, eellike bodies with laterally compressed tails. Median fins are present supported by cartilaginous fin rays. Lacking jaws, there is a round, suctorial mouth. The skin is soft and devoid of scales.

ORDER I. PETROMYZONTIA. Lampreys are not to be confused with eels, which belong to a different class. Both fresh-water and marine forms exist. Some fresh-water forms are nonparasitic, but most lampreys are parasitic, the adults preying upon fishes. The marine lamprey, *Petromyzon marinus* (Fig. 15.1), is a parasitic form often used for dissection in courses in comparative anatomy. The animal, which attains a length of about 3 ft., lives in the sea but ascends rivers to spawn. The larval form, known as the *ammocoetes*, lives in burrows in the sand for 3 years or more before undergoing metamorphosis. The young lampreys migrate downstream and out to sea where they remain 3 or 4 years before becoming sexually mature.

FIG. 2.7. *Pterichthys cornutus*, an ostracoderm. (*After Agassiz, from Nicholson, "The Ancient Life History of the Earth," Appleton-Century-Crofts, Inc. By permission.*)

Seven pairs of gill slits are present, each opening separately to the outside. The suctorial funnel at the anterior end is ventral in position and beset with horny teeth. When feeding, the lamprey fastens its funnel to the side of a fish, usually just in back of the pectoral fin. Horny teeth on the tongue are used in rasping, the animal feeding upon blood and mucus obtained in this manner.

The harmless ammocoetes larva is of special interest to the comparative anatomist since it is a very primitive and generalized vertebrate.

The marine lamprey has invaded the upper Great Lakes where it has become firmly established. The fishing industry has been virtually destroyed, presumably by the ravages of the lamprey, although it is possible that other factors may be at least partially responsible. A detailed description of the anatomy of *Petromyzon marinus* is given in Part III, Representative Animals.

ORDER II. MYXINOIDEA. *Myxine glutinosa*, the hagfish (Fig. 2.8), is the most common species included in the order. It is a marine form somewhat like the lamprey in appearance. Its mouth is terminal and has four pairs of tentacles about its margin. Only a single pair of external gill openings is present, located some distance behind the head. The animal feeds by rasping a hole in the side of a large fish, crawling inside the body cavity, and eating the viscera.

In members of the genus *Bdellostoma* there are 6 to 14 pairs of external gill openings, depending upon the species.

SUBPHYLUM V. GNATHOSTOMATA

Members of the subphylum *Gnathostomata* have paired pectoral and pelvic appendages, true upper and lower jaws, paired nostrils, and a well-developed endoskeleton. The cranium is better developed than in agnathans. The subphylum is divided into two great superclasses which include the fishes and the four-footed animals, respectively.

Superclass I. Pisces. Fishes are entirely aquatic and in most cases respire by means of gills lining the pharyngeal gill slits. The paired appendages are fins, of which there are usually two pairs. Median fins are also present. Dermal scales of various types are found in the skin with few exceptions. Fishes are generally divided into three classes: *Placodermi, Chondrichthyes,* and *Osteichthyes.* Placoderms are known only through fossil remains.

Class I. Placodermi. During Devonian times approximately 400 million years ago ostracoderms gradually became extinct and primitive placo-

Fig. 2.8. The glutinous hagfish, *Myxine glutinosa.*

derms replaced them. The placoderms developed primitive jaws and paired fins but retained, to varying degrees, the bony armor of ostracoderms. This consisted of large bony plates arranged in different ways, and which probably gave rise to the several types of dermal scales found in modern fishes. Placoderms were not successful on the earth from a long-range point of view. They gradually disappeared as two new types of fishes evolved—the cartilaginous and the bony fishes.

Class II. Chondrichthyes. Sharks, dogfishes, skates, rays, and chimaeras are examples of cartilaginous fishes. Most are marine forms with cartilaginous skeletons, placoid scales, and ventral, subterminal mouths. All have tails of the heterocercal type (Fig. 10.44) in which the dorsal flange is larger than the ventral. These fishes are descendants of those which lived in Devonian times and which evolved from placoderms or placodermlike ancestors.

The skeleton in this class of fishes is primitive in many respects but not in the fact that it lacks bone and is entirely cartilaginous. The lack of bone is believed to represent a retrograde condition. The bone in the basal plates of the placoid scales in the skin is all that remains of the ancient bony armor.

ORDER I. SELACHII (ELASMOBRANCHII). The elasmobranch fishes, as members of this order are generally called, include those cartilaginous fishes in which the gill slits open separately to the outside. There are five to seven pairs of gill slits in addition to a modified pair, the *spiracles*, opening on top of the skull, just posterior to the eyes.

SUBORDER I. SQUALI. Sharks and dogfishes living today, as well as numerous extinct forms, belong to the suborder *Squali*. They differ from skates and rays in that their pectoral fins are distinctly marked off from cylindrical bodies and in their laterally placed gill slits (Fig. 16.1). Since many structures in elasmobranchs are primitive or generalized in character,

FIG. 2.9. Adaptive radiations among selachians.

the shark or dogfish is an ideal animal for laboratory study as an introduction to the anatomy of higher vertebrates. Dogfish, which are among the smaller species, are plentiful. The detailed characteristics of the anatomy of a common dogfish, *Squalus acanthias*, is described in Part III, Representative Animals.

Among the better-known sharks are the hammerhead, white shark, sand shark, and whale shark, the latter being the largest living fish.

SUBORDER II. BATOIDEA. Skates and rays are included in this suborder. They might be regarded as modified sharks which have become flattened in a dorsoventral direction. Head and trunk are widened considerably, and the pectoral fins are not distinctly marked off from the body. There is a distinct demarcation between body and tail, however. The gill slits are located ventrally. Skates are egg-laying forms, whereas rays give birth to living young. Among batoideans are included such forms as the gigantic devilfish, or Manta ray; the sting ray, or stingaree; the torpedo, or electric ray; and the sawfish. The body of the last is not flattened to the same extent as in most members of the suborder. The varied body forms of skates and rays are regarded as adaptive radiations from primitive sharklike ancestors (Fig. 2.9).

ORDER II. HOLOCEPHALI. This order is made up of a small group of fishes called chimaeras (Fig. 2.10). They are of special interest because they occupy a position between selachians and higher fishes. Among primi-

FIG. 2.10. Lateral view of *Chimaera monstrosa*. (*Drawn by A. Page.*)

tive features are a persistent notochord and poorly developed vertebrae. Advance is indicated by the presence of an *operculum* which covers the gill chamber on each side. Scales are practically absent in the adult.

Class III. Osteichthyes. This class includes the bony fishes, the skeletons of which are bony to some degree. Several types of dermal scales are found within the group. The mouth is usually terminal, and an operculum covers each gill chamber. These fishes are divided into three subclasses, the distinctions among them being based primarily on fin structure. Members of the first two subclasses, *Paleopterygii* and *Neopterygii*, are often referred to as ray-finned fishes; those of the third, the *Choanichthyes*, include the lobe-fins and lungfishes.

Subclass I. Paleopterygii. Only two orders of living forms belong to this subclass of "ancient fishes." Here the dermal fin rays supporting the dorsal and anal fins are more numerous than the vertebral elements at their bases.

ORDER I. CLADISTIA. The two living genera of cladistians include *Polypterus* (Fig. 2.11) and *Calamoichthys*, both found in Africa. It was formerly believed that cladistians were lobe-fins because their pectoral fins have a fleshy basal portion. The structure, however, differs from that of true lobe-fins. The caudal fin, unlike the heterocercal structure of the

Chondrichthyes, is of the symmetrical diphycercal type (Fig. 10.44). These fishes are often referred to as the fringe-finned ganoids because of the fringe-like appearance of the eight or more dorsal fin elements and the presence of ganoid scales. In some ways the larvae of *Polypterus* resemble amphibian tadpoles.

ORDER II. CHONDROSTEI. The two families which comprise this order include the spoonbill, or paddlefish, and the sturgeons. They too are believed to be survivors of primitive ray-finned fishes which have lost their bony skeleton. The skeleton is almost entirely cartilaginous. Teeth are lacking. The tail is of the heterocercal type.

Polyodon, the spoonbill, inhabits the Mississippi River and its larger tributaries. A close relative, *Psephurus*, is found in China. Large speci-

Fig. 2.11. *Polypterus bichir.* (*Courtesy of the American Museum of Natural History.*)

mens may weigh from 80 to 150 lb. A unique feature is the large paddle extending from the anterior end of the snout. A few small placoid scales lie in back of the operculum, indicating an elasmobranch relationship.

Adult sturgeons are large animals with five rows of keeled, bony, modified ganoid scales running the length of the body. The snout is prominent, and the mouth is located ventrally. Caviar is prepared from eggs taken from the body of the female.

Subclass II. Neopterygii. About 20,000 species, separated into 31 orders, are included in the subclass. In all, the posterior, or occipital, region of the skull is bony. The tail is usually of the homocercal type (Fig. 10.44), but in some it is diphycercal. It is never heterocercal.

Holosteans. The first 2 of the 31 orders include a few fishes formerly grouped under the name *Holostei*, which most taxonomists have now discarded. *Amia*, the bowfin, and *Lepisosteus*, the gar pike, are examples. Both are survivors of very old groups of fishes. Paleopterygians, holosteans, and numerous extinct forms were formerly referred to as *ganoid fishes*, a term no longer in general use.

Teleosts. The remaining 29 orders of neopterygians are commonly referred to as the *teleost fishes*. Ninety-five per cent of the fishes of the world come under this category.

Subclass III. Choanichthyes. The fishes belonging to this subclass are the first vertebrates in which the nasal passages connect the mouth cavity to the outside. Internal nares, or *choanae* (hence the name), are present for the first time. Although it is possible that some of the extinct members of the subclass used their nasal passages in connection with lung respiration, there is no evidence that species living today employ them in such a manner. Nevertheless, the presence of choanae is of great importance from an evolutionary point of view, for it suggests that amphibians, the first air-breathing terrestrial vertebrates, may have evolved from similar fishes. The subclass is divided into two superorders which include the lobe-finned fishes and the true lungfishes, respectively.

SUPERORDER I. CROSSOPTERYGII. These are the lobe-fins which make up a small but ancient group known mostly from fossil forms which ap-

FIG. 2.12. *Latimeria chalumnae*, a coelacanth. (*Drawn by Roswitha Schugt.*)

peared on earth some 400 million years ago at the beginning of the Devonian Period. The fins of crossopterygians differ from those of all other fishes. Each is borne on a fleshy, lobelike, scaly stalk extending from the body. Pectoral and pelvic fins have articulations resembling those of tetrapod limbs. Crossopterygians apparently took two different lines of descent since they may be divided into two groups, the rhipidistians and the coelacanths.

ORDER I. RHIPIDISTIA. The rhipidistian crossopterygians became extinct near the end of the Devonian Period. There is considerable evidence that it was through members of this order that evolutionary progress was made. The skeletal elements in the paired fins of the fossil *Eusthenopteron*, one of the better-known rhipidistians, have been rather clearly homologized with those in the limbs of tetrapods. Fossils of primitive amphibians have been found together with those of rhipidistians in the same geological deposits.

ORDER II. COELACANTHINI. The coelacanth crossopterygians were a more stable and conservative group which showed but little change for millions of years. Until 1938 it was believed that coelacanths had become extinct about 70 million years ago. In that year a strange fish was caught off

the east coast of South Africa.   To the surprise of zoologists and paleontologists this animal proved to be a coelacanth.   It was named *Latimeria
chalumnae* (Fig. 2.12).   In more recent years several additional specimens
of this species have been obtained.   There is no doubt that *Latimeria* is a
survivor of the oldest stock represented among living vertebrates.   In all
the time that has elapsed since coelacanths were plentiful on the earth,

Fig. 2.13.   The Australian lungfish, *Neoceratodus forsteri*.   (*Courtesy of the Chicago
Natural History Museum.*)

Fig. 2.14.   The African lungfish, *Protopterus*.   (*Courtesy of the American Museum of
Natural History.*)

Latimeria has remained relatively unchanged.   In addition to its rather
complex paired pectoral and pelvic fins it has two unpaired dorsal fins and
a single, ventral anal fin.   All except the first dorsal fin are typical lobe fins.
Singularly enough, internal nares seem to be lacking in *Latimeria*.   Nevertheless it is included in the subclass *Choanichthyes*.   The scientific world is
waiting eagerly for complete reports on the internal anatomy of this relic
of the past.

    superorder II.   dipnoi.   Three different genera of so-called lungfishes
are included in the order *Dipnoi*.   They include the Australian lungfish,
Neoceratodus (Fig. 2.13), the South American lungfish, *Lepidosiren*, and the
African lungfish, *Protopterus* (Fig. 2.14).   Most members of the class
Osteichthyes possess an internal saclike structure called the swim bladder.
This arises as a single or paired diverticulum of the digestive tract in the

region of the pharynx. It may retain its connection with the pharynx (*physostomous* condition) or lose it and become a blind sac (*physoclistous* condition). In the true lungfishes the swim bladder is of the physostomous type. It is well developed, highly vascularized, and used as a lung in respiration. Such swim bladders are more efficient respiratory organs than the lungs of many amphibians. Nevertheless, because of certain other characteristics, notably the structure of the fins, it is believed that rhipidistian crossopterygians, rather than dipnoans, were ancestors of amphibians.

Superclass II. Tetrapoda. Tetrapods are those members of the subphylum *Gnathostomata* having paired appendages in the form of limbs rather than fins. In some, the limbs have been lost or modified, but the basic plan from which all tetrapod limbs have evolved is the five-toed, or pentadactyl, appendage. Among other characteristics which distinguish tetrapods from fishes are a cornified, or horny, outer layer of skin; nasal passages communicating with the mouth cavity and which transport air; lungs used in respiration; and a bony skeleton. There has also been a reduction in number of skull bones.

The first tetrapods are believed to have evolved from rhipidistian crossopterygian fishes which they closely resembled. Such primitive tetrapods were far different from any living today. The superclass is divided into four classes made up of amphibians, reptiles, birds, and mammals, respectively.

Class I. Amphibia. The living representatives of the class include salamanders, newts, frogs, toads, and some less familiar burrowing, legless forms, the *caecilians*. Frogs and toads, often thought of as primitive tetrapods, are actually far removed from the original amphibian stock. Some skeletal structures of certain amphibians show a higher degree of specialization than do corresponding parts of lizards, which belong to the class *Reptilia*. Not all amphibians, therefore, are at a lower level in the evolutionary scale than reptiles. It is probable that both groups arose from a common ancestral stock but that amphibians, in most cases, failed to attain the degree of advancement and specialization generally found among reptiles.

The transition from aquatic to terrestrial life is clearly indicated in the class *Amphibia*. These are the first vertebrates to live on land, although all lay their eggs in water or in moist situations. Larvae with integumentary gills develop from the eggs. After a varying period of time, depending upon the species, metamorphosis usually occurs, after which the animal may spend the greater part of its life on land, although generally in a moist situation. Upon metamorphosis, among other changes, the gills usually disappear and lungs develop, supplementing the vascular skin as organs of respiration. Some salamanders never develop lungs even though they lose their gills. A few salamanders like the mud puppy, *Necturus* (Fig. 17.1), never undergo complete metamorphosis, retaining their gills throughout life. They are known as *perennibranchiates*.

The chief differences between amphibians and the truly terrestrial vertebrates lie in their aquatic reproductive habits, the lack of certain embryonic membranes, and the rather poorly developed corneal layer of the epidermis of the skin. The ends of the digits lack claws. The failure of amphibians to rise to a more dominant position lies chiefly in their mode of development. They are, so to speak, "chained to the water." Although some are fairly well fitted for life on land, their conquest of the land has been only partially successful.

Subclass I. Stegocephalia. Four orders of stegocephalians have been recognized, the first three being comprised only of fossil forms. These three groups of early tetrapods are known, respectively, as *labyrinthodonts*, *lepospondyls*, and *phyllospondyls* and are distinguished by differences in structure of their vertebral columns. The labyrinthodonts were probably closest of all to the rhipidistian crossopterygian stock. They may have given rise to modern amphibians, on one hand, and to primitive reptiles, on the other. It has been suggested (G. K. Noble, 1931, "The Biology of the Amphibia," McGraw-Hill Book Company, Inc.) that phyllospondyl stegocephalians were in the line of descent of frogs and salamanders and that caecilians may have evolved via the lepospondyl line.

Many stegocephalians had a ventral armor of overlapping bony plates, or scales, and in a few, dorsal scales were also present. The number of skull elements was greater than in any modern amphibian.

ORDER IV. APODA (GYMNOPHIONA). Living members of the order *Apoda* are found only in India, Africa, and tropical America. They include the caecilians, which are burrowing forms with snakelike bodies, lacking limbs. The tail is very short, and the anus is almost terminal. Unlike other amphibians, some caecilians have dermal, fishlike scales in the skin. Adults lack gills and gill slits. The very small eyes are buried beneath the skin or under the skull bones. Large caecilians may attain a length of 26 in. or more.

Subclass II. Caudata (Urodela). The caudates include salamanders (Fig. 2.15) and newts, the latter being small, semiaquatic forms. Caudates are found, for the most part, in temperate and subtropical climates in the Northern Hemisphere. The elongated body consists of head, trunk, and tail, the tail being retained throughout life. Two pairs of weak limbs are present in most species. Larvae closely resemble adults and, like adults, possess true teeth in both upper and lower jaws. Salamanders are common in the United States and may often be found under rotten logs in wooded areas and in moist situations. The detailed characteristics of the anatomy of the perennibranchiate salamander *Necturus* are described in Part III, Representative Animals.

Subclass III. Salientia (Anura). Frogs and toads lack a tail in the adult stage. Head and trunk are fused, and there is no neck region. Two pairs of well-developed limbs are present, the hind pair being particularly fitted for leaping. The feet are webbed and adapted for swimming. Frogs and toads are the first vertebrates to have vocal cords for sound production. The salientian larva, or tadpole, does not resemble the parent. Head and body are fused into a single, egg-shaped mass, and the long tail is equipped with median fins. Horny jaws are used in lieu of teeth in feeding. Metamorphosis is more clearly defined than in caudates. At this time not only are the gills lost as lungs develop, but legs appear and the tail is resorbed. Salientians as a group are better fitted for terrestrial existence than are caudates.

There are no superficial characters which distinguish frogs from toads.

Fig. 2.15. The marbled salamander, *Ambystoma opacum*, showing eggs in nest.

Frogs usually have a smoother and more moist body surface than do toads with their warty skin.

Amniota and anamniota. The three remaining classes of tetrapods, reptiles, birds, and mammals, are referred to collectively as the *Amniota.* The lower classes together form a group called the *Anamniota.* The essential difference between the two lies in the presence of certain membranes associated with the embryos of terrestrial forms during development. These membranes are the amnion, chorion, and allantois. The name Amniota is, of course, taken from the first of these. The amnion is a fluid-filled sac which comes to surround the embryo completely soon after development has begun. It first appears in reptiles and is of definite advantage to the embryo in preventing desiccation and otherwise offering protection during developmental stages. The other membranes are concerned with respiration and other processes essential to the developing amniote embryo.

Class II. Reptilia. Reptiles are represented today by four orders of living forms which include turtles and tortoises, alligators and crocodiles, lizards and snakes, and a peculiar, aberrant, lizardlike animal, the tuatara, *Sphenodon punctatum*, of New Zealand. Most reptiles live in tropical and subtropical regions. The reptiles of today are small and insignificant compared with the tremendous monsters of prehistoric times. During the Age of Reptiles, about 150 million years ago, reptiles dominated the earth.

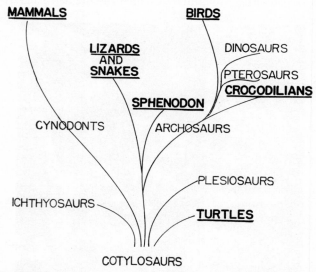

FIG. 2.16. Simplified diagram showing possible direction of evolution of reptiles, birds, and mammals from primitive cotylosaurs. The larger lettering indicates forms surviving today.

These ancient forms, known only by their fossil remains, have been grouped into 10 different orders. Some lived on land, others took to the air, and still others were adapted to an aquatic habitat.

The most ancient reptiles were the *cotylosaurs*, sometimes called the "stem reptiles." The best-known of these, *Seymouria*, so closely resembled the labyrinthodont stegocephalian amphibians that it has not been easy for paleontologists to set the two groups apart. Several groups of reptiles seem to have evolved from the cotylosaurs. Some were important for a time and then lost ground and disappeared; others have persisted to the present day with but little change; still others evolved further and not only gave rise to most of our modern reptiles but to birds and mammals as well (Fig. 2.16).

Among early forms which went up a blind alley, so to speak, were such large aquatic reptiles as the short-necked icthyosaurs and long-necked plesiosaurs. Modern turtles also are believed to have stemmed directly from an early side shoot of the cotylosaurs. They have shown but little advance. Another group tracing its origin to any early branch of the cotylosaurs was that which gave rise to mammals. Among the earliest of these mammal-like reptiles were the *cynodonts*, the skulls and teeth of which more nearly resembled those of mammals than those of other reptiles. Still another stem from the early base is believed to have branched in two directions. One branch gave rise to *Sphenodon* and to the lizards and snakes of today. The other was made up of a great group of reptiles, the *archosaurs*, sometimes called the "ruling reptiles." The varied types of dinosaurs and the flying pterosaurs belonged to the subclass *Archosauria*. The only reptilian survivors of archosaurian origin are crocodiles and alligators. Even they have become considerably modified from the ancestral stock. Birds probably evolved from another branch of archosaurs. Like pterosaurs they developed the ability to fly, but the structure of the wings in the two groups is very different (Fig. 10.57).

At the close of the Age of Reptiles great climatic changes occurred affecting both animal and plant life. Thousands of years elapsed before the great dinosaurs, their smaller relatives, and the pterosaurs disappeared and mammals, heretofore an insignificant group, began to flourish.

Although reptiles and amphibians are believed to have arisen from a common ancestral stock, the gap between the two groups is large. This is most strikingly brought out by their manner of development. Eggs of reptiles are always laid on land, and a resistant shell covers the large-yolked eggs. Of even greater significance is the presence of the embryonic membranes mentioned above.

As in lower forms, the body temperature of reptiles varies with the environment. In this respect they are said to be *poikilothermous*. The skeletons of reptiles are more completely bony than those of amphibians; their bodies are covered with dry, horny scales, and the skin is practically devoid of glands. Except in snakes, and in certain lizards which lack appendages, the limbs are characteristically pentadactyl. Gill pouches are present only in the embryo, and respiration is entirely by means of lungs except in certain aquatic turtles in which cloacal respiration is employed as well. The young resemble their parents, and metamorphosis does not occur.

ORDER I. CHELONIA. Chelonians are not closely related to other modern reptiles since they represent a very old group which has persisted with but little change for some 175 million years. Terrestrial forms are usually called tortoises, whereas turtles are generally semiaquatic. Terrapins are edible fresh-water species.

The bodies of chelonians are relatively short and wide. In certain marine forms the pentadactyl limbs have been modified to form flippers. Teeth are lacking, the jaws being covered with sharp horny beaks. The anal opening is in the form of an elongated, longitudinal slit. Most noteworthy is the presence of a shell which encases the body. The more rounded dorsal portion is the *carapace;* the flatter ventral region is the *plastron.* The shell has an underlying layer of bone over which horny scales are arranged in a rather similar manner in most species.

Variations in size are extreme among turtles, some large marine forms attaining a weight of 1,500 to 2,000 lb.

ORDER II. RHYNCHOCEPHALIA. The tuatara of New Zealand, *Sphenodon punctatum* (Fig. 2.17), is the only living member of the order. *Sphenodon* has been called a living "fossil" because of its primitive and generalized structure. It is one of the oldest types of reptiles known, even when extinct forms are taken into consideration. A significant feature is the presence of a well-developed, median, parietal, third eye in the middle of its forehead.

FIG. 2.17. *Sphenodon punctatum.* (*Courtesy of the American Museum of Natural History.*)

Some lizards have a similar median eye, but it is never as well developed as that of the tuatara. The anal opening is a transverse slit.

Despite its lizardlike appearance, *Sphenodon* is more closely related to crocodiles and alligators than to lizards. It is rapidly approaching extinction.

ORDER III. SQUAMATA. The order includes lizards and snakes. They are placed in separate suborders. These reptiles apparently came from the same ancestral stock which gave rise to *Sphenodon* but have flourished and evolved further instead of remaining at a stationary level. In evolutionary terms they represent the most recent of reptiles. Snakes are believed to have sprung from lizard stock.

The horny scales of snakes and lizards are derived from the epidermis of the skin. Sometimes bony dermal scales lie under the horny scales. As in *Sphenodon,* the anal opening is in the form of a transverse slit.

SUBORDER I. SAURIA (LACERTILIA). Lizards usually have two pairs of pentadactyl limbs, but some, known as *glass snakes*, as well as certain others, do not have legs, so this feature cannot be used to characterize lizards as a group. The eardrum, or tympanic membrane, is not flush with the surface, and external ear pits are visible. Contrary to the condition in snakes, lizards have movable upper and lower eyelids as well as a nictitating membrane. The two halves of the lower jaw are united, and the animals lack the ability to open their mouths in the manner of snakes.

Lizards and salamanders are commonly confused by the layman. The shape of the body in these two groups is essentially similar, but the smooth moist skin of the salamander and its toes without claws are quite in contrast to the dry scaly skin of the lizard, the toes of which bear claws.

One characteristic for which certain species of lizard are famous is their ability to change color rapidly (*metachrosis*) so as to blend in with the background of their environment. Not all lizards have this ability, however.

The largest species of lizard extant is the dragon lizard, *Varanus komodoenis*, of the East Indies. It may reach a length of 12 ft. The gila monster, *Heloderma*, is the only poisonous lizard known. There are two species.

SUBORDER II. SERPENTES (OPHIDIA). Snakes have lost their limbs in the course of evolution, but some, like pythons and boa constrictors, still retain vestiges of the pelvic girdle and limbs. Locomotion is accomplished in two ways, by sideward muscular undulations of the body and by movements of the transverse ventral scales. Snakes lack external ear pits and tympanic membranes. The eyelids are immovably fused, and are transparent. The loose ligamentous attachment of the jaw bones to each other and to the cranium enables the snake to stretch its mouth to a remarkable degree. Snakes vary greatly in size, ranging from species only 5 or 6 in. long to 30-ft. pythons.

Poisonous snakes fall into two groups, the vipers and the cobras. Some of the more familiar vipers, such as the rattlesnake and copperhead, are called *pit vipers* because of the presence of a pitlike depression between the eye and the nostril. The pit is a sense organ, sensitive to heat, enabling the animal to become aware of a warm object some distance away.

ORDER IV. CROCODILIA (LORICATA). Crocodilians are the only reptilian survivors of the ancient terrestrial archosaurs. The hind legs of many archosaurs were elongated and fitted for bipedal locomotion. With the demise of the archosaurs apparently one branch survived. The animals gradually changed back to the quadruped method of locomotion and assumed an amphibious life. Crocodilians are modified descendants of these archosaurs and are quite unlike other reptiles living today. In certain respects they show affinities to ancient rhynchocephalians.

Crocodilians have laterally compressed tails and two pairs of short legs. There are five toes on the forefeet and four on the hind feet. The toes are webbed. The tympanic membrane is exposed but protected by a fold of

Fig. 2.18.   Fossil remains of *Archaeopteryx*.   (*Courtesy of the American Museum of Natural History.*)

skin.   Eyes, nostrils, and ears are in a straight line on top of the head.   This enables the animal to use its major sense organs when only a small part of the body is exposed above water.   The anal opening, like that of chelonians, is a longitudinal slit.   The skin is thick, with bony plates underlying the horny scales on the back and ventral sides.

Fig. 2.19.   *Hesperornis regalis.*   (*Courtesy of the Chicago Natural History Museum.*)

Crocodiles and alligators are the largest reptiles living today.   Caymans and gavials are also included in the order.   The feature that distinguishes crocodiles from alligators is that in alligators the fourth tooth on each side of the lower jaw fits into a pit in the upper jaw when the mouth is closed. In most crocodiles the fourth tooth of the lower jaw fits into a notch on the *outer* side of the upper jaw and is exposed when the mouth is closed. The snout of the American crocodile is much narrower than that of the American alligator.

Class III. Aves. Birds are the only animals which possess feathers. Feathers are modifications of the reptilian type of epidermal scale. They, together with the scales on feet and legs of birds, indicate a close relationship between birds and reptiles. This is also borne out in many other features. We have already alluded to the fact that birds

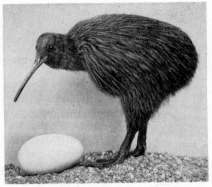

FIG. 2.20.   The kiwi, *Apteryx australis*, with egg. (*Courtesy of the Chicago Natural History Museum.*)

did not evolve from pterosaurs. They probably arose from another type of archosaur with bi-pedal locomotion and in which the scales covering the body had become modified into feathers. Feathers on the forelimbs, rather than membranous wings, are used to resist the air in flight (Fig. 10.57).

Birds are the most highly specialized of vertebrates. As a group they have become adapted to aerial life, although there are a number of exceptions. Adaptive features include the light, hollow bones; loss of right ovary and oviduct in females of most species; the exceptionally well-developed eyes; the highly specialized lung and air-sac system; the modifications of the forelimbs to form wings; the presence of feathers which although light in weight offer an effective resistance to air when the bird is in flight. Birds have a constant body temperature, independent of that of the environment, and are said to be *homoiothermous*. There is less deviation within the entire class than can be found within a single order in some of the other classes.

FIG. 2.21.   Jackass penguin. (*Courtesy of the Chicago Natural History Museum.*)

Although the forelimbs of most birds have been modified into wings, they are not always adapted for flight. The hind limbs of various

FIG. 2.22. Types of birds' feet showing various adaptations to different modes of life: *A*, duck (swimming); *B*, robin (perching); *C*, heron (wading); *D*, cuckoo (climbing); *E*, hawk (seizing); *F*, grebe (swimming); *G*, woodpecker (clinging); *H*, rail (walking and running); *I*, ruffed grouse (scratching). (*Drawn by A. Page.*)

Fig. 2.23. Types of beaks in birds, showing various adaptations to different kinds of food: *A*, red-tailed hawk (flesh); *B*, robin (worms, insects, berries); *C*, cardinal (seeds); *D*, flycatcher (insects); *E*, red-breasted merganser (fish); *F*, wood duck (aquatic vegetation, fish); *G*, American bittern (fish, crustaceans); *H*, warbler (insects); *I*, woodpecker (grubs); *J*, crossbill (seeds in fir and pine cones). (*Drawn by A. Page.*)

types of birds show much variation. The feet usually have four toes terminating in claws.

Birds are divided into two subclasses, one of which contains one or two species known only by fossil remains. The second includes all other birds, extinct and modern.

Subclass I. Archaeornithes. The famous *Archaeopteryx lithographica* (Fig. 2.18) represents the subclass. It is known from two specimens and from the impression of a single feather found in the lithographic limestone in a quarry at Solenhofen in Bavaria, Germany. This bird was about the size of a crow. Its long jointed tail bore feathers along each side. Each wing had three clawed digits. The hind feet had four toes as in modern birds. Teeth, set in sockets, were present in both jaws. Riblike dermal bones, called *gastralia*, found in numerous reptiles but not in other birds, were present in *Archaeopteryx*. In many respects, then, this fossil bird showed distinct reptilian characteristics. The presence of feathers, however, makes it imperative to classify it with birds, for in this feature it differs from any known reptile. *Archaeopteryx* is regarded as an almost ideal connecting link between these two great classes of gnathostomes.

Subclass II. Neornithes. In members of the *Neornithes* there are 13 or fewer compressed vertebrae in the tail. The wing bones have been reduced in number, and, with rare exceptions, there are no free, clawed digits on the wings. A few primitive fossil forms, some extinct flightless species, and all modern forms are included in the subclass.

SUPERORDER I. ODONTOGNATHAE. The fossil *Neornithes* includes *Hesperornis regalis* (Fig. 2.19), a flightless, swimming bird, and *Ichthyornis victor*, with well-developed wings. Both birds had true teeth.

SUPERORDER II. PALEOGNATHAE (RATITAE). To this group belong seven orders of flightless, toothless, running birds. A few, such as the giant moas and elephant birds, have become extinct within memory of man. Living examples include the ostrich, rhea, emu, cassowary, and kiwi (Fig. 2.20). Lacking the ability to fly, they have failed to become widely distributed. Their wings are rudimentary or are too small and weak to be used in flight. The tinamous of Central and South America are exceptions.

SUPERORDER III. NEOGNATHAE. All remaining birds belong to this group. Twenty-two orders are recognized. All are flying birds, except the penguins, in which the forelimbs have been modified into paddlelike swimming organs (Fig. 2.21). No teeth are present.

Numerous adaptations of birds are of interest to the comparative anatomist. Those which fit them for aerial life as well as for life on land or water; the extraordinary migrations of many species; their methods of courtship and nest building have all been carefully studied. The feet and bills of birds show many curious adaptive variations (Figs. 2.22 and 2.23).

Class IV. Mammalia. Mammals are homoiothermous gnathostomes which have hair and mammary glands. All mammals have some hair, and only mammals have hair. Mammary glands are special skin glands which secrete milk used to nourish the young.

It is believed that mammals evolved from cynodont reptiles. Probably the intricate mechanism which ensures a constant body temperature independent of the environment has had much to do with the present wide distribution and supremacy of mammals. Birds, the only other homoiothermous animals, are also widely distributed. They have specialized along lines which enable them to fly. Mammals have specialized in another direction, *i.e.*, development of the nervous system, particularly the cerebral portion of the brain.

Mammals have become adapted to a diversity of habitats. Some, like moles, live almost entirely underground; whales are at home only in the water; bats rival birds in their ability to fly; most monkeys are arboreal; but the large majority of mammals walk or run on the ground. Many mammals, entire orders in some cases, have become extinct. In the following account only living forms are stressed.

A few mammals (three species) lay eggs, but the rest give birth to living young. Accordingly, the class has been divided into two subclasses, of which the first contains only the egg-laying forms.

Subclass I. Prototheria. Eggs of prototherians are incubated outside the body, but the young are nourished by milk from mammary glands. No nipples are present, the glands opening directly on the surface of the skin. The three living species are included in a single order.

FIG. 2.24. Duckbill platypus, *Ornithorhynchus anatinus*. (*Courtesy of the American Museum of Natural History.*)

ORDER I. MONOTREMATA. The monotremes include the duckbill platypus, *Ornithorhynchus anatinus*, of Australia, and two species of *Echidna* (*Tachyglossus*), the spiny anteaters of Australia and New Guinea. The platypus (Fig. 2.24) is semiaquatic in habit, its beaverlike body, tail, and webbed feet adapting it to life in the water. Its ducklike bill is soft, flexible, and moist and richly supplied with sense organs. It bears only a superficial resemblance to the bills of certain birds. No biologist today believes that the platypus is a connecting link between birds and mammals.

In the spiny anteaters the skin is covered with spines and coarse hair (Fig. 2.25). A short tail and external ears are present. The protrusible tongue is used for feeding on ants and termites.

Monotremes do not have a highly developed mechanism for controlling body temperature, which is, therefore, rather inconstant. This group of mammals apparently has no close relatives. Several features indicate that they are more closely related to marsupials than to placental mammals.

Subclass II.   Theria.   Therians bring forth their young alive and have mammary glands provided with nipples or teats. The subclass is divided into two infraclasses.

Infraclass I.   Metatheria.   The young of metatherians are usually born

Fig. 2.25.   Spiny anteater, *Echidna*. (*Courtesy of the Chicago Natural History Museum.*)

in an extremely immature condition and undergo further development in a marsupial pouch on the ventral side of the mother (Fig. 2.26). The term *mammary fetus* is sometimes applied to the pouch young. In some metatherians the marsupial pouch is reduced or wanting.

ORDER I.   MARSUPIALIA.   The marsupials of today are confined almost entirely to Australia and the neighboring islands. Exceptions include the opossums of North, Central, and South America and the small opossum rat, *Caenolestes*, of South America. The Australian group embraces such forms as the thylacine, or marsupial wolf; the wombat, a small bearlike animal; the bandicoot, which resembles a rabbit; the marsupial mole; the marsupial flying squirrel; and a host of other forms which show likenesses to rodents, carnivores, and insectivores of other climes—but only in a superficial way.

In both sexes of most marsupials a pair of long, flat, *epipubic bones* extends forward from the lower part of the pelvic girdle. They are embedded in the muscles of the lower abdominal wall which they help support. Similar bones are found in monotremes. The fact that certain primitive reptiles also possessed a similar support of the ventral abdominal wall offers a possible clue to the ancestral relations of metatherians.

The peculiar geographical distribution of marsupials is difficult to explain and has aroused many interesting speculations. Fossil remains of numerous marsupials have been found in South America, indicating that they once were a thriving race on that continent. A rather widely accepted explanation suggests that when mammals arose to a dominant position they had already split into two basic groups, the marsupials and the placentals. At this time Europe, Africa, Asia, and North America were united into a continuous land mass, or World Continent, whereas Australia and South America were probably island continents. It is known from the fossil record that primitive marsupials of little relative importance were present, at least in

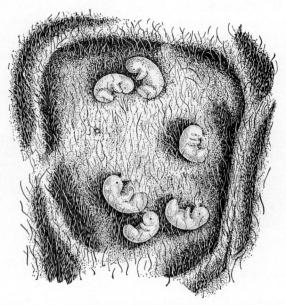

Fig. 2.26. Open marsupial pouch of Virginia opossum, *Didelphis virginiana*, showing young at about the third day after birth.

the European and North American regions of the World Continent. Placental mammals, however, were predominant. In Australia and South America the mammalian populations differed from those of the World Continent. The Australian forms were probably all marsupials, whatever their origin may have been. In South America herbivorous placental mammals and carnivorous marsupials seem to have coexisted for some time. Later on, when South America and North America became reconnected, there was apparently an invasion of competitively superior carnivorous placental mammals from the north, and the marsupials in South America gradually became extinct except for a few surviving forms. Those in Australia, on the other hand, not in competition with placentals, flourished and slowly evolved into the many types now indigenous to that continent.

Many biologists today are of the opinion that both marsupial and placental mammals originally sprang from the same basic mammalian stock which underwent an early dichotomy.   Neither type was more primitive or more advanced than the other, and both were equally progressive in their evolution and ability to adapt themselves efficiently to changing environmental conditions.   The extinction of South American marsupials in competition with placental carnivores does not necessarily imply that marsupial mammals were inferior or more primitive than placentals, but rather that the types of placental mammals which invaded South America from the World Continent had already become competitively superior.

Infraclass II.   Eutheria.   Eutherians are often referred to as placental mammals since their developing young are nourished by means of a placenta attached to the lining of the uterus of the mother.   An exchange of

Fig. 2.27.   European shrew, *Sorex oraneus castaneus.   (Courtesy of the American Museum of Natural History.)*

gases, nutritional substances, and excretory products between mother and young takes place at the placenta.   Marsupial pouches and epipubic bones are never found in eutherians.   To this infraclass belong most of the familiar mammals.   Although as many as 24 separate orders, including fossil forms, have been recognized, we shall list only 16, which include the more familar forms living today.

ORDER I.   INSECTIVORA.   To this rather primitive order belong the moles, shrews, and hedgehogs.   They are rather small mammals, usually with elongated snouts.

Moles live underground in burrows.   Their eyes are extremely small and hidden in the fur.   The heavily clawed, paddle-shaped forelimbs are used in digging; the hind limbs are small and weak.

Shrews (Fig. 2.27) include the smallest of all mammals and are frequently confused with mice.   They are voracious and pugnacious.

In America the name hedgehog is often used to refer to the porcupine, which belongs to the order *Rodentia.*   The European hedgehog, *Erinaceus,* is a true insectivore, the body of which is covered with short spines intermingled with hair.

ORDER II. DERMOPTERA. Only one genus, consisting of two species, is included in the order. *Galeopithecus*, the flying lemur of the Malay region (Fig. 2.28), is representative. It is larger than any of the insectivores and approximately the size of a cat. A well-developed fold of skin, the *patagium*, extends along either side of the body from neck to tail, enclosing the limbs. The feet are webbed. The presence of the patagium enables the animal to soar for some distance.

ORDER III. CHIROPTERA. The bats are highly specialized mammals

FIG. 2.28. Flying lemur, *Galeopithecus*. (*From a painting of a live animal by W. A. Weber. Courtesy of the Chicago Natural History Museum.*)

which show unmistakable relations to insectivores. They are the only mammals that can actually fly. The wing of the bat (Fig. 10.57) is constructed entirely differently from the wing of the bird. The fingers are greatly elongated and connected by a web which offers resistance to the air. The web is attached to the body, hind limbs, and tail, if a tail is present.

ORDER IV. PRIMATES. It may seem strange to the student that the order of mammals to which man belongs should be placed among the lowest orders. Although the nervous system, especially the cerebral portion of the brain, is best developed of all in primates, nevertheless in other respects they show many generalized characteristics. The development of the human brain far exceeds that of other primates, but aside from this man is

Fig. 2.29. Sportive lemur.
(*Courtesy of the Chicago Natural History Museum.*)

clearly related, even in minor details, to the rest of the animals making up the order.

In primates the limbs are unusually long and the pentadactyl hands and feet are relatively large. In many forms both thumb and big toe are opposable, although in man this applies only to the thumb. The limbs, in general, are adapted for arboreal existence. The eyes are directed forward. The order is divided into three suborders.

SUBORDER I. LEMUROIDEA. The lemurs (Fig. 2.29) of today are confined to Madagascar, Ethiopia, and parts of Asia. Fossil remains indicate, however, that they once were widely distributed. Lemurs are arboreal animals of moderate size, and nocturnal or crepuscular as to habit. The head is foxlike with a pointed muzzle; the tail is long but not prehensile. The second digit on each hind foot bears a sharp claw, whereas the other digits on both forefeet and hind feet are provided with flattened nails.

SUBORDER II. TARSIOIDEA. Tarsiers (Fig. 2.30) are small lemurlike creatures with long ears, large and protruding eyes, and elongated heels. The second and third digits of the hind feet bear claws; those of the forefeet and the remainder on the hind feet have nails. These animals occur in the Philippines and in the islands between India and Australia. They are arboreal and nocturnal.

SUBORDER III. ANTHROPOIDEA. Monkeys, apes, and man, all of which are included in this order, bear digits with flattened or slightly rounded nails. They are arboreal or terrestrial, and diurnal as to habit. Within the group there is a tendency to walk upright, but only man has actually attained the upright posture. The increased specialization of the nervous system, with its epitome in man, is the most prominent feature of the group.

The suborder is made up of two large divisions, the *Platyrhinii*, or South American monkeys, and the *Catarrhini*, or Old World forms. The chief anatomical feature which distinguishes the two groups lies in the wide

Fig. 2.30. Tarsier, *Tarsius spectrum.* (*Courtesy of the American Museum of Natural History.*)

distance between the outwardly directed nostrils in the former and the narrow septum between the downwardly directed nostrils of the latter. Although some of the *Platyrhinii* have prehensile tails, this is never true of the *Catarrhini*. No connecting links have been found which give a clue to the relations of the two groups.

Among the *Platyrhinii* are included marmosets, and capuchin, spider, howling, and squirrel monkeys. The *Catarrhini* include macaques, Barbary apes, baboons, gibbons, orangutans, gorillas, chimpanzees, and man. The term *ape* may be used to designate any monkey, but it is generally applied to the larger Old World forms. The anthropoid apes are those which most closely resemble man.

The well-developed brain, the generalized condition of parts of the skeleton and other body structures, together with the fact that he is homoio-

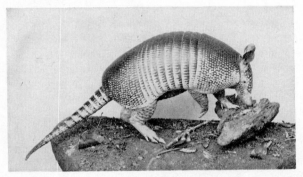

Fig. 2.31. Nine-banded armadillo. (*Courtesy of the Chicago Natural History Museum.*)

thermous and can adapt himself to almost any climatic condition, all account for the success of *Homo sapiens* (man) in attaining his present leading position in the animal world.

Biologists do not believe that man arose from the apes in evolution but rather that man and the apes sprang from a common ancestral stock, each having diverged in a different direction. No single fossil has yet been found which might be considered as the ancestral form. Discovery of the remains of manlike apes in South Africa within recent years indicates that in this region paleontologists may ultimately find missing links in the human pedigree.

ORDER V. EDENTATA. The lack of teeth or the presence only of poorly developed molar teeth characterizes the edentates. Some forms that are toothless as adults have teeth when young, but they are lost as the animals grow older. Among the edentates are included the South American anteaters, armadillos (Fig. 2.31), and sloths. Only one species, the nine-banded armadillo, is native to the United States. It is found in the southwestern part of the country but is spreading eastward.

ORDER VI. PHOLIDOTA. Only a single genus, *Manis*, the pangolin, or scaly anteater (Fig. 2.32), is included in the order. Its native habitat is in eastern Asia and Africa. The animal is covered with large, horny, overlapping scales among which a few hairs are interspersed. Teeth are lacking.

ORDER VII. RODENTIA. The gnawing incisor teeth of rodents are their most outstanding feature. These are the two chisel-shaped incisor teeth in front of both upper and lower jaws. They continue to grow through-

FIG. 2.32. Asiatic pangolin, or scaly anteater. (*Courtesy of the Chicago Natural History Museum.*)

out life. Canine teeth are lacking, but grinding, posteriorly located premolar and molar teeth are present.

Rodents are by far the most numerous of mammals and are distributed all over the world. Among the more familiar forms are rats, mice, squirrels, beavers, chipmunks, porcupines, and guinea pigs. The largest rodent of all is the capybara, *Hydrochoerus*, a South American form.

ORDER VIII. LAGOMORPHA. Rabbits, hares, and pikas are included among the lagomorphs. Like rodents they lack canine teeth and their incisors grow continually. They differ from true rodents, however, in other respects. They have four incisor teeth in the upper jaw rather than two. The second pair lies behind the first and is smaller. Their tails are short and stubby.

ORDER IX. CARNIVORA. Carnivores are flesh-eaters, for the most part, although some are omnivorous. All have three pairs of small incisor teeth in both upper and lower jaws and large well-developed canine teeth. Their limbs are typically pentadactyl. There are two suborders, the distinctive features of which have to do with the condition of the toes. In the suborder *Fissipedia* the toes are separated, whereas in the *Pinnipedia* they are webbed, forming flippers.

The fissiped carnivores include bears, doglike mammals, cats, raccoons, weasels, skunks, and others. Seals, sea lions, and walruses are placed in the suborder *Pinnipedia*. They are well adapted for aquatic life but move about on land with difficulty. Most are fish-eaters. The detailed anatomy

FIG. 2.33. Sperm whale. (*Courtesy of the Chicago Natural History Museum.*)

of one of the fissiped carnivores, the cat, *Felis domestica*, is described in Part III, Representative Animals.

ORDER X. CETACEA. Whales, porpoises, and dolphins are members of the order *Cetacea*. Although porpoises and dolphins are relatively small in size, in this group are found the largest animals inhabiting the earth. Cetaceans have undergone profound modifications in adapting themselves to marine conditions. Nevertheless, they are true mammals. They are homoiothermous, breathe air by means of lungs, bring forth their young alive, and nurse them with mammary glands. Only traces of a hairy covering remain, shown by a few scattered hairs on the snout. The webbed pectoral appendages are flippers. Pelvic appendages are lacking, except for rudiments of the pelvic girdle, embedded in the flesh. The tail is flattened horizontally and is referred to as the "flukes." Since whales are homoiothermous and have a thick, insulating layer of fat, or blubber, beneath the skin, they are at home even in Arctic and Antarctic seas.

Whales are separated into two large groups, the toothed whales and the whalebone whales. The toothed whales are primarily fish-eaters. They are usually not of exceptional size and include the dolphin, porpoise, and grampus. The sperm whale (Fig. 2.33) and the bottle-nosed whale are among the larger species. The whalebone whales (Fig. 2.34) have no teeth and are characterized by the great sheets of baleen, or whalebone, which hang from the roof of the mouth. The baleen is used in straining from the water the great numbers of microscopic plants and animals which form the chief food supply of these huge animals. The giant whales are members of this group. They include the gray, blue, sulfur-bottomed, hump-backed, and right whales.

The so-called "spout" of the whale is not a column of water, nor is it merely a condensation of moisture from the warm, exhaled air coming from the lungs. It is composed largely of mucus, gas, and emulsified oil

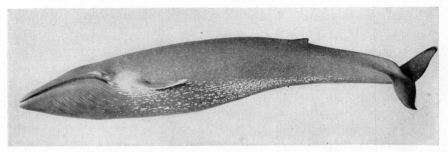

Fig. 2.34. Blue whale. (*Courtesy of the Chicago Natural History Museum.*)

that gather in the lungs. The mixture is expelled in the form of foam through the nostrils located on top of the head.

ORDER XI. TUBULIDENTATA. The aardvark, *Orycteropus*, is the only representative of the order. It is a rather large, African, ant-eating, burrowing mammal with a thickset body, large pointed ears, and a long snout. There are a few poorly developed permanent teeth. Incisors and canines are lacking.

ORDER XII. PROBOSCIDEA. Elephants are characterized by their large size, thick skin, and scanty hair coat. The nose and upper lip have been extended to an extreme degree to form a long, prehensile proboscis, called the trunk, with nostrils at its free end. There are two large species of elephant living today, the African and Indian forms. Indian elephants have small ears, tusks in the male only, a single pointed fingerlike tip at the end of the proboscis; five toes on the forefeet and four on the hind feet. These animals are rather easily tamed. African elephants have large, fanlike ears, tusks in both sexes but larger in males, two opposable fingerlike tips at the end of the proboscis, four toes on the forefeet and three on the hind feet. They are savage and not easily tamed. The pygmy elephants of the Congo are small animals of the African type. Extinct members of the order include the mastodon and the mammoth. Mastodons were older and more primitive.

ORDER XIII. HYRACOIDEA. Only one genus, *Hyrax (Procavia)*, belongs to this order. These small herbivorous creatures, commonly known as conies, inhabit certain regions of Arabia, Syria, and Africa. They somewhat resemble guinea pigs in shape and size. Four digits are present on the forefeet, and three on the hind feet. All digits are provided with hooflike nails, with the exception of the second digit on the hind foot, which bears a claw. The upper incisor teeth, like those of rodents, grow continually.

ORDER XIV. SIRENIA. The manatees (Fig. 2.35) and dugongs, commonly called sea cows, are the only representatives of the order. They are

FIG. 2.35. Florida manatees. (*Courtesy of the Chicago Natural History Museum.*)

herbivorous, and whalelike in external form, but are actually more closely related to members of the orders *Hyracoidea* and *Proboscidea*. Their bones are heavy and dense, a feature of importance in connection with their bottom-feeding habits. Manatees are about 9 or 10 ft. long. They inhabit the rivers along the Atlantic coasts of South America and Africa. Some go as far north as the Everglades of Florida. Dugongs are oriental and Australian forms.

ORDER XV. PERISSODACTYLA. This order of odd-toed, hoofed mammals includes horses, donkeys, zebras, tapirs, and rhinoceri. All are herbivorous. They walk on their nails (hoofs) and usually only on the middle finger or toe. The functional axis of the leg passes through the middle toe. The toes of the tapir have not been reduced to the extent of those of the horse family, there being four toes (one of them small) on the forefeet and three on the hind feet. The nose and upper lip have been drawn out into a relatively short proboscis.

There are one-horned and two-horned species of rhinoceri. The horns are located on the median line of the snout. Here, too, there are four toes on the forefeet (one of them small) and three on the hind feet.

ORDER XVI. ARTIODACTYLA. These are the even-toed hoofed mammals. All members of the order walk on the nails (hoofs) of the third and fourth toes. The other digits are greatly reduced or absent. The functional axis of the leg passes between the third and fourth toes. Members of the orders *Perissodactyla* and *Artiodactyla* are often called ungulates because of their unguligrade foot posture in which only the hoof is in contact with the ground.

In the *Artiodactyla* there is a division into two groups: the cud-chewers, or *ruminants*, and the *nonruminants*. The first includes cattle, sheep, goats, camels, llamas, antelopes, deer, and giraffes. Among nonruminants are pigs, hippopotami, and peccaries. Cud-chewers first swallow their food which is later regurgitated into the mouth for thorough mastication. Many members of the order bear horns or antlers projecting from the frontal bones of the skull.

SUMMARY OF CLASSIFICATION

Phylum Chordata
  Group A. Acrania
    Subphylum I. Hemichordata. *Dolichoglossus*
    Subphylum II. Tunicata. *Molgula*
    Subphylum III. Cephalochordata. Amphioxus
  Group B. Vertebrata (Craniata)
    Subphylum IV. Agnatha
      Class I. Ostracodermi. Fossil ostracoderms
      Class II. Cyclostomata
        Order I. Petromyzontia. Lampreys
        Order II. Myxinoidea. Hagfishes
    Subphylum V. Gnathostomata
     Superclass I. Pisces
      Class I. Placodermi. Fossil placoderms
      Class II. Chondrichthyes
        Order I. Selachii (Elasmobranchii)
          Suborder I. Squali. Sharks; dogfishes
          Suborder II. Batoidea. Skates; rays
        Order II. Holocephali. Chimaeras
      Class III. Osteichthyes
       Subclass I. Paleopterygii
        Order I. Cladistia. *Polypterus; Calamoichthys*
        Order II. Chondrostei. *Polyodon; Acipenser*
       Subclass II. Neopterygii. *Amia; Lepisosteus;* teleosts
       Subclass III. Choanichthyes
        Superorder I. Crossopterygii. Lobe-fins
         Order I. Rhipidistia. *Eusthenopteron*
         Order II. Coelacanthini. *Latimeria*
        Superorder II. Dipnoi. Lungfishes

Superclass II. Tetrapoda
  Class I. Amphibia
    Subclass I. Stegocephalia
          Orders I to III. Fossil labyrinthodonts; lepospondyls and phyl-
                lospondyls
          Order IV. Apoda (Gymnophiona). Caecilians
      Subclass II. Caudata (Urodela). Salamanders; newts
      Subclass III. Salientia (Anura). Frogs; toads
  Class II. Reptilia
          Order I. Chelonia. Turtles; tortoises
          Order II. Rhynchocephalia. *Sphenodon*
          Order III. Squamata
            Suborder I. Sauria (Lacertilia). Lizards
            Suborder II. Serpentes (Ophidia). Snakes
          Order IV. Crocodilia (Loricata). Alligators; crocodiles
  Class III. Aves
      Subclass I. Archaeornithes. Fossil *Archaeopteryx*
      Subclass II. Neornithes
          Superorder I. Odontognathae. Fossil *Hesperornis*
          Superorder II. Paleognathae (Ratitae). Ostrich; kiwi
          Superorder III. Neognathae. Most familar birds
  Class IV. Mammalia
      Subclass I. Prototheria
          Order I. Monotremata. Platypus; *Echidna*
      Subclass II. Theria
      Infraclass I. Metatheria
          Order I. Marsupialia. Opossum; kangaroo
      Infraclass II. Eutheria
          Order I. Insectivora. Moles; shrews
          Order II. Dermoptera. Flying lemur
          Order III. Chiroptera. Bats
          Order IV. Primates
            Suborder I. Lemuroidea. Lemurs
            Suborder II. Tarsioidea. Tarsiers
            Suborder III. Anthropoidea. Monkeys; man
          Order V. Edentata. Sloths; South American anteaters
          Order VI. Pholidota. Scaly anteater
          Order VII. Rodentia. Rats; mice; squirrels
          Order VIII. Lagomorpha. Rabbits; hares; pikas
          Order IX. Carnivora. Dogs; cats; seals; walrus
          Order X. Cetacea. Whales; porpoise
          Order XI. Tubulidentata. Aardvark
          Order XII. Proboscidea. Elephants
          Order XIII. Hyracoidea. Cony
          Order XIV. Sirenia. Manatee; dugong
          Order XV. Perissodactyla. Horse; zebra
          Order XVI. Artiodactyla. Cattle; deer; sheep

CHAPTER 3

DEVELOPMENT OF THE INDIVIDUAL

In both plants and animals there are two general types of reproduction, asexual and sexual. The asexual, or agamic, method of reproduction in animals is confined to members of some of the lower phyla. Budding and fission are examples of this method.

Sexual reproduction is the rule in the phylum Chordata. There is no scientific evidence that natural parthenogenesis (the development of ova without fertilization) occurs in members of this phylum, although under experimental conditions eggs of such vertebrates as frogs and rabbits (G. Pincus, 1939, *J. Exptl. Zool.*, **82**:85) have been induced to develop parthenogenetically.

EARLY EMBRYOLOGY

In the usual type of sexual reproduction the union of egg and spermatozoön results in a fertilized egg, or *zygote*. Fertilization of the egg brings about changes which result in the development of an embryo. The embryo is built up by a series of cell divisions in which the resulting cellular units do not dissociate but remain attached to each other and become differentiated or specialized to form the tissues and organs of the adult. Although it might appear that the stages in embryonic development differ in the several chordate groups, nevertheless the significant phases are basically similar in all. Such variations as do occur are primarily related to differences in the sizes of egg cells. The size of the egg depends, for the most part, upon the quantity of yolk that is present.

Yolk content of eggs. Eggs may be classified according to the amount of yolk which they contain. *Alecithal* eggs are those without yolk or with a very small amount of yolk. Many mammals and numerous invertebrates have eggs of the alecithal type. Some embryologists are of the opinion that there are no eggs totally lacking in yolk content. *Meiolecithal* eggs, such as those of amphioxus, contain a small amount of yolk. *Mesolecithal* ova, typical of amphibians (Fig. 8.8), have a medium amount of yolk and are quite in contrast to the large, yolk-laden *polylecithal* eggs of reptiles and birds.

Distribution of yolk. Eggs are also classified according to the manner in which yolk is distributed throughout the ovum. In *isolecithal*, or *homolecithal*, eggs the yolk is rather evenly distributed throughout the cytoplasm. Microscopic mammalian eggs are of this type. *Telolecithal* ova, on the other hand, are those in which the yolk is concentrated more on one side than the other. This condition is encountered in the eggs of fishes, amphibians, reptiles, and birds. In insects and other arthropods the ova are usually *centrolecithal*, since the yolk is confined to the central region of the egg. No chordate has centrolecithal ova.

Polarity. In most forms, even in the single-cell stage and during subsequent development, it is possible to recognize a definite axis in the embryo. The extremes of the axis consist of unlike *poles*, which are called

FIG. 3.1. Cleavage stages of amphioxus egg. The figure to the lower right is that of a blastula shown as though it were cut in half. (*Drawn by G. Schwenk.*)

the *animal* and *vegetal poles*, respectively. The existence of such an axis is termed *polarity*. It is first expressed by the arrangement of egg substances (yolk, nucleus, etc.) and later by differential rates of cleavage. In most eggs there is a tendency for the nucleus and the clear cytoplasm to be located near the animal pole and for the yolk to concentrate at the vegetal pole.

Cleavage.   The term *cleavage* is applied to the early mitotic divisions of the fertilized egg, the resulting cells being called *blastomeres*. During cleavage the zygote first divides into two smaller cells of equal size. These in turn divide into smaller and smaller units with no perceptible increase in the size of the original mass. In this respect cleavage differs from the mitotic divisions of ordinary cells which usually grow to a size equal to that of the parent cell before dividing. When growth begins and differentiation of parts become apparent, the cleavage stage of development has been completed. The rate of cleavage is determined to a great extent by the amount of yolk present in the egg. Cleavage stages of amphioxus and frog eggs are shown in Figs. 3.1 and 3.2.

Types of cleavage.   The type of cleavage which takes place in an ovum is also governed largely by the amount of yolk present. *Complete*, or *holoblastic, cleavage* is typical of alecithal, meiolecithal, and mesolecithal ova. The first cleavage plane divides the egg into two complete halves, passing through both animal and vegetal poles. The second cleavage is at right angles to the first and is also meridional since it passes through the poles. There is, however, a difference in various eggs in regard to the third cleavage plane. This is latitudinal in relation to the two poles, so that after the third cleavage the embryo is in the eight-cell stage. In alecithal eggs the eight cells are approximately equal in size. This type of cleavage is called *holoblastic equal cleavage*. On the other hand, in meiolecithal and mesolecithal ova the third cleavage, though latitudinal, is nearer the animal pole. As a result, the four cells near the animal pole are smaller than the four yolk-laden cells near the vegetal pole. They are referred to as *micromeres* and *macromeres*, respectively. In this case the type of cleavage is termed *holoblastic unequal cleavage*.

In large polylecithal ova complete cleavage does not take place. Instead, the nucleus and the clear cytoplasm undergo a series of incomplete divisions which are confined to the animal-pole area. As a result, a small disclike area composed of cleaving cells appears at the animal pole. Cleavage of this type is referred to as *incomplete*, or *meroblastic*, *discoidal cleavage*. It is typical of the eggs of fishes, reptiles, and birds (Fig. 3.3).

Blastula.   As cleavage progresses and the original ovum becomes subdivided to form the multicellular embryo, the cells usually become arranged so as to form a sphere with a single layer of cells surrounding a central cavity (Figs. 3.1 and 3.2). At this stage the embryo is referred to as a *blastula* and the central cavity is spoken of as the *blastocoele*, or *segmenta-*

tion cavity.   Polarity is still evident in the blastula stage.   The cells at the vegetal pole are generally larger than those at the animal pole because of the greater amount of yolk which they contain.   The blastula of amphioxus never consists of more than a single layer of cells.   In the frog, however, the cells of the blastula multiply in such a manner that several layers of cells ultimately surround the blastocoele.

Gastrula: epiblast and hypoblast.   The blastula stage is succeeded by the *gastrula,* the process bringing about the change being called *gastrulation.*   In amphioxus, as a result of gastrulation, a double-walled, cuplike structure is formed (Fig. 3.4).   The larger, yolk-laden cells from the original vegetal pole form the *hypoblast,* or inner layer of the cup, and the smaller,

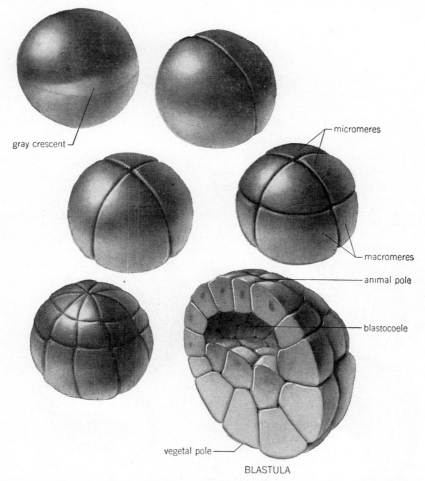

gray crescent

micromeres

macromeres

animal pole

blastocoele

vegetal pole

BLASTULA

Fig. 3.2.   Cleavage stages of frog egg.   The enlarged figure to the lower right is that of an early blastula, shown as though it were cut in half.   (*Drawn by G. Schwenk.*)

animal-pole cells make up the *epiblast*, or outer wall.   The terms *endoderm* and *ectoderm* are frequently used for hypoblast and epiblast, respectively. Since, however, in later development the hypoblast of amphioxus gives rise to endoderm, mesoderm, and notochord, it is preferable to apply the

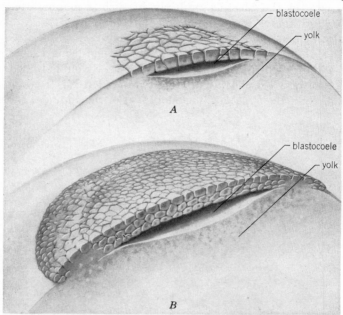

Fig. 3.3.   Meroblastic discoidal cleavage of the polylecithal bird ovum: *A*, early blastula stage; *B*, later blastula stage.   (*Drawn by G. Schwenk.*)

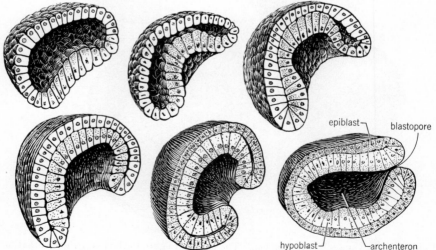

Fig. 3.4.   Successive stages during gastrulation in amphioxus.   (*Drawn by G. Schwenk.*)

terms ectoderm and endoderm at a later stage when all three *germ layers* as well as the notochord have become established.   The original blasto-coele is obliterated during gastrulation, and a new cavity, the *gastrocoele*, or *archenteron*, is formed.   This is lined entirely with hypoblast and opens to the outside through the *blastopore*.   The endoderm derived from the hypoblast is destined to form the lining of the alimentary, or digestive, tract and its derivatives.   In mesolecithal ova the larger amount of yolk

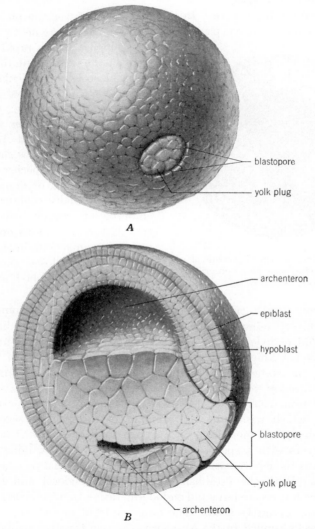

blastopore

yolk plug

A

archenteron

epiblast

hypoblast

blastopore

yolk plug

archenteron

B

FIG. 3.5.   Gastrula stage in development of frog: *A*, external view showing yolk plug filling the blastopore; *B*, median sagittal section of same, showing internal arrangement of cells making up epiblast and hypoblast.   (*Drawn by G. Schwenk.*)

in the vegetal-pole cells is responsible for the fact that in the gastrula stage a plug of yolk-filled cells usually protrudes through the blastopore (Fig. 3.5). Moreover, in such gastrulae the hypoblast cells lining the archenteron are not of equal size. The manner in which blastula and gastrula are formed in polylecithal ova differs somewhat from the above description, the differences being related to the relatively enormous amount of yolk that is present. It is not essential for our purposes here to discuss the details of these processes.

Closure of the blastopore. In the usual type of gastrula an elongation in the direction of the axis passing through the blastopore next takes place.

FIG. 3.6. Posterior view of gastrula of amphioxus, showing germ ring bordering the open blastopore. (*Drawn by G. Schwenk.*)

It is chiefly due to rapid cell divisions in the area about the margins of the blastopore, particularly on the dorsal side where epiblast and hypoblast are in continuity. This area is known as the *germ ring* (Fig. 3.6). As development progresses, the blastopore becomes smaller and smaller. In most species the edges of the germ ring, or margin of the blastopore, finally coalesce. In the embryos of certain invertebrates the blastopore remains open to become the anus, but in vertebrates the blastopore closes and an anal aperture is established at a later stage.

Mesoderm. After gastrulation is complete or is nearing completion, a third germ layer, designated as *mesoderm*, appears and comes to lie between ectoderm and endoderm. In amphioxus the mesoderm first arises as a series of pouches which pinch off from the dorsolateral angles of the hypoblast lining the archenteron (Fig. 3.7). In higher forms it usually originates by a proliferation of cells in the region of the germ ring (Fig. 3.8). The mesodermal cells push in between epiblast and hypoblast and fill the crevice which represents the remnant of the original segmentation cavity. Usually the mesoderm is at first a solid mass, but it soon splits into two layers with a space, the body cavity, or *coelom*, lying between. In amphioxus the cavities within the original mesodermal pouches become the coelom. With the establishment of the mesoderm and notochord (page 57) the terms ectoderm and endoderm, rather than epiblast and hypoblast, are appropriately used. The outer layer of mesoderm, or *somatic layer*, is closely applied to the ectoderm, the two together being destined to form the definitive body wall. The inner, or *splanchnic, layer* of mesoderm fuses with the endoderm, the two together giving rise to the digestive

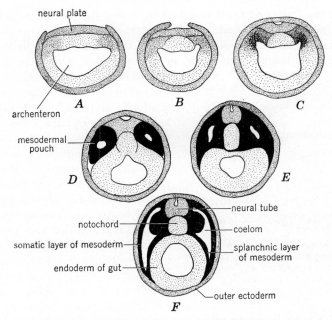

FIG. 3.7. Diagrams illustrating method of mesoderm formation in amphioxus.

tract and its derivatives. The coelom, which is thus lined entirely with mesoderm, represents the future peritoneal, pericardial, and pleural cavities of higher forms, as the case may be.

Differentiation. The cells making up the germ layers of an embryo are said to be undifferentiated; *i.e.*, they do not possess distinctive or individual characteristics. Further development of an embryo entails, among other things, a differentiation or specialization of various groups of cells to form the several types of tissues and organs which make up the body of the individual.

Notochord. At about the time that the mesoderm is differentiating into somatic and splanchnic layers, the notochord begins to form. In amphioxus it arises as a middorsal thickening of the wall of the archenteron (Fig. 3.7). In most chordates, however, it originates from cellular proliferation in the region of the dorsal lip of the blastopore between epiblast and hypoblast. It forms an elongated, rodlike structure which comes to lie in the middorsal region of the body, between ectoderm and endoderm, separating the dorsal mesoderm of the two sides (Fig. 3.8). In most chordates the vertebral column later forms about the notochord, which is gradually replaced.

Neural tube. In the details of its development the nervous system of amphioxus differs somewhat from that of higher chordates and need not be considered here. In vertebrates, as the above-mentioned changes are going on, the flattened layer of ectoderm along the middorsal side of the gastrula becomes thickened. It is known as the *neural,* or *medullary, plate.* Proliferative changes in the cells of this region result in the formation of a longitudinal depression, or *neural groove,* along the middorsal line, flanked on either side by an elevated *neural fold.* The neural folds gradually approach each other dorsally and fuse in such a manner as to form a hollow *neural tube* (Fig. 11.1). During its formation the neural tube gradually sinks down to a deeper position in the embryo. The neural tube is the forerunner of the brain and spinal cord. An opening, the *neuropore,* at the anterior end, persists for a time but ultimately closes. The outer ectodermal fold on each side meets its partner along the midline above the neural tube, forming a continuous layer from which the

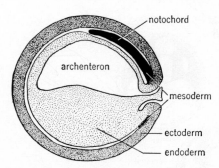

Fig. 3.8. Diagram of median sagittal section of frog gastrula in late yolk plug stage, showing mesoderm and notochord (chordamesoderm) proliferating from germ ring.

neural tube soon becomes completely separated. Thus the neural tube lies under the outer surface of the body. Small dorsolateral masses of ectodermal cells grow out on each side in the crevices formed between neural tube and outer ectoderm (Figs. 3.9 and 11.1). They are termed

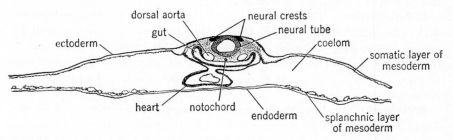

Fig. 3.9. Cross section of 33-hour chick embryo, showing neural tube and neural crests in relation to other embryonic structures.

neural crests. The neural crests are of significance in the development of numerous nerve ganglia and in the formation of certain pigment cells, known as chromatophores, found in many lower vertebrates.

Further differentiation of mesoderm. Mesoderm exists in the body either in the form of sheets of cells lining cavities of one kind or another, or as masses of loose, branching cells called *mesenchyme,* sometimes referred to as *embryonic connective tissue.* Sheets of mesodermal cells lining the body cavities are known as *mesothelia;* those lining the cavities of blood vessels, lymphatic vessels, and the heart are *endothelia.* Both epiblast and hypoblast may originally contribute to mesenchyme formation. Mesenchymal cells may migrate from their place of origin and fill in spaces between other structures.

During the time that the above changes have been taking place in vertebrate embryos, the mesoderm not only has pushed in between ectoderm and endoderm but has grown dorsally on either side of the notochord and neural tube. Three different regions or levels of mesoderm may then be recognized: (1) an upper, or dorsal, *epimere,* (2) an intermediate *mesomere,* or *nephrotome,* and (3) a lower *hypomere,* or *lateral plate* (Fig. 3.10). The epimeric mesoderm becomes marked off into a longitudinal,

FIG. 3.10. Diagram of cross section of hypothetical vertebrate embryo, illustrating the three different regions, or levels, of mesoderm.

FIG. 3.11. Rabbit embryo, 190 hours after copulation, showing series of paired mesoblastic somites in process of forming.

metameric series of blocklike masses, the *mesodermal,* or *mesoblastic, somites,* which form in succession, beginning toward the anterior end of the embryo (Fig. 3.11). The somites later become separated from the remainder of the mesoderm. Although the mesoderm of the mesomere shows evidence of metamerism in some lower forms, this is not evident in embryos of higher vertebrates except, perhaps, toward the anterior end of the body. The hypomeric mesoderm does not become segmented.

DERIVATIVES OF THE PRIMARY GERM LAYERS

All structures of the body trace their origin to one or more of the three primary germ layers. Further development is the result of the operation of a number of processes which are effective in shaping the body and in forming the various tissues and organs. Multiplication of cells goes on at a rapid rate, and the newly formed cells increase in size. Some clumps of cells form localized thickenings or swellings; others undergo a thinning or spreading out. Certain masses of cells may evaginate (push outward) or invaginate (push inward) from a surface. Some groups of cells migrate to different parts of the body and become rearranged. Diverse masses of cells may fuse or else may split apart from each other; structures or even regions may form temporarily and then undergo resorption and disappear. Various cell aggregates differentiate to form tissues of different types.

Growth of the embryo and differentiation of organs from germ layers begin before the germ layers are completely formed. The entire process of development is gradual, and although the various phases occur in a logical, step-by-step order, they are not in themselves distinct but one merges imperceptibly into the next. Experimental work has shown that the determination of cells, germ layers, tissues, and organs is not invariably the same but is directed, in the main, by relationships to other cells and by the influence of outside factors of various kinds. The different germ layers and the structures which arise from them are, nevertheless, considered to be homologous in all vertebrates. The germ-layer concept is of importance chiefly because it furnishes a convenient method of classifying organs according to their embryonic derivation and in tracing their homologies.

Ectoderm. The entire outer covering of the body of the developing vertebrate embryo consists of a layer of ectodermal cells referred to as the *superficial ectoderm*. During development when the somites, which have formed from the epimeric region of mesoderm, are undergoing differentiation, the outer portion of each somite becomes mesenchymatous. These mesenchymal cells proliferate and migrate in such a manner as to underlie the outer ectodermal covering of the body. The two layers together will form the future skin, or integument. The ectoderm gives rise to the *epidermis* of the skin; the underlying mesenchyme forms the *dermis*. Many structures associated with the skin are derived from the epidermis and are, therefore, of ectodermal origin. They include various kinds of skin glands, epidermal scales, hair, feathers, nails, claws, hoofs, and horns.

The archenteron, which is destined to form the digestive tract, is lined with endoderm. At first it opens to the outside through the blastopore, which soon closes, leaving the archenteron as a blind tube without mouth or anus. At the anterior end of the embryo an ectodermal invagination occurs, pushing inward to meet the endoderm of the archenteron. The ectodermal invagination is referred to as the *stomodaeum*, or primitive mouth. A two-layered membrane, the *oral plate*, or *oral membrane*, at first separates the two cavities. This persists but for a short time and then ruptures, so that the stomodaeum, or mouth, becomes continuous with the remainder of the digestive tract. A similar ectodermal invagination forms at the posterior end of the embryo. This is the *proctodaeum*. An *anal plate*, or *anal membrane*, at first separates archenteron and proctodaeum. With the perforation of the anal plate a complete tube is established which terminates anteriorly with the mouth and posteriorly with the anus. Derivatives of the ectoderm lining the stomodaeum include the lining of the lips and mouth, enamel of the teeth, glands of the oral cavity, covering of the tongue, and the anterior and intermediate lobes of the pituitary gland. The proctodaeal ectoderm gives rise to the lining of the anal canal or, in most forms, to a portion of the cloacal lining. It is very difficult to ascertain the exact point of transition between endoderm and proctodaeal ectoderm. For this reason there is some question as to the precise germ layer from which some cloacal derivatives arise. Certain anal and cloacal glands are believed to be derived from ectoderm of the proctodaeum.

The origin of the neural tube and neural crests has already been reviewed. The neural tube is the primordium of the brain and spinal cord, which make up the *central nervous system*. Early evidence of metamerism in the neural tube is shown by the temporary appearance of segments known as *neuromeres*. The anterior end of the neural tube enlarges rapidly to form the brain, the remainder becoming the spinal cord. The brain has three primary divisions referred to, respectively, as *forebrain* (*prosencephalon*), *midbrain* (*mesencephalon*), and *hindbrain* (*rhombencephalon*). From the posterior part of the forebrain a pair of lateral evaginations, the *optic vesicles*, grows out to come in contact with the superficial ectoderm of the head. The optic vesicles soon become flattened and then indented in such a manner that an incompletely double-walled *optic cup* is formed. This gives rise to the *retina* and to part of the *iris* of the eye. The lens of the eye develops from the outer, or superficial, layer of ectoderm opposite the optic cup. With the exception of the conjunctiva and a portion of the cornea, both of which are derived from superficial ectoderm, and the muscles of the iris which come from the outer layer of the optic cup, the remaining structures of the eye are of mesodermal origin.

The sensory parts of the remaining sense organs also come from ectoderm. The organs for the sense of smell first make their appearance as a pair of thickenings, the *olfactory placodes*, situated on either side of the head. These thickenings invaginate to become *olfactory pits*. In those vertebrates which breathe by means of lungs, and in a few others, the olfactory pits establish connection with the stomodaeum. A membranous *olfactory plate* at first separates the olfactory pit from the stomodaeum, but this soon ruptures and the two cavities become continuous. Some of the cells lining the olfactory pit become sensory and send out fibers which grow back to the forebrain with which they make connection. These fibers form the *olfactory nerve*.

On each side of the head, opposite the hindbrain, a thickened mass of superficial ectodermal cells, the *auditory placode*, is destined to form the inner ear. An invagination, the *auditory pit*, appears which soon pinches off from the outer ectodermal layer. It is then called the *auditory vesicle*. The auditory vesicle undergoes rather complex changes, ultimately forming the semicircular ducts and other portions of the inner ear which in their aggregate make up the *membranous labyrinth*. Groups of cells in various portions of the membranous labyrinth develop sensory functions. In lower aquatic vertebrates similar placodes on the head and along the sides of the body give rise to the sensory elements of the *lateral-line system*.

The organs for the sense of taste arise, for the most part, from stomodaeal ectoderm, but some are of endodermal origin. They consist of clusters of *taste cells* and supporting nonsensory cells. Fibers of the seventh and ninth cranial nerves supply the gustatory receptors.

The various *cranial* and *spinal nerves*, which form connections with the brain and spinal cord, as the case may be, make up the *peripheral nervous system*. The fibers of the peripheral nerves, depending upon the nerve in question, arise from neural-crest cells, cells from the ventrolateral parts of the neural tube, or from thickened placodes of superficial ectoderm. The *autonomic portions* of the peripheral nervous system, regulating those activities of the body under involuntary control, are derived, for the most part, from neural-crest cells, but in some forms the ventrolateral portions of the neural tube contribute certain components. The peripheral nervous system is entirely ectodermal in origin, since the neural crests, neural tube, and placodes from which it arises are all ectodermal structures.

Some neural-crest cells migrate to a position near the kidneys, where they become differentiated as suprarenal tissue or, in mammals, as the medulla, or central portion, of the adrenal glands. These tissues are endocrine in nature and secrete substances of great physiological importance into the blood stream.

Associated with tissues of the central nervous system and giving them support and protection are some other components known as *neuroglia*. Several types of neuroglia cells, all of ectodermal origin, are recognized. They are derived originally from the neural tube.

Two or three other structures of ectodermal origin should also be mentioned here. They are derivatives of the posterior portion of the forebrain. A ventral evagination of the floor of the brain in this region is called the *infundibulum*. It grows down to meet an evagination from the roof of the stomodaeum called *Rathke's pocket*. A portion of the infundibulum together with Rathke's pocket gives rise to the pituitary body. The portion derived from the infundibulum becomes the posterior lobe. The anterior and intermediate lobes of the pituitary gland come from Rathke's pocket which, except in a few lower forms, loses its connection with the stomodaeum. One or two dorsal evaginations grow out from the posterior part of the forebrain. In some forms the more anterior of the two, the *parietal body*, becomes a median, eyelike organ. The posterior evagination differentiates into a structure called the *pineal body*. The former is lacking in higher vertebrates.

Endoderm. The archenteron, or primitive digestive tube, is lined entirely with endoderm. Its communication with the stomodaeum anteriorly and with the proctodaeum posteriorly has already been alluded to. All endodermal structures of the body are derived from the archenteron. This structure elongates as the embryo grows. With progressive development it gradually differentiates into various parts which, beginning from the anterior end, include the pharynx, esophagus, stomach, intestine, and the greater part of the cloaca when such a structure is present. The inner portion of the splanchnic, or visceral, layer of mesoderm surrounding the archenteron becomes differentiated into mesenchyme. From this come the connective tissues and smooth muscle coats which, together with the endoderm, make up the wall of the digestive tract and of the various structures derived from it.

Two important digestive glands, liver and pancreas, arise as evaginations, or diverticula, of the digestive tract. The endodermal cells push out into masses of mesenchyme where they branch profusely. These organs are thus actually made up of tissues coming from two germ layers, the epithelial cells alone being of endodermal origin. The ducts of the liver and pancreas usually open into the digestive tract at the points where the original evaginations occurred.

The pharyngeal region is of particular interest, since many important organs are derived from it. Several pairs (usually four or five in higher vertebrates) of lateral pharyngeal pouches push out from the walls of the pharynx through the mesoderm until they come in contact with the outer, superficial ectodermal covering of the body with which they fuse. In cyclostomes, fishes, and amphibians the pouches break through to the outside and thus form a series of gill slits. In cyclostomes and fishes, but not in amphibians, gill lamellae, richly supplied with blood vessels, arise from the walls of the pharyngeal pouches. Larval amphibians develop external gills of a different type. Although in higher vertebrates (amniotes) the pouches form in the characteristic manner, they rarely break through to the outside. Their existence is temporary, except for the first pouch which persists in modified form as the middle ear and Eustachian tube. From the others are budded off groups of cells which go to form portions of such structures as the palatine tonsils, thymus, and parathyroid glands, and the small, irregular ultimobranchial bodies frequently found in the neck region. The appearance of pharyngeal pouches in higher forms of vertebrates is indicative of their ancestry from gill-breathing, aquatic predecessors.

The thyroid gland originates as a small, midventral evagination of the pharynx. In some groups certain pharyngeal pouches contribute to the formation of the thyroid gland.

Another midventral outgrowth of the pharynx in air-breathing vertebrates develops into larynx, trachea, and lungs. It soon divides into two branches, each of which may divide many times to form the lobes of the lungs.

The yolk sac is an additional endodermal structure which is attached to the midventral part of the archenteron somewhat near its middle portion. In embryos in which abundant yolk is present, it grows out to surround the yolk. The yolk sac is a typically embryonic structure. It becomes smaller and smaller as the yolk which it contains is utilized in nourishing the developing embryo. Eventually it disappears except in unusual and abnormal cases. It is of interest that in such forms as mammals, the eggs of which contain practically no yolk, a yolk sac appears, nevertheless, as a transitory structure.

Still another endodermal structure of great significance in the development of reptiles, birds, and mammals is an embryonic, membranous sac, the allantois, which consists of a more or less extensive outpocketing of the posterior end of the archenteron. The allantois is lost at birth. A portion of the allantois may be utilized in the development of the urinary bladder, although the greater part of this organ is derived from cloacal endoderm, as is the urethra, which carries urine from the bladder to the outside.

Mesoderm. The origin and differentiation of mesoderm into epimere, mesomere, and hypomere has already been referred to. The segmentally arranged somites, derived from the epimeric mesoderm, become mesenchymatous in their dorsolateral and midventral portions. As previously mentioned, the cells of the dorsolateral mesenchyme (*dermatome*) proliferate and migrate so as to lie under the layer of ectoderm covering the body. They give rise to the dermis of the skin. The mesenchyme from the midventral portion of the somite (*sclerotome*) grows in and fills the spaces about the notochord and neural tube. In most forms it is destined to form the various elements of the vertebral column. The remaining portion of the somite is called the *myotome*, or muscle segment. Adjacent myotomes are separated from each other by partitions of connective tissue, the *myocommata*. During development each myotome grows down in the body wall between the superficial ectoderm and the somatic layer of mesoderm to meet its partner from the other side at the midventral line of the embryo (Fig. 11.3). With some exceptions the myotomes give rise to the greater part of the voluntary musculature of the body. The precise origin of the voluntary muscle of the limbs in most vertebrates has been debated. Whether or not they are derived from myotomes, they are, at any rate, of mesodermal origin.

The mesomere which, except in lower forms, is for the most part unsegmented is concerned with the development of the urogenital organs and their ducts. The terminal parts of these ducts may, however, be lined with epithelia of ectodermal or, in some cases, of endodermal origin.

The mesothelial splanchnic layer of the hypomere surrounding the archenteron, or primitive gut, becomes mesenchymatous on the side adjacent to the endoderm. From this mesenchyme arise the involuntary muscles and connective tissues of the gut and other structures which ultimately come to surround the endodermal lining of the digestive tract and its derivatives. The heart itself is derived from splanchnic mesoderm. The remainder of the splanchnic layer, together with the somatic layer, forms the mesothelium lining the coelom and contributes to the pericardium, pleura, or peritoneum, as the case may be. Mesenteries and omenta are also derived from the splanchnic mesoderm.

The parts of the skeleton other than the vertebral column, whether made up of cartilage, bone, or other connective tissues, are all derived from mesenchyme in different parts of the body and of various origins. Mesenchyme also gives rise to blood and lymphatic vessels, blood corpuscles, lymph glands, and other blood-forming tissues. The heart, however, comes from the splanchnic mesoderm of the hypomere, as mentioned above.

Other structures derived from mesenchyme include various parts of the eye, dentine of the teeth, interrenal bodies, or, in mammals, the cortices of the adrenal glands.

TISSUES

Formation of Tissues

When tissues form from the undifferentiated cells of which the germ layers are composed, two general processes are concerned: (1) the cells multiply by numerous mitotic divisions; (2) they then undergo differentiation.

Undifferentiated cells are characterized by having relatively large nuclei and but little cytoplasm. They also have exceptional ability to divide mitotically. With a subsequent increase in cytoplasm the rate of cell division is retarded. Differentiation consists of the cell taking on a new form and changing its arrangement in relation to surrounding cells. Changes in the cytoplasm are most characteristic of differentiating cells, although the nuclei are frequently involved but to a lesser degree. Secretions or products given off by the cells may in some cases contribute to tissue formation. In other cases, accumulations of cell products within the cells themselves may characterize certain kinds of tissues. The physical and chemical properties of the cells actually undergo changes which fit the tissue to carry on the specialized function that it performs in the body.

Types of Tissues

Four general types of tissues are recognized: (1) epithelial, (2) connective, (3) muscular, and (4) nervous.

Epithelial tissue. An epithelium may be defined as a tissue composed of one or more layers of cells covering an external or internal surface of the body or embryonically derived from such a surface. Epithelia generally consist of closely connected cells which have very little intercellular substance between them. They cover the outside of the body, give rise to most glandular structures, form parts of all the sense organs, and line all internal cavities of the body which communicate with the outside. The term *endothelium*, instead of epithelium, is used to designate the simple layer of cells lining the inner surfaces of the walls of blood vessels and lymphatic vessels and of the heart. Similarly, the word *mesothelium* is used for the layer covering the surface of the membrane lining the various parts of the coelom. All canals and cavities of the body which communicate with the exterior are lined with *mucous membrane* which is composed of a superficial layer of epithelium together with a layer of connective tissue called the *lamina propria*. The alimentary canal and its diverticula, the respiratory tract and its connections, and the urogenital tract are all lined with mucous membrane. The term *serous membrane* is applied to the thin layer of loose connective tissue covered with mesothelium which lines the body cavities. Peritoneum, pleura, and pericardium are serous membranes. Mesenteries and omenta are covered with serous membrane on both surfaces. Such membranes produce a watery fluid which serves to lubricate the surfaces of organs as they move over one another when carrying on their activities. Cells which are present in the serous fluid are derived from the serous membrane.

Epithelia play an important role in the metabolism of the body and are concerned with secretion, respiration, assimilation of nutritive substances, and elimination of waste products. Various types of epithelia are present in the body. They are usually classified according to the form and arrangement of the cells of which they are composed. Two main types are recognized: (1) *simple epithelia*, composed of a single layer of cells, and (2) *stratified epithelia*, made up of several cellular layers.

In general, three varities of epithelial cells, differing primarily as to shape, may be distinguished. *Squamous cells* are broad and flat. Their height is insignificant in comparison with their length and breadth. They may be so thin that the nucleus, which is generally in the center, causes a slight bulge. *Cuboidal cells*, as their name implies, are about as tall as they they are long or wide. In cross section they appear to be square. *Columnar cells*, on the other hand, are much taller than they are wide. The shapes of these three types of cells are subject to considerable variation depending upon whether the surface which they form is stretched or contracted. The more they are stretched, the flatter they become. Conversely, contraction of the surface tends to increase their height.

Simple epithelia. Seven types of simple epithelia are usually recognized. They are distinguished basically by the type of cell of which they are composed.

SIMPLE SQUAMOUS EPITHELIUM is made up of flat, platelike, squamous cells which fit together in the manner of tiles on a floor (Fig. 3.12*A*). This type of epithelium is found lining the membranous labyrinth of the inner ear, in portions of the kidney tubules, and in the minute ducts of numerous glands. Mesothelium and endothelium are also composed of squamous cells but are not usually considered to be epithelia.

SIMPLE CUBOIDAL EPITHELIUM appears in cross section as a sheet of cells which are approximately square in shape (Fig. 3.12*B*). The free surface may appear, however, as a mosaic of irregularly hexagonal units. Cuboidal epithelium is found in many glands and lining numerous ducts. The thyroid gland and portions of the kidney tubules are typically composed of epithelium of this type. In the thyroid gland a basement membrane may be indistinct or lacking altogether. In some lower vertebrates the mesothelium over the peritoneum and mesenteries may be of the cuboidal rather than of the squamous type.

FIG. 3.12. Various types of simple and stratified epithelia: *A*, two views of simple squamous epithelium, top view above and side view below; *B*, simple cuboidal epithelium; *C*, simple columnar epithelium; *D*, simple columnar ciliated epithelium; *E*, pseudostratified columnar epithelium; *F*, stratified squamous epithelium; *G*, stratified columnar ciliated epithelium.

SIMPLE CUBOIDAL CILIATED EPITHELIUM may frequently be found in such places as portions of the kidney tubules. The free borders of the cuboidal cells bear cilia.

SIMPLE COLUMNAR EPITHELIUM is composed of a sheet of columnar cells which adhere to each other along their lateral or longitudinal surfaces. The nuclei of the columnar cells are sometimes located in the center of the cell but are more commonly found in the basal portion (Fig. 3.12*C*). The lining of the alimentary canal, from stomach to anal region, is of the simple columnar type of epithelium.

SIMPLE COLUMNAR CILIATED EPITHELIUM is similar to the plain columnar type except for the presence of cilia on the free surface of the cells. Oviducts, small bronchi, and the central canal of the spinal cord of embryos are lined with this type of columnar epithelium (Fig. 3.12*D*).

PSEUDOSTRATIFIED COLUMNAR EPITHELIUM, when viewed in cross section, gives the impression of being made up of a number of layers of cells. Close examination, however, shows that there is actually only a single layer of columnar cells but that their nuclei are at different levels, thus giving the illusory effect (Fig. 3.12*E*). The fact that certain cells taper at either or both ends and appear to be squeezed in between other and wider cells helps to give the impression of stratification. The tapering terminal portions may even fail to reach the surface of the epithelium. Pseudostratified epithelium occurs in the urethra of the male human being and in the large ducts of a number of glands, as in that of the parotid salivary gland.

PSEUDOSTRATIFIED COLUMNAR CILIATED EPITHELIUM is similar to ordinary pseudostratified columnar epithelium, but the free borders of the cells bear either motile *kinocilia* or nonmotile *stereocilia*. Examples of this type of epithelium are to be found lining the respiratory passages, Eustachian tubes and middle ears, and the ducts of the male reproductive system (epididymis and ductus deferens).

Stratified epithelia. Stratified epithelia are generally divided into five different types. Their names are based primarily on the shape of the cells forming the outermost layer.

STRATIFIED SQUAMOUS EPITHELIUM (Fig. 3.12*F*) is composed of several layers of cells. The number of layers shows much variation in different regions of the body. The basal layer appears to be of the low columnar or cuboidal type. The cells of this layer, by mitotic proliferation, bring about the formation of the other layers which are nearer the surface. A gradual change in shape of the cells occurs as they approach the surface, which is composed of flat, platelike, squamous cells. The squamous cells are either sloughed or wear away and are constantly being replaced by new cells beneath. Stratified squamous epithelium makes up the outer part (epidermis) of the skin, the lining of the mouth and esophagus, the outer portion of the cornea of the eye, and the lining of the vagina and is present in other regions as well.

STRATIFIED CUBOIDAL EPITHELIUM is similar to stratified squamous epithelium in the basal layers. The superficial layer, however, is composed of cuboidal cells. This type of epithelium is found in the epidermis of many tailed amphibians (caudates). Secretory activity of certain epidermal cells may account for their cuboidal shape when they are distended with accumulated secretory products.

STRATIFIED COLUMNAR EPITHELIUM is also similar to the aforementioned types in the lower layers, but the outer layer is made up of columnar cells. This type of epithelium is not found in abundance and is usually confined to restricted areas such as on the epiglottis, on a part of the urethra, in the folds of the conjunctiva, and in other scattered places.

STRATIFIED COLUMNAR CILIATED EPITHELIUM is like that just described, but the superficial cells are ciliated (Fig. 3.12*G*). The larynx and upper surface of the soft palate are lined with epithelium of this type.

TRANSITIONAL EPITHELIUM was formerly thought to represent a transition between stratified squamous and columnar epithelia such as occurs at the point where the esophagus joins the stomach. However, since it occurs in the lining of the pelvis of the kidney, ureters, urinary bladder, and part of the mammalian urethra, all of which are nontransitory zones, the original name does not seem particularly apt. Transitional epithelium is found in areas which frequently undergo distention and contraction. Its appearance, therefore, varies considerably. The deeper portion is like that of other stratified epithelia, but the cells of the outer layer differ. They are convex on the free edge but are concave below. They are so arranged as to be able to slide past each other when the epithelium is stretched and yet return to their original position when contraction occurs. When the epithelium is stretched, only two layers of cells may appear to be present, an underlying, cuboidal layer and an outer squamous layer. The stratified appearance is assumed during the contracted state.

General remarks about epithelia. Although structural characteristics have been used here as a basis for classifying epithelia, functional properties are sometimes utilized in describing them. The term *glandular epithelium*, for example, is frequently used in referring to columnar epithelium, which not only lines glandular organs but the cells of which actually produce the secretion characteristic of the gland. *Sensory epithelia* form the sensory portions of sense organs, such as the retina of the eye and the olfactory region of the nasal passages. *Germinal epithelium* is that part of the sex glands from which the germinal elements (eggs and spermatozoa) arise. *Cuticular epithelium* secretes a substance, the *cuticle*, which covers the cells and forms a tough, resistant, noncellular, protective layer. The chitinous exoskeleton of certain arthropods represents such a secretion.

Adjacent cells in epithelia adhere to one another with considerable tenacity. Many investigators have attempted to determine the nature of the cohesive force or substance. Some are of the opinion that intercellular, protoplasmic bridges connect adjacent cells.   In certain specially stained preparations the presence of such bridges seems clearly evident.   Other investigators hold that a cement substance fastens neighboring cells firmly together or that the adhesion of cell membranes is the important factor.   In some cases special structures, such as interdigitating ridges and grooves, hold cells in position.   When, in certain specialized tissues, no cell walls can be detected between adjacent cells and the nuclei seem to be lying in the same cytoplasmic mass, the term *syncitium* is used.   Syncitia are rare among epithelia.   In a developing embryo, the outer layer of one of the embryonic membranes (plasmoditrophoblast of the chorion) is in the form of a syncitium.

Connective tissue.   The principal function of connective tissue is to bind other tissues together and to give support to various structures in the body.   In contrast to epithelia, in which the intercellular substance is reduced or lacking, connective tissues are distinguished by the presence of *intercellular material,* or *matrix.*   The nature of the intercellular substance is characteristic of each type of connective tissue.   Connective-tissue cells themselves do not form the greater part of the tissue.   It is the intercellular substance produced by the cells which furnishes the main bulk of the connective-tissue mass.

Connective tissues are of mesodermal origin and develop from mesenchyme.   Mesenchyme is often referred to as *embryonic connective tissue.* There are four main types of connective tissue: (1) connective tissue proper, (2) blood and lymph, (3) cartilage, (4) bone.   It is not always possible to make a sharp distinction between the various types of connective tissues since there are several intergrading forms.

Connective tissue proper consists of several types showing rather wide differences in the nature of the intercellular substance.   It is composed primarily of fibers, among which various types of cells are scattered.   Most authorities believe that the fibers appear among the cellular elements and within the intercellular substance as a result of a sort of precipitating process or crystallization of the intercellular substance itself.   Mechanical forces undoubtedly are important in influencing the manner and direction in which the fibers are arranged.

LOOSELY ORGANIZED CONNECTIVE TISSUE is the most widely distributed type.   The subcutaneous tissue between skin and underlying muscles is the most familiar example.   It is composed of loose fibers, which ramify in all directions, and of scattered cells of various types.   The term *areolar tissue* has often been used for this kind of connective tissue because under certain conditions it appears as though bubblelike spaces were present among the fibers.   During life, however, the spaces are filled with tissue juices or an amorphous ground substance, so that the name "areolar" is not quite appropriate.

Two types of fibers, collagenous and elastic, are usually recognized in loosely organized connective tissue (Fig. 3.13). *Collagenous fibers* course in all directions and have the appearance of striated ribbons. The striated appearance is due to the presence of fine fibrils which run parallel to each other. The fibrils themselves do not branch, but groups of them may separate so as to give a branched appearance to the fiber as a whole. It is not possible to find the ends of collagenous fibers. They are very tough and resistant to stretching and do not have elastic properties. *Elastic fibers* are fairly long. They show no striations and are not composed of fibrils. They branch and unite with other similar fibers so as to form a rather loose network. Numbers of elastic fibers, when viewed together, may have a yellowish appearance. They may be pulled or stretched rather easily but

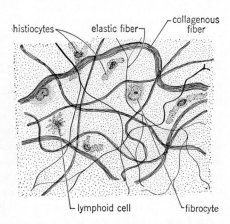

FIG. 3.13. Loosely organized connective tissue.

spring back to normal position when the tensile force is released. Existence of an *amorphous ground substance* in which the collagenous and elastic fibers are supposed to be embedded is difficult to demonstrate even in stained preparations. A very pale, barely perceptible film shows up between the fibers when the tissue is stained deeply. It has not been definitely determined whether the ground substance is jellylike or consists of thin sheets between which lie small amounts of tissue fluid.

The cellular elements in loosely organized connective tissue are of several types. Some apparently *undifferentiated mesenchymal cells* persist, usually in close proximity to blood vessels. They may at times, however, give rise to other types of connective-tissue cells. *Fibrocytes*, or *fibroblasts*, are flattened cells which are found in close association with collagenous fibers and in some cases may also be observed along the surfaces of elastic fibers. These cells may possibly be of importance in the formation of the fibers. *Histiocytes*, or *macrophages*, are almost as numerous as fibrocytes. Their nuclei, which have a rather characteristic shape, are smaller than those of fibrocytes. Under normal conditions they do not move about. They are able to ingest and store certain kinds of microscopic particles. Under inflammatory conditions they may become wandering cells which migrate about the tissue spaces by ameboid movement, engulfing bacteria and other small particles. The shape of these cells varies, their cytoplasm extending out in the form of blunt, irregular processes. *Lymphoid cells* which wander throughout the tissues appear to be identical with certain white corpuscles, or leukocytes, of the blood. They are irregular in appearance and have a phagocytic action. *Mast cells,* which show distinctive staining properties with basic aniline dyes, are also present in loosely organized connective tissue. In amphibians their cytoplasm may be extended out into fairly long processes, whereas in mammals they are more nearly rounded. It is believed that the mast cells may secrete a substance which inhibits the clotting of blood. *Fat cells* may occur singly or in groups, usually along blood vessels in loosely organized connective tissue. Fatty droplets accumulate within the cytoplasm. The droplets within a cell gradually coalesce until the cell is filled with fat. The cytoplasm of the distended cell is stretched out to a thin layer, and the nucleus is pushed to the outer edge. *Chromatophores,* or *pigment cells,* of lower forms are derived from neural crests and are therefore of ectodermal origin. In such animals as fishes, amphibians, and reptiles, they are present in connective tissue, particularly in the upper part of the dermis of the skin. They are irregularly branched cells in which the pigment granules which they contain show, at different times, varying degrees of dispersion or concentration within the cells. The pigment is in the form of small granules which are incorporated within the cytoplasm. Different names are applied to chromatophores, depending upon the color of the pigment (page 96). In mammals such pigment cells are rare. Dermal chromatophores are frequently present in the outer part of the dermis of mammals, but it is not certain that these cells are the same as those of lower forms and actually form the pigment granules which they contain. They may merely be phagocytic cells which have engulfed pigment granules coming from the overlying epidermis. An exception seems to occur in newborn babies of the Mongol race in which a dark area in the skin over the sacral region owes its color to dermal melanoblasts which contain pigment formed by the cells themselves.

Loosely organized connective tissue is so constructed as to be strong as well as elastic. It forms an ideal groundwork for supporting and holding together other tissues and fills in spaces between certain structures. In parts which undergo movement, and those which are concerned with such processes as secretion, absorption, and excretion, the loose connective tissue plays an important role. It is present in the walls of blood vessels and supports the intricate capillary network of the lungs. Gases, water, nutritive substances, and excretory products must pass through the amorphous ground substance on their way to and from the capillaries. The part played by the ground substance in metabolism should be apparent. This type of connective tissue is of great importance in reconstruction or repair after injury and also in combating infection.

DENSELY ORGANIZED CONNECTIVE TISSUE is composed of essentially the same materials that are found in loosely organized connective tissue, but the collagenous fibers are more numerous and thicker. They are very closely interwoven so as to form a dense matting. Cellular elements are relatively few in number. The dermis of the skin, portions of the walls of the digestive tract and blood vessels, as well as certain parts of the urinary excretory ducts are composed of densely organized connective tissue.

REGULARLY ARRANGED CONNECTIVE TISSUE is made up for the most part of densely organized collagenous fibers which show a definite arrangement. The fibers run parallel to each other, and fibrocytes are the only cellular elements present. *Tendons,* by means of which muscles are attached to bones or other structures, are composed of regularly arranged connective tissue. They are very strong and inelastic. The fibers are arranged in bundles which are fastened together with loosely organized connective tissue. *Ligaments,* which connect bones or support internal organs, are somewhat similar in structure to tendons. However, the collagenous fibers are not so regularly arranged as those of tendons, and elastic fibers are present in addition. The *nuchal ligament* at the nape of the neck of certain grazing mammals has an abundance of yellow elastic fibers. In these animals it serves to sustain the weight of the head and thus helps to prevent fatigue.

SPECIALIZED CONNECTIVE TISSUES are present in addition to those already referred to. *Mucous connective tissue* is a type found in embryos. It is composed of scattered cells which seem to be connected with each other by means of long, fine, branching processes. The intercellular substance, or matrix, is abundant and gives the staining reaction for mucin. In the umbilical cord the so-called *Wharton's jelly* is perhaps the best example of mucous connective tissue (Fig. 3.14). It lies between blood vessels and certain ducts which are connected to the body of the embryos (yolk stalk and allantois). The comb of the cock is largely made up of this type of tissue, the development of which, in this case, is regulated by the male hormone secreted by the testes. *Elastic tissue,* in which parallel yellow elastic fibers predominate, is found in various parts of the body. The fact that it can be stretched and then springs back to its normal position when released is of great importance in the region where this tissue occurs. The true vocal cords and the flaval ligaments between adjacent vertebrae which serve to maintain the

FIG. 3.14.   Mucous connective tissue, showing a few cells from Wharton's jelly in the umbilical cord of a pig embryo.

upright posture of man are examples of elastic tissue. *Adipose,* or *fatty, tissue* is really loosely organized connective tissue in which fat cells are particularly abundant. They take the place of other connective-tissue cells which are, therefore, far less numerous than otherwise. Adipose tissue serves to store neutral fat which is then available as a source of heat and other forms of energy for the body. In histological preparations, unless special techniques are followed, the fat is dissolved out of the cells and only a skeletal framework of adipose tissue remains (Fig.3.15).   In certain rodents a peculiar type of tissue, called *brown fat,* is present in such

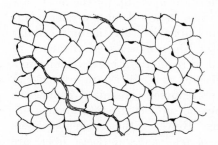

regions as the neck, between the scapulae, etc. Pigment, incorporated in the fat, is responsible for the color.   Some investigators have referred to the brown fat as the *hibernating gland.* Its histological appearance and its behavior in response to nutritional factors differ from ordinary fatty tissue.   More experimental study of brown fat is required before its true function can be unequivocally determined.   *Reticular tissue* consists of fibers which have a special affinity for silver salts and turn black

FIG. 3.15.   Adipose, or fatty, tissue. In this preparation the fat has been dissolved and removed from the cells so that only a skeletal framework remains.

when impregnated with them.   Except for this staining reaction, they rather closely resemble fine collagenous fibers.   They are present in certain regions where loosely arranged connective tissue lies close to other tissues. A network of reticular fibers which ramify in all directions is to be found supporting and surrounding the cells of lymph nodes, spleen, liver, and bone marrow.   *Pigment tissue* is characterized by the presence of numerous pigment-laden cells in the loosely organized connective tissue in certain regions.   The tissue between the sclerotic and choroid coats of the eye is of this type.   It is actually a part of the choroid coat, but when choroid and sclera are separated, portions of the tissue cling to each.   *Vesicular connective tissue* is present in the notochords of vertebrates.   It consists of large cells which are distended with fluid and closely packed together (Fig. 1.4).   The intercellular substance is reduced in amount.   This type of connective tissue is usually considered to be of mesodermal origin, but it is really derived from the undifferentiated region at the dorsal lip of the blastophore.

Blood and lymph are classified with the connective tissues even though the cellular elements are free and the intercellular substance is fluid.   Both cells and fluid course through the body in vessels which are lined with endothelium.   Since certain cellular elements, the leukocytes, are constantly passing back and forth between the connective tissue proper and the blood or lymph, it is somewhat difficult to separate these two types of connective tissue categorically.   The behavior and even the form of leukocytes may differ greatly in these different kinds of environment.

The fluid part of the blood is known as the *plasma.* The part which plasma plays in the metabolism of the body is of great importance.   It is composed mostly of water but contains a number of organic and inorganic substances in solution.   Plasma is the medium which carries nutritive substances, waste products, hormones, and even gases (to a minor extent) all over the body to the places where they are utilized or eliminated, as the case may be. The constancy in the percentage of its various constituents is one of the marvels of nature and is brought about by exchange of substances between the tissue juices and plasma.

The cellular, or formed, elements of the blood include red corpuscles, or *erythrocytes;* white corpuscles, or *leukocytes;* and *blood platelets,* which are found only in mammals but may be similar to the *thrombocytes* seen in the blood of lower vertebrates.

Although the erythrocytes in various vertebrates differ in structure and appearance, their function in all is to carry oxygen to the tissues and to aid

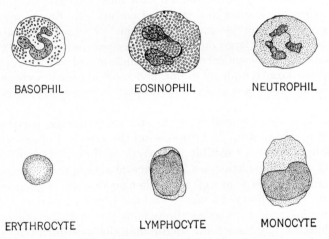

BASOPHIL   EOSINOPHIL   NEUTROPHIL

ERYTHROCYTE   LYMPHOCYTE   MONOCYTE

FIG. 3.16. Some types of formed elements in the blood of mammals.

in the removal of carbon dioxide. The erythrocytes are confined to the blood vessels under normal conditions. In mammals they lose their nuclei before entering the blood stream. They are absent from the lymph.

Leukocytes are of several types (Fig. 3.16) but may be separated into two main groups on the basis of whether they possess granules in the cytoplasm or lack them. *Granular leukocytes* are of three main types, although intergrading forms are abundant. They are all rather similar in size and are distinguished chiefly by the staining properties of the granules which they contain. *Basophils,* which stain with basic dyes, contain relatively large granules which are less abundant than in the other types of granular leukocytes. The nuclei are twisted and show two or more constrictions. These corpuscles are seen infrequently in human blood. In some vertebrates they may be absent entirely; in others they are more numerous and show considerable variation in the size and staining properties of the granules. *Eosinophils,* the granules which have an affinity for acid dyes, possess nuclei which are made up of two lobes connected by a very fine thread. The coarse granules are more numerous than those of basophils. Eosinophilic leukocytes are not abundant but are present in all vertebrates except certain species of fishes. *Neutrophils*, often called *heterophils* in the human being, are by far the most numerous type of leukocyte. Their granules are very fine and stain with neutral dyes, but in other vertebrates they may react to acid and basic dyes as well. The nuclei show great variation in shape but usually appear in the form of three lobelike regions connected with delicate strands. The term *polymorphonuclear leukocyte* is frequently applied to this type of white corpuscle.

Nongranular, or *agranular*, *leukocytes* are of two kinds, *lymphocytes* and *monocytes*. Lymphocytes are small for the most part and in human beings are approximately similar in size to red corpuscles. Small, medium, and large lymphocytes are recognized, however. The cells are more or less rounded and contain large nuclei which have an indentation on one side. A thin layer of cytoplasm surrounds the nucleus. Monocytes appear to be somewhat like large lymphocytes but have more abundant cytoplasm. The nucleus, which does not stain very deeply, is sometimes markedly constricted.

Certain leukocytes engulf bacteria and other foreign particles. They are known as *phagocytes*. Neutrophils are the principal phagocytic agents. Occasionally monocytes exhibit phagocytic activity. It will be recalled that fixed and free histiocytes, or macrophages, present in loosely arranged connective tissue as well as in other regions, are of great importance because of their ability to ingest various types of particulate matter. Leukocytes are able to migrate throughout the body by ameboid movement as long as they have some solid foundation on which they can move. They may enter and leave capillaries by squeezing between the squamous endothelial cells. This process is referred to as *diapedesis*.

Tissue which gives rise to the various types of blood corpuscles is called *hemopoietic tissue*. Lymphocytes and monocytes are formed for the most part in *lymphatic tissue*. Erythrocytes and granular leukocytes trace their origin to the red bone marrow to which the name *myeloid tissue* has been applied. It is in salientian amphibians that the red bone marrow first becomes hemopoietic tissue. During embryonic development, before spleen and bone marrow are formed, mesenchyme and liver are the chief tissues in which red corpuscles are formed. Later the spleen and bone marrow take over this function, but after birth the red bone marrow is the chief seat of erythrocyte formation.

In vertebrates below mammals the blood contains *thrombocytes*, or *spindle cells*, which are believed to play an important part in the clotting of blood. These cells are of approximately the same size as small lymphocytes. The cytoplasm is clear, and the nucleus, which stains deeply, is oval or rounded. A nucleolus is absent. In mammals there are no thrombocytes, but other formed elements called *blood platelets* are present instead. They are thought to function in a manner similar to thrombocytes. Platelets are cytoplasmic structures even smaller in size than red corpuscles. No nucleus is present. It is difficult to study them because they clump together readily as soon as blood leaves the blood vessels and stick to any surface with which they happen to come in contact. They disintegrate rapidly. The blood platelets are believed to be fragments of cytoplasm pinched off certain giant cells, called *megakaryocytes,* present in the red bone marrow.

Cartilage is a form of connective tissue in which the intercellular matrix is abundant and firm. The cellular elements, or *chondrocytes,* give rise to the intercellular substance and are embedded within it (Fig. 3.17). They lie in and completely fill small spaces in the intercellular substance called *cartilage lacunae.* In early embryonic stages and at the borders of cartilages the chondrocytes closely resemble fibrocytes in appearance. When a chondrocyte divides in a young or developing animal, each daughter cell soon forms a matrix about itself, so that usually only one or two cells are seen within a single lacuna. Cell division occurs rapidly, so that occasionally three or four cells, but seldom

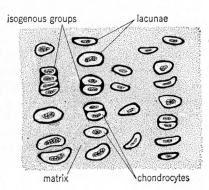

FIG. 3.17. Microscopic structure of hyaline cartilage.

more, are present in a lacuna. In any case the daughter cells appear to lie in groups within the matrix. Such a group is said to be *isogenous.* Cartilage, which is sometimes called gristle, forms an important part of the skeleton. It is also present in certain organs and in other parts of the body as well. In cyclostomes, elasmobranchs, and certain other fishes, the entire skeleton is cartilaginous. In other vertebrates, although varying amounts of bone are present in the skeleton, some cartilage is always present. The skeleton goes through a cartilaginous stage in the embryos of most vertebrates. In some elasmobranchs the cartilage in certain regions becomes calcified, or impregnated with calcium salts, and is hard and rigid. Upon superficial examination calcified cartilage may be mistaken for bone, but it has an entirely different histological structure. Cartilage is surrounded with a layer of densely arranged connective tissue called the *perichondrium.* The transition zone between these two types of connective tissue shows that they are closely related. It is to the perichondrium that tendons and muscles are attached.

Cartilage exists in three main forms, hyaline, elastic, and fibrous. In *hyaline cartilage* the matrix is homogeneous, translucent, and of a bluish-green cast. It is found in such places as the lower parts of the ribs (costal cartilages) and at the ends of bones in joint cavities. *Elastic cartilage* has elastic fibers incorporated in the matrix, which is not very abundant. This type of cartilage is more flexible than others and possesses some degree of elasticity. In the fresh state it is opaque and of a yellowish color. The external ear of mammals, epiglottis, walls of the Eustachian tube, and external auditory canal are composed in part of elastic cartilage. *Fibrous cartilage* has but little intercellular substance, but it contains large collagenous fibers which run parallel to each other. It is really an intermediate type of connective tissue and represents a transition between true cartilage and densely arranged connective tissue. It is found in the discs between vertebrae and also in regions where tendons and ligaments are attached to cartilage of the hyaline or elastic types.

Bone, which forms the greater part of the skeleton in most vertebrates, is the last type of connective tissue to make its appearance during embryonic development. The intercellular substance of bone is very dense, and the bone cells, or *osteocytes*, lie in spaces called *lacunae*, scattered throughout the matrix. The osteocytes have numerous, irregularly branching processes which, during development, join similar processes of other bone cells. Thus they penetrate or pass through the boundaries of lacunae into the matrix through small canals called *canaliculi*. Whether these connections are retained throughout life is not known with certainty. Fibers apparently identical with those of loosely organized connective tissue are present in the matrix but are difficult to demonstrate unless very special techniques are used. The fibers are so arranged as to provide for maximum strength. The hard, rigid consistency of bone is the result of impregnation of the matrix with certain inorganic salts which make up about 30 per cent of the weight of bony tissue. Calcium carbonate, calcium phosphate, sodium chloride, and magnesium phosphate are the principal compounds concerned.

Bone generally exists either in spongy or compact form. *Spongy*, or *cancellous*, *bone* consists of numerous small bony plates and bars, irregularly joined together in an intricate manner. The small spaces between the plates and bars contain *bone marrow*. *Compact*, or *periosteal*, *bone* appears as a hard solid mass without any spaces except those of microscopic size. The two types of bone are not basically different but merely represent a different arrangement of the elements of which they are composed. The expanded extremities of long bones of the body are composed of spongy bone underlying an outer compact layer which is of variable thickness. In the bones of the skull a layer of spongy bone (diploë) lies between two layers of compact bone, the *inner* and *outer tables*.

Spongy bone ensures considerable strength with a minimum of weight. Compact bone generally encloses a variable amount of spongy bone. It forms the hard, tubular shaft of the typical long bone and encloses the marrow cavity.   The outer surfaces of bones are made up of compact bone except on their articular portions.   Compact bone is covered with a dense layer of connective tissue, the *periosteum*.   It is by means of the periosteum that muscles and tendons are attached to bones.   The cavities of bones which are filled with bone marrow are lined with a thin layer of connective tissue called the *endosteum*.

A properly prepared cross section of compact, or periosteal, bone, when examined under the microscope (Fig. 3.18), gives a typical picture of bony

lamellae

Haversian canal

lacunae

canaliculi

Fig. 3.18.   Microscopic structure of bone.   (*Drawn by G. Schwenk.*)

connective tissue.   Rounded, relatively large spaces, the *Haversian canals*, are numerous.   In living bone they serve for the passage of blood vessels. Arranged in fairly regular concentric circles about each Haversian canal are the bony *lamellae*.   Between adjacent lamellae are located the lacunae in which the osteocytes are situated.   Canaliculi may be seen to extend from one lacuna to another.   The blood vessels in Haversian canals supply nourishment to the osteocytes by cell-to-cell transfer through the cytoplasmic processes lying in the canaliculi.   A *Haversian system* consists of a Haversian canal together with the surrounding lamellae, lacunae, and canaliculi.   Between adjacent Haversian systems are irregularly diposed *interstitial lamellae*, lacking Haversian canals.   They represent the remains of former Haversian systems which persist while new systems are being formed during growth processes, when reconstruction of bone is taking place.   *Circumferential lamellae*, also lacking Haversian systems, are present just adjacent to periosteum and endosteum of compact bone.   They run parallel to the outer and inner surfaces.   The bone making up the irregular plates and bars of spongy bone lacks Haversian systems, but the osseous tissue usually shows a lamellar arrangement.   It is an interesting fact that the Haversian systems of different mammals, although basically similar in structure, show enough species variation to make it possible to identify certain animals by the idiosyncrasies in arrangement of their Haversian systems.

Muscular tissue. Although the property of contractility is possessed by all living protoplasm, it is particularly well developed in muscular tissue. In such tissue the direction of contraction is along definite lines which correspond to the long axes of the muscle cells. Although animals in some of the lower phyla move by means of contraction of certain *epitheliomuscular cells*, in most metazoan animals all movement is brought about by the contraction of muscle cells. Such contractions are responsible, not only for locomotion, but also for movements of the various internal organs, for the beat of the heart, for the propulsion of blood and lymph through vessels, for the passage of food through the digestive tract, and for the passage of glandular secretions and excretory products through ducts leading from one part of the body to another.

Three main types of muscular tissue are recognized. The distinction between them is based both on structural and functional differences. *Smooth*, or *involuntary*, *muscle* makes up the contractile tissue of hollow visceral organs, ducts, and blood vessels. The action of this type of muscular tissue is not under control of the will. *Striated, voluntary,* or *skeletal muscle* forms the greater part of the body musculature and is under control of the will. A third type of muscular tissue, called *cardiac* muscle, represents an intermediate form, since it is striated in the manner of skeletal muscle but is, nevertheless, free of voluntary control.

Fig. 3.19. Smooth muscle cells teased apart.

Smooth muscle tissue (Fig. 3.19) is composed of long, narrow, spindle-shaped cells each of which bears a nucleus in its central portion. Thread-like *myofibrils*, which are demonstrated with difficulty, run in a longitudinal direction through the cytoplasm, or *sarcoplasm* as it is called in muscle cells. They are thought to be the actual contractile elements. Smooth muscle cells may occur individually or in the form of bundles or sheets. Individual fibers in close association with collagenous and elastic connective-tissue fibers are found in such regions as the skin about the nipples, the wall of the scrotum, and the villi of the small intestine. Bundles of smooth muscle fibers surrounded by connective tissue are represented by the *arrector pili* muscles which are attached to the bases of hairs and cause hair to stand erect at certain times. The most usual arrangement of smooth muscle fibers, however, is in the form of sheets composed of several layers of cells. In the walls of hollow viscera they are usually arranged in two main layers called *circular* or *longitudinal*, depending on the direction in which the fibers extend. These layers vary in thickness according to the state of contractility. The longitudinal layer is external to the circular layer. This arrangement is characteristic of the muscular wall of the intestine and certain other organs. In some regions the fibers may not show such a distinct stratification. Bundles of fibers may run in different directions, but the fibers within a bundle are parallel to each other.

The close association of connective tissue and smooth muscle is everywhere apparent. Loosely organized connective-tissue fibers gather muscle cells together in bundles and even penetrate between individual cells. Connective-tissue cells, however, do not appear between individual muscle cells of the smooth type. Smooth muscle undergoes slow and rhythmic contractions controlled by the autonomic nervous system which functions independently of the will. Peristaltic and segmenting contractions of the digestive tract, responsible for the propulsion of food down the digestive tract and for mixing it thoroughly with digestive juices and enzymes, are brought about by contraction of smooth muscle. Contraction of the circular layer causes a narrowing of the lumen and a lengthening of the organ; constriction of the longitudinally arranged fibers increases the diameter of the lumen and causes the digestive tract to shorten. In this manner ingested food is propelled down the alimentary tract, in the various parts of which different phases of digestion occur.

Striated, or *skeletal, muscle tissue,* of which all voluntary muscles are composed, consists of long fibers which are, in reality, multinucleated cells. Since the nuclei are not separated by individual cell walls, their grouping forms a syncitium. A *muscle* consists of a bundle of striated muscle fibers bound together in a sheath of connective tissue. The length of the fibers varies somewhat. In short muscles they may extend the entire length of the muscle, but in longer muscles they are attached to tendons or to other muscle fibers in most cases. Individual fibers are independent, show no branching, and course parallel to each other (Fig. 3.20). Each fiber is bounded by a membrane, the *sarcolemma.* Numerous *myofibrils,* which are present within the fiber, are surrounded by cytoplasmic sarcoplasm. The

Fig. 3.20. Three striated muscle fibers teased apart.

myofibrils consist of minute, alternating dark and light plates, or discs. These are so arranged within a fiber that all the dark discs lie at the same level, giving the appearance of dark bands within the boundaries of the sarcolemma. The light discs, lying side by side, form light bands in a similar manner.

The close association between muscular tissue and connective tissue is again brought out in a study of striated muscle, particularly in the region where the muscle is attached to bone or cartilage by means of a tendon. A sheath of connective tissue, the *epimysium*, surrounds an entire muscle. Bundles of muscle fibers are intimately interdigitated with the collagenous fibers of the tendon. Tendons are actually continuations of the *perimysium*, the regularly arranged connective-tissue fibers which lie between bundles of muscle fibers which they help to bind together and with which they form a close union. A thin network of connective tissue, the *endomysium*, surrounds the individual muscle fibers. It is continuous with the perimysium and contains connective-tissue cells in addition to the fibrous elements. Elastic fibers may be found in more than ordinary numbers in certain muscles such as those which cause eye movements and those of the tongue and face.

Cardiac muscle tissue, which is confined to the muscular wall of the heart, is an intermediate type of muscular tissue and shows some characteristics of both smooth and skeletal types. It contracts rhythmically and involuntarily in the manner of smooth muscle. In structure, however, it more closely resembles skeletal muscle, since it is striated. Alternating dark and light discs are present in the myofibrils. The nuclei of the fibers, however, are spaced at more or less regular intervals, lie deeper within the fiber in its axial portion, and are in contrast to the arrangement of the nuclei in skeletal muscle. Moreover, cardiac muscle fibers branch so as to form a network. Peculiar, transverse, *intercalated discs* give the impression of separating the muscle fibers into cells (Fig. 3.21), but researches have shown that cardiac muscle is syncitial, nevertheless. The significance of the intercalated discs is not understood.

FIG. 3.21. Cardiac muscle fibers showing intercalated discs.

Connective tissue penetrates between the cardiac muscle fibers only in mammals. Numerous capillaries course through the connective tissue. In fishes and amphibians the endothelium of the blood vessels which ramify among the bundles of muscle fibers seems to be in direct contact with the bundles.

Nervous tissue. All protoplasm is irritable. It has the power of responding to stimuli or disturbing influences such as may be produced by mechanical forces, sound, heat, cold, light, chemical action, and electricity. Protoplasm also has the property of conductivity, by means of which impulses set up by stimuli are transmitted from one portion of the protoplasmic mass to another. In the cells which make up *nervous tissue,* the properties of irritability and conductivity are more highly developed than in any other tissue within the body. The greater part of the *nervous system* is composed of nervous tissue. Its function is to receive stimuli and to send impulses from one part of the body to another. In this manner the functions of many organs and parts of the body are coordinated and integrated. Nervous tissue is also the seat of all conscious experience. The nervous system is a dominant system. It must function properly if the integrity of the body is to be maintained.

The structural units of nervous tissue are *neurons*, or *nerve cells*, together with their processes. The part of the cell in which the nucleus lies is called the *cell body*. Masses of nerve-cell bodies, if located in the brain or spinal cord, are referred to as *nuclei*. Such nuclei should not be confused with nuclei of individual cells. A mass of nerve-cell bodies located *outside* the central nervous system is called a *ganglion*.

The processes of a neuron are of two kinds: (1) *dendrites*, usually numerous, which are short processes showing a high degree of branching close to the nerve-cell body, (2) a single, slender, *axon*, or *axis cylinder*, which is a long process with branches, the *axon ending*, or *terminal arborization*, at its end (Fig. 3.22). Collateral branches may be given off by the axon along its course, but these are frequently lacking. Axons of certain neurons may be very long, as in those which conduct impulses from the spinal cord to the extremities of the appendages. The number of cytoplasmic processes extending from a nerve-cell body varies and forms the basis for classifying different types of neurons.

The nucleus of a nerve cell is large and spherical and contains a single, distinct, densely staining nucleolus. Special staining techniques

FIG. 3.22. Diagram of a typical medullated neuron.

reveal the presence of numerous basophilic bodies in the cytoplasm. They are called *Nissl's granules*, or *bodies*. The significance of the Nissl's granules is not understood, but their importance in the metabolism of neurons is indicated by the very definite changes which they undergo under varying physiological conditions. Nissl's granules are present in the cytoplasm of dendrites, particularly in the region adjacent to the cell body. They are not present in the axon. Very fine *neurofibrils*, in the form of an intricate network of threads, are also present in the cytoplasm. They extend even into the smallest branches of both dendrites and axon. The neurofibrils may possibly play a part in the transmission of impulses.

The axon with its enveloping sheath or sheaths is spoken of as a *nerve fiber*. Those nerve fibers located outside the brain and spinal cord are covered by a thin, continuous, encapsulating membrane, the *neurolemma (sheath of Schwann)*. The neurolemma is composed of *sheath cells (Schwann's cells)* which are present in series beginning at the brain or spinal cord, or at a ganglion, and ending almost at the terminal arborization. Each sheath cell with its cytoplasm and flattened nucleus surrounds a section of the axon. The sheath cells, like neurons, are of ectodermal origin. Some believe that they represent neuroglia cells from the central nervous system which have moved out to a peripheral position. They are not connective-tissue cells. Their presence is essential for the proper functioning of the axons of peripheral nerves since they seem to play a role in the metabolism of the axis cylinders.

Nerve fibers are said to be either *medullated* or *nonmedullated,* depending upon whether or not they are surrounded by a sheath of glistening-white material called *myelin* which lies between the axon and the neurolemma. However, unlike the neurolemma, which is continuous, the myelin sheath is interrupted at rather regular intervals by circular constrictions, the *nodes of Ranvier*. Sections between adjacent nodes are called *internodes*. A single sheath cell of neurolemma covers an internode. It has been shown that the myelin sheath is composed of alternating concentric layers of lipid (fatty) and protein materials. It is believed that it may serve as an insulating substance, much in the manner of the coating on an electric wire, preventing loss of energy of the nerve impulse during its passage along the fiber. The origin of myelin in peripheral nerve fibers is also questionable, but it appears as though the presence of the neurolemma is necessary for its formation. Nonmedullated fibers lack myelin sheaths, and the neurolemma surrounds the axon directly. Lacking a myelin sheath, they appear gray in color, in contrast to the glistening-white appearance of medullated fibers.

A *nerve*, or *nerve trunk*, is made up of numerous nerve fibers outside the central nervous system, bound together in parallel bundles by connective tissue. Most peripheral nerves are composed of medullated fibers. Nonmedullated fibers are found chiefly as components of nerves making up the sympathetic nervous system. Nerve fibers located in the brain and spinal cord are medullated but lack a neurolemma. Instead, they are surrounded by neuroglia cells which are believed to produce the myelin sheath surrounding the axons.

Generally speaking, the presence of medullated fibers occurs only among vertebrates, cyclostomes being the only ones in which the nerve fibers lack myelin sheaths.

In the animal body, impulses always travel in one direction in nerve cells, passing from dendrites to cell body and then down the axon. Thus one end has a receptive function, whereas impulses are discharged at the other. This is spoken of as the *polarity* of the neuron. It has been shown, however, that under experimental conditions it is possible for impulses to travel in the reverse direction. This does not occur in the body because of the manner in which the various neurons are arranged and because of the fact that they are polarized. The nervous system is mostly made up of neurons arranged in chains in such a manner that impulses can be transmitted from one to another in series. The terminal arborization of one cell comes in close, and even intimate, contact with the dendrites of one or more other neurons. The cells do not fuse, however, and the substance of one cell is separated from that of the next. Such a point of junction is known as a *synapse*. An impulse does not travel across the synapse from the terminal arborization of one cell to the dendrites of the next. Rather, a fresh impulse is set up on the other side of the synapse. In this manner impulses are conducted from one part of the body to another. One neuron in most cases forms synapses with many other neurons. There have been many speculations as to the nature of the synapse and the manner in which impulses are transmitted. The two sides of the synapse are not alike structurally or functionally. Often the terminal branches of the axon bear small, clublike enlargements which are closely applied to the dendrites or even to the cell body of another neuron. In some cells they form small networks which appear to be in contact with dendrites of another cell. One idea, supported by considerable evidence, holds that in peripheral nerves a minute amount of a chemical substance (acetylcholine) is given off by the very small terminal fibers of the axon and that this sets up an impulse in the next cell. Another theory suggests that the properties of the synapse depend upon electrical phenomena. It is not definitely known whether synapses in the central nervous system involve chemical mediation like those of peripheral synapses, although it appears probable that they operate in the same manner. It is known that if a stimulus is too weak to initiate a nerve impulse, and another stimulus of the same magnitude is applied immediately afterward, a nerve impulse will then start up. The first seems to sensitize the nerve substance in such a manner that the second stimulus may then act. The combined activity of two such stimuli applied close together is known as *summation*. The presence of the synapse may possibly be of importance in connection with this phenomenon.

The terminal processes of neurons in contact with epithelial, muscle, glandular, and even certain connective-tissue cells show many interesting variations. Some are *receptors*, capable of receiving sensory stimuli; others are *effectors*, either causing muscle cells to contract or glandular cells to secrete. Receptors are dendrites, modifications of dendrites, or are comparable to dendrites. Effectors are homologous with the terminal arborizations of axons. The various modifications of receptor and effector nerve endings are discussed in Chap. 14.

Types of neurons. A great number of types of neurons may be observed in various parts of the nervous system. *Unipolar neurons* are those in which only a single process, the axon, passes from the cell body and no dendrites are present. Such neurons are rarely found in the central nervous system of adults, but they are present in abundance during developmental stages in early embryonic life.

Typical *bipolar neurons* have a single dendrite and a single axon projecting from opposite ends of the cell. Such neurons are present in the retina of

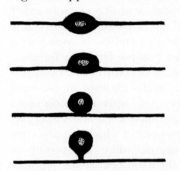

the eye, in the olfactory epithelium, and in the ganglia of the auditory nerve. In certain regions a further differentiation occurs, so that both axon and dendrite appear to arise from the nerve cell by a single process. Intermediate stages are shown in Fig. 3.23. Neurons of this type are found in the ganglia of cranial and spinal nerves. They are sometimes spoken of as *pseudounipolar,* or *unipolar-ganglion, neurons.* The dendrite of such a cell is highly specialized. It may be

FIG. 3.23. Intermediate stages in the transition of a bipolar neuron to one of the pseudo-unipolar type.

very long, and its microscopic structure similar to that of the axon. The chief difference between an axon and a dendrite of this type is that they conduct impulses in opposite directions in reference to the cell body. Sometimes such dendrites are even referred to as peripheral sensory axons.

The shape of *multipolar neurons,* which are most numerous of all, is variable and depends upon the number, arrangement, and length of the processes. They may, in general, be resolved into two main types. In *Golgi Type I* there is a single long axon and numerous short dendrites; in *Golgi Type II* the axon is very short. The cell bodies of multipolar neurons are located in the gray matter of the brain and spinal cord. In Golgi Type II the cells are confined to the central nervous system, but the axons of many neurons of Golgi Type I form the motor components of spinal nerves and of certain cranial nerves.

Gray matter and white matter. Groups of nerve-cell bodies, their dendrites, and the proximal ends of medullated axons have a grayish appearance. The term *gray matter* is applied to such parts of the brain, spinal cord, and peripheral ganglia in which nervous tissue of this type is present. *White matter,* on the other hand, is present in the brain, spinal cord, and most peripheral nerves. It is composed of large bundles of medullated nerve fibers with their glistening-white myelin sheaths. Generally speaking, white matter serves to conduct impulses from one part of the body to another. Gray matter, on the other hand, functions in integrating impulses. It should be recalled that supporting, ectodermal *neuroglia cells* are present in the brain and spinal cord where they serve to bind together the various nervous elements.

Postganglionic fibers of the sympathetic nervous system lack myelin sheaths and appear gray in color. In contrast, the peripheral cranial and spinal nerves are white, since their fibers are medullated.

ORGANS AND ORGAN SYSTEMS

As observed in an earlier part of the chapter, any part of the body which carries on some special function is referred to as an *organ*. Organs are composed of several types of tissues which work in harmony in the normal functioning of the body. Organ systems are composed of several organs which unite in a common function. The organ systems of the body include the following:

1. Integumentary system
2. Digestive system
3. Respiratory system
4. Excretory system
5. Reproductive system
6. Endocrine system
7. Skeletal system
8. Muscular system
9. Circulatory system
10. Nervous system and receptor organs

In the following pages a comparative study of the organ systems of vertebrates is presented.

SUMMARY

The sexual method of reproduction is the rule in members of the phylum Chordata. A fertilized egg or zygote undergoes a series of cell divisions resulting in the development of an embryo. The manner of development is influenced greatly by the amount and distribution of yolk within the egg cell. An embryo during early development passes through blastula and gastrula stages during which two layers, epiblast and hypoblast, are formed. A third layer soon appears which comes to lie between the other two. Three germ layers are thus established, ectoderm, mesoderm, and endoderm. All structures in the body trace their origin to one or more of these three primary germ layers. The following outline summarizes the derivation of the various structures of the body from the three primary layers.

I. Ectoderm
  A. Skin. Epidermis, skin glands, hair, feathers, nails, claws, hoofs, horns, epidermal scales, covering of external gills
  B. Lining of mouth. Enamel of teeth, glands of the mouth, covering of tongue and lips, anterior and intermediate lobes of the pituitary gland
  C. Nervous system. Brain and spinal cord, cranial and spinal nerves, autonomic portion of peripheral nervous system, sensory parts of all sense organs, medulla of adrenal gland, infundibulum, and posterior lobe of the pituitary gland
  D. Miscellaneous. Lens of eye, intrinsic eye muscles, neuroglia, pineal body, lining of anal canal and derivatives, lining of a portion of cloaca
II. Endoderm*

* The listing refers only to the epithelial lining of the organs. All are surrounded or supported by tissues of mesodermal origin.

    A. Alimentary canal. Pharynx, esophagus, stomach, intestine, liver, pancreas, lining of most of cloaca

    B. Pharyngeal derivatives. Larynx, trachea, lungs, gills of the internal type, middle ear, Eustachian tube, tonsils, thyroid, parathyroids, thymus, ultimobranchial bodies

    C. Miscellaneous. Allantois, urinary bladder, urethra, yolk sac

III. Mesoderm

    A. Muscles. Smooth, striated, cardiac

    B. Skeleton. Cartilage, bone, other connective tissues

    C. Excretory organs. Kidneys and their ducts

    D. Reproductive organs. Gonads, ducts, accessory structures

    E. Circulatory system. Heart, blood vessels, blood, spleen, lymphatics, blood-forming tissues

    F. Miscellaneous. Dentine of teeth, dermis of skin, cortex of adrenal glands, lining of body cavities, mesenteries and omenta, portions of the eye

The cells making up the germ layers do not possess distinctive differences and are said to be undifferentiated. Further development of the embryo entails, among other things, a differentiation or specialization of groups of cells to form the several types of tissues which make up the body of an individual. A tissue is an aggregation of similarly specialized cells united in the performance of a particular function such as secretion, support, protection, or contraction. A complex of several tissues may together form an organ. Organs have definite form and perform special functions. Groups of organs, working together in performing one or more closely allied functions, constitute an organ system.

Tissues are classified as follows:

  I. Epithelial tissue. Composed of one or more layers of cells covering an external or internal surface of the body or embryonically derived from such a surface

    A. Simple epithelia. Consisting of a single layer of cells

      1. Simple squamous epithelium. Lining of blood vessels and body cavities

      2. Simple cuboidal epithelium. Lining of many glands and their ducts

      3. Simple cuboidal ciliated epithelium. Portions of lining of kidney tubules

      4. Simple columnar epithelium. Lining of alimentary canal

      5. Simple columnar ciliated epithelium. Oviducts, small bronchi

      6. Pseudostratified columnar epithelium. Urethra of human male, large ducts of certain glands (parotid)

      7. Pseudostratified columnar ciliated epithelium. Respiratory passages, ducts of male reproductive system

    B. Stratified epithelia. Composed of several layers of cells

      1. Stratified squamous epithelium. Epidermis of skin, lining of mouth

      2. Stratified cuboidal epithelium. Epidermis of many tailed amphibians

      3. Stratified columnar epithelium. Epiglottis, part of urethra

      4. Stratified columnar ciliated epithelium. Larynx, upper surface of soft palate

      5. Transitional epithelium. Urinary bladder, pelvis of kidney

 II. Connective tissue. Binds other tissues together and gives support to various structures in the body. It is distinguished by the presence of intercellular material, or matrix

    A. Connective tissue proper
        1. Loosely organized connective tissue. Under skin, walls of lungs, most visceral organs
        2. Densely organized connective tissue. Dermis of skin, part of walls of urinary ducts
        3. Regularly arranged connective tissue. Tendons, ligaments
        4. Specialized connective tissues
            a. Mucous. Umbilical cord, cock's comb
            b. Elastic. True vocal cords, flaval ligaments
            c. Adipose. Fat
            d. Reticular. Groundwork of most glandular organs
            e. Pigmented. Choroid coat of eye
            f. Vesicular. Notochord
    B. Blood and lymph. Fluid connective tissue
    C. Cartilage. Firm and abundant intercellular matrix
        1. Hyaline. Costal cartilages
        2. Elastic. External ear, epiglottis
        3. Fibrous. Intervertebral discs
    D. Bone. Dense, hard, intercellular matrix
III. Muscular tissue. Composed of cells in which the property of contractility is particularly well developed
    A. Smooth or involuntary. Arrector pili muscles, walls of intestine and blood vessels
    B. Striated, skeletal, or voluntary. All voluntary muscles
    C. Cardiac. In wall of heart
IV. Nervous tissue. Composed of cells in which the properties of irritability and conductivity are extremely well developed. The greater part of the nervous system of the body is composed of nervous tissue

PART II. ORGAN SYSTEMS OF VERTEBRATES

CHAPTER 4

INTEGUMENTARY SYSTEM

The integument, or outer covering of the body, is commonly referred to as the skin. Together with its derivatives it makes up an important organ system of the body, the *integumentary system*. It is continuous with the mucous membrane lining the eyelids, mouth, nostrils, and the openings of the rectum and urogenital organs. The primary function of the skin is to cover and protect the tissues lying beneath it, since this is the part of the body which comes in contact with the environment. It is abundantly supplied with sensory nerve endings which are affected by environmental stimuli. The character of the skin and its derivatives shows much variation in the different groups of vertebrates. The type of environment, whether aquatic or terrestrial, is an important influence in determining the character of the variations.

INTEGUMENT PROPER

In such invertebrates as arthropods, annelids, mollusks, and some others, the integument consists of a single layer of cells, the *epidermis*, together with a noncellular *cuticle* (Fig. 4.1) secreted by the cells. The cuticle may be very thin, as in annelids, or a heavy layer composed of chitin, calcareous material, or other substances. In arthropods the rigid cuticle makes up the *exoskeleton.* The term *ecdysis* refers to the periodic shedding of this outer layer. The integument of vertebrates (Fig. 4.2) consists of an outer layer, the *epidermis*, composed of cells which are derived from ectoderm, and an underlying mesodermal layer known as the *dermis*, or *corium.* In tetrapods, ecdysis consists of a shedding, or sloughing, of the outer layer of the epidermis. In some forms this is shed as a whole, but in others it is given off in fragments of various sizes. Under the dermis lies a loose layer of connective tissue, the *subcutaneous tissue.* In skinning an animal the integument is readily detached from the rest of the body. In many regions fat may be deposited in the subcutaneous tissue. The fatty layer is known as the *panniculus adiposus.* In obese individuals, the panniculus may be extensively developed and several inches in thickness. In such places as the palms of the hands and soles of the feet the fibers of the dermis are more or less tightly interwoven with those of the subcutaneous layer so that the skin in these regions is more firmly attached.

Skin of man. In order to understand more readily the modifications of the integument found in various vertebrates, it is convenient first to discuss that of the human being, since it is most familiar.

Epidermis.   The outer epithelium, or epidermis, is made up entirely of cells which are arranged in more or less distinct layers.   It is closely applied to the corium beneath.   In the deepest layer the cells are columnar in shape and arranged perpendicular to the corium.   These cells are con-

FIG. 4.1.   Section through a portion of the integument of a crayfish, a typical invertebrate.

FIG. 4.2.   Section through a portion of the integument of a typical tetrapod (semidiagrammatic).

tinually dividing mitotically and make up the *stratum germinativum,* or *Malpighian layer.*   As new cells are formed they gradually approach the surface, becoming flattened as they do so.   The region in which this occurs is called the *transitional layer.*   On the outer surface the cells are dead and have lost their nuclei.   The outer layer of flattened cells is the *stratum corneum,* or *horny layer* of the skin.   Its chief constituent is keratin, a very hard, tough, insoluble protein.   The stratum corneum is known as the horny, or cornified, layer because in some vertebrates it becomes very hard in certain regions.   The epidermis of man is an excellent example of stratified squamous epithelium (Fig. 4.3).

The cells of the stratum germinativum lie in direct contact with the dermis.   It is from the dermis with its rich supply of blood vessels that they derive their nourishment and are thus able to grow and divide.   As new cells are constantly forming, the outer, flattened cells of the stratum corneum would ultimately form a very thick layer were it not for the fact that they are continually being sloughed or worn off from the surface and replaced by new cells.   The rate of proliferation of the cells of the stratum germinativum is approximately the same as that at which the outer corneal cells are being desquamated, so that the thickness of the epidermis is relatively constant.   An increased amount of friction in a given area of the epidermis seems to stimulate the cells to divide more rapidly and results in the formation of calluses.   Such thickened areas afford a greater protection to the delicate tissues lying beneath.

In many tetrapods the dead corneal layer is shed at intervals as a continuous sheet, but in man small fragments are continually being given off, and shedding is ordinarily not noticeable.   After a severe sunburn the corneal layer of the human skin may, however, be sloughed in fairly large shreds.   It is a familiar experience that after perspiring, portions of the skin may easily be rubbed off in small fragments.   Shedding of the corneal

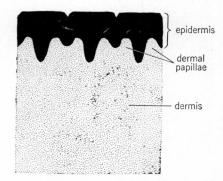

Fig. 4.4.   Diagram showing relation of dermal papillae to epidermis in friction area of skin.

Fig. 4.3.   Section through thick integument on the palm of a human being (semidiagrammatic).

layer seems to be at least partly controlled by the secretion of the thyroid gland.

The epidermis in certain parts of the body in man shows modifications from the conditions described above.   For example, in the thick skin on the soles of the feet and palms of the hands (Fig. 4.3), the transition from columnar Malpighian cells to flattened corneal cells is not so abrupt.   A granular layer intervenes to form the lower part of the transitional layer. This is called the *stratum granulosum*.   Another layer, the *stratum lucidum*, lies just above the stratum granulosum in these thickened regions of the integument and forms the remainder of the transitional layer.   The stratum lucidum is rather transparent and resists ordinary stains in sections prepared for histological study.   These tough layers serve as a protection to the cells of the stratum germinativum in regions most likely to come in contact with external objects.

Dermis. The dermis, sometimes called the true skin, is best developed in mammals. In contrast to the epidermis it is not composed entirely of cells but consists largely of connective-tissue fibers extending in all directions and forming a fairly elastic covering which makes up the greater portion of the skin. Cells appear among these fibers. In addition to connective tissue, the dermis contains nerves, smooth muscle fibers, blood vessels, and certain glands. In preparing leather, the epidermis is first removed by maceration and the connective-tissue fibers of the dermis are thickened and toughened by the action of tannin, alum, chromium salts, or other so-called tanning agents.

Patterns. On the surface of the human skin are many small grooves and ridges which intersect so as to bound small triangular and quadrangular areas. On the palms and soles the grooves and ridges generally run parallel to each other for some distance. The side of the dermis in contact with the epidermis is thrown into rows of *papillae* which are most prominent on the palms and soles. The papillae are quite definitely arranged so that a double row lies beneath one of the external ridges (Fig. 4.4). The grooves between the external ridges correspond to the depressions of the Malpighian layer in the dermis. In other regions the papillae show variations in size and arrangement. The ridges on the palms and soles are arranged in such a manner as to provide the greatest possible friction with a surface. They tend to prevent slipping should the surface be very smooth.

The finely detailed patterns formed by depressions and friction ridges are very useful in making fingerprints and footprints. The patterns do not change from birth to death. There is no longer any question as to the constancy of fingerprints, and this fact has been used extensively in preparing systems of identification now so widely used. Use of fingerprints as a means of identification goes back to ancient times when the thumb impression of a monarch was used as a signature. The patterns on the various fingers and toes of a single individual show as much variation as do those of separate persons. With millions of fingerprints now on record, a system of cataloguing them had to be devised in order to identify quickly any print that was being traced. There are four main types of patterns: arches, whorls, loops, and composites. In each type distinct subdivisions occur, and these in turn show detailed variations. The number of possible patterns is almost limitless. The Federal Bureau of Investigation in Washington maintains the largest collection of fingerprints in the world. It cooperates with 81 foreign countries and territorial possessions in the international exchange of fingerprint-identification data. So well catalogued are the prints that one can be traced almost in a matter of minutes.

Pigment. Pigment in vertebrates occurs in certain cells in the form of small granules. The human integument does not contain special *chromatophores* (pigment-bearing cells) such as are found in cyclostomes, fishes, amphibians, and reptiles and which respond to stimulation by changing the distribution of the pigment granules within the cells. Instead, the color of the skin depends upon the presence of pigment granules in the lowest layers of epidermal cells. With the exception of certain white animals and albinos the integument of all vertebrates bears pigment granules. In true albinos there is a total lack of pigment in all parts of the body.

In man pigment granules are present in the basal cells of the stratum germinativum. Some additional, branched pigment cells called *melanoblasts* lie at the point of junction between dermis and epidermis. A few pigment cells may also be scattered throughout the dermis. Their relation to other pigment cells is not clear. It might be supposed that all the cells of the epidermis would contain pigment since they are derived from the stratum germinativum. This, however, is not the case, for most of the pigment is lost as the cells approach the surface. When a water blister forms in the skin, the fluid collects between the outer and inner layers of epidermis. The skin covering a blister in a Negro as well as in a white man is almost devoid of pigment.

Wide variations in skin color exist among races of man and even among individuals of the same race. The color of the human skin actually depends upon three varying factors: its basic color is yellowish; the blood vessels in the skin give it a reddish hue; the pigment *melanin* in different concentrations causes various shades of brown. The actual amount of pigment present is relatively small. It has been estimated that there is about 1 g. of pigment in the entire skin of an average Negro.

A contested point but one of considerable interest is that of the relationship between the degree of human pigmentation and the degree of intensity of the sun's ultraviolet rays in different regions of the earth. In general, the Negroid races nearest the equator are the darkest. In the area about the Mediterranean Sea the dark Spanish and Italian races are to be found, while the regions farther north are inhabited by the lighter Germanic and Scandinavian races with the least degree of pigmentation. There are many exceptions, however, to the general rule. The Eskimo, for example, with dark skin and hair inhabits the most northern regions. The discrepancy may perhaps be attributed to migration from a more southerly clime. At any rate, the degree of pigmentation seems to be associated with protection from the sun's rays. Formation of pigment is stimulated by mild exposure to ultraviolet light. In the lighter-colored races this is commonly known as "tanning." A dense pigmentation gives its possessor a certain advantage in his power of enduring the heat of the sun. It is probable that a heavy layer of pigment in the stratum germinativum of the epidermis prevents the actinic rays from reaching the capillaries nearest the surface. These may then expand so that a relatively large amount of blood is brought to the surface of the body from which excess heat is given off by radiation.

In cases of sunburn the ultraviolet rays apparently kill the outer cells of the skin. The cells are believed to release a metabolic substance which has the effect of dilating the skin capillaries. Hence the sunburned area becomes flushed. Evidence that the local reaction spreads beyond the limits of skin exposed to light gives conclusive support to the view that a vasodilator substance is released. In cases of severe sunburn, blisters form in regions where the capillaries are excessively dilated. The fluid contained within the blister is exuded by the capillaries. Leukocytes may gather and give the affected area a yellow color. The dead skin is finally sloughed.

The difference between becoming sunburned and tanned should be apparent. Two entirely different processes are involved. In sunburn a severe, rapid, and harmful action occurs; whereas in tanning, which is at best a slow process, there is but mild or short exposure and the skin is stimulated to form pigment which acts as a protection from too great exposure to the sun's rays.

The degree of pigmentation in various parts of the body of an individual also shows variation. In the darker races the back and dorsal regions of the arms and legs are darker than the ventral aspects. The palms and soles in particular are lighter in color. Such a distribution of pigment might be correlated with exposure to light if man were to assume the position taken by most tetrapods. On the other hand, regions such as the axillae, nipples, external genitalia, and groin, as well as the circumanal area, all show a greater degree of pigmentation than do other parts of the body. A pigmented area appears in the skin over the sacral region in young babies of the Mongol race. No satisfactory explanation has been offered which throws any light on the function of pigment in these regions. It scarcely seems plausible that it can be correlated with exposure to the sun's rays.

Generally speaking, the skin is pigmented in those vertebrates which lack accessory integumentary structures such as hair or feathers. In those in which the body is thickly covered, the accessory structures receive the pigment and the integument proper has a scant supply.

Comparative anatomy of the integument proper. *Amphioxus.* The skin of amphioxus represents chordate integument reduced to its simplest form. The epidermis consists only of one layer of columnar epithelial cells which secrete a thin, noncellular cuticle perforated by minute pores. The dermis is thin and made up of soft connective tissue. Pigment is lacking.

Cyclostomes. Cyclostome integument shows a greater degree of development than that of amphioxus. The epidermis is made up of several layers of cells. There is no dead stratum corneum, since the outer cells have nuclei, are living, and are active enough to secrete a thin cuticular covering. The dermis is even thinner than the epidermis and consists merely of a meshwork of connective-tissue fibers intermingled with blood vessels, nerves, and smooth muscle fibers. Horizontal bands of fibrous tissue are interrupted at definite intervals by vertical strands, the *myocommata*, which lie between successive myotomes. The color of the skin is due to the presence of chromatophores which, as in fishes, are located in the dermis.

Fishes. In fishes the integument shows little if any change over the condition in cyclostomes. There is no dead corneal layer. However, in certain teleosts during the breeding season, so-called "pearl organs" appear on the skin. These are cornified areas of the epidermis. The dermis consists of connective tissue, nerves, blood vessels, and smooth muscle fibers and shows some degree of stratification. Scales are embedded in the dermis.

The color of fishes is due primarily to the presence of *chromatophores* in the dermis. These pigment cells sometimes wander into the epidermis. Crystals of guanin located in cells called *iridocytes*, or *guanophores*, associated with scales, are responsible for the iridescence and reflection so charac-

| A | B | C |

FIG. 4.5. Three stages in concentration and dispersion of pigment in chromatophores in the skin of certain vertebrates: *A*, pigment concentrated in center of cell; *B*, intermediate condition; *C*, pigment dispersed throughout cytoplasm of chromatophores.

teristic of the integument of many fishes. The chromatophores of lower forms are specialized cells which are derived from the neural crests and are, therefore, of ectodermal origin. They contain pigments of various colors. *Melanophores* contain black or brown pigment; *erythrophores*, red pigment; *xanthophores*, yellow pigment. Other chromatophores may contain granules of an orange color. The red, yellow, and orange types are sometimes referred to collectively as *lipophores*. Chromatophores have many irregular, branching processes. When the pigment granules are dispersed throughout the cell it displays the greatest amount of color (Fig. 4.5). When the granules become concentrated about the nucleus only a small spot of color is visible. Various colors may be produced by combinations and blending of chromatophores bearing different kinds of pigment granules and by various degrees of dispersion of the granules. The background color of pigment in the cells of the stratum germinativum is also of importance in producing any effect. The ability to change color is known as *metachrosis*. Changes are probably mediated, for the most part, by impulses reaching the brain from the eyes. Two methods of control have been discovered; nervous and endocrine. In elasmobranch fishes, amphibians, and most reptiles, epinephrine from the adrenal gland brings about a concentration of pigment, and intermedin from the intermediate lobe of the pituitary gland brings about its dispersion. Many teleost fishes, and chameleons, among lizards, evidence a nervous control of chromatophore-pigment dispersion and concentration, via the autonomic nervous system. The nerve endings presumably give off certain chemicals such as epinephrine or sympathin which actually bring about the reaction.

Amphibians. The epidermis of amphibians (Fig. 4.6) is composed of several layers of cells and is the first to have a dead stratum corneum. The

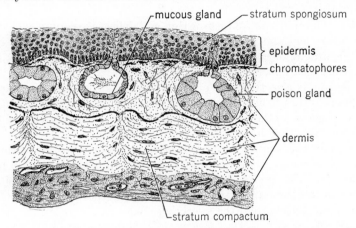

Fig. 4.6. Section through integument of frog, *Rana pipiens*. Note upper loose layer (stratum spongiosum) and lower compact layer (stratum compactum) of dermis.

stratum corneum is best developed in those amphibians which customarily spend considerable time on land. The dead corneal layer is an adaptation to terrestrial life. It not only aids in protecting the body but helps prevent loss of excessive amounts of moisture. When ecdysis occurs, the corneal layer may be shed as a whole or come off in fragments. In the larval or tadpole stage, the epidermis is unusual in that even prior to hatching it is made up of two layers of cells. In the earliest stages the epidermis is ciliated.

The dermis is relatively thin in amphibians. It is composed of two layers: an outer looser layer, the *stratum spongiosum*, and an inner, more compact layer, the *stratum compactum*. The outer part of the stratum spongiosum is often more compact than the remainder of this layer. Blood vessels, lymph spaces, nerves, and glands are abundant in the stratum spongiosum. The amphibian skin is an important organ of respiration, and the dermis is supplied with an unusually large number of blood vessels.

The ability of the integument to change color so as to blend in with the environment is related to the chromatophores which are present, for the most part, between epidermis and dermis.

Reptiles. The epidermis of reptiles is characterized by the extremely well-developed corneal layer and is admirably adapted to life on land. The scales of reptiles are derived from the horny stratum corneum. Ecdysis occurs at intervals and is necessary for removal of dead outer layers.

The dermis consists of superficial and deep layers. In many snakes and lizards the superficial layer has an abundance of chromatophores, but these are not particularly conspicuous in other reptiles. The deep layer is composed mostly of bundles of connective tissue. Leather can be prepared from the skins of certain reptiles. Some reptilian leathers have a high commercial value.

Birds. The epidermis of birds is thin and delicate except in such exposed regions as the legs and feet, where the thick, corneal layer forms protective scales. Feathers, of course, cover and protect the bodies of birds. They, too, are modifications of the stratum corneum.

The dermis is also thin and made up mostly of interlacing connective-tissue fibers. Muscle fibers are particularly abundant, being used in raising and lowering the feathers. In a few birds, such as the ostrich, the integument is so thick that it can be prepared as leather.

Pigment in the skin of birds is generally confined to the feathers and scales. No chromatophores of the type found in lower forms are present.

Mammals. The human skin, previously discussed, is typical of the mammalian integument. A major distinction is that the dermis of mammals is much thicker than the overlying epidermis.

STRUCTURES DERIVED FROM THE INTEGUMENT

Glands

One of the most important functions of epithelial tissues is the part played by them in the metabolism of the body. Absorption of external substances and the liberation of others may take place through the epithelium. Modifications of the epithelium in the form of glands aid in carrying on its secretory function. The many and varied types of glands found in the skin are not essentially different from those found in other parts of the body, but the stratum germinativum alone is concerned with their formation. All of them are *exocrine*, or externally secreting, glands which pour their secretions onto an epithelial surface. Although *endocrine*, or internally secreting, glands are usually derived from epithelial surfaces, none is associated with the integument except as it may be derived from ectodermal epithelium in the embryo.

Structure

According to structure, the exocrine glands of the skin are of two general types, *unicellular* or *multicellular*, depending upon whether they consist of isolated units or numbers of similar cells joined together to form the glandular element.

Unicellular glands. The simplest of all glands found in the skin are unicellular glands, which may be scattered as modified single cells among other epithelial cells covering the body in amphioxus, cyclostomes, fishes, and amphibian larvae. These glandular cells are, for the most part, known as *mucous,* or *goblet, cells.* They secrete a substance known as *mucin,* which is protein in nature. Mucin together with water forms a slimy, viscid material called mucus. When a unicellular gland of the goblet type is secreting, it contains a mass of mucin somewhat resembling a goblet in shape, with its wide end near the surface and a more or less narrow stalk at its base. The nucleus is generally located at the basal end of the cell. Mucin protrudes through an opening on the free surface. In some cases the elimination of mucin is gradual, and it retains its gobletlike shape. In others, the mass of mucin is liberated and the cell collapses, only to fill up gradually again with secretion, after which the process is repeated. Goblet cells may pass through a number of such phases of secretory activity but finally die and are shed. In the meantime, new goblet cells have been formed. The slippery mucus serves to lubricate the surface of the body, thus lessening the degree of friction with surrounding water. Other types of unicellular glands include *granular gland cells* and large *beaker cells* of cyclostomes and fishes. A beaker cell may extend from the lowest layer of epidermis to the surface. The secretion of the unicellular glands of amphibian larvae digests the egg capsule and frees the embryo.

Multicellular glands. The multicellular glands of the skin are formed by ingrowths of the stratum germinativum into the dermis. In some cases the ingrowth may be a hollow structure from the beginning, but in others it is a solid structure in which a lumen appears later. As development progresses, the mass of cells may give off side shoots, resulting in the formation of compound glands. The branches in most cases, therefore, connect to a single duct which opens onto the outer surface. The glandular portions push deeper down into the dermis where their actively secreting cells are nourished by the blood vessels so abundant in that region. Multicellular glands are classified according to shape.

Tubular glands. The tubular gland, as one would infer from its name, is a tube of practically uniform diameter without any bulblike expansion at its end.

SIMPLE TUBULAR GLANDS. Glands of the simple tubular type are short, blind tubes lying partly in the dermis but extending to the outer epithelial surface (Fig. 4.7*A*). The skin of *Mormyrus,* a fresh-water fish inhabiting some of the larger streams of northern and central Africa, contains such glands. Certain specialized glandular areas in amphibians, such as the swollen thumb pads of male salientians and the *mental glands* of male plethodontid salamanders, appear to be masses of simple tubular glands. The *glands of Moll,* which are found on the margin of the human eyelid, might be considered to be of this type. They apparently are modified sweat glands.

SIMPLE COILED TUBULAR GLANDS. Sweat glands are typical examples of the simple coiled tubular type of integumentary gland and are present only in the mammalian skin. Each gland consists of a long narrow tube, the distal end of which is coiled into a small ball that lies in the dermis (Fig. 4.7*B*). The proximal end serves as a duct which courses through the epidermis and opens onto the surface of the skin by a slightly widened aper-

FIG. 4.7. Diagrams representing various types of integumentary glands, all of epidermal origin: *A*, simple tubular gland; *B*, simple coiled tubular gland; *C*, simple branched tubular gland; *D*, compound tubular gland; *E*, simple saccular gland; *F* and *G*, two types of simple branched saccular glands; *H*, compound saccular gland.

ture. The openings are sometimes referred to as the "pores" of the skin. The glandular epithelium itself is composed of a layer of cuboidal or columnar cells.

SIMPLE BRANCHED TUBULAR GLANDS. The duct of the simple branched tubular gland, which leads to the surface, divides at its lower end into two or more branches (Fig. 4.7*C*). They may or may not be coiled in their terminal portions. Some of the large sweat glands in the axillae, or armpits, are of this type, since the coiled terminal portions show some branching.

COMPOUND TUBULAR GLANDS. Compound tubular glands consist of a varing number of tubules the excretory ducts of which unite to form tubules of a higher order. These tubules in turn combine to form others of a still higher order, etc. (Fig. 4.7*D*). The unit structure of the compound tubular gland is like a simple tubular gland. Mammary glands of monotremes are compound tubular glands. Except for these it is doubtful if any other integumentary glands of this type exist in vertebrates, although several glands associated with internal organs are classified as compound tubular glands.

Saccular glands. The saccular, acinous, or alveolar gland differs from the tubular gland in that there is a spherical expansion at the terminal portion of a tubular duct. The actual secretory cells are in the expanded portion, which lies in the dermis. The duct serves as a passageway by means of which the secretion is discharged onto the epithelial surface. There are three general types of saccular glands.

SIMPLE SACCULAR GLANDS. If only one expanded bulb, or acinus, is at the end of a duct, the gland is of the simple saccular type (Fig. 4.7E). Numerous simple saccular mucous and poison glands are found in the skin of amphibians.

SIMPLE BRANCHED SACCULAR GLANDS. If several acini are arranged along a single excretory duct, as in the *Meibomian glands* of the eyelid, or if a single acinus is divided by partitions into several smaller acini (Fig. 4.7F and G), as in the sebaceous or oil glands of the skin, the gland is said to be of the simple branched saccular type.

COMPOUND SACCULAR GLANDS. Compound saccular glands consist of several portions called *lobules*. The smallest unit of the lobule corresponds to a simple saccular gland. Several of these unit structures unite to form a common duct. This in turn unites with similar ducts of other lobules to discharge the secretion through a main duct which opens on the surface (Fig. 4.7H). The mammary glands of metatherians and eutherians are examples of such glands. Each lobe of the mammary gland is a compound saccular gland.

Method of Secretion

In addition to the classification of glands based on structural characteristics, glands are sometimes classified according to their manner of secreting.

Merocrine glands include those in which the glandular cell bodies are not injured or destroyed during secretion. A cycle of discharge, formation, discharge, and reformation continues. The unicellular integumentary glands are of this type. Among nonintegumentary glands which secrete in this manner are the salivary glands and pancreas.

Holocrine glands are those in which there is an accumulation of secretion within the cell bodies. The cells die and are discharged with their contained secretion. New cells are constantly being produced, so that the process is continuous. Sebaceous glands of the skin are of the holocrine type. The term *necrobiotic* is frequently applied to holocrine glands.

Apocrine glands are those in which the secretion gathers at the outer ends of the glandular cells. The accumulated secretion is pinched off with a portion of the cytoplasm. Most of the cytoplasm, however, as well as the nucleus, remains unchanged, and after a time the process is repeated. Mammary glands are integumentary glands of this type.

Type of Secretion

Glands are also sometimes classified according to the type of secretion which they produce.

Mucous glands secrete mucus. The unicellular glands of cyclostomes and the simple saccular glands in the integument of fishes and amphibians are examples.

Serous glands form a thin, watery secretion. Sweat glands are examples.

Fat, or oil, glands are exemplified by sebaceous glands of the skin and Meibomian glands of the eyelids which are considered to be modified sebaceous glands.

Comparative Anatomy of Integumentary Glands

Amphioxus. Only unicellular mucous glands of the merocrine type are present in the integument of amphioxus. They are mostly goblet cells and are scattered among the other columnar epithelial cells which cover the body.

Cyclostomes. Goblet cells, granular gland cells, and beaker cells, all of which are unicellular merocrine glands, are the only integumentary glands found in cyclostomes. The mucus secreted by them renders the surface of the body extremely slippery. In the hagfish the skin may give off an almost incredible amount of mucus. The hagfish integument also possesses pockets of so-called *thread cells*. The protoplasm in each of these cells secretes a spirally coiled thread which, under the proper stimulus, is shot out and unwound, often to a considerable distance. The threads are added to the other mucous secretion so that a protective layer is formed about the animal.

Fishes. The skin of fishes is particularly abundant in unicellular and multicellular mucous glands. The unicellular glands are like those of cyclostomes, whereas the multicellular glands are of the simple saccular type.

An unusual adaptation in which mucous integumentary glands play an important part is to be found in the South American and African lung-fishes *Lepidosiren* and *Protopterus*. During the dry season these fishes bury themselves in the mud of dried-up river beds. The abundant secretion of mucous glands of the skin forms a sort of "cocoon," or capsule, about the fish in which it lies during estivation.

A few elasmobranch and teleost fishes have multicellular poison glands derived from the epidermis, which are used in a protective manner. In one species, *Synancia*, from the Indian Ocean, the poison organ is well developed. The terminal half of each dorsal spine is provided with a deep groove on both sides. A sac containing the poison lies at the lower end of each groove. A duct from the sac extends to the top of the spine and runs along the groove. Fisherman accustomed to these fish are adept at handling them without injury. The fish generally lies hidden in the sand. Not infrequently a person wading with bare feet will step upon the spines and by causing pressure on the poison sac will inject the poisonous secretion into the wound. The common catfish has a poison gland opening at the base of a spine on each pectoral fin. The spine, when erected, may inflict painful wounds. Other fishes have similar glands associated with spines on the operculum. The spines are often hollow tubes with a poison sac opening at the base. They function in a manner analogous to a hypodermic needle. Erection of the spine brings pressure to bear on the gland, causing the poison to be ejected. This is, perhaps, the first example where the vertebrate skin is modified as a special device for protection from enemies.

Some of the deep-sea elasmobranchs and teleosts, living in total darkness, have luminous phosphorescent organs in the skin. The arrangement of these organs varies considerably, but most frequently they lie in longitudinal lines near the ventral surface of the body. The luminous organs, or *photophores*, are modifications of integumentary glands. Some are quite complicated in structure. In one particular species, *Porichthys*, in which development of photophores has been studied, certain cells bud off the stratum germinativum and come to lie in the dermis. Here they become differentiated into a lower glandular layer and an upper layer which forms a lenslike structure. A reflecting layer surrounded by pigment forms below the glandular layer. The glandular cells give off phosphorescent light, and the other structures serve to transmit it to the outside (Fig. 4.8). The light emitted by luminous organs of this sort undoubtedly helps certain deep-sea fishes to attract their prey.

Fig. 4.8. Section through luminous photophore of the fish, *Porichthys: e*, epidermis with unicellular mucous glands; *gl*, glandular layer; *l*, lens; *r*, reflector surrounded by pigment. (*Redrawn from Kingsley, after Greene.*)

Still another type of integumentary gland found in fishes is the *pterygopodial gland* located at the base of the clasping organs of certain species of skates and rays. Pterygopodial glands are multicellular mucous glands, the function of which is little understood.

Amphibians. Since the skin of many amphibians is an important respiratory organ, it must be kept moist so that exchange of gases may take place between the surface capillaries and the environment. In these forms the large numbers of integumentary glands that are present aid in keeping the skin moist. The glands are usually simple saccular structures, the bulb-like expansions of which lie in the stratum spongiosum of the dermis. Because of differences in structure and secretion, two varieties are recognized: mucous and poison glands (Fig. 4.6).

Mucous glands are generally more numerous and smaller than poison glands. They are found all over the surface of the body but are more abundant in some parts than in others. In one species of frog, *Rana fusca*, there may be as many as 60 to each square millimeter of surface. Around each gland is a coat of smooth muscle fibers which aids in expelling mucus from the cavity of the gland.

Poison glands are larger but not so numerous as mucous glands and are not so evenly distributed over the surface of the skin. In many species

Fig. 4.9. Mental gland of male salamander, *Eurycea bislineata*, as it appears prior to and during the breeding season: *A*, ventral view of head showing position of glandular area; *B*, the same as *A* with the skin below the gland removed to expose the tubular nature of the gland.

they are more abundant on the dorsal side of the body and hind legs. The so-called "warts" of toads and the *parotoid glands* which lie on the neck are actually masses of poison glands. The secretion of these poison glands appears as a whitish fluid which is said to have a burning taste. It may be secured by compressing the glands in the skin of a toad or by exciting the animal and thus causing a natural exudation of poison. When given to a dog the poison brings about trembling, weakness of legs, and nausea. A large dose may cause death, acting upon the heart and nervous system. A small quantity placed on the tongue causes a great stimulation of the salivary glands and induces nausea. A young dog that catches his first toad quickly learns to let toads alone. A tree frog, *Hyla vasta*, which is found in

Haiti, gives off a poisonous secretion so strong that when the animal is handled the poison causes inflammation of the skin. The poison glands in the skin are thus an adaptation for protection. Many amphibian collectors have had the experience of finding all their specimens dead after a day of collecting, with the exception of perhaps one species. The poison of the one species has a lethal effect on the others, but apparently members of its own kind are immune. Stories of getting warts from handling toads are fictitious. Poison glands, in general, are more abundant in toads than in frogs.

Some specialized integumentary glands in amphibians have a tubular structure. They include those on the feet of certain tree-dwelling frogs and toads. Suctorial discs on the toes aid in climbing. The swollen glandular thumb pads of male frogs and toads during the breeding season aid them in clasping the females in amplexus. The males of some plethodontid salamanders develop a glandular area, the *mental gland,* on the chin as the breeding season approaches (Fig. 4.9). Its secretion seems to attract the female. Unicellular glands also occur in amphibians, being present on the snouts of tadpoles and caudate larvae. Their secretion is believed to have digestive properties, thus aiding in freeing the larva from the egg capsule during early development. Large *glands of Leydig* are unicellular glands of uncertain function in the epidermis of adult caudates.

Reptiles. Reptiles, contrary to amphibians, have rough and scaly skins which are primarily adapted for life on land. Correlated with this is an almost total lack of integumentary glands. This paucity of glands in the skin is an adaptation which prevents any unnecessary evaporation of water from the body and accounts for the fact that reptiles can generally live for a considerable time without water. In many species the water contained in the food is enough to give them an adequate supply. Many snakes, however, contrary to popular opinion, do drink water when it is available. The integumentary glands of reptiles, therefore, are fewer in number, and those which are present are scent glands, for the most part associated with sexual activity.

Crocodilians have two pairs of skin glands which secrete musk. One pair is located on the throat on the inner halves of the lower jaw. A slitlike external opening leads to a sac which, in large specimens, is about the size of a walnut. The sac contains a pale, brownish substance which is concentrated essence of musk, much prized by the natives of certain localities. These glands secrete most actively during the breeding season. A second pair of glands of the same type lies just within the cloacal aperture. They are possessed by both sexes and are undoubtedly hedonic in function. In crocodilians a row of glands runs down either side of the back between the first and second rows of dermal plates. If any function is attached to these glands it is unknown.

The skin of lizards is devoid of glands. So-called *femoral glands* found in males on the undersurfaces of the thighs may not be glands at all. They consist of small pits filled with a yellowish debris which projects above the surface as a small hard cone. Little is known of the nature of this "secretion." The short spiny projections are used as an aid in copulation.

Some snakes have glands in the cloacal region which seem to be used in defense. They secrete a milky fluid which has a nauseating odor. The fluid cannot be projected but has a high protective value, as anyone who has handled snakes will agree.

In certain turtles musk glands are present beneath the lower jaw and also along the line of junction of plastron and carapace. They are probably used in sexual allurement.

Birds. As we shall learn later, birds have many characteristics resembling those of reptiles. Like the reptilian integument, the skin of birds is

FIG. 4.10. Section through uropygial gland of bird. (*After Schuhmacher.*)

practically devoid of glands. Usually the only gland that is present in the skin of birds is the *uropygial gland*, a simple branched saccular oil gland located on the dorsal side of the body at the base of the *uropygium*, or tail rudiment. In the chicken it is made up of two lobes which in most cases have separate openings (Fig. 4.10). A septum divides the gland into two halves. The oil collects in a central cavity. The bird, by squeezing out a quantity of oil on its beak, or bill, oils its feathers as it preens them, making them quite impervious to water. The uropygial gland is best developed in aquatic birds. In some, several ducts lead from the gland. It is said that if a duck is washed thoroughly with soap and water so as to remove the oil, the animal will sink when it takes to water.

Not all birds possess a uropygial gland, it being notably absent in the Paleognathae and in a few other species such as parrots and some varieties of pigeons.

The only other skin glands found in birds are certain modified oil glands in the region of the external ear opening. These are found in only a few gallinaceous birds such as the American turkey.

Mammals. The skin of mammals is particularly abundant in glands, and a considerable variety is found. There are two essential types from which all are probably derived, sebaceous glands and sweat glands.

Sebaceous glands. Sebaceous, or oil, glands are distributed over the greater part of the surface of the skin, being absent, however, from the palms and soles. With few exceptions, the duct of the gland opens into a hair follicle. Often several glands are associated with a single hair follicle. The oily secretion given off by these glands serves to keep the hair and skin smooth and soft and also imparts to the animal an individual scent, or odor. Sebaceous glands are present, without being connected to hairs, on the corners of the mouth and lips, the glans penis, internal surface of the prepuce, labia minora, and mammary papillae. These glands, although associated with sexual activity, should not be confused with primary sex glands. The Meibomian, or tarsal, glands of the eyelids also have no connection with hairs, although it seems probable that at one time they were associated with them. They are sebaceous glands with fairly long, straight ducts into which the separate alveoli open. There are about 30 Meibomian glands in the upper eyelid of man and about 20 in the lower. Their oily secretion forms a film over the layer of lacrimal fluid which is thus held evenly over the surface of the eyeball. The film also prevents tears from overflowing onto the cheeks under normal conditions. Small *glands of Zeis* on the eyelids are sebaceous glands which open into the hair follicles of the eyelashes. Infection of one of the glands of Zeis results in a *sty*.

Sweat glands. Sweat glands, or sudoriparous glands, in man are abundantly distributed all over the surface of the body except on the lips, glans penis, and nail bed. They are simple coiled tubular glands which, in the region of the axillae, may show some branching. Sweat glands have two very important functions: getting rid of metabolic wastes and helping to maintain a constant body temperature. In hot weather or after strenuous exercise when the body temperature tends to be higher than normal, the sweat glands pour out their secretion onto the surface of the skin. The cooling effect of evaporation of sweat is important in maintaining a constant body temperature. As much as 2 or 3 liters of sweat may be given off in a 24-hour period.

Deficiency or absence of sweat glands occurs occasionally in man. Several individuals lacking sweat glands have been reported in the state of Mississippi. Frequent plunges in cool water enable them to keep their body temperature down to the normal level in warm weather.

It has been estimated that in an average human being there are about $2\frac{1}{2}$ million sweat glands in the skin. They are most numerous in regions devoid of hair but may occur in all parts of the skin and may even open into hair follicles. According to Krause, there are about 370 sweat glands per square centimeter on the palm of the hand and a slightly smaller number on a corresponding area of the sole of the foot. Krause has made the following estimates for the number of sweat glands in the various regions of the body: 200 per square centimeter on the back of the hand; 175 per square centimeter on the forehead, front, and sides of the neck; 155 per square centimeter on the chest, abdomen, and forearm; 60 to 80 on the legs, back of the neck, and trunk. The size of the sweat glands also varies. According to Krause, the average diameter of the coil is 0.17 to 1.25 mm., and some are nearly 4 mm. in diameter.

In some regions pigment granules are incorporated with the secretion, which explains why the sweat in certain parts of the body, such as the axillary region, appears stained. The sweat of the hippopotamus has a reddish color and is rather albuminous in consistency. In a certain South African antelope, *Cephalophus*, it is of a bluish color.

The horse is supplied with an abundance of exceptionally large sweat glands. In the bear and hippopotamus, sweat glands are present all over the body. Several mammals have no sweat glands. Among these are the spiny anteater, moles, sirenians, cetaceans, scaly anteater, and certain edentates such as the two-toed sloth. Many textbooks and articles state that sweat glands are lacking in the hairy skin of the dog. On the contrary, large numbers of sweat glands are present. Experiments have shown that the sweat glands in the hairy part of the dog's skin do not play an important part in regulating body temperature but serve chiefly in protecting the skin from an excessive rise in temperature (T. Aoki and M. Wada, 1951, *Science*, **114**:123). Many mammals have a limited number of sweat glands confined to certain localities. Sweat glands in the platypus are present in the snout region. In deer they are arranged about the base of the tail. In mice, rats, and cats they are present on the undersides of the paws. Rabbits have them around the lips. The moisture on the muzzles of sheep, goats, cattle, pigs, dogs, and others is due to the secretion of sweat glands. It is improbable that the presence of sweat glands in such restricted areas is related to the temperature-regulating mechanism of the body.

The *ceruminous*, or wax-producing, glands in the external ear passages consist of tubes coiled into small balls like those of sweat glands. There is, of course, a difference in the nature of the secretion, which is fatty; but because of the similarity of the two in structure and manner of development, the ceruminous glands are considered to be modified sweat glands. They are, however, considerably larger than ordinary sweat glands, and their ducts often join those of large sebaceous glands, frequently opening into hair follicles. The mixture of the two kinds of secretion forms what is known as earwax.

The glands of Moll in the eyelids and the circumanal glands are also considered to be modified sweat glands. They, too, are larger than those of the ordinary type.

Scent glands. Scent glands are found in many mammals. Their structure indicates that they are either modified sweat glands or sebaceous glands, but the nature of their secretion is known in only a few cases. Scent glands of various types serve several functions. In some animals they are useful in attracting members of the same species. In other forms they are used in attracting members of the opposite sex and may be present only in the male. In skunks and some others, scent glands have a definite function in serving as a protection from enemies. It is possible that in certain other cases the scent may act as a lure or even to frighten foes away.

The location of scent glands varies greatly. In the deer family they are located on the head in the region of the eyes. Many carnivores have scent glands near the anal opening. Skunks and weasels have saclike scent glands which open into the rectum just inside the anus. They may be everted, and since they are surrounded with muscle fibers, their foul-smelling secretion may be expressed. Scent glands may be located at the openings of the reproductive organs as in many rodents; on the face, as in bats; between the hoofs, as in pigs; at the base of the tail in dogs; over the temporal bone in the elephant; and in still other animals on the arms, legs, and other parts of the body. The callosities on the legs of horses and closely related forms are believed to be vestiges of former glandular areas.

Mammary glands. The mammary, or milk-producing, glands which are present in all mammals and only in mammals are really modified sweat glands. Their ducts open directly or indirectly onto the surface of the skin. The apocrine type of secretion is typical of mammary glands.

Milk is essentially of the same composition in all forms of mammals. The percentages of the different constituents, however, vary in different species. Mammary glands are active only at certain times; immediately after the young are born and generally as long as active sucking continues. The development and functioning of the mammary glands are largely controlled by hormones secreted by the ovaries, the anterior lobe of the pituitary gland, and the adrenal cortex.

Although the details of development show variations in different species, nevertheless most mammary glands are built on the same general plan. The actively secreting mammary gland is made up of many small masses called *lobules*. Each lobule, in turn, consists of large numbers of alveoli which contain the actual secretory cells. The small ducts leading from the alveoli in a lobule gradually converge to form a larger duct. This generally unites with similar ducts from other lobules, and the common duct or ducts thus formed lead to the outside. In the inactive mammary gland the alveoli and lobules are reduced or wanting and the glandular tissue consists mainly of branching ducts. Since abundant adipose, or fatty, tissue usually surrounds the ducts and alveoli, this contributes much to the size of the *mammae*, or breasts.

In the Prototheria the mammary glands are of the compound tubular type. No nipples are present, and the glands open directly onto the surface of the skin. The mammary area, however, is depressed, and the milk is exuded onto this depressed area. The young animals grasp tufts of hair, which project from the depression, in lieu of nipples, and thus obtain their nourishment by lapping, licking, or sucking. In the Metatheria and Eutheria the mammary ducts lead to nipples or teats which are grasped by the mouths of the young when sucking.

The distinction between a nipple and teat is not always apparent on superficial examination (Fig. 4.11). A nipple is a raised area on the breast through which the mammary duct or ducts open directly to the outside. In some mammals, a single duct leads to the surface, as in certain rodents,

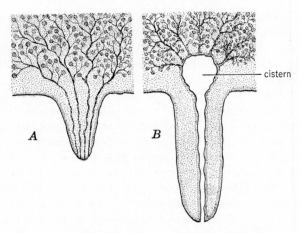

Fig. 4.11.   Diagrammatic sections: *A*, through nipple; *B*, through teat.

marsupials, and insectivores. In other forms, several ducts may open on the nipple, as is the case in some carnivores and in man, in which as many as 20 separate ducts may be present. In the false nipple or teat, which is present in horses, cattle, and others, the skin of the mammary area grows outward to form a large projection. The mammary ducts open into a "cistern" at the base of the teat, and the milk is then carried by the secondary duct, or tube, to the surface.

Many laymen believe that the udder of the cow is a simple sac which fills with milk and must be drained periodically by milking. Nothing is further from the truth. The udder is made up of mammary and other tissues through which the mammary ducts ramify and converge at the bases of the teats (Fig. 4.12). If a milch cow which has been giving several quarts of milk per day is slaughtered, it is doubtful if more than a pint of milk can be obtained from her udder. It is the secretory activity of the cells in the living alveoli which forms milk from substances brought to them by the blood stream.

Although nipples, teats, and mammary tissue may be present in both sexes, functional mammary glands occur normally only in lactating females. In exceptional cases, functional mammary glands have been known to occur in males. Such a condition is referred to as *gynecomastia*. Although there have been reports that in certain species the male may actually aid in nursing the young, these have not been well authenticated. It is more probable that such cases as have been observed have been abnormal, intersexual individuals. It is, however, not uncommon for milk to be present in the mammary glands of human males as well as females at birth and at puberty. The milk which is present in the mammary glands of the human infant at birth is sometimes called "witches' milk."

During early embryonic development in mammals an elevated band of

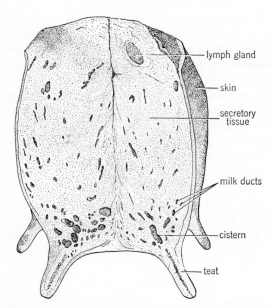

FIG. 4.12. Cross section through the rear quarters of a cow's udder. (*From C. W. Turner, Univ. Missouri Agr. Expt. Sta. Research Bull.* 211. *By permission.*)

ectoderm, called the *mammary ridge*, or *milk line*, appears on either side of the body, extending from the base of the pectoral limb bud to the pelvic limb bud. Depending upon the species, thickenings appear at various points along the mammary ridge, each of which develops into a separate mammary gland with its nipple or teat, as the case may be. The tissue between adjacent glands reverts to normal. Nipples and teats are usually paired, their number being roughly proportional to the number of young delivered at birth. They vary from 1 pair in man and some others to 11 pairs in certain insectivores. Occasionally, in a particular species, extra nipples or teats may be present, a variation which harks back to primitive ancestral conditions and to abnormal embryonic development in which more than the usual number of glandular areas develop in the mammary ridge. If only supernumerary nipples are present, the condition is known as *hyperthelia*, but if more than the usual number of mammary glands or breasts occur, it is referred to as *hypermastia*, or *polymastia*. Hyperthelia is not uncommon in man in which the extra nipples appear as small pigmented areas on the thoracic or abdominal walls. Perhaps the most interesting case on record is that of a Polish woman who possessed eight functional breasts.

The distribution of mammary glands varies greatly in different groups of mammals and is related to the habit of the mother when nursing her young. Animals such as dogs, cats, and pigs, which lie on their sides when the young are feeding, have mammary glands in two ventrolateral rows extending from axilla to groin.   Horses and cows, which stand up when nursing, have their teats in a protected location between the hind legs.   In elephants a single pair is located between the front legs, whereas in whales they are confined to the inguinal region.   Primates, with their arboreal habits, have pectoral mammary glands, as do the manatees and dugongs of the order Sirenia.   In human beings mammary glands occasionally are found in such unusual situations as the axillae, hips, thighs, or back.   This has no real morphological significance and is due to displacement rather than reversion to ancestral conditions.

Scales

In many vertebrates the body has a covering of scales, which gives it protection.   Scales, in general, are of two types: epidermal and dermal. The structure and mode of development of these two types are very different, and it is important not to confuse them.

Epidermal Scales

These are cornified derivatives of the stratum germinativum of the epidermis and are found primarily in terrestrial animals.   A well-developed stratum corneum is characteristic of vertebrates living on land.   Thus, few examples of epidermal scales are to be found in amphibians, but in reptiles, birds, and certain mammals they are very well developed.   Epidermal scales, with few exceptions, are usually shed and replaced.   Large epidermal scales, such as those on the shell of the turtle or the head of a snake, are often called *scutes.*

Dermal Scales

As their name implies, these scales are located in the dermis of the skin and are mesenchymal in origin.   They are found, for the most part, in fishes, and take the form of small bony or calcareous plates which fit closely together or overlap.   Both epidermal and dermal scales are present in certain reptiles and a few other forms.   It is important to distinguish between the two.   Dermal scales are remnants of the dermal skeleton.

Comparative Anatomy of Scales

Amphioxus.   No scales of any kind are present in the skin of amphioxus.

Cyclostomes.   Integumentary scales are absent in modern cyclostomes. However, the epidermal teeth found in the buccal funnel and on the tongue (Fig. 15.2) are really modified epidermal scales.

Fishes.   Epidermal scales are lacking in fishes, but dermal scales, making up part of what is known as the *dermal skeleton* (page 374), are abundant and of several types in this class of vertebrates.   Not all fish have scales.

The common catfish, or bullhead, and *Torpedo*, the electric ray, are examples of fishes which lack integumentary scales. It is commonly believed that eels have no scales, but they are present, nevertheless. Scales of eels are very small and are deeply embedded in the dermis. In certain other fishes, as in chimaeras, scales may occur only in localized regions. The scales of fishes are colorless. Numerous pigment cells (chromatophores), which give the fish its color, are located in the outer part of the dermis both above and below the scale. The presence of water on a descaled fish will frequently reveal the pattern of the scales. In the sea horse and a few other fishes, bony plates form a veritable armor which covers the entire body.

Fish scales as well as the flat, membrane bones in the skulls of fishes and higher vertebrates are believed to be remnants of the bony armor present in ostracoderms and found also in a number of placoderms. The armor of these extinct forms consisted of four rather distinct layers. The deepest layer (*isopedine*) resembled compact bone; the next layer was composed of spongy bone containing numerous vascular spaces; the third layer was of more compact consistency and made up of a hard dentine (*cosmine*) often in the form of separate elevations or ridges; the outer layer was thin and of a hard, enamellike consistency.

Two types of scales have been identified among the earliest primitive bony fishes. One type, the *cosmoid scale*, not found in any form living today, was constructed essentially on the plan of ostracoderm or placoderm armor plates. The scales, however, were in the form of small, separate elements. Cosmoid scales were present in primitive members of the subclass Choanichthyes, *i.e.*, crossopterygians and dipnoans. The other type, the *ganoid scale*, found in primitive ray-finned fishes, existed in two forms. One, the *paleoniscoid ganoid scale*, persists today in *Polypterus*. Here the basal layer is of compact bone (isopedine); the spongy-bone layer has been lost; the cosmine layer has been reduced; the outer portion of the scale is composed of layers of a hard, shiny, translucent material of mesodermal origin and called *ganoin*. The other, or *lepisosteoid ganoid scale*, has eliminated both the spongy-bone and cosmoid layers so that the ganoin lies directly upon the layer of compact bone. This type of scale persists today in the garpike.

Dermal fish scales of four types, ganoid, placoid, ctenoid, and cycloid, are recognized in species living today. They are all fundamentally similar in origin, but their form varies considerably.

Ganoid scales. The structure of the two types of ganoid scales as found in *Polypterus* and *Lepisosteus* has already been described. The scales fit closely together like tiles on a floor and are arranged in diagonal rows (Fig. 4.13). *Amia* has modified ganoid scales on the head. Sturgeons have similar scales in the tail region. In both these fishes the layer of ganoin is lacking.

Fig. 4.13. Ganoid scales of the gar, *Lepisosteus*. Note perforations for openings of the lateral-line canal. (*Drawn by G. Schwenk.*)

Placoid scales. With few exceptions, placoid scales are found only in the elasmobranch fishes. Each scale consists of a basal bony plate which is rounded or rhomboid in shape and embedded in the dermis. From the plate a spine projects outward through the epidermis and points pos-

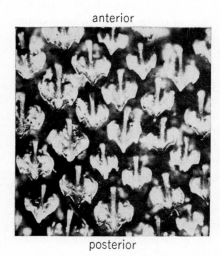

Fig. 4.14. Enlarged photograph of skin of shark, *Squalus acanthias*, showing numerous placoid scales.

teriorly (Fig. 4.14). The spine is made up of dentine covered with a hard layer of *vitrodentine*, both of mesodermal origin. A pulp cavity lies within the spine and opens through the basal plate. This offers a point through which blood vessels enter the pulp cavity. Many authorities have stated in the past that the placoid scale is covered by a layer of enamel. Researches indicate, however, that although the scale may be formed under the organizing influence of an enamel organ (page 154), no actual enamel is formed and the spine is composed of dentine alone. The general similarity in structure of placoid scales to teeth of higher forms should be apparent. Both are considered to be modified remnants of the bony armor of such primitive vertebrates as ostracoderms and certain placoderms.

The scales of dogfishes and sharks are numerous and set closely together, but in other forms they are usually large and scattered about on different parts of the body. They are frequently particularly well developed along the middorsal line. The teeth on the rostrum, or saw, of the sawfish (Fig. 4.15) are actually the extremely large spines of modified placoid scales embedded in sockets at their bases. Placoid scales may develop during embryonic life in chimaeras but soon disappear except in certain scattered areas.

FIG. 4.16.   Ctenoid scale.

FIG. 4.15. Saw of sawfish, *Pristis pectinatus.* The teeth are modified placoid scales.

Ctenoid scales. The ctenoid scale derives its name from the fact that its free edge bears numerous comblike projections (Gr. *ctenos,* comb). It is a rather common type and present in most teleost fishes. Ctenoid scales are thin, translucent plates composed of an underlying layer of fibrous material covered by a layer which somewhat resembles bone. These scales might be compared with ganoid scales from which the layer of ganoin has disappeared and the underlying layer of bone modified. Each scale is embedded in a small pocket in the dermis. The scales are obliquely arranged so that the posterior end of one scale overlaps the anterior edge of the scale behind it. When a fish is scaled preparatory to cooking, the scales are readily flipped out of their pockets by scraping with a knife in a tail-to-head direction. The basal end of the ctenoid scale is usually scalloped (Fig. 4.16). Lines of growth are present which, if examined under a microscope, will give an exact indication of the age of the fish. The number of lines of growth varies according to the species in question and the part of the scale examined. When several lines of growth are widely separated, it indicates that that portion of the scale was formed during the warm season when food was plentiful and rapid growth took place. When several lines of growth are placed close together, the cold season is denoted. Thus, an area on a scale which covers a series of wide lines and a series of close lines would correspond to a year in the life of the fish.

Cycloid scales. The cycloid scale seems rather primitive in structure as

compared with a ctenoid scale. It is roughly circular in outline (Fig. 4.17) with concentric lines of growth which may be used as a means of determining the age of the animal. Cycloid scales are also located in pockets in the dermis but are somewhat more loosely attached than ctenoid scales.

Both ctenoid and cycloid scales overlap, much in the manner of shingles on a roof. In certain fishes, such as flounders, scales of both types may be present, those on the underside being cycloid and those on the upper side being ctenoid. It is probable that complicated ctenoid scales were developed from the more

Fig. 4.17. Cycloid scale of white sucker. From a fish that has lived through eight winters. (*From a photograph by Dr. W. A. Spoor.*)

simple cycloid type. Intermediate types of scales, some of which bear spines, are present in a variety of fishes. It is interesting to note that the scales covering the lateral line (page 677) are frequently perforated and permit the passage of the small connectives of the lateral-line canal to the outside (Fig. 4.13).

Amphibians. The skin of modern amphibians lacks scales except in a few toads and in some of the burrowing, limbless caecilians. The skin is usually smooth and moist.

Epidermal scales. In the spade-foot toads, *Scaphiopus* (American) and *Pelobates* (European), a highly cornified area of epidermis on the inner side of the hind foot, which is used in digging, might be considered to be an epidermal scale. In the South African toad, *Xenopus laevis*, the dark cornified epidermis at the ends of the first three digits on the hind feet has a clawlike appearance.

Dermal scales. In a few toads bony plates are embedded in the skin of the head or back. Extinct stegocephalians, which are usually considered to be the ancestors of modern amphibians, possessed large bony plates in the skin. True dermal scales are found in the integument of certain caecilians. They lie between ringlike folds in the skin of these animals and alternate with areas which are typically glandular in nature. The scales of caecilians resemble those of fishes in that they are embedded in pockets in the dermis, but instead of a single scale being confined to a pocket, several (four to six) may be present.

Reptiles. Both dermal and epidermal scales exist in the class Reptilia, and the two types are frequently associated with each other.

Epidermal scales. Epidermal scales are extremely well developed and are characteristic of the class as a whole. The scales are of two general types: those present in snakes and lizards and those found in turtles, crocodiles, and alligators. In the former type each scale projects backward and overlaps the scales behind (Fig. 4.18). The formation of this type of scale is of interest. Thickened areas separated by thinner regions appear in the integument (Fig. 4.19). Each thickened area, which consists of a covering of epidermis together with the dermis beneath, is known as a *papilla.* The flattened papillae grow upward and posteriorly and become lopsided, since the cells on the upper or outer surface multiply faster than do those beneath. The rapidly dividing epidermal cells are nourished by

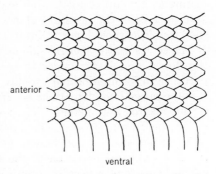

FIG. 4.18. Overlapping epidermal scales of snake (diagrammatic).

materials brought to them by the blood vessels in the dermis. Dermis and stratum germinativum of the epidermis gradually retract, leaving the dead, cornified scale on the surface. The hollow scale soon collapses, and all that is left is a flat, thin structure. Thus, although the fully formed scale is entirely epidermal, it is formed under the influence of the dermis. The scales are continuous with each other at their bases. Snakes and lizards periodically undergo ecdysis. Before ecdysis occurs a new set of scales has been formed beneath the old. The old corneal layer is shed as a whole and

FIG. 4.19. Stages in development of epidermal reptilian scale (diagrammatic).

in snakes is turned inside out. Several days before the layer is to be cast off, the colors of the snake seem to fade and the scales over the eyes become whitish. This is because the colorless, semitransparent old corneal layer is separating from the new one beneath. It first loosens on the top of the head and margins of the mouth. The snake then literally crawls out of its old skin, aided partially by squeezing its body through a narrow place. Lizards might be said to creep out of their castoff scaly covering, for it is not turned inside out during ecdysis. The frequency of shedding depends on such factors as amount of food eaten and the activity of the thyroid gland and anterior lobe of the pituitary gland. A healthy snake that is well fed may shed its old corneal layer at intervals of 2 months or less.

The scales on the ventral side of the body in snakes differ from those on the dorsal and lateral sides in being transversely arranged. Their importance in locomotion has already been discussed.

Some special modifications of epidermal scales are to be observed in certain lizards and snakes. The so-called horns of the horned lizard are really specialized scales. The rattle of the rattlesnake is made up of a series of old, dried scales loosely attached to each other in sequence. At the time of ecdysis the scale at the very tip of the tail is not shed with the others because of a peculiar bump which causes it to adhere to the newly formed scale (Fig. 4.20). Thus a series of scales forms the rattle, each new

Fig. 4.20. Rattle of rattlesnake: *A*, median sagittal section of end of tail; *B*, a single horny element of the rattle. (*After Czermak.*)

scale being slightly larger than its predecessor. The exact age of a rattlesnake cannot be determined by counting the number of rattles, since ecdysis may occur several times a year. Old rattles at the tip may gradually wear off or be broken off. There are usually less than 10 rattles, although more than this number is frequently observed. The so-called "warning" of the rattlesnake is not a warning in the real sense of the word. The vibration of the tail, which produces the buzzing sound of the rattler, is, however, of protective value to the snake, since the sound is enough to frighten even the most formidable of enemies.

In most turtles large epidermal scales cover the carapace and plastron, but the pattern of the scales does not conform to that of the bony plates beneath. Each scale develops separately. Periodically the stratum germinativum under each scale grows peripherally, and thus the area of each scale is increased. A new cornified layer is then formed, which pushes the older scales away from the shell. This results in a piling up of the older scales, which then appear from above as a series of irregular concentric rings (Fig. 4.21). The number of rings indicates the number of growth

Fig. 4.21. Arrangement of scales on carapace of wood turtle.

periods, and hence the number of ecdyses. In temperate zones each ring represents a year's growth, since during hibernation there is an almost complete cessation of growth. The old, smaller, outer scales frequently break off or are worn off, so that the number of rings does not necessarily represent the exact age of the animal. In such forms as the painted turtle the old scales characteristically peel off and only the smooth, most recently formed scale is present at any one time. Scales also cover the softer parts such as the neck and legs.

Pigment in the turtle's integument is located in the stratum germinativum. In some cases it diffuses into the horny layers above. The beautiful tortoise shell of commerce owes its color to the various combinations of pigment which have diffused into the corneal layer.

Epidermal scales of crocodilians (Fig. 4.22) cover the entire body. On the lateral and ventral sides, as well as on the tail, each scale bears a pitlike depression. A small sensory capsule is located at this point, and the scale is not cornified in the region of the capsule. Crocodilian scales do not undergo periodic ecdyses as in other reptiles. Instead there is a wearing away and a gradual replacement. Alligator skins that are used commercially consist of the tanned dermis with the epidermal scales removed.

Dermal scales. Perhaps the best example of highly developed dermal scales exists in the turtles. Here the bony plates in the dermis form a rigid dermal skeleton which becomes intimately connected with the endoskeleton. The carapace, or dorsal part of the turtle's shell, beneath the epi-

dermal scales is composed of bony costal plates fused to the neural arches of vertebrae in the midline, and laterally to the ribs beneath (Fig. 10.40). The plastron, or ventral part of the shell, is usually made up of nine large dermal plates covered with epidermal scales.

In crocodilians the dermis is thick and soft except on the dorsal side of the body and occasionally on the throat, where bony plates lie beneath the epidermal scales. The dermal plates are much reduced in size and are not fused to one another. Also present in these reptiles are dermal *"ribs,"* called *gastralia*, located in the ventral abdominal region. The rhynchocephalian *Sphenodon* also possesses gastralia. They should not be confused with true ribs.

Fig. 4.22. Arrangement of scales on neck and shoulder region of alligator.

Small dermal scales are present in certain lizards and snakes, but most of these animals lack such bony elements. The membrane bones of the skull, however, represent dermal scales.

Birds. With the exception of the membrane bones of the skull, dermal skeletal structures, or scales, are usually lacking in this class of vertebrates. Epidermal scales and their derivatives, however, are exceptionally well developed.

Epidermal scales. Epidermal scales of the reptilian type are confined to the legs and feet. They generally overlap and are formed in the same manner as those of lizards and snakes.

A bony projection of the tarsometatarsus in the males of certain species of birds is known as the *spur*. It is covered with a horny, scalelike epidermal sheath which may be very sharp and pointed. The spur is best developed in some gallinaceous birds in which it is used in fighting. Spurs may also occur on the wings (metacarpus) in certain forms.

The webs on the feet of aquatic birds, such as geese, ducks, and swans, are modified regions of the integument. The skin forming the web is characteristically scaled.

Feathers. The outstanding feature of birds is the presence of feathers, which are found in no other group of animals. Feathers are actually modified reptilian scales. This is very well shown in certain varieties of chickens such as cochins, brahmas, and langshans in which feathers appear on the legs and toes in close relation to the scales. In feathers the stratum corneum has reached the climax of modification and specialization, as witness the elaborate tail feathers of the peacock and the beautiful plumage of certain birds of paradise.

The varied and sometimes gorgeous coloring of feathers is based upon two main factors: (1) pigmentary, or chemical, coloration and (2) structural, or physical, coloration. Presence of pigment in the feather substance, deposited during development, is the most common basis for coloration. The color that is observed is due to the absorption of certain wavelengths of light by the pigment. The light that is not absorbed is that which affects the eye of the observer. Black, red, and yellow pigments in various combinations have been identified. Perhaps green should be added to the list, although most greens are due to physical factors mentioned below. White color is not due to white pigment but rather to an altogether different principle. Whiteness is caused by reflection of light without the absorption of any of its component rays. Reflection from a polished surface like that of a mirror does not cause whiteness. Irregular reflection which scatters or reflects light in all directions is responsible for the white color. The presence of innumerable air spaces in a white feather causes irregular reflection. This embodies the same principle as that involved when a transparent piece of ice is crushed into many smaller particles which then give the mass a white appearance.

Structural, or physical, coloration is brought about by such physical phenomena as refraction and interference of light rays as they are reflected from minute, irregular surfaces of parts of the feather. Iridescent hues, metallic colors, grays, and certain shades of blue are due to such structural irregularities. When physical coloration is superimposed upon the effect of the basic pigment, it may result in a color which differs considerably from that of the pigment itself.

Endocrine factors have been shown to play an important part in deposition of feather pigments during development.

In general, there are three main types of feathers, known, respectively, as *filoplumes*, or hair feathers; *plumulae*, or down feathers; and *plumae*, or contour feathers.

FILOPLUMES. Hair feathers, as their name implies, appear superficially like hairs but have an entirely different structure and origin. They can usually be observed on a chicken after it has been plucked preparatory to cooking and are commonly singed or burned off. The structure of a hair feather is simple, since it consists only of a long, slender shaft which may bear a few barbs at its distal end (Fig. 4.23). The shaft is embedded in the skin and surrounded by the *feather follicle* at its base. Hair feathers are usually scattered over the surface of the body, but in some birds, such as flycatchers, they are concentrated about the mouth and serve as an aid in catching insects.

PLUMULAE. The down feather is more complex than the hair feather (Fig. 4.24). It is composed of a basal, short, hollow *quill* which is embedded in the integument. Numerous *barbs* arise from the free end of the quill, and these bear tiny *barbules* along their edges. The transient nestling down which may be observed on the young bird as its first feather covering

FIG. 4.23. A hair feather.   FIG. 4.24. A down feather.   FIG. 4.25. Distribution of feather tracts in the pigeon. (*After Nitsch.*)

is shed when the later-appearing contour feathers emerge. Nestling downs often adhere to the tips of the newly erupting contour feathers. The type of down feather seen in an adult bird is sometimes called "powder" down. Such feathers lie under the larger contour feathers and in many cases form a warm insulating layer which not only aids in keeping the body temperature of the bird constant but assists in warming the eggs during incubation.

PLUMAE. Except in penguins, ostriches, and toucans, plumae, or contour feathers, arise from certain areas of skin called feather tracts, or *pterylae* (Fig. 4.25). Large areas between the pterylae are devoid of contour feathers and are known as *apteria*. Hair feathers and down feathers may occur in the apteria, however. Contour feathers are so named because they give the body its outline, or contour. If they are removed by plucking, the body configuration is decidedly altered. Special contour feathers located on the wings are referred to as *remiges*, or flight feathers. Those on the tail are *rectrices*, or tail feathers.

The typical contour feather (Fig. 4.26) consists of a long *shaft* and a broad, flat portion called the *vane*. The shaft is made up of two parts: the hollow *quill* which is embedded in the skin and a solid *rachis* which bears the vane. At the lower end of the quill is a small opening, the *inferior umbilicus*. At the junction of rachis and quill is another opening, the *superior umbilicus*. On the underside of the rachis and extending from the

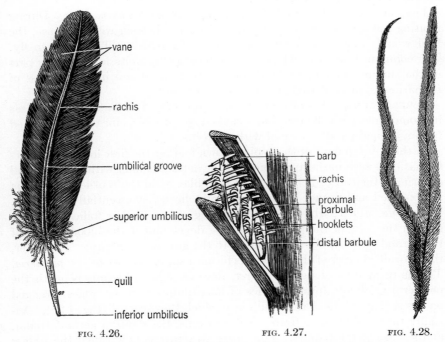

FIG. 4.26.   FIG. 4.27.   FIG. 4.28.

FIG. 4.26. A contour feather from the wing of a chicken. (*Drawn by G. Schwenk.*)

FIG. 4.27. Arrangement by means of which barbs of a feather are held together. (*Drawn by G. Schwenk.*)

FIG. 4.28. Feather from a cassowary. The mainshaft and aftershaft are of similar dimensions.

superior umbilicus to the tip is a groove, the *umbilical groove*. The vane is composed of a number of *barbs* which arise from the rachis. Each barb in turn bears small *barbules* on both distal and proximal sides. The lower part of each distal barbule bears tiny *hooklets* which fasten onto the proximal barbules of the next adjacent barb. Hooklets are lacking from the proximal barbules (Fig. 4.27). As a result of this arrangement the barbs are hooked together via their barbules, and the vane offers a flat, wide, firm, and unbroken surface. Should certain barbs become separated, the bird can easily put them in place again by preening, or drawing the barbs together with its beak or bill.

In many birds at the junction of rachis and quill is located what appears to be another feather. This is called the *aftershaft*, or *hyporachis*. It also bears barbs and barbules, but hooklets are lacking. The aftershaft is generally smaller than the main shaft and may consist only of a small downy tuft. In some birds, such as the emu and cassowary, the aftershaft with its accessory parts may be as long as the main shaft and the feather appears to be double (Fig. 4.28).

Feathers are shed periodically in a process known as *molting*. During molting not all the feathers are shed at once. If such were the case, the bird would be greatly handicapped by being temporarily unable to fly. The common barnyard chicken characteristically molts in the latter part of the summer in temperate zones. New feathers are in the process of formation at the time that the old ones are shed.

DEVELOPMENT. A study of the development of a feather emphasizes its homologies with the lizard and snake type of scale, since each is formed from a dermal papilla covered with epidermis.

In the development of the typical down feather the first indication of its formation is seen in the appearance of the dermal papilla with its epidermal covering. Instead of being flat and platelike, as in the reptile, the papilla is elongated and round. The structure is, however, essentially the same. An *annular groove*, which is the beginning of the feather follicle, appears around the base of the papilla. During development the blood vessels of the dermal pulp supply nourishment to the growing structure. The outer, thin, cornified layer of the epidermis forms a sheath known as the *periderm*. This is ultimately sloughed. First, however, the epidermis beneath the periderm gradually forms a series of longitudinal folds or ridges arranged on the surface of the dermal pulp into which they extend (Fig. 4.29). Actually these ridges arise from a collar of cells, the stratum germinativum, at the base of the papilla. The entire structure is now called the *feather germ*. The longitudinal epidermal ridges are destined to give rise to the barbs of the feather. The feather germ with its peridermal sheath grows rather rapidly and soon projects from the feather follicle above the surface of the skin as a "pinfeather." The dermal pulp and stratum germinativum gradually retract. Soon the periderm at the apex splits, and the tips of the cornified epidermal ridges dry and crack. The distal ends of the barbs can then be observed projecting from the apex of the sheath. As the feather continues to grow, the proximal parts of the elongated ridges become cornified and separate. The periderm is shed in the form of small, dandruff-like scales, and the barbs spread out. They remain attached at their bases to the quill, which lies beneath the surface of the skin and does not split. Small, pithy partitions inside the quill represent dried remnants of the dermal pulp. A small papilla remains at the base of the feather. This later gives rise to the feather which will replace its predecessor when the latter is shed.

The development of the contour feather is similar to that of the down feather up to a point, after which it becomes considerably more complex. Observations (F. R. Lillie and M. Juhn, 1938, *Physiol. Zoöl.*, **11**:434) have shown that during development a differential growth occurs on one side of a collar of stratum germinativum at the base of the feather germ. This is considered to be the dorsal surface of the developing feather, and the region opposite is the ventral surface. The middorsal portion of the collar starts

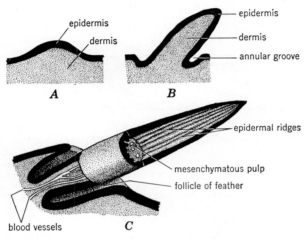

epidermis

dermis

epidermis

dermis

annular groove

A   *B*

epidermal ridges

mesenchymatous pulp

follicle of feather

blood vessels   *C*

Fig. 4.29. Stages in the development of a down feather. (*Modified from Kingsley, "Comparative Anatomy of Vertebrates," The Blakiston Division, McGraw-Hill Book Company, Inc. By permission.*)

to grow outward, carrying the barbs on either side along with it (Fig. 4.30). This becomes the rachis. The umbilical groove on its undersurface represents the line of fusion of the two sides of the collar as it grows outward. As the series of barbs moves dorsally with the concrescence of the two sides of the collar, new barbs appear in the space thus provided on the ventral side. As in the case of the down feather, the contour feather is at first enclosed by a sheath of periderm. When the periderm dries and sloughs, the developing feather splits along the midventral line and flattens out. The underside of a feather, therefore, represents that portion which was originally adjacent to the feather pulp. Again, as in the down feather, the quill is that portion which lies beneath the skin and has failed to split. Transverse, pithy partitions inside the quill represent the remainder of the dermal pulp. The superior umbilicus and inferior umbilicus are merely openings through which the dermal pulp was originally in continuity with the dermal papilla. The development of the aftershaft is like that of the main shaft except that differential growth occurs along the midventral line as well.

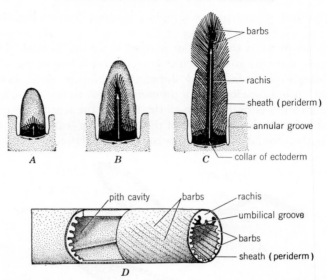

Fɪɢ. 4.30. *A*, *B*, and *C*, schematic representation of developing contour feather from a collar of ectodermal cells which shows differential rates of growth. In *C*, the periderm at the distal end has ruptured. The barbs of the two sides have separated along the midventral line and have flattened out. *D*, a stereogram of part of a developing contour feather. (*A, B, and C, based on figures by Lillie and Juhn, 1938, Physiol. Zoöl., 11:442. By permission of the University of Chicago Press. D, after Kingsley, "Comparative Anatomy of Vertebrates," The Blakiston Division, McGraw-Hill Book Company, Inc. By permission.*)

Mammals. Except for the membrane bones of the skull, most mammals lack dermal skeletal structures. Armadillos have the best-developed dermal skeletons among living mammals. Bony plates, or scales, lie under the epidermal scales which they reinforce. The extinct glyptodons, belonging to the order Edentata, possessed a rigid, bony, dermal armor. In certain whales bony plates may be present on the back and in the dorsal fins. In mammals in general, as in birds, there has been a tendency toward elaboration of epidermal structures and a loss or diminution of dermal derivatives.

Epidermal scales are present in many mammals. With the exception of the scaly anteaters and armadillos, they are generally confined to the tails and paws. When scales do occur they are usually associated with hairs. This, among other reasons, has given rise to the belief that mammalian hair was originally derived from scales. The question of the degree to which scales, feathers, and hairs are comparable is of interest, but it is clear that feathers are more closely related to scales than are hairs.

In the scaly anteaters the body, except on the ventral side, is covered with large, overlapping, horny epidermal scales (Fig. 2.32). They are typically reptilian in structure, but ecdysis occurs singly. In the armadillos the large scales fuse to form plates over the head, shoulders, and hind quarters and the ringlike bands which surround the midbody region except along the midventral line. As mentioned above, dermal bones underlie the epidermal scales. These hark back to the fishlike ancestors of prehistoric times. There is no true ecdysis, but rather a gradual wearing away from the surface and replacement from beneath. Transient scales are found on the body of the embryo of the brown bear.

On the tails of many rodents, such as the rat, mouse, muskrat, and beaver, imbricated scales are present. They are truly reptilian in structure and development, but the degree of cornification is not pronounced, nor is there a period of ecdysis.

Of great interest is the arrangement of hairs in relation to scales. The

Fig. 4.31. Arrangement of hairs in relation to scales on the tail of the rat.

Fig. 4.32. Arrangement of tori on hind foot of rat. (*Drawn by Ella K. Weichert.*)

hairs project from beneath the scales. On the tail of the rat, for example, three hairs project from beneath each scale. The one in the center is larger and coarser than the two lateral hairs (Fig. 4.31). The astonishing fact is that the hairs on other parts of the body have a similar arrangement. The skin of the pig is devoid of scales, but the grouping of the hairs, or bristles, gives evidence of origin from scaled ancestors. Coarse hairs are usually arranged in clusters of three and interspersed with finer hairs. Examination of a pair of pigskin gloves will clearly indicate this relationship. In other mammals, including man, similar arrangements are found, hairs being grouped in twos, threes, fours, and fives. Often this relationship, although clear during development, is obscured in the adult.

In most mammals the undersurfaces of the hands and feet are scaled or bear evidence of the former presence of scales. The friction ridges (page

93) familiar to everyone and which in man are used in making fingerprints really represent such scale rudiments. In certain animals definite elevated pads on the undersurfaces of the feet bear friction ridges. Such pads are known as *tori*. On the foot of a rat, for example (Fig. 4.32), there are 11 elevated tori. They include 5 *digital tori* at the ends of the digits, 4 *interdigital tori* below the spaces between the digits, 1 *thenar torus* at the base of the first digit, and 1 *hypothenar torus* at the base of the fifth. In man, in which no elevated tori are present in the adult, the friction ridges have become flattened and spread over a considerable surface. However, groupings in the regions where one would expect tori to occur indicate a relationship similar to that described above.

In the development of the integument in embryos of reptiles, birds, and mammals the first layer of cells given off by the stratum germinativum forms a continuous sheet called the *periderm*. The cells of the periderm possess characteristic staining properties. This layer is later shed as a whole during development and in mammals contributes to the *vernix caseosa*, a cheesy material present on the skin of the newborn. That the periderm may represent the scaly covering of ancestral forms is indicated by the fact that the only place where it is not shed is on the palms and soles, and in these regions it contributes to the formation of the friction ridges. The term *epitrichium* is applied to the periderm of mammals.

Hair. True hair is found in all mammals, and only mammals have hair. In most forms the entire integument is covered with hair, but in some, the hairy coat has practically disappeared and only traces remain. In the adults of some of the larger whales, for example, only a few coarse, stubby hairs are present in the region of the snout. Such a condition is referred to as *hypotrichosis*. During embryonic development in all mammals the body is at one stage covered with a coating of fine hair called the *lanugo*. This is absent only on the ventral surfaces of the hands and feet. The lanugo hair is transient and is usually shed sometime before birth. In the human embryo the lanugo is fully developed by the seventh month of fetal life. Shedding begins during the eighth month, and most of it is lost by the time of birth or shortly after. In cases where hairs have failed to develop normally, the condition is known as *atrichosis*. There are occasional human beings whose bodies are entirely devoid of hair. In such cases the nails and even the teeth may be lacking. Abnormally excessive hairiness is called *hypertrichosis*. This condition is frequently observed in men but rarely in women, in whom it is often associated with abnormal functioning of the cortical portion of the adrenal glands. In extreme cases the entire body may be covered with a thick coating of hair like that of a dog or cat. The celebrated "Jo-Jo the dog-faced man" of circus fame is an example of this condition, which is alluded to as *pseudohypertrichosis* (Fig. 4.33). It is possibly the result of overdevelopment of the lanugo hair, but this is not certain.

STRUCTURE, DEVELOPMENT, AND GROWTH OF HAIR.   Hair is entirely epidermal in origin.   During development a small thickening in the epidermis pushes down into the dermis and finally becomes cupped at its lower end (Fig. 4.34).   The dermis, which extends into the cuplike depression, makes up the *hair papilla*.   The blood vessels which extend into the papilla bring nourishment to the stratum germinativum of epidermal cells.   As this process is going on, the epithelial, epidermal ingrowth splits so as to leave a central *shaft*, the space becoming the *follicle* in which the hair lies.   The cells of the follicle at the same time are budding off one or more masses of epidermal cells which will develop into sebaceous glands.   These open

Fig. 4.33.   Jo-Jo, the dog-faced man, an example of pseudo-hypertrichosis.

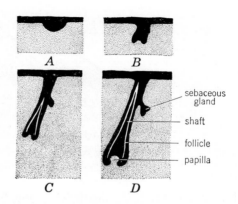

Fig. 4.34.   Stages in the development of a hair.

directly into the hair follicle.   Within the follicle (Fig. 4.35) the hair shaft is surrounded by two layers of cells which do not extend beyond the limits of the follicle.   *Huxley's layer* is the inner layer of the sheath, and *Henle's layer* lies outside this.   The hair shaft is entirely cellular and is composed of a central core, or *medulla;* a middle *cortex;* and an outer covering of scaly cells, *the cuticle.*   At the base of the follicle the hair is expanded slightly to form a bulblike enlargement, which is sometimes called the "root" of the hair.   All growth takes place in the root, where the cells of the stratum germinativum divide actively.   Beyond this point the cells gradually die and the shaft of the hair is thus composed of dead, cornified cells.

   The character of the surface of the hair varies from smooth to decidedly rough and scaly.   The hair of sheep, commonly known as wool, is an example of the latter type.   The small scales of adjacent hairs interlock in such a manner that the hairs cling together.   Wool, therefore, is admirably adapted for spinning and gives a high quality of cloth.   The smooth type of hair naturally gives a glossier appearance.   The oily secretion of the sebaceous glands which open into the hair follicles serves to keep the hair smooth and glossy and aids in shedding water.

The manner in which hairs of various types grow is said to be either *definitive* or *angora*. Angora hairs grow to a considerable length before they loosen and are shed. The head hair of man is of this type. Definitive hairs, on the other hand, grow to a certain length and then stop. They are then shed and quickly replaced. Eyelashes, eyebrows, and body hairs are of the definitive type. Angora hairs may persist for several years, but definitive hairs usually last only for a few months.

A general belief exists that hair may continue to grow after death. Since hair is made up of cells and because cells come only from preexisting cells,

Fig. 4.35. Diagram showing structure of hair. (*After Kingsley, "Comparative Anatomy of Vertebrates," The Blakiston Division, McGraw-Hill Book Company, Inc. By permission.*)

it is obvious that after death, when oxygen and nutriment are no longer supplied by the blood stream, cell division must cease. After death, especially when the body is embalmed, the skin shrinks, thus exposing hair shafts which had hitherto been concealed. A preparator not infrequently may observe what appears to be a growth of beard several days after embalming a corpse. Possibly this has given origin to the fantastic story mentioned.

Hairs do not emerge vertically from the skin but project at an acute angle. Associated with each hair is a small involuntary muscle, the *arrector pili*. It extends from the basal part of the hair to the upper part of the dermis and lies on the side toward which the hair slopes. Contraction of the arrector pili muscles, by pulling on the bases of hairs, tends to cause them to stand erect. In man this brings about a condition called *cutis anserina*, or goose flesh (duck bumps). In dogs and cats the raising of the hair, particularly along the back of the neck, is observed when the animal is confronted with danger. It is supposed that this is a protective adaptation which gives a false contour, or outline, to the body and might cause an enemy to "miss his mark" when attacking.

Variations in the shape of hairs in cross section are responsible for the degree of straightness or curliness. A straight hair, which is typical of the Mongoloid races, is round; that of the kinky-haired Negro is flat. Oval and elliptical hairs show different degrees of curliness or waviness. In the modern beauty parlor curly hair is produced by chemicals and instruments which actually flatten hair. Atmospheric humidity also has a bearing on the curliness of hair. On wet or damp days there is often a tendency for hair to curl. Since the hair is somewhat porous it will absorb a certain amount of moisture and swell along the line of least resistance, which is the diameter. If the diameter increases, the length will decrease, so that if the hair is short the end will curl in the manner of a figure 9. Long hairs do not exhibit this phenomenon to the same degree.

Hairs in different parts of the body show some variation in the direction in which they grow or slant. There are usually different patterns, or hair currents, along which the hairs grow. These are best seen when the hair is short or clipped but are more obscure when the hair is long. Where hair currents diverge, *parts* occur. When they converge, *crests* or *tufts* may be present. In certain regions *whorls*, or *vortices*, indicate a spiral arrangement. The familiar cowlick on the human forehead is an example of a whorl. Although in most mammals the hair parts on the middorsal line and slopes to the ventral side, the sloths show the opposite condition. Here, associated with the animals' habit of hanging upside down in trees, parting occurs on the midventral line and the hair actually slopes dorsally. This enhances the shedding of water in the tropical rain forests in which the sloths are at home.

COLOR OF HAIR. The color of hair in various mammals actually shows very little range, and the vivid colors seen in other vertebrate classes are lacking. To be sure, in certain apes like the mandrills, highly colored skin areas are present, but in these it is the skin itself rather than the hair which bears the pigment. There are very few mammals that can be said to be highly colored.

Four factors are responsible for the color and luster of the hair: (1) the color of pigment which is present in the cortex, (2) the amount of pigment, (3) the character of the hair surface, whether smooth or rough, (4) to amount of air contained within the intercellular spaces of the medulla.

Pigment in hair is present in the intercellular spaces of the cortex. The amount that is present determines the shade. Browns seem to predominate in most forms, but in man the color seems to have black and red pigments as its foundation. Absence of one or both or different combinations or dilutions of the two apparently bring about the many variations that may be observed.

As in the case of the white feather, white hair is not due to the presence of white pigment. Instead there is a lack of pigment, and light is reflected in all directions from the air spaces between the cells, particularly those of the medulla. Gray hair is the result of reduction of pigment and a reflection from an increased number of air spaces.

Although pigment deposition generally does not cease until the latter part of life, this is not true of all mammals.   The varying hare, arctic fox, stoat, and certain weasels are remarkable in that, as winter approaches, the old brown pelage is replaced by a white coat which provides protective or aggressive coloration, as the case may be.   In these mammals, pigment deposition is seasonal.

In man the deposit of pigment in hair may sometimes be interrupted or permanently stopped after sickness or extreme nervous shock.   It is, of course, impossible for hair to turn white overnight, since pigment already present in the hair cannot be retracted.

SHEDDING OF HAIR.   In mammals which show decided differences in their summer and winter coats, the hair is shed periodically.   Horses and cattle shed their long, thick coats in the spring.   The buffalo has a shaggy, moth-eaten appearance when large patches of hair are being shed.   In many mammals, however, there is constant shedding and renewal.   If a hair is pulled out, the place where it "gives" is usually just above the stratum germinativum at the base of the follicle.   A new hair may then grow in its place.   When there is complete destruction of the stratum germinativum and papilla, regeneration will not occur.   Under normal conditions when a hair is shed, it first ceases to grow and then loosens at its base.   A new hair then develops at the same place.   It is not certain whether new hairs usually form from old papillae or whether new papillae are constantly forming. The former method seems more probable under most conditions.

The cause of baldness in human beings is not entirely clear.   Evidence exists that there is some relationship between baldness and certain endocrine secretions of the anterior lobe of the pituitary gland and of the testes. Certainly it is a condition far more prevalent in men than in women.   Excessive masculinity is often compatible with baldness.   Some types seem to be hereditary, the determining factors being transmitted from generation to generation.   Baldness seems to be dominant in men and recessive in women, but it is not a sex-linked character.   Men become bald if they are heterozygous and only one factor for baldness is present.   Women must be homozygous for baldness if the condition is to manifest itself (D. Osborn, 1916, *J. Heredity*, **7**:347).   It is of interest that the same pattern of baldness is usually present in a family strain.

DENSITY OF THE HAIRY COAT.   The density of hair on the body shows much variation in different mammals.   Those living in cold climates, either far north or south or at high altitudes, possess the heaviest hair coats of all. Tropical forms are generally sparsely covered.   A permanent abode in the water is associated with an almost total loss of hair in sirenians and cetaceans.   Even among the races of man, rather marked variations exist.   Certain members of the white race, the aborigines of Australia, and the hairy Ainus of the isle of Yesso are at one extreme.   On the other hand, the natives of the Malay Peninsula with their smooth, practically beardless skin furnish quite a contrast.

The quality of a fur, or pelt, is determined primarily by the degree of development of the underfur. This consists of large numbers of short, densely arranged hairs interspersed among the larger and coarser ones. Animals inhabiting cold climates have the heaviest underfurs. As the cold season approaches, the underfur begins to grow; and when it is fully developed, the fur is said to be *prime*. At this time its commercial value is greatest. The reason that furs from the far north have a much greater value than those from subtropical or tropical regions should be evident.

In certain mammals, such as the fox, the long hairs are the ones which make the pelt attractive. In others the coarse, long hairs are removed in the preparation of the pelt for market. Hudson seal is really dyed muskrat with the long hairs removed. True seal and beaver pelts are also treated in the same manner.

SPECIAL TYPES OF HAIR. The type of hair in different parts of the body of the same animal varies. Manes like those of the horse or lion, crests and tufts in certain regions, long tail hairs, eyelashes, eyebrows, dust-arresting hairs in the nose, all are hairs of special types which are, in the main, adaptive in function. They serve as an aid in protection from enemies, in defense against insects, and in guarding delicate membranes from foreign particles which might otherwise be injurious. In man the head hair clearly serves the function of protection from sun and rain. Pubic and axillary hair aids in decreasing friction between the limbs or between the limbs and body during locomotion. According to one theory, the persistence of pubic and axillary hair goes back in time to arboreal ancestors in which the longer hair in these parts furnished a means by which the young could cling to the parent, thus permitting a greater freedom of limb movement.

Other special hairs include the vibrissae (whiskers or feelers) found on the snouts of many mammals. These hairs are unusually sensitive. They have an abundant nerve supply at the root and are best developed in nocturnal mammals. The spines or quills of the porcupine have barblike scales at the tips and are loosely attached at the base. They cannot be projected but are easily pulled out when the barbed ends become embedded in the flesh of an enemy.

Differences in quality and distribution of hair in different regions are often quite marked in the sexes and furnish some of the outstanding secondary sex characters that distinguish male from female. The beards of men and the hairy covering of the chest, arms, and legs are in marked contrast to the relatively smooth condition of the skin in women. The heavy mane of the lion clearly marks him from the lioness. Even in rats, where secondary sex characters are not very clear-cut, the coarser texture of the fur of the male makes it easy to distinguish the sexes by anyone who is accustomed to handling these animals in the laboratory.

Beaks and Bills

In turtles and tortoises and in all modern birds, teeth are lacking. Each jawbone is covered with a modified epidermal scale which forms the beak or bill.   In turtles and tortoises the beak is hard, and the bite of a large animal may be serious.

Among birds, great variation is to be seen in the shape of the beak (Fig. 2.23), correlated with its use in procuring food.   Seed-eating birds usually have short, rather blunt beaks; insect-eaters possess long and narrow beaks which are not so strong as those of the seed-eaters.   The long, strong, hooked beaks of birds of prey are well fitted for their methods of obtaining food.

As applied to birds the words *beak* and *bill* are used interchangeably. The use of one or the other depends on the preference of the user.   The term bill is more commonly used by ornithologists (personal communication from Dr. Harry C. Oberholser, Cleveland, Ohio).

The bill of the egg-laying mammal, the duckbill platypus, is soft and pliant.   It is not covered with a modified epidermal scale and should not be confused with the type of bill found in birds.

Claws, Nails, and Hoofs

The hard structures which are present at the distal ends of the digits are derived from the horny layer of the integument.   They differ from other epidermal structures in that they grow parallel to the surface of the skin. Wearing away occurs at the tip.   Nails, claws, and hoofs are built upon the same plan, and even superficial observation reveals their homologies.   The stratum lucidum of the epidermis is exceptionally well developed at the base of these structures.   True claws are present only in reptiles, birds, and mammals.   They have also been described in certain fossil amphibians.   In the larval stage of the salamander, *Onychodactylus*, horny epidermal caps at the ends of the digits are elongated so as to form sharp "claws" which are much like those of lizards in appearance.   The South African "clawed toad," *Xenopus laevis*, is an amphibian which has clawlike tips on the first three digits of its hind feet.   Such structures may possibly foreshadow the appearance of claws in higher classes of vertebrates but are not true claws. Mammals are sometimes grouped into those which bear claws, nails, or both, and those possessing hoofs.   The hoofed animals are usually referred to as *ungulates*.

Claws.   A claw is composed of a dorsal scalelike plate called the *unguis*, and a ventral plate, the *subunguis*, or *solehorn*.   The unguis is the better developed of the two and is of greater importance.   The claw covers the terminal bony phalanx of the digit and is thus reinforced.

In the typical reptilian claw (Fig. 4.36) the unguis is curved both longitudinally and transversely and encloses the subunguis between its lower edges.   The claw forms a sort of cap at the end of the digit.   The outer layers of reptilian claws are shed and renewed periodically.

Claws of birds are typically reptilian in structure, but many variations are to be found, associated with the mode of life of the bird (Fig. 2.22).   The strong curved talons of the birds of prey; the sturdy, stubby claws of the gallinaceous birds; and the sharp, rather slender structures of birds that perch or cling to surfaces are representative of the many types that may be observed. In birds, shedding of the entire claw is unusual, and growth and wearing away occur at a more or less constant rate. Although claws are generally present only on the feet of birds, the young hoatzin, *Opisthocomus cristatus* (Fig. 4.37), of British Guiana and the valley of the Amazon, bears claws on the first two digits of the wings, and these are used as an aid in climbing. In this respect the young hoatzin resembles the fossil *Archae-*

Fig. 4.36. Structure of a typical reptilian claw. (*After Bütschli, from Walter and Sayles, "Biology of the Vertebrates," copyright 1949 by The Macmillan Company and used with their permission.*)

Fig. 4.37. Wing of young hoatzin, showing claws on first two digits. (*After Pycraft.*)

opteryx which has three clawed digits on each wing. As the bird grows older the claws disappear.

In the claws of mammals the subunguis is reduced in size and is continuous with the torus, or pad, at the end of the digit, which bears the friction ridges. Members of the cat family possess retractile claws which, when not in use or not extended, are withdrawn into a sheath. They are thus protected and kept sharp for the purposes for which the animals use them. In some mammals, as in certain lemurs, nails are present on some digits and claws on others (page 42). The tarsier has claws on the second and third digits of the hind feet, the others being supplied with nails.

Nails. In nails the dorsal unguis is broad and flattened and the subunguis is reduced to a small remnant which lies under the tip of the nail (Fig. 4.38). The so-called "root" of the nail, or region where growth of the unguis takes place, lies embedded in a pocket under the skin called the *nail groove*, or *sulcus unguis*. The *nail bed* lies beneath both the nail and its root. It is made up of proximal, middle, and distal regions, which show differences in structure. The proximal part, or *matrix*, is the most important. It is this portion which is concerned in the formation of the nail. Its anterior portion in man may be seen through the base of the transparent thumbnail and forms

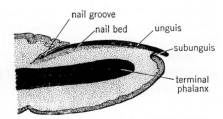

nail groove

nail bed

unguis

subunguis

terminal phalanx

Fig. 4.38. Longitudinal section through end of human finger, showing arrangement of nail.

the whitish *lunula,* a crescent-shaped area.   The lunula is not so conspicuous on the other digits.   The stratum germinativum above the base
of the nail forms a rather rough margin where the nail emerges from the
sulcus unguis.   This is called the *eponychium,* or *cuticle.*

Hoofs.   In the hoofs of ungulates the unguis curves all the way around
the end of the digit and encloses the subunguis within it (Fig. 4.39).   The
torus, or pad, lies just behind the hoof and is called the *"frog."*   Since the
unguis is of a harder consistency than the subunguis, it wears away more
slowly and a rather sharp edge is thus maintained.   The sure-footedness of

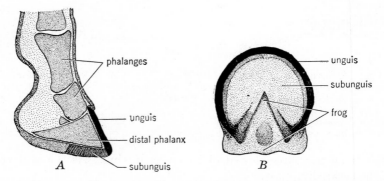

Fig. 4.39.   Structure of hoof: *A,* median sagittal section of distal end of leg of horse; *B,*
ground surface of hoof.   (*After Ellenberger in Leisering's Atlas, based on Sisson, "The
Anatomy of the Domesticated Animals," W. B. Saunders Company.   By permission.*)

many ungulates is dependent upon this factor.   Work horses are customarily shod with steel horseshoes to prevent the unguis from wearing away too
rapidly.   Shoes are nailed onto this portion of the hoof.   Since the hoof
grows continuously, the shoes must be removed at intervals.   The unguis
is then pared down, and the shoe nailed on again.

Horns and Antlers

Except for their presence in a few lizards, horns are found only in mammals.   Certain extinct dinosaurs possessed horns on the head consisting of
bony projections which were probably covered with a horny epidermal cap.
The horned toads of the genus *Phrynosoma,* indigenous to the southwestern
United States, are lizards which have numbers of such structures on their
heads.

Among mammals, horns are found only in certain members of the order
Artiodactyla and in the rhinoceros of the order Perissodactyla.   Four types
are recognized: the keratin-fiber horn, the hollow horn, the pronghorn, and
the antler.

Keratin-fiber horns.   The keratin-fiber horn is found only in the rhinoceros.   It is a conical structure composed of a mass of hardened, kerati-
nized cells growing from the epidermis covering a cluster of long, dermal

papillae. A fiber, somewhat resembling a very thick hair, grows from each papilla. Cells which develop in the spaces between the papillae serve as a cement substance, binding the whole together. The fibers are not true hairs since their bases are not located in follicles extending into the dermis. These unusual and formidable weapons are median in their position on the head. In the Indian rhinoceros only one horn is present, but in the African species there are two, the larger one being in front. A roughened, bony excrescence of the fused nasal bones supports the great horn in the Indian species. Another roughened area, posterior to the first, but less elevated, serves for attachment of the second and smaller horn of the African rhinoceros. It is located on the frontonasal region of the skull.

Hollow horns.   The hollow horn (Fig. 4.40) is the type found in cattle,

Fig. 4.40.   Hollow horn of domestic cow with bony core removed.

sheep, goats, buffaloes, and others. In certain species they are found only in males, but this is not true of all. The hollow horn consists of a projection of the frontal bone of the cranium covered by a cornified layer of epidermis. A cavity, which is continuous with the frontal sinus, extends into the bony projection. The horny layer is not shed. The powder horns of early settlers of America were prepared by loosening the horny covering from the bone beneath.

In a very young animal which will bear horns of this type, a loose button-like mass of bone, the *os cornu*, can be felt under the skin which lies over the frontal bone. If the os cornu is destroyed by caustic or is otherwise removed, the horn will not develop. If it is left intact, the horn will form and the os cornu ultimately becomes fused with the frontal bone. In certain domestic animals it is often desirable that the horns either be prevented from developing or that they be removed (polled). The former method, involving destruction of the os cornu, is more desirable, since polling cattle with well-developed horns is much more difficult and may cause harm to the animal which is treated.

Pronghorns.   A unique type of horn, the pronghorn, is found only in the antelope, *Antilocapra americana*, of the western United States. It consists of a projection of the frontal bone covered with a horny epidermal sheath. The sheath usually bears one prong (Fig. 4.41), although as many as three have been observed. The unusual feature of this type of horn is that the horny covering is shed with annual periodicity and a new horn forms from the epidermis which persists over the bony projection.

Antlers. The male members of the deer tribe possess branched antlers which project from the frontal bones. Only in the reindeer and caribou do both sexes bear antlers. In its fully developed state an antler is composed of solid bone. It is therefore entirely mesodermal in origin and properly

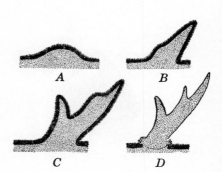

Fig. 4.41. Structure of horn of the prong-horn antelope.

Fig. 4.42. Stages in the development of an antler. *D* shows the final stage after the covering skin has been sloughed.

should not be called a horn at all. Antlers are to be considered as parts of the dermal skeleton. Since, however, the antler is formed under the influence of the integument, it is expedient to include it under the discussion of integumentary derivatives.

In the young male an outgrowth of the frontal bone develops on each side (Fig. 4.42). This is covered with soft skin, and the blood vessels in the overlying dermis bring minerals and other elements necessary for the growth of the structure. The antler is then said to be "in velvet." When it has reached the full extent of its development, a wreathlike burr grows out around the base. This cuts off the blood supply to the skin covering the antler. The skin then dries, cracks, and is rubbed off in shreds by the deer. This usually occurs as autumn approaches. At the end of the first season the antler appears as a single "spike." A young buck with a single spike on each side is referred to as a "spike buck." In the spring, because of certain degenerative processes which occur between the frontal bone and the burr, the antlers become loosened and are shed. The skin then closes over the area. Soon a new antler begins to grow, but this time it is branched. In fact, each year more branches appear, and the structure becomes more complicated. The developing antlers remain "in velvet" until autumn approaches. During this time they are sensitive and warm to the touch. Again the burr cuts off the circulation, and the skin covering the antler is sloughed. The entire bony antler is shed the following spring.

In the giraffe both sexes possess antlers. These, however, are small and rather inconspicuous. They are never shed and remain permanently "in velvet." Antlers are secondary sex characters in other species with the exception of the caribou and reindeer. They reach the height of their development just before the mating season, when it is customary for the males to fight for domination of the herd. Occasionally the antlers of two bucks become interlocked in combat in such a manner that they cannot be extricated. Starvation and death of both combatants usually follow.

Antler growth is apparently regulated by hormones secreted both by the testes and the anterior lobe of the pituitary gland (G. B. Wislocki, J. C. Aub, and C. M. Waldo, 1947, *Endocrinology*, **40**:202). In the Virginia deer, castration before the eighth month of life completely suppresses antler growth. If the antlers have already developed and if they are "in velvet" at the time when castration occurs, then they are not shed but remain permanently in velvet. However, castration of males with antlers which have lost their velvet results in a prompt shedding. Subsequently, new antlers grow, and these remain permanently "in velvet." Antler growth has been induced in castrated female Virginia deer by administration of the male hormone testosterone.

SUMMARY

1. The vertebrate integument consists of an outer, ectodermal, epithelial layer called the epidermis and an underlying mesodermal layer, the dermis, composed largely of connective tissue, blood and lymphatic vessels, nerves, and smooth muscle fibers.

2. Pigment in the integument occurs either in the form of small granules in the cells of the lowest layers of the epidermis or else in special branched cells, called chromatophores, in which the pigment may become dispersed throughout the cell or concentrated in its center around the nucleus. They are usually located between the epidermal and dermal layers. Chromatophores of this type are not generally present in birds and mammals.

3. Both epidermis and dermis give rise to various integumentary structures which are, for the most part, protective and adaptive in character.

4. From the epidermis are derived: (*a*) Skin glands of the following types: mucous, poison, sweat, sebaceous, ceruminous, mammary, and scent. (Photophores are light-producing modifications of skin glands.) (*b*) Scales, formed from the hardened, horny, corneal layer. They include epidermal

scales of reptiles, birds, and mammals; feathers; hair; claws; nails; hoofs; spurs; true horns; beaks; and bills.

5. From the dermis are derived (*a*) bony scales of the ganoid, placoid, ctenoid, and cycloid types, (*b*) bony plates in the skin of certain reptiles and mammals, (*c*) membrane bones of the skull.

6. The dermis, through its blood vessels, supplies nourishment to the developing epidermal structures but is not otherwise involved. Dermal structures arise within the dermis itself. In certain cases bony dermal plates are closely associated with epidermal scales which lie above them.

7. The evolution of the integument is fundamentally correlated with the transition from aquatic to terrestrial life. The highly developed epidermis of terrestrial forms, with its many modifications fitting the animal for life on land, is indicative of the trend. Dermal derivatives are basically more primitive.

CHAPTER 5

DIGESTIVE SYSTEM

In order to produce heat and other forms of energy, the living organism is constantly using up materials which have been stored within it in one form or another. It is clear that the body would soon be depleted of such energy-producing substances if they were not replenished. The primary concern of every living thing is to obtain certain necessary substances so that it may continue to live. Oxygen, food, and water are necessary for the continuance of life. Oxygen, present in the air (or dissolved in water), enters the body through the agency of the respiratory system, to be discussed later; but food and water are, in most animals, first taken into the digestive system. Water can be absorbed unchanged through the walls of the alimentary tract, but few kinds of food are available to a vertebrate in such a form that they can be used or absorbed directly.

The main function of the digestive system is to prepare foods so that they may be made available to the body for use in growth, structural maintenance, and the production of various forms of energy. The main principle involved in digestion is the breaking down of complex molecules of certain foods, by a series of chemical changes, into molecules of simpler structure. These can then either be absorbed in soluble form through the walls of the digestive tract and enter the blood vessels (in the case of proteins and carbohydrates) or be otherwise prepared so that they may enter the small vessels or lacteals of the lymphatic system (if the food is in the form of oil or fat).

Food that is present in the digestive tract cannot properly be said to be inside the body. Not until it has been digested and enters the blood or lymphatic systems, or is otherwise incorporated within the body tissues, can it be spoken of as actually being within or part of the body. Ingested material that cannot be digested thus never really enters the body proper. It merely passes down the digestive tract and is eliminated unchanged.

GENERAL STRUCTURE

In all vertebrates the digestive, or alimentary, tract is *complete*, having a *mouth* at one end and an *anus* at the other. The greater part of the lining of the alimentary tract (mesodaeum) is of endodermal origin, but the regions of ingress (mouth, or stomodaeum) and egress (anal canal, or proctodaeum) are lined with epithelium of ectodermal derivation. In the completely developed alimentary tract there is no exact point which would

141

indicate the original line of junction of stomodaeum or proctodaeum with the mesodaeum. Within rather rough limits it may be stated that the original stomodaeal region ends just posterior to the teeth and that the original proctodaeum extends inward only to the point where the urogenital ducts enter the cloaca.

During embryonic development in many vertebrates the endodermal portion of the digestive tract contains relatively large amounts of yolk. In embryos which develop from polylecithal ova there is so much yolk that it cannot be contained within the limits of the body wall. Most of it is located in a *yolk sac* which is attached to the alimentary canal by means of a *yolk stalk* (Fig. 5.1). As the embryo develops, the blood vessels surrounding the yolk sac gradually absorb yolk and carry it to the developing tissues which

Fig. 5.1. Embryo of dogfish shark, *Squalus acanthias*, showing yolk sac attached to body by means of yolk stalk. (*Drawn by G. Schwenk.*)

utilize it in growth processes. The yolk never enters the digestive tract directly. The yolk sac becomes smaller and smaller until finally nothing remains save a small, scarlike remnant on the intestine which indicates the original point of attachment of the yolk stalk.

The wall of the alimentary tract (Fig. 5.2), in general, is made up of four main layers, or coats: serous, muscular, submucous, and mucous. The outer *serous layer*, or *visceral peritoneum*, almost entirely surrounds those parts of the alimentary tract that lie within the coelom. This layer, then, is lacking in the region of the esophagus. Where the mesentery is attached to the alimentary tract, the serous layer is continuous with the surface layer of the mesentery on each side (Fig. 16.8). The cells of the serous layer rest on loose connective tissue. Beneath this lies the external *muscular coat*, which in turn is composed of two layers, often referred to as the *outer longitudinal* and *inner circular* layers. This is because in cross section the smooth muscle fibers of the inner layer appear to be arranged in a circular manner, whereas those of the outer layer are cut transversely. It has been demonstrated that both these layers are actually arranged in the form of spirals. The inner layer is a very close spiral with frequent turns; the outer layer is in the form of an open spiral, the turns of which are rather far apart. Some fibers from each layer cross over into the other. Between the two muscle layers lies a nervous network composed of nerve cells and bundles of nerve fibers, the sympathetic *myenteric plexus*, or *plexus of Auerbach.* Next to the circular muscle layer is the *submucosa*, composed of dense connective tissue and elastic fibers with a small island of fatty, or adipose, tissue here and there. Intestinal glands may lie in this layer, particularly in the duodenal portion of the intestine. Blood and lymphatic vessels are present in the submucosa in addition to a plexus of nerve cells and fibers, the submucous *plexus of Meissner.* The submucosa is the strongest layer of the alimentary tract. The *mucous coat (mucosa)*, or innermost layer of the alimentary tract, is in turn composed of three layers, or regions. Next to the submucosa is the *muscularis*

Fig. 5.2. Part of transverse section of ileum, showing three villi and the layers of the intestine.

mucosae, a thin layer of smooth muscle fibers and elastic connective tissue consisting of inner circular and outer longitudinal layers. Internal to the muscularis mucosae is a layer of peculiar connective tissue, the *lamina propria* of the mucosa. Numerous small nodules of lymphatic tissue lie within the lamina propria, as do blood vessels and nerves. The lamina propria is covered with a basement membrane which supports a single layer of simple, columnar, *epithelial cells.*

The muscular layers are under the involuntary control of the autonomic nervous system of which the plexuses of Auerbach and Meissner are parts. Contraction of the smooth muscle fibers is responsible for peristalsis, which propels food materials along the intestine, and for segmenting and pendular movements which do not propel food but aid in kneading it and mixing it thoroughly with digestive juices and enzymes. Striated, or voluntary, muscle fibers are found only at the two ends of the canal.

The digestive tract is admirably suited for its functions. Its wall contains muscles which thoroughly mix the contents and propel them along; it is provided with glandular elements which secrete certain fluids and ferments (enzymes) necessary for proper chemical reactions to take place. The thin cell walls of the lining epithelium are well suited for absorption, and the rich supply of blood and lymphatic vessels not only ensures the

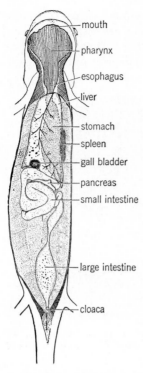

mouth

pharynx

esophagus

liver

stomach

spleen

gall bladder

pancreas

small intestine

large intestine

cloaca

Fig. 5.3. Digestive organs of salamander, *Eurycea bislineata*. The other internal organs have been removed.

proper nourishment of the tissues of the digestive tract but serves as the pathway by means of which digested substances are transported to all parts of the body.

In vertebrates the alimentary tract is typically divided into several sections. These are, in order, the *mouth, pharynx, esophagus, stomach, small intestine, large intestine,* and *cloaca* (Fig. 5.3). The term cloaca has been adopted from the Latin word meaning sewer. It is a common chamber into which the intestine, urinary ducts, and reproductive canals discharge. A cloaca is present in the adult stage of birds, reptiles, amphibians, and many fishes, beng notably absent in teleosts, chimaeras, *Polypterus*, sturgeons, and others. Among adult mammals, too, a cloaca is lacking except in monotremes and the pika. However, even in higher mammals a cloaca is present for a time during embryonic development. Such digestive glands as the *salivary glands, liver,* and *pancreas* are derived from the alimentary canal with which they are connected by means of ducts. Other structures derived from the endoderm of the primitive digestive tract in the region of the pharynx, but which are not concerned with digestion, include the *thyroid, thymus,* and *parathyroid glands; the tonsils; middle ear; Eustachian tubes;* and the *respiratory organs* (Chap. 6, pages 187 to 238).

MOUTH AND STRUCTURES ASSOCIATED WITH IT

It will be recalled that the primitive mouth, or stomodaeum, which develops early during embryonic life, is lined with ectoderm. It is, for a time, separated from the endodermal portion of the digestive tract by an oral, or pharyngeal, membrane. This soon ruptures and the stomodaeum and gut become continuous. The stomodaeum develops into part of the mouth, the lining of which is ectodermal. The exact point where ectoderm and endoderm merge is often impossible to discern, and there is much variation. It is important to remember that the various structures derived from the stomodaeum are ectodermal in origin or are at least covered with material derived from ectoderm.

Amphioxus

At the anterior end of amphioxus is a funnel-shaped structure called the *oral hood.* This is bordered by a number of tentaclelike *cirri.* The cavity within the oral hood is spoken of as the *vestibule*. This is not comparable to the mouth cavity of higher forms. The true mouth is located at the apex of the vestibule. On the walls of the oral hood are several lobelike structures covered with cilia. These form the so-called *wheel organ*. Posterior to this is a membranous *velum* which contains the true mouth opening in its center and which also bears several *velar tentacles*.

Cyclostomes

In cyclostomes a *buccal funnel* is located at the anterior end. This is bordered by many small *papillae*. In lampreys the lining of the buccal funnel is beset with numerous *horny teeth* (Fig. 15.2), not in any way comparable to the true teeth of higher forms. At the apex of the funnel is the mouth opening through which the tongue projects. The tongue also bears horny teeth. No jaws are present, and the mouth is permanently open. The name Cyclostomata (round mouth) has been given to the lowest group of vertebrates because of this characteristic.

Gnathostomes

All the remaining vertebrates have both upper and lower jaws and are placed in the subphylum Gnathostomata. The size and shape of the mouth opening are varied, being generally correlated with the type of food eaten and the manner in which it is obtained. *Cheeks* may mark the boundary of the mouth opening on either side. Many gnathostomes, however, have no cheeks and may open their mouths to an astonishing degree.

LIPS

The upper and lower boundaries of the mouth opening are known as *lips*. In all forms below mammals they are immovable and consist of epithelial folds or pads of connective tissue which meet when the mouth is closed. In turtles and birds the jaw bones are covered with hard, horny beaks. Truly movable lips occur only in mammals. The presence of muscles in the lips is associated with the development of dermal facial muscles, which reach their most complex development in man. Notable exceptions to the movable condition of the lips in mammals include the platypus and whales. The bill of the platypus is not horny but is soft, pliant, and extremely sensitive. Whales merely have soft pads of connective tissue which serve to keep the mouth tightly closed.

Mammalian lips are covered with skin on the outside and lined with mucous membrane on the inside. A modified area lies between the two. This is most conspicuous in man and is richly supplied with sensory receptors. Among other functions, the lips of mammals serve to keep the food between the teeth while eating. They may be used as prehensile organs in grasping or picking up food and other objects; they aid in the process of drinking in many species and are particularly well adapted for sucking. In

the human being they are also used in modifying the voice and in oscula-
tion.

Vestibule

The space between the lips and jaws is the *vestibule*. Lateral to the
mouth opening the vestibule may be bounded on the outside by the cheeks
and on the inside by the gums. In mammals a *labial frenum*, composed of
a fold of mucous membrane, connects the middle of each lip to the gum, or
gingiva.

In certain mammals cheek pouches of considerable size are present. In
some species, as in the pocket gopher, they are lined with fur and are used
as temporary storage places for food when these rodents are foraging.
Squirrels have the same habit but to a lesser degree. Certain Old World
monkeys also have well-developed cheek pouches. According to H. Burrell
(1927, "The Platypus," Angus and Robertson, Ltd.) the cheek pouches of
the platypus are used chiefly for holding fine gravel, which is used as an aid
in masticating chitinous or other hard food.

A variety of glands opens into the vestibule. These are, for the most
part, mucous glands. *Labial mucous glands* are small structures opening
on the inner surface of the lips. In man they may be identified as small
lumps when one pushes the tongue against the lips. In some mammals
molar mucous glands open near the molar teeth. The *parotid duct* (*Stensen's
duct*), which drains the parotid salivary gland, opens into the vestibule
opposite the first or second upper molar teeth in man and at a corresponding
point in other mammals.

Oral Cavity

In fishes, the mouth, in addition to serving as a passageway for food, is
concerned with the passage of water which contains the dissolved oxygen
used in respiration. In most fishes the nasal cavities are quite independent
of the oral cavity, but in the Choanichthyes they first communicate with
the mouth by means of a pair of *internal nares*, or *choanae*. In amphibians
the lining of the oral cavity is ciliated.

The roof of the mouth and pharynx is often referred to as the *palate*. In
most reptiles and birds a pair of *palatal folds* grows medially for a variable
distance on either side. The palatal folds do not meet in the median line,
thus forming a *palatal cleft* through which the nasal and mouth cavities are
in communication. In both crocodilians and mammals horizontal shelflike
processes of certain bones of the skull grow medially and fuse with their
partners of the opposite side, thus forming a *secondary palate* which effectively separates the nasal passages from the mouth cavity. These passages
thus communicate with each other more posteriorly than they would otherwise. The anterior part of the secondary palate is called the *hard palate*
since it is reinforced by portions of the premaxillary, maxillary, palatine,

and, in some forms, of the pterygoid bones. The posterior part in mammals is the *soft palate* since it has no bony foundation. Abnormal development of the palate in mammals may result in a condition spoken of as *cleft palate*. The nasal passages communicate with the pharynx posterior to the soft palate. In man, the soft palate ends in a fleshy, pointed elongation, the *uvula*, which hangs downward and backward. This serves to close off the nasal passageway from the mouth during the act of swallowing. In many forms the palate is thrown into transverse ridges, the *palatine rugae*. These are not so prominent in man as in such carnivores as dogs and cats in which they undoubtedly serve as an aid in securing prey.

GLANDS OF THE ORAL CAVITY

In cyclostomes a so-called *salivary gland* opens into the mouth cavity on either side just below the tongue. The gland secretes an anticoagulant, called *lamphedrin*, which facilitates the flow of blood from an animal when it is attacked by the lamprey.

Fishes, and amphibians that spend their entire life in the water, have no glands other than simple mucous cells opening into the mouth cavity. Glands first appear in the mouths of terrestrial vertebrates, their prime function being to moisten the food and render it slippery so as to facilitate swallowing. In higher forms specialization of the mouth glands occurs, and they may play an important part in capturing prey and in digestion. In poisonous snakes and lizards certain mouth glands serve as dangerous organs of defense.

Amphibians. In terrestrial amphibians a mucous gland called the *intermaxillary*, or *internasal*, *gland* lies in the nasal septum between the premaxillary bones and nasal capsule. It is larger in salientians than in caudates, but in both cases the ducts open in the front of the mouth. The secretion of this gland helps to give the tongue its adhesive properties. The intermaxillary gland is lacking in caecilians. Another gland, referred to as the *pharyngeal gland*, is present in frogs and toads. It lies near the internal nares, its secretion passing into them. Mucous *lingual glands* are numerous on the protrusible tongues of frogs and toads as well as in certain salamanders. Their secretion aids in the capture of prey. In some frogs a digestive enzyme, *ptyalin*, is secreted by the mouth glands.

Reptiles. The oral glands of reptiles show a much more distinct grouping than do those of amphibians. A *palatine gland* is present which is homologous with the intermaxillary gland of amphibians. In addition, *lingual*, *sublingual*, and *labial glands* are present.

In poisonous snakes the gland which secretes the poison, or venom, is a modification of the labial gland of the upper jaw. It is homologous with the parotid salivary gland of mammals. The labial poison gland is encapsulated by a strong sheath of connective tissue. Its duct opens into the cavity or groove of the poison fang (Fig. 5.4).

In the Gila monster, *Heloderma,* which is the only poisonous lizard extant, it is the sublingual gland which is modified to form the poisonous secretion. This passes through four ducts which penetrate the bone of the lower jaw to emerge in the vestibule in front of the grooved teeth.

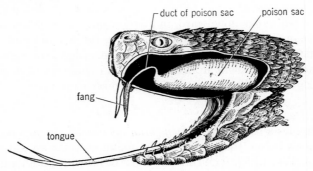

duct of poison sac   poison sac

fang

tongue

Fig. 5.4. Head of rattlesnake dissected to show relation of poison gland to hollow fang. (*Drawn by J. Dohm.*)

In marine turtles and in crocodiles and alligators, oral glands are poorly developed.

Birds. Well-developed *anterior* and *posterior sublingual glands* opening in the floor of the mouth are present in birds. Another gland at the angle of the mouth, the so-called *angle gland,* may possibly be homologous with the labial glands of reptiles. In birds, labial and intermaxillary glands are missing. Numerous groups of small glands open separately on the roof of the mouth. A digestive function has been ascribed to the mouth glands of many birds, the enzyme ptyalin being present in their secretions.

Mammals. Many small mucous glands are located on the palate and tongue in mammals. Here, however, for the first time, we find the large and distinctly grouped *salivary glands.* There are usually three sets of salivary glands, which are named according to their position. The *parotid gland* lies in the region of the ear, usually beneath and somewhat anterior to the external auditory meatus. Its position may vary within limits in different species. The *parotid duct (Stensen's duct)* courses over the masseter muscle of the cheek to enter the vestibule of the mouth opposite the upper molar teeth. The *submaxillary gland* lies in the posterior part of the lower jaw. Its duct, the *submaxillary duct (Wharton's duct),* opens in front of the tongue near the lower incisor teeth. Rabbits and horses lack the submaxillary gland. The *sublingual gland* is smaller than the other salivary glands. It is composed of a major portion, the sublingual gland proper with its duct (*of Bartholin*), and numerous smaller elements each with its own duct (*of Rivinus*). The ducts open separately into the oral cavity along the jaw-tongue groove and lateral to the submaxillary duct with which they frequently unite. The sublingual gland is not present in the mouse, mole, or shrew. Salivary glands are reduced or wanting in whales and sirenians.

The secretions of the three sets of salivary glands vary. In man the submaxillary and sublingual glands produce most of the mucin in the saliva. This gives saliva its mucilaginous character. The secretion of the parotid gland is more watery and contains the enzyme ptyalin in greater amounts than that of the other two. Ptyalin plays a role in digestion, since in its presence and in a neutral or slightly alkaline medium, starches are converted into maltose (malt sugar) in a step-by-step process. Maltose is of simpler chemical structure than starch. Ptyalin is not secreted by the salivary glands in all mammals.

The disease known as *mumps,* which affects human beings, is technically known as *contagious parotitis.* It is marked by an inflammation and swelling of the parotid gland. The causative organism is probably a virus. Mumps may occur on both sides or on one side only. Sometimes the submaxillary and sublingual glands may be involved, and occasionally the testes, mammary glands, and labia majora become swollen.

Mucous *molar glands* are especially well developed in such herbivorous forms as the Artiodactyla. Their secretion aids greatly in swallowing the coarse vegetation on which these animals feed. The large *orbital glands* of the dog family are mucous glands, the ducts of which open into the mouth in the region of the last upper molar teeth.

Tongue

The tongues of vertebrates show much diversity, and not all are homologous with the mammalian organ with which we are most familiar.

Cyclostomes. The cyclostome "tongue" is a very highly specialized structure which is not comparable to the tongues of higher vertebrates. Cyclostomes attach themselves to fishes by means of the buccal funnel which acts as a sort of suction cup. They then rasp the skin and muscles of their prey by a back-and-forth movement of the muscular tongue which bears horny teeth on its surface (Fig. 15.2).

Fishes. The tongue, or rather the *primary tongue,* of fishes should scarcely be called a tongue. It is merely a fleshy fold which develops from the floor of the mouth between the mandibular and hyoid arches. The hyoid arch frequently extends into this fold and supports it. The tongue is devoid of muscles and can be moved only within narrow limits by varying the position of the hyoid arch. Sensory receptors may be present. In some fishes the tongue bears small papillae, and in a few teleosts, such as the salmon, teeth may even be present on the tongue. These are supported by a *glossohyal bone* which unites the hyoid arches of the two sides.

Amphibians. Four different conditions pertaining to the tongue prevail in amphibians. In a certain group, called the *aglossal toads,* no tongue of any sort is present. This represents a degenerate condition. In some caudates, such as *Necturus,* in which the entire life is spent in the water, the tongue shows very little change over the condition found in fishes.   Other amphibians have movable tongues which may be thrust out of the mouth and used in capturing the animals on which they feed.   These tongues consist of a basal portion which is homologous with the primary tongue of fishes and an expanded, anterior, glandular portion which is well supplied

with protractor and retractor muscles. These together make up the so-called *definitive tongue*. In frogs and toads the base of the tongue is attached anteriorly at the margin of the jaw. Its free end is folded back on the floor of the mouth when at rest and is flipped out of the mouth during activity. In caudates the tongue has a more extensive attachment to the supporting hyoid arch. Some salamanders, like *Eurycea* (Fig. 5.5), can thrust out their

FIG. 5.5.   Head of salamander, *Eurycea bislineata*, with tongue extended.   (*Drawn by J. Dohm.*)

tongues directly and pull them back again with lightninglike rapidity.

Reptiles.   In turtles, crocodiles, and alligators the tongue is not protrusible and lies on the floor of the mouth.   Snakes and lizards, on the other hand, have well-developed tongues which can be extended and retracted. Many possess a sheath into which the greater part of the tongue can be withdrawn.   Because of the presence of a small notch at the tip of the lower jaw, snakes can extend their bifurcated tongues out of their mouths even when the latter are tightly closed.   Among the lizards, the tongue of the chameleon is best developed and is used as a prehensile organ in capturing prey.   It has been reported that the bifurcated tongues of certain lizards and of snakes, when retracted, are placed in the blind pockets of Jacobson's organ which opens on either side into the mouth cavity near the choanae. This seems to be an accessory olfactory device.   Volatile chemical substances, particles of which cling to the surface of the tongue, may thus be detected by the animal.

The reptilian tongue represents a higher degree of development than that of amphibians.   It includes a fold over the hyoid arch and a homologue of the glandular tongue, or *tuberculum impar*, seen in amphibians.   This arises between the basihyal and the lower jaw.   A pair of *lateral lingual folds* above the mandibular arch also contributes to tongue formation.   The tongue is thus composed of four portions which have fused together.

Birds.   The tongue of birds is practically lacking in intrinsic muscles. It is usually covered with horny material and may be provided with pointed, thornlike projections.   In some birds it is bifurcated, and in others it is split at the end, forming a brushlike structure.   Since the tongue lacks intrinsic muscles, the only way it may be moved is by altering the position of the hyoid apparatus which supports it at its base.   Although most birds can move the tongue only slightly, the woodpeckers can extend it for a considerable distance.   The hyoid apparatus of the woodpecker is long, slender, and coiled when at rest.   When it is extended the coils straighten out and the bird is thus able to secure the insect larvae which make up the bulk of its food.

In birds the tongue has lost the lateral lingual folds derived from the mandibular arch and which are possessed by reptiles.   It is largest in the birds of prey and in the parrots.   The familiar thick, soft tongue of the parrot is large, not because of muscular development but rather on account of the fat, blood vessels, and glandular elements which it contains.

Mammals.   The mammalian tongue is the best developed of the vertebrates and shows many modifications not only in form but in function.   In all groups except the whales it is movable because of the well-developed intrinsic muscles which are contained within it.   In the anteaters the tongue is best developed of all, and its muscles may extend back as far as the sternum.

The mammalian tongue is derived from five separate portions which have united.   These include the unpaired tuberculum impar, paired lateral lingual swellings from the mandibular arch which make up the *body* of the

tongue, and paired fleshy ridges, contributed by the hyoid arch and the third and fourth branchial arches, which form the pharyngeal portion, or *root*, of the tongue.   The hyoid apparatus supports the tongue at its base.   The thyroid gland originally arises from the midline at the point where the anterior and posterior portions of the tongue come together. A small depression, or pit, the *foramen caecum*, at the base of the tongue (Fig. 5.6), represents the point of origin of the thyroid gland.

The mucous membrane under the front of the mammalian tongue forms a median fold, the *lingual frenum*, which is attached

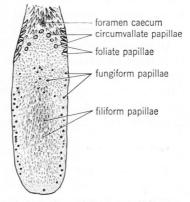

Fig. 5.6.   Tongue of cat, showing arrangement of papillae.

to the floor of the mouth.   Occasionally this frenum in human beings is too short and thus restricts the freedom of movement of the tongue.   A person with an abnormally short lingual frenum is said to be tongue-tied.   Speech may be difficult, at least when the production of certain sounds is attempted.   A simple operation which involves cutting the frenum usually will remedy this condition.

The tongue bears papillae of various kinds (Fig. 5.6) which may or may not be associated with taste buds.   Among those most commonly found in mammals are *filiform, fungiform, foliate*, and *vallate* or *circumvallate papillae*. *Filiform papillae* are small, conical projections making up the greater part of the plushy surface of the tongue. In the cat family (Felidae) the epithelium covering the filiform papillae is highly cornified. These modified papillae are used in cleaning the fur as well as in rasping the flesh off bones, which may be cleaned completely. *Fungiform papillae*, as their name implies, are toadstool-shaped structures scattered over the surface of the tongue. *Foliate* papillae are broad and leaflike. Their numbers vary in different species, but they are generally situated near the base of the tongue. *Circumvallate papillae* are few in number but large. Each is surrounded by a trench. These papillae are arranged in the form of an inverted V with the apex pointing toward the base of the tongue. The foramen caecum lies just beyond the apex of the V. For a further discussion of the lingual papillae, and the taste buds associated with them, the reader is referred to Chap. 14, pages 669 to 671.

The tongue of the dog is highly important in keeping the body temperature constant. Although dogs have sweat glands in the skin (page 108), they probably play little, if any, part in temperature regulation. Some mechanism other than evaporation of sweat is necessary for the elimination of excess heat. In the dog this is accomplished by panting. The moist, highly vascular tongue swells and hangs from the mouth. The rapidly expired and inspired air, passing over the surface of the tongue, evaporates the moisture and thus produces a cooling effect.

In ruminating animals the tongue is used as a prehensile organ and is important in browsing. In the giraffe the extremely long tongue may be twisted about a twig and strip off the leaves in a remarkable manner. Other mammals use their tongues in lapping up fluids and in manipulating food that is within the mouth. In man, articulate speech is made possible largely by movements of the tongue.

Teeth

Teeth are primarily employed by animals in manipulating food, but in some species they serve an additional function as structures used in attack or defense. In most vertebrates teeth are used only to hold captured prey. In others they may be modified and are of use in cutting, crushing, or grinding food. Among vertebrates, two types of teeth are found: *epidermal* and *true* teeth.

Epidermal teeth. These consist of hard, pointed, cornified, epithelial projections. They are present in but few vertebrates and are in no way homologous with true teeth discussed below. Perhaps the best-developed epidermal teeth are those of cyclostomes. They are conical, horny structures which in the lamprey are arranged in a definite pattern on the inner walls of the buccal funnel and on the highly specialized rasping tongue (Figs. 15.2 and 15.3). Each tooth is derived from the epidermis overlying a papilla of dermis, or corium (Fig. 5.7). In the hagfish a single median tooth lies above the mouth aperture and two rows of small teeth are located on the tongue.

Among amphibians, epidermal teeth are found on the edges of the jaws of most larval salientians. They are in reality cornified papillae which are used in scraping off algae on which the larvae feed.

Epidermal teeth are also found in the duckbill platypus. True teeth are present in this animal during developmental stages, but they are lost even before birth. When the true teeth are erupting, the surrounding ectoderm becomes cornified and grows under them. Thus, when the true teeth are shed, a horny plate remains which serves as an aid in holding and perhaps in

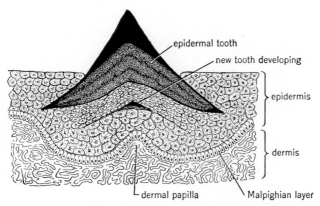

FIG. 5.7. Section through epidermal tooth of lamprey. (*After Warren.*)

crushing food. Horny crushing plates are also present in members of the order Sirenia, but these animals possess true teeth as well.

It is convenient at this point to mention the baleen, or "whalebone," found in the mouths of the so-called whalebone whales. Baleen consists of large, often enormous, horny sheets, or plates, which hang in series from the edges of the upper jaw. The lower ends of the plates are fringed and serve to strain from the water the microscopic organisms on which these huge animals feed. Baleen is formed from very large cornified papillae which become fastened together.

True teeth. All other teeth found in vertebrates are built upon the same fundamental plan, which is somewhat similar to that of the placoid scales of elasmobranch fishes (page 114). Whereas placoid scales are covered with a hard layer of *vitrodentine* of mesodermal origin, the exposed surface of true teeth is composed of shiny, translucent enamel, derived from ectoderm.

It has generally been held in the past that teeth have been derived phylogenetically from the placoid type of scale. A more recent point of view is that both are modified remnants of bony dermal plates which formed the armor of such ancestral forms as ostracoderms and certain placoderms and are, therefore, homologous. It has often been stated that the transition from placoid scale to tooth can be observed at the borders of the mouth of a shark. A more correct interpretation is that at the margins of the jaws a divergence is exhibited between enamel-covered teeth, on the one hand, and vitrodentine-covered placoid scales, on the other.

Structure and development. The portion of the true tooth that is exposed and is called the *crown* is covered with *enamel*. Under this lies the somewhat softer *dentine* (ivory), very similar in its chemical make-up to bone but differing widely in structure from bone. The dentine, in turn, sur-

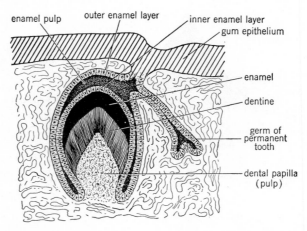

Fig. 5.8. Diagrammatic section showing structure of primary and secondary enamel organs. (*Drawn by J. Dohm.*)

rounds a *pulp cavity* filled with soft pulp. The embryonic origin of true teeth is twofold. Enamel is derived from stomodaeal ectoderm; the rest of the tooth from mesenchyme.

When teeth develop, the first indication of their formation is to be seen in a thickening in certain regions of the mouth or, in some forms, even of the pharynx. This thickening, the *dental lamina*, may be continuous or discontinuous. At intervals the ectodermal cells multiply and push into the underlying mesenchyme. The mesenchymal cells under the ectoderm also increase in number and push against the latter so that an inverted, cupshaped structure, the *enamel organ*, takes form (Fig. 5.8). Secondary enamel organs usually develop along with the primary ones being discussed. These will give rise to the teeth that appear later on in life. The mesenchyme within the enamel organ is known as the *dental papilla*. Those cells of the dental papilla next to the enamel organ become differentiated into *odontoblasts*, or dentine-forming cells; and these deposit a layer of dentine just under the ectodermal cells of the enamel organ. Dentine is harder than bone but resembles it in certain ways. The cells of the enamel organ become differentiated into two layers, the *outer* and *inner enamel layers.* Looser cells making up the *enamel pulp* lie between them. The cells of the inner enamel layer become *ameloblasts,* or enamel-forming cells. They aid in the formation of enamel which covers the dentine like a cap. Enamel is the hardest substance in the body and will give sparks when hit against steel. It is translucent and of a bluish-white cast. Continued addition of new dentine from below forces the tooth to the surface, and it is then said to erupt. The part of the dental papilla that remains after the dentine is formed makes up the pulp of the tooth, part of which is derived from odontoblasts.

In most cases after a tooth has completely formed it ceases to grow since the odontoblasts fail to function any longer. In certain special cases, as in the incisor teeth of rodents and lagomorphs and the tusks of elephants, the odontoblasts function throughout life and the teeth continue to grow. In mammals a layer of bone of peculiar histological structure, the *cementum,* forms around that part of the tooth below the crown. Cementum lacks canaliculi and Haversian systems.

Replacement of teeth. Except in mammals and a few others teeth may be replaced an indefinite number of times (*polyphyodont*). This is made possible by the formation of a succession of enamel organs. In most mammals only two sets of teeth form (*diphyodont*), but in a few there is only one set (*monophyodont*).

Location of teeth. Teeth may be located almost anywhere in the oral or pharyngeal cavities where stomodaeal ectoderm is present or where there is cartilage or bone to support them. In addition to their usual location on premaxillaries, maxillaries, and mandible, in certain forms they may be found on the vomer, palatine, pterygoid, and parasphenoid bones as well. In some fishes, teeth are located on the tongue and attached to the hyoid arch. In others they may even be found on the posterior visceral arches.

Shape of teeth. When all the teeth are of a similar form, or shape, the dentition is said to be *homodont.* When teeth are arranged in groups which differ in shape and function, the term *heterodont* is applied to the dentition. Most vertebrates below mammals that possess teeth have homodont dentition. There are several kinds of fish, however, which have heterodont dentition. In the Port Jackson shark, *Heterodontus (Cestracion),* for example, the anterior teeth in each jaw are pointed and used in a prehensile manner, whereas the posterior teeth are scroll-like and used for crushing. Although a few mammals, such as the toothed whales, have homodont dentition, most are heterodont, the teeth being differentiated into *incisors, canines, premolars,* and *molars.*

Attachment of teeth. The manner in which teeth are attached at their bases also varies. One type of arrangement found among vertebrates is the *thecodont* condition in which the teeth are set in sockets in the jawbones

(Fig. 5.9*C*). Some fishes have the thecodont method of tooth attachment, but otherwise only crocodilians and mammals, among living forms, have utilized this method. Numerous fossil reptiles had thecodont dentition, as did *Archaeopteryx*, among birds. The roots of mammalian teeth are longer and more deeply embedded than those of lower forms with thecodont dentition. There are two kinds of roots, open and closed (Fig. 5.10). In the first type the pulp cavity, or root canal, is wide open, and, by addition of new layers of dentine from beneath, such teeth may continue to grow throughout life. The tusks of elephants and the incisors of rodents and lagomorphs,

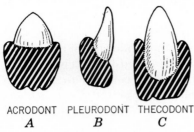

ACRODONT   PLEURODONT   THECODONT
  A   *B*   *C*

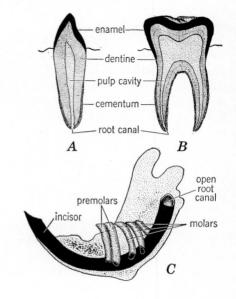

Fig. 5.9. Diagram showing three methods of tooth attachment. (*Drawn by G. Schwenk.*)

Fig. 5.10. *A*, section through incisor tooth; *B*, section through premolar tooth; both with closed pulp cavities. *C*, Lower jaw of rodent, *Geomys*, showing large incisor tooth with open pulp cavity. (*C, after Bailey, modified from Wiedersheim, "Comparative Anatomy of Vertebrates," copyright* 1907 *by The Macmillan Company and used with their permission.*)

mentioned above, are examples of this type of tooth. In the closed type, which is the usual form, the root canal is very small and serves only for the passage of nerves and blood vessels. These teeth fail to grow after they have reached their definitive size. Any increase in dentine through activity of odontoblasts would serve only to reduce the size of the pulp cavity.

In other vertebrates the method of tooth attachment is more simple. In sharks and rays the teeth are not directly attached to the cartilaginous jaws but are embedded in the fibrous and tough mucous membrane which covers the jaws. In most vertebrates, however, the teeth are fused to the underlying bone (*acrodont*) (Fig. 5.9*A*). Such teeth are apt to break off easily but may be replaced. In some fishes and snakes certain of the teeth may be *hinged*. Such teeth yield to pressure and bend backward, only to snap back to the upright position when the pressure is released. Thus, objects are permitted to pass into the mouth, but egress is prevented when the teeth assume their normal vertical position. Hinged teeth are held in position by dense, fibrous ligaments which radiate from the posterior sides of their bases to the bone supporting them. The fronts of the teeth are free at their bases and lift away from the bone when the teeth are pressed backward. Hinged teeth are found in the pike, hake, angler, and some other fishes, which also possess numerous teeth firmly fastened to the jawbones by the acrodont method of attachment. Another method of attachment of teeth is the *pleurodont* type. Here the teeth are united not only to the bone below but also along a shelflike indentation on the inside of the jawbone (Fig. 5.9*B*). In teeth of the acrodont or pleurodont types, where there are no roots, nerves and blood vessels enter the pulp cavity at the base.

Comparative anatomy of teeth. CYCLOSTOMES. Only epidermal teeth are present in cyclostomes (page 152).

FISHES. A few species of fishes are naturally toothless, at least in the adult condition. Among these are sturgeons, sea horses, and pipefish. Teeth in fishes are all of the true type. Dentition in most cases is polyphyodont, acrodont, and homodont. However, many teleosts and some elasmobranchs have heterodont dentition, and in certain forms such as the haddock, garpike, barracuda, and several others the thecodont method of attachment is to be found.

A primitive type of tooth, referred to as *labyrinthine*, occurs in fossil crossopterygians and in the living coelacanth *Latimeria*. Such teeth are of a simple, conical shape, bearing longitudinal ridges and grooves which represent a rather complex folding of the covering layer of enamel. Fish teeth usually consist of little more than conical projections, but in some, as in sharks, they are vertically flattened and triangular in shape. In chimaeras and in the Dipnoi several teeth appear to have fused to form platelike structures used for crushing. The number of teeth is highly variable, ranging from a few flattened plates up to several thousand. In different species teeth may be located in various parts of the mouth or pharynx wherever bony or hard parts are situated.

AMPHIBIANS. Save for the epidermal teeth found in larval salientians, the teeth of amphibians are all true teeth. Teeth are lacking in toads of the genera *Bufo* and *Pipa*. In several accounts the salamander *Siren* is described as being toothless. Actually it bears a patch of numerous teeth on each side of the lower jaw and two elongated patches, each containing many vomerine teeth (Fig. 5.11) in the anterior portion of the roof of the mouth (C. J. Goin, 1942, *Annals of the Carnegie Museum*, **24**:211). In frogs, teeth are lacking in the lower jaw.

Some of the ancient fossil amphibians possessed conical teeth of the labyrinthine type, but in modern forms they are simple, peglike structures. Amphibian teeth are more restricted as to location than are the teeth of fishes, being confined to the jawbones, palatines, and vomers. In a few

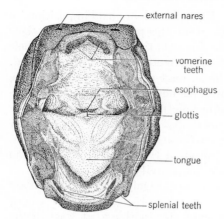

external nares

vomerine teeth

esophagus

glottis

tongue

splenial teeth

FIG. 5.11. Open mouth of salamander, *Siren*, showing numerous vomerine and splenial teeth. The angle of the mouth has been cut on each side in order to depress the lower jaw. (*Drawn by R. Speigle.*)

forms (*Spelerpes, Plethodon, Batrachoseps*) they are even attached to the parasphenoid bone. Amphibian teeth, for the most part, are polyphyodont, homodont, and acrodont.

REPTILES. Turtles are the toothless representatives of the class Reptilia. The horny beaks of these animals are sharp and strong and serve them in lieu of teeth. Some of the prehistoric pterodactyls also lacked teeth.

In other reptiles the teeth are situated on the jawbones, but in snakes and lizards they may also occur on the pterygoids and palatines. *Sphenodon* has vomerine teeth, an unusual feature among the reptiles. *Sphenodon* is also monophyodont since its single set of teeth is not replaced. Otherwise most reptiles have homodont and polyphyodont dentition, but variations occur in the method of tooth attachment. In snakes and lizards teeth are either acrodont or pleurodont, but in several ancestral fossil reptiles as well as living crocodilians thecodont dentition occurs. Certain extinct reptiles, the theriomorphs, or cynodonts, had heterodont teeth very similar to those of mammals. A few modern reptiles approach this condition.

The poison fangs of certain snakes are specialized teeth concerning which particular mention should be made. The fangs are attached to the maxillary bones. Some fangs, like those of the cobras, are permanently erect. Those of the vipers lie close to the roof of the mouth and are covered with folds of mucous membrane when not in use. When the mouth is opened to strike, however, the fangs are erected. This is made possible by the shifting in position of a chain of loosely articulated bones in the skull (page 419). There are two types of poison fangs, but both are basically similar. The first type, found in the cobras, bears a groove or poison duct on its anterior surface. In the vipers a hollow canal lined with enamel runs through the tooth and opens at the tip. In the latter type it is as though the edges of the former

poison canal

dentine

pulp cavity

enamel

FIG. 5.12. Section through poison fang of rattlesnake.

had come together and fused to form a tube (Fig. 5.12). In both cases the duct of the poison gland enters at the base of the fang. When the snake is about to strike, the muscles around the poison glands contract and the venom is forced through the fangs much in the manner of liquid passing through a hypodermic needle. It is doubtful whether a snake can strike for a distance over half the length of its body. The head of the snake lunges forward at the same time that the venom is being ejected, and when the snake strikes some soft substance, such as flesh, the poison is actually injected. It is of interest that the young of poisonous species are equipped at birth with a functional poison apparatus which, although but a miniature of the adult, is just as effective for its size. The coral snake of the south Atlantic and Gulf states is the only representative of the cobra group in the United States. Its bite is dangerous and often fatal. In the cobras the poison fangs are either the most anterior or most posterior of several maxillary teeth, but in the vipers there is but one fang on each maxilla with a few reserve fangs posterior to it. The fangs of poisonous snakes exhibited in circuses and side shows are customarily pulled out, so that there is little danger from snake bite. The operation must be performed periodically; otherwise replacement teeth will soon take over the function of the original fang.

The lower front teeth of the Gila monster are strong and slightly curved. They bear grooves on their anterior surfaces which serve for the passage of the secretion of poisonous sublingual glands. There are no true fangs, and the animal must hold tightly to its prey in order to make its virulent venom effective.

What is sometimes called an "egg tooth" is present on the tip of the upper jaw in the embryos of lizards and certain snakes. It projects beyond the other teeth and serves as an aid to the young in emerging from the leathery eggshell. It is lost soon after hatching. In *Sphenodon*, turtles, and crocodilians a *horny, epithelial* egg tooth at the tip of the snout of the embryo serves the same purpose. This is also a transitory structure and, although analogous to the egg tooth of snakes and lizards, is not homologous in any way.

BIRDS. No modern birds possess teeth. *Archaeopteryx* had thecodont teeth embedded in sockets like those of crocodilians and mammals. In *Ichthyornis* the sharp, pointed, conical teeth were set in shallow sockets; in *Hesperornis*, they were set in a continuous groove.

In many birds a transitory, horny egg tooth is present in the embryo and aids in breaking the shell at the time of hatching. It soon dries and falls off in the form of a small scale.

MAMMALS. Only a few toothless mammals are known. The adult platypus has epidermal teeth but no true teeth are present. During development a single set of teeth appears, but these are present only temporarily and are soon shed. In *Echidna* no teeth are present at any time. The whalebone whales lack teeth in the adult, as do certain anteaters. Although other anteaters, armadillos, and certain other forms possess teeth, they are imperfect structures which lack roots and enamel.

The thecodont condition is the rule in mammals. Most members of this class are diphyodont and have but two sets of teeth. The first set, known as the baby teeth, milk teeth, lacteal teeth, or deciduous teeth, are lost and then replaced by a permanent set. In certain forms, as in bats and guinea pigs, the milk teeth are lost even before birth. A few mammals are monophyodont, having but a single set of teeth. The platypus, toothed whales, sloths, and sirenians are examples. Marsupials are an intermediate group since they retain all their milk teeth except the last premolars.

In certain marsupials a prelacteal dentition has been observed, and occasionally in the human being a postpermanent dentition has been recorded. Thus in mammals it seems that there may originally have been four sets of teeth, a condition not so far removed from the polyphyodont teeth of the lower vertebrates.

Among mammals only certain cetaceans are homodont. The teeth of the toothed whales, for example, are all similar in shape. These animals feed entirely under water, and their teeth are adapted for catching and holding prey but not for chewing, since most aquatic animals swallow their food whole. These homodont mammals have anywhere from 2 to 200 teeth.

With the above exception, the heterodont condition usually prevails in mammals. Pinnepedians show a tendency toward homodont dentition, however. Four types of teeth are commonly identified in the upper jaw. *Incisors* are in front, and their roots are embedded in sockets, or *alveoli*, in the premaxillary bones. On either side the incisors are followed by a single *canine*, which is the most anterior tooth in the maxillary bone. It usually differs from the remaining teeth in being larger and having a single, pointed crown and a single root. Following the canines are the *premolars*, or bicuspid, teeth which are more complex in form and have two roots. Lastly come the *molars* with several roots. There is but a single set of molars, which should really be considered as belonging to the milk dentition but differing from the others in not being replaced. The mandible, or lower jaw, bears teeth corresponding to those just described. A natural space between two types of teeth is referred to as a *diastema*. In rodents and lagomorphs, which lack canine teeth, a diastema is present between the incisor and cheek teeth. In the cat there is a diastema between the canine and first premolar on each side of the lower jaw.

Only in mammals is there a fixed number of teeth characteristic of each species. The maximum number of teeth in *placental* mammals with the heterodont dentition is 44. There are usually fewer than this because of reduction in number of one or more types. The number of teeth in any particular species is surprisingly constant. For purposes of classification, a so-called *dental formula* has been devised. Since the two halves of the jaw correspond, only the numbers on one side are recorded. Those of the upper and lower jaws are separated by a horizontal line, so that they appear in the formula as numerator and denominator. The kind of tooth is represented by the initial letters i, c, p, m, indicating incisor, canine, premolar, and molar, respectively. Thus, the dental formula of man is $i\frac{2}{2}$, $c\frac{1}{1}$, $p\frac{2}{2}$, $m\frac{3}{3}$. In order to simplify these dental formulas the initial letter is customarily omitted, so that for man it appears as $\frac{2.1.2.3}{2.1.2.3}$. When a certain type of tooth is lacking, a zero is used to indicate this fact. Thus in a beaver, which lacks canines, the dental formula is $\frac{1.0.1.3}{1.0.1.3}$. The cow, which lacks upper incisors and canines, is represented by $\frac{0.0.3.3}{3.1.3.3}$.

From numerous studies it is believed that the hypothetical ancestral form from which existing mammalian dentitions have been derived had the formula $\frac{5.1.4.5}{5.1.4.5}$. This formula is almost attained by some marsupials, but in higher mammals there is always a reduction in the number of incisor and molar teeth. A few dental formulas of familiar mammals are given below.

Cat	$\frac{3.1.3.1}{3.1.2.1}$	Squirrel	$\frac{1.0.2.3}{1.0.1.3}$
Dog	$\frac{3.1.4.2}{3.1.4.3}$	Rat	$\frac{1.0.0.3}{1.0.0.3}$
Mole	$\frac{3.1.4.3}{3.1.4.3}$	Horse	$\frac{3.1.4.3}{3.1.4.3}$

In different mammals, the shapes of the molar and premolar teeth vary according to their feeding habits and the type of food eaten. The cheek teeth in the terrestrial carnivores have sharp, cutting crowns. This condition is known as *secodont*. A so-called *carnassial tooth* in each jaw, a premolar above and a molar below, is specially developed for shearing. In man and some other mammals, the flattened cheek teeth with their small tubercles are of the *bunodont* type and used for grinding. In ruminating mammals, the horse, and some others, the cheek teeth are characterized by the presence of vertical, crescent-shaped folds of hard enamel enclosing softer areas of dentine. Cement may fill the interstices (Fig. 5.13A). This condition is known as *selenodont*. Because the softer dentine wears away more rapidly, a rasping surface, well adapted for grinding, is maintained. In elephants, enormous grinding teeth are present which may measure as much as 1 ft. in length and 4 in. in width. There is an intricate folding of the enamel and dentine to form transverse ridges. Such teeth are of the *lophodont* type (Fig. 5.13B). In elephants as well as the manatee there is an almost constant succession of molar teeth from behind throughout life. The front ones are pushed forward and are shed as new ones form behind. Only one fully developed tooth is present at one time on each side of each jaw in elephants.

Certain unusual teeth found in mammals deserve special mention. The tusks of elephants are incisor teeth with open root canals. They grow continuously throughout life. The gnawing incisor teeth of rodents and lagomorphs are also examples of teeth with open pulp cavities. These chisellike

FIG. 5.13. *A*, grinding surface of selenodont tooth from lower jaw of a sheep; *B*, grinding surface of lophodont molar tooth of African elephant. (*B, after Tomes.*)

teeth also grow continuously. Only the anterior face of the tooth is covered with enamel. The teeth of the two jaws oppose each other and are kept sharp by whetting against each other since the softer dentine wears away more rapidly than the hard enamel. If the jaw is damaged so that one or the other incisor tooth has nothing to oppose it, it may grow in a spiral manner (Fig. 5.14) and become so large that it prevents the jaws from closing. Animals with such teeth usually die of starvation. The tusks of the male wild boar are greatly developed canine teeth which also have large, persistent pulp cavities. Both upper and lower canines curve upward and are kept sharp by working against one another. Tusks of both male and female walrus are also enlarged upper canine teeth.

FIG. 5.14. Lateral view of skull of experimental rat. The lower incisor teeth were cut off at intervals. The unopposed upper incisors then grew abnormally in the curved manner shown in the figure.

In a number of mammals rather striking sexual differences are apparent in the dentition. In addition to those animals mentioned above, the apes show sexual dimorphism in this respect. The canines and first premolars are decidedly larger in the male than in the female.

Embryonic monotremes, being the only mammals to develop within an eggshell outside the body of the mother, are the only mammals which have a horny egg tooth at the end of the snout. This serves the young in escaping from the eggshell.

The origin of the rather complex cheek teeth of mammals from the simple conical type found in most other vertebrates has long been a subject for conjecture. The simple, single-rooted incisor and canine teeth show so little modification that they need not enter into the discussion. Two main theories have been advanced to explain the origin of the more complex premolars and molars. The first theory embodies the idea that the cheek teeth originated by fusion of two or more conical teeth. Indeed, in the dugong several enamel organs fuse to form the molar teeth, but this condition is exceptional. Embryological evidence which should support the soundness of this theory is fragmentary and indecisive. The other theory, which is more generally held and for which there is considerable paleontological evidence, holds that starting with a primitive conical tooth, two additional projections, or buds, developed, giving rise to the so-called *triconodont shape*. Later these cones shifted in position so as to give rise to separate tubercles or cusps arranged in a triangle. This has been called the *tritubercular position* (Fig. 5.15). Still later, other parts may have devel-

| A | B | C | D |

FIG. 5.15.   Theoretical development of tooth cusps from a single pointed tooth.   (*After Osborn.*)

oped from these three original tubercles so as to form additional cusps, ridges, and folds, and thus are finally arrived at the many and varied types of mammalian cheek teeth that exist today. For further details and elaborations of this theory of tooth evolution the reader is referred to the works of Cope and Osborn, who originally propounded it.

Anterior and Intermediate Lobes of the Pituitary Body

The pituitary body, or gland, can under no circumstances be considered as a part of the digestive system. However, since its anterior and intermediate lobes arise from the ectodermal epithelium of the primitive mouth cavity, they should be mentioned here as stomodaeal derivative. For a complete discussion of this important endocrine organ the reader is referred to pages 352 to 361.

PHARYNX

The first part of the endodermal portion of the alimentary tract, and the portion which is directly continuous with the ectoderm-lined mouth, is the pharynx. Its function as part of the digestive system is merely to serve as a passageway between the mouth and esophagus. It is in the walls of the pharynx that the muscles which initiate swallowing movements are located. The pharynx is also very important in connection with respiration.

Gill clefts, lungs, and several other structures are derived from its walls. These are more properly described in their relation to the respiratory system and will be discussed in that connection.

ESOPHAGUS

The esophagus is that portion of the alimentary canal immediately following the pharynx. At its other end it joins the stomach. In some forms, particularly among the lower vertebrates, the point at which the esophagus ends and the stomach begins is difficult to distinguish. The length of the esophagus is related to the length of the neck region.

The histological structure of the esophagus is similar, in general, to that of the remainder of the digestive tract except that, since it does not lie within the coelom, it is not surrounded by a layer of visceral peritoneum. Furthermore, the mucous membrane lining the esophagus is of the stratified squamous type of epithelium rather than being composed of a single layer of columnar epithelial cells. In some vertebrates the squamous cells become cornified, but in others, as in man, these cells do not undergo true cornification. In the upper part of the esophagus the muscle fibers, in most cases, change gradually from the striated, or voluntary, type to the smooth, or involuntary, type. There are exceptions to this, particularly in the ruminating, or cud-chewing, mammals, in which the striated fibers extend throughout the entire length of the esophagus. Contraction of the esophagus in these animals is under voluntary control.

Cyclostomes. In the adult lamprey a very specialized condition occurs for which there is no parallel in other vertebrates. From the mouth cavity two tubes extend posteriorly (Fig. 15.3): a dorsal esophagus, and a ventral pharynx which ends blindly and is concerned entirely with respiration. At the entrance to the pharynx is a valvelike *velum*. The esophagus is lined with numerous folds. In the hagfish the condition is much as in other vertebrates, and the esophagus merely extends posteriorly from the pharynx in back of the last internal gill aperture.

Fishes. In fishes the esophagus is very short and its junction with the stomach is almost imperceptible. In certain elasmobranchs, as in *Squalus acanthias*, numerous backward-projecting papillae line the esophagus as well as the first part of the stomach. The esophagus commonly bears longitudinal folds which permit a considerable degree of distention. Some fishes are actually capable of swallowing others larger than themselves.

Amphibians. The esophagus in amphibians is extremely short and consists of little more than a constricted area of the alimentary tract. In most amphibians the lining of the esophagus as well as of the mouth is ciliated, and by this means small food particles are swept on to the stomach. Secretory cells in the esophageal epithelium of the frog are reported to have a digestive function. They secrete a substance called *propepsin*, which, however, is ineffective until it reaches the stomach. When acted upon by hydrochloric acid in the stomach, propepsin is converted to the enzyme *pepsin*, used in digestion.

Reptiles. In reptiles the esophagus is generally longer than in lower forms. Longitudinal folds in the walls permit considerable expansion, which is of special use in snakes, all of which are capable of swallowing large objects. The lining of the esophagus of a certain marine turtle is covered with cornified papillae which point backward (Fig. 5.16).

Fig. 5.16. Cornified papillae lining esophagus of a marine turtle. (*Drawn by G. Schwenk.*)

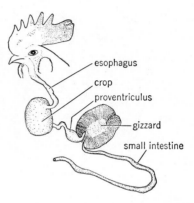

Fig. 5.17. Relations of crop and stomach regions of the domestic fowl.

Birds. In many birds the esophagus is likewise lined with horny papillae. Its junction with the stomach is abrupt. In grain-eating birds as well as birds of prey the esophagus forms a large sac, or else a ventral, pouchlike outgrowth is present (Fig. 5.17). This is called the *crop*, or *ingluvies*. It is primarily useful in permitting the bird to secure an abundance of food in a short period, thus lessening the time during which it is in danger from enemies. It also enables the bird to compete with others for a limited amount of food. Food is moistened within the crop. Although it is doubtful whether any digestion occurs here, such food particles as grain may swell and are thus rendered more capable of being digested later on. The crop releases portions of its contents at intervals. The food then passes on to the stomach. The *furcula*, or *wishbone*, supports the crop.

In pigeons a peculiar adaptation is found in the so-called *crop "glands,"* which are two modified areas in the walls of the crop in both males and females (Fig. 5.18). These are really not glands since they are cytogenic, or cell-forming, structures. Upon proper stimulation, the crop "glands" enlarge and very rapid cellular proliferation occurs. A nutritious, cheesy material called *pigeon milk* is sloughed into the cavity of the crop. This is regurgitated into the throats of the young squabs and serves as their food. It has been found that the activity of the crop "glands" is controlled by the *lactogenic hormone* secreted by the anterior lobe of the pituitary gland (page 357). Development of the crop "glands" seems to be stimulated via the pituitary by the act of incubating the eggs, in which both male and female participate. After the young are reared, the crop "glands" return to their resting condition.

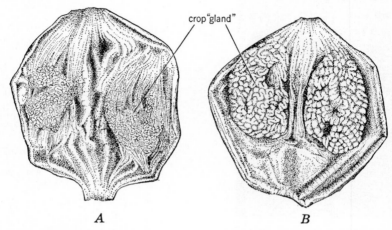

crop "gland"

A   B

Fig. 5.18.   Crops of pigeons cut open to show crop "glands": *A*, during resting, or inactive, period; *B*, from a bird previously injected with lactogenic hormone. (*Drawn by J. Dohm.*)

Mammals.   In mammals there is a clear distinction between stomach and esophagus. The length of the esophagus varies with the length of the neck, the giraffe having the longest esophagus of all. In man it is about 9 or 10 in. long, on the average. On its way to the stomach it must pass through the diaphragm. That portion below the diaphragm is covered by serosa, or visceral peritoneum, which is lacking from the upper portion.

Most textbooks state that the first three parts of the stomach region of ruminants (page 169) are actually modified regions of the esophagus. This is because these regions, like the esophagus, are lined with stratified squamous epithelium. The embryological studies of Lewis (F. T. Lewis, 1915, *Anat. Record*, **9**:102) indicate that those who hold this view are in error and that these structures are modified regions of the true stomach.

STOMACH

The stomach is basically a dilatation of the digestive tract for the temporary storage of food. Only when its lining epithelium contains gastric glands (with certain special exceptions) is it properly called a true stomach.

Its digestive function is apparently a secondary acquisition. The shape of the stomach is related to the shape of the body. In such elongated animals as snakes, it extends longitudinally, but in those with wider bodies it occupies a more transverse position. The end of the stomach which connects to the esophagus is nearer the heart and, therefore, is called the *cardiac end.* The main portion is called the *"body."* The *pyloric end* connects to the intestine and terminates at a valve, the *pylorus,* or *pyloric valve.* This consists of a fold of the lining mucous membrane surrounded by a thick sphincter muscle which regulates the passage of the contents of the stomach into the intestine.

In those animals in which the stomach has assumed a transverse position it is U-shaped or J-shaped. A twisting has occurred so that the cardiac end is on the left side of the body and the pylorus on the right. Two faces, the lesser and greater curvatures, are thus formed (Fig. 5.19). The lesser curvature is actually ventral, and the greater curvature dorsal. The expansion at the cardiac end of the stomach, formed by the greater curvature, is the sac-like *fundus.*

FIG. 5.19. Outline of human stomach, showing regions (ventral view).

The muscular walls of the stomach above the middle of the "body" do not exhibit contractions of a peristaltic nature. Those of the pyloric end contract in such a manner as to mix or churn the contents of the stomach thoroughly. Peristaltic waves originate near the body of the stomach and pass through the pyloric end down to the intestine, forcing the contents along. The rate of peristalis and the strength of the contractions vary with the type and amount of food eaten.

Cyclostomes. The cyclostome stomach is very poorly developed and consists of nothing more than an almost imperceptible enlargement at the posterior end of the esophagus.

Fishes. There is practically no distinction between esophagus and stomach in fishes, and the longitudinal folds of the former may extend for some distance into the stomach. A considerable variety of stomach shapes may be observed. Some are simple, straight tubes without any digestive function as in the Dipnoi. In others, as in *Polypterus,* the cardiac and pyloric limbs have fused along the line of the lesser curvature so that the stomach appears much as a blind pouch.

In elasmobranchs the J-shaped stomach is typical. The pyloric limb is smaller than the cardiac portion (Fig. 5.20A). Many other fishes have similarly shaped stomachs. Among teleosts there is greater variety of stomach shapes than in the other groups of fishes.   In some teleosts a ciliated lining is present.

Amphibians.   In frogs the cardiac end of the stomach is wide, there is no fundus, and the pyloric end is short and narrow.   In certain salamanders the stomach is straight.   All amphibian stomachs have a digestive function. Patches of ciliated epithelium may be found in the lining mucosa.

Reptiles.   No striking deviations are to be observed in the stomachs of reptiles.   Snakes and lizards have long, spindle-shaped stomachs in correlation with their elongated and narrow body shape.   There is a clear-cut line of demarcation between stomach and esophagus, however.   Of all the reptiles, the crocodilians have the most specialized gastric organs.   Part of the stomach is like that of birds, being modified into a gizzardlike muscular region.

Birds.   In accordance with the lack of teeth and the type of food eaten by birds, the stomach of most has been modified greatly for trituration. It has become differentiated into two regions (Fig. 5.17).   The first, which is continuous with the esophagus, has a glandular lining which secretes gastric juices.   It is known as the *proventriculus*.   Food, which is mixed

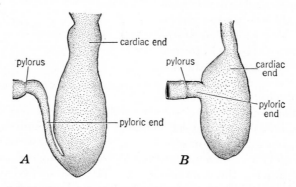

Fig. 5.20.   *A*, J-shaped stomach of elasmobranch fish; *B*, stomach of platypus in which the two limbs are fused along the lesser curvature.

with the digestive fluid in the proventriculus, passes into the much modified and highly muscular *gizzard*, which represents the pyloric portion of the stomach.   The muscles form a pair of disclike areas with tendinous centers. The glandular cells lining the gizzard secrete a tough, horny layer which in some cases bears bumps, or tubercles, on its surface.   These aid in the grinding process.   In grain-eaters, pebbles are taken into the gizzard.   They serve as an aid in reducing the contents to a pulp.   In commercial poultry establishments it is the practice to supply grit or pebbles to the birds; otherwise the food cannot be properly utilized.   The gizzard is best developed in grain-eating birds.   It is less well developed in insectivorous forms and in birds of prey, in which little differentiation is noticeable.

Mammals. *Variations in structure.* Many modifications exist in the transversely arranged stomachs of mammals, although most of them are of the typical kind. In monotremes the lining epithelium lacks glands, and the pouchlike structure, which serves merely for the storage of food, is therefore not considered to be a *true* stomach. In the platypus the two limbs are fused along the lesser curvature, so that the organ appears as a wide sac (Fig. 5.20*B*). In some monkeys, rodents, and other mammals a constriction marks off pyloric and cardiac regions. Such a stomach is often referred to as an *hourglass* stomach. It is occasionally encountered in man.

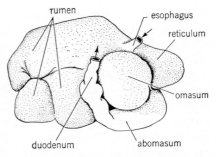

The gastric organs of herbivorous mammals are larger than those of carnivores. They are frequently divided into two or more compartments. Ruminating mammals (those which chew their cud) have the most complex stomachs of all. The stomach in cattle consists of four separate chambers: the *rumen* (*paunch*), *reticulum* (*honeycomb*), *omasum* (*psalterium* or *manyplies*), and *abomasum* (*rennet*) (Figs. 5.21 and 5.22). Although the first three,

FIG. 5.21. Stomach of ox viewed from the right side, showing normal structural relationships. (*After Sisson, "The Anatomy of the Domesticated Animals," W. B. Saunders Company. By permission.*)

as mentioned previously, are often considered to be modified portions of the esophagus, embryological studies show that they should properly be considered to be parts of the stomach. The rumen is a large, sac-

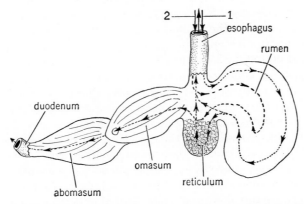

FIG. 5.22. Diagram of stomach of ruminant, showing functional relationships: *1* denotes initial swallowing; *2* indicates path taken by food upon reswallowing. (*Modified from Kingsley, "Comparative Anatomy of Vertebrates," The Blakiston Division, McGraw-Hill Book Company, Inc. By permission.*)

culated compartment which serves mainly for the storage of food. According to H. H. Dukes (1947, "The Physiology of Domestic Animals," Comstock Publishing Associates, Inc., pp. 307–325), the animal feeds fairly rapidly and fills the rumen with grain, grass, or other herbage. In cattle, fluid is added, and, by muscular contractions, the food in the rumen is churned about. The food also undergoes some bacterial fermentation during its stay in the rumen. It is believed that bacterial action on relatively simple nitrogenous compounds brings about a synthesis of proteins and vitamins of the B complex, which are important food constituents. While this is going on, the animal frequently lies down and "chews its cud" at leisure. Food in the rumen passes by degrees into the reticulum or directly to the esophagus and, together with a fair amount of fluid, is then regurgitated into the mouth. It is referred to as the cud, or bolus. The voluntary musculature of the esophagus makes this possible. When the animal begins to chew its cud it first swallows most of the fluid, which passes back into the rumen. When the cud has been well masticated and mixed with secretions of the salivary glands, it is swallowed once more and again passes into the rumen. A new bolus is then formed, regurgitated, and the entire process repeated. Most of the food which has been thoroughly masticated goes from the rumen into the reticulum and then passes directly to the omasum, a small chamber with many well-defined longitudinal folds in its walls, and thence to the abomasum. The latter is the only chamber of the stomach provided with gastric glands.

In camels the stomach is not quite so complicated, since an omasum is lacking. Pouchlike diverticula, called *water cells*, arise from both rumen and reticulum. Their openings are guarded by sphincter muscles. It is generally believed that the camel stores water in its water cells and, therefore, may go for long periods without drinking. This belief is not tenable (J. E. Hill, 1946, *Natural History*, **55**:387). The pouches can by no means hold as much water as the animal would require on a prolonged journey through the desert with no water available. Many camels have carried a standard load of 400 lb. 25 to 30 miles per day for 8 days without water. The water cells, or pouches, sometimes do contain almost pure water, but this is generally metabolic water drawn from other parts of the body and is used to moisten food undergoing digestion. Some water is stored in the muscles and connective tissues, but most of it comes indirectly from the breakdown of glycogen stored in the muscles and of fat stored in the hump. Physiologists have determined that for every 100 g. of fat oxidized in the body 110 g. of water is produced. As much as 8 gallons of water may be obtained by the animal as a result of processes involved in the breakdown of fat stored in the hump alone and which is used under certain conditions by the body as a source of energy.

The stomachs of whales and hippopotami are divided into several compartments. In the kangaroo the pyloric portion has many peculiar sacculated folds in its walls. The pyloric portion of the stomach of the blood-sucking bat, *Desmodus*, is elongated into a caecumlike structure which fills with blood when the animal is engaged in feeding.

Secretions. In the typical mammalian stomach, secretory cells are arranged so as to form a great number of tubular gastric glands. It has been estimated that there are about 35 million such glands in the stomach of a human being. Occasionally glands will show a slight degree of branching, but usually they are simple in structure. Three kinds of gastric glands are present, named according to their location: *cardiac, fundic,* and *pyloric glands.* They differ both as to histological structure and type of secretion. The cardiac and pyloric glands secrete an alkaline mucus. It is the glands of the fundus which are of greatest importance in digestion. Three kinds of cells are recognized in the fundic glands: *mucous neck cells; chief,* or *zymogen, cells;* and *parietal,* or *acid-secreting, cells.*

In most forms two *proenzymes* are secreted by the chief cells of the fundic glands. These are called *propepsin* and *prorennin,* respectively. In the presence of hydrochloric acid, secreted by the parietal cells, these are converted into the active enzymes, *pepsin* and *rennin.* Another enzyme called *gastric lipase* is also secreted by the gastric glands, but it has not as yet been determined in which cells it is formed. *Gastric juice* is a mixture of all these secretions and thus contains mucus, hydrochloric acid, pepsin, rennin, and gastric lipase. The concentration of hydrochloric acid in human gastric juice varies between 0.05 and 0.3 per cent. In the dog it may reach a concentration as high as 0.6 per cent.

Pepsin is said to be a proteolytic enzyme, since it is concerned with the digestion of *proteins.* It acts only in an acid medium and splits large protein molecules into smaller molecules of *peptones* and *proteoses.* Rennin, which is especially abundant in the gastric juice of young mammals, is a coagulating enzyme. It functions in a slightly acid medium and in the presence of calcium, to coagulate casein, the soluble protein in milk. This forms an insoluble compound called *calcium paracasein,* which is referred to as *curd.* A soluble, proteoselike substance, the *whey protein,* remains. The curd is then acted upon by pepsin in the usual manner. Gastric lipase, the third gastric enzyme, is weak and of little, if any, importance to an adult. Fats in a fine state of emulsion, such as the butterfat in milk and the fat of egg yolk, may possibly be acted upon by this enzyme. Mucus from the gastric glands has the power of combining with acid and, since it coats the lining of the stomach, may help protect the mucosa from the action of gastric juices.

The rapid passage of food through the mouth makes it almost impossible for the enzyme ptyalin to act to any great extent upon starches within the mouth by splitting them into molecules of maltose. It is a question as to how much of the starchy food that is mixed with saliva can be digested when it gets to the stomach. Ptyalin acts only in an alkaline, neutral, or faintly acid medium, and it would seem that the relatively high percentage of hydrochloric acid within the stomach would soon stop all activity. Investigations have shown that if the stomach of a rat which has been fed differently colored foods is removed, frozen, and sectioned, the food is observed to be arranged in concentric layers. Thus, before the contents of the stomach can be thoroughly churned, some time may elapse. During this interval and before the acidity increases to a point where reaction will cease, the ptyalin can act in the breaking down of starches.

It was formerly believed that the opening and closing of the pyloric valve, which regulates the passage of the contents of the stomach into the intestine, was controlled by the relative acidities of the materials in the stomach and intestine. It is now held that the pylorus is partly open most of the time and that emptying of the stomach is related to peristaltic muscular contractions, or waves, that pass from the stomach to intestine, and also to the degree to which the stomach contents have been rendered fluid or semifluid. The amount of material in the upper part of the intestine may also be a determining factor.

INTESTINE

The portion of the alimentary tract following the stomach is the *intestine*. It is the most important part of the digestive system. Here the acid *chyme* from the stomach is mixed with alkaline bile from the liver, pancreatic juice from the pancreas, and the secretions of great numbers of small glands in the walls of the intestine itself. These secretions finally convert food into such a form that it may be absorbed through the wall of the intestine into the blood or lymphatic systems, which then distribute it to all parts of the body. The intestine usually consists of two main parts: a long but narrow *small intestine* and a short, but wider, terminal portion, the *large intestine*. The part of the small intestine which immediately follows the stomach is called the *duodenum*. It is here that the ducts from liver and pancreas open.

Many modifications are to be found in the intestines of vertebrates. They serve, for the most part, to increase the surface area of the intestinal epithelium for secretion of digestive fluids and for the absorption of digested foods. The intestine may become elongated and coiled; its diameter may be increased; saclike diverticula called *caeca* may be present; the lining is often thrown into longitudinal folds; circular folds of various types may develop; there may be great numbers of tiny projections, or *villi*, all over the lining surface. In some, a fold, called the *spiral valve*, extends throughout the length of the small intestine. Alternate contractions of circular and longitudinal muscles in the intestinal wall are responsible for three types of contractions that may be observed. These include peristalsis, segmenting movements, and pendular movements. These together result in a churning and mixing of the contents and the propulsion of materials toward the posterior end.

The length of the intestine is related to the feeding habits of the animal. It is relatively short in carnivorous forms and long in herbivores. This is unusually well shown in the frog. During its existence as a larva, or tadpole, it feeds on vegetation, and the intestine is long and coiled. In the mature frog, which is carnivorous, the intestine is not only relatively but actually shorter than that of a tadpole half its size.

Cyclostomes. The cyclostome intestine is straight. At its posterior end it enlarges slightly to form a rectum which terminates in an anus. This opens into the anterior end of the cloacal depression (page 685). A longitudinal fold, the *typhlosole*, which takes a somewhat spiral course, projects into the cavity of the intestine.

Fishes. In elasmobranchs the small intestine is shorter than the stomach. It is wide, but rather straight, and contains a well-developed spiral valve which greatly increases the surface for digestion and absorption (Fig. 5.23). In *Squalus acanthias* the spiral valve takes $14\frac{1}{2}$ turns. Spiral valves are also found in the small intestines of Dipnoi, members of the subclass Paleopterygii, *Amia*, and *Lepisosteus*. Traces have been found in certain other teleosts. In elasmobranchs the large intestine, which is the short passageway from the small intestine to the anus, bends slightly and then opens into the cloaca. A long, slender, fingerlike *rectal gland* connects to the intestine by means of a duct near the point where small and large intestines join. The function of the rectal gland has not been identified with certainty. It appears to be a mucous gland the secretion of which acts as a lubricant in the voiding of fecal material. Some biologists have homologized the rectal gland with the colic caecum of higher forms (page 176). In the Dipnoi a cloacal caecum is present.

Many fishes have *pyloric caeca* coming off the part of the intestine which immediately follows the pylorus (Fig. 5.24). In *Polypterus* there is but one. In some teleosts, as in the mackerel, for example, approximately 200 separate pyloric caeca may be present. Sometimes the pyloric caeca are bound together in a compact mass by connective tissue.

A circular valve often separates the small and large intestines. In many fishes the anus opens separately to the outside. This is particularly true of teleosts, chimaeras, sturgeons, *Polypterus*, and some others. In other fishes a true cloaca is usually present. When no cloaca is present, the posterior part of the large intestine is known as the *rectum*.

Amphibians. In caecilians the intestine is not differentiated into large and small regions and shows but a slight degree of coiling. In salamanders a greater degree of coiling is evident, and in salientians this tendency is much more marked. The large intestine in caudates and salientians is short, straight, and plainly marked off from the small intestine. It opens

into a cloaca. A ventral diverticulum of the amphibian cloaca gives rise
to the *urinary bladder*. It is difficult to discern exactly from which germ
layer, ectoderm or endoderm, the lining of the cloaca is derived in amphibians. Most biologists are of the opinion that it is endodermal and that
the bladders of amphibians are homologous with those of higher forms.

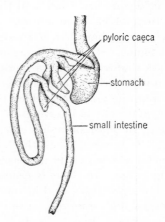

Fig. 5.24. Digestive tract of
perch, showing pyloric caeca.
(*After Wiedersheim, "Comparative Anatomy of Vertebrates," copyright* 1907 *by The
Macmillan Company and used
with their permission.*)

Fig. 5.23. Small intestine of
Squalus acanthias cut open
to show spiral valve. (*Drawn
by J. Dohm.*)

Frequently an *ileocolic valve* is present between small and large intestines.
The modification of the lining of the small intestine to form villi is first
apparent in certain members of this class although villi are lacking in the
common leopard frog and many others. Circular folds, the *valvulae conniventes*, are also present in the small intestines of some amphibians.

Reptiles. The small intestine in reptiles is elongated, coiled, and of
fairly uniform diameter. The large intestine is generally straight, is of
greater diameter, and opens into a cloaca. An ileocolic valve lies at the
junction of small and large intestines, and at this point, except in crocodilians, a *colic caecum* arises. This is the first place in the vertebrates
where true colic caeca are found.

Birds. A tendency to greater length is evident in the small intestine in
this group. The large intestine is straight and relatively short and terminates in a cloaca. A colic caecum is lacking in parrots, woodpeckers, and

some others, but in most forms one or two such structures are present at the junction of small and large intestines. They are not always functional. In certain birds (ducks, geese, turkeys, ostriches, etc.) the colic caeca attain a very large size and the walls may even bear villi. The relatively enormous caecum of the ostrich contains a spiral fold not found in other birds. An important disease causing a great mortality in chickens and turkeys is known as *coccidiosis*. The causative organism is a sporozoan parasite which lodges primarily in the caecum and attacks its walls.

Mammals. The intestines of mammals are more elaborately developed than those of other vertebrates. The coiled small intestine is made up of three regions: *duodenum, jejunum,* and *ileum*. The name duodenum is derived from the Latin word *duodecimus*, which means *twelve*. Old anatomists, accustomed to measuring things according to the breadth of the fingers, gave it this name because the average human duodenum is about as long as the combined breadths of 12 fingers. The name jejunum, which is that part of the small intestine following the duodenum, is also taken from the Latin. The word means "empty." This part of the intestine is usually found empty soon after death. It comprises about two-fifths of the small intestine. The ileum extends from the jejunum to the large intestine and makes up the remaining three-fifths.

A pouchlike structure, known as *Meckel's diverticulum*, is sometimes found projecting from the lower part of the ileum. It represents a portion of the embryonic yolk stalk which has failed to degenerate in the normal manner. A Meckel's diverticulum is found in about 2 per cent of all human adults. Its average length is about 2 in., but sometimes it is as long as 7 in. Usually the diverticulum is a blind pouch. It may be fastened by a cord of connective tissue to the abdominal wall at the umbilicus. In some cases there may even be an opening onto the outside of the abdomen at the navel through which partially digested food may escape. Although ordinarily unimportant, the presence of a Meckel's diverticulum may cause certain conditions which require surgical attention. In some cases it may push back into the cavity of the ileum and cause an intestinal obstruction. In other cases a loop of the small intestine may become strangulated if it should become twisted about the cord of connective tissue by which the diverticulum is fastened to the body wall.

It is generally stated that the average length of the small intestine in man is 22½ ft. Actually there is much variation. According to a report on 100 autopsies, the small intestines of men ranged from 16 ft. to 25 ft. 9 in.; of women from 11 ft. to 23 ft. 6 in. (B. M. L. Underhill, 1955, *Brit. Med J.*, 1243–1246). The large intestine, or *colon*, is much shorter than the small intestine but of considerably greater diameter. In man it averages about 4 to 5 ft. in length. The colon terminates in the rectum, which opens to the outside through the anus. Among mammals only the monotremes and the pika, a lagomorph, possess a cloaca. The intestine of herbivorous mammals is very long and may be from twenty to twenty-eight times the length of the body. In the cow the average length is 165 ft., and in the horse approximately 95 ft. Carnivorous forms have an intestine only five or six times the length of the body.

At the junction of the ileum and colon lies the *ileocolic* (sometimes called *ileocaecolic*) *valve,* which regulates the passage of material from the small to the large intestine (Fig. 5.25). Coming off the colon at this point of juncture is a single colic caecum, found in almost all mammals. Some edentates have two, but this is exceptional. Great variations occur in the form and size of the caecum. It is small in bats, carnivores, some edentates, and certain whales. In man its distal end has degenerated and the remnant is represented by the *vermiform appendix,* the seat of so much trouble (Fig. 5.26). The human appendix under normal conditions lies deep to

Fig. 5.25. Junction of ileum and colon of cat, showing caecum and ileocolic valve.

Fig. 5.26. Junction of ileum and colon of man, showing caecum and vermiform appendix.

McBurney's point (Fig. 5.27). This is situated on the abdomen about 2 in. from the right anterior spine of the ilium on a line between the latter and the umbilicus, or navel. A vermiform appendix is also found in certain monkeys, civets, and a few rodents. In marsupials, herbivores, and some rodents the caecum is relatively enormous and may even exceed the length of the body. In *Hyrax* a peculiar pair of caecal diverticula arises from the colon at some distance from the usual caecum.

The mucous membrane of the intestine contains myriads of intestinal glands. In the duodenal region numerous glands are also found in the submucosa. The glands are of two main types: (1) simple tubular *glands of Lieberkühn,* which are found throughout the entire length of small and large intestines, and (2) the branched tubular mucous *glands of Brunner,* which are confined to the region of the duodenum. The intestinal glands in the walls of the caecum and colon are considerably longer than those found in the small intestine. The secretion of the intestinal glands is called the *succus entericus*. Several enzymes are secreted by the intestinal glands. These include *erepsin*, a proteolytic enzyme which brings about the final breakdown of peptids into amino acids; *lipase*, which together with lipase from the pancreas aids in the digestion of fats; and various enzymes which break down complex sugars into glucose: *sucrase* for cane sugar, *maltase* for malt sugar, and *lactase* for milk sugar. A substance, *enterokinase*, formerly thought to be an enzyme, is secreted by the intestinal glands and functions to activate trypsin coming from the pancreas (page 183).

In addition to the small digestive glands, the epithelium of the small intestine bears great numbers of villi of various shapes. Those in man vary from 0.2 to 1 mm. in height. They give a velvety appearance to the lining of the small intestine. In a human embryo, villi are also present in the large intestine, but they gradually disappear, so that at birth the lining epithelium is relatively smooth. Villi contain blood vessels and lymphatics (lacteals) which collect the products of digestion after they have been absorbed.

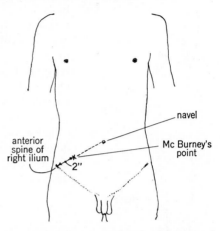

FIG. 5.27. Diagram showing location of appendix at McBurney's point.

Nodules of lymphoid tissue, called *Peyer's patches*, are large oval areas in the small intestine, most numerous in the region of the ileum. Occasionally some are present in the duodenum and jejunum. In the human intestine the average number of Peyer's patches ranges from 30 to 40, although as many as 60 have been observed. Villi are lacking from the epithelium which covers these structures. In old age the patches of Peyer undergo a retrogression. Lesions of these structures occur in typhoid fever.

Several types of folds in the intestinal lining are found in mammals. In man these include (1) *plicae circulares*, or *valvulae conniventes*, which are circular folds found only in the jejunum and ileum, (2) *plicae semilunares*, or internal transverse folds of the colon, containing circular muscle fibers, (3) *plicae transversales* in the lining of the rectum. Bulges of the colon between the plicae semilunares are known as *haustra*. In the region of the anal canal several longitudinal folds called *rectal columns* are present.

PROCTODAEAL DERIVATIVES

Derivatives of the proctodaeum are few in number when compared with those of stomodaeal origin. It is very difficult to determine the point of transition between the endoderm lining the cloaca and the ectoderm lining the proctodaeum. Although some disagree, it is generally conceded that the urinary bladder of amphibians, which opens directly into the cloaca (Fig. 5.28), is lined with *endoderm* derived from the cloaca and *not* with proctodaeal ectoderm. The *bursa Fabricii*, present in most young birds, is another endodermal cloacal derivative, often thought to be derived from the proctodaeum. It forms a secondary connection, however, with the proctodaeum during early development. The bursa Fabricii comes to lie in the body cavity between the spinal column and posterior part of the large intestine and enters the cloacal orifice just beyond the openings of the urogenital ducts. It apparently functions as a lymphoid organ during early life but degenerates as the animal approaches sexual maturity. In this way it somewhat resembles the thymus gland, another lymphatic organ. Certain so-called *anal*, or *cloacal*, *glands*, used primarily for defense or sexual allurement, are probably derived from the ectodermal, proctodaeal invagination.

position of mental gland

heart

stomach

liver

spleen

gall bladder

pancreas

testis

ductus deferens

urinary bladder

cloaca

FIG. 5.28. Internal organs of male salamander, *Eurycea bislineata*, showing relation of urinary bladder to cloaca.

LIVER

The liver is primarily a digestive gland, although it has many other functions. It is the largest gland in the body. During embryonic development it arises as a ventral outgrowth of the endodermal wall of the primitive gut, or archenteron. The region from which it arises becomes the duodenal portion of the small intestine. The original outgrowth gives rise to a hollow hepatic diverticulum, which soon differentiates into two parts: an anterior, or cranial, portion which proliferates to become the large, glandular mass of the liver and its bile ducts; a posterior, or caudal, part which gives rise to the gall bladder and cystic duct. A fairly typical arrangement of these various parts is to be found in man (Fig. 5.29). Two main ducts, one from the right lobe and one from the left, drain the liver. These unite to form a single *hepatic duct*. The *gall bladder*, in which bile is stored, is an enlarged, pear-shaped, saccular structure, its narrow neck connecting with a *cystic duct*, which in turn joins the hepatic duct to form the *common bile duct*, or *ductus choledochus*, which opens into the duodenum. The *pancreatic duct* (ventral pancreatic duct, duct of Wirsung) joins the common bile duct shortly before it enters the duodenum. The common orifice of the two ducts opens at the tip of a *duodenal papilla*. The short segment common to the bile and pancreatic ducts is dilated, forming an *ampulla* (*ampulla of Vater*). The opening of the ductus choledochus is guarded by a sphincter muscle, the *sphincter of Oddi*. The liver proper consists of great numbers of branched columns of cells called the *liver trabeculae* which are separated from one another by small blood spaces, or *sinusoids*. Narrow *bile capillaries* course between the cells and anastomose with each other. Larger ducts drain the bile capillaries, and these finally unite to form the hepatic duct.

There are many variations from the arrangement just described to be

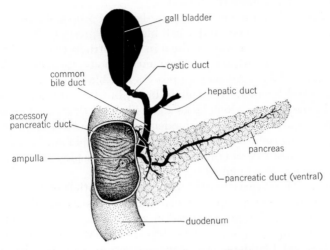

Fig. 5.29. Fairly typical arrangement of gall bladder, bile ducts, and pancreatic ducts in relation to duodenum, as found in man (semidiagrammatic).

found in different vertebrates. Some of the variations are described below. The shape of the liver varies according to the shape of the animal and is typically divided into right and left lobes. It is generally larger in herbivorous forms than in carnivores. The liver is held firmly in place by folds of peritoneum. Its main attachment is to the *septum transversum*, a structure which in mammals contributes to the formation of the diaphragm.

Comparative anatomy of the liver. *Amphioxus.* Although no true liver is found in amphioxus, the presence of such a structure in higher chordates is foreshadowed in amphioxus by a hollow, forward-projecting, ventral *hepatic caecum* which comes off the intestine just posterior to the branchial region (Fig. 2.5). The lining of this pouch is ciliated, and it may have some digestive function. A system of veins coming from the intestine breaks up in capillaries on the hepatic caecum, thus presaging the appearance of the hepatic portal vein of higher forms.

Cyclostomes. The liver in cyclostomes is unusually small. In the lamprey it appears to be single-lobed, but in the hagfish it consists of two halves, this representing the most typical condition of the liver. The ducts from these two parts in myxinoids open separately into the gall bladder. Neither gall bladder nor bile duct is present in an adult lamprey. It is of interest, however, that the ammocoetes larva of the lamprey possesses both these structures which degenerate during metamorphosis.

Fishes. The livers of fishes are lobed and relatively very large. Some are of considerable economic value because of the oil and vitamins which they contain. A gall bladder is almost uniformly present, being lacking only in a few species of sharks. The color of fish livers shows a great range, particularly among the teleosts.

Amphibians. Amphibians' livers are large in proportion to the size of the body. They are lobed, and a gall bladder is present.

Reptiles. No important deviations in liver structure occur in reptiles. In snakes, correlated with the long and narrow body, the liver consists only of one elongated lobe. All reptiles possess gall bladders.

Birds. Lobed livers are the rule in birds, but in many a gall bladder is lacking. In the pigeon, which lacks a gall bladder, there are two bile ducts which open separately into the duodenum. One comes from each main liver lobe, but the right one is the more slender of the two. It has been reported that a transitory gall bladder is present in the pigeon for a short time during embryonic development.

Mammals. More variations occur in the lobulation of the mammalian liver than in any other group. The two main lobes are usually subdivided into smaller units which are arranged in various ways. In some mammals there may be as many as six or seven lobes. In man there are five. Many mammals lack gall bladders. These include certain rodents, whales, *Hyrax*, some of the *Artiodactyla*, and all the *Perissodactyla*. Although the rat lacks a gall bladder, there is some evidence that a minute rudiment of a gall bladder is present for a day or two during early embryonic development.

Functions of the liver. The functions of the liver are numerous. Bile, which is secreted by the liver cells, is a complex fluid. It has an alkaline reaction and contains, among other things, bile pigments, bile salts, lecithin, and cholesterol. No digestive enzymes are present in bile, but nevertheless it plays a very important part in digestion. Certain excretory products are also eliminated by the liver and discharged with the bile into the intestine, from which they are expelled with the feces. Other functions of the liver include formation of blood corpuscles in the embryo, storage of excess carbohydrate in the form of glycogen, liberation of glycogen in the form of glucose when the concentration of the latter in the blood stream falls below normal, formation of urea, storage of copper and iron, formation of vitamin A from carotene, enzyme formation, and the elaboration of fibrinogen which is very important in the clotting of blood. The liver is also of great importance in the metabolism of fats and proteins.

A gall bladder is not indispensable, since it is lacking in many mammals and can be removed from human beings and other mammals without serious effects. It functions mainly as a storage place for bile. When bile is secreted by the liver, it cannot enter the duodenum unless the sphincter of Oddi is relaxed. It therefore backs up into the gall bladder, where it accumulates and from which it is discharged intermittently.

If bile pigments are not properly eliminated from the body, they escape into the tissues and impart a yellow color to them. This shows up most noticeably in the "whites" of the eyes, but the entire skin may be affected. Such a condition is known as yellow jaundice and is caused by mechanical blocking of the hepatic duct or ductus choledochus. Tumors, gallstones, or parasites may be instrumental in causing such a blockage. In jaundice, normal digestion, particularly of fats, is interfered with.

Gallstones are usually composed of cholesterol, a polyatomic alcohol normally present in solution in bile. When this is thrown out of solution under certain abnormal conditions, it will deposit concretions about tiny fragments of tissue or pigment to form gallstones. In some types, calcium and bile pigments also contribute to their formation. There may be a single large stone, a few smaller ones, or even hundreds of tiny stones which appear much like gravel. The passage of gallstones is not only excruciatingly painful but may block the duct and cause jaundice. Bile may even back up into the pancreatic duct and cause acute pancreatitis, a very serious condition.

In so-called typhoid carriers, or persons who carry and distribute typhoid germs without necessarily having the disease themselves, the organisms usually grow in the gall bladder and are discharged from the body with the feces.

Liver contains a factor, formed in the mucosa of the pyloric end of the stomach and of the duodenum and stored in the liver, which is specific in treating a disease of the blood known as pernicious anemia. It may be taken by mouth or intramuscular injection. The latter method is more effective. The factor stimulates the formation of red corpuscles in the bone marrow.

The liver receives its blood supply from two sources. The first is the usual type of oxygenated blood which supplies all organs. It reaches the liver through a hepatic artery, which is a branch of one of the main vessels coming off the aorta. The hepatic portal vein, which begins in capillaries in the digestive tract and spleen, brings the products of digestion, especially those of carbohydrates and proteins, to the liver. Here the vein breaks up into capillaries (sinusoids), which ramify throughout that structure. The two types of blood lose their identity in the liver.

PANCREAS

The pancreas is the second largest of the digestive glands. It arises from the endoderm of the primitive gut in the same general region from which the liver develops. A single dorsal, and usually one or two ventral, pancreatic diverticula develop in most vertebrates. The proximal portions of the diverticula form the pancreatic ducts, and the distal parts, by an intricate process of budding, give rise to the main mass of pancreatic tissue. The ducts undergo various degrees of fusion or reduction, so that the number and arrangement show considerable diversity. Usually only one or two ducts persist. They may open independently into the duodenum or may join the bile duct. The chief *pancreatic duct (ventral pancreatic duct, duct of Wirsung)* arises in the embryo as a diverticulum of the bile duct. This duct and the common bile duct have a common opening into the duodenum. A *dorsal pancreatic duct (accessory pancreatic duct, duct of Santorini)* opens into the duodenum independently. The pancreas is a single organ of irregular shape and may consist of several lobes. It generally lies in a loop between the stomach and duodenum. In such animals as calves and sheep it is large enough to serve as food for human beings and is sold on the market under the name "stomach sweetbreads."

The pancreas plays a dual role in the body, serving both as an exocrine and endocrine gland. The structure of the exocrine portion of the pancreas closely resembles that of the salivary glands. Only one type of cell is present. The exocrine secretion of the pancreas is called *pancreatic juice.* That part of the pancreas which is responsible for the endocrine secretion consists of small groups of cells called the *islands (islets) of Langerhans* which in most forms are scattered throughout the main mass of the gland. Since they are not concerned in the digestive processes, they are more properly discussed in Chap. 9, Endocrine System (pages 337 to 341).

Comparative anatomy of the pancreas. *Amphioxus.* No pancreas is present in amphioxus. The hepatic caecum is considered by some authorities to be a possible homologue of both liver and pancreas, but this is doubtful.

Cyclostomes. In the adult lamprey no well-defined pancreas is evident. Recognizable pancreatic tissue is present, however, embedded within the liver and in the wall and typhlosole of the intestine. This probably represents only the endocrine portion of the pancreas. No traces of an exocrine part are to be found. The hagfish possesses a small pancreas located near the bile duct into which several pancreatic ducts open independently.

Fishes. In certain fishes (Dipnoi and many teleosts) the pancreas is so diffuse as to be almost unrecognizable. In some, the endocrine portion is separated from the remainder of the pancreas and is spoken of as the *principal island* (page 338). Elasmobranchs have a well-defined pancreas consisting of dorsal and ventral lobes connected, in many cases, by a narrow isthmus. A single duct enters the intestine. The pancreas of elasmobranchs arises entirely from a single dorsal diverticulum of the archenteron.

Amphibians, reptiles, and birds. No noteworthy features are exhibited by the pancreas in members of these three classes of vertebrates. One duct or several may be present, and they may open directly into the duodenum or indirectly through the bile duct.

Mammals. Generally two pancreatic ducts are present in mammals. The ventral duct opens into the bile duct near the ampulla (Fig. 5.29). The dorsal duct enters the duodenum directly, although its position varies in different forms. Both ducts are functional in the horse and dog. In the cat, sheep, and man the ventral duct is the functional duct, although the dorsal accessory duct may persist in reduced form. In the pig and ox only the dorsal duct persists. A *pancreatic bladder* is sometimes found in the cat. Pancreatic juice may accumulate here and then be released into the intestine in much the same manner as bile is released from the gall bladder.

Digestive function of the pancreas. Pancreatic juice is alkaline in reaction and contains a number of enzymes. They include *amylase, trypsin, lipase, maltase,* and *rennin.* Amylase has an action similar to ptyalin from the salivary glands but is much stronger. Any starches that have escaped the action of ptyalin in the mouth or stomach are broken down to maltose, or malt sugar, by the action of amylase in the intestine. Only traces of the enzyme maltase are present in pancreatic juice, and this together with the maltase secreted by the intestinal glands effects the final breakdown of malt sugar to glucose. Trypsin acts only in an alkaline medium. In the form in which it is secreted by the pancreas it is practically inactive. *Enterokinase* in the small intestine activates the trypsin. The action of trypsin, which is a proteolytic enzyme, carries the digestion of proteins further than does pepsin from the stomach. It serves to break down peptones and proteoses into smaller units called peptids, which are really small groups of amino acids. These are finally acted upon by erepsin secreted by the intestinal glands. Pancreatic lipase acts in the intestine to split fats into fatty acids and glycerine. Pancreatic rennin is similar in action to the rennin secreted by gastric glands.

It should be clear that the pancreatic enzymes serve both to initiate action on foods that have escaped the effect of salivary and gastric enzymes and to carry the breaking-down processes still further. It is the intestinal enzymes which in most cases complete the digestive activity.

DIGESTION OF FOOD (A SUMMARY)

The principles of digestion have been most thoroughly worked out in man. With minor variations, the same processes take place in other vertebrates. The following account embraces the main factors concerned in digestion.

Foods exist in three main forms: carbohydrates, fats, and proteins. In order to produce food substances, a great deal of energy is required. In the last analysis it is the energy from the sun which is used in food production. Plants, under the influence of sunlight, can synthesize carbohydrates from water and carbon dioxide. Other inorganic elements may be taken from the soil or air to manufacture fats and proteins. Herbivorous animals can make use of this stored-up energy in building up their own bodies. Carnivores are but one step further removed.

When food is taken into the mouth, mucus is added which renders it capable of being swallowed more easily. Ptyalin in the saliva may begin to break down starches into the smaller molecules of malt sugar. This process may even continue for a time after the food has reached the stomach, because of the process of *layering*. In the stomach, hydrochloric acid, propepsin, prorennin, and perhaps some gastric lipase are secreted by the glands in the fundic region. Additional mucus is added by gastric glands, particularly those in the cardiac and pyloric regions. The muscular walls of the stomach contract and churn the contents thoroughly. The acid in the stomach soon stops the action of ptyalin on starches but activates the proenzymes to form pepsin and rennin. Rennin, in the presence of calcium, acts upon the soluble protein, or casein, in milk to form the curd referred to as calcium paracasein. The proteoselike whey protein remains. If not all the milk is changed in this way, pancreatic rennin will later act upon the remainder in the intestine. Pepsin, in the acid medium of the stomach, acts upon proteins, including calcium paracasein, and breaks them down into peptones and proteoses. This reaction, however, may not be completed in the stomach.

When the food in the stomach has reached a fluid or semifluid state, it is known as *chyme*. Muscular peristaltic waves intermittently force the chyme through the pylorus into the duodenum. The waves of peristalsis continue throughout the entire length of the intestine. Bile, which has been stored in the gall bladder, is released into the duodenum, and to this is added the alkaline pancreatic juice which contains the enzymes amylase, maltase, trypsin, lipase, and rennin. Amylase continues the breaking down of starches which have escaped the action of ptyalin and reduces them to malt sugar. Maltase from the pancreas, together with that formed in the intestine, splits the malt sugar into molecules of the more simple sugar, glucose. This passes through the wall of the intestine into small blood vessels which lead into the hepatic portal vein. Other sugars such as sucrose and lactose, which may be present in the food and cannot be absorbed as such, are acted upon by the intestinal enzymes sucrase and lactase, respectively, and are also reduced to glucose.

Proteins, peptones, and proteoses are at the same time acted upon by trypsin, which becomes activated by enterokinase from the small intestine. Trypsin carries the digestion of proteins past the peptone stage until only peptids remain. The final breakdown of peptids to amino acids, the "building stones" of proteins, is accomplished by the intestinal enzyme erepsin. Amino acids pass into the blood vessels of the intestinal wall, and thence to the liver via the hepatic portal vein.

Fats are not appreciably digested until they reach the intestine. Lipase from the pancreas and intestinal glands breaks the fat molecules down into fatty acids and glycerine. The alkali in the intestine forms soaps with some of the fatty acids, and this aids in the emulsification of the remaining fats. Bile salts which are present in the bile are even more important in this respect, since they are instrumental in lowering surface tension. A greater surface of fat particles is thus exposed to the action of lipase. Bile salts also assist in the passage of fatty acids through the intestinal wall. About 60 per cent of the digested fat passes into the lacteals, which are small lymphatic vessels, to enter ultimately the thoracic lymph duct which joins the left subclavian vein. The remainder of the digested fat is apparently absorbed into the capillaries which lead into the hepatic portal vein.

In the ileum, the chyme is still fluid in consistency. When it reaches the caecum and colon, the remaining products of digestion are absorbed. The absorption of water takes place, for the most part, in the first part of the colon, and the indigestible residue becomes firmer and is known as *feces.* Very little undigested food is present in feces. It is composed mostly of indigestible matter, old epithelial cells, leukocytes, and great numbers of bacteria.

In herbivorous animals, cellulose, which makes up the walls of plant cells and which is ordinarily not digested, is acted upon for the most part by bacteria in the colon and broken down into substances which can be utilized by the body.

The structure of the digestive tract is admirably suited and adapted for the functions it performs. When one considers the labors that a chemist would have to go through to bring about all the reactions that take place within a relatively short time in the digestive tract, one must marvel at the provisions made by nature whereby animals can utilize the foods that are available to them.

SUMMARY

The digestive tracts of vertebrates are built upon the same fundamental plan and function in a comparable manner. Many variations are to be found which may be considered as adaptations to meet particular needs. The signs of evolution are not so apparent in a study of the digestive system as in some of the other organ systems, but the adaptive radiations from a simple plan are strikingly brought out.

Among the more important advances that are to be noted within the group are:

1. Separation of mouth and nasal passages
2. Change to heterodont condition of teeth
3. Development of muscles in lips and tongue
4. Beginning of digestive function on part of mouth glands

5. Distinct separation of esophagus and stomach
6. Digestive function of stomach added to that of mere storage
7. Complicated stomachs in many forms providing for proper utilization of type of food eaten
8. Differentiation of intestine into distinct regions
9. Tendency toward lengthening of alimentary canal as a whole
10. Provisions for increasing surface for absorption and secretion
11. Differentiation of cloaca so that openings of digestive and urogenital systems are separate

CHAPTER 6

RESPIRATORY SYSTEM AND RELATED STRUCTURES

Every living cell in an organism consumes oxygen. A supply of oxygen is essential to that phase of metabolism known as *catabolism*. Oxidation of substances within the cells results in the liberation of heat and other forms of energy and in the production of carbon dioxide. This end product of metabolism, unless removed from the cell (or body), acts as a poison which is harmful to protoplasm. It has been estimated that the average human adult exhales about 20 liters of carbon dioxide per hour. In a poorly ventilated room occupied by several people, the percentage of carbon dioxide is not poisonous unless the gas is present in large quantities; air containing more than 15 parts in 10,000 is not fit for respiration under any conditions.

RESPIRATION

Aerobic respiration. The term *aerobic respiration* is used to denote the exchange of oxygen and carbon dioxide between an organism and its environment. In this type of respiration oxygen is taken into the body and carbon dioxide is given off.

Anaerobic respiration. In certain organisms *anaerobic* respiration takes place. Carbon dioxide is given off, but no oxygen is taken in. The necessary oxygen is obtained, in such forms, by the incomplete breakdown of carbohydrates, and possibly of fats, in the body.

The role of blood in respiration. Although in members of certain lower phyla there is a direct exchange of gases between the cells and the environment, in vertebrates and some other forms the blood serves to bring oxygen from the environment to the cells and to carry carbon dioxide from the cells to the environment. It is the presence of the pigment hemoglobin that gives vertebrate blood its unusual capacity for carrying oxygen. Hemoglobin is present in the blood of all vertebrates and even in certain invertebrates. In vertebrates it is confined to the red blood corpuscles, or erythrocytes. There are minor differences in the hemoglobins of different forms, and they vary somewhat in their properties. It is interesting that the muscles of birds and mammals also contain hemoglobin. The importance of hemoglobin in connection with respiration lies in its ability to combine with oxygen through the medium of iron which it contains. Two atoms of oxygen, under favorable conditions, unite with each atom of iron in the hemoglobin complex. Thus $Hb_4 + 4O_2 = Hb_4O_8$. Hemoglobin which has combined with oxygen in this manner is spoken of as *oxyhemoglobin*. It is scarlet red in color and a very unstable compound, since it gives up its oxygen so readily. After having given off its oxygen it is known as *reduced hemoglobin*, or simply *hemoglobin*, and has a purplish-blue color.

The red corpuscles with their contained hemoglobin also play a prominent role in transporting carbon dioxide. When carbon dioxide leaves the cells and tissues of the body it enters the blood stream and diffuses into the red blood corpuscles. Here most of the carbon dioxide combines with water to form carbonic acid as follows: $CO_2 + H_2O = H_2CO_3$. An enzyme, *carbonic anhydrase*, present in the red cells, facilitates the reaction. The carbonic acid thus formed combines with potassium (formerly in combination with hemoglobin) to form potassium bicarbonate. Bicarbonate ions then diffuse out into the plasma in exchange for chloride ions which enter the cell. In the plasma the bicarbonate ions combine with sodium to form sodium bicarbonate. Thus, carbon dioxide is transported by the plasma as well as by the red corpuscles. At the respiratory surface oxygen enters the red blood corpuscles and the above processes are reversed. Carbon dioxide is then liberated as a free gas.

Phases of respiration. In animals in which the blood is used in carrying oxygen and carbon dioxide two phases are involved in respiration. They are referred to as *external* and *internal respiration*. The term external respiration is used to denote the exchange of gases between the blood and the environment. This usually takes place in the capillaries of the gills or lungs, but in some cases other structures such as the skin are utilized. In gills the capillaries are almost in direct contact with the water in which oxygen is dissolved. In lungs they are practically in contact with air that has been taken into the cavities of the lungs. Even though lungs are situated within the body, nevertheless the term external respiration is used. During external respiration the blood takes up oxygen and loses most of the carbon dioxide which it is carrying. Internal respiration refers to the gaseous exchange between the blood and the tissues or cells of the body. Oxygen is taken from the blood, which in turn gains carbon dioxide given off by the tissues. The principles involved in internal and external respiration follow the "laws of gases" and are physical rather than biological in nature.

In vertebrates, respiratory organs are present which serve to facilitate external respiration. Certain requirements are demanded in respiratory organs in order that they may function properly: (1) a large, vascular surface area must be provided so that an ample capillary network may be exposed to the environment; (2) the membrane surfaces through which gaseous exchange occurs must be moist at all times and be thin enough to permit the passage of gases; (3) provision must be made for renewing the supply of the oxygen-containing medium (air or water) which comes in contact with the respiratory surface and for removing the carbon dioxide which has been given off from that surface.

With few exceptions, the organs of respiration in vertebrates are formed in connection with the pharynx. In some forms, notably amphibians, the skin itself is an important respiratory organ. In a fish, the loach, *Misgurnus fossilis,* a peculiar method of respiration is utilized. The animal has the habit of swallowing air, passing the air bubble the length of the intestine, and voiding it at the anus, oxygen being absorbed en route by blood vessels in the extremely vascular intestine.

The function of the pharynx as part of the digestive tract is merely to serve as a passageway from mouth to esophagus and to initiate swallowing movements. However, the part which it plays in respiration is of much greater importance. The gills of aquatic vertebrates and the lungs of air-breathers are structures, derived from the pharynx, which are particularly adapted for respiration. In some cases the vascular epithelium of the pharyngeal wall itself is important in respiration. Other structures not associated with respiratory activity are derived from the pharynx. Among these are certain glands such as the thyroid, thymus, and parathyroids.

NASAL PASSAGES

In air-breathing vertebrates there is a close association between the olfactory organs and the organs of respiration. In lower aquatic forms, however, these structures are usually completely divorced from each other. The advantages of a close relationship between the organs of smell and those of respiration should be obvious. When air is drawn from the outside environment into the lungs, volatile substances carried by the air may stimulate the sensitive endings of the olfactory nerves situated in the nasal passages. In the Dipnoi and in the larval forms of some of the more primitive salamanders, such as the newt, water enters the mouth through the nares and leaves via pharyngeal gill slits. Chemical substances in the water may be detected by the olfactory apparatus located in the nasal passages.

Comparative anatomy of nasal passages. *Fishes.* In most fishes there is no connection between nostrils and mouth cavity. In some elasmobranchs, however, an open *oronasal groove* on each side forms a channel connecting the olfactory pit to the mouth. There is some dispute as to whether the *labial grooves* at the lateral edges of the mouth in *Squalus acanthias* (Fig. 6.1) are homologous with the oronasal grooves of other elasmobranchs. Oronasal grooves foreshadow the appearance of a direct connection between the two in higher forms. It is in the fishes of the subclass Choanichthyes that for the first time a direct connection exists between nasal and mouth cavities in the form of a pair of closed tubes. The openings to the outside are known as the *external nares;* those opening into the mouth are the *internal nares,* or *choanae,* hence the name *Choanichthyes.* In these fishes the external nares open to the outside beneath the upper lip but outside the mouth. They cannot be seen when the mouth is shut. Internal nares apparently were secondarily lost in the coelacanths and are not present in *Latimeria,* which, nevertheless, and for other reasons, is classified with the Choanichthyes. In a certain group of teleosts, the stargazers (*Astroscopus*), a well-developed passageway leads to the oral cavity and internal nares are present (J. W. Atz, 1952, *Anat. Record*, **113**:105). These, however, are not homologous with the nasal passages of the Choanichthyes or tetrapods even though they are used to some extent in respiration and probably have an olfactory function. None of the living fishes possessing internal nares is known to use them to breathe atmospheric air (J. W. Atz, 1953, *Quart. J. Biol.*, **27**:366). Water is drawn into the mouth through both the mouth and nasal passages. In the Dipnoi, olfactory epithe-

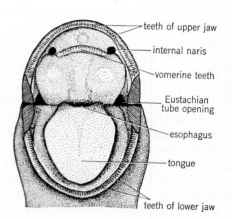

Fig. 6.1. Head of dogfish shark, *Squalus acanthias*, ventral view.

Fig. 6.2. Oral cavity of salamander, *Ambystoma texanum*. The angle of the mouth on each side has been cut in order to depress the lower jaw.

lium is located in the dorsal part of each nasal passage, thus indicating that the nasal passages serve primarily to increase the effectiveness of olfaction.

In most vertebrates during embryonic development two ectodermal thickenings appear in the surface epithelium at the ventrolateral portions of the head. These are the *olfactory placodes* which soon invaginate to form *olfactory pits*. They form connections with the oral cavity by means of a groove similar to the oronasal groove of elasmobranchs. The edges of the olfactory pits and grooves fuse together, forming a pair of tubular connections between the external nares and the mouth.

Amphibians. External and internal nares are present in amphibians. The nasal passages connecting them are short, the internal nares being located just inside the upper jaw (Fig. 6.2). In larval caudates the current of water passing through the nasal passages is produced either by ciliary action or by movements of the gill apparatus and muscles of the lower jaw. In many caudate larvae and in the tadpoles of salientians, valves around the internal nares control the direction of flow of water.

With the appearance of lungs at the time of metamorphosis in most caudates, smooth muscle fibers are generally found to be present around the external nares, thus providing a means for regulating the size of the aperture. This is the first place in which atmospheric air is drawn through the nasal passages. Adult salientians use a peculiar device for closing their nostrils. A small, rounded, conical projection, the *tuberculum prelinguale*, at the tip of the lower jaw, is thrust forward and upward and pushes apart the two premaxillary bones which lie above it in the upper jaw. The movement of these bones, by changing the position of a portion of the nasal cartilages, effectively closes the nasal passages.

The nasal passages of amphibians are surrounded by a cartilaginous *nasal capsule*, which is bounded by nasal, premaxillary, maxillary, and vomer (prevomer) bones. In a few caudates a projection into the nasal passage from the lateral wall on each side indicates the first appearance of the *conchae*, which become highly developed in certain mammalian forms. The nasal passages themselves consist of upper olfactory and lower respiratory regions.

Reptiles. Beginning with reptiles there is a tendency toward elongation of the passageway between the external and internal nares. This is brought about by the development of a pair of palatal folds. These are horizontal, shelflike projections of the premaxillary, maxillary, palatine, and even of the pterygoid bones. Only in the crocodilians among reptiles, however, do the processes from the two sides fuse along the median line, thus forming a bony *secondary palate* which separates the nasal passages from the mouth cavity. The internal nares communicate with the mouth cavity posterior to the secondary palate. In crocodiles and alligators they are located rather far down the throat. In reptiles a single concha, supported by bone, projects into the nasal passage on each side from its lateral wall.

Birds. The greater part of the upper portion of the beak, or bill, of birds consists of the very much enlarged and fused premaxillary bones, together with the maxillaries at the base. The bones are covered with a hard, horny sheath. The external nares are usually located at the base of the beak, but those of the kiwi are placed almost at the tip. The secondary palate, like that of most reptiles, is incomplete, consisting of a pair of palatal folds which fail to fuse medially. The choanae lie above the palatal folds. In most birds the nasal passages are relatively short because of the basal position of the external nares and the cleft condition of the palate.

Three folds, or conchae, extend into the nasal passages of birds. They are supported by *turbinate bones*. Only the posterior concha is covered with olfactory epithelium. The mucous membrane covering the conchae aids in warming and moistening the air on its way to the lungs. The choanae connect with the pharynx posterior to the conchae.

Mammals. The nasal passages of mammals have been greatly elongated and are larger and more complicated than in lower forms. Median projections from the premaxillary, maxillary, and palatine bones fuse in the midline to form the *hard palate*. The pterygoids, which are reduced in mammals, do not contribute to palate formation. Extending posteriorly from the hard palate is the *soft palate* composed of connective tissue covered with epithelium and without any bony foundation. The presence of the soft palate carries the nasal passages posteriorly, so that the choanae open into the pharyngeal region.

The presence of a *nose* is characteristic of mammals. That of man is of a special nature and not comparable to those found in most other forms. In some mammals the nose is excessively developed and forms a proboscis at the end of which the external nares are located. A proboscis is more or less well developed in moles, shrews, tapirs, and elephants. The trunk of the elephant actually represents the very much drawn-out nose and upper lip.

The nasal passages of mammals are divided into three general regions: vestibular, respiratory, and olfactory. The *vestibular region*, lined with skin, leads from the outside to the inner mucous membrane. Hairs and sebaceous glands may be abundant in this area. Into the *respiratory* and *olfactory regions*, which make up the greater part of the nasal cavity, extends a veritable labyrinth of conchae. These are coiled and scroll-like projections of the nasal, maxillary, and ethmoid bones. They are called the *superior nasal conchae* (nasoturbinates), *ventral nasal conchae* (maxillo-turbinates), and *lateral nasal conchae* (ethmoturbinates), respectively. The *respiratory region* is lined with "respiratory" epithelium. This is a ciliated, pseudostratified, columnar epithelium, rich in goblet cells. The superior and ventral nasal conchae are covered with respiratory epithelium, which keeps the nasal passages moist. The *olfactory region* occupies the innermost upper recesses. It is covered with "olfactory" epithelium which contains nerve endings for the sense of smell. The olfactory epithelium lies over much of the surface of the lateral nasal conchae, thus increasing the sensory area. In man, with his relatively poorly developed sense of smell, there has been a great reduction of the conchae as compared with many other mammals. For this reason they merely project into the nasal passages in the form of rather shallow ridges. The olfactory epithelium in man is confined on each side to an irregular area measuring roughly 250 sq. mm.

Sinuses, or spaces, within certain bones communicate with the nasal passages. The chief sinuses found in mammals are those of the frontal, maxillary, ethmoid, and sphenoid bones. They are lined with ciliated mucous membrane like that of the respiratory region, but glandular cells are smaller and less numerous. The sinuses, which in man are so often the seat of infection and give so much trouble, have no known function. Their presence lightens the skull and gives resonance to the voice.

The nasal passages of mammals are formed in a manner somewhat different from that of lower forms. On each side of the head an olfactory pit develops which communicates with the mouth cavity by a groove similar to the oronasal groove of certain elasmobranchs. Here the similarity ends, for the nasal pits grow inward and establish secondary connections with the oral cavity. The original grooves close over and fuse. Failure of the grooves to close on one or both sides results in unilateral or bilateral *harelip*, as the case may be (Fig. 6.3).

A   B

Fig. 6.3. *A*, unilateral harelip; *B*, bilateral harelip.

Jacobson's organ. In many tetrapods a peculiar structure, the *vomeronasal organ* of Jacobson, is present. It consists of a pair of blind diverticula usually extending from the ventromedial portion of the nasal cavity. In amphibians, reptiles, and mammals it receives branches from the terminal (O), olfactory (I), and trigeminal (V) cranial nerves. Although the function of Jacobson's organ is obscure, it is believed to aid in the recognition of food, since it is best developed in animals which hold food in their mouths.

The vomeronasal organ first appears in amphibians. In frogs it is situated in the anteromedial portion of each of the nasal cavities, but in caudates it is usually lateral in position. Its connection with the nasal cavity is constricted, so that it appears in the nature of a duct. The organ is lacking in *Necturus* and in the cave salamander, *Proteus*.

In *Sphenodon*, snakes, and lizards (Fig. 6.4), Jacobson's organ is best de-

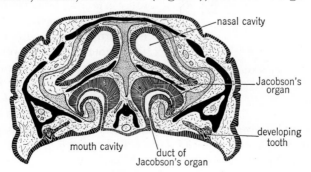

Fig. 6.4. Cross section through head of lizard, showing Jacobson's organ. Black areas represent bone; stippled areas represent cartilage. (*After Schimkewitsch.*)

veloped of all. Instead of opening into the nasal cavity, in these forms, the duct connects directly with the mouth cavity but near the choanae. In other reptiles and in birds the organ appears only as a rudiment during embryonic development. The tips of the forked tongues of snakes and of some lizards, when retracted, are placed in the small, blind pockets of the vomeronasal organs. These apparently serve as an accessory olfactory device, detecting volatile chemical substances that may have adhered to the surface of the tongue when it was thrust out of the mouth. In mammals there is much variation. In some, as in man, it appears only as an embryonic vestige in the lower medial side of each nasal cavity, but in others it persists throughout life as a definite structure. Jacobson's organ is best developed in monotremes in which it is surrounded by cartilage through which a branch of the olfactory nerve passes. A small concha even projects into its cavity, much in the manner of the conchae of the main nasal cavity referred to above. The organ is small but well-developed in marsupials, insectivores, and rodents.

PHARYNGEAL POUCHES

In the embryos of all chordates a series of pouches develops on either side of the pharynx. These endodermal structures push through the mesenchyme until they come in contact with invaginated *visceral furrows* of the outer ectoderm to which they fuse, forming thin, platelike areas. The pharyngeal pouches arise in succession in an anterior-posterior direction. They develop in such a manner that they become successively smaller from first to last (Fig. 6.5), and the pharynx therefore is more or less funnel-shaped and tapers toward the esophagus. Except in the highest vertebrate classes perforations usually occur where endoderm and ectoderm come in contact. Even in the higher classes, however, temporary openings are occasionally established. The *visceral,* or *pharyngeal, pouches* are then called *clefts.* Primitively the cavity of the pharynx is thus connected by a series of clefts to the outside. The openings connecting the pharynx proper with the clefts are called *internal gill slits;* those connecting the clefts with the outside are *external gill slits.*

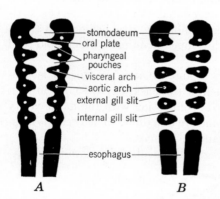

stomodaeum
oral plate
pharyngeal pouches
visceral arch
aortic arch
external gill slit
internal gill slit
esophagus

A   *B*

Fig. 6.5. Diagram showing arrangement of pharyngeal pouches: *A*, during development; *B*, after connection with the outside has been established and the oral plate has disappeared.

The number of pharyngeal pouches or clefts is greatest in the lowest groups of vertebrates and least in the higher classes. Thus, among cyclostomes, certain forms (*Bdellostoma*) possess as many as 14 pairs, although the lamprey (*Petromyzon*) has 7 pairs and the hagfish (*Myxine*) but 6. In fishes, amphibians, and reptiles 5 or 6 pairs commonly appear in the embryo, but birds and mammals possess the reduced number of 5 or 4 as the typical condition. The pharyngeal pouches are of greatest significance in the lower aquatic vertebrates since they bear gills and are directly concerned with respiration. Those of amniotes do not bear gills and generally disappear, except for the first which becomes the Eustachian tube and middle ear. Remnants of the others persist in the form of certain glandular structures, to be discussed later.

The visceral clefts are separated from one another by septa, which are mesodermal structures, covered with epithelium derived either from ectoderm or endoderm, depending upon whether it is toward the exterior or interior surface. Within each septum lies a cartilaginous or bony barlike structure, the *visceral arch*. This serves to support the septum. Blood vessels, called *aortic arches*, branch from the ventral aorta and course through the septa. The visceral arches, which make up the so-called *visceral skeleton*, are modified in higher vertebrates to form various portions of the skeleton in the head region (pages 396 to 404). The aortic arches also undergo changes in the different classes (pages 518 to 528).

GILLS

Gills are composed of numerous *gill filaments* or *gill lamellae*, which are thin-walled extensions of epithelial surfaces. Each contains a vascular network. Blood is brought extremely close to the surface, thus facilitating the ready exchange of gases. In their aggregate, gills present a relatively large surface for respiratory exchange.

Types of gills. Gills are of two general types, external and internal. *External gills* (Fig. 6.6) develop from the integument covering the outer surfaces of visceral arches. They are usually branched, filamentous structures covered entirely with ectoderm and are not related to the visceral pouches. *Internal gills* (Fig. 6.7) are usually composed of a series of parallel *gill lamellae*, although in some forms they may be filamentous. They may be borne on both sides of the interbranchial septa but in some cases are present on one side alone. A series of lamellae on one side of an interbranchial septum is termed a *half gill*, or *hemibranch*. Two hemibranchs enclosing between them an interbranchial septum make up a *complete gill*, or *holobranch*. The two hemibranchs bounding a gill cleft thus belong to different holobranchs. It is generally assumed that internal gills are covered entirely with endoderm, but there is some controversy on this point and the question of exact origin has not been definitely settled. In some animals both external and internal gills are present.

The functioning of external gills poses no problems since the filaments are in direct contact with the water containing dissolved oxygen. When internal gills are used in respiration, water, containing dissolved oxygen, is generally taken into the mouth and passes through the internal gill slits into the gill clefts. As the water passes over the gill lamellae, oxygen is taken from the water and carbon dioxide is released. The water then passes through the external gill slits to the outside.

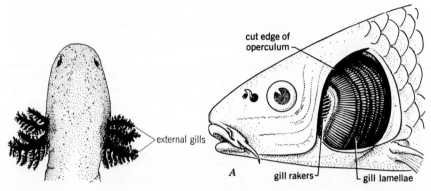

Fig. 6.6. Head of salamander larva with external gills.

Fig. 6.7. Head of bony fish (carp). The operculum has been cut away in order to expose the internal gills. (*From Storer, "General Zoology," McGraw-Hill Book Company, Inc. By permission.*)

Comparative anatomy of gills. *Amphioxus.* The mouth of amphioxus leads into the pharynx, the opening being guarded by a fold called the *velum*, bearing 12 *velar tentacles*. The walls of the pharynx are provided with large numbers of vertically elongated gill clefts. Over a hundred of these may be present. The gill clefts are separated by *primary gill bars* of a stiff, gelatinous consistency, somewhat resembling chitin which makes up the exoskeleton of insects. The primary gill bars bifurcate at their ventral ends. During development a *secondary bar*, or *tongue bar*, grows down from dorsal to ventral sides between two primary gill bars and thus divides each primary gill cleft in two. The secondary bars are *not* bifurcated at their lower ends. Still later, small *crossbars* appear, connecting one primary bar with the next so that the gill clefts become further subdivided. The crossbars pass *over* the secondary bars, but the two usually fuse after a time. There are no gill filaments or lamellae, and blood vessels course through the pharyngeal bars. A few of the anterior gill slits, for a time, open directly to the outside. With the development of the ectoderm-lined *atrium*, however, the pharynx no longer forms direct connections with the outside and all gill clefts come to open into the *atrial cavity*, or *peripharyngeal chamber*. A single opening to the outside, the *atriopore*, is located on the ventral side of the animal, about two-thirds of the way back.

Although much of the respiration of amphioxus takes place through the skin, a constantly renewed stream of water passes from mouth to pharynx, through the gill clefts, and into the peripharyngeal chamber. In passing over the gill bars, the blood within them is oxygenated. Water leaves the peripharyngeal chamber through the atriopore.

Cyclostomes. The respiratory system of an adult lamprey is highly specialized and on first inspection seems to be atypical. Study of its development in the ammocoetes larva, however, reveals that it is built upon the typical vertebrate plan. In the pharyngeal wall of the larva eight pairs of gill pouches begin to develop, but the first pair flattens out before long and disappears. Seven pairs of gill clefts remain, each with its internal and external gill slits. At this stage the pharynx connects with the mouth in front and with the esophagus behind. During further development, and with the formation of the round, sucking mouth, a peculiar change occurs in the pharynx-esophagus relationship. These structures become split apart, or separated in such a manner that each has its own connection with the mouth (Fig. 6.8). The esophagus then lies dorsal to the pharynx. The latter becomes a blind pouch, the opening of which is guarded by a *velum*. Seven pairs of internal gill slits open from the pharynx into seven pairs of gill clefts which are rather large and spherical in shape. The gill lamellae are arranged in a more or less circular fashion, but, nevertheless, each gill cleft is bordered by a hemibranch on both anterior and posterior walls. There are thus 14 hemibranchs on each side, but only 6 holobranchs, since the first and last hemibranchs are not parts of holobranchs (Figs. 12.16 and 15.5).

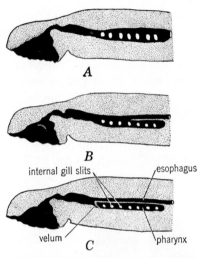

FIG. 6.8. Stages *A*, *B*, and *C* in separation of esophagus and pharynx in lamprey (semidiagrammatic).

During respiration the lamprey normally takes water in and out of the gill clefts through the external gill slits. Thus the gill lamellae are bathed by a constantly replenished supply of water. This method of respiration is quite in contrast to that employed by true fishes in which water enters the mouth and passes over the gills on its way to the outside through the external gill openings. The method utilized by the lamprey is necessary because when the animal is attached to some object or engaged in feeding, the mouth opening is blocked. It is, of course, possible that when the animal is free, water may pass through the buccal funnel into the mouth cavity and to the outside via pharynx, internal gill slits, gill clefts, and external gill slits. It is doubtful, however, whether this method is employed, at least to any appreciable extent.

When blood, mucus, and tissue fragments, on which the animal feeds, pass into the mouth cavity, they go down the esophagus to the remainder of the digestive tract. The velum at the anterior end of the pharynx prevents the passage of the bloody food into the respiratory system and also prevents dilution of the blood with water which might enter the mouth from the pharynx. When the lamprey is getting ready to feed (T. E. Reynolds, 1931, *Univ. Calif. Publs. Zoöl.*, **37**:15), the buccal funnel is first collapsed or flattened and the water already in it is forced over the tongue into the mouth cavity and *hydrosinus* above. The hydrosinus is an anterodorsal extension of the mouth cavity. Next, the tongue is used to block the passage between the buccal funnel and the mouth cavity. The suctorial disc is then arched, or warped, outward, thereby increasing the volume and the degree of suction of the buccal funnel. Water in the hydrosinus and oral cavity is then forced past the velum into the pharynx, the velum serving as a one-way valve which prevents the return of water into the mouth cavity. The tongue, up to this point, is still blocking the passage between the buccal funnel and mouth cavity. The discharge of water from mouth cavity to pharynx creates a low-pressure area extending from the attached disc to the velum. The tongue is now free to move back and forth in rasping. Tissue fragments, and blood flowing from the wound, pass readily into the mouth cavity and thence to the esophagus and remainder of the digestive tract. In the meantime the animal is respiring by taking water in and forcing it out of the external gill slits as described above.

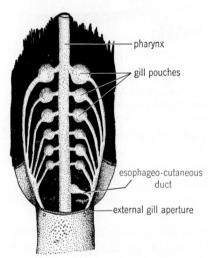

In the hagfish the pharynx forms a direct connection between mouth and esophagus. Six pairs of internal gill slits and gill pouches are present. Only a single pair of external openings exists, however. A series of long tubes coming from the gill pouches unites to form a common duct on each side, and this leads to the external aperture (Fig. 6.9), which is situated near the midventral line at some distance from the anterior end. This may be of advantage to the animal when it is feeding, or boring its way into the body of a fish in order to devour the soft internal organs. An *esophageo-cutaneous duct* connects the

Fig. 6.9. Diagram showing relation of gill pouches of hagfish, *Myxine*, to the pharynx and to the single pair of external gill apertures, ventral view. (*After Müller.*)

esophagus with the common duct on the left side in *Myxine*. It lies posterior to the last gill pouch on that side and is similar to a gill cleft but lacks gills.

In cyclostomes of the genus *Bdellostoma* the number of gill clefts varies from 6 or 7 up to 13 or 14 pairs. The gill clefts connect internally with the pharynx which is similar to that of the hagfish and not a blind pouch of the type found in the lamprey. An esophageo-cutaneous duct is also found on the left side in *Bdellostoma*. The animal resembles lampreys, however, in that the external gill slits open separately to the outside through small apertures.

In cyclostomes, with their poorly developed skeletons, visceral arches homologous with those of higher forms are essentially lacking. A peculiar,

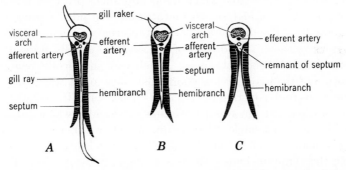

FIG. 6.10. Types of fish gills: *A*, elasmobranch; *B*, chimaera; *C*, teleost.

irregular, cartilaginous *branchial basket* (page 405) provides some support but lies peripheral to the gill clefts, just beneath the skin.

Fishes. In fishes and tetrapods a series of skeletogenous *visceral arches* encircles the pharynx. In tetrapods these become greatly modified, but in fishes they serve primarily to support the gills. They are located between the gill clefts, one behind the other, at the bases of the interbranchial septa. The *first* is called the *mandibular arch;* the *second* is the *hyoid arch*. The remaining visceral arches are referred to by number (3, 4, 5, 6, etc.). The first gill pouch or cleft lies between the mandibular and hyoid arches and is often referred to as the hyomandibular cleft. In fishes it is either modified to form a *spiracle* or is closed altogether. The ancestral placoderms had a full-sized gill slit between the mandibular and hyoid arches.

Two main types of *internal* gills are to be found among fishes. The first and more primitive type is typical of elasmobranchs. In this group the interbranchial septa are exceptionally well developed and extend beyond the hemibranchs (Figs. 6.10*A* and 6.11*A*). Each bends posteriorly at its distal end in such a manner that a row of separate external gill slits is formed. Thus the interbranchial septa, in addition to separating the gill clefts, serve to protect the gills themselves. In the frilled shark, *Chlamydoselachus*, the interbranchial septa are continued distally to an unusual degree and project *over* the external gill slits. In the dogfishes and sharks the external gill slits are lateral in position, but in adult skates and rays they are ventrally located even though they are in a lateral position during the early part of embryonic life.

Small cartilaginous *gill rays*, or *branchial rays*, in the form of a single row, project from each visceral arch into the interbranchial septum to which they give support. Rigid, comblike, *gill rakers* usually project from the gill arches. Their function is to prevent food and foreign bodies from entering the gill clefts.

The second type of gill is found in the remaining fishes. In these the interbranchial septa are reduced to varying degrees (Fig. 6.10*B* and *C*) to form slender structures from which the hemibranchs protrude into a single *branchial*, or *extrabranchial*, *chamber* located on each side between the operculum and gills. The distinction between internal and external gill slits is less obvious in these. Two rows of gill rays are usually present, rather than one as in the elasmobranchs. Each row supports a hemibranch. The septum of the hyoid arch is enormously developed and grows caudad as a cutaneous fold, covering the gill clefts posterior to it. The gill cover, or *operculum*, protects the gills in the branchial chamber which thus opens to the outside through a single gill aperture. In a few forms, as in the eel, the opening is small and round, but it is usually long and slitlike. In one group of fishes, the symbranchiates, there is a single, midventral opening. Although in elasmobranchs, chimaeras, sturgeons, and some others a true hemibranch receiving unoxygenated blood is located on the posterior side of the hyoid arch, this is lacking in *Polypterus*, *Amia*, *Polyodon*, teleosts, and Dipnoi. Teleosts have four complete holobranchs on each side. Since in fishes no aortic arch courses through the tissue posterior to the last gill cleft, no hemibranch is found on the posterior wall of the last gill cleft except in *Protopterus* in which its homologies are doubtful.

In fishes having an operculum, a pliant, *branchiostegal membrane* supported by bony *branchiostegal rays* usually extends from the inner surface of the operculum to the body wall. It serves as a one-way valve which permits water to leave the branchial chamber through the opercular opening but does not allow it to enter. Other folds, from the maxillary and mandibular regions, form *oral valves* located just within the mouth opening. These permit water to enter the mouth but not to leave it. Gill respiration in these fishes (Fig. 6.11*B* and *C*) is brought about by raising the opercula and closing the branchiostegal folds. This causes a change in pressure within mouth and pharynx, so that the oral valves are opened and water enters the mouth. Lowering the operculum, with a resulting increase in pressure, causes the oral valves to close and the branchiostegal valves to open. As water passes over the gills, emerging through the opercular slit, oxygen is taken up and carbon dioxide liberated. Respiration in fishes thus involves a series of muscular contractions in the walls of mouth and pharynx, bringing about a flow of water. The act of inspiration causes water to enter the mouth and pharynx, and expiration results in its expulsion. According to J. F. Daniel (1934, "The Elasmobranch Fishes," University of California Press), respiration in elasmobranchs is brought about by the interaction of a complicated series of buccal and pharyngeal muscles which, in the absence of specific valves, in most cases, regulate the passage of water over the gills. When water enters the mouth the external gill slits close, and when the

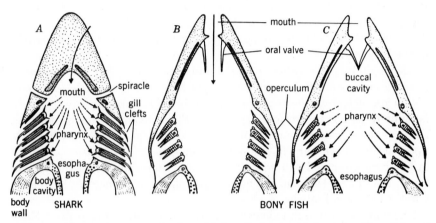

Fig. 6.11. The respiratory mechanism of fishes; diagrammatic frontal sections (lobes of oral valve actually are dorsal and ventral); arrows show paths of water currents. Shark: *A*, water enters ventrally placed mouth which then closes and floor of mouth region rises to force water over the gills and out the separate gill clefts. Bony fish: *B*, inhalent, opercula closed, oral valve open, cavity dilated, and water enters; *C*, exhalent, oral valve closes, buccal cavity contracts, water passes over gills in common cavities at sides of pharynx and out beneath opercula. (*From Storer, "General Zoology," McGraw-Hill Book Company, Inc. By permission.*)

slits open, the mouth closes. In one species, *Heterodontus francisci*, the number of respirations has been observed to be approximately 35 per minute when the animal is at rest.

In most elasmobranchs and in a few other fishes (*Acipenser, Polyodon,* and *Polypterus*) the first gill pouch has become modified and opens to the outside by means of a *spiracle.* Rudimentary gill lamellae may be located on the *anterior* wall of the spiracle. Since the blood supply to these lamellae consists of oxygenated blood, they do not perform a respiratory function, and the term *false gill,* or *pseudobranch,* is customarily applied to them. The spiracles generally open on the top of the head posterior to the eyes. Even in skates and rays with their ventrally disposed gill slits, the spiracles are in a dorsal position. In most of the free-swimming sharks water passes *out* of the pharynx through the spiracles as well as through the external gill slits. In many species the spiracles are provided with valves. In the rays, which are bottom-dwelling forms, most of the water *enters* the pharynx through the spiracles and little comes through the mouth. The spiracular valve closes by contraction of the first dorsal constrictor muscle (page 487), and water is forced out through the external gill slits. Other valves in rays prevent water from leaving through the mouth which does not usually close entirely. Under certain conditions rays have been observed to reverse the usual procedure and to "spout" water *out* through the spiracles. This seems to be a protective device enabling the animal to eject foreign matter that has entered the pharynx with the incurrent stream of water. It is of interest that in one of the viviparous elasmobranchs, *Petroplatea micrura*, certain villous projections from the uterine wall of the mother enter the spiracles of the developing young, supplying nutriment directly to the walls of their digestive tracts.

Although in most fishes a *true* hemibranch, receiving unoxygenated blood, is lacking on the posterior side of the hyoid arch, a modified *opercular gill*, or *pseudobranch*, receiving oxygenated blood may be present. Opercular gills of this type are found in *Amia*, the Dipnoi, and many teleosts. Such opercular gills probably represent the spiracular pseudobranch which, upon closure of the spiracle, has shifted its position. *Lepisosteus* is peculiar in having both dorsal and ventral gills on the inner surface of the operculum. The dorsal lamellae belong to a pseudobranch, whereas the ventral gill is a true hemibranch.

The number of gills and gill clefts varies among fishes (Fig. 6.12). There is some confusion as to just what each represents since different authors use different numbers in designating them. Throughout this volume we shall consider the mandibular arch to be the *first* visceral arch, the hyoid the *second*, and shall refer to the remaining arches as 3, 4, 5, 6, etc. The hyomandibular cleft between the mandibular and hyoid arches is actually the first cleft. However, since it is either modified to form a spiracle, or is closed altogether, and because it never bears true gills, we shall refer to it only as the spiracle, spiracular cleft, or hyomandibular cleft. The cleft between the hyoid and third visceral arches is the first *typical* gill cleft and, therefore, will here be designated as gill cleft 1.

Most elasmobranchs have five pairs of clefts in addition to the spiracles. One form, however, *Hexanchus*, has six, and another, *Heptanchus*, has seven, exclusive of the spiracles. *Heptanchus* has the largest number of gill clefts of any gnathostome. Chimaeras have but four pairs of clefts, the spiracles being absent and the last cleft closed. *Polypterus*, *Acipenser*, and *Polyodon*, like most elasmobranchs, have five pairs in addition to the spiracles. *Amia*, *Lepisosteus*, and teleosts, all of which lack spiracles, also have five pairs of clefts. The Dipnoi, which lack spiracles, show the greatest variations. *Neoceratodus* and *Protopterus* have five pairs of clefts, but *Lepidosiren* has only four. There seems to be some difference of opinion as to which numbers these represent in the three forms being considered. In *Protopterus* no gill lamellae border the first two clefts or the anterior wall of the third. A hyoidean pseudobranch lies anterior to the first gill cleft.

The presence of external gills is rare among fishes. In the larva of *Polypterus* a single pair of external integumentary gills is present in the region of the hyoid arch. Each gill consists of a narrow, main, central portion which bears a double row of filaments. Larval Dipnoi possess four

Fig. 6.12. Diagrams showing number of gill slits and arrangement of hemibranchs in lamprey (*Petromyzon*) and seven representative fishes. Dotted line indicates gill slit or spiracle which has failed to open to the outside; solid, parallel lines indicate lamellae of true hemibranchs; stippled areas indicate pseudobranchs; 1–9, position of visceral arches; I–VII, typical gill slits.

pairs of external cutaneous gills located on the visceral arches. These external gills disappear in adult life, although vestiges may remain. In certain elasmobranchs during embryonic life the gill filaments are so long that they extend out the pharynx through the spiracles and function in the manner of external gill filaments. It is believed that they may even aid in the absorption of nutriment.

Most fishes die soon after being exposed to air, even though their gills are kept moist. Lack of water in the branchial chambers, as well as the accumulation of mucus, causes the gills to stick to each other with the result that the exposed respiratory surface is decreased to the point that exchange of gases is no longer adequate.

Some fishes, such as eels, which can migrate for some distance on the land, are able to retain water in the branchial chamber. The opercular aperture is small and rounded, thus more readily permitting the retention of water.

Although gills serve as the chief organs of respiration in most fishes, other respiratory mechanisms may be present in addition. Vascular areas in the skin, in some forms, may aid in respiration. Some fishes possess pockets, projecting from the branchial chambers, in which water may be carried. Other accessory respiratory organs in fishes may enable the animals to utilize oxygen taken from the air. Certain species have posterior extensions of the gill chamber, filled with air and extending the entire length of the coelom. Another very important structure, which in some of the lower fishes serves as a lung, is the *swim bladder*, or *air bladder*, to be discussed in detail further in this chapter.

Amphibians. Most members of the class Amphibia spend their larval life in water and, after a period of metamorphosis, go to the land. During the larval state gills of the external integumentary type are used as organs of respiration in addition to the highly vascular skin. In a few caudates the gills are retained throughout life, but in most caudates and all the tailless amphibians, they disappear at the time of metamorphosis. Newly developed lungs then take over the respiratory function. Cutaneous respiration is very important in this class both in larval and adult life. In adult salamanders of the family Plethodontidae lungs fail to develop, and, with the loss of the gills, the animals depend entirely upon cutaneous and buccopharyngeal respiration (page 227).

During embryonic development, with few exceptions, five pairs of pharyngeal pouches form in the characteristic manner. The first and usually the last do not become perforated, so that only numbers 2, 3, and 4 actually connect to the outside. The first gill pouch gives rise to the *Eustachian tube* and *middle ear*, at least in salientians. In most amphibians all the gill slits become closed over at the time of metamorphosis, but in certain caudates some of them persist throughout adult life. In *Siren* all three clefts remain. *Necturus*, *Typhlomolge*, and *Proteus* possess only two pairs of clefts, representing pharyngeal pouches 3 and 4, during the adult stage. In *Amphiuma* only one pair persists (pharyngeal pouch 4). In the hellbender, *Cryptobranchus alleganiensis*, at the time that the external gills disappear, the edges of the operculum (page 205) fuse to the throat except on the dorsal side, leaving an opening on either side. These openings serve as outlets for water taken into the mouth during feeding. These animals depend upon their skin and lungs for respiration. Frequently one or the other of the openings fails to develop.

The external gills of amphibians consist of tufts of filaments with bases on the third, fourth, and fifth visceral arches. Arterial loops coming off the main aortic arches ramify through the external gills. In caudate amphibians and in early stages of development of salientian larvae the aortic arches are not interrupted by gill capillaries as in fishes. Blood, therefore, may go either directly through the aortic arches or through the arterial loops in the external gill filaments. The gills are covered with ciliated epithelium. Waving movements of the gills themselves, together with movements of the cilia, ensure a constant change in the water with which they are in contact.

In the larvae of salientians an operculum develops shortly after the external gills appear. It arises from the hyoid region but does not contain any skeletal elements. The operculum grows posteriorly and covers over the gill clefts, gills, and the region from which the forelimbs will later develop. It then fuses with the body, behind and below the gill region, in such a manner that the gills are confined to an *opercular chamber* (Fig. 6.13). The opercular aperture becomes greatly reduced in size and is sometimes referred to as the *spiracle*. It should not be confused with the spiracle present in certain fishes. There may be either a single midventral aperture or one that is more lateral in position. In a few forms paired apertures are present. The external gills soon degenerate, and a new set of gills develops from the tissue covering the same visceral arches. These are often referred to as *internal gills* because of their location *within* the opercular cavity. The entire opercular cavity is lined with ectoderm, a portion of which covers the internal gills. These, as well as the external gills, should be considered as integumentary derivatives, and it is indeed questionable whether they should be homologized with the internal gills of fishes. When the "internal" gills develop in salientian larvae the continuity of the aortic arches is temporarily interrupted as new arterial loops appear. Upon metamorphosis, however, the aortic arches once more make direct connections with the dorsal aorta. Water passes from mouth to pharynx and then through the gill slits into the opercular chamber. It finally leaves through the opercular aperture.

An opercular fold, as mentioned in connection with *Cryptobranchus*, also forms in caudate amphibians, but it is usually much reduced in size

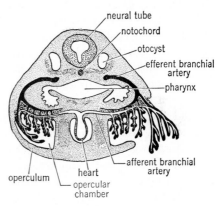

FIG. 6.13.   Diagram showing relations of external gills of salientian larva before (*right*) and after (*left*) the operculum has grown back to enclose the gills in an opercular chamber. (*After Maurer.*)

and consists of a mere crease immediately anterior to the gill region.

The gills of larval caecilians are, in general, similar to those of caudates, a reduced opercular fold also being present in this group. In one form, *Caecilia compressicauda*, the gills are in the form of large, leaflike folds.

The gills of salientians are resorbed during metamorphosis. Among other changes which occur in this transformation from tadpole to adult, the developing forelimbs push out into the opercular chamber. In the leopard frog, *Rana pipiens*, the left limb passes through the opercular aperture, whereas the right one pushes through the wall of the operculum itself.

In caudates several conditions obtain. Three pairs of gills and two pairs of gill clefts persist during adult life in *Necturus*. In *Amphiuma* the gills are resorbed, but a single pair of gill slits remains. In most salamanders, however, both gills and gill slits usually disappear during metamorphosis. A condition referred to as *neoteny* is encountered in certain salamanders. This term is used to denote the retention of certain larval characteristics beyond the normal period, or during adult life. For example, the tiger salamander, *Ambystoma tigrinum*, normally loses its gills at the time of metamorphosis and becomes a terrestrial animal. The Mexican *axolotl*, formerly believed to be another species, is an aquatic, gill-breathing animal even during its adult life. In 1876 Duméril demonstrated that under certain conditions the axolotl could be induced to lose its gills and become a typical lung-breathing salamander, in every way identical with *Ambystoma tigrinum*. No satisfactory explanation of the meaning of neoteny has been advanced. Not all caudates which retain their gills may be induced to lose them under experimental conditions (page 524).

In some amphibians the gill stage is passed through very rapidly while the embryo is still enclosed within the jellylike egg envelopes. By the time of hatching, metamorphosis may already have occurred, and the animal is fitted for a terrestrial existence rather early in life. The salamander, *Plethodon cinereus*, exemplifies this type of development.

Reptiles, birds, and mammals. Five pairs of pharyngeal pouches are formed in reptiles during early embryonic life, but only four develop in birds and mammals. Although a fifth pair may form in these latter groups, it is rudimentary and attached to the fourth pair. The pouches do not usually break through to the outside, but they may do so occasionally. The first pharyngeal pouch persists to become the Eustachian tube and middle ear, but the other pouches become reduced and disappear except for certain vestiges and derivatives to be discussed later in the chapter. The homologies of these pouches with those of lower forms should be apparent. Their development furnishes an excellent example illustrating the law of biogenesis. If the pharyngeal pouches fail to become obliterated in the normal manner, they may lead to the formation of branchial cysts and fistulae. In the latter condition there is an opening in the neck region which communicates with the pharynx. In such cases a perforated gill cleft has failed to disappear. Gills do not develop in association with the pharyngeal pouches of the three highest classes of vertebrates. Some transitory structures, which appear for a short time during development as outgrowths of the gill pouches in chick embryos and the embryos of certain turtles, may possibly be homologues of gills. It is certain that they have no respiratory function.

PHYLOGENETIC ORIGIN OF LUNGS AND SWIM BLADDERS

The swim bladder in various fishes shows a rather wide diversity in structure and function. Generally speaking, it is a gas-filled diverticulum which arises from the pharyngeal or esophageal region of the digestive tract. In certain primitive fishes its structure and function are such that it is difficult to make a distinction between swim bladder and lung. In fact, the swim bladder is a better lung in some fishes (Dipnoi) than are the lungs of most amphibians. The term *lung* is usually applied specifically to the respiratory organs of terrestrial vertebrates. The similarity of the lungs of tetrapods to the swim bladders of such fishes really makes such a distinction artificial. Some authors refer to the swim bladder as a lung if it has a ventral connection with the digestive tract. Nevertheless, in the following pages we shall refer to these structures in fishes as swim bladders since in most cases their primary function is not respiratory. A swim bladder may be single or double and may open into the digestive tract dorsally, ventrally, or not at all. It may be large and extend the entire length of the coelom or may be so small as to be practically indistinguishable. It is usually located dorsally and lies directly beneath the vertebral column, dorsal aorta, and opisthonephric kidneys, but outside the coelom. The peritoneum covers only its ventral surface. Swim bladders which retain the open *pneumatic duct*, or connection with the digestive tract, are said to be *physostomous*, whereas those which are completely closed are *physoclistous*.

Many authorities in the past have considered the swim bladder to be the forerunner of the lungs of higher forms. It was supposed to have arisen in fishes as an unpaired, dorsal evagination from the digestive tract and to have become modified gradually, in subsequent evolution, into the bilobed, ventrally located lungs of the higher vertebrates. The modern point of view, however, is that the presence of lungs was a primitive character and that the swim bladder of higher fishes is probably a specialized modification of the lung.

The origin of the swim bladder in the phylogenetic series has been obscure, and several theories, now only of historical interest, have been advanced to explain a possible mode of derivation. R. H. Denison (1941, *J. Paleontol.*, **15**:553) discovered that lungs were present in the fossil remains of the Devonian placoderm, *Bothriolepis*. The placoderms, all of which are extinct, are considered to be the most primitive of the gnathostomes. It is now thought probable that the lungs of the lower fishes and of the tetrapods, together with the modified swim bladders of higher fishes, came from a common source among the placoderms. But few connecting links among the various groups have been discovered up to the present time.

Although in some of the lower fishes the swim bladder functions chiefly as an accessory respiratory organ, supplementing the gills in this respect, it may also serve as a hydrostatic organ and, in certain cases, as an organ for sound production and sound reception as well. The modified swim bladders of higher fishes seem to play little or no part in respiration and serve almost entirely as hydrostatic or equilibratory organs, enabling the fish to swim at different levels of water with but little effort.

Comparative anatomy of swim bladders. *Placoderms.* The lungs (swim bladders) of placoderms, as evidenced by study of *Bothriolepis*, consisted of little more than a posterior pair of pharyngeal pouches extending ventrally and which, in all probability, functioned as primitive pneumatic organs.

Elasmobranchs. No swim bladder is present in elasmobranchs. In several species, however, a transitory rudiment appears during development. Opinions differ as to the significance of the rudiment. Nevertheless, it is entirely possible that it represents a lunglike development which was present in some remote progenitor.

Cladistians. Of the two genera of cladistians living today, *Polypterus* is the more widely known. It is of particular interest because of the peculiar structure of its swim bladder. *Polypterus* is the most primitive of all the ray-finned fishes living at the present time. Its smooth-walled swim bladder is bilobed and its pneumatic duct lies ventral to the digestive tract. It opens into the ventral part of the anterior end of the esophagus by means of a small, muscular *glottis*. The opening is slightly to the right of the midventral line. The two lobes of the swim bladder are of unequal size, the left being considerably smaller than the right. Where the right lobe extends beyond the left, it curves around the right side of the digestive tract and is dorsal to the intestine at its posterior end.

The arteries which supply the swim bladder of *Polypterus* arise from the last pair of efferent branchial arteries. Blood going to the structure has therefore already passed through the capillaries of the gills and under normal conditions would be oxygenated. The veins which drain the swim bladder enter the hepatic veins a short distance below the sinus venosus.

Dipnoi. The true lungfishes include but three surviving genera: *Protopterus*, *Lepidosiren*, and *Neoceratodus*. Study of the *sacculated* swim bladders of these three forms offers a clue to the origin of the specialized types of swim bladders found in the teleost fishes. During the dry season some of the Dipnoi estivate in burrows in the mud and utilize their swim bladders (lungs) in respiration. *Protopterus* and *Lepidosiren* are similar to *Polypterus* in that their swim bladders are bilobed and connect with the esophagus on its ventral side. The two lobes are, however, of practically the same size, although during development the left lobe is, for a time, smaller than the right. The blood supply of the swim bladder is derived from pulmonary arteries which arise directly from the dorsal aorta posterior to the last pair of aortic arches. In these fishes, nevertheless, at least partially oxygenated blood is carried to the swim bladder (page 510).

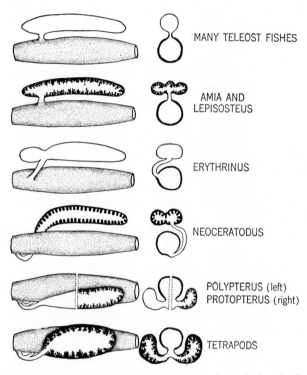

MANY TELEOST FISHES

AMIA AND LEPISOSTEUS

ERYTHRINUS

NEOCERATODUS

POLYPTERUS (left)
PROTOPTERUS (right)

TETRAPODS

Fig. 6.14. Various types of swim bladders (or lungs), shown in longitudinal and cross section (diagrammatic). (*After Dean.*)

Pulmonary veins carry the blood directly to the left atrium of the heart. Two atria, right and left, appear in the Dipnoi for the first time in the vertebrate series.

Neoceratodus is of particular interest because its swim bladder consists of a single lobe lying *dorsal* to the digestive tract and communicating with the esophagus by a tube, the *pneumatic duct*. The duct courses around the right side of the esophagus and opens through a glottis on its *ventral* side. A small diverticulum, present only during embryonic development, represents the left lobe, which is altogether lacking in the adult. A pulmonary artery arises from each posterior efferent branchial artery to supply the swim bladder. Two pulmonary veins unite to form a single vessel which opens into the left atrium of the heart. In *Neoceratodus* there is not so complete a separation of right and left atria as in *Protopterus* and *Lepido-siren*. Blood going to the swim bladder has, under normal conditions, been oxygenated in the gills.

The evolutionary step from the double, ventrally connecting type of swim bladder, as found in *Protopterus*, to the lungs of tetrapods would seem to be comparatively simple and logical. The origin of the physoclistous organs of many teleosts from the dorsally located, single-lobed swim blad-der of the type present in *Neoceratodus* would also appear to follow a logical sequence (Fig. 6.14).

Tetrapods. In amphibians, reptiles, birds, and mammals the lungs arise during embryonic development as a diverticulum from the ventral portion of the pharynx. The diverticulum becomes bilobed. In most forms there is a tendency for the left lung to be smaller than the right, as is true of *Polypterus* and some other species of fishes. The walls of the lungs become subdivided into compartments of varying degrees of complexity. In mam-mals each lung is commonly divided into two or more large lobes. In structure and method of development, the tetrapod lung so closely re-sembles the swim bladder of *Protopterus* and certain other fishes that there is little doubt concerning homologies and the phylogenetic origin of the lungs of higher vertebrates.

Neopterygii. The two lowest orders of the subclass Neopterygii include the bowfin, *Amia*, and the garpike, *Lepisosteus*. The swim bladder of *Amia* is unpaired, large, and highly vascular. It lies dorsal to the digestive tract and extends almost the entire length of the coelom. Contrary to the condi-tion in *Neoceratodus*, however, the pneumatic duct opens through a muscu-lar glottis on the *dorsal* side of the esophagus just behind the pharynx. In *Amia*, also, a rudiment of the left lobe appears during development, but it persists only for a short time. The arterial supply to the swim bladder is similar to that of *Polypterus* and *Neoceratodus*, coming from the last pair of efferent branchial arteries. The venous drainage is like that of *Polypterus*.

The swim bladder of *Lepisosteus* is very much like that of *Amia*. It is, however, supplied with arteries which arise directly from the dorsal aorta, and the veins leading from the organ enter the hepatic portal and post-cardinal veins. This condition is similar to that encountered in the teleosts.

Among the teleost fishes which make up the remainder of the subclass Neopterygii are found the most specialized swim bladders of all. They bear the least resemblance to the primitive structure of *Polypterus*. There are several families of teleosts, however, in which a swim bladder is al-together lacking. Bottom-dwelling flatfishes, such as the flounder and halibut, lack a swim bladder in adult life. The typical teleostean swim bladder is a thin-walled gas-filled sac which lies dorsal to the digestive tract and extends the entire length of the body cavity. Branches of the coeliac artery supply it with blood, and the venous return is through the hepatic portal or postcardinal veins. Teleostean swim bladders probably play little or no part in respiration, their primary function being concerned with hydrostasis and equilibration.

Among the major specializations to be found within the group is the loss of the pneumatic duct, which may atrophy and either disappear altogether or persist as a remnant in the form of a solid, fibrous cord.

The salmon, carp, pickerel, and eel are among commonly known teleosts which retain the open pneumatic duct. The swim bladder of the salmon is of simple construction. It consists of a single sac connected with the dorsal side of the esophagus. A sphincter muscle is present at the esophageal end of the pneumatic duct.

In the carp family there is a reduction in size of the swim bladder and a diverticulum grows forward into the head region. This is the *anterior*

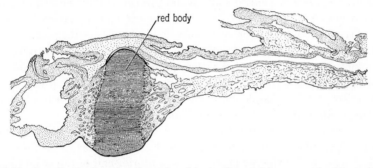

red body

FIG. 6.15. Longitudinal section through red body dissected from an eel. The red body proper consists of numerous blood vessels of capillary dimensions, compactly arranged and running parallel to each other.

chamber. The *posterior chamber* is joined to the esophagus by a pneumatic duct. The anterior chamber is connected by a chain of four small bones, the *Weberian ossicles*, to the inner ear. Weberian ossicles, which are derived from portions of the anterior four vertebrae, are found in members of the order Ostariophysi to which the carp, catfish, and sucker belong. In some other teleosts (herring, etc.) extensions of the swim bladder itself make direct contact with parts of the inner ear. They may thus be of importance in static or even auditory perception.

There is much variation in the degree of vascularity of the swim bladders of teleosts. In some the entire inner surface is uniformly vascular; in others, rather localized masses of interlacing, tightly packed capillaries called *retia mirabilia* are present. In certain teleosts with physostomous swim bladders, one or more retia mirabilia become further specialized to form peculiar structures known as *red bodies* which project into the cavity of the swim bladder near its anterior end. The lining epithelium of the swim bladder is continued over the red bodies, apparently without any modification. The common eel possesses several red bodies (Fig. 6.15), the largest of which lie near the opening of the pneumatic duct. Red bodies are able to remove oxygen, nitrogen, and carbon dioxide from the blood that is circulating through them and to pass these gases into the cavity of the swim bladder. The structures are unique in being able to remove free oxygen (O_2) from the oxyhemoglobin contained within the red corpuscles. How this is accomplished is little understood.

Completely closed, physoclistous swim bladders are found in such teleosts as the perch, toadfish, cod, and haddock. With the disappearance of the pneumatic duct a modification of the red body occurs. The capillaries are still densely arranged, but the epithelium covering the projecting portion of these structures is of a glandular nature with numerous crypts and folds. The red body has now become the *red gland*. A single red gland is found in the cod and haddock, but in other teleosts several may be present, projecting from the dorsal or ventral walls of the anterior end of the swim bladder.

Physoclistous swim bladders show rather extreme variations in shape. Some have the configuration of a horseshoe. In others there may be distinct anterior and posterior chambers separated by a narrow opening or by a constriction which is provided with a sphincter muscle. In some there are two constrictions, so that it appears as though three sacs are present. Still other teleosts have simple or even complexly branched caecalike outgrowths, or diverticula, of the swim bladder.

Any excess gas secreted into the swim bladder in physostomous fishes may be liberated via the pneumatic duct. In physoclistous forms, gas which is secreted by the red glands at the anterior end of the swim bladder is, under certain conditions, absorbed by vessels which form a more diffuse rete mirabile at the posterior end. In species having two chambers in the swim bladder the sphincter muscle separating them may regulate the passage of gas from anterior to posterior chambers and thus control the amount of gas which may be absorbed by the rete mirabile in the wall of the posterior chamber. In certain forms the posterior chamber with its rete mirabile is reduced to a small pocket, the *oval*, the entrance to which is guarded by a sphincter.

Chondrostei. The swim bladders of the paddlefish and sturgeons, which are grouped together with the cladistians, *Polypterus* and *Calamoichthys*, in the subclass *Paleopterygii*, have not been discussed prior to this point since they do not fit into the general scheme of things as outlined here. Some sturgeons lack a swim bladder altogether. In others it is oval in shape, with a smooth inner surface lined with ciliated epithelium. It opens into the dorsal side of the esophagus by means of a rather wide aperture. During embryonic development the swim bladders of sturgeons seem to rise more posteriorly and nearer the stomach than in other fishes. In such forms gastric glands may be present in its walls for a time during development. This group of fishes is considered to be degenerate in other respects, and the loss or degenerate condition of the swim bladder may be nothing more than an association with bottom-dwelling habits.

Functions of the swim bladder. It has been mentioned that in some of the lower fishes the swim bladder serves as an important adjunct to the gills in respiration. The observed behavior of such fishes, and the structure of the swim bladder with its blood supply, support such an assumption. Its position in the body, and the fact that it contains gas within its cavity, indicate that the swim bladder may function also in hydrostasis, equilibration, and sound production. It is doubtful whether the physoclistous swim bladders of the higher teleost fishes are of any importance in respiration. They seem to serve chiefly as hydrostatic and equilibratory organs. Those teleosts having Weberian ossicles may possibly use their swim bladders in sound reception.

Respiration. It is well known that *Lepisosteus*, the dipnoans, and a few other species of fishes are unable to live for any length of time if kept sub-

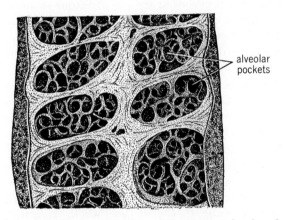

alveolar pockets

Fig. 6.16. Lining of portion of swim bladder of *Lepisosteus*, showing alveolar pockets.

merged and prevented from coming to the surface of the water to gulp air. Observations of *Lepisosteus* show that under normal conditions the animal comes to the surface and "breaks water" every 7 or 8 minutes. Such fishes normally inhabit rather shallow waters or stay rather close to the surface.

In most of these lower fishes the lining of the physostomous swim bladder is thrown into a complicated series of highly vascular folds and sacculations of an alveolar nature (Fig. 6.16), thus providing an excellent respiratory surface. Blood going to the swim bladder under normal conditions, however, has already been oxygenated in the gills since the arteries with which it is supplied arise from the posterior efferent branchial arteries or directly from the dorsal aorta. If the oxygen content of the water in which these fishes live is depleted and the gills cannot obtain enough oxygen, the ability of the swim bladder to take over the respiratory function entirely is of great adaptive value to the animal. On the other hand, it would seem that perhaps the respiratory surface of the gills is inadequate to secure the necessary amount of oxygen, and a supplemental supply may be obtained at the swim bladder. This seems to be particularly true of *Protopterus* in which gills are lacking on the borders of the first two gill slits and anterior portion of the third. The anterior aortic arches in *Protopterus* thus form direct channels from ventral to dorsal aortae, and the pulmonary arteries, which arise from the dorsal aorta posterior to the gill region, supply the swim bladder with blood which has been only partially oxygenated.

The exact mechanism by means of which air can be taken into the swim bladder is not well understood. Muscles are present in its walls in certain forms, and these may possibly play a part in inhalation and exhalation of air. It has been reported that in certain fishes muscles at the entrance of the pneumatic duct enable the animal literally to swallow air which then enters the swim bladder.

Some investigators believe that the physoclistous swim bladder may be used for the storage of oxygen which has been separated from the blood by the red glands. This oxygen then may be utilized when the oxygen content of the surrounding water is low. If this is true, then in such a sense the swim bladder may be considered to be an accessory organ of respiration. However, it has been demonstrated, under experimental conditions, that certain fishes may be asphyxiated even though the swim bladder contains a considerable amount of oxygen. The amount of carbon dioxide in the swim bladder has a very definite influence upon the amount of oxygen that may be absorbed by this organ. A more satisfactory interpretation of the role of the physoclistous swim bladder in respiration is indicated by experiments which show that if the amount of carbon dioxide in the water increases, the red gland secretes more gas into the swim bladder, thus causing the fish to rise almost automatically to the surface, where oxygen is available in greater quantities.

Hydrostasis. The hydrostatic function of the swim bladder has been amply demonstrated by experimental work. The organ serves to equilibrate the body of the fish with the surrounding water at any level. The animal literally "floats" *in* the water. Adjustment of the body in changing from one level in the water to another is not usually accomplished quickly. Change in the volume of the contained gas is one method by which this may possibly be effected. Muscular contractions, at least in part, may be used to change the volume. Increasing or decreasing the amount of gas contained within the swim bladder, however, is the more probable explanation, pressure within the bladder being maintained by muscles in the wall of the organ. In physostomous fishes passage of gases in or out of the swim bladder seems to be associated with the pneumatic duct. However, in physostomous teleosts, gulping of air has been shown to be but one means of increasing the volume of gas. Gases may also pass in a free state directly, from the blood in the retia mirabilia, or red bodies, into the swim bladder. The latter method of increasing the amount of gas requires a greater length of time than the former and is probably used primarily when the fish does not have ready access to surface air.

In physoclistous fishes, inasmuch as no pneumatic duct is present, any changes in the gaseous content of the swim bladder must be brought about solely by exchange of gases between the swim bladder and blood stream. The peculiar concentration of parallel capillaries of the red glands is believed to be the chief center of gas secretion or diffusion. At the time when a red gland is giving off free oxygen, there is an increased flow of blood through the gland; the capillaries dilate, and the oxygen dissociates from the oxyhemoglobin in the red corpuscles. In fishes with closed swim bladders and lacking red glands, there is a physical diffusion of gases between the swim bladder and the blood vessels in its walls. In such cases diffusion does not take place so rapidly as in those in which red glands are present.

Gases pass into and out of the swim bladder depending upon environmental conditions, particularly in relation to pressure changes. The composition of the contained gas also shows variations in relation to pressure. The chief gases in the swim bladder, as previously stated, are oxygen, carbon dioxide, and nitrogen, with traces of other inert gases that are normally present in the atmosphere. When a fish is swimming near the surface the gases are in approximately the same concentration as in the air. But as the depth increases, the per cent of oxygen in the swim bladder increases. In some deep-sea species oxygen may make up as much as 87 per cent of the gaseous content of the swim bladder.

When fishes are suddenly brought to the surface from depths where the pressure of water on the body is great, various results are noted. Physostomous fishes release bubbles of gas from their swim bladders, thus adapting themselves to the change in pressure. Physoclistous fishes, however, do not have any such means of gas release. In some cases the swim bladder may burst, but more frequently the expansion of gas, which naturally follows when pressure is released, causes the swim bladder to become abnormally distended, and the fish is then incapable of swimming. The stomach may be pushed out through the mouth, or the intestine everted through the anus. Pressure of the inflated organ upon neighboring viscera is probably the major cause of their extrusion. Under normal conditions ascent and descent between surface water and depths take place rather gradually.

Sound production. Among other functions of the swim bladder, the part which it may play in sound production is important. Sound production in fishes is by no means so rare as is generally supposed. Many are able to produce rasping or strident sounds by rubbing such structures as teeth, bones, and spines against one another. Sounds comparable to those made by higher vertebrates, in which passage of air forms the basis of sound production, occur but rarely among fishes. In some cases the sounds originate by expulsion of air from the swim bladder through the pneumatic duct and mouth. In the loach, which employs intestinal respiration, voiding of air bubbles through the anus causes sound production of a sort.

In those fishes in which gas in the swim bladder is used in making sounds, some mechanism is generally present which is capable of compressing the contained gas. Muscles attached to the swim bladder, on the one hand, and to bony structures, on the other, may serve alternately to compress and expand the swim bladder. In some species, in which the swim bladder lacks muscles of its own, the organ may be at least partially invested with tendinous or muscular extensions of the body wall which can be utilized in producing pressure upon the gas contained within. In cases in which the organ is divided by constrictions into two or three chambers, the passage of gas from one chamber to another over the edges of loose septa may cause sounds to be produced.

Cyclostomes and elasmobranchs are not known to be capable of emitting sounds. Sound production in fishes is confined mostly to the teleosts, although there is evidence that *Polypterus, Protopterus, Calamoichthys,* and *Lepidosiren* are capable of sound production. The mechanism by means of which this is accomplished is not understood. In none of the fishes are skeletal supports to be found in the region of the glottis, which might be considered as homologues of the laryngeal structures of higher vertebrates.

Since water is a much better conductor of sound waves than is air, sounds produced by fishes may be carried for considerable distances. In certain cases the sounds may have some relation to mating activities, species recognition, or defense from enemies.

LUNGS AND AIR DUCTS

The diverticulum which in the embryo gives rise to lungs grows out ventrally from the floor of the pharynx posterior to the last gill pouch. It soon divides into two halves, the *lung buds,* which are destined to give rise to the bronchi, and the lungs proper. The lung buds grow posteriorly, invested by an envelope of mesoderm, until they reach their final destination in the body. They may branch to varying degrees, depending upon the species. The original unpaired duct which connects the lungs to the pharynx serves to carry air back and forth and is known, in most forms, as the windpipe, or *trachea.* In most salientian amphibians the duct is so short as to be practically nonexistent. In many tetrapods the anterior end of the trachea becomes modified to form a voice box, or *larynx,* which opens into the pharynx by means of a slitlike *glottis,* the walls of which are supported by cartilages. At its lower end the trachea usually divides into two bronchi which lead directly to the lungs.

Larynx. The skeletal elements supporting the walls of the larynx are derivatives of certain visceral arches which, along with the loss of gills, have become modified during development.   No such structural modifications have been observed to be associated with the pneumatic duct in fishes, the visceral arches of which are retained as such.

Amphibians.   The simplest condition of the larynx is to be found in certain caudate amphibians, such as *Necturus*, in which a pair of *lateral cartilages* bounds the slitlike glottis.   These cartilages are derived from the last pair of visceral arches.   Other amphibians show further modification in that the lateral cartilages are supplanted by an upper pair of *arytenoid cartilages*, bounding the glottis, and a lower pair of *cricoid cartilages* (Fig. 6.17).   The two cricoids may fuse to form a cartilaginous ring located

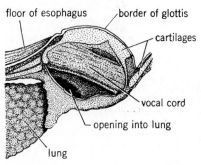

Fig. 6.17.   Dorsal view of laryngeal cartilages of frog, *Rana esculenta*. Black represents bone; stippled areas, cartilage. (*After Gaupp.*)

Fig. 6.18.   View of interior of left half of larynx of bullfrog, *Rana catesbeiana*, showing position of vocal cord, attached at its ends and along its length to the wall of the larynx.

within the walls of the larynx.   The arytenoid cartilages are moved by muscles which work in antagonistic pairs and which are also derived from the gill region.   They serve to open and close the glottis.   In salientians two thickened ridges of tissue, composed of elastic fibers for the most part, project into the cavity of the larynx.   These are the *vocal cords* (Fig. 6.18). They are arranged so as to parallel the glottis.   The inner, or lower, rim of each vocal cord is set into vibration as air is forced from the lungs, thus bringing about the production of sound.   Alterations of pitch are influenced by tightening or relaxing the vocal cords to different degrees.   Although a few caudates can produce sounds, they rarely amount to much more than a slight squeak or hiss.   In salientians, sound production is often well developed, particularly in males.   Not only is the larynx usually much larger in males, but they also possess *vocal sacs* which, when dilated, act as resonators.   The vocal sacs are diverticula of the mouth cavity which extend ventrally and laterally so as to lie under the outer skin and muscles of the throat region (Fig. 6.19).   Air is forced back and forth between the inflated vocal sacs and lungs, the nostrils generally remaining closed.

Sounds therefore may be produced when the animal is under water as well as when on land. Many curious variations of the vocal sacs are to be found within the group. They are usually paired. However, in some forms they are unpaired, median structures. In certain species the vocal sacs are very large and extend posteriorly into the large lymphatic spaces. Sounds produced by female salientians, with their smaller larynges and

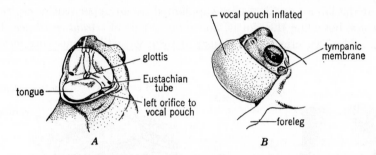

Fig. 6.19. Vocal pouch of American spadefoot toad, *Scaphiopus holbrookii*. *A*, showing location of openings to vocal pouch; *B*, the vocal pouch inflated. (*From Noble, "Biology of the Amphibia," McGraw-Hill Book Company, Inc. By permission.*)

in the absence of vocal sacs, are of much less magnitude than those of males.

Reptiles.   The larynx in reptiles is generally no better developed than in amphibians. It is closely associated with the hyoid apparatus, and its skeletal support consists of a well-developed pair of arytenoid cartilages and an incomplete cricoid ring. In crocodilians another cartilaginous element, the *thyroid cartilage*, is present in the larynx. Otherwise a thyroid cartilage appears only in mammals. A fold of mucous membrane of the mouth, which in certain lizards and turtles lies anterior to the glottis, is thought to represent the beginning of an *epiglottis* such as is found in mammals. In chameleons the lining of the larynx between the cricoid cartilage and the first tracheal cartilage extends outward, forming an inflatable *gular pouch*.

Most reptiles lack the ability to produce sounds except for a sort of hissing noise which may result from the rapid expulsion of air from the lungs. Vocal cords are present in the larynges of certain lizards (geckos and chameleons), and these are able to produce guttural noises. Male alligators make loud, bellowing sounds, particularly during the mating season when they may be heard over distances of a mile or more.

Birds.   One would expect that in the highly vocal birds a well-developed larynx would be present. This is not the case, however. Another structure, the *syrinx*, located at the lower end of the trachea, is responsible for sound production (page 221). The larynx in birds is poorly developed and incapable of producing sounds. Arytenoid cartilages, which are sometimes ossified, guard the glottis.   In some birds the upper portions of the cricoids have separated into additional elements called the *procricoids.*

Mammals.   The mammalian larynx is more complicated than that of other groups of vertebrates.   In addition to the arytenoid and cricoid cartilages, other skeletal elements are present.   A *thyroid cartilage,* derived from portions of the fourth and fifth visceral arches, is located on the ventral side of the larynx.   It articulates with the hyoid apparatus at its anterodorsal angles.   The thyroid cartilage usually consists of two parts which, except in monotremes, are fused along the midventral line.   In man this portion forms a prominent protuberance called the *pomum Adami* (*Adam's apple*).   The arytenoid cartilages, covered with mucous membrane, form the lateral boundaries of the posterior portion of the larynx; the cricoid makes up the posterodorsal portion.   Its middorsal part is frequently separated from the rest of the cricoid and forms the *procricoid.* The arytenoid and thyroid cartilages articulate with the cricoid.   In some mammals small *corniculate* and *cuneiform* cartilages are arranged in close association with the arytenoid cartilages.

An epiglottis is characteristically present in mammals.   It is composed of elastic cartilage and extends dorsally from the anterior, median portion of the thyroid cartilage in front of the glottis.   It was formerly thought that the epiglottis served as a sort of cover, or lid, for the glottis over which food passed on its way to the esophagus.   This view is no longer held.   During the act of swallowing, however, the epiglottis stands erect and the larynx is raised by muscular contraction in such a manner that the glottis is sheltered by the epiglottis and root of the tongue.   Even if the epiglottis is removed, little trouble is encountered from food entering the larynx.   Elevation of the larynx and closure of the glottis itself during the act of swallowing are the important factors in preventing food from entering the respiratory passages.   If the larynx cannot be raised, as in certain diseased conditions, swallowing is virtually impossible.   The homologies of the epiglottis are not clear.

The larynx extends from the root of the tongue to the posterior end of the cricoid cartilage where it is continuous with the trachea.   It is divided into two regions by the presence of vocal folds, or *true vocal cords.*   Each of these consists of a bandlike fold of yellow elastic tissue stretched between the anterior portion of the thyroid cartilage and the posterior part of the arytenoid.   The vocal cords are covered by a thin layer of mucous membrane with a stratified squamous epithelium.   The glottis lies between the vocal cords in front and is bounded by the arytenoid cartilages behind. Air, going through the narrow passage between the true vocal cords, causes them to vibrate and produce sounds.   Pitch is regulated by the degree to which the cords are contracted or relaxed by laryngeal muscles. The portion of the larynx in front of the true vocal cords is called the *vestibule.*   A pair of crescentic *false vocal cords (ventricular folds)* extends into the vestibule for a short distance on either side. The portion of the vestibule between the true and false vocal cords is called the ventricle of the larynx. It is usually small but in some forms assumes considerable proportions. In the howling monkeys, for example, a large, saccular diverticulum of the ventricular portion of the larynx forms a resonating chamber

portion of hyoid bone

FIG. 6.20. Resonating chamber of larynx of howling monkey.

(Fig. 6.20), supported by a greatly enlarged basihyal, which is responsible for the howling noises made by these forms. Such noises may be audible for considerable distances. Although both true and false vocal cords are present in most mammals, there are some exceptions. Elephants lack false vocal cords, and the hippopotamus lacks true ones.

In man the larynges of the two sexes differ but little in size until the age of puberty is reached. At that time the larynx of the male increases considerably in size and becomes much larger than that of the female. All the cartilages enlarge, and the thyroid cartilage forms a rather marked protuberance in the midline of the neck. The enlarged vocal cords are responsible for the lower pitch of the masculine voice. Growth of the male larynx at the time of puberty is a response of that structure to the hormone secreted by the testes. Removal of the testes before the age of puberty results in a failure of the larynx to grow to normal proportions, and the high-pitched voice of the boy is retained. After the larynx has grown to adult size, castration has little, if any, effect upon the pitch of the voice.

Trachea and bronchi. The trachea is the main trunk of a system of tubes through which air passes between larynx and lungs. It is a cartilaginous and membranous tube the walls of which are composed of fibrous and muscular tissue stiffened by cartilages which prevent it from collapsing. The trachea is lined with mucous membrane, the epithelium of which is composed of columnar-ciliated and mucus-secreting cells.

Amphibians. The trachea in most of the tailless amphibians is so short that it can scarcely be said to exist. However, in one group, the Pipidae, in which the lungs function as hydrostatic organs, a definite trachea is present. It divides into two bronchi at its lower end. In caudate amphibians the trachea is short but nevertheless exists as a definite structure which in some forms (*Amphiuma* and *Siren*) may be 4 or 5 cm. long. The tracheal cartilages are small and irregular. They show a tendency to form bands. In caecilians the cartilages are in the form of half rings. The trachea in either case divides at its lower end into two bronchi which lead directly to the lungs.

Reptiles. In amniotes the trachea is elongated to varying degrees, depending upon the length of the neck. Among reptiles, the trachea of lizards is relatively shorter than in other groups. In crocodilians and turtles it is considerably elongated and in some turtles is even convoluted. The tracheal cartilages have become better developed and more complete. In *Sphenodon*, lizards, and some snakes, certain anterior cartilages are present in the form of complete rings. The remainder appear as imperfect bands located on the ventral and lateral parts of the trachea. These bands are deficient on the dorsal side. In snakes successive tracheal cartilages are frequently united. Supporting cartilages are also present in the walls of the bronchi in many reptiles. In some snakes only one bronchus and one lung (the right) are present.

Birds. In correlation with the long necks of many birds, and the location of lungs in the thoracic region, the trachea may be of unusual length. In many birds the length of the trachea even exceeds that of the neck. In such cases it is convoluted, the loops lying under the skin of the thoracic or abdominal region or between the muscles and the sternum. In swans and cranes a loop of the trachea lies within a peculiar cavity located in the modified keel of the sternum, which thus serves as a resonator. An unusual condition is encountered in the penguins in which the trachea is double (Fig. 6.21). The duplication begins about 1 cm. from the larynx. The tracheal cartilages in birds are usually in the form of complete rings and are often calcified or ossified. The bronchi are also provided with supporting cartilaginous rings.

It has already been emphasized that the larynx is poorly developed in birds and is not concerned with sound production. The *syrinx*, found only in birds, is the true organ of sound production. It is located at the lower end of the trachea where that structure divides into the two bronchi.

The syringes of birds show much variation in structure, but in general three different types are recognized: *tracheal*, *bronchotracheal*, and *bronchial*. In the *tracheal syrinx* the lateral parts of the posterior tracheal rings have disappeared and a vibratile membrane closes over the gap thus formed. The *bronchotracheal syrinx* is the more usual type. Here the posterior tracheal rings are modified to form an enlarged resonating chamber, the *tympanum*, which often becomes ossified. Membranous folds, the *internal* and *external tympanic membranes*, project into the cavity from the medial and lateral walls of each bronchus. Often there is a skeletal structure, the *pessulus*, crossing the trachea in a dorsoventral direction at the point where it bifurcates. The lower portion of the pessulus bears a *semilunar membrane*. In certain aquatic birds, such as the male duck, the tympanum is very large and asymmetrical. In the *bronchial syrinx*, membranes between two successive cartilaginous rings of each bronchus form vibratile folds when the bronchi are contracted and the cartilages pulled closer together.   In these various types of syringes the positions of the different membranes and skeletal elements are altered by the action of complicated sets of muscles so that production of a variety of sounds is made possible.

Mammals.   Although the trachea is relatively short in the aquatic cetaceans and sirenians, in other mammals it is elongated and straight, its length varying with the length of the neck.   The trachea in a human adult measures about 4 to 5 in. in length.   Tracheal cartilages in mammals are

Fig. 6.21.   Trachea of jackass penguin, dissected to show duplication which begins about 1 cm. past the larynx.   (*From a photograph by Dr. Pearl M. Zeek.*)

usually incomplete on the dorsal side, the esophagus pressing against the gap thus formed.   In whales and sirenians they are arranged in the form of a spiral.   In man the number of tracheal rings varies from 16 to 20, whereas in the long-necked giraffe over 100 may be present.

In most mammals the trachea divides into two main bronchi; but in pigs, whales, and some ruminants a third, the *apical,* or *eparterial, bronchus* arises independently from the right side of the trachea anterior to the main point of bifurcation.   In some other forms the apical bronchus is a main branch of the right bronchus.   Cartilaginous rings support the walls of the bronchi in mammals.

Lungs.   The lung buds of terrestrial vertebrates give rise to two saclike structures, the walls of which become subdivided in most cases.   The divisions become more and more numerous and complex as the vertebrate scale is ascended, reaching the highest degree of branching in mammals.

In the latter group the lungs form a spongy mass composed of minute chambers called *infundibula*, or *alveolar sacs*, lined with *alveoli*. The alveoli make up the respiratory surface of the lung. The greater the degree of branching, the greater is the area of respiratory surface.

Amphibians. The lungs of amphibians are relatively simple in structure. They connect directly with the larynx in most forms, although a short trachea may be present. In caudate amphibians the lungs consist of a pair of elongated sacs, the left often being longer than the right. In some the lining is smooth, whereas in others alveoli may be present. In many cases the alveoli are confined to the basal portion. The left lung is very short in caecilians, and alveoli are present over the entire surface lining the right lung. In frogs and toads the lining of the lung sacs is somewhat more complex since the wall is thrown into numerous infundibular folds, which are, in turn, lined with alveoli. The more terrestrial amphibians generally possess a larger alveolar respiratory surface than do those which remain close to the water or which retain the aquatic mode of life.

Although it is usual for amphibians to develop lungs at the time of metamorphosis, this is not always the case. In some salamanders and frogs they develop during larval life. In salamanders of the family Plethodontidae no larynx, trachea, or lungs develop at the time that the gills are resorbed. The animals depend upon cutaneous and buccopharyngeal respiration during adult life. In certain forms, such as *Necturus*, which retains its gills, lungs are present in addition. It is doubtful whether they are used very effectively since they are supplied with blood which has already been oxygenated (page 525). However, they may be utilized in times of emergency when the oxygen supply of the water in which the animal lives becomes depleted.

Reptiles. The lungs of reptiles are more complex structures than those of amphibians. Snakes and lizards are characterized by a lack of symmetry between the two sides. In some lizards the right lung is the larger, whereas in others the condition is exactly the opposite. In snakes the left lobe is smaller than the right or is altogether absent.

Sphenodon illustrates the most primitive reptilian condition, in which the lungs are rather simple sacs lined uniformly with infundibula. In snakes the infundibula are usually confined to the basal portion of the lung. The next advancement is seen in the lizards. In this group septa, or partitions, divide the cavity of the lung into several chambers. In some cases the chambers communicate with each other at the proximal end of the lung, and in others at the distal end. In some of the higher lizards, turtles, and crocodilians the bronchi divide into smaller and smaller branches which finally terminate in infundibula lined with alveoli. This arrangement gives the lungs a spongy consistency. The crocodilian lung most nearly approaches the condition found in mammals. In chameleons several thin-walled, saclike diverticula, which ramify among the viscera, come off the distal portion of the lung. Only the proximal part of the lungs is spongy. The projecting diverticula seem to foreshadow the appearance of air sacs which reach their climax of development in birds. Throughout the reptilian class there is a tendency toward an increase in the alveolar respiratory surface.

Birds. The lungs of birds show many peculiarities not found in other groups. They are perhaps the most efficient of all from a physiological point of view. The lungs are small, very vascular, and capable of but little expansion. They are firmly attached to the ribs and thoracic vertebrae. The lower surface of each lung is covered by a membrane into which are inserted several muscles that arise from the ribs.

The main bronchus on each side enters the lung on its medial ventral surface and passes to the distal end. The portion within the lung proper

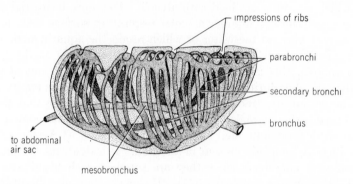

Fig. 6.22. Diagrammatic medial view of left lung of chicken, illustrating relations of bronchus, mesobronchus, secondary bronchi, and parabronchi. (*After Locy and Larsell.*)

is referred to as the *mesobronchus*. As it passes through the lung its cartilaginous rings disappear and a number of *secondary bronchi* arise from it. The secondary bronchi branch into numerous small tubes of rather uniform diameter called *parabronchi* which form loops connecting with other secondary bronchi (Fig. 6.22). Surrounding each parabronchus are large numbers of minute tubules, the *air capillaries*, which form anastomosing networks and loops with each other and which open into the parabronchi. The arrangement is not that of a branching system as in the lungs of mammals and some other vertebrates, but is, rather, a system of intercommunicating tubes within the lung itself. The actual respiratory surface consists of the very vascular lining of the air capillaries. The mesobronchus and several (usually four) secondary bronchi continue on through the walls of the lung and expand into large *air sacs* which ramify among the viscera. Branches even enter the cavities of several of the bones. Only in the primitive kiwi are the air sacs so poorly developed that they fail to enter the bones or to pass into the abdominal cavity. The air sacs do not furnish an increased respiratory surface since their walls are smooth and have a poor blood supply. Moreover, they are furnished with oxygenated blood. In addition to the one large tube which enters each air sac, there are several small tubes, called *recurrent bronchi*, which connect the sac with the adjacent portion of the lung.

During inhalation, at times when the bird is at rest, air is drawn from the outside through the trachea, bronchi, mesobronchi, and secondary bronchi, into the air sacs. This is accomplished by the action of intercostal muscles which raise and lower the ribs and sternum, thereby varying the volume of the body cavity in the thoracic region. Air, however, is not simply drawn *into* the lungs; it actually passes *through* them in a much larger volume than these small structures could possibly accommodate. Upon exhalation, it is believed, a large quantity of air in the air sacs, on its way to the outside, instead of returning directly to the mesobronchus, passes throught the recurrent bronchi to the lungs. The air is then forced, under pressure, into the intercommunicating system of parabronchi and air capillaries, the latter furnishing the surface where actual respiratory exchange takes place. The air continues its passage into one or another secondary bronchus and thence to the mesobronchus. From here it may possibly go back again to an air sac and be recirculated. Finally, however, it passes through the bronchus and trachea to the outside. Since there are no blind alveolar pockets in the lungs of the bird, and a constantly renewed supply of air passes over the respiratory surface, there is no stagnation of air as in the lungs of other vertebrates (residual air). During flight, movement of air in the air sacs is effected by pressure from surrounding viscera and by movements of the flight muscles and hollow wing bones which contain diverticula of the air sacs. At such times the skeleton must be kept rigid in order to brace the wings, and the ordinary method of inspiring and expiring air by the use of intercostal muscles must be abandoned temporarily. The more rapidly a bird flies, the more rapid is the circulation of air back and forth through the respiratory channels. The efficiency of this type of respiration should be obvious. The best fliers among birds are those having the most highly developed air sacs.

In addition to furnishing the lungs with oxygen, the air sacs may be of importance in reducing the specific gravity of the bird when in flight by reason of the warmer air which they contain. They may also play a significant role in temperature regulation by serving as an internal cooling device. The skin is of little help in this respect. Unlike that of mammals, it is practically devoid of glands and is covered with insulating feathers.

Mammals. In the development of mammalian lungs the original lung buds, which arise from the midventral wall of the pharynx, divide many times to form primary, secondary, tertiary, etc., bronchi. The smaller bronchi, in turn, give rise to *bronchioles* which are of several orders of magnitude. The terminal bronchioles usually divide into two or more *respiratory bronchioles* which then branch into several *alveolar ducts*. From these arise *alveolar sacs* and terminal *alveoli* (Fig. 6.23). The alveoli are supplied with a rich capillary meshwork; and since the alveolar walls are very thin, it is they which make up the true respiratory surface. The respiratory bronchioles derive their name from the fact that a few alveoli may be found projecting from their walls.

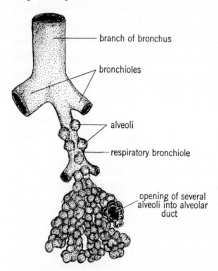

branch of bronchus

bronchioles

alveoli

respiratory bronchiole

opening of several alveoli into alveolar duct

The entire respiratory surface is of endodermal origin, since it is a derivative of the pharyngeal epithelium. The remainder of the lung is mesodermal and is composed of reticular and collagenous connective tissues together with a large number of elastic fibers. The epithelial lining of the greater part of the "respiratory tree" is of the ciliated columnar type, but the cilia end a short distance down the respiratory bronchioles. Here the epithelium changes to a low cuboidal type. There is some dispute about the actual nature of the epithelium lining the alveolar ducts, alveolar sacs, and alveoli. No cilia are present, and the lining cells are unusually thin. The cilia in the upper regions beat toward the trachea, serving to remove dust and other particles from the lungs.

FIG. 6.23.   Diagram showing terminal branching of a small bronchus in a typical mammalian lung.

Cartilaginous rings, similar in structure to those of the trachea, are present in the portion of the bronchus between trachea and lung. Within the lungs they become smaller and smaller, and in their place are found small, irregular plates of cartilage. When the bronchioles are no more than 1 mm. in diameter, the cartilaginous supports disappear altogether.

The entire outer surface of the lung down to the root, where bronchi and pulmonary vessels enter or leave, is covered with serous membrane, the *visceral pleura*. The lungs of mammals lie entirely within a pair of pleural cavities which are separated from each other as well as from the rest of the coelom.

In most mammals the lungs are subdivided externally into lobes, the number varying somewhat in different species. The lobulation depends to some extent on the manner in which the bronchi branch or divide during development. In some forms the lobes are completely separated from each other except for their connection by the bronchi and connective tissues. In others the separation is not so complete. The number of lobes on the right side generally exceeds that on the left. Thus in man there are three lobes on the right and two on the left. The cat has four on the right and three on the left. In cattle four or five lobes may be present on the right side but only three on the left. The left lung of the rat is not lobulated even though the right side has three large lobes and one small one.

In many mammals the most anterior lobe on the right side of the lung is called the *superior,* or *apical, lobe.* It is supplied by the *apical,* or *eparterial, bronchus* which is an anteriorly directed branch of the right bronchus. The name *eparterial* is applied because it lies upon, or is dorsal to, the right pulmonary artery. The lungs of some mammals show little, if any, indication of lobulation. Whales, sirenians, elephants, *Hyrax,* and many members of the order Perissodactyla have lungs of this type.

MECHANISM OF LUNG RESPIRATION

The exact mechanism by means of which air is taken in and forced out of the physostomous swim bladder of the lungfishes is not clear. In higher forms inhalation and exhalation are accomplished in various ways, some of which are fairly well understood.

Amphibians. The lungs of amphibians lie in that portion of the coelom referred to as the *pleuroperitoneal cavity.* A partition, the *septum transversum,* has developed posterior to the heart, cutting off a part of the coelom, the *pericardial cavity,* in which the heart lies, from the rest of the body cavity. The lungs of amphibians are located in the anterior lateral portions of the pleuroperitoneal cavity.

In several amphibians the lungs develop before metamorphosis when the larvae are still living in an aquatic environment. Such larvae frequently come to the surface and seem to snap for air. The air bubble thus obtained may be forced through the glottis and into the lungs by elevating the floor of the mouth. This method of obtaining air is sometimes employed by the adult *Necturus* in which the rather poorly developed lungs serve only as accessory respiratory organs. In such cases expiration is brought about by the pressure exerted by the elastic walls of the lungs when the glottis is opened. A means is thus provided for the escape of air which may or may not be depleted of its oxygen content.

When breathing air, both caudates and salientians keep their mouths tightly closed. Air is sucked into the mouth and forced out again through the nares by alternately lowering and raising the muscular floor of the mouth. Smooth-muscle fibers around the external nares of caudates help to control the respiratory current. Salientians, as has been alluded to previously, utilize the tuberculum prelinguale in moving the premaxillary bones and thus regulate the opening and closing of the nasal passages. This method of breathing is known as *buccopharyngeal respiration.* Some oxygen is absorbed by blood vessels in the lining of mouth and pharynx. Filling the lungs with air is accomplished in a somewhat different manner.

The throat muscles are lowered to a greater degree than in buccopharyngeal respiration, and the nostrils are then closed. The glottis is opened, and air from the lungs enters the mouth cavity, mixing with fresh air just obtained from the outside. Raising the floor of the mouth and keeping the nostrils closed forces the mixed air back through the glottis into the lungs. This process may be repeated one or more times. Sometimes when frogs are making strong respiratory movements, their eyes may be observed to sink down into the orbit for a moment. Since mouth and orbit are separated only by a thin layer composed of connective tissue and mucous membrane, retraction of the eyes aids in compressing the air in the mouth cavity and helps to force air into the lungs. After the lungs are filled, buccopharyngeal respiration may again be employed, and a fresh supply of air enters the mouth and pharynx. Repetition of these processes ensures a slow but adequate supply of oxygen to the lungs. The elasticity of the lungs themselves, possibly aided by pressure exerted upon them by contraction of the muscles of the body wall, is responsible for the escape of air from the lungs into the buccopharyngeal cavity. Even though many amphibians employ the above-described mechanisms in respiration, cutaneous respiration, in most forms, continues to be of utmost importance. It has been demonstrated that in the frog more carbon dioxide is released from the skin than from the lungs.

Reptiles. As in amphibians, the lungs of reptiles lie in that part of the coelom referred to as the pleuroperitoneal cavity; specifically in the anterolateral portions. In many reptiles, respiration is accomplished in the manner of amphibians in which throat movements and opening and closing of valves in the nostrils are utilized. However, the presence of ribs and rib muscles in reptiles aids these animals in carrying on respiration more effectively than is possible in the ribless amphibians. Raising the ribs and increasing the size of the pleuroperitoneal cavity reduces the pressure within the cavity. This, in turn, brings about an expansion of the lungs. Conversely, lowering the ribs results in an increased pressure upon the lungs, and expiration is the result. In certain reptiles, as in crocodilians, the pleuroperitoneal cavity is divided by coelomic folds into anterior and posterior portions. The lungs are shut off from the remainder of the coelom by these folds.

The presence in turtles of a hard, rigid shell, formed in part by fusion of the ribs with the dermal plates of the carapace, makes general expansion and contraction of the body cavity by the usual method impossible. Turtle respiration, therefore, presents some unusual physiological problems. It was formerly thought that these animals employed throat movements, similar to those of amphibians, in respiration. However, it has been demonstrated (F. H. McCutcheon, 1943, *Physiol. Zoöl.*, **16**:255) that this is not the case and that turtles utilize a unique method of breathing. Expiration is the result of contraction of paired muscular membranes which enclose the viscera. Inspiration is brought about by the contraction of other paired muscular membranes enclosing the flank cavities. This brings about an increase in volume of the pleuroperitoneal cavity. The glottis remains closed except when movements of expiration and inspiration are in progress. When the glottis is closed, pressure on the air within the lungs, brought about by various degrees of contraction of the paired muscular membranes, varies independently of the atmospheric pressure. Alteration in pressure brings about changes in the diffusion gradient across the lung epithelium and results in an exchange of gases from lung cavities to blood, or vice versa. The term *poikilobaric* has been proposed for air breathers of this type. *Homeobaric respiration* is the common type in which the respiratory organ is in continuous equilibrium with the atmosphere.

Birds. A membrane on each side, known as the *oblique septum* and sparsely supplied with muscle fibers, extends from the dorsal body wall to the septum transversum. This separates the lungs from the other viscera so that they are enclosed in separate *pleural cavities*. The remainder of the coelom is the *peritoneal*, or *abdominal*, *cavity*. The lungs are small and closely adherent to the thoracic vertebrae and ribs. *Costo-pulmonary muscles*, inserted in the membrane covering the lower surface of each lung, bring about expansion and contraction of these respiratory organs under normal conditions when the bird is not in flight. During flight, however, the body must be kept as rigid as possible so that the well-developed flight muscles are firmly anchored. At such times contraction and expansion of the air sacs, brought about by movements of viscera, muscles, and bones, cause air to circulate back and forth through the intercommunicating parabronchi and secondary bronchi. It has been shown under experimental conditions that if the trachea of a bird is occluded and an air sac, such as that in the humerus of the wing, is opened, the bird can continue to breathe without any difficulty. The fact that air may pass over the respiratory epithelium of the air capillaries several times in birds indicates that their lungs function more efficiently than those of most other forms.

Mammals. A muscular diaphragm, present only in mammals, separates the pleuroperitoneal cavity into two parts. That portion anterior to the diaphragm contains the lungs. Each lung is enclosed in a separate *pleural cavity* which is lined with serous membrane called the *pleura*. The part of the pleura lining the wall of the pleural cavity is referred to as the *parietal pleura*. The lung itself is invested by a layer of *visceral pleura* reflected over its surface (Fig. 6.24). Visceral and parietal pleurae are continuous with each other at the root of the lung where the bronchi enter. Pleurisy is a disease marked by inflammation of the pleura. Toward the median line the parietal pleurae of the two sides come close together so as to form a two-layered septum, the *mediastinum*, separating the two pleural cavities. The space between the two layers of the mediastinum is called the *mediastinal space*. It widens as it nears the diaphragm and contains the aorta, esophagus, and posterior vena cava. In the region of the heart the mediastinal membrane passes over the parietal layer of the pericardium. The pleural membrane is rich in capillaries and lymphatic vessels. Lymphatic fluid, present in the pleural cavities, enhances the movement of the lungs within the cavities. Under normal conditions there are practically no pleural cavities in existence, since the spaces are completely filled by the lungs except for the small amount of lymph which serves as a lubricant.

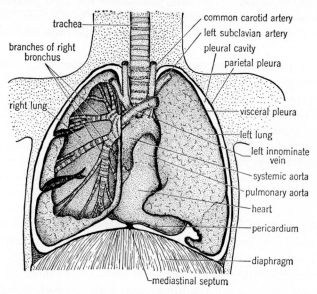

Fig. 6.24. Relations of lungs, pleural cavities, and heart in man, ventral view (semi-diagrammatic). The pleural cavities have been exaggerated for the sake of clarity, since in life the visceral and parietal pleurae are in apposition.

The pleural cavities are airtight. Increasing their size results in an expansion of the lungs, and air from the outside is drawn inside, passively. Reduction in the size of the pleural cavities forces air out of the lungs. The mechanism of respiration in mammals, therefore, consists of alternately increasing and decreasing the size of the pleural cavities. This is generally accomplished in two ways. Contraction of the muscles of the arched diaphragm flattens or lowers that structure. This increases the size of the pleural cavities, causing inspiration, and brings about an increased pressure on the abdominal viscera. Contraction of the abdominal muscles causes the abdominal viscera to push against the diaphragm, bringing about a reduction in size of the pleural cavities and a resulting expiration of air from the lungs. This method of breathing is known as abdominal respiration. The other method of expanding the pleural cavities is brought about by contraction of the external intercostal muscles. These pass from the lower border of one rib to the upper border of the rib below. Contraction brings about an elevation of the ribs. The method by which expiration is brought about in this type of breathing is not so well understood. In some mammals, such as the cat, contraction of the internal intercostal muscles reduces the size of the thoracic cavity. The elasticity of the expanded lung walls, together with the tension of the stretched body wall and ribs, undoubtedly accounts for the greater part of expiratory movement.

If the air enters the pleural cavity through a wound, or because of a rupture of the lung wall in certain diseased conditions, the lung on that side will collapse. Such a condition is known as a *pneumothorax*. As a therapeutic measure, collapse of the lung is induced artificially in certain pulmonary lesions (tuberculosis) in which the disease is confined mostly to one lung. The theory behind such treatment is to permit the lung to rest for a time by making it functionless. A pneumothorax is usually induced by injecting air into the pleural cavity. The air is gradually absorbed, and the procedure must be repeated at intervals. Although the two pleural cavities are completely separated by the mediastinum, that membrane is so pliant that a pneumothorax on one side affects the other side to some degree.

MISCELLANEOUS RESPIRATORY ORGANS

Although gills are the chief respiratory organs of aquatic vertebrates, and lungs serve terrestrial forms in a similar capacity, other structures are present in certain vertebrates which may be considered to belong to the category of respiratory organs.

Yolk sac. The blood vessels (vitelline arteries and veins) which supply the yolk sac, a structure present during embryonic stages of many vertebrates, not only function in absorbing yolk, which is used as food, but may serve in a respiratory capacity as well. In ovoviviparous sharks, for example, the blood vessels of the yolk sac (Fig. 5.1) lie in close apposition to highly vascular, villuslike projections of the lining of the uterus. Here the exchange of gases takes place between embryo and mother. In the bird embryo the yolk sac is the respiratory organ for the first few days of development or until another embryonic membranous sac, the allantois, pushes between yolk sac and porous shell and takes over the respiratory function. Even in the embryos of certain lower mammals (some marsupials) a *yolk-sac placenta* is present through which gaseous exchange occurs. The yolk sacs of most mammals, on the other hand, are but rudimentary vestiges.

Allantois. The allantoic sac, present in the embryonic stages of reptiles, birds, and mammals, is an important, if temporary, respiratory organ. The allantoic, or umbilical, blood vessels, with which it is furnished, are the ones through which oxygen is obtained and carbon dioxide eliminated during embryonic life. Even though the allantois is not well developed in many mammals, the allantoic circulation is of great importance in the exchange of gases in the placenta. The allantois is lost at birth.

Skin. In some fishes the skin, in addition to the gills, may function in respiration. For example, the walking goby, *Periophthalmus*, on the shore of the island of Celebes, has been observed to emerge from the water, its head and trunk completely exposed but its very vascular caudal fin remaining submerged and undoubtedly functioning as a breathing organ.

A highly vascular integument is very important in amphibian respiration. In some species of frogs, over 70 per cent of the carbon dioxide may leave the body through the skin. Only in forms in which the skin is kept moist can it be used in respiration, since the presence of a moist membrane is one of the requirements for respiratory exchange. In the lungless salamanders of the family Plethodontidae, which also lack gills in the adult stage, the integument is highly important in respiration. Buccopharyngeal breathing is also employed by these amphibians. In the "hairy" frog, *Astylosternus robustus*, the sides of the body and thighs are covered with many filamentous, cutaneous outgrowths which give the animal a hairy appearance. These furnish an additional respiratory surface. Barbels on the head of the African clawed toad, *Xenopus laevis*, are thought to be respiratory in function. Even the skin of man might in one sense be considered as a respiratory organ of a sort, since a small amount of carbon dioxide is eliminated in the sweat.

Rectum and cloaca. A highly vascular rectum serves some fishes as an accessory organ of respiration. Water is alternately taken in and squirted out of the rectal chamber. Some aquatic turtles have a pair of thin-walled saclike extensions of the cloaca which are sometimes referred to as accessory urinary bladders. These sacs, which are abundantly supplied with blood vessels, are frequently filled and emptied of water through the anus and, therefore, may act as important respiratory organs, particularly when in emergencies the animal may remain submerged for an undue length of time.

OTHER DERIVATIVES OF THE PHARYNX

A number of structures derived from the pharynx, but not associated in any way with respiration, may be conveniently discussed at this point.

Except for the thyroid gland, the structures derived from the pharynx arise as modifications of pharyngeal pouches. During development, small dorsal and ventral recesses appear at the outer ends of the pouches. Cellular proliferation about these recesses brings about the formation of small, budlike masses of endodermal origin which represent the primordia of certain glands confined to the neck region. The thymus, tonsils (palatine), parathyroids, and ultimobranchial bodies are derived from these primordia. The history of the various structures arising from different pharyngeal pouches varies somewhat in the different vertebrate classes, and there is much confusion, particularly in the lower forms, as to what the various structures in the neck region actually represent. They are often referred to collectively as *epithelial bodies.*

Thyroid gland. The thyroid gland in lower vertebrates arises as a midventral, endodermal diverticulum of the pharynx in the region between the second and fourth visceral pouches. In higher forms it usually develops between the first and second pouches. In some it is paired, but in others it is a single organ. In the human embryo it has been reported that small, paired primordia from the fourth pair of visceral pouches are added to the median thyroid diverticulum and that all three parts combine to form the thyroid gland. Since the thyroid is an endocrine organ, the reader is referred to Chap. 9, Endocrine System, for a more complete discussion.

Thymus gland. For many years the thymus was included in the category of endocrine glands. However, its activity as an endocrine organ is now considered very doubtful. Evidence indicates that it belongs to the lymphatic system rather than to the endocrine system. In lower vertebrates it is difficult to ascertain whether certain tissues, ordinarily referred to as thymus tissue, are actually homologues of the thymus gland as we recognize it in higher forms.

Comparative anatomy of the thymus. CYCLOSTOMES. In the lampreys all seven pairs of pharyngeal pouches are reported to be involved in the development of a number of separate elements which may possibly represent thymus tissue. Small primordia arise as buds from the dorsal angles of the pouches. These later become separated from the pharynx, come to lie dorsal to the gill region, and persist throughout life. The ventral portions of the pouches have also been reported to contribute to the thymus. If these structures actually represent thymus tissue, the lampreys exhibit the most generalized condition of all vertebrates in respect to thymus development, since all pharyngeal pouches contribute to its formation. Several lobulelike structures located posterior to the gill region in the hagfish are regarded by some authorities as thymus tissue. This is questioned by others.

FISHES. In fishes, in correlation with the reduced number of pharyngeal pouches, there is a reduction in the number of thymus primordia as compared with cyclostomes, and considerable variation is to be found within the superclass. Primordia arise from the dorsal angles of all the pharyngeal pouches except the first, and in a few species even the first pair of pouches is involved. In teleosts there is usually a fusion of the separate components on each side to form a single lobulated mass. It lies dorsal to the gill region beneath the dorsal musculature. In some forms (*Heptanchus*) connections with the pharyngeal epithelium are retained.

AMPHIBIANS. Except in caecilians in which all six pouches seem to be concerned in contributing to the thymus gland, amphibians exhibit a reduction in number of thymus primordia. In caudates the dorsal angles of pouches 1 to 5 are concerned with thymus formation but the portions from pouches 1 and 2 degenerate. In salientians the second pair of pouches alone furnishes permanent contributions. The thymus gland in caudates usually consists of a lobulated mass of tissue on each side of the neck region representing the fused elements of that side. In the adult frog the thymus lies behind the tympanic membrane and under the depressor mandibulae muscle. It is a compact structure, lymphoid in character, and is reported to be considerably smaller in the adult stage than during larval life.

REPTILES. In lizards the second and third pharyngeal pouches apparently give rise to thymus primordia from their dorsal angles, whereas in snakes thymus buds have been described as arising from pouches 4 and 5. The elements may form separate compact masses, but there is a tendency toward fusion into lobular strands of tissue. This is best shown in crocodilians.

BIRDS. Only pharyngeal pouches 3 and 4 are responsible for thymus development in birds. The dorsal primordia arising from these pouches fuse to form an elongated thymus body on each side of the throat.

MAMMALS. Mammals are exceptional in that the thymus arises from the *ventral* portions of the pharyngeal pouches rather than from the dorsal. Only pouches 3 and 4 are involved, but the fourth contributes little and the main mass of the thymus is therefore derived from the ventral angles of the third pair of pouches. When fully developed, the portions from the two sides, although not actually fused, are bound together with connective tissue so that the thymus appears to be a single structure. It is located along the ventral surface of the trachea and extends as far back as the base of the heart. The thymus has commercial value as food and is sold on the market under the name of neck, or throat, "sweetbreads."

It has been reported that in some mammals the part of the thymus lying in the cervical region is derived from skin ectoderm. Since it is sometimes difficult to distinguish the point of transition between ectoderm and endoderm on the borders of a pharyngeal pouch, variations such as this may only be apparent. It is therefore unnecessary to assume that differences in homology exist.

Histological structure. The histological structure of the thymus tissue in lower forms is but little known. In higher vertebrates it is divided by connective tissue into lobes which are further subdivided into numbers of lobules. Each lobule consists of a peripheral cortical area surrounding an inner, medullary portion. The cortex is made up of small cells which seem to be identical in structure with small lymphocytes. Some authorities challenge their identity and have called them *small thymocytes*. Elongated, *reticular cells* lie scattered among the smaller cells. The medulla, which is more vascular than the cortex, is made up of reticular cells which are similar to those of the cortex but are more conspicuous. The lymphocytes are less numerous in the medulla. Small rounded bodies called *Hassall's corpuscles*, which are characteristic of the thymus gland, are also found in the medulla. The cells are arranged in concentric circles. Hassall's corpuscles and the reticular cells are of epithelial origin. Their significance is not understood.

Function. The function of the thymus gland remains obscure despite the great deal of investigation that has been carried out to determine its role in the general body economy.

Perhaps the best-known fact concerning the thymus gland is that, although it is a comparatively large organ in the young animal or human being, it becomes relatively much smaller during adulthood. In man the cortical portions normally begin to involute at about four years of age, but the medullary regions do not begin to atrophy until the age of puberty. The gland reaches its greatest size between the eleventh and fifteenth years and then begins to decrease in size. Involution consists of a reduction in the number of reticular cells and lymphocytes and a replacement by adipose tissue. This is referred to as "age involution" and is a normal occurrence. Age involution of the thymus, more than any other factor, has given rise to the belief that it is an endocrine organ in some way associated with growth. The general concept has been in the past that the thymus stimulates growth and suppresses genital development and activity. Carefully controlled experiments indicate that removal of the thymus has no effect upon body growth nor does it affect the activity or size of the gonads. On the other hand, gonadectomy is known to delay involution of the thymus, especially in the male. Administration of sex hormones, either estrogenic or androgenic, by injection is known to hasten involution.

Experiments have been reported which claim that thymus extracts injected into parent rats bring about precocious development and growth of the young and that, if such injections are continued over several generations, there is a gradual acceleration in the time when certain physical manifestations first appear, *e.g.*, opening of eyes, eruption of teeth, appearance of fur, descent of the testes, etc. Efforts have been made to repeat these experiments, but they have not been successful.

Enlargement of the thymus has been thought to be responsible for a condition in infants and young children referred to as *status thymicolymphaticus*. The sudden death of affected children has been attributed to interference of the thymus with normal respiration. Investigations have thrown doubt upon this belief, and the very existence of such a condition as status thymicolymphaticus has been challenged.

At the present time it would seem that the thymus is a lymphoid organ, despite its epithelial origin, and that it possesses the ability to form lymphocytes and some other types of cells (plasma cells and myelocytes). Little else is known about the physiology of this structure, and the significance of age involution remains obscure.

Parathyroid glands. Definite parathyroid glands are lacking in cyclostomes and fishes. They first make their appearance in members of the class Amphibia. The parathyroids arise from the ventral angles of certain visceral pouches in amphibians, reptiles, and birds. In mammals, however, they come from the *dorsal* angles. These derivatives of the pharynx are endocrine glands related in function to the calcium and phosphorus metabolism of the body. Detailed discussion is reserved for Chap. 9, Endocrine System.

Tonsils. Lymphoid masses derived from the ends of the second pair of visceral pouches give rise to the *palatine tonsils* which are present only in mammals and are located on either side where mouth and pharynx join. The pouch itself on each side becomes very much reduced and forms the fossa and covering epithelium of the tonsil. *Lingual tonsils* are also present only in mammals. They consist of lymphoid masses which develop in relation to lingual glands. The lingual tonsils are situated at the base of the tongue. In reptiles and birds and occasionally in mammals, *pharyngeal tonsils* are present. These appear in the mucous membrane on the roof of the pharynx and come to lie behind the choanae. Certain lymphoid masses in the roof of the pharynx in amphibians may be homologous with pharyngeal tonsils. In man, enlargements of these structures are known as *adenoids*. Adenoid tissue may occlude the nasal passages, necessitating breathing through the mouth. If adenoids are not removed in the young, malformations of the face may result. Thus in mammals a partial ring of lymphoid tissue composed of palatine, lingual, and pharyngeal tonsils surrounds the opening into the pharynx.

Whether the tonsils have any function aside from being part of the lymphatic system is not known. The palatine tonsils are frequently the site of infection and often must be removed. Tonsillectomy is a relatively simple operation. However, since the ascending branch of the external carotid artery lies in close proximity to the tonsil, there is danger of severe and sometimes fatal hemorrhage.

Middle ear and Eustachian tube. The first, or hyomandibular, pharyngeal pouch in elasmobranchs and some other fishes forms the spiracle, which has already been discussed. In most fishes as well as in amphibians, reptiles, birds, and mammals, the first pouch fails to break through to the outside or becomes secondarily closed. In salientians, for the first time, the tissue between the pouch and the exterior forms the *tympanic membrane*, or eardrum. The pouch itself becomes somewhat enlarged at its outer end to form the *middle ear*. The narrowed portion connecting the middle ear to the pharynx is called the *Eustachian tube*. Middle ear and Eustachian tube function primarily as a pressure-regulating mechanism which keeps the pressure on the two sides of the tympanic membrane equal. Description of the middle ear and Eustachian tube is more properly included under a discussion of the ear (Chap. 14, pages 658 to 661). In caecilians, caudate amphibians, a few salientians, snakes, and certain other reptiles, middle ears and Eustachian tubes have degenerated and are lacking.

Other structures. Among the derivatives of the pharyngeal pouches are some small, glandular-appearing structures variously known as post-branchial or ultimobranchial bodies. They arise from, or close behind, the fifth pair of pharyngeal pouches and come to lie in the region of the thyroid gland. If they have any function, it is unknown. They are frequently confused with the parathyroid glands and may possibly represent accessory parathyroid tissue.

The so-called *carotid body*, closely associated with the carotid artery at the point where it bifurcates into internal and external branches, is conspicuous in frogs and toads and is also found in the higher vertebrates. It possesses a rich network of capillaries and contains chromaffin cells which stain brown with the salts of chromic acid (page 330). This suggests a relation to the sympathetic nervous system. The carotid body may or may not play a role in controlling circulation in the carotid vessels. Its function may be that of other chromaffin tissues in general (page 337). In amphibians the carotid bodies arise near the ventral portions of the second pair of pharyngeal pouches, whereas in lizards they appear in the vicinity of the third pair. Their origin in birds and mammals is questionable. It is somewhat doubtful whether the carotid bodies actually contain any epithelial cellular elements. If not, the pharyngeal epithelium may not in any way be concerned with their formation. Confusion in regard to the carotid body has arisen from the fact that various investigators appear to have assigned the name *carotid body* to different structures in the neck region which vary from species to species.

SUMMARY

1. The organs of respiration in vertebrates are formed in connection with that part of the digestive tract known as the pharynx. With few exceptions they are covered or lined with epithelia derived from endoderm.

2. In all chordate embryos a series of visceral pouches develops on either side of the pharynx. The number of visceral pouches is greatest in the lowest groups of vertebrates and least in the higher classes. The pouches push through the mesenchyme to fuse with the outer ectoderm, forming thin, platelike areas. In fishes and larval amphibians perforations occur, forming gill slits which connect the pharynx to the outside. The pouches are then called gill clefts. They are separated from each other by visceral arches composed of skeletal material.

Internal gills, supported by visceral arches, are vascular, lamellar, or even filamentous extensions of the epithelial surface of the gill pouches. External gills, generally covered with ectoderm, may project from the outer surfaces of the visceral arches as filamentous outgrowths.

3. In lampreys and elasmobranch fishes each gill cleft opens separately

to the outside.   In higher fishes an operculum, which is an extension of the hyoid arch, covers the gill chamber.   Although most fishes possess internal gills, some have external gills in addition, at least during larval life.

4. Only external gills occur in amphibians.   With few exceptions they disappear upon metamorphosis and the gill slits close over.   In reptiles, birds, and mammals the pharyngeal pouches usually fail to break through to the outside and gills are lacking.

5. In salientians, most reptiles, birds, and mammals, the first gill pouch gives rise to the Eustachian tube and middle ear.   The original lining of the remaining pouches gives rise to such structures as tonsils, parathyroid and thymus glands, and ultimobranchial bodies.   The thyroid gland arises as a midventral outgrowth of the pharynx.

6. Lungs develop as a bilobed diverticulum from the floor of the pharynx posterior to the last gill pouch.   In higher forms the connection between lungs and pharynx lengthens and is called the trachea.   Lungs show unmistakable homologies to the swim bladders of fishes, which in certain cases are used as lungs but in others have become specialized as hydrostatic organs.   Many modifications of the swim bladder occur.

7. The upper part of the trachea becomes modified as a larynx, or voice box, the walls of which are supported by skeletal elements derived from the visceral arches.   In birds, a syrinx which develops at the lower end of the trachea is the organ of sound production.

8. The lungs of lower forms are rather simple, vascular sacs, but in higher vertebrates the walls become subdivided into numerous pocketlike air spaces.   The divisions become more and more complex as the vertebrate scale is ascended and reach the highest degree of branching in mammals. The lungs of birds are complicated in that they give rise to air sacs which penetrate among the viscera and even enter the hollow bones.   Similar structures in certain lizards foreshadow their appearance in birds.   The thin-walled, moist, highly vascular lining of the lungs forms an ideal respiratory surface.

9. Various methods are employed by vertebrates in inflating and deflating the lungs.   The most complex condition is encountered in mammals, in which the lungs lie in separate pleural cavities partitioned from the abdominal cavity by a muscular diaphragm.

10. Nasal passages develop in connection with the olfactory apparatus. Blind nasal pits are found in most fishes, but in the Choanichthyes they form connections between the oral cavity and the outside.   This condition is retained in amphibians which, for the first time, employ the nasal passages for intake and outgo of air.   In reptiles a secondary palate begins to form, partially separating the nasal and mouth cavities.   In crocodilians and mammals the secondary palate becomes complete so that the two passageways are in communication only in the region of the pharynx.   In these forms the internal nasal openings are located relatively far back and are situated near the opening of the trachea.

CHAPTER 7

EXCRETORY SYSTEM

The word *metabolism* is used to designate the different chemical changes that take place in the tissues of the body upon which heat production, muscular energy, growth, and maintenance of vital life processes depend. The part played by the end products of digestion, after they have passed into the circulatory system, in building up protoplasm and in providing materials to be used in essential body processes is but one phase of metabolism. The term *anabolism* is used to designate this positive, or building-up, phase. *Catabolism* is the expression which is used to signify the reactions involved in the breaking down of chemical substances in the body to simpler compounds by oxidation, with the release of energy in its various forms.

Some of the products of metabolism cannot be used as a source of energy. They are called the end products of metabolism, or *wastes*. Since they are of no further use to the body, they must be eliminated. Among the waste products of metabolism are carbon dioxide, urea, ammonia, uric acid, creatinine, various pigments, and inorganic salts. Carbon dioxide is eliminated, for the most part, through the gills in aquatic forms, through the skin and lungs in amphibians, and through the lungs in terrestrial vertebrates. The remaining substances are excreted almost entirely through what are called the *excretory*, or *urinary*, *organs*. It has been demonstrated, however, that in certain fishes nitrogenous and other wastes may be excreted in considerable quantity by way of the gills. In man, small amounts may be eliminated through the sweat glands of the skin. It should be recalled at this point that although feces may contain substances excreted through the bile or by the cells of the intestine, the greater bulk of it is not true excreta but is indigestible material which has never entered the body proper.

Most excretory substances are in solution in water. Water itself is not considered to be a waste product, but any excess is eliminated along with substances dissolved in it. The final product is known as *urine*. The organs which eliminate the urine are called *kidneys*.

Although the excretory system, particularly in the male, is usually closely associated with the reproductive system, nevertheless as far as possible the two systems will be discussed separately. Frequently the excretory and reproductive systems are grouped together and spoken of as the *urogenital*, or *urinogenital*, *system*. All parts of the excretory system in vertebrates, except for a few structures near the terminal duct openings, are mesodermal structures derived from the embryonic mesomere.

239

TYPES OF KIDNEYS

In some of the invertebrates, excretory organs called *nephridia*, or *nephridial tubules*, are present. These are frequently segmentally arranged, with a pair in each segment. Each tubule is an independent structure connecting with the coelom by means of a small pore, or *nephrostome*. There is little or no evidence that the nephridial tubules of invertebrates have any relationship to the kidney tubules of vertebrates, and no evolutionary trends are indicated.

external pore

solenocytes

excretory canal

Fig. 7.1. One of the numerous excretory tubules of amphioxus. (*After Goodrich.*)

Even the excretory tubules of amphioxus (Fig. 7.1) are of an entirely different type from those of vertebrates and seem to be more closely related to invertebrate structures. In amphioxus there is a series of excretory tubules opening into the atrium, or peribranchial space. Each lies on the outer dorsal side of a secondary gill bar. These are apparently of ectodermal origin, have no connection with the coelom, and are composed of numerous flame cells called *solenocytes* which collect wastes. The solenocytes are attached to the walls of blood vessels and are also bathed by coelomic fluid. Those belonging to a given tubule enter a common excretory canal, which in turn opens into the atrium through a small excretory pore (nephridiopore).

It is rather difficult to work out homologies among the many and varied types of excretory organs found among vertebrates. The variations that are encountered are, in all probability, correlated with problems with which vertebrates have had to cope in adapting themselves to the different environmental conditions under which they have lived. Whether animals remained aquatic or took to terrestrial existence posed important problems in connection with excretion. Whether aquatic forms lived in fresh water or salt water made a great difference in their adapting themselves to changes in osmotic pressures, variations in salt concentration, and the like. Comparative anatomists have long speculated concerning the evolution of the various types of vertebrate kidneys. Gradually a fairly logical sequence of events has been postulated. There has been, and still is, much confusion in this field, particularly in regard to terminology. Investigators who have studied kidney development in embryos of birds and mammals in the past have attempted to homologize these structures with the excretory organs of lower forms. It now appears that many of these speculations were erroneous. The student, therefore, should be wary in accepting certain interpretations of homologies that appear in the older literature on the subject. Often the ideas advanced have been correct, yet the terminology used has confused the issue.

Archinephros

The belief is now generally held that the primitive vertebrate ancestor possessed an excretory organ which is referred to as an *archinephros*, or *holonephros* (Fig. 7.2). This is supposed to have consisted of a pair of ducts located on the dorsal side of the body cavity and extending the length of the coelom. Each duct was joined by a series of segmentally arranged tubules, one pair of tubules to a segment. At its other end the tubule opened into the coelom by a ciliated, funnel-shaped, peritoneal aperture called the *nephrostome*. Also formed in connection with each tubule was a *renal (Malpighian) corpuscle* (Fig. 7.3), a double-walled, cup-shaped structure called *Bowman's capsule*, enclosing a small knot of arterial blood vessels referred to as an *internal glomerulus*. From this type of kidney, with

FIG. 7.2. Diagram showing hypothetical structure of archinephros.

its *archinephric duct*, the various kidneys of present-day forms may have been originally derived. It is interesting to note that the larval form of

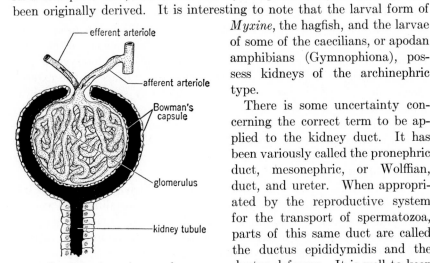

FIG. 7.3. A renal corpuscle.

Myxine, the hagfish, and the larvae of some of the caecilians, or apodan amphibians (Gymnophiona), possess kidneys of the archinephric type.

There is some uncertainty concerning the correct term to be applied to the kidney duct. It has been variously called the pronephric duct, mesonephric, or Wolffian, duct, and ureter. When appropriated by the reproductive system for the transport of spermatozoa, parts of this same duct are called the ductus epididymidis and the ductus deferens. It is well to keep these terms in mind since different authors use them all rather freely and students of anatomy and embryology may become rather confused by the variations in nomenclature. The term *ureter*, as applied to this duct, should be avoided, however, as it is most properly applied only to the kidney duct of the metanephros in reptiles, birds, and mammals (*amniota*). We shall use the term *archinephric duct* here in referring to the primitive kidney duct as it appears in cyclostomes, fishes, and amphibians (*anamniota*).

The Anamniote Kidney

The anterior portion of the archinephric kidney does not persist in many adult vertebrates. Even in the adult hagfish it is a modified structure. Nevertheless, it appears in the embryos of most vertebrates as a transitory structure to which the name *pronephros* has been applied. It usually degenerates soon after it is formed. In those vertebrates in which the pronephros persists in the adult stage it is called the *head kidney*. The remainder of the kidney posterior to the pronephric region is known as the *opisthonephros*.

Pronephros. The pronephros in anamniotes actually consists of a varying number of anteriorly located pronephric tubules, together with a pair of archinephric ducts. The tubules and ducts lie in the dorsolateral mesoderm on either side of the mesentery that supports the gut. The ducts extend posteriorly and usually open into the cloaca. One end of each of the segmentally arranged tubules connects with the archinephric duct near its anterior end; in fact the duct is actually formed by successive tubules bending posteriorly and fusing with adjacent tubules. The other end of the tubule opens into the coelom by means of a nephrostome. The nephrostome and the part of the tubule near the nephrostome are ciliated. In a few forms, rounded masses of arterial vessels of capillary dimensions called *external glomeruli* (Fig. 7.4), coming from segmental branches of the dorsal aorta, project into the coelom near the nephrostomes. A thin layer of peritoneal epithelium is reflected over the projecting surface of the external glomerulus. *Internal glomeruli*, almost completely surrounded by Bowman's capsules of the type previously described, are usually associated with pronephric tubules, however (Fig. 7.5). The blood in the glomerulus is returned to the heart via the postcardinal veins. Whether the glomeruli are of the external or internal type is of no particular significance in their relation to the pronephros.

From the glomerulus a protein-free filtrate of blood plasma passes into the coelom or into the cavity of Bowman's capsule, depending upon whether the glomerulus is of the external or internal type. Cilia sweep this fluid into the tubule by way of the nephrostome or down the tubule from the capsule. Certain cells in the wall of the tubule probably excrete wastes into the lumen where they are added to those in the fluid filtered from the glomerulus. A selective reabsorption of water and other constituents occurs as the fluid passes along the tubule so that a much smaller amount of fluid with a higher concentration of wastes in solution finally enters the archinephric duct.

Sometimes several glomeruli unite to form a larger *glomus*. In some cases pronephric tubules expand so as to form *pronephric chambers*, or else several tubules may fuse to form one large chamber.

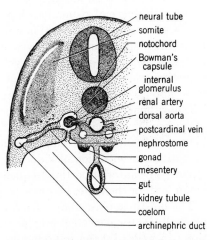

Fig. 7.4. Diagrammatic section through part of a vertebrate embryo, showing relation of external glomerulus to pronephric tubule and nephrostome.

FIG. 7.5. Diagrammatic section through part of vertebrate embryo, showing relation of internal glomerulus to kidney tubule and archinephric duct.

The importance of the pronephros consists chiefly in the part it plays in forming the archinephric duct, which persists even though the pronephros disappears. In some larval forms the pronephros itself is important, for it functions in getting rid of wastes at a time when the opisthonephros is in the process of formation.

In members of the class Chondrichthyes the pronephros degenerates soon after it is formed and no vestiges remain. In many fishes and larval amphibians, however, it becomes modified and functions for a time as a true excretory organ. It is only in the hagfish and certain teleost fishes, such as *Zoarces, Fierasfer,* and *Lepadogaster,* that the head kidney with its coelomic connections persists in adult life. In myxinoids, the pronephros and opisthonephros become completely separated by degeneration of the portion between them. The nephrostomes of the pronephros connect with the pericardial cavity, and the fluid drained by the tubules passes into a nearby vein instead of entering a duct.

Opisthonephros.   Since the pronephros in most cases is but a transient structure, the opisthonephros is actually the more important part.   It serves as the adult kidney in lampreys, most fishes, and amphibians.

In many accounts the term *mesonephros* is used in describing what we are here calling the opisthonephros.   Zoologists have come to realize that the opisthonephros of cyclostomes, fishes, and amphibians is not quite comparable to the mesonephros of embryonic amniotes even though the two are structurally similar in many ways.   We shall therefore in the following account use the term mesonephros only in referring to the structure which appears during embryonic development in reptiles, birds, and mammals.

The reason for the distinction lies in the fact that the three types of kidneys which appear in the embryos of amniotes—pronephros, mesonephros, and metanephros—represent developments from different levels of the primitive archinephros which appear in succession in an anterior-posterior direction.   The transition from one to the next is almost imperceptible. The opisthonephros of cyclostomes, fishes, and amphibians actually extends over a region which in amniotes will form the mesonephric and metanephric kidneys.   In forms possessing an opisthonephros there is a general tendency toward a concentration of kidney tubules toward the posterior end of the organ.   The anterior portion frequently loses its significance as an excretory organ and, in the male, becomes part of the reproductive system.

The opisthonephros differs from the pronephros in several respects.   As we shall see, the persistent archinephric duct may be taken over almost entirely in males by the reproductive system, in which case additional, or accessory, urinary ducts are formed to carry away waste materials.   The chief difference between the pronephros and opisthonephros lies in the fact that the segmental arrangement of the kidney tubules no longer exists and *many* tubules may lie within the confines of a single segment, this being particularly evident in the posterior portion of the opisthonephros.   Furthermore, the connection of the kidney tubules with the coelom is lost in most cases, renal corpuscles with internal glomeruli being typical.

The kidney tubules, of which the bulk of the opisthonephros is composed, develop from the intermediate cell mass (mesomere, nephrotome, intermediate mesoderm) which lies between the somite and the lateral plate mesoderm of the embryo or larva (Fig. 3.10).   The archinephric duct, formed during development of the pronephros, is already present in this region.   In some forms the anterior tubules of the opisthonephros appear in the same segments as the posterior pronephric tubules, so that there is some degree of overlapping.

At first the opisthonephric tubules are solid structures, but they soon develop lumina and begin to grow.   One end of each tubule extends out to establish a connection with the archinephric duct.   The tubule grows and becomes S-shaped.   Its other end enlarges.   This is soon invaginated by a tuft of tortuous blood vessels formed by a small, segmental, renal artery coming from the dorsal aorta. The end of the tubule thus becomes a double-walled Bowman's capsule with its contained internal glomerulus, the two together forming a renal (Malpighian) corpuscle. The tubules themselves vary somewhat in structure in different forms. Generally speaking, however, each tubule differentiates into a narrow neck at the end near the renal corpuscle, followed in turn by secretory and collecting portions. The collecting portion connects with the archinephric duct. The secretory part of the tubule forms two loops named the *proximal* and *distal convoluted tubules* in relation to their proximity to the renal corpuscle (Fig. 7.6).

FIG. 7.6. An amphibian kidney tubule of opisthonephros, showing renal corpuscle and secretory and collecting portions.

At first the opisthonephric tubules have a metameric arrangement, but secondary, tertiary, etc., tubules soon arise so that the segmental character of the opisthonephros becomes obscured. Each tubule has its own renal corpuscle, but the collecting ends of several tubules may unite to form a ureterlike duct which either opens into the archinephric duct or establishes an independent opening into the cloaca. In some forms several such urinary ducts may be present.

A glomerulus is really a tuft of tortuous small vessels of capillary dimensions in the form of loops which intervene within the course of an arteriole. Such an arrangement is sometimes referred to as a *rete mirabile*. Anastomoses between loops seldom occur. The small vessels finally converge and leave the glomerulus through an efferent arteriole. As this small vessel leaves the glomerulus, it is distributed along the proximal part of the kidney tubule where it breaks up into true capillaries. The vessels that collect the blood enter the postcardinal veins, which also receive blood from the renal portal system supplying the greater part of the kidney tubules proper.

There is not complete agreement as to the method of functioning of the kidney tubules, mostly because of technical difficulties involved in such studies. Portions of the tubule may be ciliated. In the frog, for example, long cilia project into the lumen from the cells of the neck. Shorter cilia are present for a slight distance in the part of the tubule just beyond the neck. The beat of the cilia is directed toward the proximal convoluted tubule. Experiments on amphibians indicate that at the glomerulus a protein-free filtrate of blood plasma is eliminated, probably because of pressure differences. A higher pressure (both blood and osmotic) exists in the glomerular vessels than on the other side of the membrane of Bowman's capsule which closely invests the glomerulus. The efferent vessel leaving the glomerulus is of smaller caliber than the afferent vessel. This discrepancy in size is of importance in building up pressure within the glomerulus. The cells of the secretory portion of the tubule secrete some urinary wastes into the lumen of the tubule. The secretory tubule, particularly in its distal portion, is known to reabsorb water, chlorides, bicarbonates, and reducing substances from the contents of its lumen. The rate of reabsorption of each of these substances differs. Thus the fluid (urine) which reaches the collecting tubule is in a more concentrated form. It then passes into the archinephric duct or to an accessory ureterlike duct which leads to the cloaca. According to this concept, then, glomerular filtration, secretion by certain cells of the tubule, and selective reabsorption by the secretory tubules are the important factors in kidney function.

Only internal glomeruli are present in the opisthonephros. Peritoneal funnels connect the tubules with the coelom in certain forms, but this is unusual. In most species such connections are lost, and the coelom is no longer continuous with the outside through the excretory system.

Comparative anatomy of the opisthonephros. cyclostomes. In the embryo hagfish the kidney is of the archinephric, or holonephric, type. In the adult, however, as has been pointed out, the anterior end has become modified to form a persistent pronephros, or head kidney. The remainder of the kidney, which is separated from the pronephros, becomes an opisthonephros which, in this species, differs but little in structure from the original archinephros except that the posterior tubules lose their peritoneal connections.

The opisthonephros of the lamprey consists on each side of a long, strap-shaped body without any peritoneal connections in the adult. The kidneys lie on either side of the middorsal line from which they are suspended by mesenterylike membranes. The archinephric duct runs along the free edge of the kidney (Fig. 15.6). In *Petromyzon* a vestige of the part of the archinephric duct, which was associated with the degenerated pronephros, extends forward from the opisthonephros (Fig. 15.4). The ducts from the two sides unite posteriorly to open into a *urogenital sinus* which leads to the outside through an aperture at the tip of a small *urogenital papilla*. Two slitlike openings, the *genital pores*, connect the urogenital sinus with the coelom (Fig. 7.7). Reproductive cells (eggs or spermatozoa) escape from the body cavity through the genital pores and leave through the urogenital aperture. It is only here that the reproductive and excretory systems of the lamprey are associated. The condition is similar in both sexes.

fishes. The opisthonephric kidneys of fishes show great variation in shape but are fundamentally similar in structure. They are dorsal in position in all species. In some fishes, as in elasmobranchs, they are long, narrow, strap-shaped bodies, lying against the dorsal body wall above the parietal peritoneum, on either side of the median line. The dorsal aorta and postcardinal veins lie between them. The kidneys extend almost the entire length of the body cavity. In other fishes they may be more voluminous, the two sides showing various degrees of fusion. In still others they are short and confined to the posterior part of the body cavity. Peritoneal funnels are retained in only a few forms, notably *Amia*, sturgeons, and certain elasmobranchs, such as *Squalus acanthias*. In the latter they lose their connections with the kidney tubules and end blindly. In certain marine teleosts no external or internal glomeruli are present, and their kidneys therefore are said to be of the *aglomerular type*.

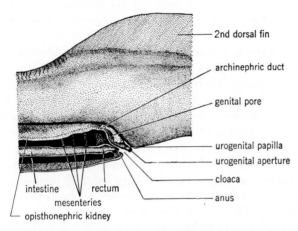

Fig. 7.7.   Position and arrangement of left genital pore of lamprey. It is through the genital pores that the reproductive elements leave the coelom to enter the urogenital sinus.

Generally speaking, the opisthonephric kidneys of male fishes are longer than those of females, the anterior ends in males having been appropriated by the reproductive system. In the males of some groups small modified kidney tubules, now called *efferent ductules*, connect the testes with the archinephric duct. The archinephric duct then becomes the *ductus deferens*, serving primarily for sperm transport. It may, in addition, continue to carry wastes. However, there is a marked tendency in such cases for the posterior portion of the opisthonephros to assume the greater part of the excretory function, with separate ureterlike ducts developing to carry wastes directly to the cloaca or to the outside. Usually the connection of the testis and archinephric duct occurs at the anterior end of the opisthonephros (selachians, chondrosteans, and some others). In *Polypterus* the connection is confined to the posterior portion (Fig. 8.27). In teleost fishes there is no connection between the testes and the opisthonephric kidneys, and the ducts from the testes may either join the archinephric ducts near their posterior ends or open independently to the exterior. Accessory ureterlike ducts may be present in some species in addition to the archinephric ducts. The term *ductus deferens* is properly used only in reference to an archinephric duct when it is used for sperm transport. Thus in teleosts and some other fishes, the sperm duct which transports spermatozoa to the outside, and which has no connection with the archinephros or archinephric duct (having an entirely different origin), should not be called a ductus deferens.

In female fishes the posterior ends of the archinephric ducts may enter a common cavity, the *urinary sinus,* inside a small *urinary papilla.* In Dipnoi and elasmobranchs this enters the cloaca, but in most other fishes it opens directly to the outside, a cloaca being absent. A similar union occurs in male elasmobranchs, but because of the association of excretory and reproductive systems in that sex, the terms *urogenital sinus* and *urogenital papilla* are used.

Dilatations of the archinephric ducts may form bladderlike enlargements for the temporary storage of urine, or, in forms in which the archinephric duct becomes a ductus deferens, seminal vesicles and sperm sacs may develop and serve for the temporary storage of spermatozoa. The anterior part of the archinephric duct sometimes becomes highly convoluted, in which case it is called the *ductus epididymidis,* or simply the *epididymis.*

AMPHIBIANS. The primitive archinephric type of kidney, found in the larval stage of the hagfish, also occurs in larval caecilians in which there is a distinct metameric arrangement of kidney tubules, renal corpuscles, and nephrostomes. In an adult, the opisthonephros extends the greater part of the length of the coelom and is lobulated.

Although a small head kidney with peritoneal connections is present in many larval amphibians, it does not persist in the adult stage. It is of interest, though, that in adult frogs ciliated nephrostomes are found on the ventral surfaces of the kidneys. These are no longer connected with kidney tubules but have become secondarily associated with the renal veins. Coelomic fluid may enter the circulatory system directly by this means. In *Necturus,* however, peritoneal connections with some of the kidney tubules persist throughout life.

Caudate amphibians have opisthonephric kidneys much like those of elasmobranchs. They consist of two regions: an anterior narrow portion, which in males is concerned more with genital than urinary functions, and a posterior expanded region which makes up the main part or body of the opisthonephros. The archinephric duct courses along the lateral edge of the kidney a short distance from the kidney proper. Numerous collecting ducts or tubules leave the opisthonephros at intervals to join the archinephric duct. These are considerably shorter in females than in males (Figs. 7.8 and 7.9). In males, the collecting tubules, particularly those from the posterior portion, are much larger, longer, and more prominent than in females. They run a parallel course around the ventrolateral part of the kidney, converging before joining the archinephric duct proper at a point quite close to its entry into the cloaca. Although renal corpuscles are present in both portions of the opisthonephros, they are far more numerous in the posterior portion. The archinephric duct in the male serves as a ductus deferens in addition to transporting wastes, but in the female it has only the latter function. The archinephric ducts in both sexes open into the cloaca on either side through a small papilla.

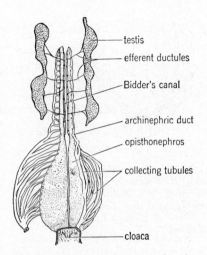

Fig. 7.8. Urogenital organs of female salamander, ventral view. The ovary on the left side and the oviduct on the right side have been removed for the sake of clarity.

Fig. 7.9. Urogenital organs of male salamander, ventral view. The collecting ducts on the right side are shown detached from the cloaca and spread out for the sake of clarity.

The opisthonephric kidneys of salientians show a more posterior concentration of tubules and are confined to the posterior part of the abdominal cavity. They are dorsally located, retroperitoneal, and flattened in a dorsoventral direction. There is no clear-cut distinction between anterior and posterior ends as in caudates. An adrenal gland of a yellowish-orange color is located on the ventral side of the kidney to which it is closely attached (Fig. 7.10). The kidneys of female frogs and toads show no relation to the reproductive system, but in males an intimate connection exists. Certain anterior kidney tubules become modified as efferent ductules connecting the testis with the kidney and archinephric duct which serves, therefore, as a ductus deferens in addition to transporting urinary wastes. The archinephric duct, contrary to the condition in caudates, is located *within* the kidney along its lateral margin. It leaves the opisthonephros near its posterior end and passes to the cloaca.

A thin-walled urinary bladder arises as a diverticulum from the ventral wall of the amphibian cloaca a short distance beyond the openings of the archinephric ducts. It is bilobed. There is no direct connection of the ducts with the bladder, so that the thin, watery urine first passes directly

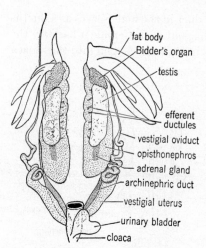

fat body
Bidder's organ
testis
efferent ductules
vestigial oviduct
opisthonephros
adrenal gland
archinephric duct
vestigial uterus
urinary bladder
cloaca

Fig. 7.10. Urogenital organs of male toad, *Bufo americanus*, ventral view. (*Modified from Witschi in Allen, "Sex and Internal Secretions," 2d ed., The Williams & Wilkins Company. By permission.*)

to the cloaca. Since the terminal cloacal opening is constricted most of the time, fluid is forced into the bladder, which may become distended to a considerable degree. The animal expels urine intermittently by opening the cloacal orifice and contracting the muscular wall of the bladder. It is possible that there may be some resorption of water through the bladder wall into the blood stream. As stated previously, the amphibian bladder originates from the cloaca. It is extremely difficult to discern, in this region, the exact point of transition between the endoderm lining the cloaca and the ectoderm lining the proctodaeum. There is some difference of opinion, therefore, regarding the germ layer from which the urinary bladder of amphibians is derived. Most authorities are of the opinion, however, that it is of endodermal origin and homologous with the urinary bladders of higher forms.

The Amniote Kidney

In reptiles, birds, and mammals, three types of kidneys are usually recognized: pronephros, mesonephros, and metanephros. These appear in succession during embryonic development, but only one, the metanephros, persists to become the functional adult kidney. Mesonephros and metanephros actually represent different levels of the opisthonephros of the anamniota, the metanephros being the equivalent of the posterior portion. In all forms, an anteriorly located pronephros is present during very early stages of development, but it soon degenerates and the more posterior mesonephros then develops. The duct of the pronephros, however, persists to become the duct of the mesonephros. This is actually the same as the archinephric duct, to which considerable reference has been made. Since most accounts refer to this duct as the *mesonephric*, or *Wolffian*, *duct* and to avoid further confusion on the part of the student, we shall use the term Wolffian duct here in referring to the archinephric duct as it appears in amniotes.

The mesonephros persists for a time and then degenerates. In the meantime the metanephros has begun to develop from the region posterior to the mesonephros. Portions of the mesonephros may persist to contribute to the reproductive system in the male or to remain as mere vestigial structures without any apparent function.

Pronephros. The pronephric kidney in amniotes forms in a manner similar to that of anamniotes. Segmentally arranged pronephric tubules appear in the intermediate cell mass in some of the anterior segments of the body. These are at first solid structures, but they soon hollow out, one end establishing a connection with the coelom. The tubules appear in succession in an anterior-posterior direction. The distal end of each tubule bends backward and fuses with the adjacent tubule. A variable number of such tubules forms in different species. In the chick, for example, 10 or 11 pronephric tubules form on each side from the fifth to the fifteenth or sixteenth segments. The last tubule grows posteriorly and establishes a connection with the cloaca. Thus, a long pronephric duct is formed, the anterior end of which is connected to a series of tubules with coelomic connections. The tubules soon disappear; in fact the anterior tubules may degenerate before the posterior ones even form. External glomeruli may or may not form. If they do, the sequence of their appearance may not even coincide with the time when the tubules are forming. Thus the amniote pronephros is little more than a transient structure which undoubtedly has no value at all as an excretory organ. To the comparative anatomist it is of interest because its presence indicates that the amniote kidney, like that of the anamniotes, has evolved from the ancestral archinephric, or holonephric, type. When the duct of the pronephros becomes the duct of the mesonephros the name Wolffian duct is applied to it.

Mesonephros. The mesonephros is sometimes called the *Wolffian body.* It extends over a greater number of segments than does the pronephros and develops after the pronephros has formed. Mesonephric tubules appear in the intermediate cell mass in the region where the pronephric duct is located, but posterior to the pronephric tubules. In some forms the anterior mesonephric tubules appear in the same segments as the posterior pronephric tubules, so that there is a slight degree of overlapping. The mesonephric tubules differentiate in the same manner as the opisthonephric tubules described earlier (page 244). Some of the anterior tubules may form peritoneal connections, but this is unusual. Contrary to the condition in the pronephros, several tubules may form in a single segment. In the human embryo from 2 to 9 mesonephric tubules may develop in one segment, making a total of between 30 and 40 for each mesonephros. In other forms the number may be even greater. As a result, the mesonephric kidneys, at least in some forms, become rather voluminous structures (Fig. 7.11) occupying an extensive portion of the body cavity.

In reptiles, birds, and mammals the mesonephros exists only temporarily and is followed in development by the metanephros, which becomes the functional adult kidney. In the embryonic stages of the mouse and guinea pig, the mesonephros is so poorly developed and appears so early that it can scarcely be regarded as functional at any time. Certain embryonic membranes in these animals may possibly help to rid the body of excretory products in the interval before the metanephros develops. On the other hand, in reptiles and in such mammals as *Echidna* and certain marsupials, the mesonephros may persist for a time after birth. Well-developed peritoneal funnels, associated with the mesonephros, have been described for the monotremes.

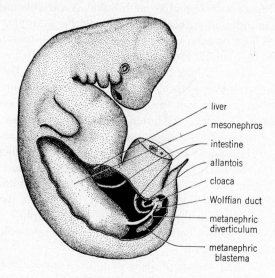

liver
mesonephros
intestine
allantois
cloaca
Wolffian duct
metanephric diverticulum
metanephric blastema

Fig. 7.11.   Pig embryo of about 10 mm. dissected to show position and relative size of mesonephros.

As long as the mesonephros functions, the Wolffian duct is the urinary passage; but as soon as the metanephros becomes functional this duct degenerates in the female although it persists in the male. The remnants of the mesonephros, which are left after the main part has degenerated, include portions which become associated with the reproductive system. The male structures derived from mesonephric components include the *epididymis, ductus deferens, seminal vesicles, paradidymis*, and *ductus aberrans*. In the female such rudimentary structures as the *paraoöphoron, epoöphoron*, and *canal of Gärtner* represent remains of the mesonephros (page 289).

Metanephros.   The metanephric kidney, found only in amniotes, arises posterior to the mesonephros on each side and is more compact than the latter organ. It comes from a level which corresponds to the most posterior portion of the opisthonephros of the anamniota. The metanephros is made up of essentially the same parts as the mesonephros and consists of renal corpuscles, secretory tubules, and collecting tubules. No nephrostomes are present. Each kidney has a twofold origin. A diverticulum, the *ureteric bud*, or *metanephric diverticulum*, from the Wolffian duct near its posterior end grows forward into the so-called *metanephrogenous tissue*, or *metanephric blastema*, which lies posterior to the mesonephros. The metanephric blastema is continuous with the nephrogenous tissue which gave rise to the mesonephric tubules. The diverticulum of the Wolffian duct, which is destined to form the *ureter*, branches and rebranches a varying number of times and ultimately forms large numbers of very fine *collecting tubules*. An expansion at the point where the ureter undergoes its primary divisions, at least in mammals, becomes the pelvis of the kidney (Fig. 7.12). Condensations in the mesenchyme of the adjacent metaneph-

FIG. 7.12. Manner of branching of diverticulum of Wolffian duct during early development of metanephric kidney. (*After Huber.*)

FIG. 7.13. A mammalian metanephric tubule, showing the renal corpuscle and secretory and collecting portions.

ric blastema soon give rise to hollow *secretory tubules* which grow longer and become S-shaped. One end of each secretory tubule establishes a connection with a collecting tubule. The other end expands and is soon invaded by a glomerular tuft from a branch of the renal artery so that a typical renal corpuscle is formed. All blood going to the metanephros is arterial, since the renal portal system of veins does not exist in these forms. As development progresses, there is a great increase in the number of secretory tubules.

The differentiation of a secretory tubule of the metanephros in mammals and, to a lesser extent, in birds is somewhat more elaborate than in the case of the mesonephros (Fig. 7.13). Each tubule, as it leaves Bowman's capsule, consists of a *proximal convoluted* tubule, a long *loop of Henle* with its *descending* and *ascending portions*, and a *distal convoluted tubule*. Secretory tubules with their Bowman's capsules are very numerous. It has been estimated that in the human being there are about 1 million renal corpuscles in each kidney. The loop of Henle functions primarily in reabsorption of water. Only when such a loop is present is the urine hypertonic to the blood. This is of great importance to terrestrial animals in which water conservation is of advantage. Otherwise the metanephros functions in a manner similar to that of the mesonephros. Wastes are carried from the kidneys by the ureters, which enter the cloaca or urinary bladder as the case may be. Reabsorption of water in reptiles and birds also occurs in the cloaca, into which the ureters open. This results in a partial solidification of urine as well as of feces.

Comparative anatomy of metanephros. REPTILES. The kidneys of reptiles are restricted to the posterior half of the abdominal cavity and are usually confined to the pelvic region. They are generally small and compact, but the surface is lobulated (Fig. 7.14). The posterior portion narrows down on each side, and in some lizards the hind parts may even fuse. The degree of symmetry may vary and is most divergent in snakes and limbless lizards, which have excessively lobulated, long, narrow kidneys in correlation with the shape of the body. One kidney may lie entirely posterior to the other. The ureters in these reptiles are extremely long. Turtles and crocodilians have very short ureters.

Fig. 7.14. Lobulated metanephric kidneys of lizard, *Monitor indicus.* (*After Wiedersheim, "Comparative Anatomy of Vertebrates," copyright 1907 by The Macmillan Company and used with their permission.*)

A urinary bladder is lacking in snakes, crocodiles, and alligators. Most lizards and turtles, however, have well-developed and usually bilobed bladders which open into the cloaca. The ureters from the metanephric kidneys open separately into the cloaca and, except in turtles, are not connected with the bladder. In reptilians the bladder is derived partly from the cloaca and partly from the base of the *allantois*, an endodermal embryonic structure important in fetal respiration. In some turtles a pair of accessory urinary bladders is also connected to the cloaca. They have been shown to function as accessory organs of respiration. In females they may be filled with water, which is used to soften the ground when a nest is being prepared.

BIRDS. In all birds the kidneys are situated in the pelvic region of the body cavity, and the two frequently unite at their posterior ends. They are lobed structures, deep fissures between the lobes serving for the passage of branches of the renal veins. The ureters of birds are short and open independently into the cloaca.

Except for the ostrich, birds have no urinary bladders. Urinary wastes, chiefly in the form of uric acid, are eliminated in a semisolid form along with the feces. The lack of a urinary bladder facilitates flight in birds since unnecessary ballast in the form of liquid urine need not be carried about.

MAMMALS. The typical mammalian metanephric kidney (Fig. 7.15) is a compact, bean-shaped organ attached to the dorsal body wall. It is retroperitoneal. The ureter leaves the median side at a depression called the *hilum*. At this point a *renal vein* also leaves the kidney and a *renal artery* and nerves enter it. The metanephros is surrounded by a *capsule* of connective tissue under which lies the *cortex*. The renal corpuscles and con-

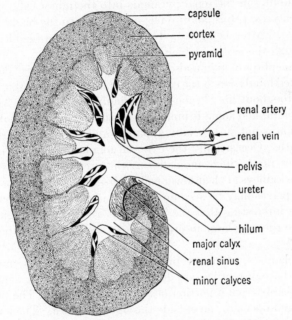

FIG. 7.15. Sagittal section of metanephric kidney of man (semidiagrammatic).

voluted portions of the secretory tubules are confined to the cortical region. Immediately beneath the cortex is the *medulla*, with which it is intimately connected. It is made up of large areas known as *renal pyramids* between which extend the *renal columns of Bertini* made up of cortical tissue. The pyramids, at their outer borders, are subdivided into smaller units called *lobules*. The collecting tubules are usually confined to the renal pyramids but may extend well up into the cortex. The inner border of each pyramid, in the form of a blunt *papilla*, projects into an outpocketing of the pelvis, which is known as a *minor calyx*. Several minor calyces join together to enter *major calyces*, which in turn open into the pelvis.

In the center of the kidney is the *sinus* of the metanephros. It contains blood vessels, nerves, and fatty tissue in addition to the pelvis and calyces.

Fluid which has been removed from the blood in the renal corpuscles passes down the proximal convoluted tubules to the descending and ascending portions of the loops of Henle and into the distal convoluted tubules. Some wastes are probably eliminated by the cells of the secretory tubule. At any rate, during its passage through the loop of Henle much fluid is reabsorbed. It has been estimated that in human kidneys, within a 24-hour period, between 150 and 200 qt. of fluid are filtered through the glomeruli into the secretory tubules. Approximately 99 per cent of the filtrate is absorbed through the walls of the secretory tubules and returned to the blood stream. The concentrated remainder is *urine*, which passes down the collecting tubules in the renal pyramids into the minor calyces; then into the major calyces, pelvis, and ureter; and thence to the bladder (cloaca in monotremes). After being stored temporarily in the bladder, the urine passes through the *urethra*, which opens to the outside.

The metanephros of mammals, in accord with its manner of development, shows marked lobulation in the embryo, and in many forms this condition is retained throughout life (Proboscidea, Pinnipedia, Cetacea, Artiodactyla, some Carnivora, and some Primates). In other adult mammals, however, the lobulation is not superficially apparent and the kidney surface is relatively smooth. Occasionally the external lobulation persists in man, but this is rather rare. Such anomalies as the presence of an extra kidney, fusion of the kidneys at their lower ends (horseshoe kidney), double ureters, and double pelves may be accounted for by abnormal embryonic development. It is interesting that the kidneys of a newborn child are approximately three times as large in proportion to body weight as they are in an adult.

Urinary bladders, which are present in all mammals, are muscular sacs which, like those of reptiles, are derived from a part of the ventral cloacal wall and possibly from a portion of the allantoic stalk. The bladder narrows down and opens to the outside through a urethra. The lower ends of the ureters, except in the monotremes, open directly into the bladder on its dorsal posterior surface and usually near the urethral end. In the monotremes the ureters open into the urethra through small papillae opposite the base of the bladder.

A sphincter muscle at the junction of bladder and urethra regulates the passage of urine from the bladder. It is contracted except during the act of urination. In males the urethra passes through the penis and opens at the tip of that organ through the *external urethral orifice*, or *meatus*. In females the condition varies, for in some, as in the rat and mouse, the urethra opens independently to the outside, passing through the clitoris; whereas in others it enters the urogenital sinus, or vestibule, which is the terminal part of the genital tract.

Even in monotremes, which, with the exception of the pika, are the only mammals having a cloaca, a urogenital portion is partially separated by means of a fold from the region into which the intestine opens. In Eutheria, the embryonic cloaca becomes separated into two distinct parts, each of which has an independent opening to the outside. The dorsal portion becomes the rectum with its anal opening; the ventral part becomes the urogenital sinus which receives the ducts of the reproductive system as as well as the urethra. In certain marsupials the division of the cloaca is not complete and a slightly depressed area receives the urogenital ducts and rectum. In females of certain species (rats, mice, and most primates) further separation of the urogenital sinus brings about a condition in which urethral and reproductive openings are independent.

EFFECT OF ENVIRONMENT ON KIDNEY STRUCTURE AND FUNCTION

Some interesting speculations have been advanced in attempting to correlate various details in the evolution of kidney structure and function with environmental factors. The speculations are based upon the assumption that vertebrates evolved from ancestors inhabiting continental fresh waters. There is some disagreement concerning this theory; nevertheless the concept is supported by considerable paleontological evidence.

The fresh-water ancestor was undoubtedly an organism with a relatively high concentration of salts in the blood. The osmotic pressure of the body fluids would thus be considerably higher than that of the water in which the animal lived. Under such conditions water would be constantly entering the body because of osmotic inflow. The necessity of ridding the body of this water was essential in maintaining a constant concentration of salts and other constituents of the blood. The glomerulus is believed to have arisen in evolution as a mechanism for ridding the body of excess water.

Those fishes which took to life in the sea had problems to contend with associated with the relatively high salt concentration and osmotic pressure of sea water. Osmotic extraction would tend to deplete the body of its water. But water must be retained so that the kidneys can form dilute urine for the elimination of wastes. One way in which this can be accomplished is by taking sea water into the digestive tract and absorbing most of the water and salts. The salts may be excreted through the gills, leaving the water free for the formation of urine. Another method of absorbing water is to be found in the elasmobranchs, in which, owing to a high concentration of urea in the blood under normal conditions, the osmotic pressure is higher than that of the salt-water environment. Water can then be absorbed directly through gills and other membranes. It need not go through the digestive route. The permeability of the gills and membranes of the mouth to urea is diminished in these fishes, a factor of importance in retaining a high concentration of urea in the blood.

In certain marine teleosts there is no need to remove water from the body, since the osmotic pressure of the blood is lower than that of sea water. Nitrogenous wastes, as well as others, have been shown to be eliminated via the gills. In these marine teleosts, glomeruli appear during developmental stages, but they later degenerate, the adults having aglomerular kidneys. Such kidneys are of little functional importance, and only a very small volume of urine is secreted in these fishes. The elasmobranch fishes, on the other hand, have well-developed kidneys with numerous glomeruli. In this group the osmotic pressure of the blood is high and, as in fresh-water fishes, water must be constantly removed by glomerular filtration.

Since the filtered fluid, like the blood, has a high concentration of chemicals which are essential for life, it is important that they be retained by the body. The kidney tubules with their ability to reabsorb these chemicals selectively have undoubtedly arisen in evolution as a means of effecting such a conservation.

Kidney tubules show much variation in vertebrates, although all possess a proximal convoluted tubule. It has been demonstrated that glucose is reabsorbed in the proximal convoluted tubules, at least in those amphibians which have been studied. In the aglomerular kidneys of the marine teleosts, mentioned above, the proximal convoluted tubule seems to be the only portion that is functional, yet the urine of these fishes does not differ basically from urine of fishes possessing glomeruli. The proximal convoluted tubule in such cases is undoubtedly secretory. Its secretory activity in glomerular kidneys has been demonstrated under experimental conditions. In all vertebrates except birds and mammals a ciliated neck connects Bowman's capsule with the proximal convoluted tubule. The ciliary current set up may facilitate glomerular filtration.

Elasmobranch kidney tubules differ from those of other vertebrates in possessing two portions, or segments, of peculiar structure. They are often referred to as the *elasmobranch segments*. The first is situated between Bowman's capsule and the proximal convoluted tubule; the second follows the proximal convoluted tubule. It has been known for a long time that elasmobranch fishes differ from all other vertebrates in the large percentage of urea present in tissues, blood, and other body fluids. The urine is particularly low in its concentration of urea, showing that most of the urea filtered through the glomeruli is absorbed. The unique segments in the elasmobranch kidney tubule seem to be specially adapted for selective reabsorption of urea.

The activity of the distal convoluted tubule remains somewhat obscure. It seems that among amphibians, at any rate, a degree of selective reabsorption also takes place here, particularly of chloride and bicarbonate.

SUMMARY

1. The excretory organs of vertebrates consist of paired kidneys together with their ducts. Several types of kidney are recognized within the group.

2. The various kinds of kidneys have probably all been derived from a primitive structure referred to as the archinephros, or holonephros. This

consisted of a pair of archinephric ducts which extended the length of the coelom. They were joined by segmentally arranged tubules, one to each segment on each side. The free end of each tubule opened into the coelom by means of a ciliated, funnel-shaped nephrostome. Connected to each tubule was a renal corpuscle consisting of a double-walled cup-shaped structure called Bowman's capsule, enclosing a small knot of arterial blood vessels known as a glomerulus. The larval stages of hagfishes and caecilians have archinephric kidneys. The various types of vertebrate kidneys may be regarded as successive stages which have evolved in an anterior-posterior direction from the original archinephros.

3. In adult anamniotes (cyclostomes, fishes, and amphibians) the anterior portion of the primitive archinephros usually becomes modified or degenerates. In the embryo, however, it appears as a transitory structure called the pronephros. In a few vertebrates the pronephros persists in the adult stage and then is called the head kidney. A head kidney is found in the adult hagfish and in certain teleost fishes.

4. The remainder of the anamniote kidney is the opisthonephros. It retains the original archinephric duct but differs from the pronephros in that several kidney tubules may be present in each segment and the tubules usually lose their peritoneal connections. The opisthnephros actually comes from levels which in amniotes will form both mesonephric and metanephric kidneys.

5. There is a general tendency toward a concentration of kidney tubules toward the posterior end of the opisthonephros. The anterior end loses its significance as an excretory organ and, in the male, is appropriated by the reproductive system, the archinephric duct becoming the ductus epididymidis and ductus deferens. Additional urinary ducts may then form by a fusion of two or more kidney tubules and serve to drain the urinary wastes.

6. In amniotes (reptiles, birds, and mammals) three types of kidneys are recognized: pronephros, mesonephros, and metanephros. These appear in succession during embryonic development, but only the metanephros persists to become the adult kidney. Mesonephros and metanephros represent different levels of the opisthonephros of the anamniota, the metanephros being the equivalent of the posterior portion. The archinephric duct is now called the Wolffian duct.

7. The pronephros of amniotes with its metamerically arranged tubules with peritoneal connections is merely a transient structure of no functional importance. Its duct, however, persists as the Wolffian duct.

8. The mesonephros appears only in the embryos of amniotes. Several kidney tubules are present in each segment, and most, or all, peritoneal connections are lost. This kidney may function for a time but then degenerates and disappears. Vestiges of the mesonephros and the Wolffian duct persist. In males, the latter gives rise to the epididymis and ductus deferens and certain other parts of the reproductive system.

9. The metanephric kidneys have no peritoneal connections. Their

origin is twofold. The collecting portion, including the ureter, is derived from a diverticulum of the Wolffian duct; the secretory portion arises from nephrogenous tissue, the metanephric blastema, which lies posterior to the mesonephros.

10. The important factors in kidney function involve glomerular filtration at the renal corpuscle, secretion of certain wastes by cells of the secretory tubule, and selective reabsorption by the secretory tubules.

11. Ducts from the kidneys lead to the cloaca in most forms. In teleost fishes they open directly to the outside. In mammals they enter the urinary bladder (monotremes are exceptions). Urinary bladders, when present, represent ventral outpocketings of the wall of the cloaca. In mammals, the bladder opens to the outside through a urethra, which in the males of all forms except monotremes is also utilized by the reproductive system.

12. The important factors in the evolution of the basic structure and function of the vertebrate kidney appear to have been associated with body-fluid regulation, involving the maintenance of a constant water and salt content of the body, regardless of the type of environment.

CHAPTER 8

REPRODUCTIVE SYSTEM

The two cardinal concerns of living things are the maintenance of self and the perpetuation of the species. All activities of plants and animals are, in the last analysis, related to one or the other of these two fundamental matters. Reproduction is essential only so that the species may continue to live upon the earth. Two methods of reproduction, *asexual* and *sexual*, are recognized.

Asexual reproduction. Asexual, or agamic, reproduction does not involve sex. In the animal kingdom it occurs only in members of certain lower phyla. Some animals reproduce asexually by a process called *fission*, in which the body is divided into two approximately equal parts, each part being capable of independent existence. Fission is a method of reproduction in such invertebrate animals as *Hydra* and *Planaria*. Budding, which may also be observed in *Hydra* and other coelenterates, is another form of asexual reproduction. Asexual reproduction is not known to occur in the chordates.

Sexual reproduction. Sexual, or gamic, reproduction is the most common method of propagation and takes place in animals which have the power of reproducing asexually as well. In all cases it involves development from an egg which may or may not be fertilized. In the rather rare eventuality of an egg developing without fertilization, the term *parthenogenesis* is used. This is considered to be a form of sexual reproduction because a sexual element, the egg, is involved. The word *amphigony* is used to denote the more usual type of sexual reproduction in which an egg cell must be fertilized by a sperm cell before development can occur. The fertilized egg is known as a *zygote* which, under proper conditions and by a series of complicated processes, develops into an *embryo*.

Reproductive organs. Egg cells, or *ova*, and sperm cells, or *spermatozoa*, are formed in the *primary reproductive organs*, which are spoken of collectively as the *gonads*. The gonads in the male are known as the *testes* and in the female as the *ovaries*. Besides forming *gametes*, or reproductive cells, both ovaries and testes give off endocrine secretions, or *hormones*, which pass into the blood or lymphatic streams and are carried to all parts of the body, where they bring about profound effects. A discussion of the endocrine activity of the gonads is included in Chap. 9.

The gonads are paired structures, although in such forms as cyclostomes, certain fishes, and female birds of most species, what seems to be an un-

261

paired gonad is the result either of fusion of paired structures or else of unilateral degeneration. It was formerly believed that the gonads were derived from tissues which showed evidence of segmentation, or metamerism. This concept has been discarded, and except for such a primitive form as amphioxus in which the gonads are distinctly segmented, it is clear that no metamerism exists in the gonads of chordates.

The gonads are mesodermal derivatives. In both sexes they arise as paired thickenings of the coelomic epithelium along the dorsal surface of the body cavity on either side of the dorsal mesentery of the gut. The

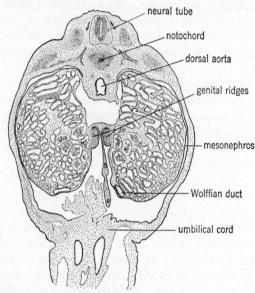

Fig. 8.1.   Cross section through 12-mm. pig embryo, showing relation of genital ridges to mesonephric kidneys.

underlying mesenchyme condenses and proliferates, and soon a pair of *genital ridges* can be observed coursing longitudinally along the median sides of the opisthonephric or mesonephric kidneys close to the base of the dorsal mesentery (Fig. 8.1). It is remarkable that development of the gonads in the earliest stages is similar in both sexes and that sexual differences cannot at first be recognized even under the microscope. The ovaries and testes eventually come to be attached to the dorsal body wall by mesenterylike bands of tissue, the *mesorchium* in the male and the *mesovarium* in the female. These bear the same relation to the gonads as does the dorsal mesentery to the gut.

The exact point of origin of the *germ plasm*, or the cells from which eggs and sperm ultimately arise, is still not known with certainty since so many variations among different species exist. In some they seem to arise in the yolk-sac endoderm and to migrate by way of the mesentery of the gut or by way of the blood stream to the genital ridges; in others they apparently appear *in situ* in the germinal epithelium of the genital ridges.

The reproductive elements formed in the gonads must be transported to the outside of the body either as ova or spermatozoa or as young which have developed from fertilized eggs within the body of the female. For this purpose, in most vertebrates, ducts are utilized, those of the male being known as the *deferent ducts* and those of the female as oviducts, or *Müllerian ducts*. In a few forms, such as cyclostomes, no ducts are present in either sex, and eggs and sperm escape from the body cavity through *genital* or *abdominal* pores (Fig. 7.7). The deferent ducts of the male are usually the archinephric, or the Wolffian, ducts which in some cases also serve to carry urinary wastes from the opisthonephric or mesonephric kidneys in those animals in which these kidneys function either during embryonic or adult life. In reptiles, birds, and mammals in which the metanephros is the functional adult kidney and the mesonephros degenerates, the Wolffian duct on each side persists as the ductus deferens.

When the reproductive ducts first develop, in most cases they open posteriorly into the cloaca in both sexes. This relationship persists throughout life in many vertebrates, but in some, modifications in the cloacal region occur and the reproductive ducts either open separately to the outside, or else, in the male, join with the excretory ducts to emerge by a common orifice.

In many aquatic vertebrates, fertilization is external. However, in all terrestrial forms and even in many aquatic species, internal fertilization is the rule. The passage of sperm from male to female is brought about in some by apposition of the cloacae of the two sexes. More commonly, however, copulatory organs are present in the male which are employed in an intromittent manner in depositing spermatozoa in the reproductive tract of the female. A variety of types of copulatory organs is found among the vertebrates.

In both sexes, all structures or organs which serve to bring the germ cells, or products of the primary sex organs, together are known as the *accessory sex organs*. They include the reproductive ducts, associated glands, and intromittent organs. *Secondary sex characters*, which are not directly concerned with sex, play a part in the reproductive scheme. Sexual differences in such secondary sex characters as ornamental plumage, body size and strength, and vocal apparatus are indirectly related to reproduction. The development and maintenance of the secondary sex characters and accessory sex organs are controlled, at least in part, by the endocrine secretions of the gonads.

THE FEMALE

Ovaries. A typical ovary is a solid structure made up of an inner medullary region composed of connective tissue, blood and lymphatic vessels, smooth muscle, and nerve fibers. Indistinctly separated from the *medulla* is the outer *cortex*, in which the cytogenic and endocrine elements are situated. The cortex in a mature ovary is usually irregular in shape because of *ovarian*, or *Graafian*, *follicles*, which are developing there. An *ovum*, or egg cell, lies within each follicle, and the *follicular cells* which surround it supply nourishment. After growing to a certain extent, and at the proper time, certain follicles push out to the surface of the ovary. Either the follicle ruptures, liberating the ovum into the coelom (*ovulation*), or else the follicle and its contained ovum degenerate. Degenerating ovarian follicles are said to be *atretic*.

In certain fishes, and in amphibians, snakes, and lizards, the ovaries are of the saccular type and are hollow. In most teleost fishes the cavities are actually closed-off portions of the coelom into which the ripe ova are liberated. This is not the case in amphibians, snakes, and lizards, in which the ovarian cavity is not homologous with that of teleosts and in which ripe ova escape into the coelom through the *external* surface of the ovaries (page 266). It is a general rule in vertebrates that ova are shed into the coelom. Often this is not apparent since the opening into the oviduct is so close to the ovaries that there is little chance for them to escape into the main part of the body cavity.

New ova are formed periodically by mitotic activity of oöcytes which are present in the *germinal epithelium*. This is a narrow band or layer of cells located on the outer border of the cortex. Each developing ovum is soon surrounded by one or more layers of small epithelial cells which make up the follicle.

The size of an ovarian follicle differs greatly in various vertebrates. It depends mostly upon the volume of the ovum which is characteristic of each particular species and upon the season of the year when the ovaries are examined. The mature ova of all forms below mammals are relatively large because of the yolk which they contain. They range in size from those of certain fishes, in which the ova are just visible to the unaided eye, to the enormous "yolk," or ovum, of the ostrich and the mackerel shark. In vertebrates below mammals in the evolutionary scale, the ovum completely fills the cavity of the follicle. The relationship of the microscopic mammalian ovum to the Graafian follicle is discussed elsewhere (page 268).

In most annual-breeding vertebrates there is a seasonal fluctuation in the size of the ovaries, which is maximum at the breeding season. After the eggs have been discharged, the ovaries become relatively small and remain in a "resting" condition until called into activity with the approach of the next breeding period, when a new series of ova and follicles develops. Most domestic animals are not limited to an annual breeding period but have definite times during the year when reproductive activity is manifested. Cyclic changes in the ovaries accompany these periods but are not of the same magnitude as is observed in annual breeders.

Amphioxus. The ovaries of amphioxus are metameric structures consisting of approximately 26 pairs of gonads projecting into the atrium, or peribranchial space, from the inner surface of the body wall. The most anterior gonads are located at about the middle of the pharyngeal region. Those in the center are larger than the ones at the anterior and posterior extremes. Each gonad has a layer of atrial epithelium reflected over its free surface. Under this is a double layer of coelomic epithelium which almost completely surrounds the gonad. Thus, each ovary lies in a closed pocket of coelom, the *gonocoele.* When the eggs are ripe, the coelomic pouches and atrial epithelium rupture. Eggs are forced into the peribranchial space from which they pass directly to the outside through the atriopore. Some observers report that spawning amphioxus often discharge their eggs through the mouth. If this is true, they must pass from the peribranchial space through the gill slits into the pharynx and then forward, through the mouth, to the vestibule.

Cyclostomes. The adult female lamprey has a single gonad, representing a fusion of two, which runs the length of the body cavity and is attached to the middorsal body wall by a thin sheet of tissue continuous on either side with the peritoneum. This is the mesovarium. At the height of the breeding season the ovary occupies the greater part of the abdominal cavity. In the ammocoetes larva two ovaries are present, separated by the dorsal mesentery of the gut. The mesentery disappears, and the gonads of the two sides fuse.

The hagfish is *hermaphroditic,* the anterior part of the single gonad being ovarian in nature and the posterior portion testicular. Usually one or the other region matures and becomes predominant. Only the left gonad develops fully.

In cyclostomes, ripe eggs are shed directly into the coelom.

Fishes. It is unusual to find unpaired ovaries in fishes. Even when this condition seems to occur, there is actually a fusion of the two gonads. The ovaries are sometimes asymmetrical in position. In a number of elasmobranchs only the right ovary becomes fully developed and the left ovary atrophies in the adult.

The eggs of elasmobranchs are discharged from the anteriorly located ovaries directly into the body cavity. Few eggs are produced at a time. In correlation with the small number, the ova contain relatively enormous amounts of yolk. It has been reported that in ovoviviparous elasmobranchs certain bodies, called corpora lutea, presumably having an endocrine function, are formed from the ovarian follicles after ovulation.

In most teleosts the ovaries are of the saccular type. During development they become folded or else form a pocket (Fig. 8.2) in such a way as to enclose part of the coelom within them. This loses all connection with the rest of the coelom. The anterior end of the cavity is blind, but in most cases the posterior end connects directly with the cavity of the very short oviduct formed from peritoneal folds which are continuous with the ovaries. Teleost ovaries are very large during the breeding season, and ripe ova, which are sometimes numbered in the millions, are discharged directly into the central ovarian cavity from which they pass down the oviduct to the outside. In adult teleosts a cloaca does not exist, the oviducts having separate openings from the urinary and digestive systems. In some, the urinary and genital systems have a common opening but the anus opens independently. It would seem that the condition in these teleosts is an exception to the rule that ova are liberated into the coelom. However,

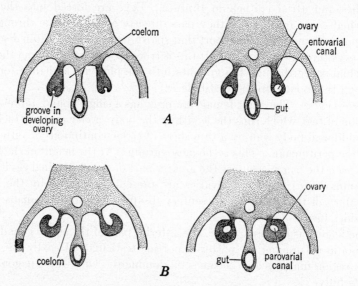

FIG. 8.2. Diagrams showing two methods of formation of hollow teleost ovaries: *A*, entovarial canal formation; *B*, parovarial canal formation.

since the hollow cavity within the ovary is really a portion of the coelom that has been cut off, the exception is only apparent. The gar pike, *Lepisosteus*, is the only member of the "ganoid" fishes that has a saccular type of ovary. In most other members of the group, the solid ovaries are flattened, elongated structures from which mature ova break out into the coelom in the orthodox manner.

Amphibians. Although amphibian ovaries are saccular structures, ova escape into the coelom through their *external* walls. The cavity within each ovary becomes lymphoid in character and does not correspond morphologically or functionally to the cavity of the teleost ovary. Amphibian ova are of the *mesolecithal* type, with a medium amount of yolk. Ovaries filled with ripe ova are, therefore, large irregular structures which at the breeding season fill the greater part of the body cavity. The shape of the ovaries varies with the shape of the body. They are long and narrow in caecilians. In caudates the ovaries are also elongated but to a lesser degree. In salientians they are decidedly shortened and more compact. The cavity within the caudate ovary is single and continuous, but in salientians it becomes divided into a number of pockets.

Closely associated with the ovaries in amphibians are the *fat bodies*, or *corpora adiposa*. In salientians they are yellowish structures situated anterior to the gonads and consist of a number of fingerlike processes. In caudates they are long and slender and run parallel to the ovaries along their medial edges. Apparently the fat bodies serve as a storage place for nutriment. They undergo profound changes during the year and are smallest at the approach of and during the breeding season. After this they gradually increase in size until a maximum is reached.

A peculiar structure in the male toad, known as *Bidder's organ*, may under certain conditions develop into a true ovary (page 315).

Reptiles. Snakes and lizards possess saccular ovaries of the amphibian type, whereas turtles and crocodilians have solid ovaries. In the latter animals the gonads of the female are rather broad and symmetrically disposed, but in snakes and lizards there is a tendency toward elongation. This is more pronounced in snakes, where the right ovary lies in advance of the left.

Eggs of reptiles are of the *polylecithal* type. Only that part of the reptilian egg which is called the "yolk" is formed in the ovaries, and this represents the true ovum. The size of the large eggs is in proportion to the size of the animal which lays them.

In certain ovoviviparous snakes and lizards, following ovulation, corpora lutea form from the ruptured follicles and persist throughout pregnancy. It seems likely that these structures, as in mammals, secrete a hormone (progesterone?) necessary for the maintenance of pregnancy.

Birds. Although both ovaries are present during embryonic development, in most birds (excepting birds of prey) the right ovary degenerates and the left becomes the functional adult gonad. This is in keeping with the elimination of unnecessary ballast observed in connection with other structures of birds. Mature ova of the polylecithal type escape from the ovarian follicles into the coelom through a preformed, nonvascular band, the *stigma*, or *cicatrix*, located on the surface of the follicle (Fig. 8.11). As in the case of reptiles, only the yolk of the egg represents the true ovum formed in the ovary.

Experiments have shown that if the functional left ovary is removed from domestic fowls the rudimentary right gonad will develop into a testis-like organ. In many birds an increase in the number of hours of daylight stimulates ovarian activity.

Mammals. Cortical and medullary portions of the mammalian ovary are more clearly marked off from each other than in most other vertebrates. The cortex consists chiefly of a compact *stroma* made up, for the most part, of connective tissue. The Graafian follicles lie in the cortex and form its most significant components. The relationship of the small mammalian ovum to the ovarian follicle differs somewhat from conditions in other vertebrates. Follicles vary in size according to their state of development and can be grouped into *primary, growing,* and *mature* follicles. Generally, the youngest lie near the surface of the ovary; those which are growing advance toward the medulla; and mature follicles appear as large vesicles which may extend throughout the thickness of the cortex and even produce rounded elevations of the outer ovarian surface.

A young, or primary, follicle consists of a centrally disposed ovum which is surrounded by a single layer of epithelial *follicular cells.* The stroma separates the follicles from each other. In a growing follicle the follicular cells have increased greatly in number and form several layers about the ovum. A sort of capsular arrangement of cells known as the *theca* now surrounds the follicle. The theca is arranged in two layers: an outer *theca externa,* the cells of which are long and spindle-shaped, and an inner, vascular *theca interna,* made up of more rounded cells which, however, are sharply delineated from the follicular cells. It is highly probable that the cells of the theca interna secrete the female sex hormone, *estradiol.* The ovum, which has been growing up to this point, now ceases to enlarge. It is surrounded by a clear, thick, transparent envelope, the *zona pellucida,* which has been produced by the follicular cells. Tiny canals traverse the zona pellucida, furnishing a pathway through which the ovum is nourished. The follicular cells making up the first layer around the zona pellucida are more columnar in shape, stain somewhat differently, and are more conspicuous than the others. They form what has been termed the *corona radiata.* So far the follicle is solid but is soon converted into a fluid-filled vesicle by intercellular vacuolation and a rearrangement of the follicular cells. The cavity thus formed, known as the *antrum,* or *follicular cavity,* is filled with a semiviscous fluid, the *liquor folliculi,* or *follicular fluid.* A small hillock of follicular cells, the *cumulus oöphorus,* or *germ hill,* within which lies the ovum surrounded by the zona pellucida and corona radiata, protrudes into the antrum (Fig. 8.3). The follicular cells bordering the antrum are several layers in thickness and are collectively referred to as the *stratum granulosum.*

Many follicles in the mammalian ovary begin to grow, but most of them degenerate before long and become *atretic.* In a mature female, at periodic intervals which are typical of each species, one or more follicles grow to maturity, the number being closely correlated with the number of offspring cast in a single litter. When these follicles have become fully developed, the cumulus with its contained ovum separates from the remainder of the follicle; the follicle ruptures; and the ovum, with its surrounding layers, is extruded into the coelom. It then passes through the *ostium tubae* into the *Fallopian tube.* It is of interest that in the rabbit, ferret, cat, mink, shrew, and possibly others, ovulation will not take place unless the animal copu-

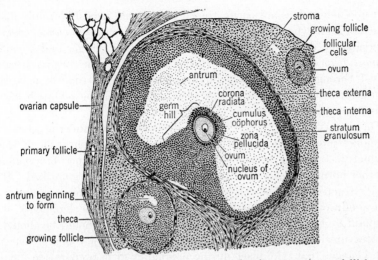

Fig. 8.3. Section of portion of cortex of rat ovary, showing one primary follicle, two growing follicles, and a single large mature follicle.

lates. In these forms, then, ovulation is not spontaneous, and the nervous stimulation of copulation brings about changes which result in the rupture of the Graafian follicles.

In some mammals the antrum of the follicle fills with a clot of blood coming from the small, ruptured blood vessels in the theca. Such a body is called a *corpus hemorrhagicum*. In other mammals a corpus hemorrhagicum does not form. In either case the cells of the stratum granulosum and theca interna undergo a transformation. They enlarge and push into the antrum, which is thus gradually obliterated. If a corpus hemorrhagicum is present, the blood is soon resorbed. Finally, a relatively large, rounded mass of cells is formed which is known as a *corpus luteum*, or *yellow body*. This name is derived from the fact that in the human being, cow, and some other mammals the corpus luteum has a characteristic yellow-orange color. In most mammals, however, the corpora lutea are of a pinkish hue. The corpus luteum of the human being rarely becomes solid. The luteal cells form the thick wall of a hollow vesicle (Fig. 8.4) which fills with the secretion of former follicular cells. This later either acquires a gelatinous consistency or is replaced by an ingrowth of the connective-tissue cells.

Fig. 8.4. Section through human corpus luteum of pregnancy.

If pregnancy does not occur, the corpus luteum persists for only a short time and is known as a *corpus luteum spurium*, or *corpus luteum of ovulation*. If pregnancy does ensue, the corpus luteum grows larger and is called a *corpus luteum verum*, or *corpus luteum of pregnancy*. The corpora lutea vera persist throughout pregnancy but degenerate as the time of parturition approaches. In either case all that ultimately remains is a whitish, scarlike remnant of connective tissue, the *corpus albicans*.

The corpus luteum is of primary importance as an endocrine gland. Its hormone, *progesterone*, is essential for the proper preparation of the reproductive tract for pregnancy and for the maintenance of pregnancy. Another hormone, *relaxin*, of uncertain origin, has been identified. It has been extracted from the corpora lutea of sows. This hormone under certain conditions brings about a relaxation of the pubic ligaments of the pregnant guinea pig (page 350). The corpora lutea should be thought of as structures of transitory appearance, the function of which is concerned with changes that take place during pregnancy or in preparation for pregnancy.

Ovaries in mammals are located in the lumbar or pelvic regions. During development they arise at a level anterior to the metanephric kidneys, but later descend to their permanent and more posterior location.

In the monotremes the left ovary shows a much greater degree of development than the right and it appears as though only the left gonad is functional. Eggs with shells are laid by the monotremes. The ovum of the platypus at the time of ovulation measures approximately 3 mm. in diameter. Albumen and shell are added later when the ovum is passing down the oviduct.

Mammalian ovaries are usually small in relation to the size of the body. They are suspended from the middorsal body wall by mesovaria. Blood vessels and nerves enter at a point called the *hilum*. The ovaries are usually so situated that the surface is exposed to the coelomic cavity, but the ostium tubae, or opening into the oviduct, is so close to the ovary that ova generally enter the oviduct directly rather than getting lost in the body cavity. Experiments on the sow indicate that external migration of ova is possible, since ova from one ovary have been shown to pass across the body cavity and enter the ostium on the other side. Whether this occurs under normal conditions or in other species has not been determined. In forms with closed ovarian capsules (rat, mouse), external migration of ova is impossible.

Ovulation, as has been mentioned previously, occurs at rather regular intervals. Most vertebrates are annual breeders, and ovulation in such forms takes place but once a year. In many mammals, particularly in domesticated forms, ovulatory cycles occur at shorter intervals. At such times the females are in a condition referred to as *estrus*, or "animal heat," and at this time only will they accept the male in copulation. The primates seem to be an exception to this rule. The following table gives the average length of the ovulatory cycle in some familiar mammals. If pregnancy supervenes, ovulation is suspended until after birth of the young and in many cases even during the period of lactation.

Opossum	28 days
Guinea pig	16 days
Rat	5 days
Mouse	5 days
Dog	6 to 7 months
Sheep	Twice a year (many variations)
Sow	2 to 4 weeks
Cow	21 days
Mare	21 days
Woman	28 days
Macaque monkey	24 to 26 days
Chimpanzee	37 days

Although in species having several young at a time both ovaries may form numerous follicles and corpora lutea, it has been reported that in certain others, in which only one young normally develops during a given gestation period, there is a sequence between the two ovaries in regard to follicular development, ovulation, and corpus luteum formation. This may or may not be uniformly true.

Oviducts. The oviducts of the female, except in teleosts and some other fishes, are modifications of the *Müllerian ducts*. The latter are formed in either of two ways during embryonic development. In elasmobranchs and caudate amphibians the archinephric duct splits longitudinally, one part remaining as the kidney duct and the other forming the Müllerian duct. In elasmobranchs, after the splitting occurs, the Müllerian duct opens anteriorly into the coelom by means of one, or possibly more, of the pronephric tubules and nephrostomes. In other vertebrates the usual method of Müllerian-duct formation is by the appearance of a groove or an invagination of the peritoneum covering the ventrolateral part of the opisthonephros or mesonephros, as the case may be, near its cephalic end and near the archinephric, or Wolffian, duct (Fig. 8.5). The edges of the groove come together and fuse, thus forming a tube, the Müllerian duct, which grows caudad to join the cloaca. The anterior end does not close, and the opening becomes the *ostium tubae abdominale*. In certain amphibians, pronephric tubules and nephrostomes play a part in forming the ostium tubae as well as the anterior end of the Müllerian duct. Whether the oviducts of elasmobranchs and caudate amphibians are actually homologous with those of higher forms is a matter for speculation. It is generally assumed, however, that the elasmobranch and caudate condition is the more primitive and that rather definite homologies exist. At any rate, in both male and female the close relationship of the reproductive ducts to the excretory organs and ducts is obvious.

In much the same manner as the Wolffian ducts of amniotes degenerate in the female except for certain vestiges, the Müllerian ducts in the male usually become atrophic and only a few remnants persist. However, in the males of some groups, amphibians and certain fishes in particular, the Müllerian ducts may persist in the adult as rather prominent structures. It is doubtful if any function can be assigned to these vestigial oviducts, but their presence is strongly indicative of the bisexual nature of certain amphibians.

Although the reproductive ducts of the male are invariably paired, and the paired condition is typical of the female, in birds only one oviduct, the left, generally persists. The oviducts in most vertebrates become differentiated into regions which are associated with particular functions. Commonly the lower portion is expanded to form a *uterus*. This may serve as a temporary storage place for eggs and in many vertebrates affords a site in which the young develop.

dorsal mesentery of gut

genital ridge

mesonephros

Müllerian groove

A   Wolffian duct

B   Müllerian duct

C   Müllerian duct

FIG. 8.5.   Successive stages, *A*, *B*, and *C*, in the formation of the Müllerian duct.

Amphioxus.   No reproductive ducts are present in amphioxus. Ripe ova which have been discharged into the atrium, or peribranchial space, aided by muscular contractions, are carried along by the respiratory current out the atriopore into the surrounding sea water.   In some cases the ova may be discharged through the mouth (page 265).   Fertilization is external.

Cyclostomes.   Reproductive ducts are lacking in cyclostomes.   Ova make their way from the coelom through the genital pores at the posterior end of the abdominal cavity into the urogenital sinus and out the aperture at the tip of the urogenital papilla (Fig. 7.7).   External fertilization also occurs in this group.

Fishes.   Structures for transport of ova from coelom to the outside show a great diversity in fishes.   In some teleosts of the family Salmonidae, as well as in occasional members of other groups, eggs escape through modified abdominal pores which connect the coelom with the cloaca. These are frequently continued a short distance within the body cavity by short, funnellike projections.   It is not certain whether these are homologous with the oviducts of other classes.   In other fishes, as in certain elasmobranchs, abdominal pores may be present, but their function is unknown.   It is possible that they may not be homologous with those of teleosts.   In addition to abdominal pores, elaborately developed ducts for the transport of ova are usually present in fishes.

The two Müllerian ducts in elasmobranchs fuse at their anterior ends so that a single ostium tubae connects with the coelom (Fig. 16.11).   A narrow, but distensible, oviduct leads from the ostium on each side.   An

Fig. 8.6.   *A,* egg case of dogfish, *Scyllium; B,* egg case of bullhead shark, *Heterodontus galeatus.* (*After Waite.*)

enlargement called the *shell gland* is present on each oviduct.   Beyond the shell gland the Müllerian duct enlarges on each side to form a uterus which opens into the cloaca.

In all elasmobranchs, fertilization takes place internally.   However, the method of reproduction is varied, there being both oviparous and ovoviviparous species.   Oviparous forms lay eggs encased in elaborate horny shells formed by the shell gland.   The cases protect the embryos during development.   An egg case usually contains one egg, but in some species three or four eggs may be present.   In general, there are two types of egg cases (Fig. 8.6*A* and *B*).   That of the dogfish *Scyllium,* for example, is rectangular with a tendrillike projection extending from each corner.   The second type of egg case is screw-shaped and has long, filamentous projections coming off the apex.   The Port Jackson shark has an egg case of this type.   The tendrils are usually coiled about upright masses of seaweed in such a manner as to fix the egg firmly in position.   In *Scyllium,* depending upon temperature and other factors, it takes from 6 to 9 months for the embryo to develop. The shell is ruptured by the fully developed embryo at the time of hatching.

The shell formed about the ova in ovoviviparous species is very much reduced. In accord with this, the shell gland in oviparous species is better developed than in ovoviviparous forms. On the contrary, the uteri of ovoviviparous elasmobranchs are larger and more highly developed than those of egg-laying species, for they serve as structures in which the young undergo a considerable part of their development.

In the dogfish, *Squalus acanthias*, which is ovoviviparous, a beautifully clear, amber-colored, temporary shell at first surrounds several eggs in the uterus. The eggs undergo early development within the shell. At about the time that the transient external gills of the embryo are being absorbed, the shell breaks down. Numerous villuslike folds appear in the lining of the uterus during pregnancy. They are in close contact with blood vessels in the yolk sac of the embryo, and an exchange of metabolic substances takes place between the circulatory systems of the mother and her developing young. In oviparous species the lining of the uterus is almost smooth.

It has been reported that the spiny dogfish, *Squalus acanthias*, has a 2-year gestation period. In the Woods Hole region of Massachusetts the animals migrate northward in late April and early May toward the coast of Newfoundland. Pregnant females caught at this time fall into to groups: those having "pups" with large yolk sacs (Fig. 5.1) and those in the so-called "candle" stage. The latter have large undeveloped ova in the uteri. In October and November the fish again pass Woods Hole, migrating to the South. The females that bore candles in May have pups that are 3 or 4 in. long. Those which carried pups in May either have given birth or else the yolk sacs of the almost fully developed young have been practically resorbed, indicating that birth is about to occur. In the following spring the females which were in the candle stage the previous year are carrying pups and those which have given birth to young are once more in the candle stage.

In still other elasmobranchs, as in the ovoviviparous *Mustelus laevis*, there is an even closer relation between mother and young, for the yolk sac gives off branched processes which are closely attached to the uterine wall.

The eggs of holocephalians are much like those of selachians. Development takes place within the uterus.

Teleosts with saccular ovaries have short oviducts which are directly continuous with the ovaries. They are derived from peritoneal folds continuous with the gonads (Fig. 8.2) and should probably be distinguished from true Müllerian ducts since there is some question about their homologies. The two oviducts often fuse, continuing posteriorly as a single structure which may open by a genital pore either between the rectum and urinary aperture or else at the tip of a papilla. Such papillae are occasionally elongated to form tubelike *ovipositors* through which ova are discharged. A cloaca is lacking in teleosts. In some forms the oviducts enter a urogenital sinus in common with the archinephric ducts. Most teleosts are oviparous, but numbers of ovoviviparous species are known. Internal fertilization in these species is accomplished by copulatory organs which are generally modifications of the anal fin of the male. Development of young may take place within the cavities of the ovaries in some cases, but more commonly it occurs within the oviducts.

In most of the ganoid fishes and in many teleosts, as previously indicated, the ovaries are solid and eggs are shed into the general coelomic cavity.

A   *B*

Fig. 8.7. Cross section of oviduct of salamander, *Eurycea bislineata: A*, during breeding season (Apr. 11); *B*, after the breeding season is over (June 21).

The oviducts in these species are not continuous with the ovaries, although the ostia are in close proximity. Whether such oviducts are true Müllerian ducts has been questioned.

The oviducts in Dipnoi are long, paired, coiled structures which are true Müllerian ducts. They open anteriorly by funnel-shaped apertures. At the posterior end they unite and have a common opening into the cloaca. A gelatinous coating is secreted about the eggs as they pass down the oviducts.

Amphibians. Oviducts in amphibians are of the same general pattern throughout the class. They are paired, elongated tubes with ostia situated well forward in the body cavity. Posteriorly, each Müllerian duct is enlarged somewhat to form a short uterus, which in most species opens independently into the cloaca. In certain toads, however, the oviducts unite before entering the cloaca. The uteri in most amphibians serve only as temporary storage places for ova that are soon to be laid. The lining of the oviducts is glandular. During the breeding season the ducts become greatly enlarged (Fig. 8.7) and markedly coiled and the glandular lining epithelium begins to secrete a clear, gelatinous substance. Eggs escaping from the ovaries into the body cavity are directed toward the ostia by cilia located on the peritoneum lining the body wall, liver, and adjacent structures. After entering the ostia, the eggs pass down the oviducts in a twisting, spiral motion and are forced along by muscular peristaltic waves. The oviducal glands deposit several layers of jellylike material about each ovum. This swells when the egg enters the water (Fig. 8.8).

In salientians fertilization is external. The male grasps the female in a process called *amplexus*, and as the eggs emerge from the cloaca, spermato-

Fig. 8.8. Stereogram showing fertilized frog's ovum surrounded by three layers of "jelly." (*Drawn by G. Schwenk.*)

zoa are shed over them. No copulatory organs are present. Nevertheless, one group of African frogs (*Nectophrynoides*) is apparently ovoviviparous.

The reproductive habits of many frogs and toads are of extraordinary interest. The Surinam toad, *Pipa americana*, of South America, is probably one of the most remarkable of the group. When the eggs are laid, the male places them on the back of the female. The eggs adhere by means of a sticky secretion. Gradually they sink into the skin in small, pitlike depressions which are finally closed over by a membrane. Here they are kept moist. The young develop in the cell-like depressions and do not emerge until they have metamorphosed. After the young have departed, the depressions on the back of the female gradually flatten out.

In the "pouched," or marsupial, frog, *Gastrotheca pygmaea* of South America, the female has a large permanent pouch on her back, not possessed by the male. Here the eggs are placed and carried about while the young develop. The opening to the pouch is inconspicuous and hidden among the folds of the skin.

The obstetrical toad, *Alytes obstetricans* of western Europe, is curious in that the male wraps strings of eggs about his body and hind legs, protecting them and keeping them moist until the tadpoles emerge, well advanced in development.

FIG. 8.9.   Three types of salamander spermatophores: *A, Triturus viridescens; B, Desmognathus fuscus; C, Eurycea bislineata.*   (*From Noble, "Biology of the Amphibia," McGraw-Hill Book Company, Inc. By permission.*)

In a certain species of frog, *Rhinoderma*, found in Chile, the eggs are carried in the large vocal sacs of the male, where they are protected during development. The eggs in this case are large and fewer in number than usual.

A tree frog of Paraguay, *Phyllomedusa hypochondrialis*, is known to glue its eggs to the folded leaves of trees. The leaves are in a position overhanging the water, so that, when the tadpoles hatch, they fall into the water below.

Tree frogs of the genus *Hyla* in Jamaica place their eggs in little pools of rain water which have collected between the large leaves of certain tropical plants.

Internal fertilization occurs in most caudates, but no copulatory organs are present. In these amphibians the males deposit *spermatophores*, which are actually small packets of spermatozoa held together by secretions of the cloacal glands. The spermatophores are placed here and there in pond or stream and even on the land in certain species. The structure of the spermatophores shows some variation. In most species the spermatozoa are gathered together at the tip of the spermatophore (Fig. 8.9). The females

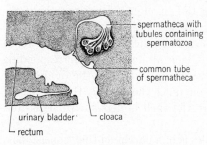

spermatheca with tubules containing spermatozoa

common tube of spermatheca

urinary bladder   cloaca

rectum

FIG. 8.10.   Diagram showing relation of spermatheca to cloaca in the salamander, *Eurycea bislineata.*

search for the spermatophores and take the spermatozoa gathered together at the tip into the cloaca. This is accomplished by muscular movements of the cloacal lips. A dorsal diverticulum of the cloaca, the *spermatheca* (Fig. 8.10), serves as a receptacle for the spermatozoa, which are thus available for fertilizing the ova as they pass down the oviducts to the cloaca.

In several species of salamander the female protects the eggs by coiling her body about them. Fertilization is external in *Cryptobranchus*, in the Asiatic land salamanders, and also, apparently, in the Sirenidae.

The breeding habits of *Salamandra atra*, the black salamander of Switzerland, are of special interest. The animal lives in the rushing waters of mountain streams. Two eggs are retained in the reproductive tract of the female, where they undergo development. When the young hatch, they are well enough developed to be safe in the turbulent waters. Another exception is *Salamandra maculosa*, the fire salamander. About 15 young develop within the oviducts, but at the time they are born gills are still present and metamorphosis occurs considerably later. Some plethodontid salamanders are ovoviviparous.

Internal fertilization is the rule in caecilians. The eversible cloaca of the male is considered by some authorities to serve as a copulatory organ. In a certain species of caecilian, *Ichthyophis*, native to Ceylon, breeding takes place in the spring. A burrow is prepared by the female in the moist ground in close proximity to running water. She coils her body about the relatively large-yolked eggs, which number 20 or more, and guards them during development, protecting them from predaceous snakes and lizards. The eggs gradually swell until they are double their original size, and the embryo, when about to hatch, weighs about four times as much as the original egg. External gills are present at first but are lost soon after hatching. The larvae, which are fishlike in form, metamorphose into the burrowing, limbless adults which will drown if kept under water. Another genus, *Typhlonectes*, is aquatic and gives birth to living young.

Reptiles. The oviducts of reptiles open into the coelom by means of large, slitlike ostia. Each oviduct is differentiated into regions which mediate different functions in forming the envelopes deposited about the ova prior to laying. In *Sphenodon*, turtles, crocodiles, and alligators, oviducal glands lining the upper part of each oviduct secrete albumen about the ovum. Eggs of snakes and lizards lack albumen, and corresponding glands are missing in these forms. Ova are forced down the oviducts by ciliary action and muscular contraction until they reach the uterus, or shell gland, at the posterior end where the shell is deposited. The uteri enter the cloaca independently.

The eggshell in most oviparous reptiles is of a parchmentlike consistency, but in some lizards and in crocodilians it is hard and rigid like that of a bird's egg. Turtle eggs are usually round, but most reptilian eggs are elongated and elliptical.

The size of the oviducts varies with the season and is at its maximum at the breeding period. In a number of reptiles the right oviduct is longer than the left. This is particularly true of snakes, in which the right ovary is situated farther anteriorly. Vestiges of the degenerate Wolffian duct are frequently found in close association with the ovaries of snakes and turtles and to a lesser degree in other reptiles.

In all reptiles, fertilization is internal and occurs in the upper part of the oviduct. The lining of this portion of the Müllerian duct is ciliated, but the beat of the cilia is in an abovarian direction, *i.e.*, away from the ovary and toward the uterus. It would seem that this would tend to prevent the ascent of spermatozoa. However, it has been discovered that in the reproductive tract of the turtle there is a narrow band of ciliated cells along the side of the oviduct where the mesotubarium is attached in which the ciliary beat is in a pro-ovarian direction. It is believed that the ascent of spermatozoa in the oviduct, at least in the turtle, is brought about by the action of this narrow band of ciliated epithelium. It has not been reported whether a similar condition exists in other reptiles. The males of all reptilian species, with the exception of *Sphenodon*, possess copulatory organs by means of which spermatozoa are introduced into the cloaca of the female.

Most reptiles are oviparous. In such forms the eggs are usually incubated by the warmth of the sun. When the young hatch they must fend for themselves.

An alligator may have from 20 to 40 eggs in a nest. The female prepares a hollow in the sand in the bank of a river or stream, places some eggs in the hollow, and then covers them over with leaves, grass, and mud. Another batch of eggs is placed on top of this, and these in turn are covered as before. Several such layers may be prepared. It takes about 2 months for the eggs to hatch. The warmth of the sun and the heat generated by the decaying vegetation aid in the incubation of the eggs. The female guards the nest, and, when the young are hatched, leads them to water and watches over them until they are strong enough to care for themselves.

In some egg-laying snakes, such as the python, the mother coils her body about the eggs and guards them throughout the period of incubation. During this time her body temperature may be from 3 to 4 degrees higher than that of the environment.

Some snakes and lizards furnish good examples of ovoviviparity, since their eggs are retained in the oviducts until the young are hatched.

Cloacal glands are present in many reptiles. They are, for the most part, hedonic in nature, but in some forms they give off a secretion with a nauseating odor and thus serve as organs of defense.

Birds. The right Müllerian duct as well as the right ovary in most birds is degenerate, and only the left oviduct is functional. Both oviducts are formed in the embryo at the same time, but that on the right side fails to develop further and only vestiges remain. Both ovaries and oviducts are functional in certain raptorial birds.

The left oviduct is long, coiled, and made up of several regions. The ostium tubae is bordered by the *fimbriated funnel*, or *infundibulum*. This is followed by a *glandular portion* in which albumen is secreted. Then follows a short *isthmus* leading to a dilated *uterus*, or *shell gland*, which opens into the cloaca by a short terminal *vagina*.

Fig. 8.11. Reproductive organs of hen. Only the left ovary and oviduct are functional. A portion of the oviduct has been cut away to expose a descending ovum. Actually only one ovum is in the reproductive tract at any one time. (*Drawn by G. Schwenk, after Duvall.*)

The reproductive tract of the hen (Fig. 8.11) has been studied thoroughly. An egg which has ruptured from the ovarian follicle through the stigma is literally swallowed by the infundibulum. Cases have been observed in which the infundibulum was seen to surround the follicle and exert a sort of tugging action, possibly facilitating the emergence of the ovum from the follicle. The egg passes down the oviduct by peristaltic contractions of the oviducal muscles and pursues a spiral course. In the upper part of the glandular region a thin but very dense layer of albumen is deposited about the *vitelline membrane* which encloses the yolk. This is known as the *chalaziferous layer*. At either end, in the longitudinal axis, the chalaziferous layer is twisted into a spiral strand, the *chalaza*. As the ovum travels farther down the oviduct, a thick, *dense layer* of albumen is wrapped about the chalaziferous layer. This forms about half of the ultimate albumen content of the egg of the hen. At this point the egg enters the isthmus. *Inner* and *outer shell membranes* (Fig. 8.12), made up

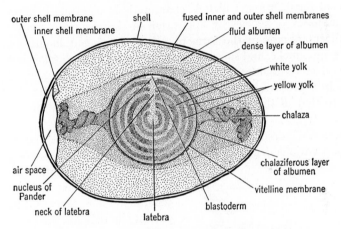

FIG. 8.12. Diagram of sagittal section of hen's egg, showing the stratification of yolk frequently encountered.

of a fibrous meshwork, are deposited in the isthmus. The so-called *fluid albumen* enters the egg in both isthmus and uterus and actually passes through the shell membranes. The hard calcareous shell is formed in the uterus. It has been estimated that under normal conditions, the time occupied by an egg in passing down the oviduct, from the time of ovulation until it is ready to be laid, is approximately 21 to 23 hours. Of this, 3 hours are spent in the glandular part of the oviduct, 2 to 3 hours in the isthmus, and 16 to 17 hours in the uterus. Conditions in other birds are undoubtedly similar to those observed in the fowl.

The formation of abnormal eggs, which are occasionally encountered, can be readily understood on the basis of the foregoing description. Double-yolked or extremely rare triple-yolked eggs are the result of almost simultaneous ovulation of more than one ovum. In passing down the oviduct in close proximity to one another, a single mass of albumen is wrapped about the yolks and a single membrane and shell is formed about the mass. Such eggs are much larger than ordinary hen's eggs. Sometimes a fully formed egg is found within another and larger egg. This unusual state of affairs can be explained by assuming that a reversal of peristalsis has occurred and that a fully formed egg from the uterus has been forced back into the glandular portion of the oviduct. When it again passes down the oviduct in the usual manner, the normal reactions of the various parts of the oviduct are evoked.

Experiments in which small cork balls were placed in the abdominal cavities of hens resulted in eggs being laid with cork balls instead of yolks. Blood clots and tissue fragments entering the oviducts may, in a similar manner, stimulate the various parts to activity. Very small or abnormally shaped eggs are frequently the result of such processes.

Internal fertilization, which is characteristic of birds, is accomplished in the majority of species by apposition of the cloacae of the two sexes. Intromittent organs in the form of *penes* are present in male ostriches, swans, geese, ducks, and some other birds. Fertilization takes place in the upper end of the oviduct. In the oviduct of the pigeon a band of cilia beating in a pro-ovarian direction has been described. The condition is similar to that of the turtle. Movement of spermatozoa up the oviduct is apparently mediated by the action of these cilia.

Mammals. Paired Müllerian ducts are present in all mammals. In this group various degrees of fusion occur between the two sides and the ducts become differentiated into regions. Fertilization is internal and generally takes place in the upper part of the oviduct.

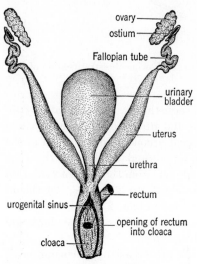

The most primitive condition found in mammals is that of monotremes, in which the Müllerian ducts remain separate and terminate independently in a urogenital sinus anterior to ureters and bladder (Fig. 8.13). Each duct consists of a narrow anterior *Fallopian tube* and a posterior expanded *uterus*. Although both oviducts are present in the platypus, apparently only the left side is functional. No eggs have ever been found in the right oviduct. The Fallopian tube opens into the coelom by an ostium bordered by a fimbriated, or fringed, infundibulum. A very thin layer of albumen

Fig. 8.13. Reproductive tract of monotreme (diagrammatic).

is formed about the small ovum in the Fallopian tube. A horny shell is deposited when the ovum reaches the uterus. When the shell of the platypus egg is first formed it is round and measures only 4 mm. in diameter, but while still in the uterus it increases in size until its diameter is approximately 10 mm. Calcium salts are then deposited in the shell, which thickens, continues to increase in size, and becomes elliptical in shape. The long axis is similar to that of the developing embryo. The size of the egg just prior to hatching is about 14.5 by 17 mm. The shell is thin and easily indented. The continued growth of the monotreme egg, after the shell has been deposited, is unique. It is due to the absorption of uterine fluids and to the plasticity of the horny shell. Usually two eggs are laid, although in some cases one or three have been observed. At the time of laying, the embryos are well along in their development and at about the same stage as a 36-hour chick embryo. They probably have been nourished to some extent by the imbibed uterine fluid. The eggs are incubated outside the body for about 2 weeks before hatching takes place. During this time the mother does not leave the nest and the eggs are kept warm by being placed between the abdomen and upturned tail. Apparently, after hatching, the young are not fed by the mother for a week or more. Not until that time are the mammary glands of the parent developed sufficiently to secrete milk. The young are born naked and rather incompletely developed. At 6 weeks of age they are about a foot long, their eyes have opened, and they are able to crawl about the burrow. Before long they begin to swim.

The egg of *Echidna*, like that of the platypus, grows while in the uterus. Nutriment from the uterus is absorbed through the shell. An average-sized egg, just after laying, measures 15 by 17 mm. The females have a depressed mammary area on the ventral side of the abdomen. A temporary brood pouch develops about this area, and here the eggs are placed and incubated until they have hatched. A group of mammary glands opens on each side of this temporary structure. After the young animal has grown to a certain size, the mother removes it from the brood pouch but returns it from time to time for feeding. At night when she is out searching for food, the baby is left in a special burrow which has been prepared for that purpose.

In other mammals the Müllerian ducts become differentiated into three distinct regions. The upper, narrow Fallopian tube, which is sometimes spoken of as the oviduct, is sharply marked off from the expanded uterus. It opens into the coelom by a funnel-shaped opening which is sometimes fimbriated. In certain species, as in the rat and mouse, the free end of each Fallopian tube is modified so as to form a completely closed capsule about the ovary (Fig. 8.16). In such forms there is no communication between the general coelom and the outside. The uterus leads to a terminal vagina which serves for the reception of the penis of the male during copulation. The lower part, or neck, of the uterus is usually telescoped into the vagina to a slight degree. This portion is referred to as the *cervix*. A canal passing through the cervix communicates with the uterine cavity by a small opening, the *os uteri internum*. Its opening into the vagina is the *os uteri externum*.

Marsupials retain the primitive paired condition of the Müllerian ducts, and two vaginae open into a urogenital sinus. In some, the vaginae fuse at their upper ends so as to form a vaginal sinus which extends posteriorly as a blind pocket or tube (Fig. 8.14). This caecumlike structure may even

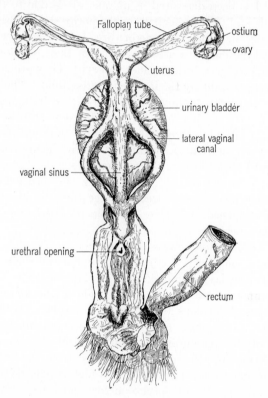

FIG. 8.14.   Dorsal view of reproductive tract of female kangaroo which had recently given birth. A single sucking young, 9 cm. long (crown-rump), was in the marsupial pouch at time of mother's death. The urogenital sinus region has been slit longitudinally and the edges spread apart.

open independently into the urogenital sinus and is sometimes referred to as a third vagina. Young which become lodged in this structure at the time of birth pass directly into the urogenital sinus. In the event that the pouchlike caecum has no opening, a rupture takes place at its blind end.

The method of reproduction in the opossum is fairly typical of the group. The eggs of the opossum, when liberated from the ovary, are microscopic in size and contain but a small amount of yolk material. Development takes place in the uteri, but the period of gestation is short and extends only over a 12-day period. There is no true placental attachment, and the young derive their nourishment from secretions coming from glands which line the uterine walls. The uterine secretion which bathes the developing embryos is often referred to as uterine "milk." It bears no resemblance to true milk formed in the mammary glands. Uterine "milk," nevertheless, is highly nutritious. The number of young developing at any one time varies from 5 to 14. Two or three litters are generally reared in 1 year.

When the young are born they are far from being fully developed (Fig. 2.26) and are slightly less than ½ in. long. It has been estimated

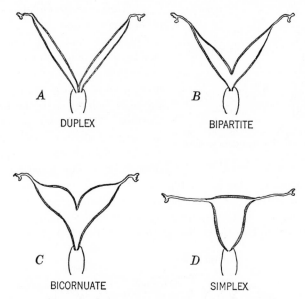

FIG. 8.15. Diagram illustrating degrees of fusion of the uterine portions of the two Müllerian ducts in four types of mammalian uteri.

that it would take about 1,750 newborn young to weigh a pound. Nevertheless, the forelimbs at birth are large and provided with strong claws which are later shed, whereas the hind legs are scarcely further developed than the embryonic limb buds of other forms. The young opossums exhibit negative geotropism (a reaction causing them to crawl upward, or against the pull of gravity) and climb with their strong claws along the fur on the underside of the mother to the fur-lined marsupial pouch. Inside the pouch is the mammary area, where they attach themselves to nipples.

The nipples then enlarge somewhat and become firmly fastened in the mouths of the young, which hold on to them securely by means of a well-developed sphincter muscle. At first the young are too weak and undeveloped to suck actively, and the mother, by contracting her abdominal muscles, actually forces milk down their throats. The milk does not get into the trachea and lungs, because at this time the opening of the trachea

FIG. 8.16. Duplex uterus of rat. The position of the cervices is indicated.

extends upward into the back part of the nasal passages. As the young animals grow and develop further, they begin to suck of their own accord.

Reproduction in the kangaroo is similar to that of the opossum. The gestation period is about 3 weeks in the large kangaroos. When the young are born, they are about the size of the little finger in man.

Eutherian mammals are characterized by possessing a single vagina which represents a fusion of two. A cloaca is present only in the embryo except in the pika, belonging to the order Lagomorpha. The uterine portions of the Müllerian ducts may fuse to varying degrees, resulting in different types of uteri (Fig. 8.15). The *duplex* uterus (Fig. 8.16), found in many rodents, elephants, some bats, conies, and the aardvark, is the most primitive of these types, with two *ora uterorum* opening separately into the vagina. In the *bipartite* uterus (carnivores, pigs, cattle, few bats, some rodents) the two sides fuse at their lower ends and open by a single

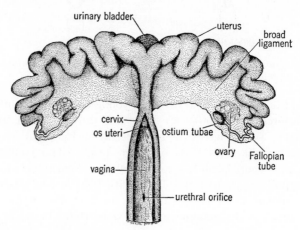

FIG. 8.17. Bipartite uterus of sow as viewed from the dorsal side. The two uterine cornua are fused at their lower ends.

os uteri (Fig. 8.17). The *bicornuate* uterus (sheep, whales, insectivores, most bats, some carnivores, many hoofed animals) is the result of a still greater degree of fusion (Fig. 8.18). In the *simplex* uterus of apes (Fig. 8.19) and man the fusion of the two sides is complete. Only the bilaterally disposed Fallopian tubes indicate the paired origin of the simplex type of uterus. Anomalous uteri of the duplex, bipartite, and bicornuate types are occasionally encountered in the human being.

The urethra coming from the bladder may join the vagina to form a urogenital sinus, or *vestibule*, which opens to the outside. In marsupials the urogenital canal is considerably elongated. In other forms it is short, and in still others, urethra and vagina have independent openings (rats, mice). Often a more or less complete fold of mucous membrane called the *hymen* marks the border of the vagina where it opens into the vestibule.

The external part of the female reproductive system is called the *vulva*. In primates, two folds of skin,

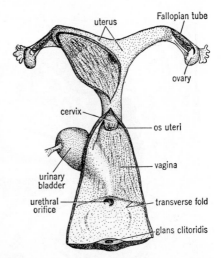

Fig. 8.18. Bicornuate uterus of mare, dorsal view. The uterine cornua are fused to a greater degree than in the bipartite type. (*After Ellenberger in Leisering's Atlas, from Sisson, "The Anatomy of the Domesticated Animals," W. B. Saunders Company. By permission.*)

the *labia minora*, are located about the margins of the opening of the vestibule. In some apes and in the human female (Fig. 8.20) two additional outer folds, the *labia majora*, make up part of the vulva. They correspond to the scrotal swellings of the male (page 295).

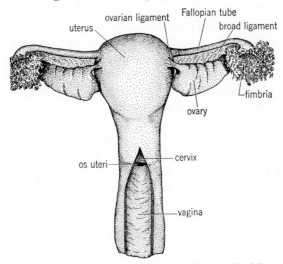

Fig. 8.19. Simplex uterus of the gorilla. The only evidence of its bilateral origin is indicated by the paired Fallopian tubes.

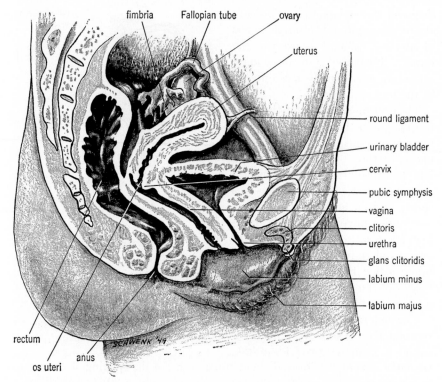

fimbria   Fallopian tube   ovary

uterus

round ligament

urinary bladder

cervix

pubic symphysis

vagina

clitoris

urethra

glans clitoridis

labium minus

labium majus

rectum

SCHWENK '49

anus

os uteri

Fig. 8.20.   Urogenital system of the human female.   (*Drawn by G. Schwenk.*)

On the ventral wall of the vestibule a small *clitoris* is situated.   It bears a rudimentary *glans clitoridis* at its tip, which is homologous with the glans penis of the male but is much smaller.   The clitoris, like the penis, is partly composed of erectile tissue and becomes erect and distended with blood during sexual excitement.   It differs from the penis, however, in that it has no connection with the urethra except in a few cases, as in rats and mice. In some forms a *clitoris bone*, homologous with the *os penis* in males of certain species, is found within the clitoris.

In addition to the above structures, certain glands, as well as rudiments remaining from the degenerated mesonephros, are associated with the female reproductive system.   The glands are generally homologues of similar structures present in the male reproductive system.   *Glands of Bartholin* correspond to Cowper's glands (bulbo-urethral glands) of males. They open into the vestibule near the hymen and secrete a clear, viscid, fluid under sexual excitement.   This serves as a lubricant during copulation. *Paraurethral glands* (*of Skene*), corresponding to the prostate glands of males, are occasionally encountered in females but are inconstant in appearance and of doubtful function.   Small *vestibular glands*, homologous with the glands of Littré, are located around the opening of the urethra and on the clitoris.   They are mucus-secreting structures.

Among the remnants of the degenerated mesonephros which are found in association with the reproductive organs of the female is the *epoöphoron,* a complex of degenerate anterior mesonephric tubules connecting to a persistent portion of the Wolffian duct. The *paraoöphoron,* a similar group of more posterior tubules, is located farther caudad. Both epoöphoron and paraoöphoron are situated in the *broad ligament* and near the ovaries. A *canal of Gärtner,* located in the wall of uterus or vagina, represents a vestige of the Wolffian duct proper. None of these structures is functional.

The wall of the Fallopian tube consists of an outer serous layer, an intermediate muscular layer, and an inner mucous membrane. The muscular coat is made up of inner circular and outer longitudinal fibers. The mucous membrane is rather thick and thrown into ridges or folds.

The epithelium lining the Fallopian tube consists of two kinds of cells: ciliated cells, which are most numerous on the fimbriated funnel and upper part of the Fallopian tube, and others of a glandular nature. No true glands are present in this part of the oviduct, however. The beat of the cilia is abovarian in direction, and this, together with peristaltic muscular contractions, serves to transport ova down the Fallopian tube. In most species of mammals it takes 3 or 4 days for fertile ova to pass down the Fallopian tube to the uterus. If fertilization does not occur, the ova die and probably disintegrate before they have even reached the uterus. How spermatozoa can ascend the Fallopian tube against the beat of the cilia has been the subject of much conjecture. Since the tubes of most mammals are coiled to some extent and undergo rhythmic peristaltic contractions, it is possible that a churning of the contents, together with movements of the spermatozoa themselves, and constantly changing ciliary eddies, currents, and whorls may result in the passage of spermatozoa up the tube against the movement of the cilia. No cilia beating in a pro-ovarian direction, and similar to those described for the pigeon and turtle, have been observed in mammals.

The wall of the uterus is also made up of three layers: a thin outer layer of *visceral peritoneum,* or *serous membrane;* a thick, middle layer of smooth muscle, the *myometrium;* and an inner layer of mucous membrane, the *endometrium.* The myometrium consists of an inner layer of interwoven circular and oblique muscle fibers and an outer longitudinal layer next to the serous membrane. The endometrium, with its *lamina propria* of reticular fibers and blood vessels, is characterized by the presence of *uterine glands* which extend down toward the muscular layer. They are simple tubular glands which often show some branching toward their blind ends. The epithelium of the uterine glands is continuous with that lining the uterine cavity. Cilia occur only sporadically.

The state of development of the endometrium with its uterine glands varies during the reproductive cycle and shows a definite periodicity correlated with changes taking place in the ovaries. The ovarian hormones *estrogen* and *progesterone* have been shown to control these endometrial changes. In primates, at rather definite intervals, a phenomenon known as *menstruation* occurs. This involves a degeneration and sloughing of the superficial portion of the endometrium accompanied by hemorrhage from the blood vessels of the tunica propria. This process lasts from 3 to 5 days, on the average. The endometrial lining is then regenerated. Further details are discussed in Chap. 9.

The vagina consists of three layers: an outer, thin layer of connective tissue which joins the vagina to surrounding tissues; a middle muscular

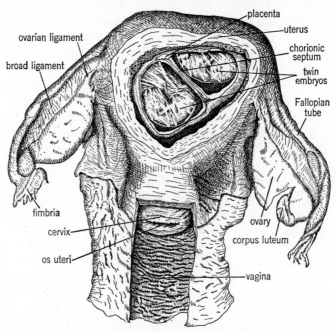

Fig. 8.21. Reproductive tract of pregnant woman, containing twin embryos. In this specimen only a single corpus luteum is present. (*Drawn by Dr. H. L. Wieman.*)

layer made up of inner circular and outer longitudinal smooth muscle fibers; and an inner mucosa. Between the mucosa and muscular layers is a zone of erectile tissue. The lining of the mucosa is thrown into folds which may be in contact under normal conditions. Longitudinal folds or columns may be present as well as transverse ridges known as *rugae*. The mucosa is devoid of glands. The mucus which lubricates the vagina comes from glands located on the cervix of the uterus. The vaginal epithelium is of a stratified, squamous type. It undergoes periodic changes in correlation with the stage of the sexual cycle. So clear-cut is this correlation that in many forms an examination of scrapings of the vaginal wall can be used with precision in determining the exact stage of the reproductive cycle. In primates these changes are not so definite as in rodents and some others.

During pregnancy profound changes occur in the uterus. The fertilized ovum becomes embedded, or implanted, in the endometrium, where it undergoes development. The *placenta* (Fig. 8.21) also forms at the implantation site. This is an organ which establishes communication between the mother and developing young by means of the umbilical cord.

Among the armadillos there is one phase of reproduction which is unique. Four young are born at a time. They are always of the same sex and are identical quadruplets. There is only one placenta, but four umbilical cords are present. All four young come from the same fertilized egg which during the early developmental stages has divided into four parts. Occasionally eight young are born. In such cases they represent two sets of quadruplets.

The connective tissue of the uterus increases in amount during pregnancy, and histological changes occur in both myometrium and endometrium. There is a marked augmentation and extension of the blood vessels which supply and drain the uterus. The entire organ grows until it is many times its original size. In animals that normally have several young at a time, there is a fairly even spacing of the embryos along the cornua of the uterus (Fig. 8.22).

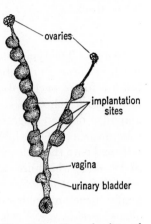

Fig. 8.22. Ventral view of rat uterus on fourteenth day of pregnancy; eight implantation sites in right horn, three in left.

The length of the *gestation period*, which extends from the time of fertilization to *parturition*, or time at which the young are born, shows great variation among mammals. The number of young born at a single delivery also is highly variable. The following table of averages lists these data for certain familiar mammals:

Animal	Gestation period, days	Number of young
Dog (collie)	63	6 to 7
Black bear	208	2 to 3
Rat	22	6 to 10
Guinea pig	62	5 to 6
Rabbit	30	4 to 6
Elephant	641	1
Cow	270	1
Sow	112 to 115	4 to 10
Mare	335	1
Chimpanzee	231	1
Man	266	1
Monkey (rhesus)	213	1
Opossum	12½	12
Kangaroo	40	1
Cat	63	4 to 7
Lion	106	2 to 3

The state of development of mammalian young at the time of birth shows a great diversity. Many marsupials are developed only to a stage that is comparable to that of an embryo of higher forms. The young of rats, mice, rabbits, and even of the human being are born in a helpless condition and require a great deal of parental care before being capable of fending for themselves. On the other hand, a guinea pig at birth has its eyes open, is covered with fur, and does not even depend on milk from its mother for food.

THE MALE

Testes. The typical testis is a compact organ, the shape of which shows much variation in members of different vertebrate classes. In all except a few low forms, each testis is composed of numbers of *seminiferous ampullae* or *tubules* which connect by means of ducts to the outside. The rounded ampullae or the elongated tubules, as the case may be, at first consist of solid masses of cells which later develop lumina, or cavities. Two types of cells make up the walls. The first of these are large, but not too abundant, *Sertoli cells*, which are supporting and nutrient elements. The others are *sex cells* (*spermatogonia*) which, by a complicated series of cell divisions, and finally a metamorphic change (*spermiogenesis*), give rise to spermatozoa. The several layers of cells that can be seen in a cross section of a fully developed seminiferous tubule (Fig. 9.11) represent different stages in the development of mature spermatozoa which finally are set free in the lumen of the tubule. At a certain stage of spermatogenesis the developing sperm cells become embedded in the Sertoli cells. It is believed that the latter serve in some manner as "nurse" cells, but the exact significance of this relationship is obscure.

In addition to their sperm-producing function, the testes of vertebrates are endocrine organs which elaborate the male hormone *testosterone*. The actual tissue in the testes which secretes testosterone has not been definitely determined, at least in the lower classes of vertebrates. In mammals, groups of cells which lie in the interstices between adjacent seminiferous tubules undoubtedly represent the endocrine elements of the testes. They are called *interstitial cells*, or *cells of Leydig*. In lower forms this tissue is apparently lacking, is obscure, or else appears only at certain times. It is thus difficult to assign an endocrine role to any specific testicular component in such animals.

In most vertebrates the testes are located in the dorsal part of the body cavity, where they first appear during embryonic development. In the majority of mammals, however, they undergo a descent to a position outside the coelom proper and come to lie in a special, pouchlike structure called the *scrotum*.

In most annual breeders the size of the testes, like that of the ovaries, fluctuates. In such forms they are largest just before the breeding period, but after the spermatozoa have been discharged, they shrink to only a fraction of their former size. Spermatogenesis begins once more, following a "resting period," and the testes return to their fully mature condition.

Amphioxus. The gonads of the male amphioxus (Fig. 2.6) are similar in form to those of the female. They are metameric structures which consist of about 26 pairs of testes projecting from the body wall into the peribranchial, or atrial, cavity. Each is almost completely surrounded by a closed coelomic pouch, the *gonocoele*. With the rupture of the wall of the gonad, spermatozoa pass into the peribranchial space and thence to the outside via the atriopore.

Cyclostomes. The gonad of the male lamprey differs but little in general appearance from that of the female. In the adult it is an unpaired structure which represents a fusion of two. The testis, even when fully developed, does not become so voluminous as does the ovary in the female. This is because of the small size of spermatozoa as compared with ova. Sperm cells break through the outer wall of the testis and are shed directly into the coelom.

The hermaphroditic condition of the gonad of the hagfish has already been alluded to (page 265).

Fishes. In elasmobranchs, the testes are paired, symmetrical structures situated at the anterior end of the coelom. There is a tendency for the right testis to be somewhat larger than the left and for the two gonads to fuse at their posterior ends. As in other vertebrates, each is suspended from the middorsal body wall by a mesorchium. In shape, the testes are roughly oval or elongated. In most other fishes they are elongated and often lobulated as well. The position of the testes corresponds in general to that of the ovaries in the female. In Dipnoi the testes are enveloped in a mass of lymphoid tissue. The male gonads vary greatly in size during the year and are extremely large at the breeding season.

Amphibians. The shape of amphibian testes shows a rough correlation with body shape. Thus, in caecilians each testis is an elongated structure which appears like a string of beads. The swellings consist of masses of seminiferous ampullae, and these are connected by a longitudinal collecting duct. In caudates the testes are somewhat shorter and irregular in outline (Fig. 8.23); in salientians they are more compact and of an oval or rounded shape (Fig. 7.10). A pronounced difference in size is apparent during breeding and nonbreeding seasons. Fat bodies are also associated with the gonads of male amphibians. They resemble those of the females in position and appearance. The size of the fat bodies varies or fluctuates with the seasons. They become smaller as the breeding season approaches and enlarge again after this season has passed.

Reptiles. The testes of reptiles are compact structures of an oval, rounded, or pyriform shape. Seminiferous tubules within the testes are long and convoluted. In snakes and lizards there is a tendency for one

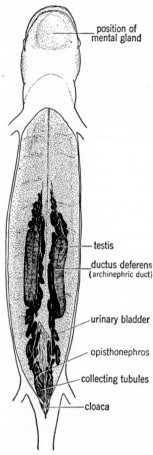

position of
mental gland

testis

ductus deferens
(archinephric duct)

urinary bladder

opisthonephros

collecting tubules

cloaca

Fig. 8.23. Urogenital organs of male salamander, *Eurycea bislineata*. The other abdominal organs have been removed. In this species the opisthonephric kidneys are reduced and practically confined to the posterior part of the body cavity.

testis to lie farther forward in the body cavity than the other. Periodic fluctuations in size of the gonads are clearly indicated in reptilians.

Birds. The round or oval shape of the bird's testis is characteristic. There is a tendency for the left gonad to be larger than the right. In such birds as the domestic fowl the testes are functional throughout the year and no periodic variations in size are noted. In others, as in the sparrow and junco, which have a limited breeding period, the testes enlarge conspicuously at the approach of the mating season. They become many times larger than the inactive gonads of the non-breeding period. Increase in the number of hours of daylight has a very definite effect in stimulating spermatogenesis in certain birds, and hence in bringing about testicular enlargement which, therefore, generally occurs during the spring of the year. This reaction is undoubtedly mediated through the pituitary gland.

Mammals. The smooth, oval-shaped mammalian testes are enclosed in a tough, fibrous envelope, the *tunica albuginea*. Each testis is divided internally into a number of *lobules* which show occasional intercommunications. Several seminiferous tubules lie within each lobule. The tubules are very much convoluted and compactly arranged. In man a single tubule when straightened out measures 12 to 27 in. in length. It has been estimated that their combined length in the human being is 750 ft. or more. The seminiferous tubules of the bull measure about 3 miles in combined

length. It is therefore not surprising that enormous numbers of spermatozoa are produced by such an extensive system of tubules. In all mammals except monotremes, the testes move from their place of origin to the pelvic region of the body cavity where they may remain permanently, or else descend farther into the scrotum. In some mammals the testes are located in the scrotum only during the breeding period and are withdrawn into the body cavity after this season has passed. Such testes shrink in size and become inactive. At the approach of the next breeding period they enlarge and again descend into the scrotum. In several species a relation between the number of hours of daylight and testicular activity has been demonstrated. In many other mammals the testes remain permanently in the scrotum and are capable of functioning at any time.

The condition in each of the major groups of mammals is listed below:

I. Intra-abdominal testes
    A. Monotremata
    B. Several Insectivora
    C. Most Edentata
    D. Proboscidea
    E. Hyracoidea
    F. Sirenia
    G. Cetacea
II. Periodic withdrawal into the body cavity
    A. Some Insectivora
    B. Tubulidentata
    C. Chiroptera
    D. Most Rodentia
III. Permanently in scrotum
    A. Metatheria
    B. Some Insectivora
    C. Some Edentata
    D. Carnivora
    E. Pinnipedia
    F. Artiodactyla
    G. Perissodactyla
    H. Primates

The scrotum actually represents a fusion of two *scrotal pouches* which develop during embryonic life. The two halves are separated internally by a partition, the *septum scroti*. Externally the line of fusion is represented by a scarlike *raphe*. Each scrotal pouch contains a diverticulum of the peritoneum known as the *vaginal sac*, or *process*. The opening into the vaginal sac from the coelom is called the *inguinal canal*. The testis lies under the peritoneum and, as it descends into the scrotum, pushes against the peritoneum of the vaginal process in such a manner as to become partly covered by a reflected fold which comes in close contact with the tunica albuginea. This peritoneal fold is called the *tunica vaginalis*. It may become entirely separated from the peritoneal lining of the remainder of the coelom. Thus the testis lies entirely outside the coelomic cavity but within the scrotum (Fig. 8.24). The descent is brought about by unequal rates of growth of the body and the ligaments (gubernaculum) which support the testis.

The inguinal canal remains open in those species in which the testes periodically withdraw into the body cavity. It closes in most forms in which the testes lie permanently in the scrotum. In the latter, the tunica vaginalis becomes a closed sac with a *visceral layer* partially surrounding the testis and a *parietal layer* lining the remainder of the scrotal cavity.

A fairly common condition encountered in human males is an *inguinal* or *scrotal hernia*. This may be congenital or occur later as the result of a rup-

Fig. 8.24. Diagram illustrating the descent of the testes in man.

ture or tearing of the tissues in the region where the cavity of the vaginal sac became separated from the rest of the peritoneal cavity. A loop of the intestine may then descend into the pouch (Fig. 8.25), resulting in an inguinal hernia or scrotal hernia, depending upon the extent to which the intestine descends.

The wall of the scrotum consists of layers of fascia, muscle, and skin. The integument is thin, folded, and often rather deeply pigmented. Just beneath the skin lies the *dartos tunic*. This is a thin layer of smooth muscle fibers closely connected to the integument. It reacts to variations in temperature in such a manner that under the influence of warmth the scrotum is relaxed and flaccid, but under the influence of cold it becomes contracted, thick, and corrugated, and pushes the testes up close to the body. A layer of muscle fibers and connective tissue called the *cremasteric fascia* lies between the dartos tunic and the parietal layer of the tunica vaginalis.

Fig. 8.25. Diagram showing a scrotal hernia in man. A loop of the intestine has pushed through the inguinal canal into the scrotum.

In various mammals the testes descend into the scrotum at different relative times. In some, descent takes place before birth; in others a considerable time may elapse before the testes arrive at their final destination.

In mammals which normally possess scrotal testes, if a gonad is abnormally retained in the body cavity, it is said to be *cryptorchid*. Cryptorchidism may be unilateral or bilateral. It may be induced experimentally. The single scrotal testis of the unilaterally cryptorchid individual is morphologically and functionally normal. A bilaterally cryptorchid man or animal is sterile. Cryptorchid testes are ordinarily considerably smaller than normal gonads, and spermatozoa are absent. Occasionally spermatogonia and spermatocytes may be present in the seminiferous tubules, but the process of spermatogenesis has obviously been interfered with. The small size of the cryptorchid testis is thus due to a reduction in the seminiferous tubules. The interstitial cells of Leydig are apparently unaffected except under certain conditions in which the cryptorchid condition is unduly prolonged. Bilaterally cryptorchid individuals are usually normal in every respect except that they lack the ability to procreate.

It has been definitely established that the scrotum serves as a temperature regulator and produces an environment for the testes which is several degrees lower than that of the body. A slightly lower temperature seems to be a requirement for spermatogenesis in most mammals. If the testes are made cryptorchid experimentally by securing them in the body cavity, they quickly undergo the profound changes that are characteristic of the condition. Restoring them to their scrotal environment will generally bring about a return to normal within a few weeks. It has been found that if the undescended testes of cryptorchid boys are lowered into the scrotum by surgical procedure or, in some cases, by giving injections of a hormone extracted from the urine of pregnant women, the testes often begin to function in producing spermatozoa. Under normal conditions the thin wall of the scrotum, its exposed position, and the reaction of the dartos tunic in responding to warmth and cold, all serve to keep the temperature of the testes relatively constant.

Birds, the only other homoiothermous vertebrates, have relatively high body temperatures and have intra-abdominal testes. However, there is some indication that even in birds a lowered temperature may be a requirement for full spermatogenesis to occur. In sparrows, for example, greatest mitotic activity in the seminiferous tubules occurs at night when the body temperature usually drops several degrees. In certain passerine birds a nodule, formed by coils of the ductus deferens, protrudes markedly into the cloaca during the height of the breeding season (page 304). Furthermore, it has been demonstrated that in many birds there is a preseasonal migration of the testes which push against the abdominal air sacs. This may exert a cooling effect upon the gonads.

Those mammals which under normal conditions have intra-abdominal testes would appear to be exceptions to the rule that a lowered temperature is a requirement for spermatogenesis. It is probable that the thermoregulatory mechanism of such mammals is not so highly organized as in others and that their body temperatures are not normally so high. Furthermore, in such mammals the testes usually lie in shallow pockets where the covering skin is unusually thin. In mammals in which there is a periodic withdrawal of the testes into the abdominal cavity during the nonbreeding season, the smaller size of the testes and the cessation of spermatogenesis during this period are undoubtedly caused to some extent by the cryptorchid condition.

In marsupials the scrotum is situated anterior to the penis, but in other mammals it lies posterior to that organ. In a few (rhinoceros, tapir, etc.) the scrotum is not typically pendulous and the descended testes lie in recesses in close proximity to the integument.

Spermatozoa. The size of the spermatozoön is extremely small as compared with that of the ovum. In vertebrates having eggs with an abundance of yolk (polylecithal) the ovum may be several hundred thousand times larger than the spermatozoön, yet both are single cells. Spermatozoa show a great variety of form. In certain invertebrates, such as crustaceans and nematode worms, the sperm cells are ameboid in appearance and move along the substratum on which they are deposited by a creeping ameboid movement. The spermatozoa of many invertebrates and of all vertebrates, however, possess long, filamentous, flagellalike tails. These are used in a whiplike manner in moving through the fluids in which they are deposited.

A spermatozoön, despite its small size, is an exceedingly complex cell. It is made up of a *head, middle piece,* and *tail.* The nucleus is located in the head surrounded by a small amount of cytoplasm. The head sometimes narrows down to a short *neck* to which the middle piece is attached. The tail is continuous with the middle piece. An *axial thread,* or *filament,* is continued throughout the length of the tail. It is enveloped by a thin, cytoplasmic capsule which does not extend to the tip. Other details have been described, but are of greater interest to the cytologist than to the comparative anatomist.

Many curious shapes are to be seen in the spermatozoa of vertebrates (corkscrew, oval, spiral, rod, hook, cone, etc.), particularly in the region of the head (Fig. 8.26). The tail, in some cases, bears an undulating membrane. The length also shows much variation and ranges from 0.018 mm. in amphioxus to 2.25 mm. in a certain toad.

Spermatozoa are usually not motile within the reproductive organs of the male. Movement is dependent upon the relative acidity and alkalinity of the sperm environment. Contact with water, in certain lower forms, excites them to activity. In other cases chemicals liberated by the eggs seem to be essential in activating the spermatozoa. In most mammals spermatozoa do not become active until mixed with secretions of the accessory sex glands. Contrary to many early reports, sperm cells do not live for an extended period after they have become freely motile. It is not surprising that the energy of such a small cell should soon be dissipated. Motility is not the only criterion of fertilizability, however. A spermatozoön may be motile but still not be able to fertilize an egg. Fertilizing ability is lost more quickly than motility. Loss of energy or of essential chemical constituents may possibly be the explanation.

In vertebrates with internal fertilization, secretions in the female reproductive tract apparently have a deleterious action on spermatozoa, the life of which is measured by hours rather than by days, as is generally believed. In artificial insemination, so widely practiced with domestic animals, it is better to collect semen fresh from the male rather than to recover it from the vagina of the female. The higher temperature of the vagina in mammals may also have a harmful effect on the spermatozoa. The condition in the bat is exceptional among mammals. Since copulation occurs in the autumn but ovulation and fertilization are delayed until the following spring, spermatozoa live for several months in the female reproductive tract without losing their fertilizing ability. During the period of inactivity they are nonmotile.

FIG. 8.26.   Various types of vertebrate spermatozoa.

In a number of other vertebrates a long period of survival within the female reproductive tract has been reported. In the salamander, *Eurycea bislineata*, for example, spermatophores are taken into the cloaca of the female in October although ovulation does not take place until near the end of the following March. The spermatozoa within the spermatheca are presumably nonmotile. Certain fishes are fertile several months after being isolated from males. In the domestic fowl, fertile eggs may be laid from 15 to 20 days after copulation, but in the duck the period is only about half as long.

The number of sperm cells produced by the male is enormous. In man a single ejaculate of semen measures about 4 cc. in volume. An average number of approximately 300 million spermatozoa is present in this quantity of seminal fluid. It has been estimated that an average man in his lifetime discharges about 400 billion sperm cells. This would be equivalent to a billion spermatozoa for every ovum liberated by the ovaries of the female. It is difficult to understand why there should be such a discrepancy in number of germ cells produced by male and female. The necessity for the motile sperm cell to seek out the egg and the many hazards which it encounters on its way would explain the large numbers of spermatozoa, at least to some extent. An enzyme, *hyaluronidase*, present in extracts of mammalian testes or sperm, is capable of dispersing the follicular cells around freshly ovulated mammalian ova. It has been suggested that the large numbers of sperm cells in an ejaculate of semen may be necessary in order to obtain a high enough concentration of hyaluronidase to disperse the closely adhering follicular cells from the ovum so that the sperm may have opportunity to penetrate the egg. In the absence of hyaluronidase, according to this idea, no fertilization occurs. Some authorities doubt the importance of hyaluronidase in this connection. At any rate, it would seem that nature is more than prodigal in supplying an abundant quantity of spermatozoa.

Male ducts. The ducts which in most vertebrates serve to transport spermatozoa to the outside of the body are the archinephric ducts or the Wolffian ducts formed in connection with the development of the kidneys. It will be recalled that the term *archinephric duct* is applied to the kidney duct in the anamniotes. The name *Wolffian duct* is given to the duct in amniotes, which forms in connection with the pronephric and mesonephric kidneys. These are really different names for the same thing (page 242). The original function of these ducts is elimination of urinary wastes. In a number of fishes and amphibians certain modified kidney tubules are employed in carrying spermatozoa from the testis to the archinephric duct. They are known as *efferent ductules*, and the archinephric duct then becomes the *ductus deferens*. Even in the amniotes, in which the mesonephros degenerates, its duct persists to become the ductus deferens and the *ductus epididymidis* (*epididymis*), the latter establishing connections with the testis via efferent ductules which are modified and persistent mesonephric tubules.

Amphioxus. Reproductive ducts are lacking in amphioxus. Spermatozoa, which have been discharged into the peribranchial chamber, are swept to the outside along with the respiratory current of water through the atriopore.

Cyclostomes. The reproductive system of the male lamprey functions in a manner similar to that of the female. Again, no ducts are present, and sperm cells, which have been liberated from the testis into the body cavity, leave through genital pores which enter the sinus in the urogenital papilla and thence pass out the urogenital aperture. At the approach of the breeding season the urogenital papilla becomes considerably longer and narrower.

Fishes. A variety of conditions is encountered in the reproductive systems of male fishes. In elasmobranchs (Fig. 16.10), small efferent ductules, leading from the testis, course through the mesorchium and connect with

certain anterior kidney tubules along the median border of the opisthonephros. Spermatozoa are thus conveyed from the testis through the efferent ductules and kidney tubules into the archinephric duct which now
serves almost entirely as a ductus deferens. It courses along the ventral
side of the opisthonephros and in young specimens is a straight tube with a
urinary function. In older specimens it becomes convoluted, its anterior
end sometimes being referred to as the *ductus epididymidis*. The posterior
portion is markedly dilated to form a *seminal vesicle*. The two seminal
vesicles open into a common *urogenital sinus*, which in turn communicates
with the cloaca through an aperture at the tip of a *urogenital papilla*. A
pair of blind *sperm sacs* passes forward from the ventral wall of the urogenital sinus. The sperm sacs are possibly remnants of the Müllerian ducts
which persist in the male. When the archinephric duct is utilized for sperm
transport its function in draining urinary wastes from the kidney is practically lost. Accessory, ureterlike, urinary ducts are then formed, particularly in the posterior part of the opisthonephros, and these take over
the urinary function.

Although in elasmobranchs the connection of testis and archinephric duct
occurs at the anterior end of the opisthonephros, in other fishes conditions
may be quite different. For example, in the cladistian, *Polypterus*, only
the posterior part of the opisthonephros becomes involved. The glomeruli
of the posterior kidney tubules frequently degenerate, so that this portion
of the kidney is concerned mostly with reproduction and loses much of its
excretory character. A sperm duct, running the length of the testis, connects, by means of posteriorly located efferent ductules, to a longitudinal
canal within the kidney. This is *not* the archinephric duct. The two, however, join posteriorly to open into a common urogenital sinus (Fig. 8.27*A*).

In *Protopterus* a longitudinal sperm duct also extends the length of the
testis. Each sperm duct leaves its testis at the posterior end, and those
from the two sides enter the cloaca through a median genital papilla (Fig.
8.27*B*). No relation to the archinephric duct is apparent even though the
sperm duct, which is not considered to be a true ductus deferens, may pass
through the posterior end of the opisthonephros. Only when the archinephric duct is utilized for sperm transport is it appropriate to use the term
ductus deferens.

The male ducts of teleosts (Fig. 8.27*C*) in many cases are entirely different in origin from those of most fishes. Their relation to the gonads is
similar to that of the oviducts in females. Folds of peritoneum enclose a
portion of the coelomic cavity, which is thus continuous with the gonad.
In the male the tube connects with the gonad by a number of anastomosing
canals and is not quite so simple in arrangement as that of the female. It
is not a true ductus deferens. A connection with the archinephric duct is
established posterior to the opisthonephros, but the two ducts in some
teleosts have independent openings.

The anterior connection of the testes and archinephric ducts, as seen in

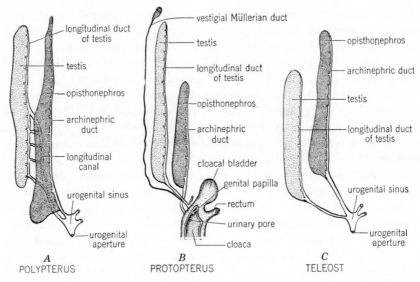

Fig. 8.27. Three types of male fish urogenital organs: *A, Polypterus; B, Protopterus;*
C, teleost. (*Modified from Goodrich.*)

elasmobranchs, seems to be most primitive. The posterior connections
found in *Polypterus* and the gradual separation of the testis duct and archinephric duct, as observed in *Protopterus* and many teleosts, probably represent deviations and specializations from the primitive condition.

Amphibians. The relationship of the reproductive and excretory systems in male amphibians is closer than is found in most fishes. It most
closely resembles the condition found in elasmobranchs. Efferent ductules
are usually connected inside the testis or along its medial border by a longitudinal canal. They course through the mesorchium, enter the anterior
part of the opisthonephros on its medial side, and may either form direct
connections with the archinephric duct or join certain kidney tubules which
in turn connect with the archinephric duct.

In caecilians the longitudinal collecting duct, which connects the lobules
of the testis, gives off small transverse canals between successive lobules.
These pass toward the kidneys to join another longitudinal duct which runs
along the lateral edge of the opisthonephros. Spermatozoa then pass
through a second series of transverse canals to join kidney tubules which
transport them to the archinephric duct.

In caudates, efferent ductules join a narrow longitudinal canal, called
Bidder's canal, which runs along *outside* the medial edge of the kidney but
within the mesorchium. Bidder's canal connects by a number of short
ducts with kidney tubules in the narrow, anterior part of the opisthonephros. Although Bidder's canal is present in females, it is rudimentary. Certain kidney tubules emerge from the lateral edge of the opisthonephros and

join the archinephric duct, which courses posteriorly (Fig. 7.9). The anterior part of the archinephric duct, or ductus deferens, is concerned primarily with transport of spermatozoa, but the posterior portion serves for elimination of urinary wastes as well. The archinephric ducts enter the cloaca independently.

In salientians (Fig. 7.10) conditions are quite similar to those of caudates, but minor variations are present. Efferent ductules enter the anterior end of the opisthonephros along its medial edge. In some forms they connect directly with the archinephric duct but in others join Bidder's canal which, in these animals, lies *within* the opisthonephros close to its medial border. Spermatozoa are then conveyed from Bidder's canal through kidney tubules to the archinephric duct, which also courses within the opisthonephros but along its *lateral* border. A Bidder's canal is present in the opisthonephros of the female, but its function, if indeed it has any, is obscure. The archinephric duct emerges from the kidney near its posterior end and passes to the cloaca. In males of several species a dilatation of the archinephric duct, as it nears the cloaca, forms a *seminal vesicle* in which spermatozoa may be stored temporarily. Seminal vesicles are very poorly developed in *Rana pipiens* and *Rana catesbeiana*, species which are commonly studied in introductory courses in zoology.

In those species having seminal vesicles, these structures are at the height of their development during the breeding season and then undergo regression. Their rise and wane, in all probability, are controlled by seasonal changes in the secretion of testosterone, the hormone secreted by the testes.

The ductus deferens proper, particularly in caudates, also varies greatly in size and is largest just prior to the breeding season. During the nonbreeding period it may be reduced to a mere thread (Fig. 8.28). The cloacae of male caudates have glandular linings, and these, too, become markedly enlarged as the mating season approaches. The cloacal glands

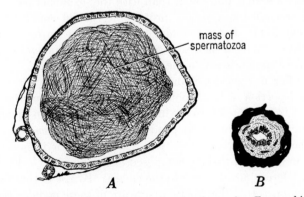

mass of spermatozoa

A   *B*

FIG. 8.28. Cross section of ductus deferens of male salamander, *Eurycea bislineata: A*, from specimen captured Mar. 21, just prior to the breeding season; *B*, from specimen obtained May 16, several weeks after the breeding season.

secrete a jellylike material which is used in forming spermatophores deposited by the males.

Reptiles. When the mesonephros of the embryo degenerates in male reptiles its duct persists as the male reproductive duct. The end of the Wolffian duct near the testis becomes greatly convoluted to become part of the epididymis. Certain persistent mesonephric tubules become modified to form efferent ductules which connect the seminiferous tubules of the testis with the epididymis. In some reptiles the epididymis is even larger than the testis. The Wolffian duct is continued posteriorly as the ductus deferens, which sometimes is straight but more often convoluted. In most reptiles the ductus deferens on each side joins the metanephric ureter, so that the two ducts enter the cloaca through a common aperture at the tip of a urogenital papilla.

Müllerian ducts commonly persist in male reptiles, but are generally very much reduced in size, and a lumen may be lacking. In the European lizard, *Lacerta viridis*, however, the Müllerian ducts of the male are as well developed as those of the female.

The epididymides and deferent ducts of such reptiles as have been studied show seasonal modifications and are apparently under endocrine control. In many lizards and other reptiles some of the posterior urinary tubules of the metanephros become enlarged periodically and produce an albuminous secretion which contributes to the seminal fluid in which spermatozoa are suspended.

Other accessory genital organs in male reptiles include glandular structures in the walls of the cloacae of snakes and lizards. In snakes these consist of a single pair of glands, but in lizards a lateral pair is present in addition. Their secretion passes into the groove formed by the hemipenes (page 311). No accessory glands are found in turtles. Scent glands in some snakes and crocodilians open into the cloaca, but these have more to do with defense or sexual allurement than with the sexual act itself. In chelonians and crocodilians a single, protrusible, penial copulatory organ is present (page 311). It bears a longitudinal groove on its upper surface. The deferent ducts from the testes open at the proximal end of the groove which conveys spermatozoa to the free end of the penis.

Birds. Efferent ductules connect with a small epididymis composed of a long coiled portion of the Wolffian duct which serves for the passage of spermatozoa from the testis to the highly convoluted ductus deferens. The deferent ducts in birds open independently into the cloaca and have no relation to the metanephric ureters (Fig. 8.29). In some passerine birds, as previously indicated, a nodule, composed of an intensely coiled portion of the ductus deferens, protrudes into the cloaca. By use of thermocouples it has been demonstrated that the temperature of these nodules is somewhat lower than body temperature. It is quite possible that this may be of importance to the spermatozoa before they can become completely mature and functional. The reproductive tracts of male birds lack accessory glands. In the few birds possessing copulatory organs (page 312), a groove on the upper surface of the single penis carries spermatozoa to its apex.

Mammals. The male duct in mammals is again the Wolffian duct. Efferent ductules which are persistent and modified kidney tubules and homologous with the similarly named structures of lower forms connect by means of a long, compactly coiled duct, the epididymis, to the ductus deferens. That portion of the epididymis to which the efferent ductules are attached is spoken of as the *globus major,* or the *caput epididymidis;* the central part is the *body,* or *corpus epididymidis;* the remainder forms the

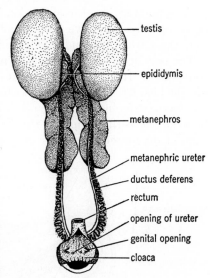

FIG. 8.29.   Urogenital system of male fowl.

tail, globus minor, or *cauda epididymidis* (Fig. 8.30). It has been estimated that in the guinea pig the total length of the portion of the Wolffian duct included in the epididymis is 9 ft. In a man it measures approximately 20 ft. Experiments have shown that when spermatozoa pass through the epididymis they undergo a physiological maturation. The secretions of the glandular lining of the epididymis may contribute to this process. In ex-

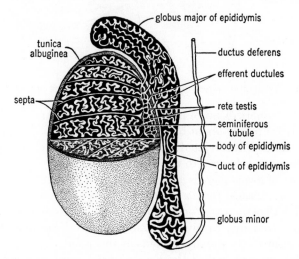

FIG. 8.30.   Diagram showing relation of mammalian testis to epididymis and ductus deferens.

periments on artificial insemination in guinea pigs, spermatozoa from the caput epididymidis have been found to be less effective in fertilizing ova than those from the cauda epididymidis.

The portion of the ductus deferens which leads from the epididymis is convoluted. It then straightens out to join the urethra a short distance below the bladder. In mammals in which the testes are located in a scrotum, the ductus deferens enters the pelvic region of the body cavity where it lies between the peritoneum and the lateral wall of the pelvis. It crosses in front of the ureter, loops over that structure (Fig. 8.31), and then courses

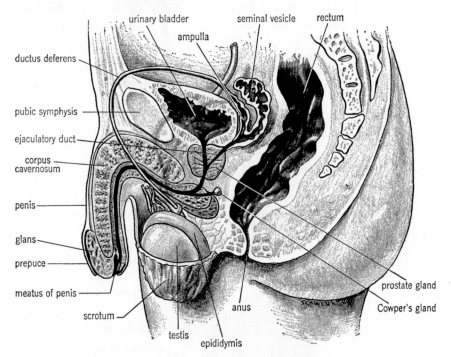

FIG. 8.31.   Urogenital system of the human male.   (*Drawn by G. Schwenk.*)

posteriorly for a short distance before entering the urethra. This peculiar state of affairs is brought about by the descent of the testis from its original abdominal position. It is related to the location of the ductus deferens during development in reference to the ureter and urethra.

In a number of forms there is an enlargement of the ductus deferens near its posterior end, termed the *ampulla*. This may function as a temporary storage place for spermatozoa and is found in such mammals as ruminants, shrews, certain rodents, carnivores, and primates. An *ampullary gland* may also connect to the ductus deferens at this point.

A glandular structure called the *seminal vesicle* may arise as a saccular diverticulum of each ductus deferens near its point of junction with the urethra. Its secretion forms an important constituent of the seminal fluid in which spermatozoa are suspended. In such mammals as monotremes, marsupials, carnivores, and cetaceans, seminal vesicles are wanting. Spermatozoa are not generally stored in mammalian seminal vesicles.

The lower portion of the ductus deferens between seminal vesicle and urethra is sometimes called the *ejaculatory duct* because of its muscular walls which aid in ejecting semen.

The urethra, which extends throughout the length of the penis, opens at the tip of that structure by means of the small *external urethral orifice*, or *meatus*. It thus serves a dual function, since both seminal fluid and urine are expelled through it. Accessory sex glands are also found associated with the urethra. The most prominent of these is the *prostate gland*. It consists of a number of large lobules opening separately into the urethra by numerous small ducts. The lobules are generally bound together by a mass of connective tissue. The prostate gland surrounds the urethra near its junction with the bladder, and its ducts enter the urethra just above the openings of the deferent ducts. Monotremes, marsupials, edentates, and cetaceans lack a prostate gland. The prostate furnishes the remainder of the seminal fluid. When the secretions of seminal vesicles and prostate gland are intermingled, they become coagulated. In the rat a special lobe of the prostate on either side lies close to the seminal vesicle (Fig. 8.32). It

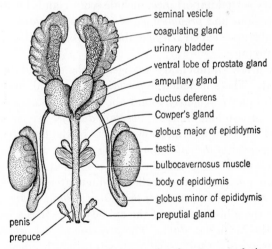

FIG. 8.32.   Urogenital organs of male rat, ventral view.

is called the *coagulating gland*, or coagulating portion of the prostate. In some species, as in the rat, just after mating a so-called *copulation plug* is present in the vagina. This is nothing more than a mass of coagulated semen. The copulation plug prevents further copulations for a time, aids in the retention of spermatozoa, and thus increases the chances of successful fertilization.

The *bulbo-urethral glands of Cowper* join the urethra at the base of the penis. During sexual excitement they secrete a clear, viscid fluid with a slightly alkaline reaction. This secretion tends to neutralize any acid which may be present in the urethra after the previous passage of urine and also helps to neutralize any acid condition in the vagina. It also facilitates the sexual act by means of its lubricating properties. Small quantities of the secretion of Cowper's glands are added to the semen. In monotremes, Cowper's glands are the only accessory reproductive glands.

In addition, numerous small *urethral glands*, or *glands of* Littré, open into the floor of the urethra. They are mucus-secreting glands.

Homologues of many of the above-mentioned accessory glands may be found in females.

The urethra is conveniently divided into three portions: (1) a *prostatic region*, surrounded by the prostate gland, (2) a short, narrow *membranous portion*, (3) a *cavernous portion* traversing the penis from base to apex.

It has been definitely established that the normal functioning of the accessory sex organs in mammals is controlled by the hormone secreted by the testes. All these structures undergo a profound regression after castration. Injection of androgenic substances (page 345) restores them to normal size, structure, and functional activity.

Other glands, which are not directly related to the sexual act but which are of secondary sexual importance, include scent glands located in the anal and inguinal regions and *preputial glands*, or *Tyson's glands*, which secrete a sebaceous substance called *smegma* about the base of the glans penis underneath the prepuce.

In the male a few rudimentary vestiges of the degenerate mesonephros may be present. These include the *paradidymis*, a small mass of surviving mesonephric tubules frequently found above the globus major of the epididymis. One or two long, narrow, *aberrant ductules* are occasionally present, connected to the upper and lower parts of the epididymis. A small vesicle, the *appendix of the epididymis*, lying against the surface of the epididymis, represents such a detached and persistent mesonephric tubule.

Persistent homologues of the Müllerian ducts are also present in males. These include the small *appendix of the testis (hydatid of Morgagni)*, which lies just under the globus major of the epididymis. It is a remnant of the upper end of the Müllerian duct. The *prostatic utricle (vagina masculina, uterus masculinus)* is a short, saclike structure which opens into the posterior portion of the prostatic urethra. It represents the fused lower, or posterior, ends of the Müllerian ducts.

Copulatory organs. Fertilization always takes place in a fluid medium. Spermatozoa, which swim by a whiplike movement of the long, flagellum-like tail, must have some medium in which they can travel in order to gain access to the ova. In most aquatic animals external fertilization takes place and water furnishes the medium by means of which spermatozoa reach the eggs. In terrestrial forms a liquid environment must be provided. In such animals internal fertilization is the rule, and fluids supplied by both male and female furnish the means by which spermatozoa may come in contact with ova. In a number of terrestrial vertebrates, spermatozoa are transferred from male to female by cloacal apposition. However, in most terrestrial forms and even in many aquatic species, intromittent, or copulatory, organs are present in the male by means of which spermatozoa suspended in seminal fluid are deposited directly within the reproductive tract of the female.

Fertilization usually takes place in the upper part of the oviduct. In those forms in which the egg is surrounded by a shell, fertilization must take place before the shell has been formed about the ovum. Sperm cells do not generally reach the upper part of the oviduct entirely under their own motive power. They are aided by churning muscular movements of the female reproductive organs, action of cilia, and other factors.

A number of types of intromittent organs exists among vertebrates. Since they are by no means all homologous, it is best to consider them separately.

Fishes. Although most fishes are oviparous, many lay fertile eggs or else give birth to living young. In fishes, copulation with internal fertilization occurs only in elasmobranchs, holocephalians, and some teleosts. Among elasmobranchs are found oviparous, ovoviviparous, and viviparous species. Copulation is accomplished by means of *clasping organs* (Fig. 8.33), modifications of the medial portions of the pelvic fins of males, used for transport of spermatozoa. Each clasper is provided with a medial groove, the middle portion of which actually serves as a closed tube, since the edges overlap in the manner of a scroll. The anterior opening into the clasper tube is termed the *apopyle;* the posterior exit is the *hypopyle.* Spermatozoa enter the apopyle which is situated close to the cloaca. In sharks and dogfish a sac, the *siphon,* with heavy muscular walls, lies just beneath the skin in the posterior, ventral, abdominal region. Its anterior portion ends blindly, but posteriorly it communicates with the apopyle. Direct observations indicate that the siphon is used with some force in the ejection of spermatozoa. Under normal conditions the apopyle is open and sea water is drawn into the siphon. The clasper tube gradually fills with spermatozoa. During

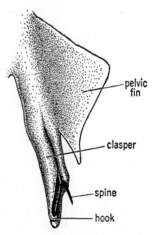

FIG. 8.33. Pelvic fin of male dogfish, *Squalus acanthias,* showing clasper in detail. (*After Petri.*)

the copulatory act the clasper is bent in such a manner as to close the apopyle. Contraction of the siphon forces water down the clasper tube, ejecting the spermatozoa already there, into the uterus of the female.

Not all elasmobranchs have hollow siphons. In skates and rays the space normally occupied by the siphon is almost filled with glandular tissue. The function of this integumentary *pterygopodial gland* is obscure.

It is probable that during copulation only one clasper is inserted into the cloaca of the female. This has been noted during observation of copulation in *Scyllium* in an aquarium. The coition lasted for 20 minutes. Motion pictures of rays, taken during the act of mating, have also revealed that but a single clasper is inserted at a time. Unqualified data are lacking, however, since the difficulty of observing such a process under natural conditions is obvious.

In holocephalians, clasping organs similar to those of elasmobranchs are present. In addition, however, a pair of *anterior claspers* extends from a pouchlike depression in front of the pelvic fins. Also a *frontal clasper* protrudes from the top of the head. It is not clear how these are used.

In those teleosts in which internal fertilization occurs, the anterior border of the anal fin of the male may be elongated posteriorly to form an intromittent organ, the *gonopodium* (Fig. 8.34). The common tropical aquarium

FIG. 8.34. *A,* showing anal fin of female poeciliid fish; *B,* illustrating how anterior portion of anal fin of male is modified to form the gonopodium.

fish called the "guppy" is an example of an ovoviviporous teleost possessing a modified fin of this type. Other copulatory organs in teleosts include modifications of the hemal spines of certain caudal vertebrae or of an outgrowth posterior to the anus.

Amphibians. Although fertilization in salientians is external, a peculiar process called *amplexus*, or false copulation, takes place. The male mounts upon the back of the female and clasps her just behind the forelegs. Swollen glandular thumb pads aid in making his hold secure. So strong is the clasp reflex that it is very difficult to dislodge a male during amplexus. The body of the female is compressed by the strong grasp of the male, and the resulting increase in internal pressure aids in extrusion of the eggs. Spermatozoa are shed over the eggs as they pass from the cloaca.

Internal fertilization in caudates has been discussed previously (page 277). No copulation or amplexus takes place in this group.

A peculiar method of internal fertilization is noted in the caecilians. The muscular cloaca of the male is protrusible to a marked degree and serves as a sort of copulatory organ when the cloacae of the two sexes are in apposition.

Reptiles. The only reptile entirely lacking in copulatory organs is *Sphenodon.* In other reptiles two types of structures are recognized, one being typical of snakes and lizards and the other of turtles and crocodilians.

In snakes and lizards, peculiar paired structures called *hemipenes* are employed in an intromittent manner. They consist of saclike structures normally lying under the skin adjacent to the cloaca at the base of the tail and frequently containing rigid spines. Although hemipenes are also present in the female they are very small and of doubtful function. Each hemipenis bears a spiral furrow which may be so deep as to give the organ a notched appearance (Fig. 8.35). The hemipenes are everted during copulation, and spermatozoa pass down the grooves into the cloaca of the female. Retractor muscles are present by means of which the hemipenes may be withdrawn. These structures do not contain erectile tissue as do the penes of higher forms and are not homologous with

FIG. 8.35. Hemipenes of lizard, *Platydactylus.* (*After Unterhössel.*)

them. In some male lizards small conelike projections from the integumentary *femoral pores,* or *glands,* which are situated on the undersurfaces of the thighs, are used in clasping the females during copulation.

A single penis is present in turtles and crocodilians. It is apparently derived from paired thickenings or ridges in the anterior and ventral walls of the cloaca and is made up of connective and erectile tissue. The paired masses of erectile tissue are called *corpora cavernosa.* The penis can be extruded and retracted. A homologous structure, the *clitoris,* is present in females. At its proximal end the penis divides, indicating a bilateral origin, but the distal end is single and free. A groove along the dorsal surface provides for the passage of spermatozoa. During the act of mating the corpora cavernosa are filled and distended with blood and the penis is firm and enlarged. It is then said to be *erect.* This property of erectile tissue makes it possible for the penis to serve as an intromittent organ during the act of copulation. Unless the penis becomes erect, copulation is impossible. In crocodilians the penis is longer and the groove is deeper than in turtles.

Birds. A penis is present in only a few birds such as ducks, geese, swans, and ostriches. It is a single structure built upon the same plan as that of crocodilians. A clitoris is present in the females of these species. In many other birds a rudimentary penis can be identified. Most birds copulate by cloacal apposition.

Mammals. A single penis is typical of mammals, and its homologue, the clitoris, is present in all females. In monotremes, under normal conditions, the penis lies on the floor of the cloaca. It is similar to the organ in turtles, crocodilians, and birds except that the groove on the dorsal side has become a closed tube. Moreover, the tube is surrounded by erectile tissue known as the *corpus spongiosum*, which differs somewhat in structure from that of the paired corpora cavernosa. The canal in monotremes is believed to carry only spermatozoa, since the urethra has a separate opening into the cloaca (Fig. 8.36). In this respect the penis of the monotreme

FIG. 8.36. Diagrammatic longitudinal section through cloacal region of male monotreme, showing penis in retracted position. (*After Boas, based on Wiedersheim, "Comparative Anatomy of Vertebrates," copyright* 1907 *by The Macmillan Company and used with their permission.*)

differs from that of all other mammals. The end of the penis is enlarged to form a sensitive, swollen *glans.* The glans penis in monotremes and other mammals differs from that of reptiles in being surrounded by a fold of skin termed the *prepuce,* or *foreskin.* Erectile tissue is present in the glans. This structure in *Echidna* is peculiar in being divided into two double-lobed knobs (Fig. 8.37*A*). In the platypus the glans is bifurcated at its tip and covered with soft spines. The sperm canal in monotremes is reported to open onto the surface of the glans through a number of small apertures. Spermatozoa are scattered over a considerable surface at the time of copulation, which, in the platypus, occurs in the water.

Marsupials lack a cloaca, at least in the adult stage. The marsupial penis, therefore, does not lie within a cloaca as in monotremes. It is covered by a sheath and opens to the outside of the body just underneath the anus. It may be protruded and retracted. As previously noted, the scrotum in marsupials is anterior to the penis. The urethra in this and subsequent groups carries both urine and spermatozoa. The urinary duct, which in the monotremes leads to the cloaca, has become closed off in marsupials. The two corpora cavernosa are separated by a septum. The urethra is surrounded by the erectile corpus spongiosum. In several marsupials the tip of the penis is bifurcated (Fig. 8.37*B*). Usually three pairs of bulbo-urethral, or Cowper's, glands open into the urethra at the base of the penis. These and the preputial glands are the only accessory glands found in marsupials.

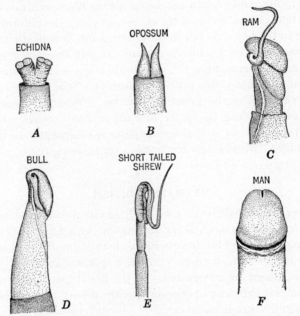

Fig. 8.37. Various types of mammalian glans penis. (*C and D, after Böhm, from Sisson, "The Anatomy of the Domesticated Animals," W. B. Saunders Company. By permission.*)

In the Eutheria, there is a tendency for the penis to be directed forward, and in all forms possessing a scrotum, the penis is located anterior to that structure. It is situated along the midline of the abdomen and usually in a horizontal position. In most forms, the penis lies within a sheath from which it can be protruded and retracted. In primates, however, it is permanently exserted and a preputial sheath, or foreskin, covers and protects only the sensitive glans. In a number of mammals a *penis bone (os penis, os priapi)* develops in the septum between the corpora cavernosa. This helps to increase the rigidity of the penis, which normally becomes erect by distension with blood. Penis bones are present in members of the orders Rodentia, Carnivora, Chiroptera, Cetacea, and lower Primates. In a walrus, the os penis is extremely large. In some species of whales it may attain a length of 6 ft.   Only a single corpus cavernosum is present in cetaceans.

The glans penis is really the enlarged distal end of the corpus spongiosum covered with thin and delicate skin.   It is supplied with numerous sensory-nerve end bulbs and is extremely sensitive to certain stimuli.   Many variations in shape and structure are to be observed (Fig. 8.37).   In the cat the glans bears numerous horny papillae or spines which undoubtedly function as a sexual irritant during copulation.   Lions and tigers possess similar spines, but they are not so prominent.   In certain ruminating animals, such as sheep, giraffes, and certain antelopes, a long filament, traversed by the urethra, extends from the tip of the glans.   In sheep the filiform appendage is attached to the left side, but in other ruminants it is median in position. It contains erectile tissue which is continuous with the corpus spongiosum.

Anomalous development of the vertebrate penis is encountered now and then.   Most frequently this takes the form of a failure of the urethra to continue to the tip of the penis, so that the urogenital opening may be located anywhere along its under (dorsal) surface.   Such a condition is known as *hypospadias*.   A hypospadic penis is comparable to the grooved penis of reptiles.   More rarely the urethra opens along the upper (ventral) side of the penis (*epispadias*).

HERMAPHRODITISM

The term *hermaphroditism* is used to designate a condition in which the reproductive organs of both sexes are present in a single individual.   In many invertebrates and lower vertebrates hermaphroditism is not uncommon, but in higher forms it appears only as a sporadic anomaly.   Two types of hermaphroditism are recognized.   In the first type, known as *true hermaphroditism*, an individual possesses gonads of both sexes either as separate ovaries and testes or as an *ovotestis*, in which elements of the two gonads are combined within a single organ.   A true hermaphrodite is said to be *monoecious*.   The opposite term, *dioecious*, is used to refer to the more usual condition in which the sexes are separate.   *False, spurious,* or *pseudohermaphroditism* is a condition in which the individual possesses the gonads of only one sex but the external genitalia and secondary sex characteristics may closely resemble those of the opposite sex.   Since the genital organs of both male and female have a common embryonic origin, and because close homologies exist between the various structures, it is not surprising that faulty development, resulting in the various forms of hermaphroditism, should occasionally be encountered.

Cyclostomes.   The hagfish is a true hermaphrodite.   Only the left gonad develops fully.   The single gonad consists of anterior ovarian and posterior testicular tissue.   A single individual, however, functions as either male or female, since either one or the other region becomes functional.   It is reported that a single animal may at times function as a male and at another time as a female. If this is true, it is an example of what is called *protandrous hermaphroditism.*

Lampreys are normally dioecious, but specimens have been found which show evidence of hermaphroditism. Ammocoetes larvae, on the other hand, show a high incidence of hermaphroditic gonads.

Fishes. Although hermaphroditism occurs but rarely in fishes, it has been observed in such teleosts as the ling, herring, cod, and mackerel. The sea basses *Serranus scriba, hepatus,* and *cabrilla* are considered to be hermaphroditic under normal conditions and have even been reported to fertilize their own eggs. In the daurade, *Chrysophrys auratus,* another teleost, eggs and sperm ripen alternately within the gonad. Specimens of other teleosts are sometimes found with an ovary on one side and a testis on the other.

Amphibians. Among salientians occasional hermaphrodites are encountered. The newt, *Triton taeniatus,* is an example of the condition in caudates. Bidder's organ in the male toad (page 267) has been shown to be capable of developing into a functional ovary. Numerous cases of sex reversal in amphibians have been reported under experimental conditions.

Reptiles. Functional hermaphroditism is not known to occur in reptiles.

Birds. The bisexual potencies of birds have been subjected to much experimental analysis. After removal of the functional left ovary, the capacity of the rudimentary right gonad of the female domestic fowl to develop into a testislike structure has been demonstrated. Such modified gonads may elaborate male hormone but have not been shown to be capable of producing mature spermatozoa. A single case of true sex reversal in birds was reported in 1923. A fowl which at one time had laid eggs and reared several broods was found at a later period to have mated successfully with a hen and fathered two chicks. This is the only case of the sort that has been scientifically verified.

A peculiar condition referred to as *gynandromorphism* has been observed in the domestic fowl, pheasant, and other birds. Of four known cases among certain European finches, three had male plumage on the right and female plumage on the left, whereas the fourth was just the opposite. Only one of the first three cases was subjected to anatomical study, and in this specimen a testis was found on the right side and an ovary on the left. The explanation of the origin of such an unusual condition is obscure.

Mammals. True hermaphroditism among mammals is extremely rare. It has frequently been described in pigs in which it occurs about once in a hundred thousand animals. Only about 25 cases of true hermaphroditism in human beings are known in all medical literature. In no case is there any record of production of both eggs and spermatozoa.

Pseudohermaphroditism in the male is the most common sexual abnormality among mammals. In human beings the presence of a hypospadic penis, accompanied by a failure of the testes to descend, brings about a condition in which the external genitalia of the male come to resemble those of the female.

Sometimes in a female the ovaries descend to the labia majora and the clitoris enlarges so that the masculine condition is simulated. Accompanying these anomalous developments, unusual endocrine factors may be at work which bring about various degrees of development of the accessory sex organs and secondary sex characters of the opposite sex. On the other hand, hormonal functioning may be perfectly normal.

All the above changes may be traced back to faulty development during embryonic life, but the actual cause of the abnormal development is unknown. Experiments involving the injection of certain hormones at various times during prenatal and early postnatal life have been successful in evoking permanent abnormalities in the reproductive organs of both sexes. Certain of these changes are comparable to conditions sometimes encountered in hermaphrodites.

Of special interest is the *freemartin*. When a cow has heterosexual twins, in a large percentage of the cases the female co-twin is sexually abnormal and is known as a freemartin. The reproductive organs of the freemartin have been modified in a masculine direction. In such cases, during early embryonic development, there is an anastomosis of the blood vessels of the two. Some humoral factor, undoubtedly carried to the female member, has a profound influence on her developing reproductive organs, bringing about an abnormal persistence and further development of Wolffian-duct derivatives and a suppression of those structures derived from the Müllerian duct. The exact factors responsible for this are obscure. On the other hand, the marmoset, a small platyrrhine monkey, also may have heterosexual twins with an anastomosing circulation, yet the female co-twin is sexually normal and a condition comparable to the freemartin does not occur.

SUMMARY

1. The reproductive system consists of primary and accessory sex organs. The primary organs are the paired gonads: testes in the male and ovaries in the female. Spermatozoa are formed in the testes, and ova in the ovaries. Gonads are derived from mesoderm and arise from the medial sides of the opisthonephric or mesonephric kidneys as thickened genital ridges which project into the coelom. The accessory sex organs are the ducts and glands which provide for the transport of eggs or spermatozoa to the outside of the body. The opisthonephric duct (in anamniotes) or the Wolffian duct (in amniotes) becomes the reproductive duct, or ductus deferens, in the male. The Müllerian duct, or oviduct, in the female of elasmobranchs and caudate amphibians arises by a splitting of the archinephric duct. In other forms an invagination of the peritoneum covering the opisthonephros or mesonephros, as the case may be, closes over to form the Müllerian duct, which,

nevertheless, is generally considered to be a phylogenetic derivative of the kidney duct. Ducts are lacking in amphioxus and cyclostomes.

2. Eggs develop in ovarian, or Graafian, follicles within the ovaries. When fully developed, they break out of the ovaries into the coelom. Each oviduct generally opens into the coelom by a funnel-shaped ostium, which has been homologized with one or more peritoneal funnels of the pronephric kidney. The oviducts of teleost fishes are derived in a different manner and may not be homologous with those of other vertebrates.

3. In forms below mammals the paired oviducts are separate and usually open independently into a cloaca. In the higher mammals a cloaca no longer is present, except in the pika. Each oviduct differentiates into three regions: Fallopian tube, uterus, and vagina. Various degrees of fusion occur from distal to proximal ends, and different types of uteri result. The Fallopian tubes always remain paired. In higher mammals, vagina and urethra usually have a common opening to the outside. In a few groups, however, separate openings are present. The young in viviparous and ovoviviparous species develop within the uterus.

4. The Wolffian duct in amniotes disappears or is nonfunctional in the female, but its remnants, together with those of the degenerated mesonephros, are frequently found associated with the female reproductive organs.

5. Certain accessory glands associated with the female reproductive tract secrete mucus, which serves to lubricate the vagina during copulation. Fluids secreted by the Fallopian tubes and uterus may aid in the passage of ova down the reproductive tract and, in those forms with internal fertilization, in the passage of spermatozoa to the upper part of the oviduct where fertilization takes place.

6. In males, spermatozoa are formed within seminiferous ampullae or tubules in the testis. Each ductus deferens establishes connections with the testis generally by means of an epididymis and persistent kidney tubules called efferent ductules. In the anamniota the epididymis and ductus deferens consist of portions of the archinephric duct which may serve in some cases as an excretory duct as well as for the passage of spermatozoa. In the amniota, however, the epididymis and ductus deferens are formed from the persistent Wolffian duct, which is entirely dissociated from the ureter of the metanephric kidney.

7. The testes are located in the abdominal cavity except in a number of mammals. In most mammals they are either temporarily or permanently situated in a pouchlike scrotum outside the body proper. The scrotum serves as a temperature regulator.

8. Remnants of the Müllerian duct persist in the males of many species and are found associated with the reproductive organs.

9. Accessory glands, particularly in mammals, secrete seminal fluid in which spermatozoa are suspended and which are necessary not only for the

viability of the spermatozoa but for their transport through the reproductive tracts of both male and female.

10. In most vertebrates with internal fertilization, copulatory organs are used in transferring spermatozoa from male to female. In fishes these usually consist of modifications of fins. In snakes and lizards, paired hemipenes are present; but in turtles, crocodilians, certain birds, and all mammals, a single penis serves the purpose. The penis consists largely of erectile tissue which, when distended with blood, causes the organ to become firm and erect, and only then can it serve as an intromittent organ. In some forms a penis bone contributes to the rigidity of the organ. The urethra coming from the urinary bladder passes through the penis in all mammals except the monotremes. It thus serves for the passage of both urinary and seminal fluids.

11. The parallel development of male and female reproductive organs is striking. The various structures in each sex have definite homologies with those of the opposite sex.

12. The close structural relationship between excretory and reproductive organs is very apparent in vertebrates, but the evolutionary trend is toward a complete separation of the two systems.

CHAPTER 9

ENDOCRINE SYSTEM

A vast amount of research has been carried out in attempting to discover the functions of the endocrine glands, or glands of internal secretion. Many extremely important discoveries have been made concerning the activities of these glands in health and disease. Of special interest to the comparative anatomist is the fact that the endocrine glands occur, with some uniformity, in all vertebrates and that they make up a definite organ system of the body. Although each gland has its particular and specific functions, nevertheless there is a rather close interrelation among them. Some of the glands making up the endocrine system, however, show closer interrelationships than do others. The science of *endocrinology* is concerned with the study of the structure, function, and interrelationships of these glands.

All the organs making up the endocrine system have one characteristic in common: no duct is present to carry off the secretory product or products. This is quite in contrast to the exocrine glands. The secretions, which are known as *hormones*, instead of passing through a duct go directly into the blood or lymph and are carried to all parts of the body by the circulating fluid. The secretions are of a chemical nature, bringing about certain changes in other parts of the body. These may affect the body generally or else act very specifically on only a certain organ or part of an organ, such tissues being referred to as "targets."

The nervous and endocrine systems are the dominating and coordinating systems of the body. The nervous system exerts its control through nerves which are distributed directly to the various body structures. The endocrine system has a simpler method in that its means of control is humoral, the secretions or hormones being carried passively to all parts of the body via the blood and lymphatic vessels.

Certain glands play a dual role as regards their method of secretion. For example, the pancreas is an exocrine gland with a duct or ducts opening directly or indirectly into the intestine. Its exocrine secretion is rich in enzymes which are of great importance in the process of digestion. Scattered among the alveoli, or groups of cells which form the exocrine secretion, are irregular masses of an entirely different type of cell. Such groups of cells are known as the *islands (islets) of Langerhans*. They are believed to elaborate the internal, or endocrine, secretions of the pancreas. The hormones, of which there are probably two, are known as *insulin* and *glucagon*, respectively. The ovaries and testes are cytogenic organs since they produce the reproductive cells. However, they have an endocrine function in addition, the endocrine secretions being formed in tissues which are quite different from those giving rise to ova and spermatozoa.

Although the thymus and pineal glands (pages 233 and 574) have long been classified as endocrine glands, their inclusion among the organs of internal secretion has been challenged. Very striking evidence has been presented to show that the thymus gland and pineal body have endocrine functions, but further work is necessary before they can be indisputably included in the endocrine system. Most endocrinologists today are of the opinion that the thymus gland is a lymphoid organ and that the pineal body is but a curious vestigial structure.

THYROID GLAND

Perhaps the most familiar gland of the endocrine system is the thyroid. In the human being it is located in the lower part of the neck region, lying ventral and lateral to the trachea just posterior to the larynx. Ordinarily the thyroid gland is inconspicuous, but when enlarged, as in certain diseases, it may protrude prominently. An enlarged thyroid gland is commonly known as a *goiter*, of which there are several types.

The thyroid may be considered to be almost as typical a vertebrate organ as the notochord. Its histological structure is similar in all vertebrates. The gland consists of varying numbers of rounded *thyroid follicles* of different sizes which are separated from each other by delicate strands of connective tissue (Fig. 9.1). Each follicle is normally lined with a single layer

A   B

FIG. 9.1. Sections through thyroid glands: *A*, salamander, *Ambystoma texanum; B*, rat (same magnification).

of cuboidal epithelial cells enclosing a mass of viscid material known as *colloid*. The colloid represents the stored-up product of the secretory epithelial cells, the amount present fluctuating with changes in physiological activity of the gland. The epithelial cells are low and flattened when the thyroid is inactive, and tall and columnar when the gland is secreting to capacity.

The hormone of the thyroid gland is *thyroxin*, an amino acid containing approximately 65 per cent iodine. It is combined with other amino acids in the gland to form a large protein molecule called *thyroglobulin*. This then passes into the follicle where it is stored as colloid. Thyroxin must be separated from the other amino acids of the thyroglobulin molecule by enzymic action before it can leave the gland and enter the body fluids. When it does so it becomes linked with blood proteins and circulates through the body in that form. It has been reported that another compound, *triiodothyronine*, much more potent in its action than thyroxin, and apparently representing thyroxin which has been altered chemically, is the actual form of the hormone affecting the tissues. The hormone controls the rate of metabolism of the entire body. It also affects other endocrine glands, particularly the anterior lobe of the pituitary body, and the thyroid may in turn be affected by them.

There is much evidence that administration of certain drugs such as thiourea, thiouracil, and sulfonamides prevents the cells of the thyroid from synthesizing the thyroid hormone.

Protochordates. No thyroid gland is present in the protochordates. Some comparative anatomists have homologized the glandular, ciliated groove in the ventral wall of the pharynx of tunicates and amphioxus, known as the *endostyle*, with the thyroid gland of the vertebrates. There is little evidence for this, however. The endostyle of the protochordates is clearly a structure which aids in trapping food particles which are carried to the remainder of the digestive tract.

Cyclostomes. A *subpharyngeal gland*, sometimes referred to as the endostyle, is present in the ammocoetes larva of the lamprey. It lies beneath the floor of the pharynx, roughly between the first and fifth gill pouches. The subpharyngeal gland is a complicated structure which possibly functions as a mucous gland. Its orifice is associated with a system of ciliated grooves in the pharyngeal wall. Five types of cells have been described in the gland. At the time of metamorphosis certain of these cells lose their cilia, change their shape, and become arranged in the form of typical thyroid follicles. Because of this, the endostyle in such protochordates as amphioxus and tunicates has been regarded in the past as the forerunner and homologue of the thyroid gland of higher forms. Experiments in which radioactive iodine has been used as a tracer substance show that the endostyles of tunicates fail to concentrate iodine, whereas this element accumulates rapidly in certain cells of the ammocoetes subpharyngeal gland even before they become organized as thyroid follicles. Other cells apparently do not have this ability. These findings indicate that only a portion of the ammocoetes subpharyngeal gland, and not the entire organ, is the homologue of the thyroid gland and that the homologies of the endostyles of the protochordates with the thyroid of higher forms are therefore questionable.

The fact that the thyroid first makes its appearance in the embryos of higher forms as a median, ventral diverticulum of the pharynx is also of special interest in this connection.

In the hagfish the thyroid is composed of rounded or ovoid capsules embedded in fat. They are in a median position, are arranged separately or in groups between the pharynx and ventral aorta, and lie between the gill pouches on either side.

Fishes. In all fishes a thyroid gland appears early in embryonic development. Its location in the adult shows considerable variation. In elasmobranchs the thyroid is a single compact organ located posterior to the mandibular symphysis and just anterior to the point where the ventral aorta bifurcates into the afferent branchial arteries.

In teleosts it is usually paired and lies near the first branchial arch on either side. In some, as in the perch, it is more diffuse and consists of small masses which lie under the ventral aorta and scattered along the paths taken by the afferent branchial arteries.

Although the thyroid gland in the Dipnoi is arranged in a single mass, it shows some indication of being a paired structure, since it is made up of two prominent lateral lobes connected by a constricted central portion. It lies under the epithelium covering the tongue, anterior to the muscles of the visceral skeleton and just above the symphysis of the hyoid apparatus.

The thyroid glands of fishes reared on inadequate diets may become goitrous. Fish hatcheries must take precautions to see that enough iodine is present in the water to prevent abnormalities in growth due to improper function of the thyroid gland.

Amphibians. In caudates the development of the thyroid gland has been studied in several species. It appears very early in a developing embryo in the ventral wall of the pharynx as an unpaired structure which soon divides into two. In the adult salamander the glands lie on either side of the throat region on the ventral side and slightly anterior to the aortic arches. The thyroid vein, a tributary of the external jugular vein, passes ventral to the gland. By following the course of this vessel the thyroid gland may easily be found (Fig. 9.2). The number of follicles in the thyroid varies considerably. Within a given species the number seems to be correlated with the size of the animal. For example, in a small species, such as *Eurycea bislineata*, as few as five follicles have been observed in the gland of a medium-sized individual, but as many as 14 may be

thyroid gland

Fig. 9.2. Ventral view of lower jaw of salamander, *Ambystoma texanum*. The skin has been removed to show the position of the thyroid glands.

present in a larger specimen.   The average number for this species is 8.8.

Among salientians the thyroid of the frog has been most carefully stud-ied.   Here too the gland is paired and on each side appears as an oval-shaped structure located lateral to the hyoid apparatus in the notch formed by the junction of the lateral- and thyro-hyoid processes.   It is rather deeply concealed, and this, together with the small size of the structure, accounts for the difficulty in finding it by ordinary dissection.

It has been demonstrated that if the thyroid rudiment is removed from amphibian tadpoles complete metamorphosis fails to occur.   The animals continue to grow; in fact they may become larger than normal tadpoles and their lungs and reproductive organs will ultimately develop.   If such ani-mals are fed thyroid substance they soon undergo metamorphosis, the tail being resorbed, the limbs developing, and the mouth undergoing a pro-

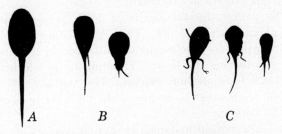

Fig. 9.3. Toad tadpoles in which acceleration of metamorphosis has been brought about by thyroid feeding: *A*, control; *B*, effect of 5 days of thyroid feeding; *C*, effect of 15 days of thyroid feeding.   (*After Gudernatsch.*)

nounced transformation.   It has long been known that when small tadpoles are fed with thyroid substance they stop growing and undergo a spectacular early metamorphosis, quickly being transformed into tiny frogs or toads (Fig. 9.3).   Even today this reaction is considered to be one of the most sensitive tests for the presence of thyroid hormone.   It seems, furthermore, that administration of elemental iodine to tadpoles will hasten metamor-phosis in both normal animals and those from which the thyroid gland has been removed.   It would seem, therefore, that when an adequate amount of iodine is present the animals can utilize it even in the absence of the gland. However, such tadpoles must have attained a certain degree of develop-ment before they are able to respond to iodine or to the thyroid hormone itself.   There is quite a marked variation in the response of different am-phibian species.   The caudate *Necturus* seems to be incapable of metamor-phosing under any conditions (page 524).

The process of ecdysis, or periodic shedding of the corneal layer of the skin, is also at least partly under control of the thyroid hormone.   Amphib-ians in which the thyroid glands have been extirpated fail to undergo ecdysis.   The dead layers of skin pile up, and the animal appears to assume a much darker color than normal (page 355).   Thyroid administration enables such animals once more to cast off the dead layers of epidermis.

Reptiles.   In snakes, turtles, and crocodilians the thyroid gland is unpaired, whereas in lizards it is bilobed in the young but paired in the adult.   In lizards it lies ventral to the trachea, approximately halfway along its course.   In other reptiles it lies farther posteriorly and immediately in front of the pericardium.

Experiments have shown that in reptiles, as in amphibians, the process of ecdysis is partly under control of the thyroid hormone.   However, it seems that in snakes, removal of the thyroid enhances ecdysis, whereas thyroid administration interferes with the normal shedding of the corneal layer (W. H. Schaefer, 1933, *Proc. Soc. Exptl. Biol. Med.*, **30**:1363).   Why the action of the thyroid hormone in respect to corneal shedding in snakes is just the reverse of its effect on amphibians is not clear.   Lizards apparently are similar to amphibians in this regard.

Birds.   The paired thyroid glands of birds possess no noteworthy features not previously considered.   They lie on either side of the trachea near the region where the trachea divides into bronchi and just anterior to the large vessels leaving the heart.   Experiments in which thyroxin has been injected into brown leghorn chickens show that the color pattern and shape of certain feathers can be decidedly altered in the presence of unusual amounts of the hormone.

Mammals.   The typical mammalian thyroid consists of right and left lobes connected across the ventral side of the trachea by a narrow *isthmus* (Fig. 9.4).   The lateral lobes are firmly attached to the larynx, and the isthmus is fastened to the trachea. Thus if the larynx and trachea move, the gland moves also.   The isthmus is the only part of the normal thyroid that is ordinarily palpable in man.   If the finger is gently pressed against the trachea at the level of the suprasternal notch and the movement of swallowing is executed, the isthmus of the thyroid will be felt to move up and back again.

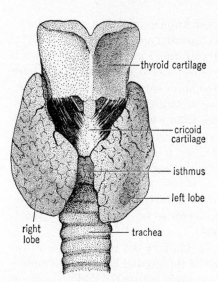

The thyroid gland arises in the mammalian embryo as a median ventral diverticulum of the pharynx between the first and second pharyngeal pouches.   Thus, for a time, it is connected to the pharynx by a duct known as the *thyroglossal duct.* Under normal conditions this connection is soon lost and the only in-

FIG. 9.4.   Ventral view of human thyroid gland shown in relation to trachea and larynx.

dication of its former point of origin is a small depression at the base of the tongue called the *foramen caecum* (Fig. 5.6). Occasionally small remnants of thyroid tissue are embedded in the substance of the tongue, and if these should undergo hypertrophy, a *lingual goiter* is the result.

In human beings, as well as in certain other mammals, several abnormal conditions are known to result from improper function of the thyroid gland. As was mentioned previously, the thyroid gland plays an important role in regulating the metabolism of the body. Excessive production of thyroxin increases heat production, sensitizes the nervous system, and accelerates the rate of heart beat. All activities of the body are speeded up. These symptoms are characteristic of a disease known as *exophthalmic goiter*, in which the thyroid gland is enlarged and the eyeballs often protrude markedly. Factors not completely understood at the present time seem to be involved in this condition. It seems as though excessive production of thyrotropic hormone from the anterior lobe of the pituitary body may be responsible both for hyperactivity of the gland and protrusion of the eyeballs. Abnormal action of the sympathetic nervous system in contracting the orbital muscle behind the eyeball may possibly be involved. Surgical removal of all or of part of the thyroid gland is often resorted to in order to reduce the amount of thyroxin being secreted.

The thyroid gland may, on the other hand, be lacking entirely or may not give off a sufficient amount of the hormone, and the resulting effects are quite the opposite of those discussed. Thyroid deficiency in the young is marked by a retardation of growth and development. In severe cases intelligence is subnormal, the teeth are slow to form and erupt, the sex organs fail to develop, the abdomen protrudes, and body temperature is low. The tongue is thick and may extend out of the mouth, the skin is wrinkled, and the hair is scant and coarse. A child having such extreme lack of thyroid is known as a *cretin*. Some cretins are born without thyroids.

If the thyroid gland degenerates during adult life, the symptoms are, in general, similar to those of cretinism except that, since growth has been completed, only degenerative changes are observed. This condition, called adult cretinism, or *myxedema*, occurs much more frequently in women than in men. The body temperature is lowered, and the person may continually complain of cold. Mental processes become dulled, the skin is thick and puffy in appearance, the tongue thickens, and speech becomes labored. The hair is dry and sparse. Persons suffering from myxedema usually gain weight and may even become quite obese.

Mild degrees of oversecretion or undersecretion of the thyroid gland show less severe symptoms than those described above.

Fortunately, the administration of thyroid substance either by mouth or by injection can bring persons who suffer from thyroid deficiency back to normal. Usually the treatment must be continued indefinitely; otherwise the patient may lapse into his former state. Persons who take thyroid without the supervision of a physician run a great risk, because the drug is so powerful that harmful effects may result from its use.

Another abnormal thyroid condition, called *endemic goiter*, is really a form of thyroid deficiency. When this occurs, the thyroid gland increases considerably in size and may cause an enlargement of the neck. In such cases, although the gland is large, it does not function properly and the body suffers from a lack of thyroid hormone. This type of goiter also occurs much more frequently in women than in men.

Endemic goiter occurs more often in certain regions of the world than in others. These areas, known as goiter belts, are alike in that the soil and drinking water are deficient in iodine. Some of the best-known goiter belts are in the Himalaya Mountains in Asia, the Swiss Alps, the Andes Mountains in South America, and, in North America, the Great Lakes basin as well as the Cascade Range in Oregon, Washington, and British Columbia. Less important regions are found in the Appalachians and in the Rocky Mountains. In general, these are either well-drained areas or places where the soil, deposited by glaciers in ancient times, has been leached thoroughly by melting ice. In either case the iodine content of soil and water is unusually low. Goiter rarely occurs along the seacoast. Before the days of extensive travel, and before the treatment of goiter was fully established, those who lived in goiter belts were so accustomed to the presence of goiter that in some cases it was considered a natural and normal development.

Administration of small amounts of iodine to persons inhabiting these areas is of great value in preventing the appearance of goiter. A number of years ago an important and interesting experiment was carried on among the school girls of Akron, Ohio, which lies in the Great Lakes goiter belt. The girls were divided into two groups. One group was untreated but observed before and after the experiment which extended over a period of $2\frac{1}{2}$ years. To the other group, for 2 weeks twice a year, small amounts of a chemical compound containing iodine were given by mouth. At the end of the experiment, out of 2,305 untreated children, 445 had developed goiter, while of the 2,190 receiving treatment, only 5 developed a thyroid enlargement. This significant work indicates in a striking manner how iodine may be used in preventing goiter. Even if a goiter has developed, the administration of iodine under the supervision of a physician may often result in its disappearance. Iodized salt is frequently used to supply small amounts of iodine which otherwise may be lacking in the diet. Because there are thyroid difficulties which may be aggravated by iodine some physicians advise against the indiscriminate use of iodized salt.

PARATHYROID GLANDS

The parathyroid glands get their name from the fact that in mammals they lie alongside of or dorsal to the thyroid gland. Frequently they are wholly or partially embedded in the thyroid or thymus glands. In early stages of development in all vertebrates small budlike masses of epithelial cells proliferate from both dorsal and ventral ends of the pharyngeal pouches. The number varies in different vertebrates and vertebrate groups. It is clear that in the higher tetrapods certain of these epithelial buds give rise to the parathyroid glands which are thus of endodermal origin. In cyclostomes and fishes, however, because of the small size, diffuse nature, and difficulty in extirpating these structures completely, it has not been conclusively determined whether any of the buds actually represent parathyroid tissue.

Cyclostomes. The lampreys possess the most complete set of these small epithelial structures, since all pharyngeal pouches give rise to both dorsal and ventral buds. Their significance is unknown.

Fishes. Glandular pharyngeal bodies of varying number have been identified in fishes, but their functional identity remains obscure. Irregular masses of soft tissue in the region above the gill slits, however, are believed to represent thymus tissue.

Amphibians. The parathyroid glands are first identified as such in amphibians. These as well as the thymus glands are usually derived from the third and fourth pairs of pharyngeal pouches. In salientians, however, the thymus arises almost entirely from the second pouch. Whereas the thymus glands arise as dorsal buds, the parathyroids come from the ventral portions of the pouches. In caudates they lie in a position lateral to the aortic arches and ventral to the thymus glands. Usually two or three parathyroids appear on each side, but in some forms only a single pair may be present. They are rather widely separated from the thyroids in caudate amphibians. In salientians the parathyroid glands are small, rounded, reddish bodies, two of which lie on either side of the posterior portion of the hyoid cartilage next to the inner ventral surface of the external jugular vein. Some authors in the past have referred to them as *pseudothyroid glands.*

Apparently the parathyroids in amphibians function in a manner similar to those of mammals, controlling the level of calcium and phosphorus salts in the blood.

Reptiles. The parathyroids of reptiles, like those of amphibians, arise from the ventral ends of pharyngeal pouches III and IV. They are frequently confused with other bodies of pharyngeal origin. In the various members of the class two pairs are present on the side of the neck, located somewhat posterior and lateral to the thyroids. In snakes the parathyroids are situated nearer the skull than in other members of this class.

Birds. The parathyroid glands of birds are derived from ventral diverticula of pharyngeal pouches III and IV. In the adult animal they may be observed as small, paired bodies, slightly posterior to the thyroid gland on each side. There are one or two pairs. Occasionally the parathyroids lie on the dorsal surface of the thyroid.

Mammals. Much more is known about the parathyroids in mammals than in any other group. In this class, contrary to the condition in lower forms, the parathyroids arise from the *dorsal* ends of pharyngeal pouches

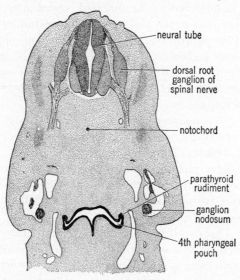

FIG. 9.5. Section through pharyngeal region of 10-mm. pig embryo, showing the parathyroid rudiments arising as dorsal diverticula from the ends of visceral pouch IV.

III and IV (Fig. 9.5). There are usually two on each side, although occasionally an additional gland may be found. They are roughly oval in shape and of a lighter color than the thyroid gland with which they are closely associated anatomically if not functionally.

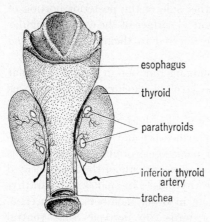

FIG. 9.6. Dorsal aspect of human esophagus and trachea, showing position of thyroid and parathyroid glands. (*After Halsted and Evans.*)

In man (Fig. 9.6) each gland is about the size of a grain of corn. The names *superior* and *inferior* parathyroids are generally applied to them, the superior pair being more cranial in position. During embryonic development their position becomes shifted so that those coming from the third pair of pharyngeal pouches are dragged along by the developing thymus rudiments and assume the more caudal position. Those coming from the fourth pouch move slowly in a cranial direction and become the superior pair. The superior parathyroids are much more constant in position than the inferior pair which are sometimes found some distance caudad the thyroid gland. Accessory islands of parathyroid tissue are occasionally encountered. In mammals the parathyroids may be embedded in the thyroid gland to varying degrees (Fig. 9.7). This is particularly trueof the superior pair.

The parathyroids are composed of rather densely packed polygonal cells which are separated into groups by delicate connective-tissue septa. Two types of cells have been described: principal, or chief, cells and colloid, or oxyphil, cells, but the significance of this dual arrangement is not clearly understood. Most investigators, however, are of the opinion that the chief cells are concerned with the elaboration of the parathyroid hormone.

The glands are essential for life unless remedial measures are instigated.

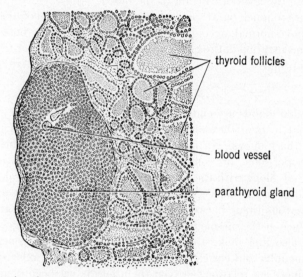

thyroid follicles

blood vessel

parathyroid gland

FIG. 9.7. Section through parathyroid and thyroid glands of rat, showing parathyroid partially embedded in thyroid tissue.

If they are removed or badly diseased, the subject suffers from severe spasms of the muscles, a condition known as *tetany*. Death usually follows within a few days. The parathyroids are also important in bone and tooth formation.

It was formerly believed that the thyroid gland was necessary for life because when it was removed death resulted. We now know that in such cases the parathyroids were probably overlooked and removed along with the thyroids. In old museum specimens of thyroid glands the parathyroids can sometimes be observed dangling from the other tissues. It is not difficult to speculate as to the fate of the patients from whom the specimens were obtained. Today, surgeons take particular care not to remove the parathyroids when they are operating on the thyroid gland.

Apparently the function of the parathyroid glands is to regulate the amount of calcium and phosphorus in the blood. The percentage of these chemical substances must be kept at a relatively constant level if the body is to function normally. If the parathyroids are removed, there is a decrease in blood calcium and an elevation of phosphorus. When this occurs there is a greater excitability of nervous tissue and muscles, resulting in tetany. A hormone, called *parathormone*, has been extracted from the parathyroid glands of cattle. It has not as yet been obtained in pure form.

Parathormone, when injected, will gradually bring about an elevation of blood calcium to the desired percentage. In the absence of the hormone, intravenous injection of calcium salts, and administration of vitamin D, which facilitates absorption of calcium from the digestive tract, may be used to raise the level of calcium in the blood.

If there is too much parathormone in the body, the level of blood calcium is raised above normal, accompanied by a softening of the bones. A high calcium concentration in the blood causes nausea, loss of appetite, and other serious symptoms.

ADRENAL GLANDS

The adrenal glands are endocrine organs which derive their name from the fact that in man they are situated in close proximity to the cranial borders of the kidneys. In mammals they are compact bodies made up of distinct portions, or components, an inner *medulla* of ectodermal origin derived, along with the sympathetic ganglia, from neural-crest cells, and an outer *cortex* derived from mesoderm. The cortex arises from mesenchymatous tissue between the dorsal mesentery of the gut and the medial surface of the mesonephric kidneys. The genital ridges, or gonad primordia, also first make their appearance in this same general region. Although medulla and cortex in mammals are so closely related anatomically, no functional relation between them has as yet been demonstrated.

The cells of the medulla stain a brownish-yellow color with chromic acid and its salts. This is called the *chromaffin reaction*. The staining reaction is correlated with the presence of the hormone *epinephrine*, or *adrenalin*, since the depth of the stain and the content of hormone rise and fall together. Chromaffin tissue has been found in such other parts of the body as the carotid body, prostate gland, seminal vesicles, cervix of the uterus, and others. In these regions there is also a close association of the chromaffin tissue with that of the sympathetic nervous system.

In the lower classes of vertebrates the homologues of medulla and cortex are usually completely divorced from one another. The parts which are homologous with the medulla of higher forms have been called the *suprarenal*, or *chromaffin*, *bodies*, and these too give the typical chromaffin reaction. Those structures corresponding to the cortex are known as the *interrenal bodies*.

Nothing corresponding to the adrenal glands has been discovered in amphioxus. In certain invertebrates, chromaffin tissue has been described, but it is doubtful whether this bears any relation to the structures being considered here.

Cyclostomes. Adrenal elements are found for the first time in cyclostomes. In *Petromyzon*, for example, there are two clearly distinguished series of bodies. The first consists of small, irregular, lobelike structures situated along the postcardinal veins, renal arteries, and the arteries running dorsal to the opisthonephric kidneys. They may even extend into the lumina of these vessels. This series of small bodies is the interrenal, or cortical, series. The other, or chromaffin series, extends from near the anterior end of the gill region (opposite the second gill cleft) to the tail. Here the chromaffin bodies consist of small strips of tissue which extend along the course of the dorsal aorta and its branches. It has been demonstrated experimentally that extracts of tissues from these regions, when injected into cats, will cause a rise in blood pressure comparable to that induced by epinephrine.

Although chromaffin tissue has been found in the hagfish, no interrenal tissue has been described.

Fishes. In elasmobranchs the interrenal bodies lie between the posterior ends of the opisthonephric kidneys. They are usually paired in the Batoidea and unpaired in the Squali. The ochre-yellow color of these structures in the living animal resembles that of the adrenals in salientian amphibians. The chromaffin bodies are paired and located on the segmental branches of the aorta on either side of the spinal column. Some of the anterior bodies may be elongated and united. The close relationship to the sympathetic ganglia is clearly shown in this group.

In teleost fishes the interrenal and chromaffin bodies again are separate entities. Interrenal bodies are arranged in a manner similar to those of elasmobranchs. They are generally paired, of a pinkish color, and may lie free on the surface of the opisthonephros or partially embedded in that structure. The name *corpuscles of Stannius* has been used in the past to designate these teleostean interrenal structures. The chromaffin bodies lie in the walls of the postcardinal veins, particularly on the right side and toward the anterior end.

In the Dipnoi no tissues corresponding to interrenal bodies have been described with certainty. Chromaffin bodies are arranged segmentally around the intersegmental arteries and in the walls of the anterior part of the postcardinal and right azygos veins.

Amphibians. Beginning with this group of vertebrates, the two components of the adrenal glands are much more closely associated. The familiar orange or yellow bands on the ventral surfaces of the opisthonephric kidneys of the frog are composed of two types of tissue closely intermixed. The interrenal elements are arranged in cell columns of different shapes and sizes. The chromaffin cells are irregularly distributed throughout the gland but are often found along the ends or borders of the interrenal cell columns. They show the typical chromaffin reaction.

In caudates the adrenal glands are by no means so compactly arranged as in salientians. Interrenal and chromaffin components are intermingled and located in strips of tissue which extend the entire length of the opisthonephros and even anterior to it, sometimes being located as far forward as the subclavian arteries.

Reptiles. In most members of this class the interrenal and chromaffin constituents are intricately intermingled. In some reptiles, however, the dorsal side of the gland is composed largely of chromaffin cells which penetrate into the mass of interrenal tissue only to a slight degree. In Crocodilia and Chelonia the arrangement is practically the same as in birds.

Birds. In birds the adrenal glands are ochre-yellow bodies lying on either side of the vena cava immediately anterior to the kidneys and close to the reproductive organs. The interrenal and chromaffin elements are closely interwoven, the chromaffin tissue lying in crevices between masses of interrenal tissue.

Mammals. In mammals the adrenals lie at the cranial ends of the kidneys (Fig. 9.8). In some forms they are in close apposition to the

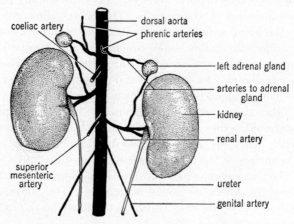

Fig. 9.8. Ventral view of kidneys and adrenal glands of rat, showing arrangement of the arteries which supply them with blood.

kidneys; in others they are separated by a space. The right gland lies closer to the inferior vena cava than does the left. These glands in mammals differ greatly from those of other vertebrates in having a true cortex and medulla. The medulla occupies the central portion of the gland, and its cells show the typical chromaffin-staining reaction. The outer cortex is homologous with the interrenal tissue of the members of the other vertebrate classes. Accessory "cortical" and "medullary" bodies are frequently found in the vicinity of the adrenal glands but may sometimes lie at a considerable distance from them. There is considerable variation in size and number of accessory bodies among individuals and species.

In some species, as in the rat, the adrenals of females are considerably larger than those of the male. Even though medulla and cortex are easily distinguishable in all mammals, the microscopic appearance of these regions varies and an experienced histologist can even distinguish species by these variations.

In the Prototheria, cortex and medulla are not so distinctly separated as in other mammals and cords of medullary tissue penetrate into the cortex. In some, as in the mouse and antbear (*Tamandua*), a layer of connective tissue separates the two types of cells. Even the proportion of cortex to medulla varies. In the porcupine and guinea pig the cortex is preponderant, whereas in the porpoise, chimpanzee, and others the medulla forms the greater part of the gland. The adrenals may appear lobulated because of strands of connective tissue from the enclosing *capsule* which may penetrate deep into the cortex.

In human embryos the adrenal glands are relatively large and even at birth are about one-third the size of the kidneys. After birth they fail to grow at the same rate as neighboring structures.

When viewed under the microscope, the typical adrenal cortex will be found to consist of three or more distinct layers, or zones (Fig. 9.9).

FIG. 9.9. Segment of adrenal gland of rat, showing zonation. The gland is shown below in cross section. The wedge above indicates the microscopic appearance of the medulla and the cortical layers.

Under the capsule of the gland lies the *zona glomerulosa*. The cells of this relatively narrow layer are arranged in alveolarlike groups and stain rather deeply. The middle and widest zone is the *zona fasciculata*. Here the cells are arranged in long columns, one to three or four cells in width, which extend from the zona glomerulosa toward the center of the gland in a radial sort of arrangement. The innermost zone of the cortex is the *zona reticularis*, the cells of which are arranged irregularly. It is this zone which lies next to the medulla. Often cords of chromaffin tissue penetrate into it.

According to one theory, cells are constantly being formed in the inner part of the zona glomerulosa and push down toward the zona reticularis, where the older cells are removed. The typical division of the adrenal cortex is not obvious in all mammals. In the opossum, for example, such a division is not discernible.

The cells of the medulla are more homogeneous than those of the cortex in appearance but are arranged irregularly about blood sinuses which are abundant in this portion of the adrenal gland. The adrenals are among the most vascular organs of the body. The medullary portion is believed by many to represent modified sympathetic ganglion cells. In man and the higher apes complete differentiation of the various parts of the adrenal glands does not occur until some time after birth.

In certain mammals, notably man and the mouse, another layer, or zone, of the adrenal cortex has been described. It lies between the medulla and zona reticularis and has variously been called the X zone, embryonic zone, fetal zone, and androgenic zone. This area has a different histological structure from that of the true, or definitive, cortex, and its cells have a distinctive staining reaction. In man it usually disappears during the first year after birth. In the male mouse the X zone persists only until about the sixth week after birth, whereas in the female it may persist for 3 months or more. Castration in the male mouse causes this zone to persist, but in the female removal of the ovaries seems to have no effect.

The full significance of the X zone is not clear. Some investigators are of the opinion that its persistence, often associated with tumors or enlargement of the adrenal cortex, may result in certain abnormalities of the reproductive system. In young girls and also in older women a pronounced *virilism* may occur in which various masculine characters may develop. The body hair increases in amount, being distributed like that of the male, the voice deepens, muscular development becomes more pronounced, the clitoris enlarges to penislike proportions, and menstruation either fails to occur or ceases, depending upon the age when these abnormal manifestations first appear.

A similar condition in young boys results in a precocious puberty in which the child may resemble an infant Hercules, with a high degree of muscular development and having fully developed accessory sex organs and secondary sex characters. In such boys, however, the testes remain infantile, indicating that the adrenal cortex is the source of an androgenic hormone similar to that normally secreted by the testes. Such a hormone, known as *adrenosterone*, has been extracted from the adrenal cortex.

More experimental work must be done before the role of the adrenal cortex in causing such abnormalities is clearly understood.

A British physician, Thomas Addison, in 1855 published a paper in which he described a disease which ever since has borne his name. Addison's disease is characterized by anemia, loss of appetite, great languor with muscular weakness, and feeble heart action. Most peculiarly the skin becomes dark and of an unusual bronze color. The bronzing of the skin is more pronounced in parts exposed to the air, such as the face and hands, and also in parts normally subjected to pressure of the clothing. The severity of the symptoms gradually increases, and before long death ensues. Addison discovered that almost all the 11 patients he had observed possessed lesions of the adrenal glands either due to tumors or to tuberculosis.

If the adrenal glands are removed from a cat, within a few days the animal weakens, becomes prostrate, and dies. If the cortex alone is removed, the same thing occurs. If, however, only the medulla is removed and the cortex left intact, harmful effects are not observed. In Addison's disease it is the destruction of the adrenal cortex that is important, since the proper functioning of this portion of the gland is necessary for life.

In recent years great advances have been made in our knowledge of the functioning of the adrenal cortex in health and disease, yet much remains to be done. Approximately 30 different crystalline compounds, known as steroids and closely allied chemically to the ovarian and testicular hormones, have been isolated from the adrenal cortex. They are referred to as *adrenocorticoids*. Only six or seven of these have been found to be physiologically active. Certain adrenocorticoids have been used on animals that were at the point of death after removal of their adrenal glands. Within a short time after injection, rapid and astonishing recovery ensues. The hormones must be administered at intervals in proper combination and amounts, or the animals will soon revert to their former state of collapse. Animals which have had their adrenal glands extirpated have been kept alive and in good health for extended periods by injecting the proper adrenocorticoids. Good results have also been obtained by the use of these hormones on patients suffering from Addison's disease and numerous other conditions. Although extensive experimental work has been carried on in this field, the problem of the function of the adrenal cortex has not as yet been completely solved. Each new discovery, however, further emphasizes the fact that the adrenal cortex, excepting only the pituitary body which controls it, is the most important of the endocrine glands

It seems that the adrenocorticoids fall into three main groups, each having a profound effect upon the body. There is, however, some overlapping of their activities. The first group, which includes such hormones as *cortisone* and *compound F* (*17-hydroxycorticosterone*), is concerned with carbohydrate and protein metabolism. The second group, of which 11-*desoxycorticosterone* is the most potent, seems to influence the sodium content of the blood and to control the electrolyte balance and fluid shifts in the body. The third group, including *adrenosterone*, mentioned above, seems to be closely related to the sex hormones.

When the adrenal cortex is removed, there is an increased elimination of salt in the urine and a loss of sodium from the blood. As the sodium in the body is depleted, there is an increased elimination of water. This causes a lowering in the volume of circulating blood, and the tissues of the body become dehydrated. The blood is consequently more concentrated and blood pressure is lowered. These symptoms are also found in patients with Addison's disease. Other symptoms are, without doubt, also related to the loss of sodium and water. Administration of quantities of salt (sodium chloride) in the diet is of benefit in these cases. Experimental adrenalectomized animals are usually maintained by adding salt to the drinking water in a concentration of about 1 per cent. Under such conditions only minimal amounts of adrenocorticoids need be administered.

Certain investigators, using cytochemical techniques, believe that they have demonstrated that two secreting zones exist in the adrenal cortex, each serving a different function. They believe that the zona glomerulosa may secrete the corticoid(s) regulating sodium balance, whereas the zona fasciculata secretes those affecting carbohydrate metabolism. This is not conclusive. Although far from being completely understood, most authorities are of the opinion that the adrenal cortex does not secrete many different substances, each a finished chemical entity in itself. It would seem more logical to assume that it acts as a sort of chemical factory, synthesizing certain substances in a series of complicated reactions. At intermediate stages certain products may be liberated to meet bodily requirements, thus accounting for the multiplicity of steroids which have been extracted from the gland.

Dramatic results have been obtained by physicians who have used cortisone and compound F on patients suffering from such diseases as rheumatoid arthritis, Addison's disease, certain leukemias, and other conditions. Administration of ACTH, the adrenocorticotropic hormone of the anterior lobe of the pituitary body (page 357), which controls the output of the adrenal cortex, is also often used successfully in such conditions.

Since treatment for adrenocortical insufficiency means supplying the body with specific hormones which its intact glands are unable to furnish, administration of adrenocorticoids must be continued indefinitely. In some cases unfortunate side reactions may take place which preclude their further use.

The adrenal cortex also plays a very important role in enabling the body to adjust itself to many kinds of stress. This is discussed briefly under the title "General Adaptation Syndrome" on page 357.

Epinephrine, or adrenalin, from the adrenal medulla, was the first of all the hormones to be discovered. Chemists have been able to synthesize it, and today epinephrine is one of the most widely used drugs in the practice of medicine.

The injection of even minute quantities of epinephrine into the body produces striking results. It causes a rise in blood pressure, due primarily to its constricting effects on peripheral blood vessels. This forces the blood to the inner parts of the body. The skin is blanched, and the blood supply to the muscles and abdominal organs is thus increased. The heart beats more forcefully, and there is an increase in the amount of sugar in the blood, providing more fuel for increased muscular activity. The air passages to the lungs dilate, and breathing is made easier. The processes of digestion stop temporarily, the hair stands on end (goose flesh in man), and the mouth becomes dry.

These reactions usually occur during periods of fear or anger and are referred to in their aggregate as the "emergency mechanism" of the body. During emotional stresses of this sort the body is better adapted for self protection.

It seems probable that little if any epinephrine is secreted by the adrenal medulla under ordinary circumstances. During emotional stresses, in all likelihood, its secretion is increased. However, all the reactions brought about by epinephrine can occur even when the adrenal medulla has been removed. Other chromaffin tissues of the body in all probability secrete epinephrine, or a similar substance, when properly stimulated. Stimulation of the sympathetic nervous system (page 607) will also bring about the reactions mentioned above. The postganglionic fibers of the sympathetic nerves are known to secrete an epinephrinelike compound called *sympathin* which can elicit the reactions normally attributed to epinephrine even in the absence of the adrenal medulla.

Practical applications for the use of epinephrine include its action as a styptic to stop bleeding from superficial blood vessels and its use in asthma to dilate the respiratory passages so that breathing can be more easily accomplished.

Several other substances have been developed which have properties similar to those of epinephrine. The most common of these are *ephedrine*, prepared from a Chinese herb, and two synthetic compounds named *synephrine* and *neosynephrine*.

In those fishes, amphibians, and reptiles capable of changing color so as to blend in with the environment (metachrosis), epinephrine is believed to be responsible for the concentration of pigment granules around the nucleus of the integumentary chromatophores, or pigment-bearing cells of the skin, thus causing a generalized pallor.

PANCREAS

The dual role of the pancreas as both an exocrine and endocrine gland has already been mentioned. This structure is made up of two distinct kinds of tissues which, although so intimately associated anatomically, are functionally entirely separate. The comparative anatomy of the pancreas as an exocrine gland has been discussed in the chapter on the Digestive System. In the exocrine portion the secretory cells making up the alveoli pour digestive juices into ducts which empty directly or indirectly into the duodenum. In most vertebrates, scattered apparently at random among the alveoli, are masses of epithelial cells of different appearance and different staining properties. These isolated masses, which are of variable size, are known as the *islands (islets) of Langerhans* (Fig. 9.10). The cells

Fig. 9.10. Photograph of a section through the pancreas of a rat, showing an islet of Langerhans surrounded by alveolar tissue.

which compose the islands have an embryonic origin in common with the cells making up the alveoli.

Cyclostomes. No discrete pancreas is present in the lamprey. A few small masses of cells have been described, buried in the substance of the liver and in the wall of the intestine. These may possibly represent pancreatic tissue. It is believed that they are comparable to the islands of Langerhans, since no duct is present.

Fishes. In elasmobranchs, the islet cells are reported to surround a lumen, or cavity. In the teleosts the pancreas is usually very diffuse. The islands are fewer in number and proportionately larger than in the mammals and, even when minute, can be identified by the unaided eye. They are of a pale color and, since they are rather thick, can easily be distinguished against the more translucent sheet of the surrounding pancreatic alveoli. In many of the teleosts there is an encapsulated island of Langerhans called the *principal island* which is of relatively large size and constant occurrence. It lies in the region of the gall bladder, pyloric caeca, or spleen, and its relation to the rest of the pancreatic tissue is slight. In some species it is the only islet tissue present. Because of this fact, in the early days of insulin research, the principal islands of certain teleosts were considered as a possible commercial source of the hormone. They are of particular value, since no other tissues or secretions are present to contaminate the extracts of insulin during their preparation. The supply of these principal islands is of necessity extremely limited. Removal of the principal island in teleosts causes a marked increase in the amount of sugar in the blood stream.

Other classes. In amphibians, reptiles, birds, and mammals the islands of Langerhans are scattered among the alveoli in the typical manner and no unusual features are to be noted. In mammals the islands are most numerous in that portion of the pancreas which lies nearest the spleen. It has been estimated that in the human pancreas there are from $\frac{3}{4}$ to $1\frac{1}{2}$ million islets, and in some mammals the number is considerably larger.

Vertebrates from which the pancreas has been completely removed soon develop characteristic symptoms. The amount of sugar in the blood increases, and the kidneys excrete large amounts of it in the urine. A loss of weight follows, especially since body fat and protein are lost rather rapidly. There is an accumulation of certain products called *ketone bodies* in the blood, leading to acidosis, a diminution of perception, and finally a loss of consciousness known as *diabetic coma*. These symptoms result from the removal of the islands of Langerhans, for although the entire pancreas is removed, the portion which secretes the digestive juices has been shown not to be concerned in this condition. The symptoms, moreover, are similar to those of human beings suffering from a disease known as *diabetes mellitus*. The islands of Langerhans seem to be affected so that insulin secretion ceases or else normal quantities of insulin are no longer secreted into the blood stream.

Three types of cells, which differ in their staining properties, have been identified in the islands of Langerhans of man. They are referred to as A, B, and D cells. A fourth type, the C cell, has been described in the islets of guinea pigs. The B cells are believed to be the source of insulin secretion. When a chemical called *alloxan* is administered for a short period, a permanent diabetes results. It has been found that in alloxan diabetes the B cells of the islets have been damaged or destroyed. The existence of still another pancreatic hormone, *glucagon*, has been reported. It seems that the A cells are the ones responsible for the secretion of glucagon. This is a blood-sugar-raising principle which seems to be controlled by a hormone from the anterior lobe of the pituitary gland. It is not clear whether the somatotropic, or growth, hormone is responsible for this or whether a separate diabetogenic factor affects the A cells.

When there is an insufficient amount of insulin being secreted, the liver is affected so that excess carbohydrates can no longer be stored in the liver cells in the form of glycogen. Thus the sugar in the blood reaches a much higher concentration than is normal. The kidneys begin to eliminate the excess sugar via the urine. Oxidation of blood sugar in producing heat and energy also seems to be impaired to some extent. The liver, which normally converts sugar to glycogen and vice versa, soon gives off its supply into the blood stream until it has been depleted of its stores. Glycogen stored in the muscles also may be reduced below normal levels in the diabetic. Fats and proteins are then broken down to provide heat and other forms of energy. Ketone bodies, which are intermediate products formed during the oxidation of fats, are produced in such large amounts that the body cannot cope with them in breaking them down as rapidly as desirable. They accumulate in the blood and, since they are acids, gradually deplete the so-called *alkaline reserve* of the body. The blood gradually becomes relatively more acid, and a condition referred to as *acidosis* occurs which will lead to coma and death unless remedial measures are taken. The body loses weight rapidly and becomes less able to combat infections.

When an animal or person suffering from diabetes is given injections of insulin, the ability of the body to utilize sugar and fat in an approximately normal manner is restored. The excessive breakdown of protein ceases, and ketone bodies disappear. The liver once more begins to store glycogen, and the glycogen in the muscles returns to its normal level. The body again becomes resistant to infections.

The discovery of insulin in 1921 was of paramount importance to mankind, for the use of this hormone has prolonged the lives of innumerable diabetic persons who otherwise would have succumbed. Insulin is now prepared in purified crystalline form, but its use is by no means a cure for diabetes. However, it enables those suffering from the disease to lead normal lives. Even when using insulin, the diabetic patient must watch his diet carefully so that the intake of carbohydrate does not exceed his impaired ability to utilize it. He must nevertheless receive an adequate amount of carbohydrate to maintain normal, healthy conditions.

Administration of insulin by mouth has but little effect. It is destroyed by the action of digestive juices. An overdose of insulin given by injection must be guarded against because it reduces the blood sugar below the normal level and may result in a condition known as *insulin shock*. This first makes its appearance as an uncomfortably weak or faint feeling; the patient breaks out in a profuse perspiration, the eyeballs are unusually firm, and the skin becomes pale. This may lead to complete unconciousness followed by convulsions. The typical signs of insulin shock are due to a loss of activity of nerve cells in the higher centers of the brain. In insulin shock, injection of sugar, or feeding sugar in some form, is necessary so as to raise the sugar concentration in the blood stream rapidly. A prompt recovery usually follows if sugar is given. Insulin shock is deliberately induced as a therapeutic measure in patients having a certain type of mental disease, and remarkable recoveries have been effected.

The cause of diabetes mellitus is not definitely known, but it is becoming apparent that other endocrine organs besides the pancreas may be involved.

TESTES

The male gonads play a dual role in the body, being both *cytogenic* (cell-producing) and *endocrine* in nature. The comparative anatomy of the testes as spermatozoa-producing organs has been discussed. To the comparative anatomist the importance of the endocrine secretion of the testes lies in the fact that the development of the *secondary sex characters* of the male, which in many cases distinguish him markedly from the female, are dependent on this secretion, or hormone. In some animals the secondary sex differences are very striking, as, for example, the presence of antlers in the male deer and their absence in the female. In other animals, such as the rat or mouse, the differences are less apparent. The normal development, growth, and functioning of the *accessory sex organs* (page 263) are also partly under control of the male hormone. Since the endocrine secretion of the testes plays so important a part in the development and maintenance of many structures of the male body, it is important that the student of anatomy have an understanding of the tissues responsible for the elaboration of the male hormone.

The nature of the cells which actually produce the endocrine secretion of the testes is rather obscure in members of the lower vertebrate classes. The cytogenic portion of the testes is made up of seminiferous ampullae or tubules in which spermatogenesis takes place. It is still a question whether, in such vertebrates, the endocrine secretion is formed by germinal cell constituents, mature spermatozoa, connective tissue, or interstitial cells lying in spaces, or interstices, between the seminiferous tubules. In all probability it is the latter cells which are responsible even though they are rather inconstant in appearance.

Amphioxus and cyclostomes. No work has been done which would demonstrate an endocrine activity on the part of the testes in these forms. Only the cytogenic portion has been described. The fact that in the lamprey the urogenital sinus assumes somewhat different forms in male and female during the breeding season would lead one to infer that sex hormones were at work. In the male, with the approach of sexual maturity the urogenital sinus becomes rather narrow and opens by means of a small pore at the end of a long tube which in some ways resembles a penis.

Fishes. Most fishes are seasonal breeders, having a definite reproductive cycle and breeding but once a year. In many forms sexual dimorphism is not very clear-cut, whereas in others marked secondary sex characters are apparent. These take the form of color patterns, modifications of fins, appearance of excrescences on the skin, etc. Such features are most prominent at the breeding season and usually regress at the termination of the nuptial period. Changes in such internal structures as kidney tubules in certain places, ductus deferens or archinephric duct, and cloacal glands occur concomitantly with the external changes mentioned above. These structures also undergo a regression at the close of the breeding season.

Observations on the testes of several species show that, as the mating period approaches, interstitial cells, which are normally absent, appear among the seminiferous tubules. Following the breeding season, these cells gradually disappear, and there is a regression of the secondary sex characters which were so prominent at the height of the reproductive period. The correlation of the appearance and disappearance of the interstitial cells with the waxing and waning of the nuptial dress is circumstantial evidence that the internal secretion of the testes may be formed by the interstitial cells.

Castration, or removal of the testes, in certain species of fishes results in a complete failure of the nuptial changes to appear. If the operation is performed while such characters are at the height of their development, there is a much more rapid regression than would normally take place.

The fact that, in other species of fishes, secondary sex characters appear with sexual maturity and are retained as such throughout life in the absence of interstitial cells has led some investigators to believe that germinal elements, especially mature spermatozoa, may be the source of the male hormone in these forms. In fishes, therefore, it has not been determined definitely whether germinal elements or interstitial cells are the seat of hormone production.

Amphibians. Among amphibians there is usually an annual breeding period which is narrowly restricted in some forms and spread out over a rather long period in others. The season also varies from early spring, as in *Rana pipiens*, *Eurycea bislineata*, *Ambystoma texanum*, and most others, to early fall in case of the salamander *Ambystoma opacum*. As in the case of seasonal breeders among the fishes, with the approach of the breeding season, certain secondary sex characters appear in male amphibians. These consist of various modifications, such as swelling of the thumb pads (*Rana pipiens*), enlargement of the mental gland (*Eurycea bislineata*) (Fig. 4.9), changes in color pattern and development of a dorsal crest (*Triton cristatus*), and enlargement of the cloacal glands (*Ambystoma texanum* and others). Changes in the reproductive ducts accompany these modifications. After the breeding season is over, there is a regression of the various organs and structures mentioned above.

The testes of amphibians, in addition to their sperm-producing function, have been shown to be responsible for the development of the male accessory sex organs and secondary sex characters. Castration prevents the appearance of these nuptial features. The seat of hormone production in the testes of amphibians is still a matter for conjecture. Whether germinal elements, mature spermatozoa, or interstitial cells, which are very inconstant in appearance, are responsible for male-hormone elaboration remains undetermined. Interstitial cells appear in most forms only after the ampullae of the testes have been emptied of spermatozoa. They consist largely of connective-tissue cells, and it would seem unreasonable to believe that these should be responsible for the development of characters which make their appearance sometime previous to the actual breeding period.

Reptiles. Seasonal reproductive activity is characteristic of most reptiles, and periodicity in the appearance and disappearance of secondary sex characters is also evident in this class of vertebrates. These characteristics are not so strikingly evident as in members of other classes. In lizards, on which most work has been done, changes in skin pigmentation and development of femoral glands and hemipenes, as well as such internal organs as epididymides, have been reported to be seasonal. Interstitial cells are present in the testes throughout the year but show a cyclic modification, increasing in number following the discharge of germ cells toward the end of the breeding period. Certain cytological studies of the interstitial cells of lizards indicate an activity which is closely correlated with the appearance of the secondary sex characters. Very little, relatively, is known concerning reproductive physiology and detailed morphology of reptilian testes.

Birds. Just as in the other classes of vertebrates, the testes of birds have an endocrine function in addition to their cytogenic activity. In the domestic fowl interstitial cells are not ordinarily observed in the testes of an adult cock, and their lack has caused much speculation as to the seat of hormone production. Experiments in which certain pituitary extracts have been injected show that such treatment brings about the definite appearance of interstitial cells. This would indicate that previous investigators had overlooked the presence of these not too abundant cellular elements. Again, the seat of hormone production is not definitely known, but evidence points to the interstitial cells as the probable source.

Castration of the male domestic fowl has long been practiced. The prepuberally castrated capon fails to develop comb and wattles, does not crow, and has a more quiet demeanor. If the operation is performed after these characteristics have developed, they show a marked regression. The flesh of the capon is richer, of better flavor, and of higher quality than that of the uncastrated rooster, and for that reason capons command a higher market price. In many birds the brilliant plumage of the male as contrasted to his rather drab mate is evidence of the activity of the male hormone, although in a number of cases certain genetic factors may also be involved. Most birds are seasonal breeders, and fluctuations in the appearance of certain characteristics (beak color, plumage changes, etc.) may be correlated with the breeding and nonbreeding seasons. In other birds, particularly the domesticated species, fully developed secondary sex characters are in evidence throughout the year. The accessory sex organs are likewise under control of the male hormone.

Experiments with birds have revealed that in a number of species an increase in the total number of daylight hours brings about a marked stimulation of testicular development. Conversely, reduction of the normal daylight period delays the normal seasonal increase. In the junco, for example, the testes are at a minimal size in November. At the height of the breeding season they weigh several hundred times as much as the inactive organs. It has been demonstrated that if juncos in Canada, kept out of doors at subzero temperatures in winter, are subjected to progressive increases in electric lighting after sunset, there is a marked increase in size and activity of the testes. Not only are the spermatogenic elements of the testes affected, but the interstitial cells respond as well. The premature changes in accessory sex organs and secondary sex characters of the experimental animals are indicative of an awakened activity of the endocrine portion of the testes which is undoubtedly brought about by stimulation from hormones elaborated by the anterior lobe of the pituitary gland.

Mammals. In the testes of mammals the interstitial cells, or *cells of Leydig*, are a constant feature. Masses of these cells, with their abun-

seminiferous tubules

interstitial cells

mass of spermatozoa

Fig. 9.11. Photograph of a section through the testis of a rat, showing cells of Leydig lying in the interstices between adjacent seminiferous tubules.

dant vascular supply, are present in the interstices formed by adjacent seminiferous tubules (Fig. 9.11). Much experimental work has been done on the mammalian testis, and the assignment of male-hormone production to the interstitial cells has been fairly well established. Even in cryptorchid individuals in which the seminiferous tubules are degenerate and spermatozoa have not formed (page 296), the secondary sex characters and the accessory sex organs develop normally. In such individuals the interstitial cells appear to be normal and are apparently not influenced by the higher body temperature as are the seminiferous tubules. Only after cryptorchidism has been in existence for a long time is there any evidence that the secretion of the interstitial cells is diminished. It seems obvious, then, that masculine characteristics are not dependent upon the presence of sperm cells and must be controlled by some other factor in the testes. The male hormone, *testosterone*, was first extracted from bull testes. It can now be prepared synthetically. Substances having the physiological properties of testosterone are referred to as *androgens*.

Castration of various domestic mammals has long been practiced to improve the quality of flesh or to make them more docile. A castrated bull is known as a *steer;* a castrated stallion is called a *gelding*. A *barrow* is a castrated boar, and a castrated man is a *eunuch*. If such animals or human beings are castrated *before* the age of puberty, typical masculine structures and characteristics fail to develop. Castration *after* the age of puberty invariably leads to a regression of such accessory sex organs as seminal vesicles, prostate, and Cowper's glands. Certain secondary sex characters of the postpuberal castrate, such as voice and beard in human beings, are altered little, if at all.

Injections of testosterone are fully capable of maintaining the activity of the accessory sex organs and will prevent any change in the secondary sex characteristics. Treatment, however, must be continued indefinitely in such cases. Two other androgens have been recovered from male urine. They are known as *androsterone* and *dehydroisoandrosterone*, possessing approximately one-sixth and one-eighteenth the potency of testosterone, respectively. Both are steroids.

It is interesting that the internal secretion of the testes has a rather profound effect on the development of certain parts of the skeleton. Modifications of the pelvis of the castrated male, when compared with a normal individual, are often obvious. Comparison of the pelves of males and females in different mammalian species often reveals differences of the nature of secondary sex characters. The resorption of the pubic bones of the female pocket gopher with the approach of sexual maturity and the failure of this process to occur in normal or castrated males are good examples of hormonal control of development of some skeletal parts (Fig. 10.56). The large larynx and deep voice of the human male contrasted with the small larynx and higher-pitched voice of the female, the presence of antlers in male deer of many species, their absence in the female, and their failure to develop in the prepuberally castrated male, all bear witness to the fact that the male hormone may determine the presence or absence of bony or cartilaginous structures. The larger size of the male mammal as compared with the female is undoubtedly a reflection of the influence of male hormone on skeletal growth.

OVARIES

As is true of the testes in the male, the ovaries in the female are both cytogenic and endocrine in nature. These two functions are mediated through tissues in the ovaries which have a much closer morphological relationship than do the corresponding parts of the testes. It has been fairly well established that the cells of the theca interna, and possibly those making up the stratum granulosum and discus proligerus of the Graafian follicle, are responsible for secretion of one of the female sex hormones. In all probability the compound which is secreted by these cells is a steroid called *estradiol*. All substances having the physiological properties of estradiol are referred to as *estrogens*. Estradiol is the most potent of the natural estrogens. Many other estrogens have been isolated from such tissues as the placenta, adrenal cortex, ovaries, and testes and from various body fluids. Several have been prepared synthetically. All natural estrogens, of which at least 10 are known, are steroids, but several other substances which are not steroids have estrogenic properties yet differ from the natural estrogens in other respects. The most important of these are diethylstilbestrol, hexestrol, and dienestrol. Many estrogens are sold commercially under a variety of names.

Ovarian estrogens are responsible for the development of the secondary sex characters of the female. The development and maintenance of the organs making up the female reproductive system are at least partially under control of this hormone.

Not a great deal is known concerning the endocrine activity of the ovaries in vertebrates below the class Mammalia. Whereas thousands of scientific papers dealing with the structure and function of mammalian ovaries have appeared in the literature, there have been relatively few reports on the endocrine functions of the ovaries of lower forms.

Amphioxus and cyclostomes. Although the cytogenic activity of the ovaries of these animals is well understood, little is known of their function as endocrine glands. In the female lamprey, with the approach of sexual maturity, the urogenital sinus forms a large vestibule with a vulva and a rather wide opening. This would appear to be a response of the urogenital organs to the presence of a female sex hormone elaborated by the ovary.

Fishes. The development of the reproductive ducts in female fishes with the approach of sexual maturity or with the advent of the breeding season indicates that endocrine factors are at work. A few experiments have been reported on fishes from which the ovaries have been removed. A small minnow, *Phoxinus laevis*, in which both male and female exhibit a red nuptial coloration along the dorsal side during the breeding season, has been the subject of some investigation. Removal of the ovaries either brings about a rapid regression of the nuptial coloring, if it is already present, or else prevents it from appearing. In this particular species an endocrine secretion of the ovary undoubtedly regulates the nuptial coloring of the female.

Although in most fishes, following ovulation, the emptied follicles shrink and are resorbed, it seems that in those elasmobranch fishes which give birth to living young, corpora lutea develop at the sites of follicular rupture. More experimental work must be done before it can be fully established that these corpora lutea are functional and whether their presence is essential for the continuance of pregnancy.

Amphibians. The actual seat of hormone production in the amphibian ovary is not definitely known, but evidence that this organ functions as an endocrine gland is clear-cut. If the ovaries are removed from a female frog, the oviducts atrophy markedly. When estrogen is injected into such an ovariectomized female, these structures may be caused to enlarge to an even greater extent than is found in the normal animal during the breeding season. This indicates that estrogen controls the functional development of the female reproductive ducts. No structures resembling corpora lutea have been described for amphibians which as a group are notable for their oviparity, only a few species of salamander giving birth to living young.

In the *male* toad, a peculiar lobelike structure called *Bidder's organ* is present at the anterior end of each testis (Fig. 7.10). It has been shown that if the testes are removed, Bidder's organs will, in the course of approximately 2 years, develop into functional ovaries, thus bringing about a complete sex reversal in the male. Under such conditions the otherwise rudimentary oviducts and uteri enlarge, seemingly in response to female sex hormone elaborated by the transformed Bidder's organs.

In normal female amphibians, with the approach of the breeding season, the oviducts and uteri enlarge greatly and the glandular cells of the lining epithelium begin to secrete actively (Fig. 8.7). Development of ova within the follicles precedes the growth changes in the oviducts by several weeks.

Reptiles. Those reptiles which hibernate have a breeding period that commences shortly after the period of hibernation has terminated. Reptiles living under tropical conditions, on the other hand, have recurrent breeding periods which may extend over many months. Very little is known about the endocrine secretions of reptilian ovaries and their action on the secondary sex characters and accessory sex organs. It is safe to assume, however, that such activity is similar to that of other vertebrates.

In certain snakes of the genera *Storeria*, *Potamophis*, *Thamnophis*, and *Natrix*, which give birth to living young, well-developed corpora lutea form in the ovaries after ovulation. It has been demonstrated that the presence of these corpora lutea is essential for the successful completion of pregnancy, for when the ovaries with their corpora lutea are removed the pregnancy is invariably terminated. The corpora presumably secrete the hormone progesterone (page 349). Some ovoviviparous lizards are also known to have corpora lutea in their ovaries during pregnancy.

Birds.   In most birds only the left ovary develops into a functional adult organ.   In birds of prey both ovaries develop, but this is the exception rather than the rule.   It is assumed that the follicular cells surrounding the large, yolk-filled ova are the seat of estrogen secretion.

If the left ovary is removed, the single left oviduct becomes greatly reduced and the convolutions which are present in the oviduct of the normal animal are lacking.   It has been clearly demonstrated that administration of estrogen results in the activation of the oviduct of the domestic fowl.   If both the functional left ovary and the rudimentary right gonad are removed, the animal, after a time, takes on characteristics which are practically indistinguishable from those of a capon.   If only the left ovary is removed, in addition to retrograde changes in the oviducts, a remarkable transformation takes place.   The rudimentary right gonad becomes modified into a testislike organ.   Although spermatozoa seldom appear in such gonads, they apparently secrete androgen, which causes the appearance of such masculine characteristics as comb and wattle growth, development of spurs, assumption of male plumage, and even such phenomena as crowing and exhibition of a pugnacious attitude.   At a later period reversion back to the female type of plumage may occur.   It has been demonstrated that in such animals certain fluid-filled nodules appear on the testislike gonads, and it is probable that estrogen given off by them is responsible for the plumage change.

It is doubtful whether anything comparable to a corpus luteum exists in birds.   However, it has been reported that after ovulation in the domestic fowl, the presence of the collapsed follicle has a definite influence upon the subsequent ovulation.

Mammals.   Whereas estrogens alone are known with certainty to be secreted by the ovaries of most vertebrates below mammals, in the mammals and possibly in ovoviviparous elasmobranchs, lizards, and snakes, an additional ovarian hormone is secreted by the corpora lutea.   It is a steroid called *progesterone*.   Another hormonal agent found in some mammalian ovaries is *relaxin*, discussed below.

Estrogen has been shown to be responsible for the development of the secondary sex characters and accessory sex organs of the female.   Progesterone and, in certain cases, relaxin are concerned only with changes occurring in preparation for and during pregnancy.

Removal of the ovaries in the prepuberal female mammal prevents the further development of uterus, vagina, and Fallopian tubes, all of which remain in an infantile condition.   Postpuberal castration brings about atrophy of these organs.   The secondary sex characters react in much the same manner as do the accessory sex organs.   Administration of estrogen prevents regressive changes and restores structures to their full size even after they have atrophied.

One very interesting response to estrogen is the resorption of the pubic bones of the female pocket gopher with the approach of sexual maturity. In this destructive rodent of the western United States, males and young females have well-developed pubic bones which unite ventrally at the pubic symphysis. In adult females the pubic bones have been resorbed, resulting in an enlargement of the restricted pelvic passageway, thus making it possible for the young to pass through the birth canal at the time of parturition. Experiments show that the hormone estrogen is responsible for the resorption of the pubic bones as the time of puberty approaches. Even the pubic bones of males, which normally never undergo resorption, can be made to disappear if injections of estrogen are given.

In females of certain species of monkeys, one of the secondary sex characters is the brilliantly colored "sexual skin" in the region of the buttocks. If the ovaries are removed, this color quickly fades but is soon restored if injections of estrogen are given. Moreover, in a young female monkey the skin is pale before the age of puberty, but as sexual maturity is reached the bright color of the sexual skin appears for the first time. The color rises and wanes in accordance with the cyclic changes in amounts of estrogen secreted by the ovaries.

Fig. 9.12. Highly magnified photograph of the ovary of a pregnant rat, showing numerous corpora lutea.

Much research has been carried on to determine the function of the corpus luteum (Fig. 9.12). It is considered to be a true endocrine gland which secretes progesterone, the action of which is necessary in preparing the uterus for pregnancy and in the maintenance of pregnancy. It has also been demonstrated that the placentas of certain mammals secrete progesterone. Functional corpora lutea must be present during the early stages of pregnancy in all mammals and, in most species, throughout the entire gestation period. Removal of the ovaries, or of corpora lutea alone, results in resorption or abortion of the developing young. In some mammals, however, as in the human being, mare, and guinea pig, extirpation of the ovaries or corpora lutea during the latter part of pregnancy has no such effect. In these animals, and probably certain others, progesterone secreted by the placenta may take over, supplementing that from the ovaries and thus enabling the pregnancy to continue without interruption. Since the corpus luteum hormone is necessary for bringing about certain essential changes in the uterine mucosa, for the early development of the placenta, and for complete development of the mammary glands, its importance can readily be appreciated. A previous sensitization of the uterus and mammary glands by estrogen is necessary before progesterone can become fully effective.

The hormone relaxin has been extracted from the corpora lutea of sows, the blood serum of pregnant rabbits, dogs, cows, and other mammals, and from rabbit placentas. Whether it is a true ovarian hormone is thus questionable since the actual site of its formation is obscure. It has not been identified chemically. The hormone is effective in relaxing the pubic ligaments of female guinea pigs which have been previously sensitized with estrogen. It is also effective to some extent in relaxation of the human pelvis during the latter part of pregnancy. In the normal pregnant guinea pig the enlargement of the birth canal, resulting from relaxation of the pubic ligaments, makes it possible for the guinea pig to deliver her relatively large young, which could not otherwise pass through the pelvic opening under ordinary conditions. It is interesting that in the female pocket gopher the resorption of the pubic bones seems to be controlled by estrogen alone, whereas in the guinea pig relaxation of the pubic ligaments is controlled by the cooperative action of estrogen and relaxin.

The activity of the reproductive organs in the female is cyclic in all species of mammals. In seasonal breeders such activity may occur but once a year. In other mammals, as in rats and mice, periods of activity take place every 5 days. Not only do the hormones estrogen and progesterone bring about periodic changes in the reproductive organs, but the very periodicity itself depends upon a reciprocal action of these hormones and the gonadotropic hormones of the anterior lobe of the pituitary gland.

The cyclic uterine changes which result in menstruation in the human being and other primates are brought about by the rise and wane of estrogen and progesterone with their subsequent effects on the uterine endometrium. Under the influence of estrogen, which increases in amount as the Graafian follicle grows to maturity, the uterine endometrium undergoes changes. It increases in thickness and receives a richer blood supply. The uterine glands also increase in size, but here the response ceases. This is the condition at the time of ovulation when the endometrium is said to be of the *mid-cycle type*. After ovulation, which takes place approximately halfway between two menstrual periods, and with the development of the corpus luteum, further changes occur which are brought about under the influence of progesterone. The endometrium becomes thicker, its blood vessels become extremely dilated, and the uterine glands not only become twisted and coiled but begin to secrete actively. The endometrium is now ready to receive the fertilized egg and is said to be a *progestational type* of endometrium. If pregnancy follows, the fertilized egg becomes implanted in the endometrium and develops into an embryo. If fertilization does not occur, part of the endometrium sloughs, accompanied by a loss of blood. Menstruation takes place approximately 2 weeks after ovulation. Following menstruation, a regeneration of the surface epithelium occurs and the endometrium increases in thickness. With the growth of a new ovarian follicle, followed by ovulation and corpus luteum formation, the whole process is repeated. Menstruation is held in abeyance during pregnancy.

The actual explanation of the mechanism responsible for the sloughing of the inner part of the endometrium with its accompanying bleeding has been clarified by studying pieces of monkey endometrium transplanted into the anterior chamber of the eye, where direct observations can be made. The observed changes have been substantiated by histological studies. The mechanism involves (1) vascular fluctuations in the coiled arteries supplying the inner third of the endometrium, (2) cyclic variations in the levels and activity of the ovarian hormones acting upon the endometrial tissues, (3) the cyclic activity of the anterior lobe of the pituitary gland in producing and releasing the gonadotropic hormones which in turn affect the ovaries. Menstruation appears to be precipitated by a decrease or withdrawal of the hormonal stimulus which is necessary to maintain the active condition of the endometrium, at the end of the cycle. Cases of menstruation without previous ovulation and corpus luteum formation are known to occur occasionally. In such instances it is the mid-cycle type of endometrium that is shed, but in this case also, withdrawal of the maintaining hormonal stimulus (estrogen) is believed to bring about sloughing.

No satisfactory suggestion has been advanced which would indicate that there is any evolutionary significance to menstruation or that it has any adaptive value. Why it should occur only in primates and in no other group of mammals remains an obscure point. The uterine bleeding observed in dogs when in estrus, or occasionally in human beings at the time when an embryo is implanting in the endometrium, should not be confused with menstrual phenomena. Menstruation might be considered to be the result of a biological failure. The uterine endometrium has been built up as though in preparation for implantation of an embryo. When fertilization does not occur and no embryo is present, the endometrium is no longer maintained and shedding and bleeding occur. It then repairs itself and starts to build up once more.

In all female mammals, at about middle age, the ovaries cease to function in the normal manner. The time at which this occurs is variously known as the *menopause, change of life,* or *climacteric.* In human beings it generally occurs around the forty-fifth year. In other mammals the time of the menopause is proportionately correlated with the life span. Changes in certain secondary sex characters occur at the menopause, and there is an accompanying atrophy of the genital organs and a cessation of periodic manifestations. In monkeys, when estrogen secretion by the ovaries ceases, there is a marked fading of the brilliantly colored sexual skin. The most important use of estrogens in medical practice is to alleviate the symptoms of the menopause, which in some cases are severe.

Extirpation of the ovaries at any time before the menopause will bring about an artificial or premature climacteric in which all the symptoms of the natural menopause are manifested.

PITUITARY GLAND

The great importance of the pituitary gland is generally recognized. It has often been referred to as the "master gland." However, as more discoveries are made it becomes increasingly evident that all the endocrine glands are dependent upon the action of others and such a designation for the pituitary gland is somewhat misleading. An outstanding feature of the pituitary gland is that, in addition to secreting agents which exert their effects on tissues other than those of an endocrine nature, it influences many other endocrine glands and is in turn influenced by them.

Sella turcica

FIG. 9.13. X-ray photograph of human skull, showing well-defined sella turcica in basal portion of sphenoid bone in which the pituitary gland lies.

The pituitary gland, or *hypophysis cerebri*, lies at the base of the brain in the region of the diencephalon, connected to the brain by a *hypophyseal* or *infundibular stalk*. It is a compound organ which in higher forms is situated in a depression in the upper face of the basal portion of the sphenoid bone (basisphenoid) called the *sella turcica* (Fig. 9.13). Because of its well-protected and inaccessible location, early anatomists thought it might be the "seat of the soul."

There has been some confusion in the literature in regard to the terminology of the various parts of the pituitary gland. Some authorities use the term "hypophysis" to denote only a portion of the pituitary; others use the two terms interchangeably. We shall follow the latter scheme here.

The pituitary gland is composed of three main parts, or lobes: anterior, intermediate, and posterior. A fourth component referred to as the *pars tuberalis* is really a modified part of the anterior lobe. The pituitary body has a dual embryonic origin and is entirely ectodermal. The *neurohypophysis* originates from the *infundibulum*, a ventral evagination of the embryonic diencephalon. From this is derived the *posterior lobe*, or *pars nervosa*. It is this part which remains attached to the brain by the infundibular stalk. From the ectodermal epithelium of the primitive mouth cavity, or stomodaeum, arises a dorsal evagination called the *adenohypophysis*, or *Rathke's pocket*. This usually constricts off the stomodaeum and becomes a closed vesicle which comes in contact with the neurohypophysis. The anterior portion of Rathke's pocket enlarges and becomes modified to form the *anterior lobe*, or *pars distalis*, from which the pars tuberalis is also derived; the posterior portion enlarges to a lesser extent to become the *intermediate lobe*, or *pars intermedia*. The original cavity of Rathke's pocket usually persists as a small space, the *hypophyseal cleft* (residual lumen).

The pars tuberalis is a vascular, collarlike mass of tissue partially surrounding the infundibular stalk and situated close to the *tuber cinereum* at the base of the diencephalon. It develops as a pair of lobelike extensions of the anterior lobe. Since the pars tuberalis is inconstant in appearance, being notably absent in snakes and lizards, and because no specific function has been assigned to it, no further mention of this part of the pituitary complex will be made. Whether it possesses a definite function or is merely rudimentary in character cannot be stated at the present time.

Each of the anterior, intermediate, and posterior lobes of this gland gives off hormones which produce different effects in the body. Although the three lobes are so closely related anatomically, they are functionally quite unrelated.

Posterior lobe. This lobe does not have the histological appearance of an endocrine gland. It seems that the hormones attributed to the posterior lobe are not actually produced in this portion of the pituitary gland but are formed by neurosecretory cells located in certain centers in the hypothalamic portion of the brain. The secretions are believed to pass down tracts formed by the axons of nerve cells to the posterior lobe where they enter the vascular plexus there. The tissue of which the pars nervosa is composed contains certain branched cells named *pituicytes*, as well as abundant unmyelinated nerve fibers. The pituicytes are not glandular cells but are probably neuroglia elements which are more of the nature of supporting tissue than secretory elements. Thus, the posterior lobe should be looked upon as a structure in which endocrine products of a neurosecretory nature are stored, rather than as a truly secreting endocrine gland.

At least two hormones from the posterior lobe have been recognized. The first of these, *vasopressin (pitressin)*, has the power of elevating the blood pressure in a manner somewhat similar to that of epinephrine, although its action is more prolonged. It also has an antidiuretic effect since, when it is administered, it seems to act upon the kidney tubules increasing resorption of water and decreasing resorption of salt. Extracts containing vasopressin are very effective in reducing to normal levels the enormous output of urine in a disease known as *diabetes insipidus* in which as much as 20 liters of urine are voided, and a corresponding amount of water taken in, during a 24-hour period. Whether the pressor and antidiuretic effects are brought about by the same or different hormones has not as yet been clarified.

The other hormone extracted from the posterior lobe is *oxytocin (pitocin)*. This acts specifically in contracting the smooth muscle of the uterus, but the response of the uterus to this hormone differs under varying conditions. It reacts best when previously sensitized with estrogen. When corpora lutea in the ovary are functioning and secreting progesterone, there is an inhibiting effect on uterine contractions and the uterus does not respond to injections of oxytocin. This hormone is used as an aid during childbirth. It is effective at this time because the corpus luteum degenerates at the end of pregnancy.

An extract of the posterior lobe of the pituitary gland, sold under the name *pituitrin*, has been used by physicians for many years. Pituitrin really contains a mixture of the two hormones, vasopressin and oxytocin. Neither of these hormones has been extracted in pure form nor has either been identified chemically. In view of the powerful effect of oxytocin on the uterus it would be logical to assume that it plays an important role during parturition. It has been demonstrated, however, that parturition can take place normally even when the pituitary gland has been extirpated.

Intermediate lobe. As was mentioned in the chapter on the Integumentary System, chromatophores, which are special pigment-bearing cells, are responsible for the color of the skin in practically all the lower vertebrates. These cells, which originate from neural crests, are located in the outer part of the dermis. They are quite different from the epidermal cells which in birds and mammals bear pigment granules. In most fishes, amphibians, and reptiles, the ability to change color within limits so as to blend in with the environment is in large part due to changes in the integumentary chromatophores (Fig. 4.5). The cytoplasm of these cells is usually spread out into a number of complex branches. The pigment granules may be dispersed evenly throughout the cytoplasm, giving the animal a darkened appearance, or they may be concentrated about the nucleus, thus making the animal appear lighter in color (Fig. 9.14). Variations in color and of patterns are often made possible by the action of chromatophores bearing pigments of different colors. The mechanism controlling the dispersion of pigment granules in these changeable chromatophores varies considerably. In some, the autonomic nervous system and neurosecretory cells are responsible. However, in elasmobranchs, amphibians, and in many reptiles, the chromatophores are under endocrine control. A hormone, *intermedin*, from the intermediate lobe of the pituitary gland has the effect of causing a dispersion of the pigment granules and thus brings about the darkening effect. Epinephrine, from the medulla of the adrenal gland, or sympathin, secreted by postganglionic fibers of sympathetic nerves, bring about an aggregation of the pigment granules. Thus the color of these animals at

FIG. 9.14. Photograph of salamanders, *Ambystoma texanum*. (*Left*) Normal control animal; (*center*) a few hours after removal of pituitary gland, pigment granules concentrated around nuclei of chromatophores; (*right*) several weeks after pituitary removal; the dark color is due to failure of the animal to shed the corneal layer of epidermis, which has become very thick. The last effect is undoubtedly caused by the failure of the thyroid gland to function in the absence of the pituitary gland.

different times appears to depend upon the relative activity of intermedin and epinephrine (or sympathin). It seems strange that intermedin should be present in the pituitary glands of birds and mammals in which there are no chromatophores of the type mentioned here on which it can act. It is, of course, possible that the hormone has some other functions in these forms which have not as yet been discovered.

Anterior lobe. The anterior lobe of the pituitary gland is particularly important and has been reported to be the source of some 9 or 10 different hormones. Whether these are distinct and separate entities is questionable.

The various actions attributed to these substances may well be due to the intrinsic action of a smaller number of hormones the existence of which is well established. Only three kinds of secretory cells are present in the anterior lobe, suggesting that the secretion of a smaller number of basic substances is more likely. The hormones seem to be of the nature of large protein molecules or of smaller units linked to such molecules. Whether they represent certain stages in the synthesis of a few basic substances remains to be determined. However, it is generally agreed that at least 6 hormones are elaborated by the anterior lobe.

Among these is the *growth*, or *somatotropic, hormone* (STH). Removal of the pituitary gland from a young animal causes an immediate cessation of growth. Extracts containing the growth hormone cause a resumption of growth when injected into such animals. The small size of the so-called *ateliotic*, or *pituitary, dwarf*, which resembles an adult in miniature and has normal body proportions, is believed to be due to a lack of sufficient pituitary-growth hormone. On the other hand, oversecretion during early life, or before normal growth has ceased, may result in *gigantism*. Again, the body proportions are normal but the bones are excessively large. One such boy at the age of eighteen was 8 ft. 3¾ in. tall and still growing. If oversecretion of growth hormone begins after the long bones of the body have stopped growing, a different condition known as *acromegaly* occurs. The long bones do not increase in length, since the epiphyses have already closed (page 370). Rather, a change takes place in the bones of the head and face. Other bones increase in diameter, and the spine may become bowed.

The diabetogenic, or blood-sugar-raising property of the growth hormone, is probably brought about by stimulating the A cells of the islands of Langerhans to secrete glucagon.

As more and more is learned about the growth hormone, the less certain it is that it is appropriately named. In addition to stimulating skeletal growth it seems to affect protein metabolism, the level of blood sugar, and other metabolic phenomena. However, it is very difficult to define exactly what is meant by "growth" since many diverse processes are involved. Growth is the result of many quantitative changes occurring in the body.

Most of the other hormones secreted by the anterior lobe of the pituitary gland affect specific structures in the body. The *thyrotropic*, or *thyroid-stimulating hormone* (TSH), stimulates the cells of the thyroid gland to secrete thyroxin. As the amount of thyroxin in the blood rises it in turn inhibits the secretion of TSH. This sort of relationship is referred to as reciprocal action. The level of these hormones in the blood stream, therefore, is controlled by a self-regulating mechanism. When drugs such as thiouracil or thiourea are administered, they prevent the synthesis of thyroxin and the normal effect of the latter in inhibiting secretion of TSH is diminished or lost. TSH is then elaborated in greater quantity, stimulating the thyroid gland to enlarge. The enlarged gland is, of course, unable to synthesize its hormone. Because of this property, which causes an enlargement of the thyroid gland, thiouracil and other closely related compounds are sometimes referred to as *goitrogenic agents.*

The *adrenocorticotropic hormone* (ACTH) stimulates the cells of the adrenal cortex to secrete adrenocorticoids which in turn inhibit production of ACTH. Here, too, we have an example of reciprocal action.

ACTH and the adrenocorticoids play a most important part in helping the body to react to prolonged, nonspecific stresses of various kinds. When subjected to such stresses as cold, burns, hemorrhage, starvation, and others, the body responds in a manner which serves to counteract the harmful effects induced by the stressing agent. The sum of responses made by the body is referred to as the *general-adaptation syndrome* (GAS). The endocrine system is of paramount importance here since one of the first reactions is an increase in output of ACTH. This causes an enlargement of the adrenal cortex and an increase in output of adrenocorticoids. These in turn, because of their various properties, increase the resistance of the body to the stressing stimulus. Overproduction or imbalance of ACTH and of cortical steroids may lead to various diseases collectively referred to as diseases of adaptation. Gastrointestinal ulcers, hypertension, rheumatic fever, and other similar conditions are examples of such diseases. A potent substance called *hypothalamic D*, or the *ACTH-hypophysiotropic hormone,* has been extracted from the hypothalamus, the ventral portion of the diencephalic region of the brain. This substance stimulates the production of ACTH by the pituitary gland and is probably an important link in the general-adaptation syndrome.

At least two *gonadotropic hormones* are secreted by the anterior lobe. The first, called the *follicle-stimulating hormone* (FSH), in the female controls the cytogenic activity of the ovary and the development of the ovarian follicles. In the male it may be responsible, at least in part, for the development of mature sperm cells in the seminiferous tubules. The second gonadotropic hormone, called the *luteinizing hormone* (LH), controls the development of corpora lutea in the ovaries of the female and the activity of the interstitial cells in the testes of the male. The existence in the male of a separate gonadotropic hormone, the *interstitial cell-stimulating hormone* (ICSH), has been claimed. This may possibly be identical with the luteinizing hormone of the female.

The periodicity, or cyclic activity, of the reproductive organs of the female is believed to be caused by interrelated activities of the gonadotropic hormones of the anterior pituitary gland and the ovarian hormones, estrogen and progesterone.

Another hormone from the anterior lobe is the *lactogenic hormone,* sometimes called *prolactin,* which causes properly prepared mammary tissue to secrete milk. In pigeons this hormone is responsible for the development and normal functioning of the crop glands (Fig. 5.18). It is now considered most likely that the lactogenic hormone also stimulates corpora lutea to secrete progesterone. Some authorities have maintained that a separate pituitary principle called *luteotropin* is responsible for this, but since purified lactogenic hormone brings about the effect, the existence of a distinct luteotropic factor is questionable.

Some investigators have suggested that a parathyrotropic hormone from the anterior lobe may affect the parathyroid glands. There is little evidence for this.

Comparative anatomy of the pituitary gland. *Tunicata*. In an adult tunicate, such as *Molgula manhattensis*, a single nerve ganglion lies embedded in the mantle between the incurrent and excurrent siphons. On the ventral side of the ganglion lies a body, the *adneural*, or *subneural*, *gland*, which some investigators have homologized with the pituitary gland of vertebrates. A duct leads from the gland into the cavity of the pharynx (Fig. 2.2 *A* and *B*). The products of secretion of the adneural gland, which are said to be cellular in nature, pass through the duct, indicating that the gland is not one of internal secretion. Furthermore it does not rise from a stomodaeal outgrowth but rather represents a degenerated cerebral vesicle which is present in the larval stage. The homologies of the adneural gland and the pituitary of higher forms are therefore far from clear. If there is any homology it would seem that this structure of tunicates possibly represents the pars nervosa, or posterior lobe, of the pituitary gland (page 353).

Amphioxus. Practically every structure in the head region of amphioxus has been examined with the view of homologizing it with the pituitary gland of higher forms. The most promising suggestion indicates that a depression in the ectoderm, called the *preoral pit*, which lies under the head and in front of the mouth of a young individual, may be the hypophyseal homologue. The left head cavity in an adult specimen opens into the preoral pit, which by that time has formed a connection with the buccal cavity. The walls of the pit become ciliated, and the structure is then known as the *organ of Müller*. If this is indeed the forerunner of the adenohypophysis, it is of interest that an organ which functions in creating a current of water should give rise to so specialized and important an organ in higher forms.

The origin of the pituitary gland from the lowest vertebrates to the highest is very constant in its fundamental constituents and method of development. The consistency shown in the differentiation of the parts of the gland may be traced from cyclostomes to the highest mammals.

Cyclostomes. In the lamprey the single nostril on top of the head leads by a short passageway into the olfactory sac which lies just in front of the brain. A large *nasopharyngeal pouch* extends in a ventroposterior direction from the olfactory sac and terminates blindly beneath the anterior end of the notochord. Between the ventral part of the diencephalon and the nasopharyngeal pouch lies the pituitary gland, consisting of the usual component parts. The homologies of the structures in this region, about which there has been much confusion in the past, have been fairly well clarified. During early development (Fig. 14.21) a *nasohypophyseal stalk* appears in close association with the developing olfactory sac at some distance from the dorsal lip and stomadaeum. The solid stalk extends posteriorly beneath the forebrain. From the caudal tip of this stalk certain cells are budded off which are to become the intermediate lobe of the pituitary gland. These intermingle with the nervous tissue forming the floor of the third ventricle. The anterior lobe tissue is budded off somewhat later from a dorsal thickening of a caudal portion of the remaining nasohypophyseal stalk. Soon the anterior lobe becomes completely detached. The nasopharyngeal *pouch* is an *adult* structure formed during metamorphosis from the persistent remnant of the larval nasohypophyseal stalk at some time after the pituitary gland has become a definite entity. It hollows out and extends caudally beneath the notochord. Although no relation of nasohypophyseal stalk or nasopharyngeal pouch to the stomodaeum is evident, it is believed that at some time a separation of the stomodaeal cavity into two parts may have occurred. The dorsal and anterior portion may then have been drawn inward with the adjacent nasal sac and have given rise to the nasopharyngeal pouch which has no counterpart in other vertebrates.

In the hagfish, *Myxine*, the nasopharyngeal pouch opens into the pharynx by an aperture which appears late during larval life. The pituitary gland is represented by clusters of cells lying between the infundibulum and the nasopharyngeal pouch. Instead of neural and stomodaeal components coming in close contact as in other forms, they are separated by a layer of connective tissue.

Fishes. In elasmobranch fishes, posterior to the optic chiasma and ventral to the diencephalon is a conspicuous projection, the *hypothalamus*. Its midventral portion consists of a narrow *infundibulum* with its two, rounded, laterally placed *inferior lobes*. The infundibulum, which appears as a thin, median stalk, extends posteriorly between the inferior lobes and then expands into a thin-walled saclike structure, the *saccus vasculosus* of unknown function. It is lined with a neurosensory epithelium. Since the saccus vasculosus is best developed in actively moving marine fishes it may possibly have a sensory function associated with awareness of change in fluid pressures. The ventral part of the saccus vasculosus is attached to the small hypophysis, or pituitary gland, which often remains in the sella turcica when the brain is removed in dissection. In the Selachii the posterior lobe of the pituitary gland is a diffuse structure and not consolidated as a distinct entity as in other vertebrates.

Not a great deal has been published concerning the structure of the pituitary gland in the higher fishes. In *Polypterus* and *Latimeria*, the gland exhibits its most primitive condition, since it connects with the mouth cavity by a persistent opening of the hypophyseal cleft, or the original cavity of Rathke's pocket. The duct passes through a foramen in the parasphenoid bone. In the haddock, the gland is flattened and closely pressed to the brain and does not lie in a sella turcica. In another fish, the angler, *Lophius piscatorius*, the pituitary is at the end of a very long infundibular stalk which extends forward so that the gland is situated about an inch in front of the expected position. In many teleosts, a large infundibulum, inferior lobes, and saccus vasculosus are present. Many minor variations may be observed in the pituitaries of fishes, but the fundamental structure is similar in all.

Amphibians. In the frog, the anterior lobe is prominent but paradoxically lies posterior to the other parts of the pituitary gland (Fig. 9.15). The

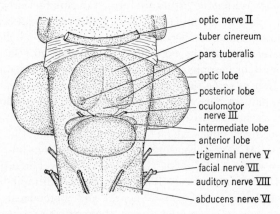

optic nerve II
tuber cinereum
pars tuberalis
optic lobe
posterior lobe
oculomotor nerve III
intermediate lobe
anterior lobe
trigeminal nerve V
facial nerve VII
auditory nerve VIII
abducens nerve VI

Fig. 9.15. Ventral view of hypophysis and adjacent parts of the brain of an adult frog, *Rana pipiens*. (*After Atwell, "The Pituitary Gland," Chap. 20, Association for Research in Nervous and Mental Disease. By permission of the Association.*)

intermediate lobe is shaped somewhat like a dumbbell and lies transversely above the anterior lobe. The posterior part of the infundibulum is thickened to form the posterior lobe. No hypophyseal cleft is present in the pituitary gland of the frog. In amphibians the stomodaeal evagination which corresponds to Rathke's pocket is, from the beginning, a solid outgrowth. This is also true in the teleost fishes. The caudate amphibians show no marked deviations from salientians in respect to the pituitary gland.

It has been shown that if the rudiment of Rathke's pocket is removed early in larval life, the neurohypophysis fails to develop normally.

Reptiles. In this class the infundibular stalk is unusually long and slender and extends posteriorly. The pituitary gland, therefore, lies in a position ventroposterior to the diencephalon. The anterior lobe is loosely connected to the rest of the pituitary gland. Otherwise the pituitary of reptiles is fairly typical of that of other vertebrates. In snakes and lizards the pars tuberalis is conspicuously absent.

Birds. The sella turcica of birds is comparatively deep, and the pituitary gland, which lies within this depression of the sphenoid bone, is farther removed from the brain than in members of the other vertebrate classes. The most unusual feature of the avian pituitary body is the lack of an intermediate lobe and hypophyseal cleft. Search for an intermediate lobe in the fowl, duck, and pigeon has failed to reveal any trace of this structure. Although a hypophyseal cleft is present during embryonic development, it becomes smaller and smaller and finally disappears altogether. The tissue which would ordinarily form the pars intermedia, lying between the hypophyseal cleft and posterior lobe, fails to develop when the hypophyseal cleft disappears.

Despite the fact that an intermediate lobe is lacking in birds, the hormone intermedin is present in the *anterior* lobe, the greatest concentration being in its cephalic portion.

Mammals. The mammalian pituitary body is typical of vertebrates in general (Fig. 9.16). Minor variations are to be observed in various species. The central cavity of the infundibular stalk is a continuation of the third ventricle of the brain. This cavity may dip deep into the posterior lobe, as in the cat, or may be short and extend only to a slight degree into the stalk of the infundibulum, as in the ox. In the ox and pig, a peculiar structure projects from the intermediate lobe into the hypophyseal cleft. This is

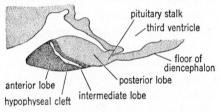

Fig. 9.16. Sagittal section of pituitary gland of rat, showing its relation to the brain.

called the *cone of Wulzen.* Its cellular structure is more like that of the anterior lobe than of the pars intermedia. The pituitary glands of whales, Indian elephants, and armadillos have no discrete intermediate lobe, and the anterior and posterior lobes are completely separated by connective tissue.

PLACENTA

That peculiarly mammalian structure, the placenta, is an important endocrine organ in addition to its other functions. Investigations have shown that hormones are undoubtedly elaborated by the placentas of various mammals, but much more systematic work must be done before the components responsible for their formation and secretion are definitely known. Since the placenta is a transitory structure, developing within the uterus early in pregnancy and being expelled at the time of parturition, its role in the endocrine system is that of an extremely specialized organ rather than one which plays a part in the general body economy.

Various types of placentas are found in mammals. Whether the more primitive types, such as the yolk sac and allantoic placentas of the Metatheria, produce endocrine secretions has not been investigated so far as the author is aware. Even in some of the higher mammals, the function of the placenta as an endocrine organ has not been established.

There is strong evidence, although actual proof is lacking, that the placenta in women, mares, cows, and some other mammals is the source of the extraovarian estrogen produced during pregnancy. In these animals large quantities of estrogen are excreted in the urine during the period of gestation. In certain cases estrogen continues to be excreted even after the ovaries have been extirpated from pregnant females. Soon after parturition there is a rapid drop to normal values, indicating that with the expulsion of the placenta the source of secretion has been removed from the body. Extracts of fetuses show rather low estrogen values, whereas extracts of the placentas of women, mares, cows, sheep, macaques, chimpanzees, and pigs have been shown to possess a much higher estrogen content.

It appears quite certain that progesterone is also secreted by the placenta in a number of species. Progesterone has been extracted from human and some other placentas. An inert steroid called *pregnandiol* appears in large quantities in the urine of pregnant women. This is believed to represent the end product of progesterone metabolism. If the ovaries are removed after a certain stage of pregnancy has been reached, pregnandiol continues to appear in the urine, indicating that some extraovarian source, presumably the placenta, is producing progesterone.

Rather clear-cut evidence exists to indicate that the placenta is the source of gonadotropic hormones found in the blood and urine of certain mammals during pregnancy. There are several reasons for believing that the chorionic portion of the placenta actually secretes these hormones which possess gonadotropic properties and are known as chorionic hormones or chorionic gonadotropins. One of these hormones, designated as PU, is excreted in the urine of women and some monkeys during pregnancy. The activity of PU is in many ways similar to that of LH from the pituitary gland but differs from it in others. These hormones also differ chemically.

Another placental gonadotropic hormone is found in the blood serum of pregnant mares during the first half of the gestation period. It does not appear in the urine. This hormone is referred to as PMS. It has the properties of a mixture of FSH with a small amount of LH. It seems likely that PMS is formed in the endometrial cups of the pregnant mare.

The pituitary gonadotropic hormones acting upon the ovaries, and the ovarian hormones estrogen and progesterone acting upon the uterus, are essential in bringing about the uterine changes necessary for implantation of the embryo and the early development of the placenta. It is probable that the placental hormones then either replace the pituitary and ovarian hormones or else exert an additive effect.

In all probability the placenta, in certain species, is also a source of the hormone relaxin. This hormone can be extracted in quantity from the placenta of the rabbit. Certain steroids similar to adrenocorticoids also have been identified in placental extracts.

The presence of chorionic gonadotropin in the urine of pregnant women is the basis for the Friedman pregnancy test, popularly known as the "rabbit test." A morning sample of urine from the patient to be tested is neutralized and filtered, and 5 cc. is injected into the marginal ear vein of a female rabbit which has been isolated for at least 2 weeks. After 24 hours the ovaries of the rabbit, which does not ovulate spontaneously, are examined for the presence or absence of corpora lutea. If developing corpora lutea (or corpora hemorrhagica) are present, the woman from whom the urine was obtained is pregnant. If no signs of corpus luteum formation are evident, the test is negative. This test is the most widely used pregnancy test in the practice of medicine. It is 99 per cent accurate. Inaccuracies may appear when certain abnormal uterine growths are present, known, respectively, as *chorioepithelioma* and *hydatidiform mole*. These abnormal chorionic tissues also give off the chorionic gonadotropic hormone which is excreted in the urine.

Another widely used pregnancy test is the Aschheim-Zondek test in which immature female mice are used as test animals. Here the action on the ovaries takes 4 or 5 days, but the principles involved are the same as those of the Friedman test. In both cases the injected gonadotropic hormone causes the rapid development of corpora lutea from follicles already present in the ovaries. The urine of men suffering from a cancerous condition, known as chorioepithelioma of the testis, will also give a positive "pregnancy" test.

Commercial preparations of the gonadotropin found in the urine of pregnancy are often used successfully in lowering the undescended testes of cryptorchid boys into their normal position in the scrotum. Hypertrophy of the interstitial cells is the primary result, and the descent into the scrotum is secondary.

The role played by the placenta as an endocrine organ thus appears to be that of an accessory ovary and pituitary gland, at least in so far as the gonadotropic properties of the latter are concerned. The degree to which it takes over such functions varies from species to species, and at the present time, no accurate generalization as to placental function can be made.

SUMMARY

1. The endocrine system consists of a number of ductless glands which secrete substances called hormones into the blood or lymph. They are carried by the circulating fluid to all parts of the body. The secretions are of a chemical nature and bring about certain changes which are either of a specific or general character.

2. Each glandular component of the system has its particular and specific functions, yet there is a close interrelationship among them.

3. The endocrine glands are all derived embryonically from epithelial surfaces.

4. Certain endocrine organs have a dual function and serve either as exocrine and endocrine glands (pancreas) or as cytogenic and endocrine glands (ovaries and testes).

5. It is doubtful whether the pineal body and thymus gland should be included in the endocrine system.

6. The thyroid gland, consisting of a number of rounded thyroid follicles, secretes a hormone, thyroxin, which controls the rate of metabolism of the entire body.

7. The parathyroids, which first make their appearance with certainty in the class Amphibia, usually lie in close proximity to the thyroids. The hormone of the parathyroids is known as parathormone. It is concerned with maintaining normal levels of calcium and phosphorus in the blood stream.

8. The adrenal glands of mammals consist of two portions: an inner medulla of ectodermal origin and an outer, mesodermal cortex. In other forms the homologues of these regions do not show similar anatomical relationships. In the lower classes they are separate entities called the chromaffin bodies and interrenal bodies, respectively. In salientians, reptiles, and birds the two types of tissues are inextricably intermingled.

The hormone of the medulla or chromaffin tissue is called epinephrine or adrenalin. Among other things it brings about an increase in blood pressure and amount of sugar in the blood. It dilates the air passages leading to the lungs. Hormones of the cortex or interrenal tissue are known as adrenocorticoids. They have to do with carbohydrate metabolism, maintenance of the volume of circulating blood, and the control of sodium balance and fluid shifts in the body. The normal functioning of this portion of the adrenal complex is necessary for life.

9. The islands of Langerhans in the pancreas are believed to secrete two hormones, both affecting carbohydrate metabolism. One of these, insulin, has the effect of lowering blood sugar; the other, glucagon, has the opposite effect.

10. The interstitial cells of the testes are believed to secrete a hormone called testosterone which controls the normal development and function of the accessory sex organs of the male and the masculine secondary sex characters.

11. Ovaries of vertebrates below mammals secrete a hormone referred to as estrogen. It is responsible for the development and maintenance of the accessory sex organs and secondary sex characters of the female. In mammals this same hormone is elaborated by the ovaries, but two additional hormones have been recognized, progesterone and relaxin. Both hormones

are probably formed by the cells of the corpus luteum although the exact origin of relaxin is still in doubt. Progesterone is concerned only with changes occurring prior to and during pregnancy. The cyclic activity of the female reproductive system is controlled by the ovarian hormones and their interaction with the anterior lobe of the pituitary gland.

12. The pituitary gland plays a dominant role in the endocrine system. It is usually made up of three parts, or lobes, which have close anatomical relationships. Each lobe elaborates one or more hormones which either affect the body generally or stimulate other endocrine glands to activity. A reciprocal relationship exists between the pituitary and several of the other endocrine glands.

13. The placenta, in addition to its other functions, secretes hormones. Its role is that of an extremely specialized organ concerned only with certain phenomena associated with pregnancy. The hormones which it elaborates are similar to certain pituitary and ovarian hormones.

14. The endocrine and nervous systems are the dominating and coordinating systems of the body. The more simple method of humoral distribution of secreted chemical substances is utilized by the endocrine system in bringing about its effects.

15. With minor variations the several endocrine organs are similar in all classes of vertebrates. Very little progressive evolution is to be observed in the endocrine system. The appearance of functional corpora lutea in mammals, ovoviviparous elasmobranchs, lizards, and snakes, and their relation to placental nourishment of intrauterine young, is perhaps the most significant development.

CHAPTER 10

SKELETAL SYSTEM

The term *skeleton* refers to the framework of the animal body. In vertebrates it is composed of cartilage, bone, or a combination of the two and serves for support, attachment of muscles, and the protection of certain delicate vital organs which it more or less completely surrounds. Furthermore, it maintains the definite form of the animal and is provided with joints so that movement is made possible.

Although the presence of an *endoskeleton* is one of the distinguishing characteristics of chordates, nevertheless many members of the phylum possess exoskeletal parts as well. The bony dermal scales of fishes, fossil amphibians, crocodilians, turtles, and even armadillos among mammals are exoskeletal structures derived from the integument. They provide the animals with a protective armor. The term *dermal skeleton* is used in referring to such structures and their derivatives. It is difficult to decide whether the endoskeleton or the dermal skeleton is older phylogenetically. The presence of bony dermal plates in the fossil remains of extinct ostracoderms and placoderms indicates that they appeared very early in the evolutionary history of vertebrates and should be considered to be primitive structures. However, during the embryonic development of animals possessing both endoskeletal and exoskeletal structures, the endoskeleton appears much earlier than the exoskeleton. This would lead one to infer that the endoskeleton is phylogenetically older. Although many modern vertebrates at first sight appear to lack a dermal skeleton, their teeth and the membrane bones of the skull are believed to represent dermal skeletal elements.

In certain animals cartilaginous or bony tissues may be present in various organs of the body, quite dissociated from the rest of the skeleton. They are spoken of as *heterotopic skeletal elements*. Examples include *sesamoid bones*, which develop within tendons at a point where the tendon moves over a bony surface; bony plates found in the diaphragmatic muscle of the camel and in the hearts of ruminants; snout bones of hogs; and the *baculum*, or *penis bone* (*os penis, os priapi*), found in the copulatory organs of many male mammals. Such heterotopic bones are special structures and are generally not considered to belong to either the endoskeleton or dermal skeleton.

Cartilage. Cartilage, or "gristle," is a type of connective tissue which forms an important part of the endoskeleton in all vertebrates, although in higher forms it is much reduced in amount, most of it having been re-placed by bone. In an embryo, much of the endoskeleton first appears in cartilaginous form. In such vertebrates as elasmobranchs the skeleton does not go beyond the cartilage stage. In higher vertebrates the cartilage which is later replaced by bone is spoken of as *temporary cartilage*, whereas that which is retained throughout life is *permanent cartilage*. The histo-logical structure of cartilage has been described in a former chapter (page 77).

During development the first indication of *hyaline cartilage* formation is to be seen as a condensation of mesenchymal cells in the place where the cartilage is going to develop. Gradually the mesenchymal cells undergo a change, losing their branching processes and becoming rounded cartilage cells, or *chondrocytes*. These cells begin to secrete a clear matrix about themselves which forces the cells apart so that they are more or less isolated from each other by the matrix which they have secreted. The surface of the developing cartilage becomes covered by a dense layer of connective tissue, the *perichondrium*, to which muscles, tendons, and ligaments may later became attached. The outer part of the perichondrium is composed of dense fibroelastic tissue and is known as the *fibrous layer*. The inner portion is at first made up of many connective-tissue cells arranged in rows parallel to the surface of the cartilage. These cells gradually differentiate into typical chondrocytes to form the *chondrogenic layer* of the perichon-drium. The very actively proliferating and secreting chondrocytes of the chondrogenic layer are responsible chiefly for the increase in diameter of the developing structure. In some cases no further change takes place and the cartilage exists as such throughout life. Examples of permanent hyaline cartilage in the body of man include the lower parts of the ribs (costal cartilages), the articular surfaces of bones, and the cartilages of the larynx, trachea, and bronchi. Other types of cartilage are also present in certain parts of the body. *Elastic cartilage* gives support to the external ear, epiglottis, and other structures. *Fibrous cartilage* is found in the inter-vertebral discs and in places where tendons and ligaments are attached to cartilage of the hyaline or elastic types.

Bone. Bone, which forms most of the skeleton in higher vertebrates, is another type of connective tissue, the structure of which has been pre-viously described. It will be recalled that bone exists in either spongy (*cancellous*) or *compact* form (page 78). Bone is formed in two ways: (1) by direct ossification in connective tissue without an intervening cartilage stage, such bone being referred to as *membrane*, or *dermal, bone*, (2) by re-placement of preexisting cartilage, in which case it is known as *cartilage bone* or *endochondral bone*.

Membrane bone. Certain flat bones of the face and of the skullcap, or vault of the cranium (*calvarium*), are typical membrane bones. The frontal and parietal bones are examples. They actually represent dermal plates, or scales, which have moved from their original peripheral location and have sunken inward to a deeper position, where they have become attached to the true endoskeleton. Although they are often considered to be parts of the endoskeleton, the manner in which they develop differs. Such bones are formed by a method known as *intramembranous ossification*.

The first indication of the formation of a membrane bone appears as an aggregation or condensation of mesenchymal cells in the region where the bone is to develop. Gradually these cells form small groups which tend to string out in various directions so as to form a sort of interlacing network commonly referred to as *membrane*. Bundles of fine collagenous fibers course in all directions among the mesenchymal cells. A semifluid, *amorphous ground substance* is present between the cells and fibers. The developing bone may first be observed as thin bars of a dense *intercellular substance* which appears between the mesenchymal cells and which is apparently secreted by them. These bars thicken and join each other in a rather haphazard manner, forming a sort of meshwork in which the original mesenchymal cells with their branching processes become trapped. These bone-forming cells are called *osteoblasts*. They gradually change their shape, but the branching processes of adjacent cells retain their connections. The intercellular substance, now known as the *matrix*, continues to increase, gradually taking the place of the amorphous ground substance. Soon the matrix is impregnated with calcium salts and becomes hard and rigid, at which time it is properly referred to as *bone*. Each individual cell, now known as an *osteocyte*, lies in a space, the *lacuna*, surrounded by matrix. The branching processes, which retain their connections with adjacent cells, lie in small canals called *canaliculi*. New osteoblasts, arising by a transformation of mesenchymal cells, arrange themselves in a continuous layer over the surface of the small bony bar, and as a result of their activity the bar increases in thickness. Each osteoblast soon becomes surrounded by matrix and is transformed into an osteocyte lying in its own lacuna. In this manner numerous, irregular bony plates and bars are formed. As they enlarge and thicken they gradually coalesce, forming what is known as *primary cancellous bone*. This has a spongy appearance. The small spaces between the plates and bars are filled with very vascular connective tissue which gradually becomes transformed into bone marrow. The spaces are then referred to as marrow cavities.

While the primary cancellous bone is developing and taking on the general configuration of the bone which is to form, the mesenchyme surrounding the developing membrane bone, above and below, differentiates into a layer of dense connective tissue, the *periosteum*. Osteoblasts appear on the inner surface of the periosteum and arrange themselves in a single layer. These osteoblasts begin to lay down strata of *compact*, or *periosteal, bone*, thus forming *inner* and *outer tables*, fusing with and enclosing the cancellous bone, or *diploë*, between them (Fig. 10.1). The periosteum becomes tightly applied to the surface. Further growth of the bone in thickness depends upon the activity of osteoblasts which lie beneath the periosteum and are derived from its innermost layer. There is no clear-cut distinction between periosteal and cancellous bone. They actually represent different arrangements of the same type of tissue.

FIG. 10.1. Section through a portion of a membrane bone (parietal bone of man) showing cancellous bone bounded by compact periosteal bone on both inner and outer surfaces.

Cartilage bone. Cartilage bones, in contrast to membrane bones, go through a cartilaginous stage in their development. The cartilage is usually a miniature of the bone which is to replace it. The term *endochondral bone formation* is used to describe this type of bone development, since it takes place within preexisting cartilage.

The main part, or shaft, of a long cartilage bone such as the tibia is called the *diaphysis*. The first indication of cartilage-bone formation consists of the appearance of a ring of bony tissue around the center of the cartilaginous diaphysis (Fig. 10.3*A*). The original perichondrium becomes the *periosteum*. Osteoblasts, derived originally from the inner, or chondrogenic layer, of the perichondrium, give rise to compact, *periosteal bone*, similar in every respect to the periosteal bone which forms the inner and outer tables of membrane bones as described above. At about the same time that this bony ring is forming, degenerative changes occur within the cartilage in the center of the diaphysis. The cartilage cells undergo certain peculiar changes and then start to degenerate. Blood vessels, accompanied by mesenchymal cells, enter the cartilage and begin to erode it in some unknown manner so as to honeycomb the area with a number of intercommunicating channels which become filled with embryonic bone marrow. The irregular cartilaginous bars, or trabeculae, which lie among the eroded spaces, become calcified and serve as centers about which osteoblasts, derived from the embryonic bone marrow and even from cartilage cells, aggregate. These cells deposit bone around the cartilaginous bars (Fig. 10.2). This forms a bony meshwork of trabeculae, with the result that the center of the diaphysis is composed of a mass of spongy bone. In the meantime osteoblasts beneath the periosteum are depositing compact bone which surrounds the cancellous bone. While these processes have been going on, the cartilage at the ends of the developing structure continues to grow cartilage cells in various stages of degeneration

blood vessel

osteoclasts

bone

osteoblasts

blood vessels

Fig. 10.2 Section through a portion of the end of a long cartilage bone, illustrating endochondral bone formation.

in length. Increase in diameter is brought about by continued deposition of bone by osteoblasts located beneath the periosteum. The center of ossification, which begins in the middle of the diaphysis, gradually extends toward the ends of the bone which, however, remain cartilaginous and continue to grow until a much later period. In mammals, and to a lesser degree in reptiles, secondary centers of ossification later appear at the ends of the bone. These are known as *epiphyses* (Fig. 10.3*D*). The time of appearance of the epiphyseal centers of ossification varies in different bones of the body. In some they appear toward the end of fetal life, but in others they do not make their appearance until some time after birth. Some bones, as in the case of certain phalanges, have only one epiphysis, although most have one at either end. Still others may have two or three separate ossification centers. The proximal end of the femur has three such centers of ossification.

Between each epiphysis and the diaphysis there remains a cartilaginous plate, or pad, known as the *epiphyseal plate*. Until adult stature is attained, increase in length of the developing bone takes place in the region of the epiphyseal plate. Its terminal portion grows by the formation of new cartilage, whereas the inner part is continually being replaced by developing bone from the diaphysis. Eventually the epiphyseal plates are entirely replaced by bone and the epiphyses are united firmly to the diaphysis (Fig. 10.3*F*). Further growth in length of the bone can then no longer occur. The ends of the bones are covered with articular cartilage throughout life. The rate of growth at the two epiphyseal plates of a long bone may differ markedly. In the femur, for example, the main increase in length takes place at the distal end.

Growth in diameter of cartilage bones takes place by the addition of new periosteal bone on the outer part of the developing diaphysis. It gradually extends toward the epiphyses. While growth is taking place, constant internal alterations and reconstruction are going on, leading to the formation of a large marrow cavity in the center of the bone. Not only does this cavity form a space to house the bone marrow, but the resulting cylindrical shape of the bone has the mechanical advantage of providing greater strength. As new bone is forming, old bone is being destroyed. This has

FIG. 10.3. Diagrams indicating progressive ossification of a long bone: *A*, collar of compact periosteal bone surrounding cartilage in middle region of diaphysis; *B*, endochondral bone appearing as primary center of ossification; *C*, marrow cavity appearing as a result of dissolution of cancellous bone in center; *D*, appearance of secondary centers of ossification, the epiphyses, at either end of structure, separated from primary center by epiphyseal plate; *E*, later stage, similar to *D; F*, closure of epiphyses with disappearance of epiphyseal plate; articular cartilage at either end of bone—no further increase in length can take place.

been demonstrated under experimental conditions in which madder leaves have been fed to growing animals. Bone which is developing during the period of madder feeding is red in color. If times of madder feeding are alternated with intervals in which no madder is given, colored and non-colored rings of bone deposits can easily be discerned. It has thus been observed that old bone is being removed in the center of the diaphysis as new bone is being added to the circumference (Fig. 10.4). Destruction or resorp-

FIG. 10.4. Diagrammatic representation of the manner in which a long bone increases in diameter: *A*, from an animal recently fed with madder, colored layer of bone (black) deposited on outside; *B*, madder feeding discontinued, new colorless bone (stippled) deposited over colored layer; *C*, still later, colorless outer layer is thicker, inner layer and part of colored layer removed by osteoclastic activity.

tion of old bone appears to be the function of certain multinucleated giant cells called *osteoclasts,* derived from the embryonic bone marrow. They are responsible for the dissolution of the central part of the diaphysis, removing the original cancellous bone and forming the marrow cavity. As a result, the shaft of the bone finally becomes a cylinder of compact bone containing a marrow cavity in its center filled with bone marrow.

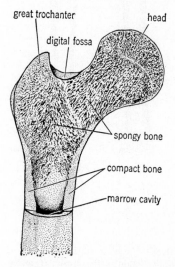

FIG. 10.5. Section through proximal end of fully developed human femur, showing relation of spongy bone, compact bone, and marrow cavity.

We have thus seen how the center of the diaphysis of a long bone is at first composed of hyaline cartilage. This becomes eroded, and the remaining cartilaginous trabeculae become calcified. Spongy bone replaces the cartilage, and later, through osteoclastic activity, is itself destroyed, so that finally only a marrow cavity remains, surrounded by compact bone of periosteal origin (Fig. 10.5).

It is of interest that once the epiphyses have united with the diaphysis, no further increase in length of a bone can occur. However, increase in diameter is still possible. This is well illustrated in the disease known as *acromegaly.* Under excessive stimulation by growth hormone from the anterior lobe of the pituitary gland, after epiphyseal closure has occurred, there may be a marked increase in diameter of the long bones as well as a thickening of other types, such as the bones of the face and of the vertebral column.

Bone marrow. *Hemopoietic tissue,* in which the various kinds of blood cells are formed, occurs in lower vertebrates in a variety of structures. Likewise, during developmental stages in higher vertebrates, several structures serve as blood-cell-forming organs (page 549). It is in the salientian amphibians that the bone marrow which occupies the cavities within certain bones is first concerned with blood-cell formation. In these amphibians, as well as in reptiles and birds, all types of blood cells are formed in the bone marrow. In mammals, however, the hemopoietic function of the bone marrow is restricted to the production of *red blood corpuscles* (*erythrocytes*) and three kinds of *white corpuscles,* the *granular leukocytes* (*heterophils, eosinophils,* and *basophils*). Other kinds of white corpuscles are formed, for the most part, in lymphoid tissue located in various parts of the body. In mammalian embryos and in newborn young the only type of bone marrow that is present is *red bone marrow,* or *myeloid tissue.* It is the red bone marrow that has hemopoietic properties. As an individual becomes older, however, the red bone marrow is replaced in many regions by *yellow,* or *fatty, bone* *marrow.* This type of bone marrow has lost its hemopoietic properties and is composed primarily of fat cells, or adipose tissue. In an adult human being, red bone marrow is confined to the diploë in the membrane bones of the skull, the proximal epiphyses of the humerus and femur, the ribs, sternum, and vertebrae. Other marrow cavities serve primarily as storage places for fat.

Joints. The term *joint* refers to an articulation between cartilages or bones. Two general types are recognized: (1) *synarthroses,* or immovable joints, and (2) *diarthroses,* or freely movable joints. There are several types in each category. Among synarthroses are included such immovable joints as *sutures,* which are the lines of junction of facial and cranial bones; *gomphoses,* in which a bony projection fits into a socket as in the case of teeth in the mandible, premaxillary, and maxillary bones; *schindyleses,* in which one bone fits into a slit in another as in the articulation of the *lamina perpendicularis* of the ethmoid bone with the vomer. Among diarthroses are *ball-and-socket joints (enarthroses), hinge joints (ginglymi), pivotal,* or *rotary, joints (rotatoria),* and *gliding joints (arthrodia).*

In the formation of synarthroses three conditions may be encountered: (1) the mesenchyme between the bones may differentiate into connective tissue proper which, as in the case of sutures, binds them firmly together (*sutural ligament*); (2) the mesenchyme may differentiate into cartilage as in the pubic symphysis; (3) the mesenchyme may differentiate into bone as in the union of the two halves of the mandible in the cat.

In the development of diarthroses, spaces appear in the mesenchyme between adjacent bones ultimately to form the *synovial,* or *joint, cavity* (Fig. 10.6). This is lined with a *synovial membrane* composed of dense, irregular connective tissue. The capsule which surrounds the joint is continuous

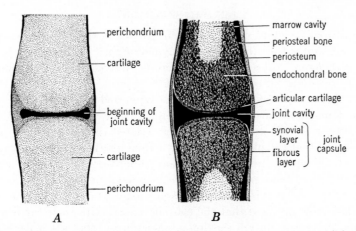

FIG. 10.6. Diagrams showing method of formation of a diarthrodial joint: *A,* beginning of joint cavity appearing in the mesenchyme between two adjacent cartilages; *B,* section through fully formed joint.

with the periosteum of the two articulating bones. It is composed of an outer, dense, *fibrous layer* and a less dense, more cellular inner *synovial layer* which encloses the synovial cavity. The synovial cavity contains a sticky, glairy, *synovial fluid* believed to be secreted by the synovial membrane. It serves to lubricate the articulating surfaces of the bones in question. The ends of the bones, it should be recalled, are covered with hyaline articular cartilage. Although the synovial membrane is said to be reflected over these cartilages during embryonic development, it is lacking in the adult.

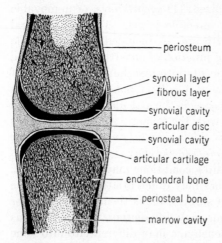

periosteum

synovial layer
fibrous layer
synovial cavity
articular disc
synovial cavity
articular cartilage

endochondral bone

periosteal bone

marrow cavity

Fig. 10.7. Diagram of diarthrosis with an articular disc and two separate synovial cavities.

Ligaments and tendons, which sometimes appear to pass through the synovial cavity, actually lie outside the cavity, since the synovial membrane is reflected over them. The *ligamentum teres femoris*, which joins the head of the femur to the acetabulum, is an example of such a structure.

In some cases the joint may be divided, completely or incompletely, by an *articular disc* or *meniscus*. Under such conditions (Fig. 10.7) the edges of the disc are continuous with the fibrous portion of the capsule and there may actually be two synovial cavities, one at the end of each of the articulating surfaces.

DERMAL SKELETON

The dermal skeleton of vertebrates originates in the corium, or dermis, of the skin and is therefore of mesenchymal origin. It should not be confused with *horny* scales or other structures derived from the epidermis, which is, of course, of ectodermal origin.

The various types of fish scales, already referred to (pages 112 to 116), represent remnants of the dermal skeleton. They are composed of membrane bone or of substances very closely related to bone. In the past it was believed that the placoid scales, or dermal denticles, of elasmobranchs represented a very primitive form of dermal derivative. With the realization that dermal bony plates were already present in the ancient ostracoderms and placoderms it became necessary to adopt a different interpretation. It is now assumed that the elasmobranchs, with their cartilaginous skeletons, have lost most of the dermal skeleton and that the placoid scales simply represent persistent remnants of such structures.

That teeth are undoubtedly dermal derivatives is strongly indicated in the elasmobranch fishes in which the transition between placoid scales and teeth is to be seen clearly at the borders of the mouth. This relationship is not surprising when one considers that the stomodaeal lining is actual invaginated integument which has retained its capacity for scale (tooth) formation. The fact that both placoid scales and teeth in elasmobranchs develop under the influence of enamel organs even though enamel is not formed over the exposed surface of the placoid scale or elasmobranch tooth further suggests a homology between teeth and placoid scales.

Fin rays, which support the peripheral portions of the fins of fishes, are also included in the dermal skeleton. However, the cartilaginous or bony elements, which support them at the base, belong to the endoskeleton.

In the evolution of the vertebrates it would seem that there has been a tendency to eliminate the dermal skeleton which is fundamentally a protective device. Epidermal derivatives such as scales, hair, and feathers have in many cases become elaborately developed, serving to protect the body in lieu of dermal structures. The dermal skeleton has been referred to in some detail in the chapter on integument and requires no further discussion here. The dermal plates of extinct stegocephalian amphibians and the integumentary scales of caecilians hark back to a fishlike ancestry. Likewise, the bony plates in the integument of crocodilians, turtles, and a few snakes and lizards, together with the ventral dermal "ribs," or *gastralia*, encountered in *Sphenodon*, crocodilians, certain lizards, and in *Archaeopteryx*, also indicate a piscine origin.

The homology of the membrane bones of the skull of modern teleosts, amphibians, reptiles, birds, and mammals to the bony dermal plates, or armor, of the earliest-known vertebrates is well established.

Except for the membrane bones of the skull, dermal skeletal elements are usually lacking in birds.

The same thing is true of most mammals. The antlers of deer are outgrowths of the frontal bones, formed under influence of the integument. They may be considered to belong to the dermal skeleton. Bony plates are present in some of the whales, in which they appear along the back and in the dorsal fins. The edentate armadillos are the only living mammals in which the dermal skeleton is well developed. The large, extinct glyptodons, which were also edentates, possessed a rigid armor somewhat like that of the armadillo but lacked movable rings. Whether the dermal skeleton of the edentates has arisen *de novo* or has been derived from reptiles has not been determined.

ENDOSKELETON

It seems somewhat artificial to make a clear-cut distinction between dermal skeleton and endoskeleton because of the fact that membrane bones, which are clearly dermal elements, contribute to what we generally consider to be the endoskeleton. In the following account we shall not stress these differences.

The endoskeleton of vertebrates is made up of *axial* and *appendicular portions*. As its name implies, the axial skeleton is that which forms the main axis of the body. It is made up of (1) the skull, (2) the vertebral column, (3) the ribs, (4) the sternum. The *visceral*, or *branchial*, *skeleton*, consisting of elements which in fishes support the gills and jaws, contributes to the skull in higher forms. It is included in the axial skeleton. The appendicular skeleton is composed of the skeletal elements of the paired anterior *pectoral* and posterior *pelvic appendages* together with their respective *girdles* by means of which the appendages are connected directly or indirectly with the axial skeleton.

Axial Skeleton

NOTOCHORD

The primitive axial skeleton consists of the notochord, present during early development in all chordates but replaced by the vertebral column and base of the skull in all but a few of the lower vertebrates. The notochord is derived, during early development, from the region of the dorsal lip of the blastopore. Embryologists refer to this tissue as *chordamesoderm*. The notochord first makes its appearance as a long, rodlike structure extending longitudinally from the infundibulum, on the ventral side of the diencephalon, to the posterior end of the body. It lies directly beneath the neural tube. It is composed of vesicular connective tissue and is unsegmented. The cells composing the notochord are usually encased within an *outer sheath* of dense fibrous connective tissue. The large, turgid cells originally inside the sheath undergo a change as development progresses. The peripheral cells secrete an *inner elastic sheath* beneath the outer sheath. The centrally located cells become vacuolated, and only their walls persist, so that this portion of the notochord has a pithy appearance (Fig. 1.4).

In amphioxus, cyclostomes, and a few fishes, the notochord persists unchanged throughout life as the main axial support. Even in the lamprey, however, the protection which the notochord gives to the spinal cord lying above it is supplemented by the presence of small, paired, segmentally arranged cartilages which abut against the dorsal side of the notochord and form a sort of incomplete arch over the spinal cord. They foreshadow the appearance of neural arches in the vertebrae of higher vertebrates.

SPINAL COLUMN

The portion of the axial skeleton which protects the spinal cord is, in most chordates, composed of a series of segmentally arranged skeletal structures, the *vertebrae*.   In their aggregate they make up the *spinal*, or *vertebral, column*.   This extends posteriorly from the base of the skull and continues to the tip of the tail.   The vertebral column gives rigidity to the body and furnishes a place for the direct or indirect attachment of the appendage girdles and numerous muscles.   A *neural arch*, on the dorsal side of each vertebra, surrounds and protects the spinal cord.   Various projections extend outward from the vertebral column, thus furnishing surfaces for attachment of muscles and ribs.   The separate elements, or vertebrae, are bound together in such a manner as to provide rigidity together with a certain degree of flexibility.   In no case is the column so flexible as to permit damage to the delicate spinal cord.   In some fishes the vertebral column is entirely cartilaginous, but in most forms it is bony, having developed, for the most part, by the endochondral method of ossification.

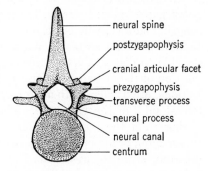

Fig. 10.8.   Anterior view of typical mammalian vertebra.

In the lower vertebrate classes there is much variation in regard to the elements of which each vertebra is composed, and considerable confusion exists concerning the homologies of the various components.   In higher forms, such as mammals, the structure is less complex.

A typical mammalian vertebra (Figs. 10.8 and 10.9) is composed of a solid, ventral, cylindrical mass, the *centrum*, or *body*, above which is the *neural arch* surrounding the *neural (vertebral) canal*.   The ends of the centrum are smooth and joined to the centra of adjacent vertebrae by means of intervening fibrocartilaginous *intervertebral discs*.   The lateral portions of the neural arch consist of two upright *pedicles*, or neural processes, fastened

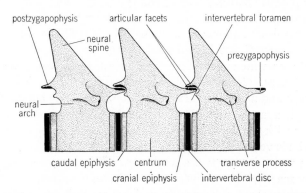

Fig. 10.9.   Lateral view of three typical vertebrae from young mammal, showing epiphyses (semidiagrammatic).

to the dorsal part of the centrum on either side. In most forms a flattened plate of bone, the *lamina*, extends medially from the upper part of each pedicle to form the roof of the neural arch. A dorsal median projection, the *neural spine*, or *spinous process*, is formed as the result of fusion of the two laminae. Anterior and posterior articular processes, the *prezygapophyses* and *postzygapophyses*, are projections which serve to join the neural arches of adjacent vertebrae. The prezygapophyses of one vertebra articulate with the postzygapophyses of the vertebra immediately anterior to it. Smooth *articular facets* are present on both prezygapophyses and postzygapophyses; those on the prezygapophyses usually are on the dorsomedial surface, whereas those of the postzygapophyses are generally on the ventrolateral surface. When examining a single vertebra, it is thus possible to distinguish anterior and posterior ends merely by noting the position of the articular surfaces of the zygapophyses. Various other projections, often referred to as *transverse processes*, extend outward from the lateral sides of the vertebrae. There are several types: (1) *diapophyses*, arising from the base of the neural arch, serve for attachment of the tuberculum, or upper head of a two-headed rib; (2) *parapophyses*, from the centrum, serve for attachment of the lower, or capitular, head of a rib (Fig. 10.41); (3) *basapophyses*, extending ventrolaterally from the centrum, are believed to be remnants of the hemal arch; (4) *pleurapophyses*, projecting laterally, are extensions with which ribs have fused. Another type of projection, the *hypapophysis*, is found in certain forms, extending ventrally from the median part of the centrum. The anterior and posterior ends of the neural arches are notched so as to form anterior and posterior *intervertebral notches*. When two vertebrae are in apposition, the anterior notch of one together with the posterior notch of the next form an *intervertebral foramen*. This serves for the passage of a spinal nerve as it emerges from the neural canal.

The vertebrae, as well as the ribs, are derived from the sclerotome regions of the mesoblastic somites during embryonic development. The mesenchymal cells of the segmentally arranged sclerotomes early come to lie in paired masses on either side of the notochord. The metameric arrangement of the sclerotomes is indicated by the presence of small intersegmental arteries which come from the dorsal aorta and course between adjacent somites. Each sclerotome soon differentiates into a compact caudal region and a less dense cranial region. Next the cranial and caudal portions split apart vertically. The less dense cranial part of one sclerotome unites with the dense caudal portion of the sclerotome in front of it to form a single vertebral mass (Figs. 10.10 and 10.11). Thus each vertebra is actually derived from two sclerotomes. The myotome regions of the somites, by reason of the above, come to alternate with the vertebrae, and the intersegmental arteries now pass under the middle of the centrum. The muscle fibers derived from a single myotome thus come to pass from one vertebra to the next. Such an arrangement must exist if movement of the vertebral column is to take place.

Further development consists of a medial extension of mesenchymal cells so that they surround the notochord, forming the primordium of the centrum; some of the cells extend dorsally on either side of the neural tube, which they gradually surround, forming the primordium of the neural arch; still others migrate in a ventrolateral direction, pushing between the myotomes, to become the *costal processes* concerned with the development

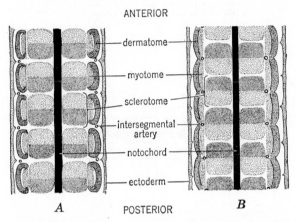

Fig. 10.10. Diagrammatic frontal sections through somite region of a typical vertebrate embryo, illustrating the differentiation of sclerotomes and vertebrae: *A*, sclerotomes differentiated into caudal compact and cranial less compact regions; *B*, union of portions of adjacent sclerotomes to form the beginnings of vertebrae. Note the relations of myotome to sclerotome in each case.

of ribs (Fig. 10.12). It is the more dense cranial portion of each vertebra primordium which is primarily concerned with this differentiation.

Mesenchyme between the centra of adjacent vertebrae, and derived from them, differentiates into the intervertebral discs. In the meantime, the notochord gradually disappears, but remnants persist between the vertebrae as the *pulpy nuclei* of the intervertebral discs.

Centers of chondrification soon appear in each developing vertebra, and before long a solid cartilaginous structure is formed. The transverse processes, neural spines, and zygapophyses are outgrowths of the cartilaginous mass. Resorption of tissue occurs at the junction of the costal processes and the remainder of the vertebral mass, so that the rib cartilages become separate from the vertebra, at least in the thoracic region. Later on, several centers of ossification appear, and the cartilage is replaced by bone by the usual method of endochondral ossification. In many vertebrates certain portions may form by direct ossification in the mesenchyme of the sclerotome. In mammals, cartilage persists at either end of the centrum. Secondary centers of ossification later appear in these cartilaginous areas to form the disclike *epiphyses* of the vertebra. An *epiphyseal plate* of cartilage persists between each epiphysis and the bony centrum until the epiphyses finally fuse with the centrum when full growth is attained.

FIG. 10.11. Diagrams indicating the manner in which vertebrae are formed from the metameric sclerotomes of somites in relation to neural tube and notochord. The position of the myotomes is indicated by the rectangular blocks in the lower part of each drawing. *A*, heavy stippling represents caudal compact portion of sclerotome; light stippling represents less dense cranial region. *B*, the two halves of the sclerotome have split vertically. *C*, the dense caudal portion of one sclerotome has united with the less dense cranial portion of the next posterior sclerotome to form the primordium of a vertebra. Four centers of ossification represent arcualia as indicated. *D*, fully formed vertebrae.

From the foregoing account it would appear that the formation of the vertebral column is relatively simple. However, comparative studies of the spinal column in different vertebrates point to a rather complex evolutionary history. In certain lower forms the vertebrae originate from a number of separate cartilaginous or bony elements which may or may not retain their integrity. The presence of these separate components has been more or less obscured in the development of vertebrae of higher forms in

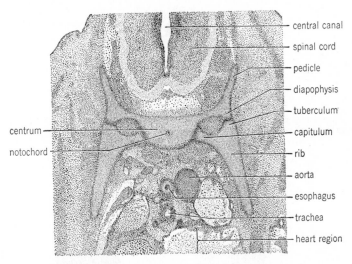

FIG. 10.12. Cross section through thoracic region of 16-day rat embryo, showing the appearance of a developing vertebra. (*Drawn by R. Speigle.*)

which the only evidence of their existence may be indicated by the appearance of separate centers of chondrification and ossification during embryonic development. Paleontological studies indicate that primitively each sclerotome gave rise to four separate cartilaginous elements, the *arcualia*, two dorsal and two ventral. The dorsal ones are referred to as *basidorsal* and *interdorsal cartilages*, and the ventral ones as *basiventral* and *interventral cartilages* (Figs. 10.11 and 10.13). The basidorsals and basiventrals are derived originally from the compact caudal regions of the sclerotomes which

FIG. 10.13. Diagram showing primitive arrangement of cartilaginous arcualia derived from the sclerotomes in relation to spinal cord, notochord, caudal artery, and caudal vein.

become the anterior parts of the separate vertebrae. Interdorsals and interventrals, which are the less conspicuous elements, are derived from the less dense cranial regions of the sclerotomes, thus contributing to the posterior parts of the vertebrae. The basidorsals of a given sclerotome fuse

F‍IG. 10.14. Diagrammatic hypothetical scheme, indicating two possible lines of evolution of vertebrae from ancestral crossopterygian fishes and the oldest known fossil amphibians; that on the left leading to the condition found in reptiles and mammals; that on the right leading to the condition found in recent amphibians. Black areas represent the hypocentrum; heavily stippled areas represent the pleurocentrum.

dorsally, giving rise to the *neural arches*. The basiventrals, at least in the tail region, similarly give rise to the *hemal arches* which serve to enclose and protect the caudal artery and vein which lie ventral to the notochord in the tail region. Anterior to the tail region the basiventrals usually contribute only to the formation of the centrum. Likewise the interdorsal and interventral cartilages may contribute to centrum formation, although in some cases the interdorsals may extend dorsally and fuse to form an arch, the *interneural,* or *intercalary, arch,* over the spinal cord (Fig. 16.2).   The cartilaginous arcualia may eventually be replaced by bone.

Although cells from the arcualia may contribute to centrum formation, the centrum is also derived in part from sclerotomal mesenchyme which appears between the arcualia and the notochord which it surrounds.   This *perichordal mesenchyme* may undergo direct ossification without passing through an intervening cartilage stage.   In teleosts and amphibians the perichordal component gives rise to the greater part of the centrum and the arcualia contribute but little.

In a few lower fishes a so-called *chordal centrum* is present.   This is formed by an invasion of cells from the arcualia into the notochordal sheath which thickens greatly as the cells increase in number within the sheath.   The sheath then undergoes chondrification and becomes a cylindrical structure surrounding the compressed or constricted notochord. A purely chordal centrum occurs but rarely.   Usually other components derived from perichordal mesenchyme and arcualia are present in addition.

The vertebrae of numerous fossil adult tetrapods possess two bony elements the exact homologies of which are somewhat questionable.   A pair of dorsolateral *pleurocentra* and a pair of ventral *hypocentra* are present in many forms.   These seem to have originated in the perichordal mesenchyme but to have fused with the interdorsal and basiventral arcualia, respectively.   Many comparative anatomists are of the opinion that the pleurocentra, by further elaboration, and with a corresponding reduction of the hypocentra, have given rise to the centrum as found in reptiles and mammals.   On the other hand, the hypocentra have played the more important role in centrum formation in amphibians.   Here the pleurocentra have been reduced or have disappeared (Fig. 10.14).   Because of insufficient embryological and paleontological evidence, the exact evolutionary history of these vertebral components remains a matter for conjecture.

Cyclostomes.   The notochord persists in cyclostomes as the main part of the axial skeleton.   It is enclosed by a thick *chordal sheath.*   In the Myxinoidea small pieces of cartilage, which appear to be neural-arch elements, are present in the tail region.   In the lampreys, on the other hand, small cartilaginous plates, two pair per segment, are present throughout the length of trunk and tail.   They abut upon the notochordal sheath but do not meet above the spinal cord.   These cartilages, which probably represent the basidorsals and interdorsals, form rudimentary neural arches. Since they first appear in the primitive cyclostomes, it is possible that neural arches were the earliest skeletal elements to make their appearance in vertebrates.   Similar cartilages in the tail region extend ventrally in lampreys to form hemal arches.

Fishes.   Among fishes the spinal column is composed of two types of vertebrae.   These consist of *trunk* vertebrae, all of which are practically alike, and *caudal* vertebrae, bearing hemal arches and confined to the tail. The position of the anus marks the point of transition between the two regions. The form of the caudal part of the vertebral column varies in the heterocercal, diphyceral, and homocercal types of tail (Fig. 10.44).

Considerable variation is to be found in the vertebral columns of fishes. In some forms, which are primitive in this respect, the condition is not much in advance of the lamprey. In the sturgeon, for example, the notochord persists unchanged and centra are lacking. Pieces of cartilage are present dorsal and ventral to the notochord. The basidorsal cartilages, forming the neural arch, fuse together above the spinal cord to form a neural spine; the interdorsal cartilages lie between the basidorsals. The basiventral carti-

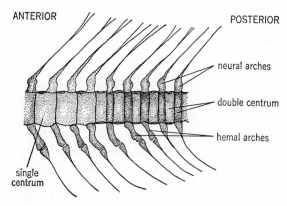

Fig. 10.15.   Diplospondyly in *Amia.* Lateral view of portion of vertebral column, showing three body vertebrae with single centra to the left, and the first five caudal vertebrae with double centra to the right. Only the posterior part of a double centrum bears neural and hemal arches.

lages form an incomplete hemal arch in the tail region, the interventral cartilages lying between them. In the Holocephali and Dipnoi a similar condition exists, but cartilage has begun to invade the notochordal sheath in which ringlike calcifications may appear, four or five to each segment. Perichordal cartilage covers the notochordal sheath to a minor degree. Interdorsals and interventrals may be lacking.

The cartilaginous spinal column of selachians is much better developed. Each vertebra bears a biconcave, or *amphicoelous, centrum* (Fig. 16.2) through the center of which the compressed notochord runs. Between the centra, however, the notochord is not constricted. If it alone were removed, it would resemble a string of beads because of the alternating arrangement of constricted and unconstricted portions. The centrum is formed by the invasion of the notochordal sheath with cartilage cells derived from the primitive cartilaginous plates as well as from mesenchyme surrounding the notochord. Neural arches are present, formed by the basidorsal cartilages, or *neural plates,* between which are interposed *intercalary plates*, representing the interdorsals.   The neural plate is perforated by a foramen for the passage of the ventral root of a spinal nerve; the intercalary plate bears a foramen for the passage of the dorsal root. In elasmobranchs dorsal and ventral roots of spinal nerves unite outside the vertebral column.   In some species the intercalary plates and even the neural plates are further subdivided.   In the tail region a complete hemal arch is formed and a *hemal spine* is present, formed by the fusion of the two hemal processes.   The hemal arch, of course, is not present in the trunk region.   Here a pair of ventrolateral projections, the transverse processes (basapophyses), representing the remnants of the hemal arch, extends toward the lateral skeletogenous septum.   Small cartilaginous ribs in the skeletogenous septum extend from the basapophyses.

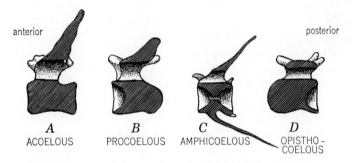

anterior   posterior

A	B	C	D
ACOELOUS	PROCOELOUS	AMPHICOELOUS	OPISTHO-COELOUS

FIG. 10.16.   Diagrammatic sagittal sections of vertebrae showing four types of centra. (*Drawn by G. Schwenk.*)

In the caudal vertebrae of some selachians and certain other fishes, such as *Amia*, there are two centra per vertebra.   This condition is referred to as *diplospondyly*.   In *Amia* only the posterior centrum bears neural arches and hemal arches (Fig. 10.15).   Paleontological evidence is incomplete in regard to the specific elements represented in the diplospondylous condition, and there is little agreement among comparative anatomists as to their exact homologies.   Diplospondyly undoubtedly permits greater flexibility in movement of the tail during locomotion.

In the gar pike, *Lepisosteus*, the centra of adjacent vertebrae form well-defined articulations of a type not found in other fishes.   The posterior end of each centrum is concave, and the anterior end convex.   Thus the convex portion of one centrum fits into the concavity of the vertebra anterior to it in the manner of a ball-and-socket joint.   Vertebrae of this type are said to be *opisthocoelous* (Fig. 10.16D).   No remnants of the notochord are to be found in the adult.

Teleost fishes, for the most part, have vertebrae with biconcave, or *amphicoelous*, centra (Figs. 10.16C and 10.17).   A small canal in the center represents the location of the remnant of the notochord which is very much reduced and compressed.   The concavities are filled with a pulpy material probably derived from the degenerate notochord. In the eel group the centra are more or less flattened or even slightly convex at the anterior end. Rather poorly defined prezygapophyses and postzygapophyses, arising from the neural arch, and otherwise appearing only in amphibians and amniotes, first make their appearance in certain bony fishes. Similar processes, but less well developed, may be associated with the hemal arches. In the trunk vertebrae of teleosts a pair of ventrolateral projections (basapophyses) represents the basal remnants of the hemal arch. Slender ventral ribs are attached to these basapophyses. The transition between ventral ribs and the hemal arches is very clearly indicated in many teleosts although it is not so apparent in others.

FIG. 10.17. Caudal vertebra of teleost fish showing biconcave centrum. (*Drawn by G. Schwenk.*)

In some fishes, as in skates and chimaeras, there is a well-defined joint between the skull and the first vertebra. In dogfishes, however, there is usually an actual fusion.

Amphibians. It has already been mentioned that it is generally believed that from a primitive ancestral condition in which two bony elements on each side, pleurocentrum and hypocentrum, made up the centrum of a vertebra, the evolutionary trend has taken place in two directions. The posterior pleurocentrum has disappeared in amphibians, and the hypocentrum has become the true centrum. Complete paleontological evidence to support this theory is lacking.

With the appearance of limbs in the evolutionary scale, a further differentiation of the spinal column into regions has occurred. This is clearly shown in amphibians with the exception of the caecilians and certain extinct forms. A single *cervical* vertebra is present which articulates with the skull at its anterior face. This is followed by a series of *trunk* vertebrae. A single *sacral* vertebra, which is connected to the pelvic girdle by means of its transverse processes (ribs), lies between the trunk vertebrae and the caudal vertebrae, which are, of course, found only in tailed forms. All the caudal vertebrae, except the first, bear hemal arches with hemal spines.

Amphibian vertebrae bear transverse processes and well-developed zygapophyses. There is some variation within the class in regard to the method of articulation of the centra of adjacent vertebrae. The vertebrae of caecilians are of the amphicoelous type. The same is true of several caudates, although most have opisthocoelous vertebrae. Salientians, for the most part, have *procoelous* vertebrae (Fig. 10.16*B*). In this type the anterior face of the centrum is concave and the posterior face convex.

Thus, adjacent vertebrae articulate in a manner just opposite to that of the opisthocoelous type.

The most striking change to be noted within the amphibian class is to be observed in salientians, since they lack a tail in the adult stage. The number of vertebrae, therefore, is less than in caudates. In most higher modern salientians there are 10 bones in the vertebral column. The number of vertebrae may, however, be reduced by fusion. Some primitive species have an additional presacral vertebra. In such common frogs as *Rana pipiens* and *Rana catesbeiana*, with 10 elements in the vertebral column, a single cervical vertebra, the *atlas*, articulates with the skull. It has no transverse processes or prezygapophyses. Instead it bears on its anterior face two concave depressions which serve for the reception of the occipital condyles of the skull. The next six vertebrae are procoelous trunk vertebrae with no unusual features. The eighth vertebra differs from the other trunk vertebrae in being amphicoelous. The ninth is the sacral vertebra in which the cranial end is convex and fits into the concavity of the caudal end of the eighth vertebra. The caudal end of the sacral vertebra bears two convex projections which fit into corresponding concavities of the

FIG. 10.18. *A*, dorsal view of pelvic girdle, last three vertebrae, and urostyle of the bullfrog, *Rana catesbeiana; B*, lateral view of the right innominate bone. (*Drawn by G. Schwenk.*)

urostyle, or tenth vertebra. The transverse processes (ribs) of the sacral vertebra are large and strong and slope posteriorly in an oblique direction (Fig. 10.18). The pelvic girdle articulates with the ends of these transverse processes. The urostyle is very much modified. It is a long bone which extends from the sacral vertebra to the posterior end of the pelvic girdle, where it rests in a depression formed by the union of the two halves of the girdle. The urostyle was formerly believed to be formed by a fusion of several caudal vertebrae and to be equivalent to the tenth, eleventh, and twelfth. There is little or no embryological evidence for this since the urostyle actually forms by ossification of a cartilaginous rod which, for a time, lies beneath the notochord. A pair of small openings near the anterior end is sometimes considered to be the equivalent of intervertebral foramina. These connect with the neural canal. In a few forms, small, rudimentary, transverse processes are present at the anterior end of the urostyle.

The transverse processes of the trunk vertebrae are tipped with small, cartilaginous projections, the *ribs.* In some species the ribs attain considerable size, but in most cases they are very small.

Reptiles.   In reptiles, contrary to amphibians, the pleurocentrum is the primitive element which has given origin to the true centrum. The hypocentrum has been reduced or has disappeared in most forms, but in *Sphenodon* it persists as a small ventral remnant.

Because of the diversity in form and habit of various reptiles, differences of considerable magnitude are to be observed in their vertebral columns. The vertebrae are ossified, but remains of the notochord may occasionally be found in the centra.

In turtles the number of vertebrae is less than in other groups. Snakes have the greatest number, over 400 being present in certain large species.

Perhaps the most noteworthy advance over fishes and amphibians to be observed in the vertebral column of reptiles is its division in most lizards and in crocodilians into different regions: *cervical, thoracic, lumbar, sacral,* and *caudal.* Cervical, or neck, vertebrae are those lying between the skull and the thoracic region. They are usually more freely movable than those in the remainder of the spinal column. Small ribs are frequently attached to the cervical vertebrae, but they do not extend ventrally to meet the sternum. Thoracic vertebrae bear ribs which articulate ventrally with the sternum. These are succeeded by the larger and more freely movable lumbar vertebrae which do not bear ribs. Next come the sacral vertebrae to the transverse processes and ribs of which the pelvic girdle is attached. Strength and rigidity are attained in the sacral region by a fusion of *two* separate vertebrae to form a *sacrum.* Caudal, or tail, vertebrae follow the sacrum. Small V-shaped *chevron bones,* on the ventral side of the caudal vertebrae of reptiles and other amniotes, probably represent the remnants of the more primitive hemal arches. They are of hypocentral origin.

Turtles, snakes, and limbless lizards do not exhibit the five divisions of the vertebral column seen in crocodilians and lizards with legs. Turtles, for example, lack a true lumbar region. Snakes and limbless lizards have only *precaudal* and *caudal* regions, and no cervical vertebrae or sacrum are present. The separate vertebrae show great similarity in structure.

All types of centra are encountered among reptiles. Amphicoelous vertebrae are present in some primitive forms such as turtles and *Sphenodon.* Opisthocoelous vertebrae occur in certain regions in a few reptiles. Most, however, have procoelous vertebrae. In some extinct forms the centra of certain vertebrae had flat ends, such vertebrae being referred to as *acoelus* or *amphiplatyan* (Fig. 10.16A). The sacral vertebrae of living crocodilians are of this type. Two or more types of vertebrae may thus be found in the same individual.

Among reptiles is found for the first time a modification of the first two cervical vertebrae, a condition which is encountered in all birds and mammals. The second vertebra, the *axis*, or *epistropheus*, in crocodilians, lizards, and chelonians, bears a projection, the *odontoid process*, at the anterior end of the centrum. This is actually the centrum (pleurocentrum) of the *atlas*, or first vertebra, which has become united secondarily to the centrum of the axis. It serves as a pivot which permits considerable freedom of movement of the head. The atlas bears an anterior concavity for the reception of the single occipital condyle of the reptilian skull. The ventral part of the atlas represents the hypocentrum. A separate bone, the *proatlas*, in the form of a neural arch, is found in *Sphenodon*, alligators, and a few other reptiles. It is located between the atlas and the occipital bone of the skull.

Although two sacral vertebrae are present in living crocodilians and lizards, in many prehistoric forms as many as five or six were present. These were firmly ankylosed.

In snakes, certain lizards, and *Sphenodon*, in addition to pre- and post-zygapophyses, other articular facets are present on the neural arches. These are called *zygosphenes* and *zygantra*. Zygosphenes are located at the anterior ends of the neural arches; zygantra are at the posterior ends. The zygosphenes of one vertebra articulate with the zygantra of the next anterior vertebra.

In *Sphenodon* and many lizards the centrum of each caudal vertebra is cut across by an unossified partition. The vertebra is rather easily broken along this septum when the tail is cast off by an animal when attempting to escape from an enemy. The condition is similar in a way to diplospondyly observed in the tails of some fishes, but probably represents a specialized rather than a primitive condition.

The 10 thoracic vertebrae of turtles differ from others in that they lack transverse processes. Their neural arches are rigidly united with the carapace. The two sacral and first caudal vertebrae are also fused to the carapace.

Some of the extinct reptiles possessed unusual variations of the vertebral column. In *Dimetrodon*, a primitive pelycosaur in the line of evolution toward mammals, the spinous processes of the thoracic vertebrae were 2 ft. long, although the centra of these vertebrae are no more than an inch in diameter.

Birds. Developmental stages of bird vertebrae indicate that they are formed in the typical manner from basidorsal, basiventral, interdorsal, and interventral components. The most characteristic feature of the spinal column of birds is its rigidity. The cervical region, however, is extremely mobile, but the remainder is, in most cases, capable of little, if any, movement. Thoracic, lumbar, and sacral regions are firmly united (Fig. 10.19) and to such an extent that it is difficult to delimit one region from another. Rigidity is of advantage in flight.

The cervical vertebrae are variable in number, there being anywhere from 8 or 9 to 25 separate vertebrae in the neck. Swans have the largest number of cervical vertebrae. The atlas differs from the others in its small size and its narrow, ringlike shape. Its centrum has become secondarily fused to the axis, forming the odontoid process of the latter. The anterior face of the atlas bears a deep depression for articulation with the single occipital condyle of the skull. The transverse processes of the cervical vertebrae are pierced by *foramina transversaria*, the presence of

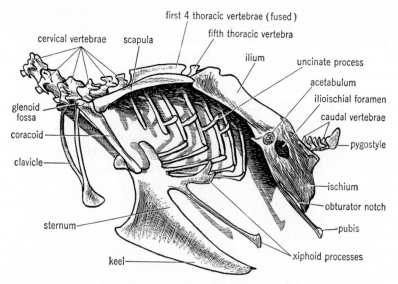

Fig. 10.19. Lateral aspect of part of skeleton of chicken, showing union of vertebrae in thoracic, lumbar, sacral, and caudal regions. The wing and leg bones are not shown. (*Drawn by G. Schwenk.*)

which is characteristic of neck vertebrae. They serve for the passage of the vertebral arteries and veins. The centra of birds' vertebrae do not usually bear epiphyses at their articular ends. In parrots, however, epiphyses are present, a condition which is otherwise confined to mammals and a few reptiles. *Archaeopteryx* had amphicoelous vertebrae, a characteristic which is not encountered in modern forms except in the caudal region. The ends of the centra in most modern birds are saddle-shaped, or *heterocoelous* (Fig. 10.20). In such vertebrae the anterior face is convex in a dorsoventral direction but concave from side to side. The posterior face, of course, has its curves in just the opposite direction, so that proper articulation is provided. Penguins, parrots, and a few others possess opisthocoelous vertebrae. Cervical ribs are frequently rather well developed in birds, and hypapophyses are of common occurrence.

Thoracic vertebrae bear ribs which unite ventrally with the sternum. The rather prominent transverse processes of the thoracic vertebrae have articular surfaces at their tips. These, together with small projections on the sides of the centra, serve for the attachment of ribs. The vertebral end of the rib, therefore, is attached at two places. Not all the thoracic vertebrae are always fused together. In the fowl, for example, there are seven thoracic vertebrae. The first four are fused, but the fifth is free. The sixth and seventh are ankylosed to the first lumbar vertebra. Posterior thoracic, lumbar, sacral, and the first few caudal vertebrae are fused into a single bony mass, the synsacrum. The number of vertebrae making up the synsacrum varies in different birds. Twenty or more elements may be included in it. Examination of the ventral side of the synsacrum will reveal the number of separate vertebrae of which it is composed, since the transverse processes of these vertebrae retain their integrity to some degree despite the fusion. It has

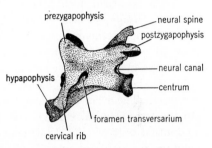

FIG. 10.20. Heterocoelous cervical vertebra of bird.

been determined from developmental studies of bird embryos that only two of the vertebrae are originally sacral, the ostrich being an exception since it has three.

Only a few free caudal vertebrae are present in birds, although *Archaeopteryx* had 20 separate vertebrae in its tail (Fig. 2.18). In most birds the posterior caudal vertebrae are fused together to form the "plowshare" bone, or *pygostyle*, which supports the large tail feathers. The pygostyle may be composed of from 6 to 10 fused vertebrae. It is poorly developed or absent in the Paleognathae. The free caudal vertebrae are usually amphicoelous.

Mammals. Fully developed vertebrae of mammals show little evidence of their ancestral origin from arcualia and such perichordal components as pleurocentra and hypocentra. During development in mammals, many ancestral stages are glossed over, and this seems to be true of vertebra development. The various separate centers of chondrification in the mesenchyme in which a vertebra is first blocked out are believed to represent the arcualia of lower forms with which they have been homologized. It will be recalled that the mammalian centrum, like that of reptiles, has probably been derived from the pleurocentrum of ancestral forms and that the hypocentrum has been lost or reduced.;

Before adult stature is attained, the centra of mammalian vertebrae, with the exception of monotremes and sirenians, bear an epiphysis at either end. In most mammals these finally become fused to the centrum. Intervertebral discs of fibrocartilage, probably representing remains of hypocentra, are also typically present in mammals.

The mammalian vertebral column, like that of many reptiles and of birds, is divided into cervical, thoracic, lumbar, sacral, and caudal regions.

Perhaps the outstanding feature of the cervical vertebrae in mammals is their constancy in number, 7 vertebrae being present with few exceptions. Length of neck, then, is determined by the length of individual vertebrae rather than by an increase in number. Three of the four mammals which are exceptions to this rule belong to the order Edentata. They include the two-toed sloth, *Choloepus*, with 6 cervical vertebrae; the three-toed sloth, *Bradypus*, with 9; and *Tamandua*, the ant-bear, with 8. The other exception is the manatee, *Trichechus manatus*, which is provided with 6 cervical vertebrae. It belongs to the order Sirenia. Fusion of some or all of the cervical vertebrae occurs in some mammals. This is true of many of the whales, armadillos, manatees, jerboas, and the marsupial mole, *Notoryctes*. The atlas is provided with a pair of concavities for articulation with the two occipital condyles of the skull (Fig. 18.5). The axis bears an odontoid process (Fig. 18.6) which is peg-shaped except in some of the ungulates in which it assumes the form of a trough. The cervical vertebrae of mammals (Fig. 18.7) may bear small ribs, but these never reach to the sternum. The transverse processes characteristically arise from two roots, one from the base of the neural arch and the other from the centrum. These transverse processes (pleurapophyses) consist for the most part of ribs which are fused to the vertebra. The foramen transversarium (vertebrarterial canal) lies between the two points of attachment of the rib. The foramen serves for the passage of the vertebral artery and vein and a sympathetic nerve plexus. The presence of foramina transversaria is diagnostic of cervical vertebrae. The seventh vertebra, however, and sometimes the sixth, may lack these foramina. In most mammals the centra of the cervical vertebrae are acoelous (amphiplatyan), but in the Perissodactyla they are distinctly opisthocoelous. This is also true of elephants but to a lesser degree. Considerable variation is to be observed in different species in regard to length of the separate vertebrae, height of neural spines, and other similar features. The seven cervical vertebrae of the giraffe are notable for their extreme length.

Thoracic vertebrae (Fig. 18.8) articulate with ventrally projecting ribs which connect directly or indirectly with the sternum. Some of the posterior ribs, however, may not reach the sternum, in which case they are known as *floating ribs*. Special articular facets are present on thoracic vertebrae for articulation with the ribs. These consist of (1) *tubercular facets* on the ventral side of the free ends of the transverse processes (diapophyses), for articulation with the *tubercle* of the rib, and (2) of costal demifacets (parapophyses) at the dorsolateral angles of the centrum, for reception of the *head*, or *capitulum*, of the rib. The caudal costal demifacet of one vertebra together with the cranial costal demifacet of the next may form a depression which serves as the point of articulation. Thus the capitulum may actually articulate with the centra of two thoracic vertebrae, although this is not always true.   In the cat, for example, each of the last three of the 13 thoracic vertebrae bears an entire facet on each side of the centrum.   Tubercular facets are also lacking in these three vertebrae. The number of thoracic vertebrae varies considerably in different mammalian species.   The smallest number is 9, as found in one of the whales, *Hyperoodon;* the greatest number is 25, as in some sloths.   Fusion of thoracic vertebrae is not known to occur in mammals except in the extinct glyptodons.   Slightly opisthocoelous vertebrae are found in the thoracic region of some of the ungulates, but in most mammals they are amphiplatyan.

Lumbar vertebrae also show great variation in number among various mammals, 4 to 7 being the usual number encountered.   The extremes in number are to be found among the whales, in which one species, *Neobalaena,* has but 2, and another, the dolphin, from 21 to 24.   Usually the number of lumbar vertebrae varies inversely with the number in the thoracic region. Lumbar vertebrae are usually large and strong.   They tend to be longer then other vertebrae.   Their transverse processes, or pleurapophyses, are prominent and directed forward.   The anterior lumbar vertebrae may bear *mammillary processes* (*metapophyses*) dorsolateral to the prezygapophyses. The mammillary processes of the armadillo are particularly large and blunt, aiding in support of the carapace.   Accessory processes may also be present, situated between the postzygapophyses and transverse processes (Fig. 18.9).

The sacrum consists of several vertebrae firmly ankylosed together and serving for articulation with the pelvic girdle.   Again, the number of separate elements which fuse to form the sacrum is variable.   There are 5 in the horse, 4 in the pig, 3 in the dog and cat (Fig. 18.10), and 5 in man. Whales lack a sacrum.   Anomalous conditions are occasionally found in which more or less than the usual number form the sacrum.   Extra elements are taken over by the sacrum from either the lumbar or caudal regions.   The presence of *sacral foramina* on both dorsal and ventral sides provides for the passage of dorsal and ventral rami of sacral spinal nerves. These foramina communicate with the neural canal within the sacrum but do not correspond to the usual intervertebral foramina.   Their location indicates the boundaries of the separate sacral vertebrae.   The first sacral vertebra is most important in supporting the pelvic girdle and hind limbs. Large *lateral masses* bear cartilage-covered *auricular surfaces* for firm articulation with the ilium.   They are composed of transverse processes and sacral ribs which have become indistinguishably fused together.   In man, with his upright posture, a loosening or slipping of the sacroiliac articulation sometimes occurs, accompanied by considerable pain.

Caudal vertebrae in mammals may vary from 3 or 4, as in man, to around 50 in the scaly anteater, *Manis,* and the insectivore, *Microgale.*   The anterior caudal vertebrae possess neural arches, spines, zygapophyses, etc. These gradually diminish in size toward the end of the tail, so that the terminal caudal vertebrae consist of little more than centra. Chevron bones, homologous with those of reptiles (page 388), are frequently present in the form of small V-shaped elements articulating with the ventral side of the centrum. They are particularly prominent in whales and edentates. The three or four caudal vertebrae in man usually unite to form a single *coccyx*. Sometimes, however, the first one or two of the coccygeal vertebrae remain free.

The number of vertebrae in any one species of mammal is quite constant except in regard to the caudal region. For convenience it is customary to use a *vertebral formula* to express succinctly the number of vertebrae found in each region. The kind of vertebrae is represented by the letters C, T, L, S, Cy, indicating cervical, thoracic, lumbar, sacral, and caudal (or coccygeal), respectively. A few vertebral formulas are given below to illustrate the kinds of variations that are met with:

Horse	$C_7T_{18}L_6S_5Cy_{15-21}$	Pig	$C_7T_{14-15}L_{6-7}S_4Cy_{20-23}$
Cow	$C_7T_{13}L_6S_5Cy_{18-20}$	Dog	$C_7T_{13}L_7S_3Cy_{20-23}$
Sheep	$C_7T_{13}L_{6-7}S_4Cy_{16-18}$	Man	$C_7T_{12}L_5S_5Cy_{3-4}$

Skull

The skeletal framework of the vertebrate head is referred to as the skull. The comparative anatomy of the skull is extremely complex, and homologies are often ascertained with difficulty. Confusion arises from the fact that such large numbers of separate elements enter into the formation of the skulls of vertebrates and that they are derived from such different sources.

The part of the skull which surrounds and protects the brain is called the *cranium* (*neurocranium*). Sense capsules associated in development with the olfactory and auditory sense organs become attached to the cranium, as do numerous components of the visceral skeleton which in fishes support the gills and jaws. All these structures in their aggregate make up the skull.

The skull of most vertebrates is derived essentially from three different embryonic components: (1) the *chondrocranium*, composed of cartilage, which contributes chiefly to the base of the skull and which in most vertebrates is replaced by bone, (2) the *splanchnocranium*, derived from the visceral, or branchial, skeleton and which is primitively cartilaginous although some of it becomes invested by or replaced by membrane bones, (3) the *dermatocranium*, made up of membrane bones which roof over the chondrocranium.*

---

* The use of these terms by different authors varies somewhat. Some use "skull" and "cranium" interchangeably. They include all parts of the skull derived from cartilage under the heading "chondrocranium" and all membrane bones under the category of "dermatocranium." The author is of the opinion that the terminology which he has employed is less confusing to the student who is attempting to understand a rather complex subject.

Early development. *Chondrocranium.* Soon after the appearance of the central nervous system during embryonic development, the mesenchymal cells which surround it begin to differentiate, forming a membranous investing layer. In the region of the brain this is referred to as the *membranous cranium.* The notochord extends forward beneath the brain, terminating near the infundibulum. The membranous layer also surrounds the anterior portion of the notochord. It furnishes the material in which the cartilaginous chondrocranium develops by histological differentiation of cartilage within the ventral region of its substance. The chondrocranium is made up of several components. First there appears a pair of flat, curved cartilages, the *parachordal plates,* which flank the notochord on either side (Fig. 10.21). They extend laterally as far as the otic capsules

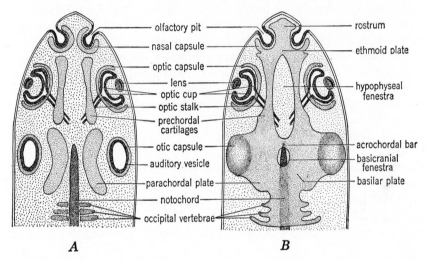

FIG. 10.21. Diagrams illustrating development of the chondrocranium: *A,* separate chondrocranial cartilages surrounding the special sense organs and flanking the notochord and brain; *B,* all the cartilages except the optic capsules have fused to form the early chondrocranium.

(page 396) and posteriorly to the point where the tenth cranial nerve emerges. In back of this point are two to four *occipital vertebrae* with which the parachordal plates later fuse and which are incorporated in the skull. The parachordal cartilages grow larger, their posterior portions fusing together in the midline to form the *basilar plate,* which encloses the tip of the notochord and becomes the floor beneath the midbrain and hindbrain. The anterior ends form a separate connection, being united by a transverse *acrochordal bar.* A small opening, the *basicranial fenestra,* often remains in the center.

Next there appears in front of the parachordals another pair of cartilages, the *prechordal cartilages,* or *trabeculae cranii.* The anterior ends of these fuse with each other, forming a transverse bar, the *ethmoid plate.* This grows anteriorly to become the *rostrum*, which later contributes to the formation of the *internasal septum* between the nasal capsules. Posteriorly the prechordal cartilages unite with the parachordals in such a manner as to leave a prominent opening in the center, the *hypophyseal fenestra*, or *pituitary space*, in which the pituitary gland lies and through which the internal carotid arteries pass.

At the same time as the parachordal and prechordal cartilages are developing, three pairs of capsules make their appearance about the developing olfactory, auditory, and optic sense organs. They are known, respectively, as the *nasal, otic,* and *optic capsules*. With the growth of the parachordal and prechordal cartilages, a union is effected with the cartilaginous nasal and otic capsules, the entire mass forming the chondrocranium. The optic capsules remain as independent elements, thus permitting unrestricted movement of the eyes. The optic capsules are seldom cartilaginous. In mammals they are of a fibrous nature.

The basal cartilaginous cranium, composed of the parts just mentioned, does not exist unchanged for very long. The side portions soon begin to grow dorsally for a short distance on either side of the brain. In such vertebrates as elasmobranchs these dorsally extending parts tend to meet above the brain and fuse, thus enclosing that structure rather completely with a true chondrocranium. In most vertebrates, however, only the most posterior, or *occipital, portion* becomes roofed over as described. The floor and sides of the more anterior region are cartilaginous, but the roof is composed of membrane. This portion of the cranium will later be covered, or roofed over, by membrane bones of the dermatocranium. The large opening at the posterior end of the chondrocranium is the *foramen magnum*. It is through the foramen magnum that the spinal cord emerges from the skull.

Dermatocranium. In addition to the chondrocranium, which appears uniformly throughout the vertebrate series, several dermal plates or membrane bones contribute to the formation of the skull. These appear first in the head region of bony fishes in the form of large scales. They are similar to scales on other parts of the body. The dermal scales gradually sink down into the head, where they roof over the more anterior region of the chondrocranium with which they fuse, thus completing the protective envelope surrounding the brain. Numerous other dermal bones become closely associated with portions of the visceral skeleton. These are discussed more fully below.

Visceral skeleton. In such primitive aquatic forms as fishes, a series of cartilaginous or bony visceral, or pharyngeal, arches encircles the pharyngeal portion of the digestive tract (Fig. 10.22). They serve primarily to support the gills and are arranged between the gill slits, one behind the other. They arise from the mesoderm surrounding the gut. The first is

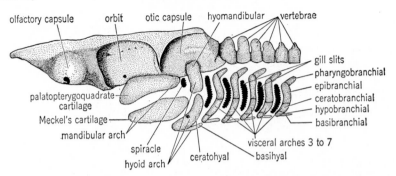

olfactory capsule	orbit	otic capsule	hyomandibular	vertebrae

gill slits
pharyngobranchial
epibranchial
palatopterygoquadrate-	ceratobranchial
cartilage	hypobranchial
Meckel's cartilage	basibranchial
mandibular arch

spiracle	visceral arches 3 to 7
ceratohyal	basihyal
hyoid arch

FIG. 10.22. Diagram showing relation of visceral arches of an elasmobranch to the chondrocranium, vertebral column, and gill slits.

the *mandibular arch*. It becomes divided into dorsal and ventral portions, the *palatopterygoquadrate bar* and *Meckel's cartilage*, which contribute to the upper and lower jaws, respectively. The second is the *hyoid arch*. It usually furnishes support to the anterior hemibranch, if present, but in many fishes its upper division, the *hyomandibular cartilage*, by means of a ligamentous connection, also serves to attach the jaws to the cranium in the otic region. This is referred to as the *hyostylic* method of jaw attachment (Fig. 10.24 *B* and *F*). The remaining visceral arches vary in number in different species, furnishing support to the remaining gills. The last visceral arch, however, usually does not bear gills. The typical number of visceral arches in fishes is seven. Each arch is usually divided into several separate cartilages.

In higher forms there has been a reduction in number of visceral arches and the entire visceral skeleton has become greatly modified. The parts of which it is composed are primitively made up of cartilage, but the cartilage, for the most part, tends to disappear, being replaced by cartilage bone or surrounded by membrane bones.

Further development. In cyclostomes, elasmobranchs, and a few of the higher fishes, no dermal bones (except those associated with scales) are present and the entire skull remains cartilaginous. Even the cranium proper is at least partially roofed over with cartilage in these forms. In most vertebrates, however, the primitive chondrocranium is replaced, at least in part, by cartilage bones. So many variations are met with that it is difficult to generalize in discussing the origin of the various bones of the skull. Nevertheless, a more or less common pattern of development is found throughout the vertebrate series.

Separate centers of ossification appear in the basilar plate of the chondrocranium in what are called, beginning from behind, the *basioccipital*, *basisphenoid*, and *presphenoid regions* (Fig. 10.23). Other centers appear in the cartilage which extends a short distance dorsally on either side of the

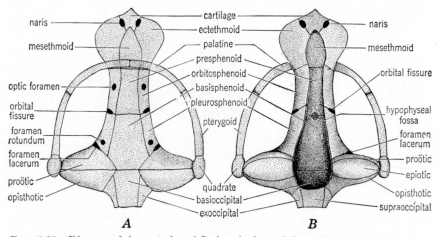

naris — mesethmoid — optic foramen — orbital fissure — foramen rotundum — foramen lacerum — proötic — opisthotic

cartilage — ectethmoid — palatine — presphenoid — orbitosphenoid — basisphenoid — pleurosphenoid — pterygoid — quadrate — basioccipital — exoccipital

naris — mesethmoid — orbital fissure — hypophyseal fossa — foramen lacerum — proötic — epiotic — opisthotic — supraoccipital

A   *B*

FIG. 10.23. Diagram of *A*, ventral, and *B*, dorsal, views of the typical tetrapod chondro-cranium, showing the main regions which ossify to form cartilage bones. The pal-atopterygoquadrate bar is also included. (*After Kingsley," "Comparative Anatomy of Vertebrates," The Blakiston Division, McGraw-Hill Book Company, Inc. By permission.*)

brain. Each center of ossification typically gives rise to a separate bony element which may or may not fuse with others, as the case may be. Three bony segments are thus formed below and along the sides of the brain. The most posterior is the *occipital segment* made up of four cartilage bones: a *basioccipital* below, two lateral *exoccipitals*, and a dorsal *supra-occipital*. It will be recalled that only the occipital region of the chondro-cranium becomes roofed over by cartilage. Anterior to the occipital seg-ment is the *parietal segment* which in reptiles and birds is composed of five elements: a *basisphenoid* below, two lateral *pleurosphenoids*, and two dorsal *parietals*, the latter being membrane bones which roof over the parietal segment. In mammals the pleurosphenoids are lacking. However, a pair of bones, the *alisphenoids*, representing the *epipterygoids* (page 425) and originating as centers of ossification in the palatopterygoquadrate bar, comes to lie on either side of the basisphenoid. The alisphenoids are *not* homologous with the pleurosphenoids. The *frontal segment*, lying anterior to this complex, is also composed of five elements: a *presphenoid* below, an *orbitosphenoid* on either side, and two membrane bones, the *frontals*, form-ing the roof. It should be noted that the frontals and parietals, being membrane bones, are not comparable to the supraoccipital, which is a cartilage bone. Sometimes some membrane bones, representing ancestral elements, are added to the dorsal portion of the occipital. For example, an *interparietal*, or *postparietal*, is usually fused to the supraoccipital in man. In the Inca Indians it was a separate bone. In such vertebrates as modern amphibians, the basioccipital and supraoccipital regions remain unossified. In mammals all four regions finally fuse to form a single *occipital bone.* The cartilage bones of the occipital segment trace their origin to the posterior portion of the parachordal plates; those of the parietal segment are derived from the anterior portions of these primitive cartilages. The cartilage bones of the frontal segment arise from the prechordal cartilages.

Certain other bones of the skull trace their origin to the olfactory and otic sense capsules as well as to the ethmoid plate lying anterior to the presphenoid region (frontal segment), all of which were parts of the original chondrocranium. Three separate centers of ossification appear in the cartilaginous otic capsules; forming three bones: (1) an anterior *pro-otic*, (2) a posterior *opisthotic*, (3) a dorsal *epiotic*. These bones may unite with each other or with neighboring bones. The complex comes to lie on either side between the pleurosphenoid and exoccipital. In bony fishes two additional bones, the *sphenotic* and *pterotic*, develop in the otic capsule.

Several cartilage bones originate in the region of the olfactory, or nasal, capsules. It will be recalled that these capsules fuse with the ethmoid plate formed by a union of the anterior portions of the prechordal cartilages. An ossification center in the middle of the ethmoid plate gives rise to the *mesethmoid* bone which contributes to the nasal septum. In some forms this region remains unossified. In fishes the nasal capsules give rise to *lateral ethmoids*, or *ectethmoids*. *Turbinate* bones (page 191) are the chief derivatives of the nasal capsules. Also from this region in mammals arises the *cribriform plate* with its numerous perforations, the *olfactory foramina*. Several of these bones may unite to form a single *ethmoid* bone. Two sets of membrane bones usually develop in this area: a pair of *nasal* bones, lying above the mesethmoid, and a pair of *vomers* below it. Often there is a single vomer. The entire nasal region anterior to the cranial cavity is commonly spoken of as the *ethmoid region*. Many variations are encountered in this portion of the skull.

Certain membrane bones, in addition to those already mentioned, are frequently present in the vertebrate skull. These include a *parasphenoid*, lying ventral to the basicranial axis; *prefrontals* and *postfrontals*, situated anterolateral or posterolateral, respectively, to the frontal bone proper; and *lacrimals*, which help to complete the inner wall of the orbit, or eye socket.

From the primitive visceral skeleton is also derived a number of separate skeletal elements. The mandibular, or first, visceral arch is very much modified. It is divided on each side into a dorsal *palatopterygoquadrate bar* and a ventral *Meckel's cartilage*. The mouth cavity is bounded by these components. The angle of the mouth is located posteriorly where the palatopterygoquadrate bar and Meckel's cartilage join at a sharp angle.

In bony fishes, centers of ossification in the more posterior portion of the palatopterygoquadrate bar give rise to such cartilage bones as *metaptery-*

*goid** and *quadrate*.   The anterior part of the bar is reduced and replaced by such membrane bones as the *palatine* and *pterygoid.**   The lower jaw articulates with the quadrate.   In these fishes the quadrate forms a connection with a *symplectic* bone, derived from the hyomandibular and attached to it.   The hyomandibular in turn unites with the otic region of the chondrocranium.   This is a variation of the hyostylic method of jaw suspension (Fig. 10.24*F*).

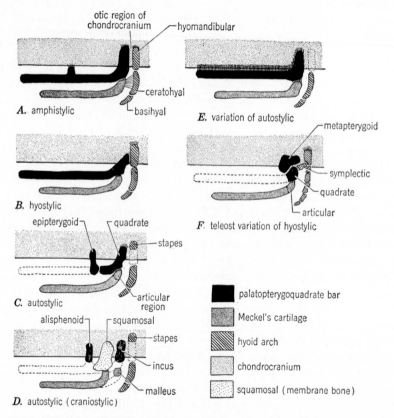

Fig. 10.24.   Diagrams indicating various methods of jaw suspension: *A*, amphistylic, found in a few primitive elasmobranchs; *B*, hyostylic, found in sharks and sturgeons; *C*, autostylic, found in tetrapods other than mammals; *D*, craniostylic, typical of mammals; *E*, variation of autostylic, found in *Polypterus*, holocephalians, and lungfishes; *F*, teleost variation of hyostylic, found in *Amia*, *Lepisosteus*, and teleosts.   The membrane bones investing Meckel's cartilage are not indicated.

    In tetrapods other than mammals a quadrate bone, with which the lower jaw articulates, is also formed by direct ossification of the posterior end of the palatopterygoquadrate bar.   An *epipterygoid,** corresponding to the

---

* Much confusion exists in regard to whether the pterygoid is a cartilage bone or a membrane bone.   Misunderstandings are largely a matter of terminology.   In this ac-

metapterygoid of fishes, develops anterior to the quadrate. The quadrate forms a firm union with the otic region of the chondrocranium. The hyomandibular cartilage is reduced in tetrapods and is not concerned with jaw suspension (Fig. 10.24C). It becomes the *stapes*, one of the auditory ossicles. This method of suspending the jaws via the quadrate is termed the *autostylic* method in contrast to the *hyostylic* method in which suspension is by means of the hyomandibular. Another type of jaw suspension found in a few primitive sharks is called the *amphistylic method* (Fig. 10.24A). Here both the palatopterygoquadrate bar and hyomandibular cartilage of the hyoid arch are united to the otic region of the chondrocranium.

In some tetrapods, as in *Sphenodon*, lizards, and turtles, the epipterygoid becomes a separate bone. In mammals, however, it comes to lie on either side of the basisphenoid and is commonly referred to as the *alisphenoid*. Pleurosphenoids, which in reptiles and birds develop on either side of the basisphenoid, are lacking in mammals.

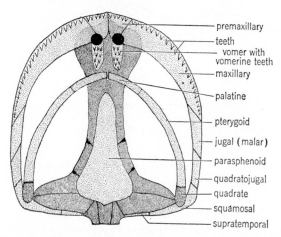

FIG. 10.25. Diagrammatic ventral view of skull of typical tetrapod, showing relationship of maxillary arch to chondrocranium and palatopterygoquadrate bar. Membrane bones are lightly stippled; cartilage bones are heavily stippled. The palatines and pterygoids, as represented here, are membrane bones which have invested the anterior portion of the palatopterygoquadrate bar. (*After Kingsley, "Comparative Anatomy of Vertebrates," The Blakiston Division, McGraw-Hill Book Company, Inc. By permission.*)

In bony vertebrates another arch, the *maxillary arch*, composed entirely of membrane bones, forms outside of and roughly parallel to the palatopterygoquadrate bar (Figs. 10.25 and 10.26). This gives rise to the greater

count we shall consider the *pterygoid* proper to be a membrane bone. *Ectopterygoids* (transpalatines, mesopterygoids) and *endopterygoids*, when present, and which are subdivisions of the pterygoid, are also membrane bones. Such bones as the *metapterygoids* of fishes and the *epipterygoids* of certain tetrapods, which develop from ossification centers in the palatopterygoquadrate bar, are clearly cartilage bones.

part of the functional upper jaw which is fused to the rest of the skull in these forms. The most anterior bones to develop in this region are the paired *premaxillaries*. They are followed by the *maxillaries*, and these in turn by the *jugals* (*malars, zygomatics*). Next in succession come the *quadratojugals, squamosals,* and *supratemporals*. Only the premaxillaries and maxillaries in this arch bear teeth.

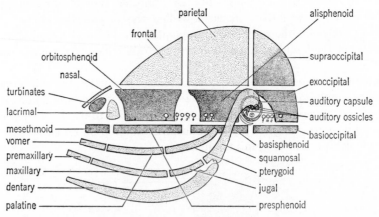

Fig. 10.26. Diagrammatic lateral view of mammalian skull, showing relationships of the various bones. Membrane bones are lightly stippled; cartilage bones are heavily stippled. The palatines and pterygoids, as represented here, are membrane bones which have invested the greater portion of the palatopterygoquadrate bar. Numbers refer to foramina through which cranial nerves emerge. (*After Flower, from Kingsley,* "*Comparative Anatomy of Vertebrates,*" *The Blakiston Division, McGraw-Hill Book Company, Inc. By permission.*)

The term *palate* is used to indicate the roof of the mouth and pharynx. In fishes and amphibians this is a flattened area directly beneath the floor of the cranium. In most reptiles and in birds a pair of longitudinal *palatal folds* grows medially for a short distance on either side. These folds do *not* meet in the median line. In crocodilians and mammals, horizontal shelf-like projections of the premaxillary, maxillary, palatine, and, in some cases, of the pterygoid bones extend medially to meet their partners of the opposite side. In this manner a complete *secondary palate* is formed separating the nasal passages above from the mouth cavity below. As a result, the nasal passages communicate with the mouth cavity much farther posteriorly than they would otherwise. The portion of the secondary palate which is bony is called the *hard palate*. In mammals the secondary palate is continued for some distance posteriorly by a *soft palate*, composed mostly of connective tissue without any bony foundation.

The original Meckel's cartilage forming the lower jaw becomes considerably modified in higher vertebrates with bony skeletons. The posterior region is usually replaced by a cartilage bone, the *articular*. This forms an articulation with the quadrate. In salientian amphibians at the point where the two halves of the lower jaw join in front, a small cartilage bone, the *mentomeckelian*, develops on either side. The remainder of Meckel's cartilage serves as a core about which a number of membrane bones forms a sheath (Fig. 10.27). The separate elements which, for the most part,

FIG. 10.27. Showing the position of membrane bones forming about Meckel's cartilage in the development of the lower jaw. (*After Kingsley, "Comparative Anatomy of Vertebrates," The Blakiston Division, McGraw-Hill Book Company, Inc. By permission.*)

enter into this complex are (1) an anterior *dentary* (*dental*), surrounding Meckel's cartilage, (2) a median *splenial*, (3) a ventral *angular*, (4) a posterolateral *surangular*, (5) a dorsolateral *coronoid*, (6) a *gonial*, lying below and to the median side of the articular. Many modifications of the above are to be found in vertebrates. Only rarely are all these bones present. They exist as separate elements in amphibians and reptiles, but in birds they begin to unite. In mammals the lower jaw consists of a single bone, the *mandible*. It represents the dentary of lower forms, the other elements having been lost except for the articular which has become the *malleus*, one of the auditory ossicles, or ear bones. Study of the fossil remains of some of the mammallike reptiles indicates clearly how, in all probability, the mammalian mandible evolved.

In tetrapods below mammals in the evolutionary scale the articular bone of the lower jaw articulates with the quadrate of the upper jaw. Both of these are cartilage bones. In mammals the articular and quadrate are modified to form the *malleus* and *incus* bones, respectively. A new articulation of the lower jaw with the squamosal, a membrane bone of the maxillary arch, is then established (Figs. 10.24 and 10.26). This occurs only in mammals. The method of jaw suspension in mammals is considered by many authorities to be autostylic even though the articulation of the lower jaw is with the squamosal bone rather than with the quadrate. Other anatomists believe that a distinction should be made and have applied the terms *craniostylic* and *amphicraniostylic* to the mammalian method.

The hyoid, or second visceral, arch does not become so highly modified as the mandibular arch during its evolutionary history. In elasmobranch fishes it is usually composed of three cartilages, a dorsal *hyomandibular*, a lower *ceratohyal*, and a small, ventral, median *basihyal* which serves to unite the ceratohyals of the two sides. In elasmobranchs the hyomandibular forms a ligamentous union with the otic region of the skull and serves as a suspensorium of the jaws (hyostylic method). In higher fishes several cartilage bones may be derived from the hyoid arch although their appearance and number are highly variable. In general they are named as follows in a dorsal-ventral sequence: *hyomandibular, interhyal, epihyal, ceratohyal,* and *hypohyal.* A small median *basihyal* unites the hypohyals of the two sides. A *symplectic* bone, derived from the hyomandibular and found only in teleost fishes (Fig. 10.24F), extends forward from the ventral end of the hyomandibular near its junction with the interhyal and articulates with the quadrate. In tetrapods the hyomandibular bone is reduced and gives rise to the *columella,* or to the *stapes* bone of the middle ear. The ceratohyal is important in elasmobranch fishes as the chief support of the gill filaments of the most anterior, or hyoid, hemibranch. In higher forms it gives rise to a portion of the hyoid apparatus which furnishes support to the tongue and larynx.

The operculum, a posteriorly directed flap of tissue which covers the gill chamber in most fishes, begins in the region of the hyoid arch. In teleosts it is strengthened by a number of thin membrane bones, the *opercular bones,* of variable size and number. The lower borders of the opercula are joined by a membranous structure which, in certain primitive fishes, contains one or two *gular* bones. In higher fishes these become *branchiostegal rays* which give support to the branchiostegal membrane. No homologues of opercular and gular bones are to be found in tetrapods.

The visceral arches posterior to the hyoid serve an important function in fishes in which they support the remaining gills. Their ventral ends are united by separate median cartilages or bones, the *basibranchials,* or *copulae.* In higher forms, the posterior visceral arches are much reduced, being of importance mainly in contributing elements to the hyoid apparatus and in furnishing cartilages to the larynx.

Skull in different classes of vertebrates. *Cyclostomes.* The skull of hagfishes is very primitive, consisting only of a floor of cartilage with side walls and roof of connective tissue. Parachordal cartilages are united with the otic capsules. The prechordal cartilages terminate abruptly at the anterior end.

In lampreys the skull is better developed. Dorsolateral extensions of the prechordal cartilages are present, forming side walls and a roof over the brain in this region. The remainder of the brain is enclosed in fibrous connective tissue. Prechordal and parachordal cartilages as well as otic capsules are homologous with similar structures in higher forms. Other cartilages of doubtful homology are present, supporting the round, suctorial mouth, the olfactory organ, and the tongue. *Posterior* and *anterior dorsal cartilages* are located anterior to the chondrocranium. They too appear to be without homologues in higher vertebrates.

The gill region in lampreys is supported by a peculiar cartilaginous *branchial basket.* The cartilage of which it is composed is continuous and not divided into separate parts. Lateral openings for the gill slits are

present in addition to other openings above and below. The branchial
basket (Fig. 10.28) lies just beneath the skin. Its posterior end furnishes
support for the pericardium. It is not homologous with the visceral skeletons of other vertebrates. In hagfishes the visceral skeleton is much re-

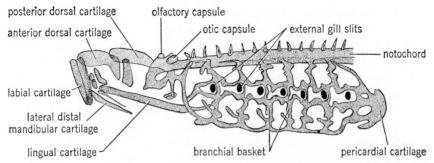

FIG. 10.28. Lateral view of chondrocranium and branchial basket of lamprey, *Petro-myzon marinus.* (*After Parker, from Schimkewitsch.*)

duced, but a hyoid arch, as well as first and second branchial arches, is
recognizable. They are located far within the head and are interpreted as
true visceral arches.

Fishes. ELASMOBRANCHS. The skull in elasmobranch fishes is entirely
cartilaginous. The cartilage is frequently calcified, however. The chondrocranium consists of a single piece of cartilage, the separate elements of
which it is formed having fused together. Nasal and otic capsules are indistinguishably united with the braincase. A large, depressed *orbit* on
either side serves to receive the eyeball. Openings are present for the passage of blood vessels and cranial nerves (Figs. 16.3 and 16.4). The floor of
the chondrocranium is complete. A cuplike depression, the *sella turcica*,
serves to receive the pituitary body. The occipital region of the chondrocranium on either side bears a posterior projection, the *occipital condyle*,
which usually forms an immovable articulation with the first vertebra.
Perhaps the most peculiar feature of the elasmobranch chondrocranium is
the *rostrum*, an anterior, troughlike extension, formed originally from the
prechordal cartilages. The presence of the rostrum causes the mouth to
be subterminal and ventral in position. In the sawfish the rostrum is a
very extensive projection, supplied along the sides with numerous sharp
teeth and forming the formidable, sawlike weapon with which this fish is
supplied (Fig. 4.15). In some of the larger sawfishes the rostrum may
reach 6 ft. in length and 1 ft. in width.

The visceral skeleton of elasmobranchs (Fig. 10.22) is typically composed of seven cartilaginous visceral arches surrounding the anterior part
of the digestive tract and furnishing support to the gills.

The first, or mandibular, arch is larger and more conspicuous than the
rest. From it are derived both upper and lower jaws. On each side the

mandibular arch divides into a dorsal palatopterygoquadrate bar and a ventral Meckel's cartilage. These articulate with each other posteriorly. Both cartilages are suspended, by means of a ligamentous attachment, from the hyomandibular cartilage of the hyoid arch which in turn is joined to the otic region of the chondrocranium. This is the hyostylic method of jaw attachment (Fig. 10.24*B*). The palatopterygoquadrate bars of the two sides make up the upper jaw. They are heavy cartilages which unite with each other anteriorly by means of a ligamentous connection. The anterior, or palatine, portion of the palatopterygoquadrate bar usually bears a *palatine,* or *orbital, process* which extends upward along the inner wall of the orbit. The two Meckel's cartilages, forming the lower jaw, are united anteriorly by a ligament. Both palatopterygoquadrate and Meckel's cartilages bear teeth. Small *labial cartilages* of doubtful homologies are embedded in the tissue just outside the upper and lower jaws near the anterior end.

The second, or *hyoid, arch* is composed of three parts. An upper *hyomandibular cartilage* articulates with the chondrocranium behind the orbit in the otic region. Below this is the *ceratohyal cartilage.* The ceratohyals of the two sides are joined together ventrally by means of a median plate, the *basihyal.* The posterior edges of both hyomandibular and ceratohyal cartilages give off numerous slender cartilaginous *gill rays* which support the tissue bearing the gill lamellae composing the first, or hyoid, hemibranch.

The number of visceral arches posterior to the hyoid varies in elasmobranchs, but usually there are five. Each consists of several cartilages on each side. Named in order from dorsal to ventral borders they are (1) *pharyngobranchial,* (2) *epibranchial,* (3) *ceratobranchial,* (4) *hypobranchial.* The pharyngobranchials slope posteriorly and terminate just below the vertebral column. They are attached to the vertebral column by fibrous bands of tissue. The hypobranchials may meet their partners in the midventral line or are connected by unpaired *basibranchial cartilages.* The epibranchials and ceratobranchials bear the gill rays which support the remaining gills. Gill rays are wanting on the fifth visceral arch which, as previously mentioned, does not bear a gill. Short but strong, pointed cartilaginous projections called *gill rakers* extend into the pharynx from the inner edges of the visceral arches. They are covered with mucous membrane and are used to strain food particles from the water.

OTHER FISHES. Among the skulls of fishes are to be found all the transitional stages from those which are completely cartilaginous to those which are almost completely bony.

In holocephalians the skull is composed entirely of cartilage. Noteworthy is the fact that the entire palatopterygoquadrate bar is immovably fused to the cranium. The lower jaw is suspended from the quadrate region, and the hyoid arch plays no part in suspending the jaws (Fig. 10.24*E*).

This is a variation of the autostylic method of jaw suspension. The skull articulates with the vertebral column by means of a movable joint. The hyoid arch is developed only slightly more than the remaining visceral arches. The hyomandibular portion is degenerate. The ceratohyal component, with its gill rays, supports the *operculum*, which first makes its appearance in this group of fishes.

The sturgeon, *Acipenser*, has a skull almost completely formed of cartilage. No cartilage bones are present although ossifications appear in the otic and orbitosphenoid regions. Several well-developed membrane bones have made their appearance. On the dorsal side they include frontals, parietals, squamosals, and others, which form a protective shield of dermal scales over the cartilaginous cranium beneath. On the ventral side are two other membrane bones, an anterior *vomer* and a more posterior *parasphenoid*. The rostrum, covered with scales, is prominent. The method of jaw attachment in the sturgeon is hyostylic. Maxillary and dentary bones are associated with the jaws, and dermal opercular bones lie over the hyomandibular cartilage. Jaws and visceral skeleton are poorly developed. In *Polyodon*, a close relative of the sturgeon, membrane bones are less prominent. Nevertheless, the snout or paddle, which is actually the enormously elongated rostrum, is covered with dermal scales.

The cladistian, *Polypterus*, exemplifies an advance over the primitive toward the more highly developed teleostean skull. The cartilaginous skull is retained for the most part, but a veritable armor of numerous membrane bones covers it. Among these are frontals, parietals, nasals, supratemporals, posttemporals, and *dermal* supraoccipitals. Since the palatopterygoquadrate bar is fused to the cranium, the method of jaw attachment is autostylic (Fig. 10.24*E*). Several important membrane bones are developed in connection with the palatopterygoquadrate bar. They include palatines and a number of pterygoids. The outer arch of membrane bones includes premaxilliaries, maxillaries, and jugals. Vomer bones are also present. In connection with Meckel's cartilage are developed dentary, angular, and splenial bones. Other membrane bones appear on the operculum.

In the gar pike, *Lepisosteus*, and in the bowfin, *Amia*, both cartilage bones and numerous membrane bones are present. Exoccipitals, prootics, and lateral ethmoids are among the cartilage bones which appear. In the gar, teeth are borne by the maxillary bones in the upper jaw. Teeth are present in *Amia* on the palatines, pterygoids, and vomers as well as on premaxillaries and maxillaries. The lower jaw of the gar consists mainly of the tooth-bearing dentary. Small angular and articular bones are also present. In *Amia* there are several splenials, an angular, surangular, coronoid, and articular. The dentary, bearing teeth, however, is the chief bone of the lower jaw. The hyostylic method of jaw attachment is found in these fishes (Fig. 10.24*F*).

A rather wide variation is to be observed among the teleosts. Their skulls have more bones than those of any other vertebrates. Numerous membrane bones are present, but most characteristic is the presence of several cartilage bones which have formed from ossification centers in the primitive chondrocranium which still persists to some degree. These bones include basioccipitals, exoccipitals, supraoccipitals, basisphenoids, pleurosphenoids, or alisphenoids (not homologous to the alisphenoids of mammals), orbitosphenoids, pro-otics, epiotics, and opisthotics. Sphenotics and pterotics, present in addition, are derived from the auditory capsules. Mesethmoid and lateral ethmoids develop anteriorly. Among the more prominent membrane bones on the roof of the skull are parietals, frontals, and nasals. A series of *circumorbital* bones affords protection to the eyes. Several other membrane bones are present in addition to those mentioned.

Forming the roof of the mouth are a large, single parasphenoid and a pair of vomers. The palatopterygoquadrate bar in these fishes ossifies to form such cartilage bones as the metapteryoid and quadrate. The posteriorly located quadrate articulates with the *symplectic*. The latter joins the hyomandibular, which in turn is fastened to the cranium. This is a variation of the hyostylic method of jaw suspension and is characteristic of teleosts (Fig. 10.24*F*). Other bones (palatine, ectopteryoid, metapterygoid) usually aid in holding the quadrate in place. Palatines and pterygoids (ectopterygoids and endopterygoids) are membrane bones formed in relation to the palatopterygoquadrate bar. The outer arch of membrane bones includes premaxillaries and maxillaries. Both usually bear teeth, but in most teleosts the maxillaries are reduced in size, do not form part of the margin of the jaw, nor do they bear teeth. Teeth are frequently present on vomers, palatines, and pterygoids. The number of bones in the lower jaw of teleosts shows a reduction. The dentary, which usually bears teeth, is the chief component. An angular bone may be present. The articular bone is small and reportedly derived from both membrane and cartilage elements. It articulates with the quadrate.

The hyoid arch is ossified in several places. A hyomandibular bone articulates with the sphenotic and pterotic bones of the auditory capsule and with the metapterygoid of the palatopterygoquadrate bar. A symplectic bone, found only in bony fishes, and segmented off the hyomandibular cartilage during development, is interposed between hyomandibular and quadrate bones. The remainder of the hyoid arch is composed of a chain of bones. First there is a small *interhyal* which articulates at the junction of hyomandibular and symplectic. This is followed ventrally and in order by an *epihyal*, a large *ceratohyal*, and a small *hypohyal*. Several sturdy, curved, bony *branchiostegal rays* project posteriorly from the ceratohyal. They are probably homologous with the gular bones which appear ventral to the operculum in some primitive fishes. The branchiostegal rays support the branchiostegal membrane (page 200). In some fishes, as in the salmon, a large, forward-projecting *glossohyal* (*entoglossal*), bearing teeth, serves to unite the hyoid arches of the two sides and to support the tongue. A posteriorly directed *urohyal* may connect with the basibranchial of the next visceral arch. Both these bones are probably hyoid-arch derivatives. In bony fishes the hyoid hemibranch is missing. It may possibly be represented by opercular gill lamellae on the inner wall of the operculum. These, however, may be remnants of the pseudobranch located on the anterior wall of the spiracle of lower fishes. The homologies of the opercular gill are uncertain. Of importance in the bony fishes are the opercular bones. They usually consist of four large membrane bones which give support to the operculum, helping to protect the gill chamber. They lie directly posterior to the hyomandibular region.

The five remaining visceral arches are often considerably reduced. They are usually composed of several separate elements named in the same manner as those of elasmobranchs. The last one consists only of a single dorsal element, the pharyngobranchial, which bears teeth but does not support a gill. Gill rakers, or strainers, project from the inner surfaces of the visceral arches. No membrane bones develop in connection with the hyoid or the remaining visceral arches.

The skull in Dipnoi is not so far advanced as that of teleosts. It is cartilaginous, for the most part, but both cartilage bones (exoccipitals) and membrane bones are found. The palatopterygoquadrate bar, like that of holocephalians, is indistinguishably fused to the cranium. No cartilage bones are derived from it. The method of jaw suspension is autostylic. Marginal teeth are lacking, but *tooth plates* are present on the vomers and pterygoids, both of which are membrane bones.

In the evolution of the skull from primitive fishes to mammals, there has been a gradual reduction in number of the separate bony elements by elimination and fusion. As many as 180 skull bones are present in certain primitive fishes. The human skull consists only of 28, including the auditory ossicles. In some cases cartilage bones and membrane bones fuse together to form a single structure. The autostylic method of jaw attachment is the rule in tetrapods.

Amphibians. Although the skulls of early tetrapods retained certain characteristics of their piscine progenitors, those of modern amphibians show considerable deviation. Among the most important changes are a reduction in the number of bones and a general flattening of the skull. In addition, the length of the skull has apparently been reduced, particularly in the occipital region. The otic capsule bears a ventral opening, the *fenestra ovalis*, into which a cartilaginous or bony plug fits. This is the *stapedial plate* of the columella which, it will be recalled, is derived from the hyomandibular cartilage. It is possible that the columella proper is

derived from the symplectic. The columella (stapes) has developed in
connection with the evolution of the sense of hearing and with the change
from the hyostylic to the autostylic method of jaw suspension in which the
hyomandibular bone loses its significance as a suspensorium.

The embryonic chondrocranium persists to a considerable extent in
amphibians, but some of it has been replaced by cartilage bones. The
basioccipital and supraoccipital regions are not ossified. Articulation of
the skull with the atlas vertebra is accomplished by means of a pair of occipital condyles, projections of the exoccipital bones. Basisphenoid and
presphenoid regions also are not ossified. Pro-otics, and in some cases
opisthotics, are ossified and fused to the exoccipitals. Much variation in
the ossification of this region is encountered.

Membrane bones form the greater part of the roof of the skull. They
are no longer closely related to the integument and occupy a deeper position in the head than in the fishes. In some of the extinct stegocephalians,
grooves for the accommodation of branches of the lateral-line canal were
present on some of the membrane bones of the skull, giving evidence of their
dermal origin. A rather large membrane bone, the parasphenoid, covers
the ventral part of the chondrocranium.

In extinct and modern stegocephalians the dorsal surface of the skull is
solidly covered by bone, leaving only openings for the nares and eyes. In
some extinct forms, however, another opening, the *interparietal foramen*, is
evident. This accommodated the stalk of the median parietal eye. The
interparietal foramen has disappeared in living species. Modern stegocephalians, or caecilians, also show great solidity of the skull. There has,
however, been a reduction in the number of skull bones. In other amphibians large spaces are present on both dorsal and ventral sides of the skull.

It has been mentioned that in forms above fishes in the evolutionary
scale the autostylic method of jaw attachment is the rule. The quadrate,
in amphibians, is fused to the otic region of the cranium. Palatine and
pterygoid membrane bones, which form about the anterior portion of the
palatopterygoquadrate bar, are well developed. The outer arch of membrane bones is represented by premaxillaries and maxillaries. Salientians
have a quadratojugal in addition. Premaxillaries and maxillaries, together
with the vomer and sometimes the palatines, bear teeth in most species.

The lower jaw consists of a core of Meckel's cartilage surrounded by
membrane bones. In early amphibians as many as 10 bones formed about
Meckel's cartilage on each half of the jaw. In modern forms the number
has been considerably reduced.

CAUDATA. In the tailed amphibians the skull is less well developed than
in salientians. The chondrocranium proper becomes ossified in only two
regions. Anteriorly there is a pair of elongated orbitosphenoids, each bearing a foramen for the passage of the optic nerve. Posteriorly are found the
paired exoccipitals which are fused with the otic bones. Two foramina in

each exoccipital near the condyle provide for the passage of the glossopharyngeal and vagus nerves. Farther anteriorly are two additional foramina for the facial and trigeminal nerves. The membrane bones on the dorsal side of the cranium consist of parietals, frontals, and *prefrontolacrimals*. A pair of nasal bones develops in the olfactory region. An unpaired parasphenoid bone, often bearing teeth, lies on the ventral surface. Anterior to this is a pair of *vomeropalatines*, usually bearing a row of teeth. The choanae open just posterior to the vomerine portion. The upper jaw consists of premaxillary and maxillary membrane bones. The premaxillaries in some cases are united and articulate with the vomeropalatines on the ventral side and with the nasals, and frequently with the frontals, on the dorsal side. Laterally the premaxillaries articulate with the maxillaries. The latter terminate freely at their posterior ends, failing to meet the quadrates. Jugals and quadratojugals are lacking. The quadrate bone, representing the remainder of the palatopterygoquadrate bar, is fused to the otic capsule and articulates with the stapes. It serves for articulation with the lower jaw. The squamosal, a membrane bone, invests the outer surface of the quadrate. A cartilage extending anteriorly from the quadrate toward the maxillary is invested ventrally and laterally by the pterygoid. In some cases the pterygoid may form a cartilaginous connection with the maxillary.

The lower jaw of caudates usually consists of two tooth-bearing membrane bones, an anterior dentary and a posterior splenial, which encase Meckel's cartilage, and a single cartilage bone, the articular, which articulates with the quadrate of the upper jaw. Another membrane bone, the angular, is also frequently present.

Although the above description applies in general to most caudates, many variations are encountered. Nasals, maxillaries, and sometimes palatines may be lacking. In *Necturus* (Figs. 17.4 and 17.5) the skull retains many primitive features. The nasal capsules are not united with other parts of the skeleton. Maxillary bones are lacking. A *palatopterygoid* membrane bone with teeth on its anterior portion unites the vomer with the quadrate on each side.

The remaining portion of the visceral skeleton in caudate amphibians is reduced in comparison with fishes (Fig. 17.6). Larval forms generally possess portions of the hyoid and four other visceral arches, but these are reduced at the time of metamorphosis. In adults the hyoid arch usually consists of two pieces on each side, a lower hypohyal and an upper ceratohyal which is frequently ossified. The hypohyals are in most cases united ventrally to a median basibranchial or *copula*. The next two arches consist of proximal ceratobranchials and distal epibranchials. The ceratobranchials unite medially with the basibranchial, which is usually composed of a single piece. After metamorphosis the last two arches are much diminished or disappear altogether. The hyoid is not always the best developed of the postmandibular visceral arches. In the caudate *Eurycea*, for example, one of the branchials is better developed than the hyoid. The entire apparatus serves to support the tongue and regions posterior to the tongue.

SALIENTIA. The broad, flat skull of the salientian amphibians (Fig. 10.29) is noteworthy for the fact that the elements composing the jaws are

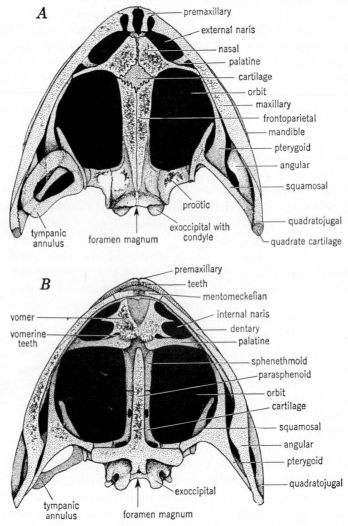

FIG. 10.29. *A*, dorsal, and *B*, ventral, views of skull of bullfrog, *Rana catesbeiana*.

so widely separated from the cranium. The cranium retains much of its original cartilaginous character. Part is replaced by cartilage bone; part is covered with membrane bone. The cartilage bones consist of (1) an unpaired *sphenethmoid*, a ringlike bone which encircles the anterior portion of the cranial cavity, (2) two *exoccipitals*, forming the margins of the foramen magnum, each bearing a condyle for articulation with the atlas, (3) *pro-otics*, of irregular shape, situated anterolaterad the exoccipitals. The fenes-tra ovalis, a well-defined opening in the cartilage lying ventral to the pro-otic, is plugged by the minute stapedial plate of the columella. The epiotic and opisthotic regions of the auditory capsule are united with the exoccipi-tals of which they are often considered to be a part. The membrane bones of the cranium include paired *frontoparietals* on the dorsal side and an un-paired *parasphenoid*, located ventrally. Three openings, or *fontanelles*, are present in the roof of the chondrocranium, but these are covered over by the frontoparietals.

The nasal capsules, although united with the cranium, usually remain unossified. Two pairs of membrane bones, however, form in connection with the nasal capsules. They are the *nasals* above and the *vomers* below, the latter bearing *vomerine teeth*. The posterior lateral borders of the vo-mers bound the median borders of the internal nares.

The upper jaw consists largely of an outer maxillary arch articulating an-teriorly and posteriorly with the rest of the skull but being rather widely separated from it in the middle. The large space thus formed on each side is the *orbit* which accommodates the eyeball. The upper jaw is composed of a series of membrane bones. From anterior to posterior ends these in-clude the premaxillaries, maxillaries, and quadratojugals. The latter are lacking in the Aglossa. Only the first two bones of this series bear teeth. At the posterior angle of the upper jaw is a small, unossified area, sometimes called the *quadrate*, with which the quadratojugal articulates. The quad-rate is connected to the cranium by a short bar of cartilage. To this, in turn, is attached a cartilaginous ring, derived from the palatopterygoquad-rate bar, which encircles and supports the tympanic membrane. The col-umella, derived from the hyomandibular cartilage of fishes, meets the tym-panic membrane distally. Its base articulates with the small stapes (sta-pedial plate) and also with a slight depression in the pro-otic bone. Three other bones complete the upper jaw. The *pterygoid* is a triradiate bone ex-tending forward from the quadrate and pro-otic to a point near the junction of the maxillary and palatine bones. The *palatine* is a small, transverse membrane bone located ventrally and crossing from sphenethmoid to max-illary. The *squamosal* is a T-shaped bone. Its base articulates at the angle of the jaw with the quadratojugal. It is separated from the pterygoid be-low by a strand of cartilage. The posterior arm of the T joins the pro-otic, whereas the anterior arm extends toward the middle of the pterygoid.

The lower jaw consists of a very small pair of anteriorly located cartilage bones, the *mentomeckelians*. Two membrane bones on each side form a sheath about Meckel's cartilage. These are the *dentary* and *angular*. Teeth are lacking on the lower jaw. There is no separate *articular* ossifica-tion which in other vertebrates forms the point of articulation with the quadrate. Articulation is by means of an *articular cartilage*.

In salientians the remainder of the visceral skeleton, or hyoid apparatus, is greatly modified. In larval forms it is much like that of caudates. In adults, however, the hyoid apparatus consists of a broad, cartilaginous *basilingual plate* with anterior and posterior projections, the *cornua*. The basilingual plate represents the united ventral portions of the visceral arches. The anterior cornua are homologous with the ceratohyals of lower forms. They curve anteriorly, then backward and upward to articulate with the auditory capsules near the fenestra ovalis. The posterior cornua, or *thyrohyals*, corresponding to the fourth visceral arches, are ossified.

The chief differences between the skulls of caudate and salientian amphibians are as follows: (1) the latter possess an unpaired sphenethmoid, homologous with the paired orbitosphenoids of caudates; (2) the frontals and parietals, which in caudates are separate bones, have fused to form the frontoparietals in salientians; (3) the maxillary bone in salientians is connected posteriorly with the cranium by means of a quadratojugal; (4) small cartilage bones, the mentomeckelians, are present at the tip of the lower jaw in salientians; (5) the skeletal elements supporting the middle ear are present in salientians in which a middle ear appears for the first time.

Reptiles. The chief differences to be noted in the reptilian skull as compared with that of amphibians is the greater degree of ossification and the increased density of bones. Little remains of the embryonic chondrocranium which has become well ossified. Only the ethmoid region has retained its primitive cartilaginous character. All four parts of the occipital complex are ossified, but all do not necessarily bound the foramen magnum. A single occipital condyle is present, formed from the basioccipital and usually by a contribution from each exoccipital. A cartilaginous or bony interorbital septum, forming a partition between the orbits, is present in many reptiles. In others, in which the brain extends farther anteriorly, the anterior part of the cranial cavity lies in this region and the septum is reduced. The pro-otic region of the auditory capsule is ossified and usually remains separate from epiotics and opisthotics. The parietal bones are paired in some species but frequently are fused. The same is true of the frontals. An *interparietal foramen* is prominent in *Sphenodon* and many lizards. Membrane bones are more numerous in reptiles than in amphibians. Prefrontal, postfrontal, postorbital, and lacrimal bones are often well developed.

CHELONIA. The skulls of turtles and tortoises (Fig. 10.30) are characterized by their solidity. The roof of membrane bones is unusually complete. Teeth are lacking within the group, although vestiges have been described in embryos of the soft-shelled turtle. Otherwise the jaws are covered with a sharp, horny beak. In chelonians the single occipital condyle is formed from contributions of the basioccipital and the two exoccipitals. The latter bound the sides and greater part of the floor of the foramen magnum. All four parts of the occipital segment form cartilage bones. Only the basisphenoid region of the remainder of the chondrocranium is ossified, however, the presphenoid and orbitosphenoid regions remaining cartilaginous. Membrane bones of the frontal segment consist of frontals, prefrontals, and postfrontals. Prefrontals join ventrally with vomers and palatines. They help to bound the external nares. The postfrontals, which articulate dorsally with the frontals, prefrontals, and parietals, extend posteriorly and ventrally to join squamosals, quadratojugals, and jugals. All three frontal bones form part of the wall of the orbit

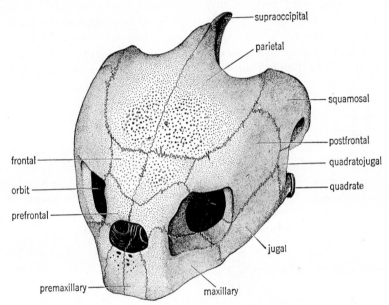

FIG. 10.30. Dorsolateral view of skull of sea turtle.

which in chelonians is completely encircled with bone. In some primitive chelonians a false roof is located above the true cranial roof, the two being separated by a wide gap. The false roof is composed of portions of the postfrontals, parietals, and squamosals.

The three elements of the otic capsule are ossified. Epiotics and opisthotics are united with the supraoccipitals, and the latter with the exoccipitals in addition. The pro-otic, in which the inner ear lies, is situated anterior to the opisthotic and supraoccipital. A large opening between the pro-otic and opisthotic on the side toward the brain is called the *internal auditory meatus*. It serves for the passage of the auditory nerve from inner ear to brain. Between these bones on the lateral surface of the head is the fenestra ovalis, which opens into the cavity of the middle ear. A large opening, the *external* auditory meatus, leads from this to the outside. One end of the bony columella fits into the fenestra ovalis. The other end articulates with a small, cartilaginous *extracolumella*, which in turn meets the tympanic membrane. A ring of bony scales, the *sclerotic bones*, encircles the eye. They are not fused with the skull. The unpaired vomer is a membrane bone in the nasal region. The mesethmoid remains cartilaginous and lies above the vomer. Nasal bones are lacking.

Only one cartilage bone is present in the upper jaw. This is the quadrate, united with exoccipital, opisthotic, and pterygoid. It joins the squamosal dorsally and the quadratojugal anteriorly. Premaxillaries are small. They articulate laterally with the maxillaries. Jugal, or malar, bones are interposed between maxillaries and quadratojugals. A dorsal extension of each jugal meets the postfrontal to complete the posterior boundary of the orbit. A parasphenoid bone is lacking. The small palatine bones are united posteriorly with strong pterygoids and in some cases with the median basisphenoid. The internal nares are bordered posteriorly by the anterior edges of the palatines. The pterygoids may join each other medially, or else the basisphenoid lies between them. Posteriorly they join the quadrate and the occipito-otic complex. A dorsal projection meets the parietal.

The bones of the lower jaw are generally fused into one piece, and the two sides are firmly ankylosed. As many as six pairs of bones enter into the formation of the lower jaw.

The remainder of the visceral skeleton is represented by components of the hyoid and next two visceral arches. The latter may be considerably larger than the part contributed by the hyoid (Fig. 10.31).

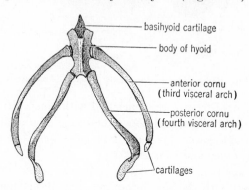

FIG. 10.31. Hyoid apparatus of turtle, showing reduction of hyoid arch. The two pairs of posteriorly projecting cornua are remnants of visceral arches 3 and 4.

RHYNCHOCEPHALIA. The skull of *Sphenodon*, the only living representative of this ancient group of reptiles, is peculiar in that it possesses two *temporal fossae*, or *fenestrae*, on each side (Fig. 10.32). The *supratemporal fossae* are separated above by the parietals. Each is bounded laterally by an arch of bone referred to as the *supratemporal arcade* and formed by the postfrontal, postorbital, and squamosal bones. The postorbital, interposed between postfrontal and jugal, makes up the greater part of the posterior wall of the orbit. Another large opening, the *lateral temporal fossa*, is situated below the supratemporal arcade. It is bounded by the ascending branch of the jugal, postorbital, squamosal, and quadratojugal bones. The jugal, quadratojugal, and part of the squamosal form the *infratemporal arcade*. A pair of *posttemporal fossae* is located pos-

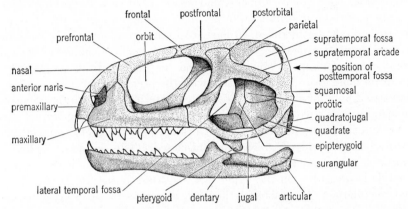

Fig. 10.32. Lateral view of skull of *Sphenodon punctatum*.

teriorly, bounded by the parietal, squamosal, exoccipital, and opisthotic bones. The quadrate bone is fused immovably to the skull. Except for certain extinct forms, only *Sphenodon* and the crocodilians, among reptiles, possess supratemporal and infratemporal arcades.

There are four conditions regarding temporal fossae which help in understanding the direction in which evolution has taken place: (1) the primitive *anapsid* condition in which no temporal vacuities exist, as in the ancient "stem" reptiles and turtles, (2) the *diapsid* condition, such as exists in *Sphenodon* and crocodilians in which supratemporal and lateral (inferior) temporal fossae are present with a supratemporal arcade passing laterally between the two, (3) the *synapsid* condition as found in mammals and mammallike reptiles in which only the lower fossa persists, and (4) the *parapsid* condition, occurring in a few extinct forms, in which only the upper fossa remains. The posttemporal fossae of *Sphenodon* are not of importance in this connection since they are of fairly common occurrence in reptiles and even in monotremes, among mammals.

Other noteworthy features of the skull of *Sphenodon* include the presence of a rather large interparietal foramen, and teeth on premaxillary, maxillary, palatine, vomer, and dentary bones. The premaxillary teeth of the adult are large and appear much like the chisel-shaped incisors of mammals.

SQUAMATA. An infratemporal arcade is lacking in the Squamata. The quadrate, except in chameleons, forms a movable union with the squamosal, and a quadratojugal is lacking. The nares are separate. In addition to the internal nares, which are anterior in position, large spaces, the *palatal vacuities*, are present in the roof of the mouth. All four parts of the occipital complex surround the foramen magnum.

Sauria. The presence of an imperfect interorbital septum characterizes the lizard skull. In only one small family of limbless lizards (Amphisbaenidae) does the cranial cavity extend forward between the orbits. Most lizards possess an interparietal foramen. In some forms the parietals and supraoccipitals are modified, in part, to form a pronounced *sagittal crest*. The orbit and temporal fossa are not confluent, nor is a complete infratemporal arcade present. Thus a modified diapsid condition exists. The quadrate bone forms an articulation with the pterygoid. A lacrimal bone, perforated by a lacrimal canal, is situated anteriorly just within the orbit. In many lizards a parasphenoid bone, homologous with that of amphibians, is present in much reduced form. It lies between the pterygoids anterior to the basisphenoid to which it is ankylosed. The secondary palate in lizards is not at all complete. As in all other reptiles a single occipital condyle is present. On the upper jaw, teeth are borne by premaxillaries and maxillaries. Occasionally they are also present on pterygoids and palatines.

The lower jaw is formed of six pairs of membrane bones surrounding Meckel's cartilage. The anterior *dentary* bears all the teeth of the lower jaw. The *coronoid* forms an upward projecting *coronoid process* immediately behind the last tooth. The coronoid process extends into the temporal fossa. The two halves of the lower jaw are firmly united by a mandibular symphysis.

Serpentes. The skull of snakes differs somewhat from that of other reptiles in correlation with their habit of swallowing large prey. Many of the facial bones are rather loosely connected, thus permitting a considerable degree of adjustment during the act of swallowing. The quadrate connects indirectly with the skull by means of the squamosal, which is interposed between quadrate and parietal (Fig. 10.33). The pterygoid articulates posteriorly with the quadrate and anteriorly with the palatine. Jugals and quadratojugals are absent. The maxillary bone is connected indirectly with the pterygoid by the *transpalatine (ectopterygoid)*. It is in the arrangement of the premaxillary and maxillary bones that the skulls of poisonous and nonpoisonous snakes differ mostly. In venomous snakes the premaxillary is very small and does not bear teeth. The maxillary is also small in venomous forms. Anteriorly it unites by a movable articulation with the lacrimal, which is in turn loosely connected to the frontal.

In such poisonous snakes as vipers and pit vipers these bones are arranged in such a manner that when the mouth is closed the fangs on the maxillary bone lie back against the roof of the mouth. This position is assumed because of traction exerted by the pterygoid on the transpalatine and hence on the maxillary. When the snake strikes, its mouth is opened and the quadrate is thrust forward. This in turn causes the pterygoid and transpalatine to be forced forward. As a result, the position of the maxillary changes so that its toothed surface turns downward and is in the most

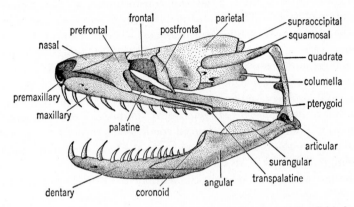

Fig. 10.33.   Lateral view of skull of snake (boa constrictor).   (*After Schimkewitsch.*)

effective position for striking. In cobras, coral snakes, and sea serpents the fangs are permanently erect.

In snakes the two halves of the lower jaw are united anteriorly by an elastic ligament which is capable of stretching to a marked degree when large prey is swallowed whole.

In the snake skull the cranial cavity extends between the orbits so that the interorbital septum is reduced. Snakes lack both supratemporal and infratemporal arcades as well as interparietal foramina. Nevertheless, this is considered to be a modified diapsid condition. A reduced parasphenoid bone is usually present as an anterior projection of the basisphenoid. It lies at the base of the interorbital septum. The lower jaw consists of several component bones surrounding Meckel's cartilage. In most species the parts of the original hyoid apparatus are lost except for an occasional remnant.

CROCODILIA. The crocodilian skull is dense and massive, with a firm union between the separate bones. The outer surface of the skull bones is unusual in being rough and pitted. Of the four occipital bones only the basioccipital and exoccipitals bound the foramen magnum. The supraoccipital is small and united with the epiotic. The basioccipital bears a single condyle to which the exoccipitals have contributed portions. The exoccipitals bear foramina for the passage of the last four cranial nerves and for the internal carotid artery. The passageway for the hypoglossal nerve lies just outside the foramen magnum.

The parietal segment is well developed with well-ossified pleurosphenoids uniting on either side with the basisphenoid. The parietal, in the adult, is a single bone representing the fusion of two embryonic components. No interparietal foramen is present.

Basal and lateral portions of the frontal segment are absent or are very imperfectly developed. An interorbital septum of cartilage is prominent. The single frontal bone is large and conspicuous. It also represents a fusion of two parts. The frontal is overlapped anteriorly by the nasals which roof over most of the nasal passages. The prefrontals form part of the inner walls of the orbits. Postfrontals are also represented by small bones lateral and posterior to the frontals. Each postfrontal sends out a postorbital process which unites with a dorsal projection of the jugal to form a *postorbital bar*, separating the orbit from the lateral temporal fossa. Crocodilians, like *Sphenodon*, have two temporal fossae on each side. This, it will be recalled, is the diapsid condition. The supratemporal fossa is located above the lateral temporal fossa, the two being separated by the supratemporal arcade. An infratemporal arcade is continuous anteriorly with the postorbital bar previously mentioned. There is no posttemporal fossa.

No unusual features are to be observed in connection with the sensory capsules. The lacrimals and supraorbitals are large bones associated with the orbit. The lacrimal forms a conspicuous part of the anterior border of the orbit. Thin vomer bones form a vertical plate which separates the two nasal passages.

The upper jaw is very well developed in crocodilians. Premaxillaries, bearing thecodont teeth, form almost the entire boundary of the external nares. These bones are partially separated on the midventral line by small *anterior palatine vacuities*. The maxillary bones are relatively large and bear the remainder of the teeth of the upper jaw. Premaxillaries and maxillaries, meeting their partners in the midline, form the anterior portion of the broad and extensive secondary palate. Palatines are long and narrow, articulating anteriorly with the maxillaries and posteriorly with the pterygoids and transpalatines. Maxillaries, palatines, pterygoids, and transpalatines bound the large *posterior palatine vacuities*. The internal nares are completely surrounded by the pterygoids. Their extremely posterior location is noteworthy. The jugal, or malar, on each side is a large bone articulating anteriorly with lacrimal and maxillary and posteriorly with the quadratojugal to form the infratemporal arcade or zygomatic arch. The jugal sends a postorbital process dorsally to meet a downward projection of the postfrontal bone, the two processes together forming the postorbital bar, previously referred to. The jugal is also united medially with the transpalatine. The quadratojugal is small and joins the quadrate posteriorly. The quadrate, in turn, articulates with exoccipital and squamosal. The latter is the chief component of the supratemporal arcade.

The two halves of the lower jaw are firmly united at the symphysis.

Each is composed of six separate bones. The dentary, which unites with its mate to form the mandibular symphysis, is the largest and bears the teeth of the lower jaw. A large opening, the *external mandibular foramen*, perforates the lateral side of the mandible near its posterior end. It is bounded by the dentary, surangular and angular. On the medial side is a smaller *internal mandibular foramen*, bounded by splenial and angular bones. These two foramina serve for the passage of blood vessels and branches of the inferior dental nerve. A small coronoid bone connects angular and splenial above the internal mandibular foramen.

The hyoid apparatus of crocodilians is represented by a cartilaginous *basilingual plate* and a pair of *cornua*. The latter articulate with the basilingual plate at about the center of its outer border. The other end passes backward and upward.

Birds. The skull of birds (Figs. 10.34 and 10.35) has not deviated far from the reptilian type. It resembles that of lizards in a number of ways. A single occipital condyle is present which, instead of being located at the posterior end of the skull, lies somewhat forward along the base. The skull articulates with the vertebral column at almost a right angle, thus accounting for the more anterior position of the condyle. With the greater development of the brain in birds, the cranial cavity has increased in size, mostly by lateral expansion. The orbit is large to accommodate the relatively massive eye. It is continuous with the single temporal fossa. A complete supratemporal arcade is lacking, but the infratemporal arcade, though slender, is completely formed. The condition in birds is essentially diapsid, although modified. The orbits are situated somewhat anterior to the cranium. Each is bounded dorsally by the frontal bone, to which the lacrimal is attached, and posteriorly by the pleurosphenoid. A thin interorbital septum is present. It is better developed, however, than in most reptiles. The chief components of the interorbital septum are the anterior mesethmoid and the posterior orbitosphenoid. A large optic foramen lies on each side of the interorbital septum in addition to openings for the passage of oculomotor and trochlear nerves. An olfactory foramen is located dorsal and anterior to each optic foramen. A ring of thin membrane bones, the *scleral ossicles*, or *sclerotic bones*, embedded in the sclerotic coat of the eye, provides protection to the eye. They are sometimes included in the category of heterotopic bones.

In correlation with their adaptation for flight, the skull in birds is unusually light in weight. The cranial bones are fused together to a high degree (Fig. 10.36). All four components of the occipital complex surround the foramen magnum. Where the supraoccipital joins the parietal a prominent crest, the *lambdoidal ridge*, is present. Epiotics and opisthotics are fused to the occipital bones. Most conspicuous is the great development of the premaxillary bones, which together with the maxillaries form the beak. Teeth, of course, are lacking in modern birds, the beak being

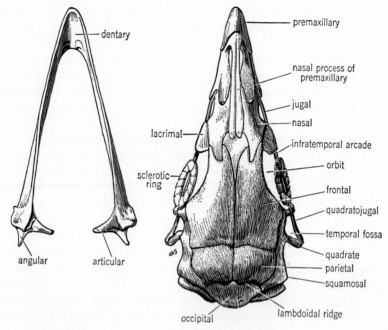

FIG. 10.34. Dorsal view of skull of chicken. (*Drawn by G. Schwenk.*)

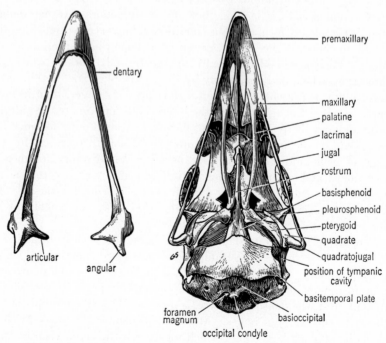

FIG. 10.35. Ventral view of skull of chicken. (*Drawn by G. Schwenk.*)

covered with a horny sheath derived from the epidermis. Premaxillaries, maxillaries, and nasals are completely fused. All three bones bound the external nares which, except in the kiwi, are located near the proximal end of the beak.

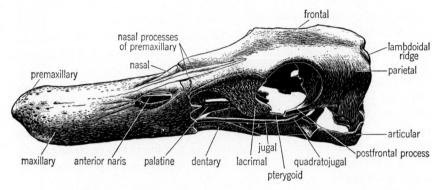

Fig. 10.36. Dorsolateral view of skull of duck. (*Drawn by G. Schwenk.*)

Contrary to the condition in crocodilians, there is no complete bony secondary palate. The inner arch, or palatopterygoquadrate bar, is slender and not connected, in most cases, with its partner across the midline. The quadrate bone is well developed and moves freely. The outer arch is also slender. It consists of a process of the maxillary together with the jugal and quadratojugal bones. The latter joins the quadrate posteriorly. Thus inner and outer arches are united at the quadrate.

An anterior prolongation of the basisphenoid, the *rostrum*, forms the base of the interorbital septum. The rostrum is believed to be homologous with the anterior part of the parasphenoid of lower forms. The posterior portion of the parasphenoid is represented by the *basitemporal plate* which lies beneath the basioccipital and basisphenoid. The pterygoids in some birds articulate with the rostral portion of the basisphenoid.

Since the quadrate is movable and the palatopterygoid can slide along the rostrum of the basisphenoid, the upper jaw can be raised or lowered within limits. The infratemporal arcade may aid in bringing about such movements. Movement of the upper jaw is best seen in parrots. In these birds the upper beak is not firmly united with the cranium but forms a flexible attachment, so that a movable joint is present. The nasals, and the loose connections of the premaxillary bones, attach the beak to the cranium.

The lower jaw consists of two rather flattened halves, united anteriorly and articulating with the quadrate posteriorly. Actually each half is composed of five bones fused together. Only the articular is a cartilage bone. The anterior dentary makes up the greater part of the lower jaw. A foramen is frequently present between the dentary and the more posterior bones. The lower jaw is covered with a hard, horny scale, the beak, or bill, in lieu of teeth.

In birds the hyoid apparatus consists of a median portion composed of three bones placed end to end, and one or two pairs of cornua, or horns. The three median bones are called, respectively, the *entoglossal, basihyal,* and *urohyal.* The anterior entoglossal, which extends into the tongue, represents the fused lower ends of the ceratohyals. The median basihyal corresponds to the basihyal of lower forms. The posterior urohyal is probably the basibranchial of the third visceral arch. The anterior cornua, which project from the entoglossal, are the free ends of the ceratohyals. The long and posteriorly directed posterior cornua, which articulate at the junction of basihyal and urohyal, represent the ceratobranchials and epibranchials of the third visceral arch. The posterior cornua are extremely long in woodpeckers in correlation with the feeding habits of these birds in which the tongue, supported by the hyoid apparatus, can be thrust out for some distance.

Mammals. Although much variation exists in the skulls of different groups of mammals, there are certain features which they share in common and which serve to distinguish them from lower forms. In general a reptilian ancestry is indicated.

Most noteworthy is the increased capacity of the cranium, which has expanded in dorsal and lateral directions in correlation with the much greater size of the mammalian brain. A firm union occurs between all the bones of the skull with the exception of mandible, hyoid, and auditory ossicles. All four components of the occipital complex are present, surrounding the foramen magnum. Two occipital condyles, formed mostly by the exoccipitals, articulate with the atlas vertebra. In higher apes and man the occipital condyles are decidedly ventral in position. Articulation of mandible and upper jaw is at the *glenoid,* or *mandibular, fossa* of the squamous region of the temporal rather than at the quadrate. This is the craniostylic or amphicraniostylic method of jaw suspension. The squamosal usually forms the squamous region of the temporal bone. The quadrate is reduced to the incus and to a bony tympanic ring, which also may form part of the temporal bone. Otic bones are fused to form the *petrosal,* which encloses the inner ear. The petrosal may fuse with squamosal and tympanic and thus becomes the *petrous region* of the temporal bone. The opisthotic is represented by the spongy *mastoid region* of the temporal.

Teeth of the upper jaw are borne only by premaxillary and maxillary bones. The premaxillaries frequently fuse together. The thecodont method of tooth attachment is the rule. Except in cetaceans the teeth of mammals are heterodont.

The number of bones in the mammalian skull (Figs. 10.37, 18.1, and 18.2) is less than in most lower forms. There are usually about 35 of them. This is the result of loss of certain bones and fusion of others. Among the elements that have disappeared in mammals are the prefrontals, postfrontals, and postorbitals. The temporal bone, just referred to, is an example of the result of fusion. Another common area of fusion is in the cartilage bones of the sphenoid complex. The basal portion of the frontal segment frequently unites with the orbitosphenoids to form a presphenoid bone. Similarly the basisphenoid and alisphenoids may fuse. In mammals there are no pleurosphenoids. Their place is taken by the epipterygoids, cartilage bones derived from the palatopterygoquadrate bar. These are then known as the alisphenoids. In some cases, as in man, all six elements of the sphenoid complex unite to form a single *sphenoid* bone. In most mammals

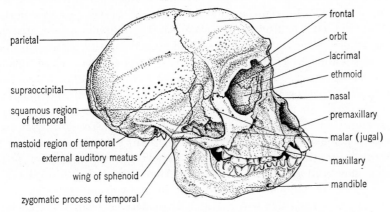

Fig. 10.37.   Lateral view of skull of monkey, *Macacus rhesus*.

a single occipital bone, containing the foramen magnum, is present. This also represents a fusion, although the four separate elements of which it is composed can easily be identified during development. Fusion of the membrane bones of the calvarium is common, particularly in the case of the frontals and parietals. A membrane bone, the *interparietal*, may develop between the parietals and supraoccipital. It may later fuse with the supraoccipital or with the parietals. The facial bones of mammals are more firmly united with the cranium than in other vertebrates. This is true both of the original maxillary arch and palatopterygoquadrate bar components. A supratemporal arcade is lacking, but the infratemporal arcade, or zygomatic arch, is invariably present. As a result, mammals possess but a single temporal fossa, an example of the synapsid condition. The zygomatic arch is composed of a posterior projection of the jugal (malar) which joins an anteriorly projecting process of the squamosal. Temporal fossa and orbit are often confluent but in many cases are separated by a bar formed by a downward-projecting postorbital process of the frontal which joins a dorsal projection of the jugal. A lacrimal bone is always present in the anterior wall of the orbit. Other bones helping to form the orbit are the maxillary, orbitosphenoid, palatine, and sometimes the ethmoid.

A hard or bony secondary palate is typically found in mammals. It is composed of premaxillary, maxillary, and palatine bones. In whales and certain edentates the pterygoids form a portion of the hard palate, but these bones are much reduced in most mammals, so that the choanae are usually bordered by the palatines alone.

The nasal cavities of mammals are large in correlation with the highly developed olfactory sense. Premaxillaries, maxillaries, and nasals surround the greater part of the nasal cavities. The ethmoid complex is well differentiated in most species. The mesethmoid forms a vertical cartilaginous plate which separates right and left nasal passages. The posterior portion becomes the bony *lamina perpendicularis*. The ethmoid also contributes the *cribriform plate*, separating nasal and cranial cavities. The cribriform plate bears numerous small *olfactory foramina* for the passage of fibers of the olfactory nerve. Ethmoturbinates are scroll-like outgrowths of the ectethmoids. Other turbinates are contributed by nasal and maxillary bones. The vomer, which is paired only during early developmental stages, lies ventral to the median nasal septum. It passes downward from the basal portion of the cranium to join the hard palate.

Many interesting variations from the above general description of the mammalian skull are to be observed. Among these is the presence of hollow, bony projections of the frontals in many members of the order Artiodactyla. They are covered with horn derived from the epidermis. The antlers of deer, which develop under the organizing influence of the integument in response to stimulation by certain hormones, when fully developed are naked projections of the frontal bones.

In some mammals a prominent sagittal crest extends forward from the posterior part of the skull on the middorsal line. A lambdoidal ridge may pass transversely across the skull along the line of junction of parietals and supraoccipital. Outgrowths of this sort provide surface area for muscle attachment.

Considerable variation occurs in the relative sizes of frontals and parietals, the latter being unusually large in primates (Fig. 10.37). In some of the whales a projection of supraoccipital and interparietal extends forward to the frontals, thus separating the parietals in the midline. Of particular interest is the fact that in some of the large whalebone whales the skull may compose as much as one-third the length of the body. Premaxillaries and maxillaries are excessively elongated. This accounts for location of the external nares, far back on the dorsal surface.

Large air spaces, or sinuses, in communication with the respiratory passages, are present to varying degrees in the skulls of mammals. The most common are the frontal, ethmoid, sphenoidal, and maxillary sinuses, the last being often referred to as the *antrum of Highmore*.

An ossified derivative of the dura mater, the *tentorium* (page 582), in such forms as the dog and cat, becomes secondarily attached to the skull on the inner surface of the parietals. It serves to separate partially the cerebral and cerebellar fossae.

The lower jaw, or mandible, of mammals (Figs. 10.37 and 18.3) differs from that of other vertebrates in its articulation with the squamosal rather than with the quadrate (page 403). This variation is linked with the developmental history of the base of Meckel's cartilage and of the quadrate. It will be recalled that these structures become independently ossified and become the *malleus* and *incus* bones of the middle ear, respectively. The third auditory ossicle, the *stapes*, is a derivative of the hyomandibular portion of the hyoid arch. The point of junction of malleus and incus thus actually represents the point of articulation of lower and upper jaws in forms below mammals in the vertebrate scale. The remainder of Meckel's cartilage becomes invested by the dentary, a membrane bone. Other membrane bones such as are present in lower forms have disappeared in mammals. The articulating surface of the mandible is the *condyle*. A *coronoid process* from the posterior portion, of various degrees of development in different species, extends into the temporal fossa. A shallow depression on the lateral surface of the mandible serves as an area for insertion of the masticating muscles. An *angular process* at the posterior ventral angle of the mandible in many species forms a prominent projection, but in others it is reduced. The two halves of the mandible are united in front at the symphysis. In primates, bats, and members of the order Perissodactyla an inseparable fusion occurs between the two halves of the mandible.

The mammalian hyoid apparatus shows much variation. Typically it consists of a body, or *basihyal*, and two pairs of *cornua*, or horns. The anterior cornua, or *styloid processes*, are attached to the otic region of the skull. In some forms (Fig. 18.4) the hyoid consists of a chain of bones extending from the basihyal to the otic region and known, respectively, as the *ceratohyal*, *epihyal*, *stylohyal*, and *tympanohyal*. The posterior cornua are sometimes smaller, each consisting of a single *thyrohyal* which forms a connection between the basihyal and the thyroid cartilage of the larynx. In other mammals the separate bones may lose their identity and are represented only by fibrous bands. The hyoid apparatus serves to support the tongue and furnishes an area for muscle attachment.

The basal portion of the hyoid apparatus together with the anterior cornua are derivatives of the original hyoid arch, which has also contributed the stapes of the middle ear. The posterior cornua represent remnants of the third visceral arch. The remaining visceral arches contribute to the laryngeal cartilages.

Ribs

Ribs consist of a series of cartilaginous or bony elongated structures attached at their proximal ends to vertebrae. In the primitive condition there is a pair of ribs for each vertebra. In some vertebrates the ribs consist of little more than small cartilaginous tips on the transverse processes of the vertebrae. They may be fused permanently with the transverse processes (pleuropophyses), or else a joint may appear between the two. In higher forms they may be stout, strongly arched structures surrounding the thoracic cavity and uniting ventrally with a median bony structure, the *sternum*, or *breastbone*. The ribs in these cases protect such vital organs as the heart and lungs by enclosing them with a basketlike framework.

Fish ribs. Ribs first appear in fishes and are of two kinds, dorsal and ventral. Many fishes possess either one type or the other, but in *Polypterus* and many teleosts, both types are present.

Dorsal ribs. The upper, or dorsal, ribs (Fig. 10.38) extend out as costal

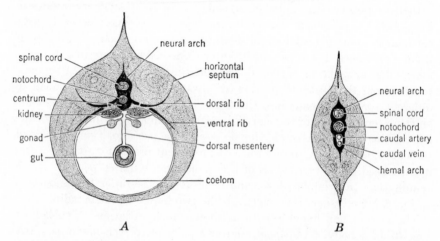

Fig. 10.38. *A*, diagrammatic cross section of typical vertebrate, showing position of dorsal and ventral ribs; *B*, section through tail of fish, showing hemal arch. (*After Parker and Haswell, "Textbook of Zoology," Vol.* II. *Used with the permission of the Macmillan Company.*)

processes from the transverse processes of vertebrae into the lateral skeletogenous septum which separates epaxial and hypaxial muscles (page 468). They occur metamerically at points where the myocommata, or septa between adjacent myotomes, cut across the lateral septum. Some authorities are of the opinion that true dorsal ribs are present only in fishes. Most, however, believe that the ribs of tetrapods are homologous with the dorsal ribs of fishes.

Ventral ribs. The ventral, or *pleural*, *ribs* of fishes are attached to the ventrolateral angles of the centrum. They lie beneath the muscles of the body wall just outside the peritoneum and are situated along the lines where the myocommata pass toward the coelom. There is general agreement that the ventral ribs represent the two halves of hemal arches of caudal vertebrae which have split ventrally and spread apart. However, this conception may be erroneous, for the caudal vertebrae of some fishes are reported to possess both ventral ribs and hemal arches. Additional intermediate bones of riblike appearance are frequently found embedded in the myocommata of fishes.

Tetrapod ribs. There is some dispute among comparative anatomists as to whether the ribs of tetrapods are homologous with the dorsal or with the ventral ribs of fishes. Most believe that they are the homologues of dorsal ribs. There is, however, some evidence that the ventral ribs, by a shifting of position during development in relation to muscles, have come to occupy a different position in the adult from that in the embryo. Some investigators are of the opinion that in tetrapods there has been a fusion of dorsal and ventral ribs, thus accounting for the two-headed, or bicipital, condition typical of tetrapod ribs. This view is not generally accepted. Regardless of homologies, each tetrapod vertebra typically bears a single pair of ribs. Except in the thoracic region the ribs are usually short and are immovably fused to the vertebrae. In most amniotes the ribs in the thoracic region are considerably modified, separating from the vertebrae with which they then form movable articulations. These ribs are elongated and unite ventrally with the ster-num. The ends attached to the sternum are usually cartilaginous and are spoken of as *costal cartilages.*

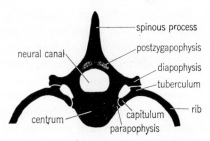

Tetrapod ribs usually form articu-lations both with the centra and neural arches of vertebrae. In these *bicipital ribs* (Fig. 10.39) the upper head of the rib, or *tuberculum*, articu-lates with a dorsal process, the *dia-pophysis*, coming from the neural arch. The lower head, or *capitulum*,

Fig. 10.39. Diagram showing method of articulation of tetrapod rib with vertebra.

joins a projection of the centrum, the *parapophysis*. The bicipital condition is considered to be primitive in tetrapods, since it exists in some of the oldest fossil amphibians and reptiles. It undoubtedly aids in terrestrial locomotion by strengthening the trunk.

In higher forms the diapophysis may be represented by a small *tuber-cular facet* on the ventral side of the transverse process; the parapophysis in such cases may consist of nothing more than a small facet on the centrum for the reception of the capitulum. The capitulum may articulate at the junction of two centra, in which case each centrum may bear a half facet, or *demifacet*, at either end. Sometimes tetrapod ribs have but a single head. This may represent either the tuberculum or capitulum or a fusion of the two.

In the cervical region, where ribs are fused to the vertebrae, the space formed between the two articulations of the rib with the vertebrae is known as the *foramen transversarium*, or *vertebrarterial canal* (page 390).

It serves as a passageway for the vertebral artery and vein and a sympathetic nerve plexus. In the lumbar, sacral, and caudal regions the ribs are fused with the vertebrae (pleurapophyses), and there is little or no evidence of the primitive bicipital condition.

Ribs in different classes of vertebrates. *Fishes.* In elasmobranchs, small ribs, attached to the ventrolateral angles of the centrum (basapophyses), extend laterally into the skeletogenous septum. It would at first sight appear as though these are dorsal ribs, but it is generally agreed that they more probably represent ventral ribs which have moved secondarily into this position. The caudal vertebrae bear hemal arches with which the ventral ribs are homologous.

In most of the higher fishes only ventral ribs are present. However, the cladistian *Polypterus*, previously mentioned, as well as the salmon and a number of other teleosts, possess both dorsal and ventral ribs.

Amphibians. In some of the fossil stegocephalian amphibians the ribs were strong structures which extended ventrally around the body for some distance. In modern amphibians they have been reduced and are small and poorly developed.

In most caudate amphibians all the vertebrae from the second to the caudal bear ribs which are typically bicipital (Fig. 10.39). The dorsal tubercular head forms a union with the diapophysis, or base of the neural arch; the lower, or capitular, head articulates with the parapophysis, a projection of the centrum. These points of attachment actually represent connections with the primitive basidorsal cartilage and the hypocentrum, respectively. In a few primitive salamanders the pointed ribs may protrude through the skin as small, naked projections of a protective nature. The strong sacral ribs are attached to the pelvic girdle. The caudal vertebrae lack ribs.

The ribs in salientians are lacking entirely except on the sacral vertebrae, or else they take the form of minute cartilages attached to the transverse processes.

Ribs in caecilians are somewhat better developed than in other amphibians. They occur on all except the first and a few of the more posterior vertebrae and are attached by means of a double or single head as the case may be. Ribs of amphibians never form connections with the sternum.

Some of the extinct fossil amphibians possessed ventral, dermal "ribs," or *gastralia.* These consisted of V-shaped, bony, riblike, dermal bones located on the ventral abdominal region and extending in a posterodorsal direction on either side. Gastralia should not be confused with true ribs, which are endoskeletal structures.

Reptiles. Rib development in reptiles has deviated far from the condition observed in amphibians. Ribs may be borne by almost all the vertebrae in trunk and tail regions. Attachment of ribs to a sternum is first observed in the class Reptilia.

Turtles lack ribs in the cervical region. The 10 trunk vertebrae bear ribs which are flat and broad and, like the vertebrae in this region, are immovably fused to the underside of the carapace (Fig. 10.40). The carapace is thus formed partly of exoskeletal dermal plates and partly of endoskeletal structures derived from vertebrae and ribs. It will be recalled that epidermal scales overlie these skeletal elements (page 118). Each rib has but a single head, the capitulum, for articulation with the vertebral column. The point of articulation is usually at the boundary of adjacent vertebral centra. The two sacral and first caudal vertebrae are also united to the carapace. The ribs of the sacral vertebrae form a union with the pelvic girdle. Those of the anterior caudal vertebrae consist of small projections, their union with the vertebrae being indicated by the presence of distinct sutures.

The ribs of *Sphenodon* are extensively developed, being present even in the caudal region. A few of the anterior thoracic ribs join a typical sternum. Most of the remaining ribs, however, join a median ventral *parasternum* which extends from sternum to pubis. The parasternum is an endoskeletal structure derived from cartilages which develop in the ventral portions of the myocommata. They should not be confused with gastralia, or dermal "ribs," previously mentioned, which are dermal derivatives and which in *Sphenodon* are present in the same region. Each rib is typically composed of three sections, an upper, ossified, *vertebral section;* a ventral cartilaginous *sternal,* or *costal, section;* and an intermediate section also composed of cartilage. In *Sphenodon* each rib bears a flattened, curved *uncinate process* which projects posteriorly from the vertebral section, overlapping the next rib and thus providing additional strength to the thoracic body wall.

FIG. 10.40. Underside of portion of carapace of young turtle, showing fusion of ribs and vertebrae to dermal bones. The marginal dermal plates in this specimen had not as yet ossified.

Small cervical ribs occur in lizards except on the atlas and axis. In the geckos, however, even the first two vertebrae bear ribs. In most lizards a few of the anterior thoracic ribs curve around the body to meet the sternum. Each of these ribs is divided into two or three sections, but only the vertebral section is bony in most cases. Articulation with the vertebra is by capitulum alone, the tuberculum being much reduced. Uncinate processes are lacking. The ribs of the flying dragon, *Draco volans*, are of particular interest, since the posterior ribs are greatly extended, supporting an extensive fold of skin on each side of the body. This provides a wide surface which, when extended, enables the animal to soar. When at rest, the "wings" are folded against the sides of the body.

In snakes all trunk vertebrae except the atlas and axis bear ribs. They articulate loosely by means of a single head, the capitulum. Since no sternum is present in these reptiles, the ribs terminate freely. The lower ends, however, have muscular connections with ventral scales which are used extensively in locomotion (Fig. 11.19).

In crocodilians the ribs are typically bicipital. All five regions of the vertebral column are rib-bearing, although the ribs are much reduced in the cervical, lumbar, and caudal regions. Even the atlas and axis bear ribs in these reptiles. The cervical ribs increase in length as they progress in an anteroposterior direction. The two heads of the cervical ribs unite with the vertebrae so as to surround an opening, the foramen transversarium. Eight or nine thoracic ribs connect with the sternum. These are composed of vertebral, intermediate, and sternal sections, of which only the vertebral section is completely ossified. Uncinate processes are present on the vertebral sections. The last two or three thoracic ribs are *floating ribs* with no sternal connections. Only the vertebral section is present in these. The two pairs of sacral ribs are strong projections which articulate with the ilium of the pelvic girdle. Some of the anterior caudal vertebrae bear ribs which are fused to the transverse processes, of which they appear to be parts. Dermal gastralia, similar to those of *Sphenodon*, are well developed in the ventral abdominal region of crocodilians.

Birds. In *Archaeopteryx* the ribs resembled those of lizards more closely than those of modern birds. They were slender, articulated by means of a single head, and lacked uncinate processes. *Archaeopteryx* also possessed gastralia, not encountered in birds of today. In modern birds some of the posterior cervical vertebrae bear movable ribs. Strong, flattened, bicipital ribs connect most of the thoracic vertebrae with the sternum. Each is typically composed of vertebral and sternal sections, both ossified. A prominent uncinate process from each vertebral section (Fig. 10.19) overlaps the rib behind, furnishing a place for muscle attachment and increasing the rigidity of the skeleton, an important factor in flight. In the posterior thoracic, lumbar, sacral, and anterior caudal regions the ribs are fused to the large synsacrum.

Mammals. Mammalian ribs are usually bicipital. In the cervical region the transverse processes are composed in part of the remains of ribs which have fused with the vertebrae. The foramina transversaria, present only in cervical vertebrae, represent the original space between the points of attachment. Thoracic ribs are well developed in mammals. The tubercular head articulates with the tubercular facet (diapophysis) on the ventral side of the transverse process; the capitulum typically articulates at the point of junction of two adjacent vertebrae, the centrum of each bearing a costal demifacet. In some posterior ribs, only the capitular head remains. Each rib consists of two sections: an upper, bony vertebral section and a lower, usually cartilaginous sternal section. The latter joins the sternum directly or indirectly and is commonly referred to as the *costal cartilage*. The ribs of monotremes are composed of three sections as in primitive reptiles. Mammalian ribs do not bear uncinate processes.

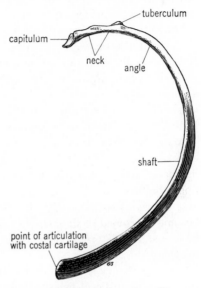

The part of the rib between the two heads is called the *neck;* the remainder is the *shaft* (Fig. 10.41). The area where the shaft curves most markedly is the *angle* of the rib. Those ribs which make a direct connection with the sternum are called *true ribs. False ribs* are located posteriorly, and their costal cartilages either unite with the costal cartilages of the last true rib, or they terminate freely. The latter are termed *floating ribs.* Mammals lack ribs in the lumbar and caudal

FIG. 10.41. Vertebral section of human rib. (*Drawn by G. Schwenk.*)

regions, although the transverse processes of the lumbar vertebrae are, in all probability, pleurapophyses.

The number of ribs in mammals shows considerable range, from 9 pairs in certain whales to 24 in the sloth. True ribs, however, range in number only from 3 to 10 pairs.

STERNUM

The sternum, or breastbone, found only in tetrapods, is composed of ventral skeletal elements closely related to the pectoral girdle of the appendicular skeleton and, except in amphibians, with the thoracic ribs. Not all tetrapods have a sternum. It is lacking in some of the elongated salamanders such as *Proteus* and the "Congo snake," *Amphiuma.* Caecilians, snakes, and limbless lizards lack a sternum, as do turtles. In the latter the plastron serves as a strengthening support in the absence of a sternum. The sternum seems to be a skeletal structure which provides greater support and a place for muscle attachment in terrestrial vertebrates, thus aiding in locomotion on land.

The origin of the sternum in evolution is obscure. Several theories have been advanced to explain its origin, none of which is wholly acceptable at the present time. According to one conception the earliest indication of a sternum is to be found in the perennibranchiate salamander, *Necturus*, in which it is referred to as the *archisternum*. In this amphibian, cartilages occur in a few of the myocommata in the ventral thoracic region. The largest and most prominent of these irregular skeletal elements is found at precisely the same region in which, in higher salamanders, a sternal plate overlaps the coracoids of the pectoral girdle. Such a theory of the origin of the sternum is plausible, relating it to the *parasternum* of such forms as *Sphenodon*, lizards, and crocodilians (page 431). The parasternum is a posterior continuation of the sternum. Fusion of some of the anterior archisternal or parasternal elements may thus possibly account for the origin of the true sternum. If this theory is correct, the connection of ribs to the sternum must be secondary.

According to another theory the sternum arises as a fusion of the ventral ends of some of the anterior ribs. This type of sternum, found in amniotes, has been spoken of as the *neosternum*. Objection to this theory is based upon the fact that although a sternum is present in most amphibians, in no case are ribs associated with it. It is possible, however, that the ribs have become shortened secondarily in amphibians in the course of evolution and have lost their sternal connections. There is no paleontological evidence for this.

Another theory seeks to derive the sternum from the median portion of the pectoral girdle of fishes. This concept has least support of all from a paleontological or an embryological point of view.

Some authorities are of the opinion that the archisternum of amphibians and the neosternum of amniotes, with its rib connections, are in no way related and are of independent origin. Since, however, there is considerable evidence from embryology that the ribs of amniotes connect with the sternum secondarily, there is no particular reason for assuming a lack of homology between the two types of sterna.

Amphibians. In caudate amphibians the sternum appears for the first time and in its most primitive form. That of *Necturus* has already been referred to. In no case, however, is the sternum very well developed. In most salamanders it consists of little more than a small, median, triangular plate, lying behind the posterior, median portions of the coracoids of the pectoral girdle (Fig. 10.52).

In salientians it is better developed. In the common frog, for example, the anterior clavicles and posterior coracoids of the pectoral girdle are separated from their partners of the opposite side only by narrow cartilaginous strips, the *epicoracoids* (Fig. 10.42). Anterior to the junction of the clavicles with the epicoracoid cartilages lies the bony *omosternum*, with an expanded, cartilaginous *episternum* joined to it anteriorly. Posterior to the junction of coracoids and epicoracoids lies the *sternum proper*.

An expanded cartilage, the *xiphisternum*, is attached to it posteriorly. The sternum is thus considered to be composed of four median elements. It is not clear as to which part corresponds to the sternum in caudates, but most anatomists consider the section referred to as the *sternum proper* to be the actual homologue.

Reptiles. Snakes, most limbless lizards, and turtles lack a sternum, but in other reptiles this portion of the axial skeleton is more fully developed than it is in amphibians. In turtles, the plastron, composed of dermal plates covered with epidermal scales, is closely associated with the pectoral girdle. The membrane bones of the plastron are usually considered to be homologous with the gastralia of such forms as *Sphenodon*, crocodilians, certain other reptiles, and *Archaeopteryx*.

In *Sphenodon* a few of the anterior thoracic ribs join a typical midventral sternum. Most of the remaining ribs, however, join the median ventral parasternum which extends from the true sternum to the pubis. It will be recalled that this endoskeletal structure is derived from cartilages which appear in the midventral portions of the myocommata in this region.

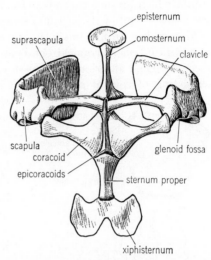

FIG. 10.42. Ventral view of sternum and pectoral girdle of bullfrog, *Rana catesbeiana*. (*Drawn by G. Schwenk.*)

In lizards the sternum usually consists of a large, cartilaginous, flattened plate to which the sternal sections of several anterior thoracic ribs are united. A membrane bone, referred to as the *episternum*, or *interclavicle*, in some cases lies ventral to the sternum. It is *not* considered to be part of the sternum.

The sternum of crocodilians is a simple cartilaginous plate which splits posteriorly into two *xiphisternal cornua*. The sternal sections of the thoracic ribs are attached to the sternum and to the xiphisternal cornua. Numerous gastralia of dermal origin are present posterior to the cornua but form no connections with them.

Birds. The sternum of birds is a well-developed bony structure to the sides of which the ribs are firmly attached. In flying birds and penguins it projects rather far posteriorly under a considerable portion of the abdominal region. The ventral portion is drawn out into a prominent *keel*, or *carina* (Fig. 10.19), which provides a large surface for attachment of the strong muscles used in flight. It is of interest to note in this connection that the extinct flying reptiles, the pterodactyls, had carinate sterna as do bats among mammals. A sternum in *Archaeopteryx* is unknown. From the posterolateral borders of the sternum extends a pair of elongated *xiphoid processes*. Running birds of the superorder Paleognathae have rounded sterna which are not carinate. In swans and cranes a peculiar cavity at the anterior end of the sternum houses a loop of the trachea.

Mammals. In mammals the sternum is typically composed of a series of separate bones arranged one behind the other. Three regions may be recognized: an anterior *presternum*, or *manubrium*; a middle *mesosternum*, consisting of several *sternebrae*; and a posterior *metasternum*, or *xiphisternum*, to the end of which a *xiphoid cartilage* is attached (Fig. 18.11). The costal cartilages of the ribs articulate with the sternum at the points of union of the separate bones. In bats the presternum is conspicuously keeled, as is the mesosternum in some cases. The number of sternebrae is variable in mammals as is the number of true ribs which articulate directly with the sternum. In some cases, as in certain cetaceans, sirenians, and primates, the separate elements may fuse. Thus, in the human being, the entire structure, which is considerably flattened, consists of only three parts: an anterior *manubrium*, a *body* (*gladiolus*), and a small posterior *xiphoid process* (Fig. 10.43). The last is long and thin and essentially cartilaginous. In older individuals the proximal portion may become ossified. The clavicles, and

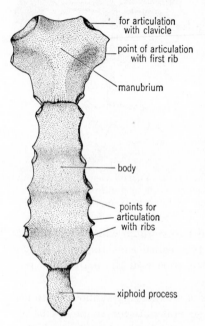

for articulation with clavicle

point of articulation with first rib

manubrium

body

points for articulation with ribs

xiphoid process

FIG. 10.43.   Sternum of man.

the costal cartilages of the first pair of ribs, join the manubrium, the second pair of costal cartilages articulating at the junction of the manubrium and body. Five more pairs of ribs join the sides of the body of the sternum at rather evenly spaced intervals. No ribs articulate with the xiphoid process. Study of development of the sternum in man shows it to be composed of separate structures, each derived from separate centers of ossification. These fuse together at various times from puberty to old age. The mammalian sternum arises quite independently of the ribs which unite with it secondarily. In such aquatic mammals as whales and sirenians the sternum has lost much of its importance. It is composed of a single bone which forms articulations with only a few of the most anterior ribs.

Median Appendages

In discussing the axial skeleton, certain unpaired, median appendages must be taken into consideration. Only aquatic vertebrates possess median appendages, which are always finlike in character. They are found in cyclostomes, fishes, larval amphibians, some adult caudate amphibians, and cetaceans. Typically they are present in dorsal, anal, and caudal regions. In some forms the median fins are continuous, but most frequently the continuity is interrupted and the various fins are separated by gaps. In some of the newts the dorsal fin of the male becomes developed only during the breeding season. At other times it is rather inconspicuous. Fin development and regression in these forms are controlled by the endocrine activity of the testes. In cyclostomes and fishes the median fins are supported by skeletal structures (fin rays) and special muscles, but in higher forms they are merely elaborations of the integument. Dorsal and anal fins are used chiefly in directing the body during locomotion. The caudal fin also helps in this respect in addition to being the main organ of propulsion.

The skeleton supporting the unpaired dorsal and anal fins in fishes consists of radial cartilaginous or bony *pterygiophores* supporting slender *fin rays* at their distal ends. Union of several pterygiophores may take place at the base of the fin to form one or more *basipterygia*, or *basalia*. These are ossified in bony fishes. Pterygiophores and basalia may form secondary connections with the neural spines of the vertebral column. There may or may not be a segmental correspondence between the skeletal elements of the fin and the vertebrae. Distal to the basalia the pterygiophores continue as cartilaginous or bony *radialia*. From the radialia extend numerous fin rays of dermal origin, supporting the greater part of the fin. Frequently the fin rays connect directly with the basalia, the radialia being absent. Various types of joints permit the fin to be moved in a complex, undulatory manner or merely to be raised or lowered as the case may be. In the males of many fishes the anal fin and its skeletal elements are modified to form a *gonopodium* (Fig. 8.34), which serves to aid in the transport of sperm from male to female in internal fertilization. Development of the gonopodium has been shown to be under control of the male hormone, testosterone.

Caudal fins are of several shapes (Fig. 10.44). Presumably the most primitive type is the *protocercal* tail of adult cyclostomes. The notochord is straight and extends to the tip of the tail, the dorsal and ventral portions of which are of practically equal dimensions. A second type, the *diphycercal* tail, found in Dipnoi, *Latimeria* (Fig. 2.12), and *Polypterus*, appears at first to be similar to the protocercal type. However, paleontological and embryological evidence indicates that the diphycercal tail may really be a secondary modification of a third type, the *heterocercal* tail. In this type the skeletal axis bends upward to enter the dorsal flange of the tail, which thus becomes more prominent than the ventral flange. A hetero-cercal tail is typical of elasmobranchs and lower fishes in general. The *homocercal* type of tail is the most common. Superficially it appears to be composed of symmetrical dorsal and ventral flanges. The posterior end of the vertebral column, the *urostyle*, is, however, deflected into the dorsal

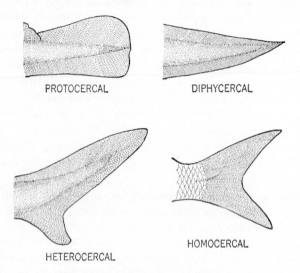

PROTOCERCAL   DIPHYCERCAL

HOMOCERCAL

HETEROCERCAL

Fig. 10.44. Four types of fish tails.

flange. This type of tail, therefore, is not far removed from the hetero-cercal type.

In caudal fins the fin rays on the dorsal side may connect with basal pterygiophores or with neural spines directly. On the ventral side, how-ever, they form connections with modified hemal spines which are spoken of as *hypurals*.

Appendicular Skeleton

Speculation as to the phylogenetic origin of the paired appendages of vertebrates has long occupied the attention of comparative anatomists. Several theories have been advanced, some of which have fallen into dis-card with new paleontological discoveries. Others have been modified from time to time as new lines of evidence have been brought to light. It is universally agreed that the limbs of tetrapods have arisen in evolution from the fins of fishes. The *fin-fold theory* of the origin of both unpaired and paired vertebrate appendages seems to be one of the most plausible and in the past has been quite generally accepted.

According to some authorities, the fin-fold theory (Fig. 10.45) goes back to amphioxus as a starting point. In this animal the single dorsal fin continues around the tail to the ventral side as far forward as the atriopore. At this point it divides in such a manner that a *metapleural fold* extends anteriorly on either side almost to the mouth region. Gaps appearing in the dorsal fin and in the metapleural folds, for one reason or another, may have resulted in the appearance of median and paired fins. Certain rather valid objections have been advanced which would make it seem improbable that the metapleural folds of amphioxus were in any way concerned with the origin of the paired appendages of vertebrates. Among these are the fact that the folds terminate at the atriopore, a structure without

FIG. 10.45. Diagrams illustrating the fin-fold theory of the origin of paired appendages: *A*, the undifferentiated condition; *B*, the manner in which permanent fins might be formed from the continuous folds. (*After Wiedersheim, "Comparative Anatomy of Vertebrates," copyright 1907 by The Macmillan Company and used with their permission.*)

homologies in higher forms. Furthermore, amphioxus has no skeletal structures other than a notochord. The so-called "fin rays" of amphioxus, which support the fins, are small rods of gelatinous connective tissue not homologous with the cartilaginous- or bony-fin supports of fishes. Usually the cyclostomes are dismissed in this connection as a specialized, limbless, divergent side shoot of the ancestral vertebral stock.

According to another idea, fin folds similar to the metapleural folds of amphioxus were present in some hypothetical ancestral fish but terminated at the anus rather than at the atriopore. In some of the very primitive acanthodian sharks a row of six or seven spiny fins extended on each side between pectoral and pelvic fins (Fig. 10.46). They have been interpreted as remnants of fin folds. Traces of lateral fin folds can be observed in embryos of certain elasmobranchs as mesodermal proliferations which develop extensively only in the pectoral and pelvic regions as metameric myotomic buds (Fig. 11.12). The pectoral and pelvic fins may thus be regarded as persistent remnants of primitive fin folds. Furthermore, the basic skeletal structure of the paired fins is essentially like that of the unpaired fins, indicating that the two have a common origin. The structure of the fins of the extinct shark, *Cladoselache* (Fig. 10.47), has been cited as providing additional support to the fin-fold theory. The fins are broad at their bases and contain numerous parallel pterygiophores which by their very arrangement suggest a primitive fin-fold-like origin.

The pterygiophores are primitively metameric, appearing in the fin along with metameric myotomic buds. Each pterygiophore is subdivided into several small pieces. Those at the base, the *basalia*, show a tendency to fuse. The *radialia* may form two or three rows of short cartilages distal to the basalia. Dermal fin rays in turn are distal to the radialia. According to one theory, fusion of the anterior basalia with their partners in the midline resulted in the formation of a transverse bar. This is the rudiment of the pectoral or pelvic girdle, as the case may be.

Another more recent theory explaining the origin of the paired appendages and girdles does not assume a primitive fin-fold origin. According to this idea the appearance of paired appendages goes back to the ostracoderms. Ostracoderms may have been the remote ancestors of existing cyclostomes. Some of the early ostracoderms had a cephalothorax covered with a shield of plates with posteriorly directed cornua. The plates in some cases are known to have contained bone cells. Certain forms possessed lateral fleshy lobes, projecting from each side, medial to the cornua of the thoracic shield. A bony skeletogenous septum passed behind the gill chamber and behind the pericardium. The fleshy lobes may have become pectoral fins, and the endoskeletal part of the pectoral girdle may have developed as an ingrowth of basal portions of the pectoral fins. The dermal bones of the pectoral girdle may have been derived from the bony plates of the thoracic shield.

Another group of ostracoderms is known to have possessed a paired row of dermal spines on the ventral side of the body not unlike the extra fins or spines of the acanthodian sharks referred to above. The spines may have been used merely as an aid in clinging to the bottom of rapidly moving

FIG. 10.46. Ventral view of acanthodian fish, *Euthacanthus macnicoli*, showing paired rows of ventral spines (fins). (*After Watson.*)

Labels on figure: pectoral fin, paired spines, pelvic fin, anal fin fresh-water streams. Loss of armor and reduction of spines, but their persistence in pectoral and pelvic regions, might well account for the origin of the paired appendages from ostracoderm ancestors. With the growth of muscles from the meta-meric myotomes into the bases of the spiny fins, their movement may first have been accomplished. Appearance of radial skeletal elements, the pterygiophores, could have accompanied the segmental muscles as they spread outward in a fanlike manner, in opposing groups, to the peripheral parts of the fin. According to this concept the basal pieces of the endoskeleton of the fin may have pushed farther into the body to give rise to the girdles. This idea holds that the paired fins were not originally parts of fin folds, but were, from the beginning, separately spaced ridges supported by spines. Much paleontological evidence has been cited in support of the ostracoderm theory.

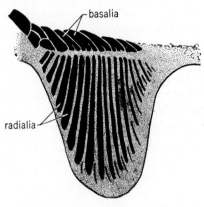

Fig. 10.47. Pectoral fin of *Cladoselache*. (*After Dean.*)

Paired fins and girdles of fishes. *Pectoral fins and girdles.* Certain extinct sharks, such as *Cladoselache*, possessed the simplest fins known to occur in vertebrates (Fig. 10.47). The skeletal structures of which they are composed consist of several basalia from which radialia extend in a fanlike manner. The basalia of the two sides do not unite as in a true pectoral girdle.

In existing elasmobranchs the pectoral girdle (Fig. 16.6) is a U-shaped cartilage in the form of an arch, located just posterior to the branchial region and open dorsally. It is not connected with the axial skeleton except in skates in which the upper portion, or *suprascapula*, joins the vertebral column on each side. The girdle consists of one piece, the *scapulocoracoid cartilage*. The ventral portion is the *coracoid bar* from which a long *scapular process* extends dorsally on each side beyond the *glenoid region* where the pectoral fin articulates. Each scapular process has a *suprascapular cartilage* attached at its free end. The fin itself consists of three basal cartilages (basalia) which articulate with the girdle at the glenoid region. They are an anterior, lateral *propterygium;* an intermediate *mesopterygium;* and a posterior, medial *metapterygium.* Numerous segmented radial cartilages extend distally from the three basal cartilages. They are arranged in rows. From the radialia many dermal fin rays extend peripherally.

In primitive bony fishes certain membrane bones have become associated with the pectoral girdle. They have been derived, in a manner similar to the membrane bones of the skull, from dermal scales which have assumed a deeper position in the body. There are usually at least two such membrane bones on each side. A pair of *clavicles* meets on the midline close to the coracoid region. A *cleithrum* overlies the scapula. In many fishes the cleithra as well as the clavicles join each other medially, thus providing additional support. In *Amia, Lepisosteus,* and teleosts, the clavicle has disappeared. Other membrane bones, *supracleithrum,* and *posttemporal,* are present in many forms, the latter forming a connection with the skull (Fig. 10.48). The original part of the pectoral girdle may remain cartilaginous but usually forms two separate bones on each side, the scapula and coracoid, articulating at the glenoid region. The two halves of the original cartilaginous girdle, as seen in elasmobranchs, no longer connect ventrally.

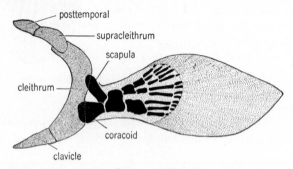

Fig. 10.48. Diagram showing the membrane bones of the pectoral girdle of a primitive fish. Membrane bones are stippled; cartilages or cartilage bones are black.

The membrane bones now make up the greater part of the pectoral girdle, the original girdle being much reduced.

In bony fishes the pectoral fins themselves exhibit much variation in their detailed structure. In the cladistian, *Polypterus,* the fin is much like that of elasmobranchs except that ossification of the separate elements has begun to take place. In most bony fishes the number of separate skeletal pieces is reduced, the dermal fin rays taking over much of the supporting function. Many separate basalia, however, may articulate with the pectoral girdle. In the dipnoan *Neoceratodus* the pectoral fin consists of a main, segmented, metapterygial, radial axis from the sides of which numerous segmented secondary rays project (Fig. 10.49). Dermal fin rays extend from the secondary rays to the periphery. In *Protopterus* and *Lepidosiren* only the main radial axis persists. The type of fin seen in *Neoceratodus* is sometimes referred to as the *archipterygium,* since it was formerly thought to be the archetype from which the tetrapod limb evolved. This view is no longer held. Instead, the type of fin found in living Dipnoi is interpreted as being a specialized derivative of the primitive, tribasic, multiradial fin of elasmobranchs. The link between the fins of fishes and the limbs of tetrapods is to be sought among the fossil crossopterygians, only a few specimens of which are known. Study of the fin structure of *Eus-thenopteron* strongly suggests that this group will provide the clue to the true explanation of the origin of tetrapod girdles and limbs (pages 446 to 447).

Pelvic fins and girdles. The pelvic fins and girdles of fishes are usually more primitive and simple in structure than those of the pectoral region. In *Cladoselache* there is but little difference between the two, although the pelvic structures are somewhat reduced. The sturgeon shows little change over the condition in *Cladoselache.* The pelvic girdle of fishes is always free of the axial skeleton. Fusion of the anterior basalia of the two sides occurs

FIG. 10.49.   Pectoral fin of *Neoceratodus.*

in elasmobranchs to form the *ischiopubic bar* (Fig. 16.7), comparable to the coracoid bar of the pectoral girdle. Attachment of the fin is at the *ace-tabular* rather than at the glenoid region. A small *iliac process*, projecting dorsally to a slight degree at either end of the ischiopubic bar, corre-sponds to the scapular region of the pectoral girdle. In the Dipnoi the pelvic girdle gives off anterior and posterior medial and lateral processes. The anterior medial projection, spoken of as the *epipubis*, has homologies with similar structures of higher forms. The posterior lateral processes serve for fin articulation. The other processes offer a surface for muscle attachment. It is rare to find any membrane bones in the pelvic region of fishes comparable to those associated with the pectoral girdle. The pelvic girdle of teleost fishes is reduced to a small element on each side with no connections between the two. It may even be lacking, as in the eels which have no pelvic fins. Often the pelvic fins have shifted so far forward that they come to lie just behind the pectoral fins and are attached at their bases to the cleithra. In elasmobranchs each pelvic fin typically consists of two basalia: a medial, posterior *metapterygium* and a small anterior *propter-ygium*. The latter may be absent. Numerous radialia extend outward from these two basal pieces. Dermal fin rays complete the skeletal struc-ture of the fins. In male elasmobranchs the skeleton supporting the clasper is a continuation of the metapterygium which is broken up into several seg-ments (Fig. 16.7). In the Dipnoi the pelvic fins are of the same archipter-ygial type as the pectoral fins. The central axis in some cases is split into two. Teleosts possess rather degenerate pelvic fins. Usually a single basal bone gives off a few poorly developed radials from which the fin rays project. Often the fin rays arise directly from the basal. A curious situation exists in certain fishes, such as the cod, in which the pelvic fins have pushed forward so as to lie *anterior* to the pectoral fins and have become attached to the throat region. The fossil crossopterygian *Eusthenopteron* shows a better-developed pelvic-fin structure than is to be found in forms living today (Fig. 10.51*B*). Although somewhat smaller in size than the pectoral fins, the basic skeletal structure is similar. A strong pelvic girdle is also present.

Paired girdles and limbs of tetrapods. The appendicular skeleton in all tetrapods shows a fundamental similarity in structure. There is a shoulder, or pectoral, girdle to which the forelimbs are attached and a hip, or pelvic, girdle supporting the hindlimbs. The pectoral girdle does not form a connection with the vertebral column except through muscles and ligaments. The pelvic girdle, however, attaches directly to the vertebral column in the sacral region. The limbs are typically pentadactyl (having five fingers or toes) or have been modified from the primitive pentadactyl type. Each girdle is composed of two halves, and each half in turn consists of three bones which show a fairly comparable arrangement in the two girdles.

In the pectoral girdle of tetrapods there has been a reduction of membrane bones, and of these only the *clavicle* sometimes persists. Connection of the pectoral girdle with the skull, as occurs in teleost fishes, is lost. The cartilage bones of the girdle in tetrapods have become the dominant elements. The bones of the pectoral girdle typically consist of a ventral *coracoid*, which meets the sternum medially; a *scapula*, extending dorsally; and a *clavicle*, which lies on the ventral side between scapula and sternum and anterior to the coracoid. In some of the lower tetrapods an additional cartilage bone, the *precoracoid*, lies anterior to the coracoid and close to the clavicle (Fig. 10.50*A*). The precoracoid probably is derived from an ossification center in a ventral projection of the scapula. At the junction of scapula and coracoid is a depression, the *glenoid fossa*, which serves as the point of articulation of the forelimb with the pectoral girdle.

The pelvic girdle (Fig. 10.50*B*) is composed of a ventral *ischium* comparable to the coracoid, a dorsal *ilium* similar to the scapula, and an anterior, ventral *pubis* corresponding in position to the clavicle and precoracoid. Clavicle and pubis are not considered to be homologous since the former is a membrane bone* and the latter a cartilage bone. Generally, pubis and precoracoid are considered to be homologous. The ilium

---

* In some higher forms, as in the rat and other placental mammals, developmental studies of the clavicle show that it is not entirely a membrane bone but some parts develop by the endochondral method of ossification and others by the intramembranous method. Therefore it is not clear just what the mammalian clavicle actually represents, and homologies are somewhat uncertain. It is possible that both clavicles and precoracoids are represented in a single element.

is the portion which forms a union with the sacrum. The two pubic bones usually unite ventrally at the *pubic symphysis.* The ischia also often come together to form an *ischial symphysis.* The two may be separated by a *puboischial foramen* or may join to form a *puboischial symphysis.* A depression, the *acetabulum,* located at the junction of the three bones serves as the point of articulation of the hindlimb with the pelvic girdle. It is comparable to the glenoid fossa of the pectoral girdle. A fourth and very small *acetabular,* or *cotyloid,* bone often enters in formation of the acetabulum in mammals. Its homologies are uncertain, but it may possibly be comparable to the precoracoid of the pectoral girdle.

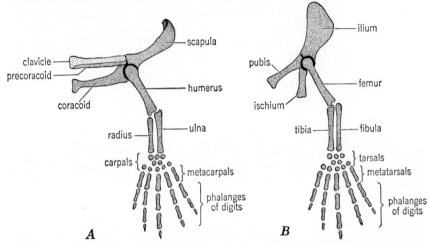

FIG. 10.50. Diagram showing skeletal structures of vertebrate limbs and girdles: *A,* pectoral girdle and limb; *B,* pelvic girdle and limb. The clavicle is lightly stippled to indicate that it is a membrane bone.

The skeletal elements of the forelimbs and hindlimbs are also arranged on the same general plan. In the forelimb there is a single bone, the *humerus,* in the upper arm, or *brachium.* The head of the humerus joins the pectoral girdle at the glenoid fossa. Two bones arranged parallel to each other are present in the forearm, or *antebrachium.* They are a lateral *radius* and a medial *ulna.* Distal to radius and ulna, in the primitive condition, are 9 or 10 *carpal,** or *wrist,* bones; 5 longer *metacarpals* in the hand; and then a few rows of small *phalanges* in the fingers. The carpal bones are primitively arranged in three rows. There are 3 bones in the proximal row, 5 in the distal row, and 1 or 2 in the middle row. Corresponding bones in the hind limb are the *femur,* which joins the acetabulum; *tibia* and *fibula,* comparable to radius and ulna; 9 or 10 *tarsal,** or *ankle,* bones; 5 *metatarsals;* and rows of *phalanges* in the toes.

* Apparently the carpal and tarsal bones of early tetrapods were originally twelve in number: 3 proximal bones, 4 central bones, and 5 distal bones. The latter articulated with the five primitive metacarpals or metatarsals.

Some remarkable specializations have taken place in the evolution of the limbs of tetrapods. These consist, for the most part, of reductions or fusions of various parts of the primitive, basic, pentadactyl limb skeleton, some notable examples of which are discussed below.

Phylogenetic origin of tetrapod girdles and limbs. Some reference to the origin of tetrapod girdles and limbs from piscine ancestors has been made previously. Several theoretical possibilities have been advanced in the past to explain such evolutionary changes. There is general agreement

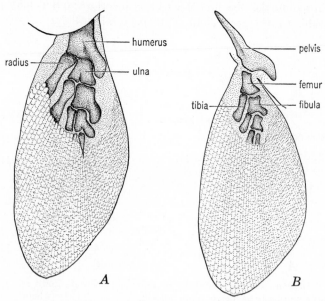

Fig. 10.51. Skeletal structure of *A*, left pectoral, and *B*, left pelvic fins of the crossopterygian fish, *Eusthenopteron*. (*After Gregory and Raven, Ann. N.Y. Acad. Sci. By permission.*)

among authorities today that connecting links are to be sought among fossil crossopterygians of the extinct order Rhipidistia. The theory of Gegenbaur, deriving the tetrapod limb from the archipterygium of the Dipnoi, has been generally discarded. A more recent theory, based upon an exhaustive study of the fossil remains of the rhipidistian crossopterygian *Eusthenopteron*, rather convincingly points out that the various skeletal parts of the fins of this primitive fish can be closely homologized with those of the pentadactyl limbs of tetrapods.

Each fin of *Eusthenopteron* consists of a chain of bones along the post-axial side, from which a series of radials comes off as indicated in Fig. 10.51. It is believed that the first skeletal element at the base of the fin is equivalent to the humerus (femur) and the second element to the ulna (fibula). The first radial is comparable to the radius (tibia). The rest of the radials are believed finally to have become carpal (tarsal) bones, whereas metacarpals (metatarsals) have arisen as new distal outgrowths from the margin of the fleshy, muscular portion of the paddlelike fin. *Eusthenopteron* itself is not considered to be the direct ancestor of tetrapods. Some close rhipidistian relative, rather, was probably the tetrapod progenitor.

Joints are believed to have developed during the evolution of such limbs at points in the appendages where bending was required to produce effective locomotion.

It has already been mentioned that in the evolution of the pectoral girdle of tetrapods there has been a loss or reduction of those portions derived from the dermal skeleton. The clavicle, however, persists in most forms, although in mammals it is frequently much reduced or absent. A new element, the *interclavicle*, a membrane bone, has been added in many tetrapods. This is an unpaired, median portion of the skeleton, lying between the coracoids just posterior to the clavicles and joining the anterior end of the sternum. It is best developed in lizards but appears also in birds as the median part of the *furcula*, or wishbone. An interclavicle is also present in monotremes among mammals. The elements derived from the original, cartilaginous pectoral arch are of most importance in the evolution of the pectoral girdle. Scapula and usually the coracoid persist. In most mammals, however, the coracoids are reduced. Precoracoids, except in mammals, are usually present but frequently remain unossified, the clavicles taking their place. The glenoid fossa is usually at the point of junction of scapula, precoracoid, and coracoid. In monotremes both precoracoids and coracoids persist, but in higher mammals the precoracoid is lost and the coracoid is represented only by a small *coracoid process* attached to the scapula.

The pelvic girdle, which in fishes is poorly developed and not attached to the vertebral column, is a much more important structure in tetrapods in which, in most groups, it forms a firm union with the sacrum. It has been suggested that the pelvis of tetrapods could have logically been derived from the primitive pelvic girdle of such a fish as *Eusthenopteron*. Changes may have involved a shifting of the acetabulum to the lateral surface, an elongation of the ischial region, and a dorsal extension of the iliac process on each side. A gradual widening of the ischial processes with the resultant formation of the ischial symphysis, posterior to the pubic symphysis, was a probable development. The union of the iliac processes with sacral ribs was the next important change to occur but probably did not take place until a later geological era. Ossifications in pubic, ischial, and iliac regions apparently resulted in the appearance of the three bony elements making up each half of the pelvic girdle.

Amphibian girdles and limbs. In some of the primitive amphibians the pectoral girdle was very similar to that of piscine ancestors except for the addition of an interclavicle. In modern amphibians the dermal elements have been lost except for the clavicle which persists in salientians. Limbs and limb girdles are much better developed in salientians than in caudates, but in both groups the basic structural plan is similar. Caecilians lack limbs and limb girdles.

The limbs and girdles of caudates are small and weak. In *Siren* both pelvic limb and girdle are absent altogether. The caudate pectoral girdle is of simple structure (Fig. 10.52) and is apt to remain cartilaginous except in the region of the glenoid fossa. The coracoids, which are united on each side with the scapula to form a single piece, are broad and overlap each other medially in a loose manner just anterior to the sternal cartilage. A precoracoid process may project anteriorly from each coracoid. Clavicles

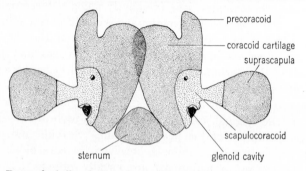

FIG. 10.52. Pectoral girdle of the salamander, *Ambystoma jeffersonianum*, shown as though it were flattened out. Actually the suprascapula arches dorsally. (*After Noble, "Biology of the Amphibia," McGraw-Hill Book Company, Inc. By permission.*)

are absent. Each scapula is connected dorsally with a broad suprascapular cartilage.

The caudate pelvis is firm, the irregular platelike puboischia being united in a median symphysis. An iliac process on each side unites with the transverse process of the sacral vertebra (Fig. 17.8). Ossification centers appear in ilium and ischium but not in the pubis. A Y-shaped *ypsiloid cartilage* lies anterior to the puboischium but is not generally regarded as part of the pelvic girdle. This cartilage and the muscles attached to it have been shown to be concerned with the hydrostatic function of the lungs.

In the caudate forelimb (Fig. 17.7), humerus, radius, and ulna are distinct. Carpal bones are reduced in number by fusion. No more than four digits are present, the first, or *pollex* (thumb), probably being the one that has been lost along with its carpal and metacarpal. In some species, only two or three digits remain. In the hind limb (Fig. 17.8), femur, tibia, and fibula remain separate, and in most cases the primitive pentadactyl condition is retained. In a few species, however, only two or three digits persist.

The salientian pectoral girdle shows several modifications within the group.   In frogs (Firmisternia) the two halves are firmly united in the midline and are closely related to the sternum (Fig. 10.42).   In toads (Arcifera) the two halves overlap in the middle.   Coracoids, precoracoids, clavicles, scapulae, and suprascapulae are present.   The clavicles are fused to or cover the cartilaginous precoracoids in the firmisternal type, whereas in toads the cartilaginous precoracoids and coracoids join their partners medially.   All stages between the two types of girdles have been identified within the group.   The pelvic girdle of salientians is V-shaped

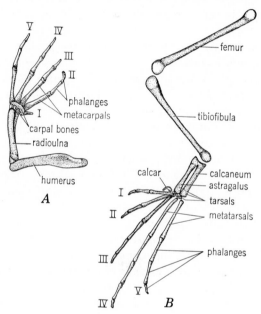

FIG. 10.53.   Arrangement of bones in *A*, pectoral, and *B*, pelvic appendages of the bull-frog, *Rana catesbeiana*.

and consists on each side of a long ilium and a small ischium and pubis. The ilium is attached anteriorly to the transverse process of the sacral vertebra.   All three bones join at the acetabulum.   The limbs of salientians are more specialized than those of caudates (Fig. 10.53).   Humerus and femur are typical, but radius and ulna in the forelimb, and tibia and fibula in the hindlimb, tend to fuse.   The hindlimb is pentadactyl, but the fore-limb usually has only four digits.   The tarsal bones are modified and consist of two rows.   The proximal row contains two long bones, an inner *astragulus* (*talus*) and an outer *calcaneum*.   The distal row of tarsals is reduced to two or three small cartilaginous or bony pieces.   Metatarsals and phalanges of the hindlimbs are long and webbed.   A small additional bone, the *prehallux*, or *calcar*, occurs on the tibial side of the tarsus in most salientians.   It is sometimes interpreted as being the rudiment of an extra digit. It is more probable, however, that the prehallux represents an additional tarsal bone.

Reptilian girdles and limbs. The girdles and limbs of reptiles are well developed except in snakes and limbless lizards. In snakes there is no trace of pectoral girdle or forelimb, but vestiges of a pelvis and hindlimb are found in members of the families Glauconiidae and Boidae. In the former group the three components of the pelvis, and even the femur, are represented. In the Boidae the pelvic vestiges appear externally in the form of small spurs on either side of the cloacal opening. Remnants of the girdles persist to some extent in most of the limbless lizards, but in a few no traces remain.

Reptilian pectoral girdles usually possess the typical three cartilage bones: coracoid, precoracoid, and scapula. The membrane bones, clavicle and interclavicle, are frequently present. In turtles the location of the pectoral girdle is peculiar in that it lies within the arch formed by the ribs or is ventral to them. A sternum is lacking in turtles. Coracoids and precoracoids are not united medially except by fibrous bands. Clavicles and interclavicles are lacking unless certain ossifications in the plastron represent these structures. Lizards have a well-developed pectoral girdle united medially with the sternum. Clavicles and interclavicles are present except in chameleons. Crocodilians, on the other hand, have an incomplete pectoral girdle. Clavicles and precoracoids are lacking. A small interclavicle lies between the coracoids ventral to the sternum but projects beyond it anteriorly. The suprascapula is represented by the small cartilaginous dorsal border of the scapula.

Pelvic girdles of reptiles are typically composed of the usual three bony elements which retain their integrity throughout life. The ilium is firmly united with the two sacral ribs. Both pubic and ischial bones form median symphyses. A small foramen in the pubic bone, serving for the passage of the obturator nerve, was the only opening or foramen in the pelvic girdle in primitive amphibians and reptiles. Next, as in *Sphenodon*, a puboischial foramen appeared between pubis and ischium. In most reptiles these two foramina have become confluent and a new name, *obturator foramen*, is then applied. In crocodilians only an ischial symphysis is present. The two pubic bones are reduced, and a pair of *epipubic bones* projects ventrally. These are separated by a membranous area and do not form a symphysis. The epipubic and pubic bones are frequently confused. According to some authorities the epipubic bones are actually pubic bones which do not enter into formation of the acetabulum and which form a movable articulation with the rest of the pelvis. In most lizards and turtles a median fibrocartilaginous bar connects the rather widely separated pubic and ischial symphyses and separates the obturator foramina of the two sides. In these groups of reptiles a median, cartilaginous *epipubis* lies anterior to the pubic symphysis. A posterior prolongation from the ischial symphysis in *Sphenodon* and in many lizards and turtles is called the *hypoischiac process*, or *cloacal bone*.

The limbs in reptiles show no very unusual features. They are typically pentadactyl, even in sea turtles, the limbs of which are in the form of paddlelike flippers. The chief differences in the limbs of the various groups are to be observed in the carpal and tarsal bones, in which the number may be reduced because of fusion. In crocodilians three tarsal bones unite just distad the tibia to form an *astragalus (talus)*. A single bone, the *calcaneum*, lies distad the fibula. The calcaneum bears a heellike projection which appears, for the first time in phylogenetic history, in this group of reptiles. A feature of the reptilian hindlimb is the presence of an intratarsal joint between the two rows of tarsal bones. Movement takes place here rather than at the junction of the tarsals with tibia and fibula. A *patella*, or kneecap, which is a sesamoid bone, appears in certain lizards for the first time.

In some of the prehistoric reptiles interesting modifications are present. The paddlelike limbs of plesiosaurs and ichthyosaurs have a very large number of phalanges (hyperphalangy). As many as a hundred phalanges to a digit have been observed. In some instances additional rows of phalanges are present in excess of the usual pentadactyl number. In the flying pterodactyls (pterosaurs) humerus, radius, and ulna are of normal proportions. One heavy metacarpal and three slender bones lie distal to radius and ulna. The slender metacarpals support the first three digits which are small and free and bear claws at their tips. The phalanges of what is presumably the fourth digit are enormously elongated. They supported the large integumentary fold which extended outward from the body from shoulder to ankle and was used as a wing. A spurlike sesamoid bone, the *pteroid*, which is *not* a modified digit, projects toward the shoulder from the base of the metacarpals. It is believed that the pteroid provided additional support to the wing. Flexure of the pterodactyl wing occurred at the junction of the fourth metacarpal and the first phalanx of that digit.

Girdles and limbs of birds. The appendicular skeleton of birds shows a remarkable uniformity within the group. The pectoral girdle consists on each side of a large coracoid, a thin, narrow scapula, and a slender clavicle. The two clavicles which are fused medially to a small interclavicle form the *furcula*, or "wishbone" (Fig. 10.19). The precoracoid has practically disappeared. The coracoids form a firm union with coracoid grooves on the sternum. The glenoid fossa is formed by an imperfect union of scapula and coracoid. In the Paleognathae the pectoral girdle is relatively small, the clavicles being much reduced or absent. In the extinct moas a pectoral girdle seems to have been missing altogether, and in the kiwi it is extremely small.

Except in *Archaeopteryx* the three bones of the very large pelvis are fused together to form the *innominate bone*. The ilium is large and projects forward and backward from the acetabulum for some distance. It is completely fused to the synsacrum along the entire length of the latter. A suture, however, indicates the line of fusion. The synsacrum, it will be recalled, is the single bony mass composed of the posterior thoracic, lumbar, sacral, and first few caudal vertebrae, all fused together. Embryological studies make it clear that only two of the vertebrae are truly sacral. The ischium extends posteriorly, paralleling the ilium and fusing with it throughout the greater part of its length. A gap, the *ilioischial foramen*, varying in size in different birds, separates the two bones for some distance (Fig. 10.19). Ischia and pubes do not form symphyses. The two pubic bones, projecting in a posteroventral direction, usually terminate freely, thus permitting passage of the relatively large eggs of birds. In a number of birds the distal end of the pubis unites with the distal end of the ischium. Only in the ostrich is there a true pubic symphysis. An ischial symphysis occurs in the rhea. Archaeopteryx may have had an ischial symphysis. The large space between pubis and ischium, whether or not these bones unite distally, represents the obturator foramen. The pelvic girdle of birds is much like that of some extinct dinosaurs.

The forelimb (wing) of birds is much modified from the primitive condition. In flying birds, humerus, radius, and ulna are exceptionally well developed, since in strong fliers the wings are much longer than the hindlimbs. Modification of carpals, metacarpals, and phalanges is primarily responsible for the specialized condition of the endoskeleton of the wing (Fig. 10.54). Carpal bones, due to fusion, are at first reduced in number to four. These are arranged in two rows of two each. The two distal carpals become fused to the corresponding metacarpals, forming the *carpometacarpus*, thus leaving the proximal carpal bones free. They are referred to as the *radiale* and *ulnare*. Three metacarpals persist in birds, but there is a difference of opinion as to which three are actually represented. In order to avoid confusion, we shall refer to them merely as metacarpals I, II, and III. Metacarpal I is much reduced. All three are united proximally, and numbers II and III unite distally in addition. The first metacarpal bears one phalanx, the second bears two, and the third only one, except in the ostrich in which two phalanges are present on the third digit. In *Archaeopteryx*, claws were present at the ends of all three digits, in which the metacarpals remained separate. In other birds, claws are sometimes encountered on digit I. The young hoatzin, *Opisthocomus*, has claws on the first two digits, but they disappear in the adult.

The various bones of the forelimb form a base supporting the large wing feathers which are called *remiges*. There are three sets of remiges: (1) *primaries*, or *metacarpodigitals*, attached to the various bones of the wrist and hand, (2) *secondaries*, or *cubitals*, attached to the ulna, and (3) *humer-*

als, supported by the humerus. The primaries are further subdivided into groups, depending upon the particular bone to which they are attached.

The hindlimbs of birds are modified for *bipedal* locomotion in contrast to the wings, which have become adapted for flight. In addition to their use in locomotion, the feet of various birds are adapted for swimming, perching, wading, running, scratching, nest building, clinging, fighting, and sundry other purposes (Fig. 2.22). Although there is so much variation, nevertheless a striking uniformity exists in the basic structure of the hindlimbs of birds. A strong femur articulates with the pelvis at the

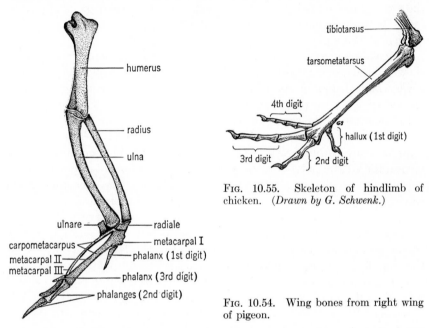

humerus

radius

ulna

tibiotarsus

tarsometatarsus

4th digit

GS

hallux (1st digit)

3rd digit

2nd digit

Fig. 10.55. Skeleton of hindlimb of chicken. (*Drawn by G. Schwenk.*)

ulnare

radiale

carpometacarpus

metacarpal I

metacarpal II

phalanx (1st digit)

metacarpal III

phalanx (3rd digit)

phalanges (2nd digit)

Fig. 10.54. Wing bones from right wing of pigeon.

acetabulum. The fibula is usually much reduced and often represented only by a small bony splint. The tibia is strong and fused to the proximal tarsal bone to form a *tibiotarsus.* A sesamoid bone, the *patella,* is found in most birds anterior to the junction of femur and tibia. The distal tarsal bones unite with the second, third, and fourth metatarsals, forming a single *tarsometatarsus,* which is thus a compound bone (Fig. 10.55). Grooves at its distal end indicate its composite origin. Because of the fusion of the tarsals with other bones, the ankle joint is said to be *intratarsal* in position. An oblique bar of bone crosses the anterior surface of the distal end of the tarsometatarsus. It is lacking in the ostrich. The first metatarsal is represented by a free projection from the distal end of the tarsometatarsus. The spur of the domestic fowl is a bony projection of the tarsometatarsus and is directed posteriorly. It is covered with an epidermal cap of horny material. No more than four digits are present in birds, the fifth metatarsal and the accompanying phalanges being lacking. The first digit (hallux) is usually directed backward, and the other three are directed forward. Some variation is met with in the direction in which the toes point. The typical number of phalanges, going from the first to the fourth digit, is 2, 3, 4, 5. The terminal phalanges bear claws.

A few variations from the above description are encountered in birds. Tibia and fibula in *Archaeopteryx* are distinct and of approximately equal length. In penguins, too, the fibula is complete. Members of the superorder Paleognathae, with the exception of the kiwi, have only three toes, the first, or hallux, being absent. In ostriches the second toe is also lacking. Of the two remaining digits in the ostrich, the third is by far the larger. It bears a claw, but the fourth digit is clawless.

Mammalian girdles and limbs. The appendicular skeleton of mammals shows considerable range from a primitive, reptilelike condition to one of a very high degree of specialization. As would be expected, the monotremes are the most primitive in this respect.

In monotremes the cartilage bones of the pectoral girdle consist on each side of scapula, coracoid, and precoracoid (epicoracoid). The coracoids form a ventral connection with the manubrium (presternum). They furnish the greater portion of the glenoid fossa. Precoracoids join a median episternum which lies anterior to the sternum. Clavicles and interclavicle are present, representing the dermal portion of the reptilian pectoral girdle. In most mammals, however, the interclavicles and precoracoids are lost and the coracoid is reduced to a small *coracoid process* on the scapula adjacent to the glenoid fossa. The latter lies entirely on the scapula. In some mammals the clavicle persists as a strong bony arch from scapula to manubrium. In others it is lost or else remains as a small, unimportant bony vestige embedded in muscle. Persistence of the clavicle is correlated with freedom of movement of the pectoral limb. In the absence of the clavicle all direct connection between axial skeleton and pectoral girdle is lost. The scapula is thus the most important part of the mammalian pectoral girdle.

The pelvic girdle of mammals is made up of the usual three bony elements which, in most cases, are united at the acetabulum. Although the three parts are distinguishable in the young, they are fused in adults to form a single *innominate* bone on each side. A small *acetabular* (*cotyloid*) bone is frequently present in the acetabulum, substituting for the pubis and sometimes the ilium in forming the acetabular depression. The ilium and sacrum are firmly ankylosed. Both pubes and ischia, in many mammals, form symphyses, but in others the ischia do not meet ventrally, so that only a pubic symphysis is present. Strong posterior projections of the ischia may develop. These support the body when in a sitting position. Even a pubic symphysis is lacking in certain mammals. In the female pocket gopher (Fig. 10.56) it undergoes resorption under the influence of the estrogenic hormone of the ovaries, thus facilitating passage of the young from the reproductive tract at the time of parturition. The presence of a large obturator foramen on each side, bounded by pubis and ischium, is characteristic of mammals. The ilium in primates, particularly in man, has become broad and flat in connection with the assumption of an upright posture. The weight of the body is then supported by ilia, sacrum, and the two femurs where they join the innominate bones. Pelvic girdle and hindlimbs are lacking in whales and sirenians. However, paired remnants of pubis and ischium remain in much reduced form.

ADULT MALE   ADULT. FEMALE

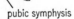
pubic symphysis

FIG. 10.56. Ventral view of pelves of adult male and female pocket gophers, showing presence and absence, respectively, of the public symphysis. (*Original by Hisaw, J. Exptl. Zool.*, **42**:437. *By permission of the Wistar Institute of Anatomy and Biology.*)

In monotremes and marsupials an additional pair of bones, preformed in cartilage, extends forward from the pubes in the ventral wall of the abdomen. They are the *marsupial*, or *epipubic*, bones. A movable articulation occurs between them and the pubes. The homologies of these bones are uncertain. Some authorities state that they are sesamoid bones which develop in the tendons of the external oblique muscles of the abdomen. Apparently they have no homologues in other vertebrates although it is possible that they represent ossifications of the epipubic cartilages of such reptiles as lizards and turtles and even are comparable to the epipubic bones of crocodilians, if indeed these reptiles actually have epipubic bones (page 450).

The forelimbs of mammals, which in many cases are highly specialized, usually deviate less than the hindlimbs from the primitive pentadactyl form. A mammalian humerus may bear a *supracondyloid foramen* near its distal end. This serves for the passage of the brachial artery and median nerve of the arm. The brachial vein does not pass through the supracondyloid foramen. In man this foramen is usually lacking but may be encountered in an occasional individual. Radius and ulna connect with the distal end of the humerus by a hinge joint which permits movement in only one plane. In primates and a few other mammals with prehensile forelimbs, radius and ulna are not arranged in a fixed position but, rather, articulate in such a manner that the distal end of the radius can rotate about the ulna so as to turn the hand in either a prone or supine position. Articulation with the humerus is chiefly through the ulna, which bears a notch and a process for junction with the *olecranon fossa* of the humerus. A projection from the proximal end of the ulna is called the *olecranon process*, commonly spoken of as the elbow. In many cases radius and ulna are fused to some extent. The ulna is most important in forming the elbow joint. The radius is chiefly concerned in forming a support for the hand.

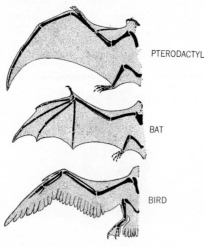

PTERODACTYL

BAT

BIRD

Fig. 10.57. Comparison of skeleton supporting wing in pterodactyl, bat, and bird. (*After Romanes.*)

In primates the pollex is usually quite independent of the other digits and more freely movable. The fact that it can be brought into opposition to the remaining digits and to the palm of the hand makes it possible for animals with opposable thumbs to pick up minute objects and to use their hands for a variety of purposes. This is one factor which has led to the superior position held by man among his contemporaries.

Carpal bones in mammals consist of several separate elements, although some fusion may occur. Metacarpals are elongated. Usually only two phalanges are present on the first digit, with three in each of the remainder. Reduction in number of digits is common in mammals, the tendency being toward reduction in the following order: 1, 5, 2, 4. In the horse and its close relatives, only the third digit remains. It is this digit which bears the hoof. Remnants of the metacarpals of digits 2 and 4 remain as the *small metacarpals*, or *splint bones*. The evolution of the limb of the horse from a primitive pentadactyl ancestor has been traced with a degree of completeness almost without parallel in paleontological investigations. In cattle there are one large and one small metacarpal. The larger of the two is actually a fusion of the third and fourth metacarpals, the line of fusion being clearly indicated by a groove. The small metacarpal is a vestige of the fifth digit. Only digits 3 and 4 are developed. Each consists of three phalanges, the terminal phalanx bearing the hoof in these split-hoofed animals. Several sesamoid bones may be present in addition to the bones just described.

Among the many interesting modifications of the mammalian forelimb is the condition found in bats. All the elements are elongated. The ulna is very much reduced, only the proximal portion being present in most cases. Its distal end is fused to the radius, which is thus the main skeletal element of the lower arm. The first digit is short and free and bears a long claw. The metacarpals and phalanges of the remaining digits are greatly elongated and support the web, or wing membrane. The third digit is the longest (Fig. 10.57). Comparison of the wings of bats and of pterodactyls is of interest. The same principle is involved in the development of wings in these two groups, but the manner in which it is accomplished differs greatly (page 451).

The pentadactyl limbs of sirenians and cetaceans are webbed to form flippers. The skeletal structure differs essentially from other mammals only in the excessive number of phalanges in the central digits.

FIG. 10.58. Skeleton of hand of kangaroo.

tarsal bones

metatarsal IV

metatarsal V

metatarsals II & III

FIG. 10.59. Skeleton of hind foot of kangaroo.

Mammalian pelvic appendages show less variation than is found in the pectoral region. A patella, or kneecap, is present in most mammals. The tibia is the chief bone of the lower leg, the fibula usually being much reduced in size or else fused to the tibia as a small splint. Tarsal bones are distinct entities. A projection of the calcaneum forms the heel. In some of the primates the large toe, or hallux, is opposable in the same manner as the pollex.

Unlike the condition in most mammals, the head of the femur of the orangutan is not attached by a *ligamentum teres femoris* to the acetabulum. This permits greater freedom of movement of the hindlimbs but makes them less strong. These apes walk with difficulty.

In mammals which show a reduction in number of digits, the hindlimbs, in most cases, show a greater reduction than the forelimbs. This is well shown in the kangaroo (Figs. 10.58 and 10.59) in which the hand is pentadactyl but the foot has lost the hallux. In addition, metacarpals 2 and 3 are very slender. The fourth toe is greatly developed and bears a formidable claw at its tip, which is of great value in defense. The fifth toe is less pronounced.

Among mammals, three types of foot posture are recognized (Fig. 10.60). The most primitive is the *plantigrade* posture, observed in the hindlimb of man, in bears, and certain insectivores. In the plantigrade animal the entire foot is in contact with the ground during locomotion. *Digitigrade* animals such as cats, dogs, etc., place only their phalanges on the ground, the wrist and ankle being elevated. In *unguligrade* forms (horse, cow, deer, etc.) only the hoof is in contact with the ground. This type of foot posture is the most specialized of the three, since it deviates most from the primitive condition and is to be found only in the most swiftly running mammals.

A
PLANTIGRADE

B
DIGITIGRADE

C
UNGULIGRADE

Fig. 10.60. Three types of foot posture in mammals: *A*, man (plantigrade); *B*, cat (digitigrade); *C*, cow (unguligrade). (*Drawn by G. Schwenk.*)

Detailed consideration of the various features of the appendicular skeleton in mammals is beyond the scope of this book. A comparative study of mammalian appendages is a most interesting field of biology. Only a few of the salient features have been presented above.

SUMMARY

1. All chordates have a supporting endoskeleton which, in the lowest forms, may consist only of a notochord. In a few groups exoskeletal structures are present in addition and are referred to as the dermal skeleton. Isolated elements, called heterotopic bones, are present in a few groups of vertebrates. Bones in the hearts of ruminants and penis bones of numerous mammals are examples.

2. The skeleton is composed of cartilage, bone, or a combination of the two. Bones are of two types: (1) membrane bones which do not go through a cartilaginous stage in development, (2) cartilage bones which do. The terms intramembranous ossification and endochondral ossification are applied, respectively, to the two types of development.

3. Joints are present at points where bones join, or articulate. There are two main kinds of joints: (1) synarthroses, or immovable joints; (2)

diarthroses, or movable joints. Several types are included under each category.

4. The *dermal skeleton* includes skeletal structures derived from the dermis of the skin. There has been a tendency in evolution to eliminate the dermal skeleton, which is fundamentally a protective device. Among structures included in the dermal skeleton are the scales and fin rays of fishes; the bony plates underlying the epidermal scales of crocodilians, turtles, and a few snakes and lizards; riblike gastralia found in certain reptiles; the bony armor of the armadillo; and the many membrane bones forming parts of the skull and pectoral girdle.

5. The *endoskeleton* consists of axial and appendicular portions. The axial skeleton includes the spinal column, skull, ribs, and sternum. The appendicular skeleton is composed of the skeletal elements of the limbs and limb girdles.

Axial skeleton. *The notochord* is the primitive axial skeleton. In amphioxus, cyclostomes, and a few fishes it persists throughout life, but in most chordates it is replaced by the centra of vertebrae.

The vertebrae are metameric structures extending from the base of the skull to the tip of the tail. They enclose and protect the spinal cord, give rigidity to the body, furnish a place for attachment of the limb girdles, and provide surfaces to which ribs and muscles are attached. A typical vertebra consists of a solid ventral body, or centrum, above which is a neural arch enclosing a neural canal in which the spinal cord lies. Various projections from the vertebrae provide for articulation with adjacent vertebrae and ribs as well as for muscle attachment. In lower forms the vertebrae tend to be similar throughout, but higher in the scale they are grouped in several regions in each of which they show certain peculiar characteristics. Cervical, thoracic, lumbar, sacral, and caudal regions are recognized. Fusion of several vertebrae is encountered in many forms but is most pronounced in birds in which rigidity of the body is important in flight. Otherwise, fusion is most common in the sacral region to which the pelvic girdle is attached in tetrapods.

The skull is derived from three different sources: (1) a chondrocranium, composed of cartilage, (2) a dermatocranium, made up of dermal bones which become attached to the chondrocranium secondarily, (3) the visceral skeleton, or splanchnocranium, derived from the visceral arches which support the gills in lower forms and which also become closely associated with the chondrocranium.

The chondrocranium is derived by histological differentiation of cartilage in a mesenchymatous condensation which early surrounds the brain. It first appears as a pair of parachordal cartilages on either side of the notochord ventral to the base of the brain. This is followed by the appearance of a pair of anterior prechordal cartilages. Three pairs of sense capsules next make their appearance in the nasal, optic, and otic regions, respectively.   A union of prechordal, parachordal, nasal, and otic cartilages results in the formation of the primitive chondrocranium.   The optic capsule does not enter into union with the others.   The side portions of the chondrocranium grow dorsally for a short distance on either side of the brain.   The posterior, or occipital, portion becomes roofed over by cartilage, but the rest remains open.   Ossification centers in various parts of the chondrocranium bring about the formation of the several cartilage bones of the cranium.

The dermatocranium consists of membrane bones derived originally from dermal plates of lower forms which have assumed a deeper position in the body.   Dermal bones roof over the more anterior part of the chondrocranium to form such bones as the parietals and frontals.   Other dermal bones become associated with the visceral skeleton.

The visceral skeleton is derived originally from the cartilaginous visceral arches which support the gills.   The first, or mandibular, arch divides into dorsal and ventral portions which become the upper and lower jaws, respectively.   Membrane bones come to invest the original cartilage which may ultimately disappear, although endochondral ossification in certain regions may result in the formation of certain cartilage bones. The second, or hyoid, arch in lower forms acts as a suspensorium of the jaws.   In higher forms it is reduced and serves merely to support tongue and larynx. The remaining visceral arches are usually lost or reduced. They may contribute certain cartilages to the hyoid apparatus and larynx.

The skulls of cyclostomes and elasmobranchs do not go beyond the cartilage stage.   In other fishes all stages can be observed, from those which are entirely cartilaginous to those which are almost completely bony. Bony fishes have the largest number of skull bones of any vertebrates.   In amphibians there is a notable reduction in the number of bones.   Articulation of the skull with the first vertebra is by means of a pair of occipital condyles.   Salientian amphibians have better-developed skulls than caudates.   Reptilian skulls show an increased degree of ossification, and several new bones make their appearance.   Fusion of various bones is most pronounced in turtles.   Articulation with the first vertebra is by means of a single, median occipital condyle.   This is also true of birds, in which the skull is light in weight, but the various bones are fused to a high degree. In all forms below mammals, articulation of the lower jaw with the rest of the skull is at the quadrate bone.   In mammals, however, the lower jaw articulates with another bone, the squamosal.   Formation of the malleus and incus bones of the middle ear is the result of this shifting in position. Mammalian skulls have an increased cranial capacity, thus accommodating the larger brain.   Two occipital condyles are utilized in articulation with the first vertebra.   The visceral skeleton shows a gradual reduction as the evolutionary scale is ascended.   The various elements of the vertebrate skull show interesting homologies, there being a surprising uniformity in the basic plan of development and arrangement.

The ribs are cartilaginous or bony rods attached at their proximal ends to vertebrae. Primitively there is one pair for each vertebra. There are two kinds of ribs, upper, or dorsal, and ventral, or pleural. The latter represent the spread-out halves of the hemal arch which, anterior to the anus, fail to unite ventrally. They lie just outside the peritoneum. Dorsal ribs appear within the myocommata and lie between hypaxial and epaxial muscle regions. They may be absent or reduced to small tips on the transverse processes of vertebrae. There is disagreement concerning homologies of tetrapod ribs. Many authorities believe that they represent the dorsal ribs of fishes. In most amniotes the ribs in the thoracic region form strong arches which unite ventrally with the sternum. Sacral ribs form a union with the pelvic girdle.

A *sternum* exists only in tetrapods. It is a midventral structure closely related to the pectoral girdle and, except in amphibians, to the ribs. A parasternum, which is a posterior continuation of the sternum in some reptiles, is derived from ossifications in the ventral portions of the myocommata. The sternum typically consists of a row of separate bones, but these may fuse, as in birds and man.

Appendicular skeleton. The appendicular skeleton consists of the anterior, or pectoral, appendages and girdle and the posterior, or pelvic, appendages and girdle. In fishes the appendages are in the form of fins; in tetrapods they are limbs. The limbs of tetrapods are believed to have evolved from the fins of fishes. The connecting links are to be sought among the fossil rhipidistian crossopterygian fishes. Several theories have been advanced to account for the origin of the paired limbs of vertebrates. The "fin-fold" and "ostracoderm" theories offer plausible suggestions.

Fishes. Neither pectoral nor pelvic girdle in fishes is connected with the vertebral column. Cartilages and cartilage bones, homologous with portions of the girdles of tetrapods, can be identified in the girdles of fishes. Several membrane bones become associated with the pectoral girdle, but not with the pelvic girdle. Of these only the ventral clavicles are represented in higher forms. Large cartilaginous or bony plates, the basalia, are located at the base of the typical fin. From these extend numerous radialia which connect distally with dermal fin rays.

Tetrapods. The girdles and limbs of all tetrapods show clear-cut homologies in fundamental structure. Pectoral girdles consist of two or three cartilages or cartilage bones. There is a single scapula and usually a coracoid and precoracoid on each side. A glenoid fossa serves as the point of articulation of girdle and forelimb. Membrane bones consisting of clavicle and interclavicle may be added. Coracoids and clavicles unite with the sternum. In higher forms the clavicles may be lost or reduced.

The coracoids of mammals, except monotremes, are reduced to a small process on each scapula. The scapula, therefore, becomes the chief component of the pectoral girdle in mammals. Pectoral girdle and vertebral column have no direct connection.

The tetrapod pelvic girdle is united firmly to the sacral region of the vertebral column. It is composed on each side of three cartilage bones: ilium, ischium, and pubis. A depression, the acetabulum, usually located at the point of junction of the three bones, furnishes the articular surface for the femur. Pubes and usually the ischia meet their fellows ventrally to form symphyses.

The limbs of tetrapods are fundamentally similar. Forelimbs and hindlimbs are also alike. The upper portion of each limb contains a single bone which articulates with the girdle. The lower portion of each limb contains two parallel bones. Next comes the ankle or wrist, as the case may be, with several small carpal or tarsal bones. This is followed by the hand or foot consisting primitively of five long, narrow bones and of five digits, each of which contains two or three small bones, the phalanges. The tetrapod limb is primitively pentadactyl. Reductions and fusions account for the many variations from the primitive condition that are encountered. Sesamoid bones, which represent ossifications in tendons, are frequently present in various parts of the limb.

CHAPTER 11

MUSCULAR SYSTEM

All movements of the body or parts of the body are brought about by muscles, at least in the higher forms of animal life. Muscular tissue, more than any other tissue in the body, has developed the power of contractility to a very high degree. Three types of muscle tissue are recognized: (1) *smooth*, or *involuntary*; (2) *striated, voluntary*, or *skeletal*; and (3) *cardiac* muscle. The detailed structure of these three types of muscle tissue has been described in Chap. 3. Muscle tissue, with few exceptions (page 628), is of mesodermal origin.

Development. It is important at this point to recall that during early development when proliferating mesodermal cells grow outward between ectoderm and endoderm, they gradually differentiate in such a manner that three different levels or regions may be recognized: (1) a dorsal *epimere*, (2) an intermediate *mesomere*, and (3) a lower *hypomere* (Fig. 3.10). It is with the epimeric and hypomeric portions that we are particularly concerned in our consideration of the muscular system. The mesomere is of importance in the development of the excretory and reproductive organs.

The epimere soon becomes marked off by a series of dorsoventral clefts which form in succession from anterior to posterior ends of the body. Thus a series of blocklike masses of mesoderm, the *mesoblastic somites*, is formed in the epimeric region. The mesomere and hypomere do not usually undergo a similar segmentation. When a somite is first formed it is made up of a practically solid mass of cells, although sometimes a small coelomic cavity is present in the center. With further differentiation of the somite the cells show a sort of radial arrangement around a central core of cells (Fig. 11.1). Next, the ventromedial cells of the somite lose their radial character and together with the cells in the central core form a mesenchymatous mass referred to as the *sclerotome*. These cells continue to proliferate and extend toward the notochord, ultimately to give rise to the vertebral column and proximal portions of the ribs. The dorsolateral part of the somite, which lies directly beneath the ectoderm, is then known as the *dermatome*. The cells of the dermatome later become mesenchymatous and contribute to the dermis of the skin. Some authorities report that the dermatome also may give rise to some muscle cells. The dorsomedial portion of the somite gives rise to the *myotome*. The cells of the myotome proliferate and grow laterally, away from the neural tube but ventral to the dermatome, finally occupying a position parallel to and ventromediad the dermatome

(Fig. 11.2). It is the myotomes which undergo the most extensive development of any parts of the somites since they give rise to the greater part of
the skeletal musculature of the body. It is with the myotomes, therefore,
that we shall be primarily concerned in our discussion of the muscular
system.

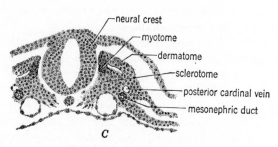

Fig. 11.1. Transverse sections through 33-hour chick embryo at three different levels,
illustrating the manner of differentiation of somites: *A*, posterior section through segmental plate; *B*, section through middle of somite region; *C*, one of the more anterior
somites showing differentiation of dermatome, myotome, and sclerotome. The formation of neural tube and neural crests is also shown.

The *hypomere* is divided into two layers of mesoderm, somatic and
splanchnic, separated by a space, the coelom, or body cavity. The somatic
layer is closely applied to the ectoderm, the two together giving rise to the
definitive body wall. The splanchnic layer surrounds the endoderm of the
gut. This layer is of importance in forming the smooth muscle of the

gut and also the cardiac muscle.
Furthermore, certain *branchial mus-*
cles in the gill region of aquatic
forms, which are voluntary and
striated, originate from the splanchnic layer of the hypomere rather
than from myotomes. They are
thus homologous with the smooth
muscle of the gut (visceral muscles)
despite their striated appearance
and the fact that they move under
voluntary control. They are used in moving the visceral arches. Derivatives of branchial muscles are also present in higher vertebrates.

FIG. 11.2. Transverse section of 48-hour
chick embryo, showing further differentiation of a somite.

The cells of the dorsally located myotomes grow down in the lateral
body wall between the outer ectoderm and the somatic layer of hypomeric
mesoderm (Fig. 11.3). The sheets of cells thus formed on the two sides

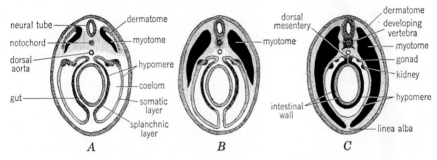

FIG. 11.3. Series of diagrams of vertebrate embryo, illustrating the epimeric origin of
the myotomes and the manner in which they grow ventrally to form the parietal musculature of the body wall. The splanchnic layer of the hypomere surrounds the gut and
contributes to the muscle and other mesodermal structures of the intestinal wall.

almost meet at the midventral line, being separated from each other only
by a longitudinal band of connective tissue, the *linea alba.* Connective
tissue also comes to occupy the spaces between adjacent myotomes. These
partitions are called *myocommata*, or *myosepta.* They extend from the
spinal column and wall of the coelom (peritoneum) outward to the dermis
of the skin. As a result of the foregoing processes, the basic musculature
of the trunk region of the body is clearly defined. The cells of the original
myotome which give rise to muscle tissue are called *myoblasts.* They begin
to differentiate, become spindle-shaped and arranged in bundles. Mitotic
divisions then occur, resulting in an increase in mass. Further differentiation takes place until the cells give the typical syncitial histological picture
of striated muscle. The muscles derived from the myotomes are referred
to as *somatic*, or *parietal*, *muscles.* These may be further subdivided into
axial and *appendicular muscles*, depending upon whether they are confined

to the region of the body wall or whether they are associated with the appendages. In fishes the axial muscles are of greater importance than the appendicular muscles since their contraction is responsible for locomotion in these animals. In tetrapods, however, in which locomotion depends largely upon movements of the limbs, the appendicular muscles have assumed greater importance and the axial muscles, although still functional, have taken a minor role.

Terminology. Smooth, or involuntary, muscles are arranged in continuous sheets as in the walls of the digestive tract, blood vessels, and the like. They are not readily dissected. Voluntary muscles, however, are arranged as separate masses which are fairly easily separated from one another. In some cases identity is difficult to establish because of fusion of two or more muscles to form a single mass or because of separation of a single mass into two or more components. Each end of a voluntary muscle is attached to some structure of the body, but the middle, or *belly*, is usually free. Although muscles are usually attached to bony or cartilaginous skeletal parts, this is not always the case. Usually one end is attached to a less movable part than the other (Fig. 11.4). This is the *origin* of the muscle. The end attached to the more movable part is the *insertion*. A single muscle may have more than one origin or insertion. In many cases muscles are attached to skeletal structures by means of *tendons*. These are white, fibrous cords or bands of regularly arranged connective tissue, strong and inelastic. The term *aponeurosis* is applied to a broad, flat, ribbon-shaped tendon. In certain regions a small bone may develop within a tendon at a point where the latter moves over a bony surface. Such bones are called *sesamoid* bones. The kneecap, or *patella*, is an example of a sesamoid bone.

FIG. 11.4. Diagram showing method of origin and insertion of flexor and extensor muscles.

[labels in figure: bone, origin, extensor muscle, flexor muscle, belly, joint, tendon, insertion, bone]

Sheets or bands of connective tissue called *fasciae* surround muscles, groups of muscles, and the body musculature as a whole. They tend to bind the parts of the body together and in some cases serve as points of muscle origin or insertion as well.

Muscles are usually present in groups of two, each group working in exactly the opposite manner of the other (Fig. 11.4). Such groups are named according to their action, thus:

Flexors tend to bend a limb or to bend one part of a limb against another.

Extensors tend to straighten a limb or one of its component parts.

Abductors draw a part away from a median line or from a neighboring part or limb. Abductors of a limb swing the limb in a direction away from the median longitudinal axis of the body; abductors of the digits move the digits in a direction away from the median longitudinal axis of the limb.

Adductors draw a part toward a median line or toward a neighboring part or limb. Adductors of a limb swing the limb in a direction toward the median longitudinal axis of the body; adductors of the digits move the digits in a direction toward the median longitudinal axis of the limb.

Rotators are muscles which revolve a part on its axis. Some rotators are called *pronators* when, as in the case of the arm, they turn the palm of the hand downward. Others, referred to as *supinators*, serve to turn the palm forward and upward.

Elevators, or *levators*, raise, or lift, a part as in the case of closing the mouth by raising the lower jaw.

Depressors are those which lower, or depress, a part, as when the lower jaw is depressed to open the mouth.

Constrictors draw parts together or contract a part. When constrictors surround an opening such as the mouth, anus, or pylorus, they are termed *sphincters*.

PARIETAL MUSCULATURE

Fundamentally the voluntary, striated, parietal musculature of chordates is made up of a linear series of myotomes extending from anterior to posterior ends. Each myotome lies opposite the point of articulation of two adjacent vertebrae and is supplied by the somatic motor fibers of a separate spinal nerve which emerges from the neural canal through an intervertebral foramen (Fig. 11.5). Whether or not the chordate head is

FIG. 11.5. Diagram showing relation of myotome to sclerotomes of vertebrae and to the somatic motor portion of a spinal nerve. (See also Fig. 10.11.)

primarily metameric has been the subject of much speculation on the part of comparative anatomists for many years. It is generally agreed that certain muscles of the head, like those of the trunk, are fundamentally metameric and are supplied by cranial rather than by spinal nerves. In higher vertebrates the metameric condition has been obscured by evolutionary changes, so that it is rather difficult to recognize homologies. Considerable confusion exists regarding homologies among the muscles of various vertebrates. In numerous cases certain muscles have been given names which are identical with those in the human being because they are located in similar positions. Such muscles may or may not be homologous with the similarly named muscles of man. One of the most reliable criteria in determining muscle homologies is the nerve supply to a muscle. This, however, is not always infallible. Despite pronounced evolutionary changes, the nerve supply has remained relatively constant. The identification and tracing of small branches of nerves is a very difficult task, and for that reason the subject of muscle homology is most complex and is far from having been completely worked out. Only some of the broader aspects of the subject are treated in this volume.

Trunk musculature. *Amphioxus.* In amphioxus the myotomes, when viewed from the side (Fig. 2.4), are observed to be V-shaped structures with the apex of the V pointing forward. The muscle fibers within the myotome course in a longitudinal direction. The fibers are interrupted from myotome to myotome by the presence of myocommata, to which they are attached anteriorly and posteriorly. The myotomes of the two sides alternate with each other in amphioxus. When the muscles of one side of the body are contracted, those on the other side are relaxed. By contracting fibers on alternate sides of the body in different regions, the animal is able to swim rather rapidly with a wriggling, undulatory motion. Because of the oblique arrangement of the myotomes, a cross section through the animal would cut through several of these structures (Fig. 2.6).

Cyclostomes. In cyclostomes, in the absence of paired appendages, the regular segmental arrangment of the myotomes has undergone little change from that of amphioxus. The myotomes, however, instead of being V-shaped, are more nearly vertical. Each is bent forward slightly at its dorsal and ventral ends (Fig. 11.6). As a result the muscle fibers have a slightly radial arrangement. Both myotomes and myocommata take a strongly oblique and posteriorly directed course in passing from the skeletal axis and peritoneum to the dermis of the skin. A cross section through the body wall, therefore, cuts across several myotomes (Fig. 15.6).

A series of *hypobranchial* muscles, not found in amphioxus, is present ventral to the gill region. These arise from the first few myotomes posterior to the gill region. During early development outgrowths extend from these postbranchial myotomes in an anteroventral direction to give rise to the hypobranchial musculature.

Fishes. Beginning with the elasmobranch fishes, the myotomes of gnathostomes are separated into dorsal, or *epaxial*, and ventral, or *hypaxial*, portions. This division is brought about by the presence of a longitudinal

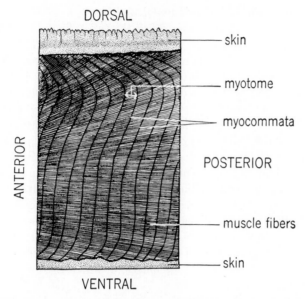

FIG. 11.6. Lateral view of several parietal myotomes of lamprey in region just anterior to the first dorsal fin. The skin has been removed to show the muscle fibers beneath.

lateral septum of connective tissue which extends laterally from the vertebral column to the skin at the point where the lateral line is located.

The myocommata now take a zigzag course (Fig. 11.7), but the muscle fibers in the myotomes, particularly those in the epaxial region, continue to run in a longitudinal direction. The epaxial muscles on each side are

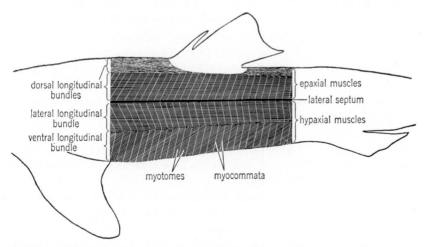

FIG. 11.7. Lateral view of portion of body wall of dogfish, *Squalus acanthias*, showing zigzag arrangement of the myotomes. The skin has been removed to expose the muscle fibers beneath.

arranged in the form of two or three *dorsal longitudinal bundles* extending from the base of the skull to the end of the tail. They form rather large muscle masses used primarily in bending the body from side to side in swimming. The hypaxial muscles are divided into *lateral* and *ventral longitudinal bundles*. The lateral longitudinal bundle lies below the lateral septum and is attached anteriorly to the scapular process. In *Squalus acanthias* it is darker than the other muscles. Anterior to the pelvic fins its fibers take a slightly oblique course anteriorly and upward, but posteriorly they course in a horizontal direction. The ventral longitudinal bundle, which in turn is divided into two parts, overlaps the lateral bundle to a slight degree. The ventral longitudinal bundle is attached anteriorly to the ventral region of the pectoral girdle. Its fibers are arranged obliquely in an anteroventral direction. This is indicative of the direction in which the "pull" caused by contraction of the muscle fibers is being exerted. In some elasmobranchs the portion of the ventral longitudinal bundle on either side of the linea alba is further differentiated into a long but narrow *rectus abdominis* muscle in which the fibers are longitudinally arranged.

Each trunk myotome is supplied by somatic motor branches of a separate spinal nerve. With the appearance of the lateral septum the epaxial muscles are innervated by the dorsal rami and the hypaxial muscles by the ventral rami of the spinal nerves.

The ventral portions of the first few myotomes posterior to the gill region grow forward in an anteroventral direction to form the hypobranchial musculature. Since the hypobranchial muscles are derived from myotomes they are supplied by somatic motor branches of spinal nerves. They should not be confused with the *branchial* muscles, to be described later, which are derivatives of the anterior visceral musculature and which are innervated by visceral motor branches of certain cranial nerves (V, VII, IX, and X).

In fishes certain of the epaxial and hypaxial muscles become specialized, sending portions to the median fins which thus can be moved in various directions.

The inner epaxial muscles of fishes are attached to the vertebral column. The deeper portions of the hypaxial muscles are attached to the ventral ribs. These presage the appearance of intercostal, oblique, and rectus abdominis muscles of higher forms. As yet they do not form distinct muscle masses but have the usual metameric appearance, with myocommata being interposed between adjacent myotomes.

Amphibians. The axial trunk musculature of tetrapods has undergone considerable modification from that observed in lower aquatic forms. The original metameric condition becomes more and more obscure as the evolutionary scale is ascended. In most tetrapods the appendicular muscles have developed extensively and the axial musculature of the trunk, which has been reduced in volume, is relatively of minor significance in relation to body movement.

Caudate amphibians do not have the epaxial muscles so well developed as do fishes, nor are they used to the same extent in locomotion. The lateral septum is more dorsal in position as are the transverse processes of the vertebrae. Despite the reduction in epaxial musculature, the arrangement of the myotomes in this region is primitive. The number of myotomes corresponds to the number of vertebrae, and the muscle fibers run from one myocomma to the next, the entire dorsal, or epaxial, muscle mass forming the *dorsalis trunci* (Fig. 11.8). The myotomes are vertical in posi-

Fig. 11.8. Muscles of portion of trunk region of *Necturus*, lateral view. In the fourth, fifth, and sixth segments from the left the external oblique layer has been removed to show the underlying internal oblique layer. In the seventh and eighth segments both external and internal oblique layers have been removed to expose the transversus. The ventral portions of the internal oblique and transversus have been removed to show the underlying peritoneum.

tion and do not exhibit the zigzag arrangement observed in faster-swimming fishes. The muscle fibers adjacent to the vertebrae are attached to them and are referred to as *intersegmental bundles*.

In salientians the epaxial muscles are still further reduced. They are utilized in bending the vertebral column dorsally rather than laterally. The dorsalis trunci has become further differentiated into *intertransversarial* muscles, between the transverse processes, and *interneural* muscles, between the neural arches. In most frogs the outer fibers of the dorsalis trunci on each side form a long muscle, the *longissimus dorsi*, which passes all the way from the head to near the end of the urostyle (Fig. 11.9). These muscles take the form of a V, the apex pointing posteriorly. The outer fibers are not attached to the vertebrae to any extent. In both caudates and salientians the anterior region of the dorsalis trunci has split up into several muscle masses, of various names, which are attached to the skull and are effective in turning the head.

The hypaxial muscles of amphibians have undergone greater modification than those in the epaxial region. In larval caudates the condition is

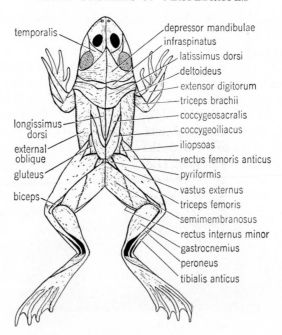

temporalis

depressor mandibulae
infraspinatus
latissimus dorsi
deltoideus
extensor digitorum
triceps brachii
coccygeosacralis
coccygeoiliacus
iliopsoas
rectus femoris anticus
pyriformis
vastus externus
triceps femoris
semimembranosus
rectus internus minor
gastrocnemius
peroneus
tibialis anticus

longissimus dorsi
external oblique
gluteus
biceps

Fig. 11.9.   Dorsal view of bullfrog, *Rana catesbeiana*, with skin removed, showing the dorsal musculature.

much like that observed in fishes, but in adults these ventral trunk muscles are arranged in four distinct layers, or sheets. Beginning from the outside there are *superficial* and *deep external obliques*, in which the muscle fibers course in a posteroventral direction, an *internal oblique* layer, in which they extend in posterodorsal direction, and a *transversus*, with fibers almost in a vertical position (Fig. 11.8). The transversus lies next to the peritoneum. On either side of the linea alba a rather well-developed *rectus abdominis*, derived from the obliques and with primitively arranged longitudinal fibers, extends from the head to the pelvic girdle. In some forms this muscle may split into superficial and deep layers.

In certain species of caudates variations from the above occur, consisting for the most part of a reduction in the number of layers. This is brought about by fusion. Within the group there is also a tendency toward reduction or loss of the myocommata, so that the muscles begin to appear as distinct entities with independent actions.

The more specialized salientians go even further in reducing the number of layers in the hypaxial trunk musculature, there being only an outer superficial external oblique layer and an underlying transversus. The rectus abdominis is now a large muscle extending from sternum to pubis, its two halves being separated in the midventral line by the linea alba. Myocommata have disappeared from the external oblique and transversus but apparently are retained to some extent in the rectus abdominis as *tendinous inscriptions*, which are transverse in position and divide the muscle into segments.

The muscles which move the tongue in amphibians are derived from the hypobranchial musculature.

Reptiles. The trunk musculature of reptiles shows a still further deviation from the primitive condition leading to the more complex arrangement found in mammals. A distinct lateral septum, separating epaxial and hypaxial muscles, is lacking in amniotes. The most conspicuous change occurs in connection with the appearance of ribs.

The epaxial muscles of reptiles become differentiated into several groups. Immediately next to the vertebral column lie the *spinalis* and the more deep and laterally situated *semispinalis* muscles. These are rather long muscles originating on the dorsal portions of the vertebrae and inserting on more anterior vertebrae or on the skull. They are sometimes referred to collectively as the *transverse-spinalis system* of muscles. The deeper muscles in this region split into numerous short muscles, of various names, located between adjacent vertebrae or between vertebrae and ribs. The longissimus dorsi of amphibians now originates at the ilium and becomes separated into (1) a *longissimus dorsi proper*, confined to the lumbar region, (2) a *longissimus capitis*, located on either side of the neck and extending to the skull in the region of the temporal bone, and (3) a laterally situated *iliocostal dorsi*, passing to the proximal ends of ribs. In the neck region the iliocostal dorsi passes to the atlas vertebra and occipital portion of the skull. In a number of forms the presence of tendinous inscriptions indicates that these muscles have originated from segmental myotomes. As would be expected, the epaxial muscles of snakes are very well developed, whereas those of turtles are greatly reduced.

The hypaxial musculature of reptiles exhibits an even greater change from the primitive condition. In such forms as lizards and crocodilians these muscles, in the abdominal region at any rate, are much like those of caudate amphibians, consisting of external and internal oblique and transversus layers. In the thoracic region, however, additional layers are present. Between external and internal obliques an *intercostal layer*, derived from the obliques, makes its appearance, with fibers connecting adjacent ribs. This is subdivided into *external* and *internal intercostals*. The fibers of these two sets of muscles run in opposite directions and are used in respiratory movements. The oblique muscles also give rise to the *scalene muscles*, which pass from the anterior ribs to the cervical vertebrae, and to the *serratus muscles* passing from the more posterior ribs to the inner surface of the scapula or to the thoracic and anterior lumbar vertebrae. The rectus abdominis is well developed in lizards and crocodilians, and tendinous inscriptions are prominent.

In snakes the ventral scales are used in locomotion. Small muscles derived from the obliques and rectus pass from the ribs to the skin under-lying the scales. These, together with certain dermal muscles, are responsible for the movement of the ventral scales (Fig. 11.19).

The hypaxial muscles of turtles are poorly developed in association with the rigid shell which narrowly restricts body movements.

The fact that the number of hypaxial muscle layers, as found in caudate amphibians, is reduced in salientians but increases in reptiles arouses interesting speculations as to evolutionary trends. In both cases animals have taken to terrestrial existence, but this factor alone would seem to be of minor importance. The increased number of layers in reptiles has developed in association with the appearance of ribs, which, of course, are lacking in salientians. This fact rather than emergence to life on land is of importance in considering evolutionary trends.

Birds. The trunk musculature of birds is quite different from that of other forms. This is not surprising when one considers their specialized mode of life. Expaxial muscles are poorly developed. Among the changes to be observed are the absence of the transversus in the abdominal region and reduction of the oblique muscles. A remnant of the transversus is recognized in the *triangularis sterni* on the inner portion of the ribs near where they are attached to the sternum.

Mammals. In mammals the trunk muscles do not deviate markedly from those observed in reptiles but the hypaxial musculature is somewhat reduced. With the greater importance of the limbs in locomotion there has been an increase in the muscles of the limbs and limb girdles. These muscles overlie the greater part of the trunk musculature. The original metameric arrangement of the trunk myotomes is now only slightly indicated. The *intercostal, serratus, scalene, intervertebral,* and *rectus abdominis* are trunk muscles in which the original segmental arrangement is retained, at least in part.

The expaxial muscles of mammals show great similarity to the reptilian condition. A bewildering variety of names is applied to the numerous muscles of this region which, if described in detail, would only add to the confusion of the student. Only a few of the more obvious muscles will be mentioned. A *sacrospinalis muscle* originates from the sacrum and spinous processes of the posterior vertebrae. Anteriorly it splits into three columns on each side: a lateral *iliocostal,* an intermediate *longissimus dorsi,* and a medial *spinalis dorsi muscle.* Each of these continues forward to the cervical region, but only the longissimus dorsi and spinalis dorsi go as far as the skull. A *multifidus muscle* represents the transverse-spinalis system of reptiles. It fills in the groove on either side of the spinous processes all the way from the sacrum to the axis. The deeper epaxial muscles again form *interspinal* and *intertransversarial* muscles between adjacent vertebrae.

The hypaxial muscles of mammals are but little modified from the reptilian condition, at least in the abdominal region. The muscles of the abdominal wall consist of an inner *transversus abdominis*, a middle *internal oblique*, and an outer *external oblique* which lies beneath the integument. The large aponeurosis of the external oblique interlaces with that of its fellow of the opposite side at the linea alba. A portion of the aponeurosis is continued posteriorly as the *inguinal ligament*. The *quadratus lumborum* is a dorsoposterior derivative of the external oblique. The internal oblique is smaller than the external and best developed in its dorsal portion. Its large aponeurosis also passes to the linea alba. The transversus is a thin muscle layer quite similar to the internal oblique in arrangement. The *cremaster muscle* of the scrotum is continuous with the internal oblique and in some cases with the transversus. The rectus abdominis in mammals lies on either side of the linea alba just as in lower forms. It is enclosed in a sheath formed from the aponeuroses of the oblique and transversus muscles. A few remnants of the rectus abdominis, which originally extended the length of the body, are to be found in mammals in the neck region. They include the *sternohyoid*, *sternothyroid*, and *thyrohyoid*. These are discussed further under the heading "Hypobranchial musculature." Tendinous inscriptions are clearly indicated on the rectus abdominis but only to a minor extent on its anterior derivatives.

In the thoracic region the mammalian hypaxial muscles show a reduction from the reptilian condition. They are almost entirely covered by the large appendicular muscles associated with the pectoral girdles and limbs. *External intercostals* pass from one rib to the next, their fibers running posteroventrally in an oblique direction. *Internal intercostals* lie beneath the external intercostals. They also pass between adjacent ribs, but their fibers run anteroventrally in an oblique direction. The intercostals are used in respiration, the external intercostals serving to pull the ribs forward, whereas the internal intercostals may pull them back to their original position. Under the internal intercostals lies the transversus which, in the thoracic region, is referred to as the *transversus thoracis*. It is confined to the inner surface of the anterior thoracic wall. *Scalene muscles* pass from the anterior ribs to the transverse processes of the cervical vertebrae. The *serratus muscles* pass from the angles of more posterior ribs to the inner surface of the scapula or to thoracic and anterior lumbar vertebrae. These are trunk muscles originally derived from the obliques, their hypaxial origin being indicated by the fact that they are supplied by the ventral rami of spinal nerves.

General. The trunk musculature of all craniates is built upon the same fundamental plan. The metameric arrangement of myotomes observed in adults of lower forms becomes less apparent with advance in the evolutionary scale. This variation from the primitive condition occurs as myotomes increase in size and thickness and as the connective-tissue septa, or myocommata, between them disappear. Many of the long trunk muscles have developed in this manner. In other cases there has been a degeneration of portions of certain myotomes leading to the formation of aponeuroses and fasciae. Other myotomes may be drawn out of position or may migrate to new regions, thus obscuring their original arrangement and position. In some cases portions of adjacent myotomes may fuse to form a single muscle.

Hypobranchial musculature. In cyclostomes and elasmobranchs, as has been mentioned previously, the hypaxial portions of the first few myotomes posterior to the gill region send buds or branches anteriorly and ventrally to form the hypobranchial musculature. The hypobranchial muscles are actually continuations of the ventral longitudinal bundles. In *Squalus acanthias* (Fig. 11.18) these muscles consist of (1) the *common coracoarcuales*, arising from the coracoid cartilage and inserting on the strong connective tissue comprising the floor of the pericardial cavity, (2) a *coracomandibular*, originating from the fascia at the anterior end of the common coracoarcuales and inserting on the symphysis of the mandible, (3) paired *coracohyoids*, coming from the coracoarcuales and passing to the basihyal and ceratohyal cartilages, (4) several *coracobranchials*, which originate from fascia above the coracoarcuales and insert on the ceratohyal and other hypobranchial cartilages. These hypobranchial muscles are considered by some to be derived from the hypomeric branchial musculature, but they are undoubtedly of myotomic origin.

In tetrapods the hypobranchial muscles have been greatly modified. Several muscles in the neck and throat regions are hypobranchial muscles which, like all trunk muscles, are innervated by spinal nerves or their derivatives. A forward continuation of the rectus abdominis in the neck region is referred to as the *rectus cervicis*. From it are derived such muscles as the *sternohyoid, thyrohyoid, sternothyroid, geniohyoid,* and *omohyoid* (Fig. 18.17). These muscles as well as the intrinsic muscles of the tongue, which are also of hypobranchial origin, are supplied by the hypoglossal nerve which is a purely somatic motor cranial nerve (XII). It is generally conceded, however, that the hypoglossal nerve, which is found only in amniotes, represents a union of the first two or three spinal (spino-occipital) nerves such as are found in lower forms and which are somatic motor nerves. The fact that the above-mentioned muscles are supplied by the hypoglossal nerve furnishes additional evidence of their hypobranchial origin.

Study of the development of the intrinsic tongue muscles of mammals shows that they do not arise as anterior extensions of postbranchial myotomes, as do the hypobranchial muscles of lower forms. Instead, they gradually differentiate directly (*in situ*) from mesenchyme within the developing tongue. Nevertheless, because the tongue muscles are innervated by the hypoglossal nerve, they are considered to be phylogenetic derivatives of hypobranchial muscles. Apparently this is an example in which a certain stage of development is omitted or glossed over so rapidly that it cannot be discerned.

Eye muscles. The hypoglossal nerve is not the only cranial nerve which bears somatic motor fibers. Certain others (III, IV, VI) are somatic motor nerves which supply the muscles moving the eyeball and which are derived from myotomes in the head region.

Primitively a series of somites existed in the head region from the anterior part of the head to the trunk. Their presence is still indicated in cyclostome and elasmobranch embryos. In the ear region, however, these somites have been crowded out and have disappeared, for the most part. Three of the most anterior ones persist and appear uniformly throughout the vertebrate series. They are known as the *pro-otic somites*, referred to respectively as the *premandibular*, *mandibular*, and *hyoid somites* in reference to their location (Fig. 11.10). The myotomes of these somites contribute to the parietal musculature. As in the case of other

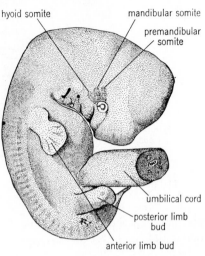

Fig. 11.10. Human embryo at an early age showing position of the pro-otic somites.

myotomes of the body, each is supplied by a single nerve. The pro-otic somites are innervated by cranial nerves III, IV, and VI, respectively, rather than by spinal nerves.

The vertebrate eye first makes its appearance in cyclostomes. Its structure is essentially similar in all vertebrate groups. With the advent of the eye, six muscles, which move the eyeball, make their appearance. All six are derived from the three pro-otic myotomes. The first of these differentiates into four eye muscles: *superior rectus, inferior rectus, internal rectus,* and *inferior oblique* (Fig. 11.11), all of which are supplied by the oculomotor nerve (III). The second pro-otic myotome develops into the *superior oblique* muscle supplied by the trochlear nerve (IV). The third myotome, which becomes the *external rectus*, is innervated by the abducens nerve (VI).

In the lamprey the abducens nerve appears to supply the inferior rectus muscle as well as the external rectus. The oculomotor nerve, on the other hand, seems to innervate only the superior rectus, internal rectus, and inferior oblique. This peculiar and seemingly paradoxical situation raises questions of homology. It has been demonstrated, however, that in the lamprey the sixth cranial nerve, which leaves the brain rather far forward

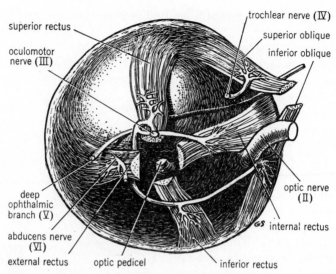

superior rectus

oculomotor
nerve (III)

trochlear nerve (IV)

superior oblique

inferior oblique

deep
ophthalmic
branch (V)

abducens nerve
(VI)

external rectus   optic pedicel

optic nerve
(II)

GS internal rectus

inferior rectus

Fig. 11.11. Posteromedian view of left eyeball of *Squalus acanthias*, showing nerve supply to the six eye muscles. (*Drawn by G. Schwenk.*)

and close to the oculomotor nerve, actually contains fibers of the third nerve and the latter are the ones which pass to the inferior rectus.

Diaphragm. The muscular diaphragm, present only in mammals, is derived embryonically from the *septum transversum* and certain other membranes. The portion adjacent to the sternum, ribs, and vertebral column becomes invaded with muscle tissue to varying degrees in different species. This is contributed by the hypaxial portion of myotomes in the cervical region. The fact that the diaphragm is innervated by branches of cervical spinal nerves indicates the embryonic origin of the muscular constituents.

Appendicular musculature. One of the most important advances in the muscular system of vertebrates takes place in connection with the appearance of paired appendages first found in the pectoral and pelvic fins of elasmobranch fishes. During early development when the myotomes are growing ventrally in the body wall, hollow buds grow out from them into the folds from which pectoral and pelvic fins arise (Fig. 11.12). They develop into the muscles which move the fins. These muscles are, therefore, derivatives of the myotomes of the trunk. Since the muscles are modified to course in different directions, their original metameric arrangement may not be apparent.

Two types of appendicular muscles are generally recognized, *i.e.*, extrinsic and *intrinsic*. The former attach the girdle or limb to the axial skeleton directly or indirectly. They originate in the axial musculature and are inserted on some skeletal element within the limb. Extrinsic muscles serve to move the entire appendage. Intrinsic muscles have both origin and insertion on parts of the limb skeleton itself, serving to move parts of the limb rather than the appendage as a whole. Actually the distinction between extrinsic and intrinsic muscles is not of too great importance since the appendicular muscles, at least in fishes, are all derived from myotomes.

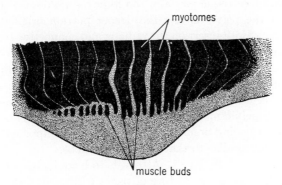

myotomes

muscle buds

Fig. 11.12.   Developing appendage of elasmobranch fish, *Pristiurus*, showing muscle buds arising from the myotomes.   (*After Rabl.*)

In various species of elasmobranchs different numbers of buds from the myotomes are concerned in the development of the fin musculature. In the electric ray, *Torpedo*, 26 myotomes are involved in forming the muscles of the pectoral fins. Each bud divides into anterior and posterior primary buds. These then give off dorsal and ventral secondary buds. The two dorsal buds of each myotome concerned give rise to the dorsal musculature of the fin; the ventral buds form the ventral fin muscles. The dorsal muscles become the extensors or levators of the fins; the ventral muscles become flexors or depressors.

In elasmobranchs, as illustrated by *Squalus acanthias* (page 487), the dorsal, or extensor, muscle of the pectoral fin consists of a single sheet some fibers of which have their origin on the scapula while others originate from the fascia covering the hypaxial myotomes. These fibers insert, respectively, on the propterygium and on the distal radialia and connective tissue covering the dermal fin rays. Other fibers originate from fascia covering the medial surface of this sheet and all three of the basal cartilages. They also insert on the radialia and connective tissue covering the fin rays. The ventral, or flexor, musculature of the pectoral fin is more elaborately developed in *Squalus acanthias*. It makes up the anterior and ventral parts of the fin and consists of three divisions all of which originate from various regions of the pectoral girdle. The *flexor protractor* inserts on the anterior border of the proterygium. The *flexor depressor* passes to the anterior half of the mesopterygium and to the radialia and dermal fin rays distal to it. The *flexor retractor* inserts on the posterior half of the mesopterygium and all the metapterygium.

The various intrinsic muscles are grouped so as to move the pectoral fin in different directions.

Muscles moving the pelvic fins of elasmobranchs are also divided into dorsal, or extensor, and ventral, or flexor, groups. The dorsal muscle consists of superficial and deep portions. The superficial portion originates from the connective-tissue fascia of the hypaxial myotomes and from the iliac region of the pelvic girdle; the deeper portion originates from the metapterygium. Both insert on the radialia and connective tissue covering the dermal fin rays. The ventral muscles likewise form two masses, one originating from the ventral side of the ischiopubic bar and linea alba and passing to the metapterygium, the other originating on the metapterygium and inserting on the radialia and dermal fin rays. Complications are introduced in the pelvic musculature of male elasmobranchs because of the presence of the clasping organs. In other fishes the appendicular musculature is generally similar to that of elasmobranchs.

scapula

developing muscles

humerus

ulna

Fig. 11.13. Anterior limb bud of 16-mm. human embryo, showing developing bones and muscle primordia. (*Redrawn from Arey, "Developmental Anatomy," W. B. Saunders Company. By permission.*)

Attempts to homologize the fin musculature of fishes with conditions in tetrapods have led only to confusion.

The limbs of tetrapods originate embryonically from limb buds which develop in pectoral and pelvic regions. These at first consist of swellings of the lateral body wall, covered with superficial ectoderm and containing an undifferentiated mass of mesenchyme. It is from this mesenchyme that the appendicular muscles are differentiated (Fig. 11.13). Only in elasmobranchs can the development of appendicular muscles be traced to myotomic buds. In higher vertebrates it is practically impossible to trace the origin of mesenchyme in limb buds so far as any relation to definite myotomes is concerned. However, the ultimate nerve supply to the appendicular muscles is precisely what one would expect were the muscles formed from outgrowths of specific myotomes as is true in elasmobranchs. It seems as though in tetrapods a certain stage in development has dropped out completely. Every other indication suggests that the appendicular muscles are of myotomic origin.

With emergence to life on land the limb musculature has undergone considerable change from the relatively simple condition observed in fishes. Separate muscles are now differentiated from the dorsal and ventral muscle masses. The muscles are larger and sturdier and have broad attachments. A clear division into extrinsic and instrinsic groups is apparent. This provides for the greater freedom of movement in many directions required in terrestrial locomotion.

At a certain point in development the muscles begin to differentiate from the mesenchyme of the limb bud. This accompanies the development of the appendicular skeleton, which is also differentiated from limb-bud mesenchyme. Those muscles which arise in the dorsal part of the appendage in most cases become extensors, whereas those in the ventral aspect become flexors. Outgrowths of these muscles toward the trunk form abductors and adductors, respectively.

So many modifications are to be found in the appendicular muscles of various tetrapods that only a brief treatment of the subject can be given here. The tailed amphibians are the first vertebrates to possess limbs terminating in digits. Accordingly they give a clue to the origin of the appendicular musculature of higher forms.

The perennibranchiate salamander *Necturus* is considered to be the most primitive tetrapod living today. It is generally available for dissection and study in the laboratory. Hence, a description of the appendicular muscles as found in *Necturus* is apt to have more meaning to the student of comparative anatomy than if a general description of the muscles of other and less familiar forms were attempted.

Extrinsic muscles of the pectoral appendages.   In *Necturus* (Fig. 11.14) a

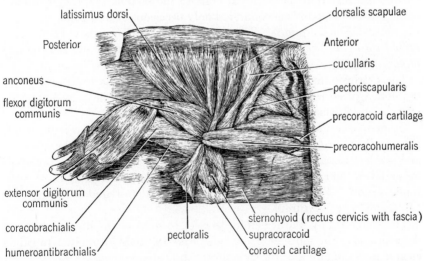

FIG. 11.14. Superficial muscles of right pectoral girdle and forelimb of *Necturus*, ventrolateral view.

rather prominent muscle, the *latissimus dorsi*, originates from myocommata and fasciae covering certain anterior myotomes of the dorsalis trunci. It passes to the humerus and vicinity of the shoulder joint. From the ventral side a *pectoralis* muscle extends from the linea alba to the ventral side of the proximal end of the humerus. Its fibers, near their origin, are continuous with the rectus abdominis and are attached to the myocommata. Deeper muscles, the *levator scapulae* and *serratus anterior*, inserting on the scapula, are clearly derived from the trunk, or axial, musculature.

The primitive condition encountered in *Necturus* becomes further modified in reptiles, which form an intermediate group as regards the evolution of the musculature of mammals. In a few reptiles and in mammals the anterior portion of the original latissimus dorsi has become a separate muscle, the *teres major*, which has been shifted so as to attach to the scapula. Posteriorly the latissimus dorsi comes to cover the greater part of the back (Fig. 11.16). The pectoralis is more highly developed and in some mammals forms superficial and deep layers. The superficial layer forms the *pectoralis major* of apes and man, the deeper layer giving rise to the *pectoralis minor*. A *subclavius* muscle may also be split off the anterior portion of the deeper layer.

The deeper extrinsic muscles, *i.e.*, the *levator scapulae* and *serratus anterior*, have become more extensive in higher vertebrates. The latter now passes between the vertebral border of the scapula and the more anterior ribs. Furthermore, the levator scapulae and serratus anterior have given rise to a series of separate muscles known as the *rhomboideus group*. Only the crocodilia among reptiles possess a rhomboideus muscle. A *rhomboideus capitis*, passing from the occipital bone to the scapula, is present in most mammals but in man is encountered only occasionally and is referred to as the *rhomboideus occipitalis*. The rhomboideus of mammals is in man separated into two distinct elements, the *rhomboideus major* and *rhomboideus minor*.

The extrinsic muscles of the pectoral limbs in birds are extremely well developed in correlation with their habit of flight. The keeled sternum offers a broad base for their attachment.

Other muscles attached to the pectoral appendage of *Necturus* include the *cucullaris* (*trapezius*) which in higher forms gives rise to the *trapezius* and *sternocleidomastoid*. These, however, are derived from the branchial musculature and are not therefore included among the muscles of myotomic origin. They are discussed in further detail under the heading "Branchial musculature."

The student may find it helpful to refer to some of the illustrations and descriptions of the muscles of the cat (pages 780 to 805) in order to gain a clearer understanding of the homologies indicated above.

Intrinsic muscles of the pectoral appendages. Turning again to the primitive caudate *Necturus* (Fig. 11.14), we find a muscle, the *dorsalis scapulae*, lying immediately anterior to the latissimus dorsi. It originates on the suprascapula and inserts on the humerus. It is thus included among the intrinsic muscles of the forelimb. In higher forms the dorsalis scapulae is represented by the *deltoid* muscles, which lie between the trapezius and latissimus dorsi. The *teres minor* is a small muscle derived from the dorsalis scapulae. A *supracoracoid* muscle extends from the coracoid cartilage to the humerus in *Necturus*. This muscle has probably given rise to the *supraspinatus* and *infraspinatus* muscles of higher vertebrates. Another muscle, the *precoracohumeralis*, in *Necturus* passes from the precoracoid cartilage to the humerus. It is believed to contribute to the deltoid group.

On the dorsal side of the upper arm of *Necturus* is the large *anconeus* muscle made up of several parts, or *heads*, which originate on the pectoral girdle and humerus and insert by means of fascia on the ulna. The number of heads varies, there being four in *Necturus* and most reptiles but usually three in mammals. In the latter group the *triceps* represents the anconeus. It serves to extend the upper arm.

On the flexor side of the upper arm lies a small *humeroantibrachialis* muscle passing from humerus to radius. A large *coracobrachialis*, arising from the coracoid cartilage, inserts on the distal end of the humerus. The humeroantibrachialis probably has given rise to both the *biceps brachii* and *brachialis* muscles of higher forms. It is frequently referred to as the biceps brachii, but this name may not be entirely appropriate. The similarly named muscle in mammals, as in *Necturus*, inserts on the radius, but its origin, from the region of the glenoid cavity of the scapula, rather than from the humerus, raises some doubts as to its homology. On the other hand, the brachialis muscle of mammals which, like the humeroantibrachialis, originates from the humerus, inserts on the ulna rather than the radius. It is possible that both biceps brachii and brachialis have been derived from the humeroantibrachialis of lower tetrapods, but this has not been established with certainty. The coracobrachialis muscles of *Necturus* and mammals are undoubtedly homologous.

The muscles of the forearm are more numerous than those of the upper arm. They provide for the more complex and diverse movements made by the forearm, hand, and digits. We shall not attempt to describe these muscles in detail since their main features are generally similar in all tetrapods. (For a detailed description of the muscles of the forearm and hand in *Necturus* the interested student may refer to H. H. Wilder, "The Human Body," Henry Holt and Company, Inc.) In general the muscles may be grouped in two main divisions, *extensors* on the dorsal surface and *flexors* on the ventral side. *Supinators*, associated with the extensor group, and *pronators*, with the flexor group, are also present in many forms.

Extrinsic muscles of the pelvic appendages. The bones comprising the pelvic girdle are directly attached to the axial skeleton via the sacrum. This firm union is quite in contrast to the attachment of the pectoral girdle which is accomplished by means of muscles, tendons, and ligaments. Accordingly the extrinsic muscles of the pelvic appendage are much less highly developed than those of the pectoral appendages.

The only extrinsic pelvic muscles present in *Necturus* (Fig. 11.15*A*) are three caudal muscles. They originate from caudal myotomes a short distance posterior to the pelvic girdle and run together in a common sheath. These muscles include the *ischiocaudalis*, with its origin on the posterior border of the ischium; the *caudofemoralis*, originating on the shaft of the femur; and the *caudopuboischiotibialis*, which joins the fascia of the *pubioschiotibialis* (see below) by means of a flat tendon. These muscles are used primarily in certain tail movements, but in some positions the caudo-

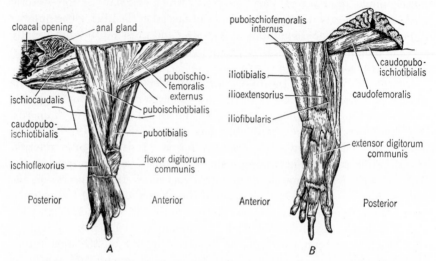

Fig. 11.15. Superficial muscles of left pelvic girdle and hind limb of *Necturus: A*, ventral view; *B*, dorsal view.

femoralis may retract the femur and the ischiocaudalis in males may compress the glandular tissue in the cloacal region. The homologies of these muscles with those of higher forms are not clear, but nevertheless it seems that the *pyriformis* in man and the higher anthropoids is a remnant of this caudal muscle complex.

Intrinsic muscles of the pelvic appendages. The proximal intrinsic muscles of the pelvic appendages as observed in *Necturus* (Fig. 11.15*A* and *B*) are not so easily homologized with those of higher forms nor with the corresponding muscles of the pectoral appendages. Much confusion exists, and there is little agreement among comparative anatomists.

On the ventral side and originating from the midventral line of the pelvic girdle, or puboischial plate, are two superficial muscles, an anterior *puboischiofemoralis externus*, passing to the femur, and a posterior *puboischiotibialis*, inserting on the proximal end of the tibia. Another muscle, the *ilioflexorius*, arising from the puboischial plate along with the puboischiotibialis, forms the posterior edge of the thigh. It inserts on fascia of the shank. A *puboischiofemoralis internus*, arising from the dorsal surface of the puboischium, passes to the shaft of the femur. Just posterior to this is the *pubotibialis*, coming from the pubic region in front of the obturator foramen and passing to the proximal end of the tibia. Three additional muscles, originating from the ilium, cover the pubotibialis. The most anterior of these is the slender *iliotibialis*. In back of it lies the *ilioextensorius*. Both these muscles insert on the tibia. Posterior to the ilioextensorius lies the *iliofibularis*, which passes to the proximal end of the fibula. Another small, deep, triangular muscle, the *iliofemoralis*, with its origin on the ilium, inserts on the posterior border of the femur. A *femorofibularis*, from the ventral face of the femur, also inserts on the fibula near the insertion of the iliofibularis.

Many investigators have attempted to homologize the proximal muscles of the caudate thigh with those of higher vertebrates, but there is little general agreement. Wilder, in his "History of the Human Body," discusses some of the more probable homologies, a few of which are listed below:

Necturus	*Mammal*
Puboischiofemoralis externus.................	Obturator externus
	Quadratus femoris
Puboischiofemoralis internus..................	Obturator internus
	Gemellus superior
	Gemellus inferior
Puboischiotibialis...........................	Adductor femoris
	Adductor longus
	Gracilis
	Sartorius
	Semimembranosus
	Semitendinosus
Ilioextensorius............................	Quadriceps femoris
	Vastus lateralis
	Vastus intermedius
	Vastus medialis
	Rectus femoris
Iliofemoralis..............................	Gluteus maximus
	Gluteus medius
	Gluteus minimus
	Short head of biceps femoris
	Tenuissimus
Iliofibularis..............................	Long head of biceps femoris

The mammalian muscles listed above exhibit many modifications associated with differences in posture and the uses to which limbs are put. Figure 11.16 illustrates some of the differences which may be observed in various muscles of the cat and man.

The distal intrinsic muscles of the pelvic limbs of *Necturus* are almost identical with those of the pectoral limbs. They too are grouped as extensors and flexors. In higher forms, however, the similarities between the two pairs of appendages, as observed in *Necturus*, are not very apparent.

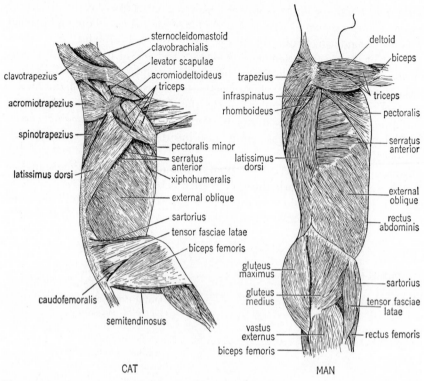

Fig. 11.16. Lateral view of superficial body muscles of cat and man, shown together for the sake of comparison.

Among mammals less variation is found in the distal muscles of the pelvic limb than in the proximal muscles.

BRANCHIAL MUSCULATURE

Turning back again to elasmobranchs, we find an important feature in the *branchial* muscles which move the visceral arches and jaws. They are voluntary striated muscles derived from the splanchnic mesoderm of the hypomere and *not* from myotomes. The branchial muscles begin anteriorly at the mandibular arch and run in series to each of the successive visceral arches. As will be pointed out in more detail in the chapter on the Nervous System, the branchial muscles are innervated by visceral motor branches of certain cranial nerves. The mandibular branch of the trigeminal nerve (V) is the nerve supplying the branchial muscles associated with the mandibular arch; the facial nerve (VII) is the nerve of the hyoid arch; the glossopharyngeal nerve (IX) innervates the branchial musculature of the third visceral arch located between the first and second *typical* gill slits; the vagus nerve (X) innervates the remainder of the branchial musculature.

The outer, or superficial, branchial muscles function as constrictors of the pharynx. They tend to close the gills and mouth during respiratory movements. They are divided into *dorsal* and *ventral* constrictors, lying above and below the gills, respectively. Each constrictor is separated from the next by a band of connective tissue, arranged vertically and known as a *raphe.*

In *Squalus acanthias* the dorsal constrictor of the first, or mandibular, arch is a small muscle which lies anterior to the spiracle. It has its origin on the otic capsule and inserts on the palatopterygoquadrate bar. The *adductor mandibulae,* which in elasmobranchs lies outside the angle of the mouth and acts in closing the jaws, is a derivative of the first dorsal constrictor. The first ventral constrictor forms the rather broad *intermandibularis* muscle which originates from a midventral raphe. Its fibers pass obliquely forward on either side to insert on Meckel's cartilage. The constrictors of the remaining visceral arches, as illustrated by *Squalus acanthias* (Fig. 11.17), are bounded anteriorly and posteriorly by the gill slits. The

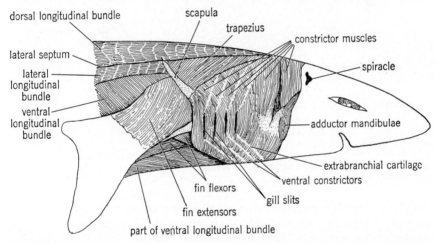

Fig. 11.17. Superficial muscles of shoulder and head of dogfish, *Squalus acanthias.* (*Original by Howell, J. Morphol.,* **54**:401. *By permission of the Wistar Institute of Anatomy and Biology.*)

second, lying between the first typical gill slit and the spiracle, is a large muscle with rather distinct dorsal and ventral portions which pass anteriorly above and below the jaws. The dorsal portion is known as the *epihyoideus* muscle. It has its origin on the otic capsule and its insertion on the hyomandibular cartilage. The anterior portion of the second ventral constrictor gives rise to the *interhyoideus* muscle which is attached to the hyoid arch and which lies just above the intermandibularis. The last four constrictors are simply arranged, their dorsal and ventral portions being rather similar in appearance.

Other branchial muscles, covered for the most part by the constrictors, serve as levators of the visceral arches. The first levator is the *levator maxillae*, which, in selachians, acts in raising the upper jaw. The second is the levator of the hyoid arch. It lies directly under the epihyoideus. The *trapezius (cucullaris)* belongs to the levator group and probably represents the posterior portion of the remaining levators. It originates from dorsal fascia and overlying skin and extends in a ventrocaudal direction to insert on the epibranchial cartilage of the last visceral arch as well as on the ventral portion of the scapula. Four small *lateral interarcual* muscles originate from pharyngobranchial cartilages of visceral arches 3, 4, 5, and 6 and are inserted on the corresponding epibranchial cartilages (Fig. 11.18).

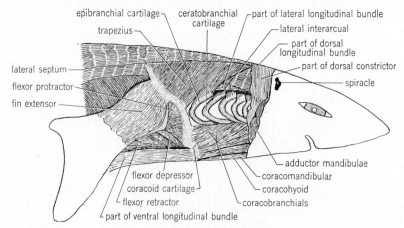

Fig. 11.18. Deeper muscles of shoulder and head of dogfish, *Squalus acanthias*. (*Original by Howell, J. Morphol.*, 54:401. *By permission of the Wistar Institute of Anatomy and Biology.*)

Since the trapezius and lateral interarcuales insert on epibranchial cartilages in series, it is believed that they represent specialized portions of a single levator group. The remaining representatives of the branchial musculature include more deeply situated *dorsal* or *medial arcuales* which connect adjacent pharyngobranchial cartilages.

Some authors consider that certain muscles ventral to the gill region should be included in the category of branchial muscles. Among these are *common arcuales*, a single *coracomandibular*, paired *coracohyoids* and *coracobranchials*. These muscles, however, are supplied by spinal nerves (hypobranchial nerve) rather than cranial nerves, indicating that they are actually hypobranchial muscles derived from anterior myotomes of the trunk musculature.

Homologues of the branchial muscles as found in higher forms have been determined mostly by tracing the visceral motor branches of the four cranial nerves which in fishes supply the branchial musculature.

The *adductor mandibulae*, derived from the first dorsal constrictor of elasmobranchs, gives rise in higher forms to the *masseter, temporal, internal pterygoid, external pterygoid*, and *tensor tympani* muscles. The *intermandibularis*, derived from the first ventral constrictor, gives rise to the *mylohyoid* and part of the *digastric* muscle of mammals. The ventral constrictor of the hyoid arch also contributes to the digastric muscle, the double innervation of which, coming from the trigeminal and facial nerves, bears witness to its homologies. Some of the muscles of the face, as well as the *platysma* of mammals, are thought to be derivatives of the hyoid constrictors. The constrictors of the remaining visceral arches are apparently not represented in higher forms.

The levator muscles of the visceral arches are also imperfectly represented in tetrapods. The *trapezius* (*cucullaris* of lower forms) and the *sternocleidomastoid*, or any of its variations such as the *sternomastoid* or *cleidomastoid*, are probably such derivatives. The voluntary muscles of the pharynx and larynx are undoubtedly derived from the branchial musculature, but their homologies are uncertain.

The anterior fibers of the eleventh cranial nerve (spinal accessory) of amniotes are so closely associated with the vagus that the muscles which it supplies are considered to be part of the branchial musculature. The sternocleidomastoid and the trapezius are such muscles. The trapezius in mammals is so obviously a muscle of the pectoral appendage that its inclusion among the branchial muscles might at first sight seem peculiar. This muscle may, however, have a twofold origin, since it is supplied by certain spinal nerves as well as by the spinal accessory (XI).

VISCERAL MUSCULATURE

The muscular tissue derived from the splanchnic layer of hypomeric mesoderm is, for the most part, of the involuntary, smooth type. An exception is the branchial musculature, already discussed, which is voluntary and composed of striated fibers. Smooth muscle is found in the walls of the digestive tract, in the ducts of digestive glands, in the walls of the respiratory passages, in the ducts of the urogenital system, in blood vessels, in lymphatic vessels in certain places, and in the spleen. The internal sphincter muscle of the anus is composed of smooth muscle as are such sphincters as the pylorus and ileocolic valve.

The peculiar cardiac muscle tissue, found only in the walls of the heart and the great vessels leaving the heart, is derived from visceral musculature. Its histological structure reveals it to be a somewhat intermediate type of muscle tissue having characteristics of both striated and smooth muscle.

The visceral muscles are more properly discussed in connection with the organs of which they form a part and will not be discussed further at this point.

DERMAL MUSCULATURE

Integumentary or dermal muscles appear, with few exceptions, only in amniotes. In some cases these muscles are attached firmly to some part of the skeleton and insert on the skin. Usually, however, both origin and insertion are in the integument. Most dermal muscles are derivatives of the parietal musculature from which they have become separated to varying degrees. Some, however, seem to have been split off the branchial musculature.

Fishes. Integumentary muscles, as such, are not present in fishes. The myocommata between myotomes are attached to the dermis, and the outermost muscle fibers of the myotomes are closely applied to the dermis. This, however, is not of the nature of a true insertion.

Amphibians. A few integumentary muscles may occur in salientians. The *gracilis minor* of the hind leg inserts in part on the neighboring *gracilis major*. It also has an insertion on the skin of the posterior region of the thigh. Another muscle, the *cutaneous pectoris*, which is located on the ventral side of the anterior part of the body, comes from the body wall and is inserted anteriorly on the skin between the forelegs. Otherwise, integumentary muscles are usually present in amphibians only in the region of the external nares. In caudates these are of the smooth involuntary type, serving to control respiratory currents. Rudimentary smooth muscles are also to be found about the external nares of salientians but, with few exceptions, are unimportant in opening and closing the nares. These amphibians utilize a different mechanism in occluding the nostrils. Movements of the premaxillary bones, which in turn move the nasal cartilages, are effective in closing the nares in most salientians.

Reptiles. Intrinsic dermal muscles in reptiles are of importance in moving the scales. Locomotion in snakes, aside from the wriggling, undulatory movements of the body proper, is accomplished by alternately elevating and lowering the ventral and ventrolateral scales. Erecting the scales provides a greater friction with the ground, furnishing a temporary anchorage from which the body can be pulled or pushed forward. *Costocutaneous* parietal muscles (Fig. 11.19), extending from ribs to scales, are also of great importance in progressive locomotion.

Birds. Movement of individual feathers in birds is accomplished by contraction of cutaneous muscles. The feathers can be made to lie smoothly or else erected to different degrees, thus enabling the bird to regulate heat radiation from the skin to some extent. The patagium, or web of skin which passes from the body to the wing, is provided with dermal *patagial* muscles. Stretching of the patagium increases the resistance of the wing to air during flight.

Mammals. Integumentary muscles are far more elaborately developed in mammals than in any other vertebrates. In such lower forms as monotremes and marsupials a broad sheet of muscular tissue, the *panniculus carnosus*, almost envelopes the entire trunk and appendages. Twitching movements of the skin, used to dislodge insects and other foreign objects, are brought about by contraction of this muscular sheet. Defensive movements of the European hedgehog and armadillos, *i.e.*, rolling into a ball when in danger, are brought about by contraction of an unusually well developed panniculus carnosus muscle. Originally derived from the *latissimus* and *pectoralis* muscles, the panniculus carnosus becomes reduced in higher forms. Remnants are most often encountered in the shoulder, sternal, and inguinal regions. In marsupials the inguinal portion forms the

FIG. 11.19. Semidiagrammatic sketch of inner side of ventral integument of snake, showing costocutaneous muscles extending from ribs to scales. The dermal layer of skin is not shown. (*Modified from Buffa.*)

sphincter muscle of the marsupial pouch. The cloacal sphincter of monotremes is also such a derivative. In horses and cattle the skin of the forelegs and shoulders can be twitched to ward off annoying flies and other insects. The posterior part of the body, which can be reached by the swishing tail, is not, however, provided with integumentary muscles to the same extent.

In lower primates both axillary and inguinal remnants of the panniculus carnosus are encountered, but in the higher apes and man only a few axillary slips may remain. A *sternalis* muscle appears occasionally even in man, overlying the pectoralis major.

In the head and neck region is another group of integumentary muscles derived from a muscular sheet, the *sphincter colli*, present in turtles and birds. The fact that these muscles are supplied by visceral motor fibers of the facial nerve (VII) indicates that they have been derived from the branchial musculature in the region of the hyoid arch. The *mimetic* muscles, or facial muscles of expression, are derivatives of the sphincter colli. In most lower mammals these muscles are poorly developed, and as a result, the facial expression of such forms does not change. In carnivores and primates, however, they are better developed, but only in man do they reflect emotion to a high degree. The original sphincter colli apparently forms two layers, an outer, or superficial, *platysma* layer and an underlying sphincter colli. The muscle fibers of these two layers course in opposite directions. Both layers form slips which serve to move special parts of the face.

From the platysma layer are derived such muscles as the *auricularis frontalis, orbicularis oculi, levator palpebrae superioris, mentalis, quadratus labii inferiores,* and *zygomatic.*

The deeper sphincter colli gives rise to the intrinsic muscles of the nose and to the *orbicularis oris, canine, buccinator,* and other muscles.

MISCELLANEOUS

Electric organs. Electric organs, consisting of modified muscular tissue, are to be found in numerous fishes. Noteworthy are those of the electric ray, *Torpedo,* and the South American electric eel, *Electrophorus (Gymnotus)*

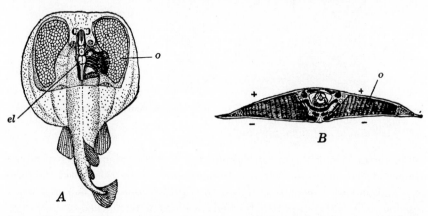

FIG. 11.20. Electric organs of *Torpedo marmorata: A,* dorsal view of entire animal, the upper surface being partially dissected away to show the electric organs, *o,* and the brain with electric lobes, *el,* from which the nerves pass to the electric organs; *B,* transverse section through the entire body at the level of the electric lobes of the brain, showing the electric organs, *o,* composed of flat discs, electroplaxes, arranged in vertical columns. The polarity of the current generated in the organ is indicated by plus and minus signs. (*After Dahlgren and Fritsch, from Wieman, "General Zoology," McGraw-Hill Book Company, Inc. By permission.*)

electricus. In *Torpedo* the electric organs lie on either side of the head between the gill region and anterior part of the pectoral fin (Fig. 11.20). In most fishes in which electric organs occur, however, they are confined to the tail. In *Electrophorus,* which grows to a length of 8 ft., the tail is very much elongated, forming approximately four-fifths of the total length of the animal. Here the electric organ is very well developed and occupies the position of the ventral longitudinal bundles. In both these fishes electric shocks of considerable intensity can be emitted at will, but those produced by *Electrophorus* are the stronger of the two. Charges of several hundred volts have been recorded. They are used by the animals in stunning or killing prey and also in self-defense. Several other fishes, including *Raja* and *Mormyrus*, possess this same ability, but the electric shocks which they produce are feeble in comparison with those mentioned above.

One of the catfishes of Africa, *Malapterurus electricus*, possesses an electric organ situated between the skin and muscles. In this fish the electric organ has been reported to be a derivative of the dermis rather than of muscular tissue. It thus differs from the electric organs of other forms.

The electric organs of fishes, with the possible exception of *Malapterurus*, are built upon the same general plan, regardless of position. Each organ is composed of many parallel prismatic columns separated from one another by partitions of connective tissue. The columns in turn consist of large numbers of minute *electric plates*, or discs (electroplaxes), piled one upon the other. Each electric plate is made up of three parts: (1) an outer *electric layer*, (2) a middle *striated layer*, and (3) an inner *alveolar layer*. The electric layer is actually composed of an outer nervous layer and an inner layer of cells with very large nuclei. Between adjacent plates lies a thick layer of gelatinous material which is thought to be metamorphosed muscle substance. The nerve fibers leading to the electric plates ramify through the connective tissue to terminate in fine networks on one side of each plate. The nervous layers of all the plates face in the same direction. These appear to be similar to motor end plates, and their relationships are like those of the endings of motor nerves on muscle fibers.

In *Electrophorus* the electric plates form columns which run in a longitudinal direction, but in *Torpedo* the columns are vertically disposed. In the former the electric current passes from the tail toward the head; in the latter, from the ventral to the dorsal surface.

The exact manner in which electricity is formed and stored in the electric organs of these fishes is not known with any degree of certainty. The fact that muscular activity produces electricity is well known and of great practical importance in electrocardiography. In any case the modified muscular tissue comprising the electric organs has developed the ability to store electricity to a remarkable degree.

The phylogenetic relationships of the electric organs are obscure. Since they occur in various parts of the body in different species of fishes, they are not even homologous within the group. This is further borne out by a study of their nerve supply. In *Torpedo* the electric organ is innervated by branches of *cranial* nerves VII, IX, and X, together with a single branch of the trigeminal nerve (V). The nerves arise from an enlarged portion of the medulla oblongata spoken of as the *electric lobe*. It is believed that the adductor muscle of the mandible and the constrictor muscles of the visceral arches have given rise to the electric organ of *Torpedo*. In *Electrophorus* and other fishes *spinal* nerves are distributed to the electric organs which are derived from the caudal musculature. More than 200 nerves pass to the electric organ in *Electrophorus*.

SUMMARY

The muscles of the vertebrate body are derived from the epimeric and hypomeric mesoderm of the embryo. The epimere, which becomes marked off into mesoblastic somites, forms segmentally arranged myotomes which give rise to the voluntary, striated, parietal musculature of the body. The hollow, unsegmented hypomere forms somatic and splanchnic layers enclosing the coelom between them. The splanchnic layer, which surrounds the gut, gives rise to the smooth, involuntary muscle of the gut and also to cardiac muscle. An exception is to be found in the voluntary branchial muscles of the gill region which are derived from the hypomeric mesoderm.

Parietal musculature. The parietal muscles consist primitively of a linear series of muscle segments, or myotomes, extending from anterior to posterior ends of the body. Each myotome lies opposite the point of articulation of two vertebrae and is supplied by a separate spinal nerve. Connective-tissue septa, the myocommata, occupy the spaces between adjacent myotomes. The myotomes of the two sides are separated at the midventral line by the linea alba composed of connective tissue.

Trunk musculature. In amphioxus, and to a lesser degree in cyclostomes, the myotomes tend to be V-shaped. In fishes they take more of a zigzag course. Beginning with elasmobranchs and in higher forms to a less conspicuous degree, the myotomes are separated into dorsal (epaxial) and ventral (hypaxial) portions. Each of these regions becomes subdivided into two or more longitudinal muscular bundles. In tetrapods the primitive metameric condition becomes more and more obscure as the evolutionary scale is ascended. This is brought about by a splitting into various layers, disappearance of myocommata, degeneration of portions of some myotomes, and a drawing out of position, a migration, or even fusion of others.

The epaxial musculature becomes reduced in higher forms but shows a tendency to split up into short and long systems of longitudinally directed muscles. The shorter ones connect adjacent vertebrae and are termed, according to position, interneural, intertransversarial, interspinal, multifidus, etc., muscles. The longer ones form such muscles as the longissimus dorsi, longissimus capitis, iliocostal dorsi, and spinalis dorsi.

The hypaxial muscles of tetrapods show greater modification than do those of the epaxial region. In caudate amphibians they split into four layers or sheets, the fibers in each sheet extending in a direction different from that of the others. These layers include the superficial and deep external obliques, an internal oblique, and a transversus. The last lies next to the peritoneum. On either side of the linea alba lies a rectus abdominis, derived from the obliques and with primitively arranged longitudinal fibers. In salientian amphibians the number of layers is reduced, but in reptiles additional layers are to be found in the thoracic region. An intercostal layer, derived from the obliques, makes its appearance. It in turn divides into external and internal intercostals which are attached to the ribs and are used in respiratory movements. Scalene and serratus muscles are also derived from the obliques. The hypaxial muscles in the thoracic region of mammals are somewhat reduced, being almost entirely covered by the large appendicular muscles of the pectoral girdle and limb.

Hypobranchial musculature. In cyclostomes and fishes, hypobranchial muscles, lying ventral to the gills, are derived from the hypaxial portion of the first few myotomes as buds which grow anteriorly. They are innervated by spinal nerves. In tetrapods these muscles have been greatly modified, but their innervation by spinal nerves bears witness to their origin. Among the muscles of hypobranchial origin are the sternohyoid, geniohyoid, thyrohyoid, sternothyroid, and omohyoid. The muscles of the tongue, supplied by cranial nerve XII, are considered to be hypobranchial in origin since this nerve, which is found only in amniotes, represents a union of the most anterior two or three spinal nerves of lower forms.

Eye muscles. The six extrinsic eye muscles of vertebrates develop from three pro-otic somites supplied by cranial nerves III, IV, and VI, respectively. From the first come the superior, inferior, and internal rectus muscles and the inferior oblique; from the second comes the superior oblique; and from the third the external rectus is differentiated.

Diaphragm. The diaphragm of mammals is composed partially of muscle fibers innervated by branches of certain cervical spinal nerves. The muscles, therefore, are believed to originate from cervical myotomes.

Appendicular musculature. In elasmobranchs hollow buds from certain myotomes grow out into the ventrolateral fin folds, accompanied by branches from corresponding spinal nerves. The original metameric arrangement of these buds is soon lost, but they give rise to the dorsal and ventral muscles moving the fins. No similar development of appendicular muscles from myotomic buds has been reported for higher forms, but in all other ways these muscles appear to be derivatives of myotomes. In tetrapods the dorsal and ventral masses differentiate into separate muscles. These are divided into extrinsic and intrinsic groups which provide for the greater freedom of movement required for terrestrial locomotion. When the complex musculature of a typical mammalian limb is compared with that of a primitive caudate amphibian, such as *Necturus*, many fairly clearcut homologies are indicated.

Branchial musculature. The striated, voluntary branchial muscles which move the visceral arches of fishes are derived from the splanchnic hypomeric mesoderm rather than from myotomes. They begin anteriorly at the mandibular arch and run in series to each of the successive visceral arches. The outer muscles serve as constrictors of the pharynx and are divided into dorsal and ventral portions. Deeper muscles serve as levators of the visceral arches. Even in fishes many of these muscles have deviated from the primitive condition, but their cranial nerve supply indicates their branchial origin. The mandibular branch of cranial nerve V supplies the muscles of the mandibular arch; the facial nerve (VII) goes to those of the hyoid arch; the third arch is innervated by the glossopharyngeal (IX), and the remaining arches by the vagus (X). In higher forms, in which the visceral arches have become greatly modified, the nerve supply to certain muscles of the neck and shoulder regions indicates that they have been derived from branchial musculature.

Visceral musculature. The smooth muscles of the hollow organs, the ducts of digestive glands, etc., as well as the cardiac muscle of the heart, all are developed from the unsegmented splanchnic layer of hypomeric mesoderm.

Dermal musculature. Integumentary, or dermal, muscles appear, with few exceptions, only in amniotes. They are, for the most part, derivatives of the parietal and branchial musculature from which they have become separated to varying degrees. In snakes the intrinsic muscles which erect the ventral scales are dermal derivatives. Movement of the feathers of birds is accomplished by integumentary muscles. Greatest development of all is to be found in mammals. In lower mammals a broad sheet of muscular tissue, the panniculus carnosus, almost envelopes the entire body. Its contraction causes twitching movements of the skin. In higher mammals this layer becomes reduced, so that remnants are found only in the axillary, sternal, or inguinal regions.

Another muscular sheet, the sphincter colli, present in turtles and birds, is most highly modified in primates, in which it gives rise to numerous "mimetic" muscles of facial expression.

Electric organs. Certain fishes such as the electric ray, *Torpedo*, and the electric eel, *Electrophorus*, possess electric organs which give off true electric shocks used to stun or kill prey and in self-defense. These organs are formed from highly modified muscular tissue. Their phylogenetic relationships and homologies are obscure.

CHAPTER 12

CIRCULATORY SYSTEM

Every living cell in the metazoan body is constantly undergoing metabolic change. Food materials in the form of glucose, amino acids, and fats must be supplied so that the anabolic phases of metabolism can take place. The cells must be furnished with oxygen so that they can utilize these food substances in the production of heat and other forms of energy and in carrying out their normal functions. Waste products of metabolism, *e.g.*, carbon dioxide, urea, uric acid, etc., given off by the cells, must be removed before they exert any deleterious effects. Hormones, the secretion products of endocrine glands, must be carried from one part of the body to other regions in order to be effective. Moreover, living cells must be kept moist in order to remain alive and to carry on their activities. This is necessary because every substance which enters or leaves the cells is in solution and can pass only through moist membranes or media. Cells that are exposed to air are usually dry and dead. Those making up the outer layers of the skin, hair, and nails, for example, are constantly being worn off or shed and replaced by new cells. All other cells are bathed by small amounts of fluid which keep them moist.

In members of some of the lower phyla most of the above functions are carried out by individual cells which are in direct contact with the environment. However, in the evolution of higher metazoan animals most of the cells making up their bodies have become further and further removed from the external environment yet their metabolic requirements have undergone little or no change. Circulatory systems of various types have developed in the evolution of higher forms in response to demands created by the increasing complexity of their bodies. Fluids carried by the circulatory system transport substances to and from cells even in the most remote parts of the body. The fluids must circulate, for only by this means can supplies of food, oxygen, and water be replenished and harmful waste products removed.

The circulatory system in vertebrates is highly complex and actually made up of two systems of elaborately branched tubes which ramify throughout the entire body and convey fluids to all the cells. These are the *blood-vascular* and *lymphatic systems*. The former is the better defined and the more obvious of the two.

Blood-vascular system. The blood-vascular system is composed of continuous tubes of various sizes known as *blood vessels* through which *blood*, a peculiar type of fluid connective tissue, is pumped to all parts of the body. This system consists of a muscular contractile organ, the *heart*, situated near the anterior end of the body and toward the ventral side. *Arteries* carry blood away from the heart. They subdivide into vessels of smaller caliber, the *arterioles*. These in turn branch into *capillaries*, which are extremely small vessels averaging from 4/1,000 to 12/1,000 mm. in diameter and 1 mm. or less in length. *Venules* collect blood from the capillaries. They combine to form *veins* which return the blood to the heart. Irrespective of the type of blood carried by the vessels, it should be clearly understood that *arteries carry blood away from the heart* and *veins carry it toward the heart*. The arteries and their branches make up the *arterial system*, and the veins with their tributaries form the *venous system*. The blood-vascular system is a closed system of blood vessels with no direct connection with any other system of the body except the lymphatic system, with which it is closely associated.

The arterial system in higher vertebrates is separated into *pulmonary* and *systemic divisions*, the former carrying blood to the lungs, the latter carrying it to all other parts of the body. The venous system likewise has pulmonary and systemic divisions, but, in addition, two or three *portal systems* may be present. A portal system is a complex of veins which begin in capillaries and end in capillaries before the blood which courses through them is returned to the heart. All vertebrates have a *hepatic portal system* in which blood collected from the digestive tract and spleen passes through capillaries (sinusoids) in the liver before reaching the heart. Adults of the lower vertebrate classes and embryos of higher forms have a *renal portal system* in addition, in which blood from the posterior part of the body passes through capillaries in the opisthonephric or mesonephric kidneys on its way to the heart. Another small but important portal system is found in association with the blood vessels draining the hypophysis, or pituitary gland.

Lymphatic system. The lymphatic system is composed in part of delicate tubes, the *lymphatic vessels*. They have their origin in very fine *lymph capillaries* which are blind at their free ends and drain the tissue spaces. Lymphatic vessels may form connections in various parts of the body with relatively large spaces called *lymph sinuses*. Some also join certain veins in the region of the heart, so that the connection between the blood-vascular and lymphatic systems is direct. The lymphatic system is a closed system, since the walls of even the lymphatic capillaries are composed of a delicate membrane made up of endothelial cells. The lymphatic system carries a fluid, *lymph*, the composition of which is, in general, rather similar to blood except that red corpuscles are lacking and the protein content is very much lower than that of blood plasma. In some animals, pulsating *lymph hearts* are present at points where lymphatic vessels enter certain veins. These aid in the propulsion of lymph into the blood-vascular system. In most forms, however, movements of the viscera and other parts of the body propel the lymph which, therefore, courses slowly through the vessels. Movement is in one direction since numerous valves are present which prevent backflow. In mammals, and to a lesser extent in birds, the lymphatic vessels are interrupted at certain places by the presence of *lymph nodes,* or *glands.* These are composed of a meshwork of reticular and collagenous connective-tissue fibers which support large masses of *lymphocytes.* Also present in lymph nodes are certain phagocytic cells known as *fixed macrophages.* These are formed from reticular cells. The lymphatic vessel breaks up into fine branches within the lymph node. The branches recombine on the other side of the node. Lymph filters slowly through the lymph nodes. Bacteria and other foreign substances are engulfed by the action of the fixed macrophages. It is here, too, that lymphocytes develop. These pass into the lymphatic stream and ultimately enter the blood-vascular system. Some of the macrophages also become free, wandering cells. The lymphatic system is of importance because lymph bathes all living cells in the body with fluid and serves as a medium of exchange between blood and the cells. The lymph nodes serve also to defend the body against invasion by bacteria and other injurious agents which might enter via the lymphatic pathway.

BLOOD VESSELS

Origin. The vessels of the blood-vascular system arise in embryonic development from mesenchyme *in situ* and are included among mesodermal derivatives. The first indication of blood-vessel formation is seen when small clumps or cords of cells, called *blood islands,* appear in certain parts of the embryo (yolk sac, body stalk, etc.). In a chick embryo, for example, at first the blood islands are solid but soon hollow out in such a manner as to form a thin, flat endothelium enclosing a fluid-filled space (Fig. 12.1). Some loose cells float about in the fluid and become blood cells, or corpuscles. The fluid, which is apparently secreted by the cells of the blood island, is blood plasma. The scattered, hollow vesicles derived from the blood islands grow and coalesce with one another to form an irregular, anastomosing network of small blood vessels. The vessels of the main part of the embryo appear as clefts in the mesenchyme. The endothelium of the original vessels proliferates, and the vascular area expands. After a primitive blood-vascular system is once established, the formation of new vessels depends upon growth and branching of previously established channels. Every blood vessel, including the heart, has an endothelial lining.

Structure. At first there is no structural difference between arteries and veins, and the early blood vessels are histologically similar to the capillaries of later stages. From the mesenchyme surrounding the endothelium of the primitive vessels are derived the coating layers found in arteries and

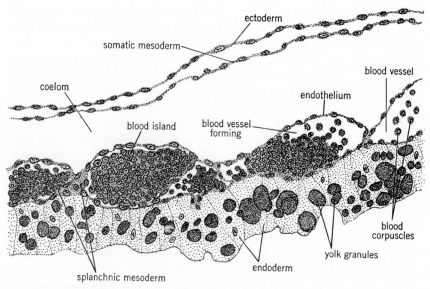

FIG. 12.1. Section through area opaca of chick embryo, showing formation of blood vessels from blood islands.

veins. The nature of the accessory coats differs in these two types of vessels.

Arteries. Every artery has a wall (Fig. 12.2) composed of three coats: (1) an inner layer, the *tunica interna,* or *intima,* which is composed of the endothelium and an *internal elastic membrane,* the structure of which differs somewhat in arteries of different caliber, (2) a thick intermediate coat, the *tunica media,* consisting of smooth muscle cells, arranged in a circular manner, as well as an elastic-fiber network also coursing circularly, (3) an outer layer, the *tunica externa,* or *adventitia,* of varying thickness in vessels of

FIG. 12.2. Section through adipose tissue adjacent to ovary of rat, showing structure of a vein and an artery.

different caliber, and made up of loosely arranged connective tissue as well as longitudinally arranged collagenous and elastic fibers. Large, medium, and small arteries differ to some degree in the detailed structure of their walls. In the tunica media of large arteries there is a preponderance of yellow elastic fibers in addition to smooth muscle cells. In general, the smaller the artery, the greater is the relative amount of smooth muscle and the less is the relative quantity of elastic connective tissue. The main distinction between large and small arteries, aside from actual size discrepancies, lies in the thickness of the tunica media.

The thick muscular and elastic walls of arteries are of great physiological significance. Blood, forced into the arteries by contraction of the heart, distends these vessels. Since backflow is prevented by certain valves in the heart, tension of the elastic walls of the larger arteries tends to force the blood farther along the vessel. This accounts for the greater part of the movement of the blood. The walls of the smaller arteries, which are predominantly muscular, are of importance in regulating the amount of blood supplied to a given area.

Veins. The walls of veins (Fig. 12.2) are much thinner than those of arteries but consist, nevertheless, of three similar coats. The tunica media is, in some cases, difficult to distinguish, particularly in the larger veins. Elastic and muscular elements are poorly developed in veins, but connective tissue is more clearly defined than in arteries. The tunica externa makes up the greater part of the wall of the vein. In birds and mammals, particularly those with long extremities, many of the medium-sized veins of the forelimbs and hindlimbs are provided with paired semilunar valves on the inner walls (Fig. 12.3). They prevent backflow of blood in the veins and are generally located distal to the point where a tributary enters a larger vessel. The valves are formed by foldings

semilunar valves

Fig. 12.3. Diagram of a portion of a vein and its tributaries, showing arrangement of semilunar valves.

of the tunica interna and contain elastic fibers. In general, the veins take the same course in the body as their corresponding arteries and usually are given similar names. A vein is always of greater diameter than its corresponding artery since its walls are thinner, not as rigid, and more capable of being distended.

In both arteries and veins of 1 mm. or more in diameter, the cells making up the walls are supplied with nutrient blood vessels of their own. They do not receive nutrient material and oxygen from the blood that is coursing through the vessel proper. The small vessels with which they are supplied are referred to as the *vasa vasorum* (vessels of the vessels).

These arise from the same vessel or a neighboring vessel some distance from the point where they are distributed. They are found in the tunica adventitia in both types of vessels but in veins may penetrate into the tunica intima.

Nerve fibers are abundant in blood vessels, particularly in arteries. They are of two types: medullated sensory fibers and nonmedullated autonomic motor fibers.

Capillaries. The endothelium of the capillary is its only component. Since it is at the capillary bed (Fig. 12.4) that exchange of gases, food materials, and wastes takes place between the blood and the extravascular fluids, the thinness of the capillary wall is of obvious advantage. Diameter

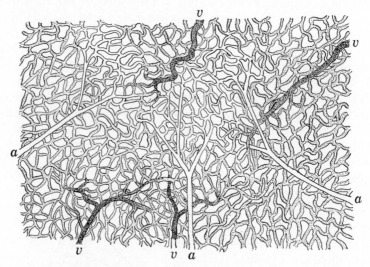

Fig. 12.4.   Diagram of a capillary bed: *a*, arterioles; *v*, venules.

of the capillaries is relatively constant for each species and is related to the size of the red corpuscles which pass through them. In man the average diameter is about 8/1,000 mm. They are seldom more than 1 mm. long. Lacking muscular and elastic coats, it has been a point of conjecture as to whether they are able to expand or contract of their own accord. In certain cases direct mechanical stimulation has been demonstrated to cause contraction of the endothelial cells which have thus been thought to be contractile. It is possible, however, that changes in diameter of capillaries may be passive rather than active and a reflection of alterations in internal and external pressures. In amphibians and some other poikilothermous vertebrates, peculiar cells having a number of long processes, called *Rouget cells,* surround walls of capillaries in certain regions. Contraction of the Rouget cells has in the past been thought to bring about contraction of capillaries, but this is now considered doubtful. Rouget cells may be nothing more than connective-tissue elements which have become located on the capillary wall. Some cells similar to Rouget cells have been described for mammals. They are too few in number to have any significance in capillary contraction.

Capillaries are so numerous that it is practically impossible to prick the skin in any part of the body without drawing blood. There are approximately 2,000 in a cubic millimeter of human muscle. It has been estimated that if all the capillaries in a man were stretched out in a single line they would measure nearly 150,000 miles.

The velocity of blood in arteries is high, but when these vessels break up into great numbers of capillaries, the corresponding increase in the vascular area brings about a considerable reduction in the velocity of the blood stream. Blood, therefore, courses more slowly through capillaries than through the larger vessels. Naturally, this is advantageous in the exchange of nutrient materials, gases, and wastes at the capillary bed.

Other vessels. In some regions there may be direct connections between arteries and veins without the intervention of a capillary network. Such vessels, which are called *arteriovenous anastomoses*, are to be found in the toes of birds, ears of rabbits, and such areas in man as the terminal phalanges of the fingers and toes, nail bed, lips, tip of tongue, nose, and eyelids. At ordinary temperatures they are closed, but when critical temperatures are reached, dilatation occurs. These vessels, according to one theory, serve in two capacities: (1) at high temperatures an increased volume of blood circulates at the surface, thereby permitting excess heat to be removed from the body by radiation; (2) at low temperatures increased circulation through these vessels prevents harmful effects which might be caused by cold. Another theory considers that arteriovenous anastomoses may be a mechanism which regulates blood pressure and circulation in various parts of the body. Their actual function is not completely understood.

Sinusoids make up another kind of connection between arteries and veins. They are unlike capillaries in structure and arrangement and are to be found in such organs as the liver, adrenal glands, bone marrow, parathyroids, pancreas, and spleen. They consist of relatively large, irregular, anastomosing vessels which, unlike capillaries with their rather constant diameter, are not lined with a continuous endothelial layer. Phagocytes and nonphagocytic cells, irregularly disposed, are present in their walls. Sinusoids are considered by some to represent a primitive form of capillary.

In some parts of the body, arteries or veins break up into capillary networks but the small vessels, which may or may not be tortuous, recombine to form larger vessels of the same type, *i.e.*, arteries or veins. Such connections of capillary dimensions are referred to as *retia mirabilia*. Examples of these structures within the course of arteries are to be found in the red bodies and red glands, in the swim bladders of certain fishes, and in the glomeruli of kidneys. The portal vein of the hypophysis, and the hepatic portal and renal portal veins which break up into sinusoids or capillaries in liver or kidney, as the case may be, are examples of venous retia mirabilia, since the capillaries in these structures recombine to form veins.

In the penis and clitoris a peculiar type of tissue, called *cavernous,* or *erectile, tissue* is to be found. It consists of large, irregular, vascular spaces interposed between arteries and veins. They are supplied directly by arteries. *Erection,* or distention, of the structure containing this type of tissue is due to a filling of the spaces with blood under high pressure and a partial closure or compression of the venous outflow.

HEART

The hearts of chordates differ from those in members of the lower phyla in their ventral, rather than dorsal, location. Blood is pumped anteriorly through arteries and is then forced to the dorsal side. The greater part then courses posteriorly where the arteries terminate in capillaries in various parts of the body. The blood finally returns to the heart through veins.

In the lowest chordates the heart consists of little more than a pulsating vessel which is sometimes referred to as a one-chambered heart. In cyclostomes and fishes the heart is still a tubular structure but is divided into a series of compartments which, in a posterior-anterior sequence, are called *sinus venosus, atrium (auricle), ventricle,* and *conus arteriosus,* respectively (Figs. 12.5, 15.7, and 16.12). The latter leads into a *ventral aorta.* Some authors refer to the hearts of cyclostomes and fishes as four-chambered hearts. This is confusing since the hearts of crocodilians, birds, and mammals, consisting of two atria and two ventricles, are also referred to as four-chambered hearts. The four chambers in the latter groups, therefore, do not correspond to the four compartments of more primitive forms. In the four-chambered hearts of higher forms there has been a division of both atrial and ventricular regions into two parts so that a double pumping mechanism is present. We shall, in the following pages, refer to atria and ventricles as *true* (in the sense of persistent) *chambers* and to the sinus venosus and conus arteriosus as *accessory chambers.* In higher forms the sinus venosus, as such, disappears since it is incorporated in the wall of the right atrium. Furthermore, the proximal part of the conus arteriosus in higher forms has become incorporated in the ventricular walls. Its distal portion and the ventral aorta have become separated, or split, into two or three arterial trunks so that the conus no longer serves as a separate compartment. Only the atrial and ventricular regions, therefore, serve as chambers throughout the entire vertebrate series.

The hearts of all vertebrates, during embryonic development, consist of a single tube which becomes twisted and compartmented in an increasingly complex manner as the evolutionary scale is ascended.   Embryological studies make it clear that definite homologies exist and that all vertebrate hearts are deviations from a relatively simple fundamental plan.

We shall, in the light of the above, consider the hearts of cyclostomes and fishes (except Dipnoi) to be two-chambered.   The conus arteriosus, coming from the ventricle, joins the ventral aorta anteriorly.   In some forms an enlargement, the *bulbus arteriosus*, is present at the proximal end of the ventral aorta.   It does not contain cardiac muscle tissue and is actually a part of the ventral aorta rather than of the conus arteriosus.   Sometimes the term *truncus arteriosus* is used as a synonym for ventral aorta.   Dipnoans, amphibians, and most reptiles have three-chambered hearts with two atria and a single ventricle.   Here the sinus venosus usually is reduced and joins the right atrium.   In crocodilians, birds, and mammals the heart finally becomes four-chambered with two atria and two ventricles.

In animals having two-chambered hearts the venous blood from all parts of the body is collected by the sinus venosus, which in turn enters the atrium.   In those having three- or four-chambered hearts, unoxygenated blood is returned to the heart through the sinus venosus or directly to the right atrium, as the case may be. Oxygenated blood, coming from the lungs, enters the heart through the left atrium.

FIG. 12.5.   Diagram of two-chambered heart, as found in cyclostomes and most fishes, showing atrium and ventricle with accessory chambers, the sinus venosus and conus arteriosus.

In lower forms the heart is located far forward in the body, but there is a gradual backward shifting as the vertebrate scale is ascended.   The heart lies in a *pericardial cavity*, which is surrounded by an investing membrane, the *pericardium*.   The pericardial cavity is a portion of the coelom which has been cut off from the remainder of the body cavity.   In such lower forms as elasmobranchs, the separation is incomplete and the two portions of the coelom are connected by a *pericardio-peritoneal canal*.   A thin, serous membrane, the *epicardium*, covers the surface of the heart.   It is similar to, and continuous with, the lining of the pericardial cavity.   It corresponds to the visceral pleura and the visceral peritoneum of the pleural and peritoneal cavities, respectively.

The heart is really a modified blood vessel.   Like other blood vessels it is lined with an endothelium, the *endocardium*.   This is surrounded by a thick muscular layer, the *myocardium*, composed of cardiac muscle tissue. Outside the myocardium lies the epicardium.

Just as the walls of blood vessels of greater caliber than 1 mm. are supplied with blood via the vasa vasorum, the tissues of the heart itself are furnished with blood vessels which bring oxygen and nutrient materials to them and remove wastes. These vessels make up the *coronary circulation* which consists of coronary arteries and veins. The blood within the chambers of the heart is too far removed from most of the tissues to be available to them. Furthermore, cardiac tissue, in order to function properly, must receive an adequate supply of oxygen. The blood in two-chambered hearts, and on the right side of three- and four-chambered hearts, has given off its oxygen supply and is inadequate in so far as furnishing oxygen to cardiac tissues is concerned. The constantly beating heart muscle perhaps uses more oxygen, per gram of tissue, than any other tissue in the body.

Origin of the heart. Although the adult heart is an unpaired structure, its bilateral origin is, in most forms, indicated by its mode of development. The ventral mesentery of the gut is concerned in the development of the

Fig. 12.6. Diagram showing method of development of heart of frog, *Rana temporaria.* (*After Schimkewitsch.*)

heart. In lower fishes and in amphibians a cavity appears in the ventral mesentery in the region of the foregut. This assumes a tubular form. From the surrounding mesoderm are differentiated the various layers of the heart. Since the ventral mesentery is formed by a coming together of the splanchnic mesoderm of the two hypomeres, the heart is basically a paired structure.

In the frog, for example, a pair of spaces appears in the mesoderm beneath the floor of the pharynx. These at first are separated from each other by a narrow strip of tissue. The lower layer of mesoderm (Fig. 12.6) is to become the parietal wall of the pericardial cavity. By a process of folding, the upper, or splanchnic, layer gives rise to the epicardium and myocardium of the heart. From the scattered cells beneath the floor of the gut comes the endothelium which forms the endocardium.

In the developing eggs of bony fishes, reptiles, and birds with their meroblastic cleavage, heart formation is somewhat different. At first the gut opens onto the yolk on the ventral side. Folds appear on either side of the midline and meet ventrally so as to close the gut (Fig. 12.7). In the region of the foregut, as this process is going on, the coelom widens to form a pair of *amniocardiac vesicles,* destined to give rise to the pericardial cavity. In the meantime a *vitelline vein* has developed from the mesoderm on either side of the foregut. With the closure of the foregut the two vitelline veins

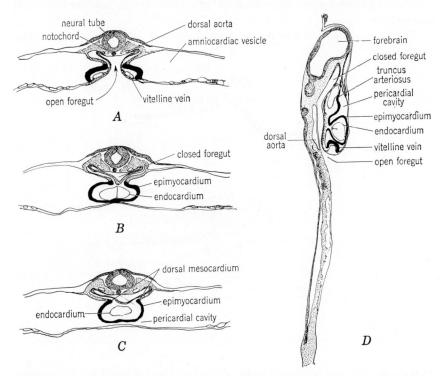

Fig. 12.7. *A–C,* transverse sections of 33-hour chick embryo, showing manner in which heart is formed; *D,* sagittal section of similar embryo.

are brought together in such a manner as to form the endothelial lining of the heart. Myocardium and epicardium are derived from thickenings in the splanchnic mesoderm on the medial sides of the amniocardiac vesicles. The fusion of the two sides leaves the primitive heart suspended from the mesoderm surrounding the foregut by a mesenterylike band of tissue, the *dorsal mesocardium,* which shortly disappears. A *ventral mesocardium* also forms, but its appearance is even more transitory than that of the dorsal mesocardium.

Heart formation in mammals differs somewhat from the foregoing account, and a bilateral origin is not so strongly indicated. The heart develops from the *cardiogenic plate,* a crescent-shaped plate of mesoderm lying anterior to the embryo. The head of the embryo gradually grows over this area so that the latter assumes a more posterior position. A space, the pericardial cavity, lies within the mesoderm just above the cardiogenic plate. As development progresses a process of folding occurs (Fig. 12.8) so that the cardiogenic plate comes to lie *above* the pericardial cavity. Two strands of cells which soon acquire cavities appear in the upper part of the cardiogenic plate. They fuse to become the endocardium of the heart. The remaining mesoderm of the plate forms myocardium and epicardium.

In all cases cited, the heart, when first formed, is a simple tube. The

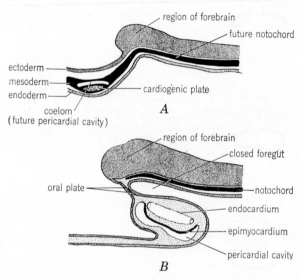

Fig. 12.8. Diagrams showing two stages in heart formation of human embryo.

appearance of constrictions, folds, and partitions of one kind or another results in the formation of two-, three-, or four-chambered hearts, as the case may be.

Comparative anatomy of the heart. *Amphioxus.* A single, median, contractile vessel lies ventral to the pharynx in amphioxus. By some authorities it is considered to be a one-chambered heart. Usually, however, it is spoken of as the *branchial artery*, *endostylar artery*, or *truncus arteriosus*. Its walls are provided with muscles which contract more or less rhythmically from posterior to anterior ends. On either side of the vessel lateral branches are given off which course through the primary gill bars. At the base of each lateral artery is a small, contractile enlargement, the *bulbillus* (Fig. 12.15). A single contraction of the "heart" followed by contraction of the bulbilli is sufficient to force blood through the entire body. It takes about 1 minute for the blood to make a complete circuit.

Contractions of the "heart" also occur at approximately 1-minute intervals. Since the primitive embryonic condition of the heart in vertebrates is that of a single tube, the "heart" of amphioxus is considered to correspond to an early stage of development of the heart in higher forms.

Cyclostomes. A two-chambered heart is present in cyclostomes. In the lamprey (Fig. 15.7) it consists of a large, thin-walled atrium which communicates with the ventricle by means of a small aperture guarded by *atrioventricular valves.* The ventricle lies on the right side of the atrium. It is smaller than the atrium and possesses thick muscular walls. The lining of the ventricle is irregular and provided with tough cords, the *chordae tendineae,* which connect to atrioventricular valves. The cords prevent the valves from being pushed into the atrium when the muscular

Fig. 12.9. Diagram of single type of circulatory system.

ventricle contracts. Blood is forced from the ventricle through a poorly developed conus into the ventral aorta which distributes it to the gills. A single set of two semilunar valves in the conus region prevents any backflow of blood. A small, thin-walled sinus venosus, which lies in the crevice between atrium and ventricle, opens into the atrium through a slitlike aperture guarded by a pair of *sinuatrial valves.* The sinus venosus receives three vessels: (1) a large, single, *common cardinal vein* on the dorsal side, (2) a small *inferior jugular vein* on its anteroventral side, (3) a small *hepatic vein* from the posterior side. The heart, which lies posterior to the last pair of gill pouches, is located in a pericardial cavity surrounded by a thick, tough pericardium. The pericardium fits into a concavity at the anterior end of the liver. In the ammocoetes stage the pericardial cavity communicates with the rest of the coelom, but the connection disappears in the adult.

Only unoxygenated blood passes through the cyclostome heart. The heart sends blood to the gills where exchange of gases takes place. This is known as the single type of circulatory system (Fig. 12.9) since but one stream of blood passes through the heart.

Fishes. The hearts of most fishes are essentially similar in structure to the two-chambered heart described for the lamprey. The single type of circulation is the rule. Variations in the relative positions of atrium and ventricle occur, but these are of minor significance. The arrangement of veins entering the sinus venosus also varies. The feature which perhaps deserves the greatest attention is the number and arrangement of the valves in the conus arteriosus (Fig. 12.10). These semilunar valves, which prevent backflow of blood into the heart, are most numerous in elasmobranchs and in the so-called ganoid fishes. In these forms the valves are arranged in three longitudinal rows, one dorsal and two ventrolateral in position. Several valves are present in each row. In *Neoceratodus* eight sets of valves are present. Many elasmobranchs have six sets. The valves of the anterior set are usually largest. The remainder decrease in size the more posterior their location. There is a tendency among fishes toward a reduction in the number of valves in the conus. Teleosts are characterized by having a single set, although in a few species (the lady fish, *Albula vulpes*, and the tarpon, *Tarpon atlanticus*) two sets are retained.

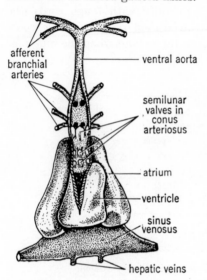

afferent branchial arteries

ventral aorta

semilunar valves in conus arteriosus

atrium

ventricle

sinus venosus

hepatic veins

Fig. 12.10. Ventral view of heart of dogfish, *Squalus acanthias.* The ventricle and conus arteriosus have been cut open to show the arrangement of the semilunar valves in the conus.

The first advance from a two- to a three-chambered condition is seen in the Dipnoi, or true lungfishes. In this group the atrium has become partially separated into right and left halves, or chambers, by an incomplete partition, or septum. In *Protopterus* unoxygenated blood from the body enters the right chamber via the sinus venosus, but oxygenated blood coming from the swim bladder (lung) enters the left atrium. Little mixing of blood occurs in the ventricle which possesses pocketlike cavities in its walls. An incomplete septum made up of fibrous and muscular tissue is also present in the ventricle and prevents mixing to some extent. In *Protopterus* the conus arteriosus has become divided into two parts so that the two streams of blood, one oxygenated and the other unoxygenated, leave the heart. This is known as the double type of circulation. The unoxygenated blood is sent to the posterior gill region and swim bladder, whereas the oxygenated stream goes to the anterior gill region and thence directly to the dorsal aorta. It will be recalled that gill lamellae are lacking in the anterior gill region of *Protopterus*.

A coronary circulation, supplying and draining the walls of the heart itself, is particularly well developed in elasmobranchs. *Hypobranchial arteries* carrying oxygenated blood usually arise from efferent arteries draining some of the anterior gills. The hypobranchials branch into various vessels among which are the coronary arteries going to the heart muscle (Fig. 16.13). Coronary veins, draining the wall of the heart, enter the sinus venosus close to the sinuatrial aperture. Similar vessels have been described in certain teleost and ganoid fishes, but in others a special coronary circulation does not seem to be evident.

Amphibians. A double type of circulation, similar to that of *Protopterus*, is characteristic of adult amphibians. Two streams of blood, one oxygenated and the other partially oxygenated, enter the heart. In am-

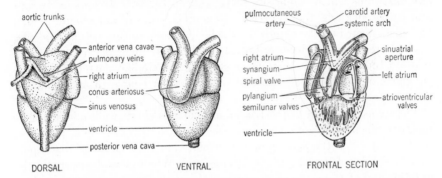

FIG. 12.11. Heart of bullfrog, enlarged. (*After Storer, "General Zoology," McGraw Hill Book Company, Inc. Drawn by R. Speigle.*)

phibians the sinus venosus has shifted in position so that it opens into the right atrium (Fig. 12.11).

The oxygenated stream coming from the lungs (also from gills via the lungs, in certain caudates) enters the left atrium and thence passes to the left side of the ventricle. The partially oxygenated stream composed of unoxygenated blood, from most of the body, mixed with oxygenated blood, from the lining of the mouth and from the skin, enters the sinus venosus from which it passes to the right atrium and thence to the right side of the ventricle.

The system of vessels coming from the lungs to the heart and those leading from the heart to the lungs is referred to as the *pulmonary circulation.* That which is distributed to the body in general and then returned to the heart is called the *systemic circulation.*

The *interatrial septum* is a thin membrane of connective tissue covered with endothelium. Perforations are frequently present in the interatrial septum of caudates but are of no special significance since little mixing of the two blood streams occurs here. The ventricle is not partitioned, but its lining is thrown into many pockets by muscular bands which, to a large extent, keep the blood coming from the right atrium separate from that coming from the left. Chordae tendineae fastened to the atrioventricular valves prevent blood from being regurgitated into the atria when the ventricle contracts.

Despite the presence of a single ventricle, the two blood streams, as previously mentioned, probably mix only to a slight degree. This, however, is not too important since the systemic blood entering the right side of the ventricle has, to a considerable extent, been oxygenated in the skin and lining of the mouth. Both these areas serve as important respiratory structures in amphibians which utilize buccal and cutaneous respiration in addition to pulmonary respiration.

Many amphibians have developed a rather complicated system of valves and partitions which ostensibly serve to keep the two streams fairly separate upon leaving the ventricle. There is some disagreement among biologists regarding the extent to which such a separation actually occurs. Variable results have been obtained by different investigators who have injected India ink, radio-opaque substances, and similar matter into different parts of the blood stream and followed their course to and from the heart.

The conus arteriosus bears striated muscle fibers in its walls and is, therefore, capable of contraction. It is made up of two regions. That part next to the ventricle is the *pylangium*. It is more muscular than the distal portion, which is referred to as the *synangium*. When viewed externally the anterior end of the synangium appears to divide into two trunks, each of which in turn separates into three arteries. The most anterior is the *carotid artery*, going to the head region; the second is the *systemic artery*, or *arch*, which gives off a few branches before the two systemic arches join each other posteriorly to form the *aorta* which in turn distributes blood to the rest of the body; the third, or *pulmocutaneous artery*, leads to the lungs and skin.

The internal structure of the conus is rather complicated. Two sets of semilunar valves are present in the conus, one set at the base of the pylangium, the other at the junction of pylangium and synangium. In most amphibians one of the latter has become modified to form the *spiral valve* (Fig. 12.11) which is generally believed to play a part in separating the two blood streams as they leave the heart.

The term *systole* is used to designate the contraction of the ventricle(s) of the heart. *Diastole*, on the other hand, refers to the state of dilatation of the heart, especially the ventricle(s), when it is being filled with blood coming from the atria.

The right atrium contracts slightly in advance of the left, and both streams of blood enter the ventricle during diastole. Little mixing of blood occurs in the ventricle. During systole the blood in the ventricle is forced into the pylangium, which leads from the right side. The atrioventricular valves prevent backflow into the atria. The mixed blood from the right side of the ventricle is the first to enter the pylangium, which then contracts in turn. The semilunar valves at the base of the pylangium prevent backflow into the ventricle.

In frogs the blood flows over the free edge of the spiral valve to the left side of the pylangium to enter a single aperture located just posterior to the synangial valves. This leads to the two pulmocutaneous arteries. The mixed blood, apparently following the path of least resistence, passes through the relatively short pulmocutaneous arteries to lungs and skin, being forced forward by contraction of the muscular wall of the pylangium. At the same time the wall of the pylangium is pressed against the free edge of the spiral valve. Therefore the remainder of the mixed blood, and the oxygenated blood which follows from the left side of the ventricle, passes through the pylangium on the *right* side of the spiral valve, finally entering the systemic and carotid arteries. A spongy mass, the carotid *"gland"* (which is not a gland at all), located at the base of the carotid arch, is believed to aid in keeping a rather constant pressure in the carotid vessels leading to the head. In salamanders all three pairs of arteries lead from the synangium. One would expect that under such conditions mixing of the two blood streams would occur in this region. Again, the results of experiments attempting to determine the extent to which separation occurs are controversial.

In perennibranchiate salamanders, such as *Necturus*, blood is sent to the gills for aeration. Blood going to the lungs through pulmonary arteries has already been oxygenated in the gills (Fig. 17.15). This would indicate that the lungs function but little as respiratory organs in such salamanders and may be used only in times of emergency.

Variations from the condition described above are to be found in the hearts of certain amphibians. The interatrial septum may be incomplete or furnished with numerous openings or a single, large aperture. This is true of the lungless salamanders and those aquatic forms in which the lungs have been reduced in size and function. The sinus venosus may open into both right and left atria, and the left atrium may be reduced in size. The spiral valve may be rudimentary or wanting in those forms in which no precise separation of the two blood streams occurs. Biologists are generally of the opinion that in its primitive condition the amphibian heart was three-chambered and capable of accommodating two separate blood streams. Any other conditions which are encountered, such as those mentioned above, may be considered to be specializations or regressions.

A special coronary circulation, supplying and draining the muscular wall of the heart itself, is apparently lacking in many amphibians. In the frog, the conus arteriosus receives a branch bearing oxygenated blood from the carotid artery. This vessel breaks up on the conus into a network of small vessels which recombine to form two small veins entering the systemic (left innominate) and hepatic portal (anterior abdominal) veins, respectively. These vessels are called the *vena bulbi anterior* and *vena bulbi posterior*.

Reptiles. The reptiles are the first group of chordates to become truly terrestrial. Except for certain aquatic turtles, which at times utilize cloacal respiration, lungs are the only respiratory organs. In this group, then, as well as in birds and mammals, an efficient pulmonary circulation is a necessity. With its development further changes have occurred in the structure of the heart.

Although a large sinus venosus is present in certain reptiles (turtles), in many it has been greatly reduced. Much of it may be incorporated within the wall of the right atrium. Valves which are present where veins enter the right atrium represent vestiges of the sinus venosus. A complete interatrial septum separates the oxygenated blood entering the left atrium from the unoxygenated blood in the right.

All reptiles have a three-chambered heart except crocodiles and alligators, in which it is four-chambered. Even in the three-chambered heart, however, the ventricle is partially divided by an incomplete *interventricular septum* which extends forward from the apex toward the center. The conus arteriosus no longer exists as such. Its distal portion as well as the ventral aorta have split into three main trunks (Fig. 12.22), each of which has a single row of semilunar valves at its base. One trunk is the *pulmonary trunk*, sometimes called the *pulmonary aorta*, which gives off two pulmonary arteries going to the lungs. The pulmonary aorta leaves the right side of the ventricle. The two remaining *systemic trunks* are called the *left* and *right aortae*, respectively. The left aorta leads from the right side of the ventricle and crosses to the left side; the right aorta leads from the left side of the ventricle and crosses to the right side. A small aperture, the *foramen Panizzae*, is located at the point where right and left aortae are in close contact and cross each other, so that their cavities are in communication. Even though the ventricle in most reptiles is only partially divided, the presence of an incomplete interventricular septum separates the two blood streams passing through the heart more effectively than is the case in amphibians. In the Crocodilia, in which a complete interventricular septum appears for the first time, a true four-chambered heart is found. Some mixing of blood occurs in these forms, however, at the foramen Panizzae and also at the point where left and right aortae unite to form the dorsal aorta.

In reptiles the right aortic arch, carrying oxygenated blood from the left side of the ventricle, gives off a large *brachiocephalic artery* which distributes blood to the anterior part of the body. At its base arise small coronary arteries which pass to the walls of the heart itself. A coronary sinus returns blood to the right atrium.

Birds. A completely double circulation (Fig. 12.12) occurs in birds for the first time, since at no point is there any opportunity for oxygenated and unoxygenated blood to mix. The sinus venosus has disappeared, and three large veins, two precavae and one postcava, enter the right atrium directly (Fig. 12.32). Pulmonary veins return oxygenated blood from the lungs to the left atrium. The heart in birds is relatively much larger and more compact than in forms previously discussed. Both atria are thin-walled. The ventricles are completely separated as in crocodilians. The muscular wall of the left ventricle is much heavier than that of the right and is par-

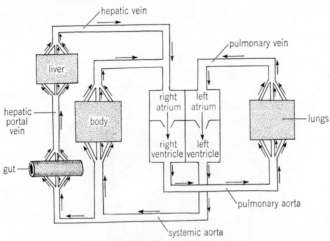

FIG. 12.12. Diagram of double type of circulatory system in a vertebrate having a four-chambered heart.

tially surrounded by the latter. Blood from the left ventricle is distributed over a considerable distance to all parts of the body, and a propulsive force of abundant power is required for such distribution. The relatively thin-walled right ventricle forces blood only a short distance through pulmonary arteries to the lungs. A single muscular and very well-developed valve separates the right atrium from the right ventricle. Two valves, however, known together as the *bicuspid valve*, are present at the left atrioventricular aperture. Chordae tendineae, which are fastened to the atrioventricular valves, are anchored at their other ends to the lining of the ventricle by heavy muscular projections called *papillary muscles*.

The main advance shown by the heart of the bird over the four-chambered crocodilian heart lies in the elimination of the left aorta. Only two vessels leave the heart in birds: a pulmonary trunk, or aorta, from the right ventricle, and a systemic aorta, corresponding to the right aorta of reptiles, from the left. A single set of three semilunar valves is present at the base of each.

In birds the circulating blood passes from the left ventricle to all parts of the body. It is collected by the two precaval and single postcaval veins and enters the right atrium. From here it passes to the right ventricle, which then sends it to the lungs for aeration. Oxygenated blood is returned to the left atrium which sends it past the bicuspid valve into the left ventricle.

A well-developed coronary system is present in birds. Coronary arteries arise from the systemic aorta. A venous, coronary sinus enters the right atrium near the entrance of the postcava.

Mammals. The four-chambered mammalian heart (Fig. 12.13) is essentially similar to that of birds, the two sides of the heart being completely

Fig. 12.13. Diagram showing internal structure of four-chambered mammalian heart, ventral view.

separated from each other by interatrial and interventricular septa. A thin area, the *fossa ovalis*, in the interatrial septum represents the position of an opening, the *foramen ovale*, which is present during fetal life. A sinus venosus, present only during early embryonic development, is lacking in the fully formed mammalian heart, having been incorporated into the wall of the right atrium.

When the atria are in a contracted state, a flaplike projection of each can be observed extending for a short distance over the ventricle. These are the *auricular appendages*. Although the inner lining of the greater part of each atrium is smooth, that of the auricular appendages is ridged by muscular bands, the *musculi pectinati*.

Some variations occur among mammals in regard to the number of systemic veins entering the right atrium. A single postcava guarded by a *valve of Eustachius* is present in all, but there may be either a single precava, as in man and the cat, or two precavae, as in the rabbit, rat, and others. Pulmonary veins, returning oxygenated blood from the lungs, enter the left atrium. Their number varies in different species.

As in birds, a *bicuspid*, or *mitral*, *valve*, consisting of two membranous flaps, prevents blood in the left ventricle from being regurgitated into the left atrium. Monotremes are exceptions in that the left atrioventricular valve is *tricuspid*. In most mammals a tricuspid valve, composed of three somewhat irregular flaps, is located between the right atrium and ventricle. Since a single valve is present in birds at this point, the presence of a tricuspid valve is a distinguishing feature of the mammalian heart. Chordae tendineae, attached to the irregular, ventricular surfaces of the bicuspid and tricuspid valves, are connected at their other ends either directly, to the inner walls of the ventricles and the interventricular septum, or indirectly to *papillary muscles* which are continuations of muscular ridges (*trabeculae carneae*) lining the inner surfaces of the ventricles.

In mammals, contrary to the condition in birds, there has been an elimination of the right aorta, so that only the left aorta persists. It arises from the left ventricle and distributes blood to all parts of the body. It is called *systemic trunk*, or *aorta*. The *pulmonary trunk*, or *aorta*, from the right ventricle carries unoxygenated blood to the lungs. A single set of three semilunar valves is located at the bases of both pulmonary and systemic aortae.

A well-developed coronary system is present in the mammalian heart. Right and left coronary arteries arise from the systemic aorta as it leaves the left ventricle and just distal to the semilunar valves. During diastole there is a rebound of blood in the aorta. The presence of semilunar valves prevents the blood from returning to the left ventricle. Some of the blood, however, is forced into the coronary arteries which distribute it to the tissues of the heart itself. Deoxygenated coronary blood is returned through several vessels which converge to enter the right atrium through the *coronary sinus* guarded by the *valve of Thebesius*. Other small openings, the *foramina of Thebesius*, are the openings of small veins, the *venae cordis minimae*, which return some blood to the right atrium directly from the heart muscle.

One form of heart failure, known as *coronary occlusion*, is caused by a blood clot or some other fragment blocking a coronary vessel. Death often results when the myocardium fails to receive its normal supply of metabolic substances. In some cases the area of myocardium supplied by the blocked vessel becomes necrotic. Either it forms scar tissue or the heart may rupture at the affected point.

Just as the walls of blood vessels are supplied with blood by the vasa vasorum, and the walls of the heart by the coronary circulation, the tissues making up the framework of the lungs, bronchi, and even the walls of the pulmonary vessels themselves receive a supply of blood distinct from that inside the pulmonary arteries and veins. *Bronchial arteries* and *veins*, branches of certain systemic vessels close to the heart, function in this manner.

Rhythmicity of the heart beat. The heart is capable of contracting rhythmically when removed from the body under experimental conditions. It would seem as though the impetus for contraction must arise within the heart itself. In the intact animal, however, the automatic beating of the heart is under the influence of nervous impulses. So-called cardiac centers in the medulla oblongata of the brain transmit impulses by means of efferent nerve fibers to the heart.

In the hearts of lower vertebrates waves of contraction may be observed to pass from the sinus venosus to atrium to ventricle. The "pacemaker," which regulates or initiates the rhythmic beat of the heart, is a bundle of atypical muscle fibers located in the wall of the sinus venosus. It is called the *sinuatrial*, or *sinuauricular, node.* In higher forms, in which the sinus venosus has been incorporated in the wall of the right atrium, the sinuatrial node lies embedded in the muscular atrial wall. Another mass of atypical muscle fibers, the *atrioventricular*, or *auriculoventricular, node*, located in the wall of the right atrium in the four-chambered heart, also acts as a pacemaker under experimental conditions when the sinuatrial node is destroyed or prevented from functioning. From the atrioventricular node a bundle of peculiar muscle tissue, the *bundle of His*, is distributed to the ventricular walls. The two nodes and the bundle of His are believed to be responsible for the rhythmic sequence of the heartbeat.

ARTERIAL SYSTEM

Although the arterial systems of various adult vertebrates appear to be different in arrangement, nevertheless a study of development reveals that all are built upon the same fundamental plan. The increasing complexity of the heart, from the simple two-chambered structure of lower forms to the four-chambered organ of crocodilians, birds, and mammals, is associated in part with the variations to be found in the blood-vascular system.

When the heart is forming in vertebrate embryos during development, a vessel, the *ventral aorta*, appears in the midline ventral to the pharynx. It soon establishes a connection with the conus arteriosus. At its anterior end the ventral aorta divides into two *aortic arches* which course dorsally in the mandibular region. Dorsal to the pharynx these are continued posteriorly, where they are known as the *paired dorsal aortae*. Additional pairs of aortic arches then appear, forming connections between ventral and dorsal aortae on each side. The aortic arches appear in sequence in an anterior-posterior direction, each coursing through the tissue between adjacent pharyngeal pouches. The typical number of aortic arches to form in vertebrates is six pairs (Fig. 12.14), although there are certain discrepancies among lower forms. The first aortic arch is known as the *mandibular aortic arch.* The second is the *hyoid aortic arch,* the remainder being referred to as the *third, fourth, fifth,* and *sixth aortic arches,* respectively. Each one lies anterior to the visceral cleft bearing the corresponding number. The two dorsal aortae soon fuse posterior to the pharyngeal region so that only a single dorsal aorta ultimately is present. It is continued into the tail region as the *caudal artery.* Various paired and unpaired vessels arise along the length of the dorsal aorta to supply all the structures of the body posterior to the pharyngeal region. Anterior continuations of the unpaired ventral aorta and the paired *radices* (singular, *radix*) of the dorsal aorta supply the head and anterior branchial regions. Although the method of branching of the dorsal aorta is fairly uniform throughout the vertebrate series,

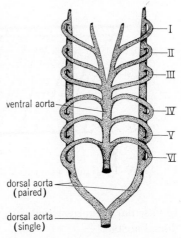

Fig. 12.14. Diagram illustrating the typical condition of aortic arches in vertebrate embryos, ventral view. Six pairs of arches connect dorsal and ventral aortae.

the aortic arches undergo rather profound modifications in different forms, the changes being rather similar in members of a given class. Blood, which is pumped anteriorly by the heart, passes through the ventral aorta to the aortic arches. These vessels then carry the blood to the paired dorsal aortae from which it either goes anteriorly to the head or posteriorly to the single dorsal aorta which distributes it to the remainder of the body. Veins return blood to the sinus venosus or right atrium, as the case may be.

Changes in the aortic arches. *Amphioxus.* The "heart" of amphioxus, sometimes called the *ventral aorta,* consists of nothing more than a single, contractile vessel lying ventral to the gill region. From the ventral aorta lateral branches, the *afferent branchial arteries,* are given off on both sides alternately. They extend up into the primary bars of the pharynx. In an adult specimen 60 or more pairs of afferent branchial arteries may be present. Each, as previously mentioned, bears a contractile enlargement, or *bulbillus,* at its base. The afferent branchial arteries give off small branches which connect with vessels in the secondary gill bars. The latter vessels have no direct connection with the ventral aorta, but those in both primary and secondary bars connect with the paired dorsal aortae by means of *efferent branchial arteries* (Fig. 12.15). The two aortae unite behind the pharynx to form a single median vessel which courses posteriorly. Oxygenation of the colorless blood takes place during its passage through the gill bars.

In amphioxus the aortic arches are much more numerous than in higher chordates. It is interesting to note that the vessels in the gill bars give rise

FIG. 12.15. Diagram of pharyngeal region of amphioxus, showing arrangement of aortic arches.

to vascular plexuses which supply the excretory tubules before joining the dorsal aortae.

Cyclostomes. The ventral aorta in cyclostomes is continued forward from the heart for a considerable distance. The number of aortic arches given off by the ventral aorta varies with the species and depends on the number of gill pouches. They are most numerous among the Myxinoidea, *Bdellostoma stouti* having 15 pairs. In the lamprey, *Petromyzon marinus*, which is representative of the group, 7 pairs of gill pouches are present. The ventral aorta leaves the heart as a single vessel which bifurcates at the level of the fourth gill pouch (Fig. 12.16*A*). Four afferent branchial arteries arise from each of the paired anterior extensions, and four pairs are given off by the unpaired portion. The first of the eight pairs of afferent branchial arteries on each side supplies the gill lamellae of the anterior hemibranch. The last furnishes blood to the most posterior hemibranch. Each of the remaining vessels arises at the level of an interbranchial septum and divides almost immediately to supply the lamellae on either side of the septum. Thus each holobranch is furnished with the two branches of an afferent branchial artery. Efferent branchial arteries, corresponding in position to the afferent vessels, collect blood from the gill lamellae (Fig. 12.16*B*). They join the single, median, dorsal aorta. The anterior end of this vessel is paired for a short distance, but the two portions come together again, thus forming what is referred to as the *cephalic circle*. From the circle arise arteries which supply the brain, eyes, tongue, and various parts of the head.

The salient features of the aortic arches in cyclostomes are (1) a reduction in number as compared with amphioxus, (2) the manner in which they break up into capillaries between afferent and efferent arteries.

Fishes. Much variation is to be observed in the aortic arches of fishes. In general, there is a reduction in number within the superclass as the evolutionary scale is ascended. The greatest number occurs in certain primitive sharks in which the number is directly related to the number of

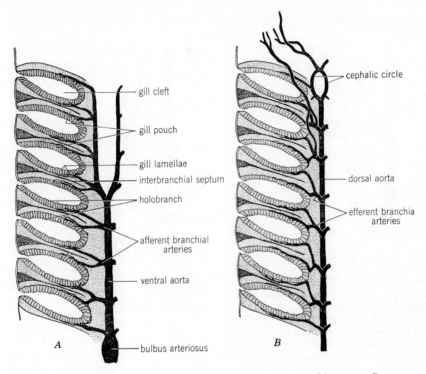

Fig. 12.16. Diagrams showing circulation through gill region of lamprey, *Petromyzon marinus*: *A*, ventral aorta and afferent branchial arteries; *B*, dorsal aorta and efferent branchial arteries.

gill pouches. In sharks of the genus *Heptanchus*, which have seven pairs of gill clefts in addition to the spiracle, there are seven pairs of aortic arches in the adult. Six pairs are to be found in adult selachians of the genera *Hexachus* and *Chlamydoselachus*. Since no hemibranch is present on the posterior wall of the last gill pouch, no arterial loop is present there.

Although in the rest of the fishes and in members of the higher classes the number of aortic arches is reduced or otherwise modified, practically all pass through a stage in embryonic development in which six pairs of aortic arches connect ventral and dorsal aortae (Fig. 12.14). Six, then, should be thought of as the primitive number of aortic arches for vertebrates whose ancestors undoubtedly possessed a greater number. The anterior continuations of the paired dorsal aortae (*radices*) give rise to the *internal carotid arteries* supplying the brain. Those of the ventral aorta form the *external carotid arteries* which supply the jaws and face. In most fishes each aortic arch, except the first, or mandibular, consists of afferent and efferent branchial portions with a capillary network interposed between. It is in the capillary network of the gill lamellae that aeration of the blood occurs. The afferent branchial arteries, as they leave the ventral aorta, course *through* the interbranchial septa, contrary to the condition

FIG. 12.17. Diagram of aortic arch region as found in most teleost fishes, ventral view. Arches I and II have degenerated. Each of the remaining arches is divided into afferent and efferent branchial arteries connected with each other by gill capillaries.

FIG. 12.18. Diagram showing modification of aortic arches as found in salientian amphibians, ventral view.

in cyclostomes, described above. The blood collected by pretrematic and posttrematic branches of the efferent branchial arteries passes to the radices of the aorta. In *Protopterus* the third and fourth aortic arches pass directly to the dorsal aorta without interruption, no internal gills being associated with these vessels.

In sharks, other than those mentioned above, only five aortic arches persist, the first having been lost or modified. Although five afferent branchial arteries are present on each side, there are usually but four pairs of efferent vessels (Fig. 16.13).

In teleost fishes and most others only the last four pairs of aortic arches remain, numbers 1 and 2 having disappeared or having been reduced to small branches of the third (Fig. 12.17). In Cladistia and Dipnoi a pulmonary artery arises from each sixth arch (or from the dorsal aorta) through which blood is carried to the swim bladder.

Amphibians. In amphibians and in the remaining vertebrate classes there is a further reduction in the number of aortic arches together with a greater modification of the entire complex of vessels in the pharyngeal region. The aortic arches do not break up into afferent and efferent portions since in these higher forms internal gill lamellae do not develop. To be

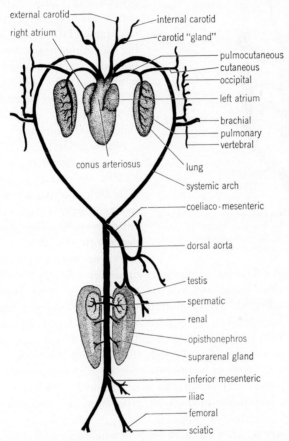

external carotid

internal carotid

right atrium

carotid "gland"

pulmocutaneous

cutaneous

occipital

left atrium

brachial

pulmonary

vertebral

conus arteriosus

lung

systemic arch

coeliaco·mesenteric

dorsal aorta

testis

spermatic

renal

opisthonephros

suprarenal gland

inferior mesenteric

iliac

femoral

sciatic

Fig. 12.19.   Diagram of arterial system of frog, ventral view.

sure, amphibians possess external gill filaments, at least during early development, but these are not homologous with the internal gill lamellae of fishes, nor are they supplied with blood in the same manner (pages 205, 524).

In salientians (Fig. 12.18), aortic arches 1, 2, and 5 disappear. The radix between arches 3 and 4 on each side gradually dwindles away. The anterior continuations of the ventral aorta become the external carotid arteries. The third arch together with the anterior portion of the radix of the aorta on that side becomes the internal carotid artery. A stapedial branch represents a remnant of the second aortic arch. The portion of the ventral aorta from which the internal and external carotid arteries arise becomes the common carotid. The fourth aortic arches persist to become the systemic arches, which unite posteriorly to form the dorsal aorta proper (Fig. 12.19). Arch 6 on each side sends a branch to the developing lung and to the skin, thus becoming the pulmocutaneous artery. The portion of arch 6 between the pulmonary artery and the radix is called the *ductus arteriosus*, or *duct of Botallus*. It disappears at the time of metamorphosis.

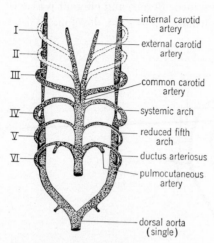

FIG. 12.20. Diagram showing modification of aortic arches as found in most caudate amphibians, ventral view.

Slight differences from the above are to be found in caudates (Fig. 12.20). In certain salamanders the fifth arch may persist in very much reduced form. Frequently the radix between aortic arches 3 and 4 fails to degenerate completely. The ductus arteriosus also persists in caudates.

The external gills of larval caudate amphibians are supplied with vascular loops connecting dorsal and ventral aortae. The loops themselves are composed of afferent and efferent vessels connected by a capillary network. They lie lateral to the aortic arches. The latter are located at the bases of the gills, each serving as a gill bypass. Blood may pass directly through the aortic arches or through the adjacent gill loops. In caudate amphibians at the time of metamorphosis the gills degenerate and the vascular loops atrophy. However, the main channel of each aortic arch concerned, which has maintained its integrity from the beginning, continues to persist.

Salientian larvae, after an early stage in which external gills like those of caudates are present (Fig. 12.21), develop peculiar gills enclosed by opercular folds. The continuity of the aortic arches is then temporarily interrupted. Upon metamorphosis, however, the arches again become continuous structures.

Certain caudate amphibians, such as *Necturus*, are called *perennibranchiates* since they retain their gills throughout life and fail to undergo metamorphosis. Attempts to induce metamorphosis in *Necturus* under experimental conditions have resulted in failure. The reason for this has long puzzled zoologists. A morphological explanation has been suggested (F. H. Figge, 1930, *J. Exptl. Zool.*, **56**:241), but its validity has been questioned. It seems that aortic arches 3, 4, and 5 persist in *Necturus* and that the ventral portion of arch 6 is missing. The dorsal portion of arch 6, representing the ductus arteriosus, is present, however, and connects the efferent portion of arch 5 to the pulmonary artery which supplies the lung (Fig. 17.15). In effect, then, the pulmonary artery comes off the fifth arch rather than the sixth as is usually the case. Blood going to the lung in *Necturus*, therefore, must first pass through a gill and has already been oxygenated. The pulmonary system, as a consequence, is of little value except in times of emergency when the oxygen content of the water may be depleted.

Experiments on larvae of the salamander *Ambystoma tigrinum* have been suggestive in this connection. In these larvae aortic arches 3, 4, 5,

Fig. 12.21. Diagrammatic cross section through gill region of early frog tadpole, showing relation of aortic arches to blood vessels in the external gills. (*After Maurer.*)

and 6 are present on each side although number 6 does not supply a gill. It gives off a pulmonary artery to the developing lung but has a short connection, the ductus arteriosus, with the fifth efferent branchial artery. Animals in which the ventral portion of aortic arch 6 has been cut or ligated fail to metamorphose even after thyroid substance has been administered. In such cases the condition which normally occurs in *Necturus* has been simulated experimentally in *Ambystoma tigrinum*. Blood going to the lungs, therefore, has been oxygenated in the fifth aortic arch, and the lungs function very little, if at all. In normal specimens of *Ambystoma tigrinum* at the time of metamorphosis the lungs begin to function as respiratory organs and the gills with their vessels are reduced. It has been suggested that in *Necturus* and in operated specimens of *Ambystoma tigrinum* it is impossible for the lungs to function because they receive only oxygenated blood. Therefore the gills are retained, and metamorphosis fails to occur. Other factors in *Necturus*, such as the absence of a spiral valve in the conus arteriosus, may also bear some relation to this peculiar state of affairs.

Reptiles. Just as in amphibians, reptiles retain aortic arches 3, 4, and 6. The fifth arch may also be retained in reduced form in certain lizards, and a remnant of the radix between arches 3 and 4 may persist on each side in certain snakes. In most reptiles, however, further modifications occur in the aortic arches. These consist chiefly of a splitting of the distal portion of the conus arteriosus and the ventral aorta into three vessels (Fig. 12.22). The fourth aortic arch on the left side establishes a separate connection with the right side of the partially divided ventricle. It, together with a portion of the radix on the left side, becomes the *left arch of the aorta*. The sixth arch on each side gives off a pulmonary artery to the lung and in most cases loses its connection (ductus arteriosus) with the radix. It persists to a minor degree in some turtles and in *Sphenodon*. The two pulmonary arteries arise from a common trunk, the *pulmonary aorta*, from the right side of the ventricle. The remaining vessel derived from the truncus arteriosus connects to the left side of the ventricle and, as it courses forward,

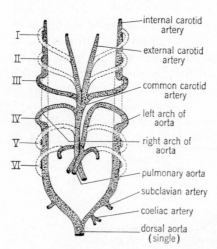

internal carotid artery

external carotid artery

common carotid artery

left arch of aorta

right arch of aorta

pulmonary aorta

subclavian artery

coeliac artery

dorsal aorta (single)

Fig. 12.22. Diagram showing modification of the aortic arches as found in reptiles, ventral view. The ventral aorta (truncus arteriosus) has split into three vessels: right and left systemic aortae and a pulmonary aorta.

gives off the fourth aortic arch on the right side and finally divides into the two common carotid arteries with their external and internal branches. The right fourth aortic arch together with a portion of the radix on that side becomes the *right arch of the aorta* which joins the posterior continuation of the left arch to form the dorsal aorta proper. A coeliac artery supplying certain viscera arises from the left aorta near its junction with the right. The portion of the left aorta between the coeliac artery and the dorsal aorta proper is somewhat reduced since the major portion of the blood in the left aorta passes into the coeliac artery. Right and left subclavian arteries arise from the right and left aortae, respectively, in those reptiles having pectoral limbs.

Since the right aorta bears mostly oxygenated blood and the left chiefly unoxygenated blood, mixing occurs in the dorsal aorta proper where these two vessels come together. Some mixing may also occur through the *foramen Panizzae* which joins the right and left aortae as they emerge from the heart. In crocodilians, in which two completely separated ventricles are present, mixing of blood occurs, as in other reptiles, at the foramen Panizzae and at the point where right and left aortae unite to form a single vessel. Mixing of oxygenated and unoxygenated blood seems to be associated with the poikilothermous mode of life.

Birds. The chief changes taking place in the aortic arches of birds correspond to those of reptiles. There is one important difference, however

(Fig. 12.23). In birds the fourth arch and radix on the left side lose their connection with the dorsal aorta and finally disappear. The ventral aorta splits into two portions, a systemic aorta and a pulmonary aorta, or trunk. The systemic aorta is connected to the left ventricle, and the pulmonary aorta to the right.

The fourth aortic arch on the right side leaves the systemic aorta and, together with the radix, leads to the main arterial channel, or dorsal aorta proper, supplying the entire body with oxygenated blood. At its anterior end the systemic aorta gives rise to external and internal carotid arteries in the same manner as described for previous groups. The fourth aortic arch on the left may possibly contribute to the left subclavian artery, but this vessel is usually a branch of the third aortic arch. The right subclavian artery either comes off the right radix or off the third aortic arch on the right side.

The pulmonary aorta leading from the right ventricle gives off the pulmonary arteries which are actually outgrowths of the sixth aortic arches. Until the time of hatching there is a ductus arteriosus on each side, representing the portion of aortic arch 6 between pulmonary artery and radix. These serve as shunts from the right ventricle to the dorsal aorta at a time when the lungs are not functioning. They close at the time of hatching, and all the blood in the right ventricle is then sent to the lungs for aeration. A cord of connective tissue on each side, the *ligamentum arteriosum*, or *ligamentum Botalli*, is all that remains of the former arterial shunt.

Mammals. The changes in the aortic arches of mammals are rather similar to those of birds except that the radix on the *right* side rather than the left loses its connection with the aorta (Fig. 12.24). The fourth aortic arch on the left side together with its radix, therefore, becomes the arch of

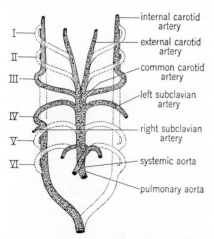

FIG. 12.23. Diagram showing modification of aortic arches as found in birds, ventral view.

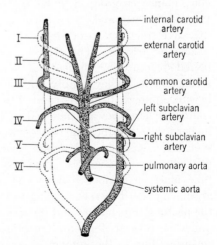

FIG. 12.24. Diagram showing modification of aortic arches as found in mammals, ventral view.

the definitive aorta. The fourth arch on the right and a portion of the right radix become the right subclavian artery, and the left subclavian develops as an enlargement of one of the intersegmental arteries coming off the aorta in this region. There is much variation among mammals in the manner in which the subclavian arteries arise. In mammalian embryos there is at first a ductus arteriosus on each side, but the one on the right persists only for a short time. The left one, which serves as a shunt between pulmonary and systemic aortae, persists until birth when it finally becomes occluded. A ligamentum arteriosum of connective tissue is finally all that remains.

In mammals, the actual presence of a fifth aortic arch during development has been questioned. However, remnants of a fifth arch have been observed in certain mammalian embryos, and there is little reason to doubt that mammals are similar to other vertebrates in passing through a primitive stage in which six aortic arches are present. In some mammals the dorsal part of the second aortic arch persists to become the stapedial artery with which the external carotid artery forms connections. Remnants of the first aortic arch may contribute to the mandibular artery.

The study of changes in the aortic arches of birds and mammals is one of the most striking illustrations of the law of biogenesis.

Remainder of the arterial system. The arteries supplying the head region are, for the most part, branches of the external and internal carotids. In some forms, branches of the fourth aortic arches or of the subclavian arteries also pass to the cephalic region. The occipitovertebral and vertebral arteries are examples. The aorta is continued posteriorly into the tail region where it becomes the *caudal artery*. Most of the vertebrate body is supplied with blood through branches of the dorsal aorta which may for convenience be grouped under two divisions: somatic arteries, supplying the body proper, and visceral arteries, distributed to various portions of the digestive tract and associated structures.

Somatic arteries. The arteries supplying the body proper are usually paired structures which clearly show evidences of metamerism or segmental arrangement. They supply portions of the body derived from the embryonic epimere, being distributed to the dorsal musculature and vertebral column, where they are referred to as *parietal*, or *segmental, arteries*. In higher forms, in which the body is divided into more or less definite regions, such terms as *intercostal, dorsolumbar*, and *sacral* are applied to these segmentally arranged vessels. Fusion of two or more segmental arteries may take place in various regions and obscure the fundamental metameric arrangement. The vessels going to the appendages, *i.e.*, the *subclavians* to the pectoral appendages and the *iliacs* to the pelvic, may be composed of a union of several segmental arteries, the number of vessels concerned corresponding to the number of somites involved in the formation of the limb.   During development a considerable shifting of vessels leading to the appendages occurs, and the end result shows little evidence of metameric origin.

Visceral arteries.   The arteries supplying the viscera are of two kinds, paired and unpaired.   The paired arteries are segmentally arranged and supply portions derived from the embryonic mesomere, or nephrotome, from which the urogenital organs and their ducts arise.   Although the mesomere itself is, for the most part, unsegmented, the arteries supplying its derivatives show pronounced evidences of metamerism, particularly in regard to the manner in which they supply the pronephric, opisthonephric, and mesonephric kidneys.   Such terms as *renal, genital, ovarian, spermatic, and urogenital arteries* are applied to the paired visceral arteries.   Renal and genital arteries are numerous in the lower vertebrates, but the number is markedly reduced in higher forms.

The unpaired visceral arteries supplying the spleen and the digestive track, and its derivatives, are vessels which course through the dorsal mesentery of the gut.   They branch profusely, the method of branching showing great variation even in members of the same species.   There are usually three unpaired visceral arteries in vertebrates.   The most anterior of these is the *coeliac artery,* supplying the anterior viscera, including stomach (*gastric*), spleen (*splenic* or *lienal*), pancreas (*pancreatic*), liver (*hepatic*), and duodenum (*duodenal*).

The second unpaired visceral artery is the *superior mesenteric* which supplies the entire length of the small intestine with the exception of the pyloric end of the duodenum.   This is taken care of by the coeliac artery. Branches of the superior mesenteric at its anterior end also supply a portion of the pancreas.   The remainder of the vessel is distributed to the caecum and upper half of the large intestine.

The third unpaired artery is the *inferior mesenteric,* supplying the posterior part of the large intestine and rectum.

Variations from the above condition may be accounted for by fusions or separations.   For example, in frogs and other amphibians, the coeliac and superior mesenteric arteries have united into a single coeliacomesenteric artery.   In the dogfish, *Squalus acanthias,* an unpaired gastrosplenic artery arises directly from the aorta just posterior to the origin of the superior mesenteric to supply the spleen and posterior part of the stomach. It actually represents a branch of the superior mesenteric which has become secondarily connected with the aorta.

Certain arteries play an important role during embryonic development and are, therefore, of unusual significance.   The superior mesenteric artery, for example, is derived embryonically from a fusion of paired *vitelline arteries* which originally branch off the aorta to supply the yolk sac (Fig. 12.25).   A pair of *umbilical,* or *allantoic,* arteries, also present during de-aortic arches I to IV

anterior cardinal vein

conus

sinus venosus

common cardinal vein

dorsal aorta

postcardinal vein

vitelline vein

atrium
ventricle

ductus venosus

vitelline artery

Fig. 12.25. Seventy-two-hour chick embryo, showing the main parts of the circulatory system, dorsal view.

velopment in higher forms, is lost at the time of hatching or birth. Their remnants are known as the *hypogastric*, or *internal iliac*, arteries, which branch to supply urinary bladder, rectum, tail, and thigh.

VENOUS SYSTEM

As in the case of the arterial system, a comparison of veins in the various vertebrate groups shows that they are arranged according to the same fundamental plan and that the variations encountered form a logical sequence as the vertebrate scale is ascended. In its development, the venous system of higher forms passes through certain stages common to the embryos of lower forms.

There is some difference in the formation of the earliest veins which appear in an embryo, depending upon whether or not a yolk sac is present. In forms without a yolk sac, a pair of *subintestinal* veins appears in the splanchnic mesoderm ventral to the gut. These veins soon fuse except in the region of the anus around which they form a loop, only to unite posteriorly where they continue on into the tail as the *caudal* vein. In animals having a yolk sac, a pair of *vitelline* (*omphalomesenteric*) veins, draining the yolk sac (Fig. 12.25), joins the posterior end of the heart. Indeed, their fusion is primarily responsible for heart formation. The part of the heart into which the vitelline veins enter is destined to become the *sinus venosus*. The vitelline veins are concerned with obtaining nourishment used by the embryo during its development. Even though the yolk sac in mammals contains no yolk, vitelline veins (and arteries) are present. Each vitelline vein is joined posteriorly by a subintestinal vein arranged in a manner similar to that in forms in which a yolk sac is lacking.

Before long, two additional pairs of veins, *anterior cardinals* from the dorsal side of the head region and *posterior cardinals* from the posterior end of the body, establish connections with the fused vitelline veins. They join the sinus venosus on each side by a common vessel variously known as the *common cardinal, duct of Cuvier,* or *Cuvierian sinus.* The anterior cardinals are generally referred to as *jugular* veins which receive *internal* and *external* tributaries. In fishes and salamanders an *inferior jugular* vein, draining the ventrolateral portions of the head, also enters the common cardinal on each side. It apparently has no homologues in higher forms.

In lower vertebrates a pair of *ventral abdominal* or *lateral abdominal* veins, located in the ventral or lateral portions of the body wall, also enters the common cardinal veins. In amniotes these veins form secondary connections with vessels draining the allantois. Blood in the allantois or umbilical cord, as the case may be, therefore, courses through the abdominal veins in the body wall and enters the sinus venosus via the common cardinal veins. The term *allantoic,* or *umbilical,* veins is then applied to these vessels in amniote embryos. Although both left and right umbilical veins are present in reptiles, only the left persists in birds and mammals. When the liver develops, the umbilical veins lose their connection to the sinus venosus and course through the liver via a large channel, the *ductus venosus,* which in turn connects with the sinus venosus.

From the primitive venous complex just described (Fig. 12.26) are derived the principal veins of the body. Changes in the course of the blood as it returns to the heart account for the variations observed in venous vessels which, nevertheless, show a consistent arrangement within each vertebrate class. The vitelline and umbilical vessels are lost, as such, at birth or hatching, but remnants persist even in adult life.

The primitive veins so far described correspond, in the main, to the chief divisions of the arteries but are not generally so clear-cut. The vitelline veins and the subintestinals give rise to the *unpaired visceral* veins, which later drain the digestive tract and its associated organs. They become lo-

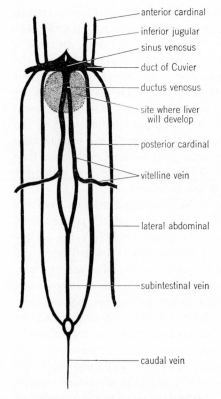

anterior cardinal
inferior jugular
sinus venosus
duct of Cuvier
ductus venosus
site where liver will develop
posterior cardinal
vitelline vein
lateral abdominal
subintestinal vein
caudal vein

Fig. 12.26. Diagram of primitive venous complex from which the venous systems of vertebrates are derived, ventral view.

cated in the mesentery of the gut. *Paired lateral visceral* veins drain the urogenital organs derived from the embryonic mesomere. *Somatic* veins are generally paired structures which drain the body wall.

Hepatic portal circulation. All vertebrates have a hepatic portal system. A portal system, it will be recalled, is a system of veins that breaks up into a capillary network before the blood which courses through it is returned to the heart. It is the vitelline-subintestinal group of vessels which is concerned in the formation of the hepatic portal system.

In an embryo the liver develops as an outgrowth of the gut in the region just posterior to the heart. As the liver grows out it soon surrounds the vitelline (or subintestinal) veins. These veins break up into a network of small vessels (sinusoids) which ramify through the liver. Posterior to the liver several anastomoses, or junctures, form between the vitelline veins. The right vessel gradually dwindles away, leaving the left vitelline vein with its subintestinal tributary as the main vessel draining the digestive tract. This then becomes the hepatic portal vein which collects blood from all portions of the alimentary canal as well as the spleen. It enters the liver, where it breaks up into sinusoids. The original connections of the vitelline veins to the sinus venosus become the *hepatic* veins which return the blood collected from the liver sinusoids to the heart.

Venous systems of different chordates. *Amphioxus.* The veins of amphioxus represent the vertebrate venous system reduced to its simplest terms. The caudal vein from the tail is continued forward as the subintestinal vein. It also connects to the postcardinal on each side, so that blood can be returned from the tail via either channel. An anterior cardinal joins the postcardinal on each side, and they enter the posterior end of the heart (sinus venosus) by means of a common cardinal vein. The subintestinal vein breaks up in capillaries in the intestine. Another vein, beginning in capillaries in the intestine, leads to the hepatic caecum, where it breaks up into capillaries again. This vessel is a true hepatic portal vein. A contractile hepatic vein beginning in the hepatic caecum carries blood to the heart (Fig. 12.27). A pair of parietal veins draining the dorsal

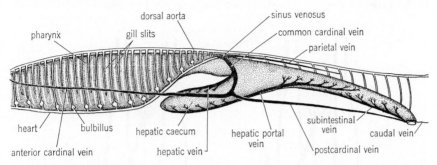

FIG. 12.27. Diagram showing the essential features of the circulatory system of amphioxus, lateral view.

body wall and located dorsal to the gut furnishes additional somatic vessels which enter the posterior end of the heart.

Cyclostomes. The venous system of the lamprey does not differ greatly from that of amphioxus. Two inferior jugular veins unite to form a single vessel which returns blood to the sinus venosus from the ventral, anterior region of the body. Paired anterior cardinals (jugulars) and posterior cardinals are present. The common cardinal veins appear to have fused, or else the left one has degenerated in the adult so that but a single common cardinal enters the sinus venosus on its dorsal side (Fig. 15.7). The caudal vein, which divides at the cloacal region, connects to the postcardinal veins which course on either side slightly ventrolateral to the dorsal aorta. They fuse as they approach the heart.

The anterior part of the subintestinal vein remains as a small vessel which is found in the typhlosole of the intestine. Its posterior end has lost all connection with the caudal vein. The subintestinal vein becomes the hepatic portal vein, which also receives a branch from the head. A contractile *portal heart* is present in the hepatic portal vein of cyclostomes. Blood from the liver is collected by a single hepatic vein which joins the sinus venosus. No renal portal system exists in cyclostomes. Segmentally arranged veins from the kidneys and gonad enter the postcardinal veins as do those from the body wall.

Fishes. Many primitive features are retained by the venous systems of fishes, but important advances over the conditions in amphioxus and cyclostomes are to be found.

The sinus venosus receives a duct of Cuvier on each side (Fig. 12.28A). An anterior cardinal, or jugular, vein brings blood from the dorsal side of the head region to the duct of Cuvier. In most fishes a pair of inferior jugular veins from the ventrolateral part of the head also enters the com-

mon cardinal vein.   These are lacking in *Polypterus* and are fused in
Lepisosteus.   The common cardinal on each side also receives a postcardinal vein from the posterior end of the body.   Since fishes are the first
vertebrates to possess paired appendages, veins bringing blood from the

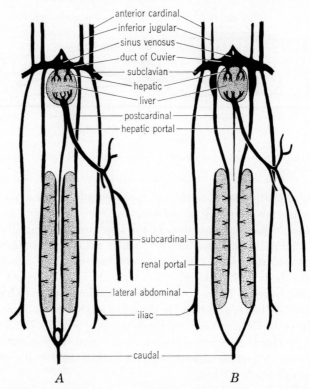

anterior cardinal
inferior jugular
sinus venosus
duct of Cuvier
subclavian
hepatic
liver
postcardinal
hepatic portal

subcardinal

renal portal

lateral abdominal

iliac

caudal

A   *B*

FIG. 12.28. Diagrams *A* and *B*, illustrating the changes over the primitive condition
which occur in the venous system of fishes, ventral view.

appendages first make their appearance in this group.   Those from the
pectoral appendages are called *subclavian* veins, and those from the pelvic
are the *iliac* veins.

In young fishes the subclavian veins may enter the anterior ends of the
postcardinals, but in adults a shifting has occurred so that the subclavian
veins frequently enter the common cardinals directly.   The iliac vein from
each pelvic fin joins the *lateral abdominal* vein which courses through the
body wall also to join the duct of Cuvier.

The posterior wall of the sinus venosus usually receives two hepatic
veins of similar size which return blood from the liver to the heart.   The
hepatic portal vein of fishes is well developed and, as in other forms, is
composed of the left vitelline vein and its subintestinal tributary.   The

subintestinal vein has, in most cases, lost its connection with the caudal vein.

The chief differences over the primitive condition to be found in the veins of fishes are concerned with changes which occur in the posterior part of the body and which result in the development of the renal portal system.

With the development of the opisthonephric kidneys and their posterior elongation, the postcardinals grow backward, ultimately to unite with the caudal vein at the point where it divides to form a ring about the anus. A new vessel or pair of vessels, the *subcardinal* veins, now develops between the opisthonephric kidneys, and a connection with the caudal vein is established near the point where it is joined by the postcardinals. Small blood vessels, passing through the opisthonephric kidneys, connect the postcardinal and subcardinal veins. They are not associated with the glomeruli, which receive arterial blood. Blood in the caudal vein now has two alternative routes through which it may pass on its way to the heart. It may go through the postcardinals directly or through the subcardinals and renal veins to the postcardinals.

The next change which takes place involves an interruption in the course of each postcardinal vein, so that anterior and posterior portions are no longer continuous (Fig. 12.28*B*). The anterior ends of the subcardinals join the anterior portions of the postcardinals. The posterior ends of the subcardinals lose their direct connection with the caudal vein. Blood from the tail now can travel only by one route. It goes up the caudal vein into the original posterior portions of the postcardinals, which are now termed the *renal portal* veins. It then passes through the renal veins, which have assumed capillary dimensions, finally to enter the subcardinal veins. The blood then courses through the postcardinal veins, which join the duct of Cuvier. The postcardinals usually receive veins from the gonads en route to the heart.

The newly developed renal portal vein falls within the definition of a portal system, since it breaks up into a capillary network before the blood which it contains enters the heart. It is interesting to note that the blood passing through the renal veins, once the renal portal circulation is established, flows in a direction reverse to that occurring during an early stage of development.

The changes in the venous system described above have now reached the stage found in the elasmobranch fishes (Fig. 16.15). Interesting variations in the venous systems of other fishes are encountered, a few of which will be considered. Many of the differences involve only minor details, but certain major deviations are noteworthy.

In elasmobranchs, large cavernous *sinuses* occur in certain portions of the anterior and posterior cardinal veins.

In the catfish, *Ameiurus*, the caudal vein continues forward, after giving off the renal portal veins, and communicates with the hepatic portal vein. The connecting vessel undoubtedly represents the original connection of the subintestinal and caudal veins. In the eel, *Anguilla,* several vessels from each renal portal vein connect with the hepatic portal vein.

In such fishes as the tench and the cod the renal portal system is imperfectly developed and some blood from the caudal vein may pass directly to the heart through a postcardinal vein which has not undergone the usual separation into anterior and posterior portions. In such cases there is an asymmetry in the development of the posterior veins. The tench and cod, like the catfish and eel, also possess connections between caudal and hepatic portal veins.

In teleost fishes the lateral abdominal veins, so conspicuous in elasmobranchs, are not present. In these fishes the subclavians enter the common cardinals and the iliacs join the postcardinals.

Veins from the swim bladder usually join the hepatic portal vein. This is a logical state of affairs, since the swim bladder is a derivative of the gut. However, in certain forms the connection is with the postcardinal veins instead. In *Polypterus* they join the hepatic veins directly. In the Dipnoi the pulmonary veins from the swim bladder enter the newly formed left atrium of the heart. In this group of fishes the double type of circulatory system appears for the first time.

It is in the true lungfishes that a connecting link is found which indicates how the venous system of amphibians may have arisen in evolution from the more simple and primitive arrangement found in other fishes. The veins of *Neoceratodus* show this transition most clearly.

In *Neoceratodus* a single, midventral, *anterior abdominal* vein, similar to that of amphibians, makes its appearance. The lateral abdominal veins have fused to form the anterior abdominal, which courses forward to enter the sinus venosus. In the meantime the iliac vein has formed a connection with the renal portal vein on each side (Fig. 12.29). The branch of the iliac which joins the anterior abdominal vein is called the *pelvic* vein.

The right postcardinal, including its posterior portion (originally the right subcardinal), becomes much larger than its counterpart on the left side. The connection with the caudal vein on both sides is retained. The large vessel on the right side is now called the *postcaval* vein. It passes through the liver to open into the sinus venosus. The smaller left postcardinal passes over the liver and enters the left duct of Cuvier. The presence of the postcava in *Neoceratodus* clearly presages the appearance of the postcaval vein in amphibians, the anterior portion of which, however, has a different origin.

The venous system of *Protopterus,* except for the lack of an anterior abdominal vein, even more closely resembles that of amphibians than does that of *Neoceratodus.*

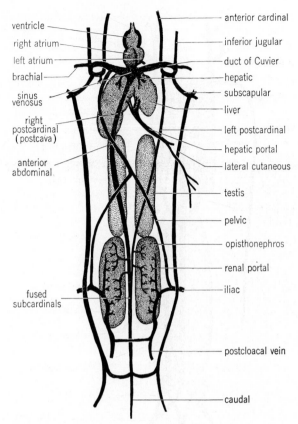

FIG. 12.29.   Diagram of venous system of *Neoceratodus*, ventral view.   (*Modified from B. Spencer.*)

Amphibians.   The venous system in amphibians bears such a close resemblance to that of *Neoceratodus* that only salient differences need be mentioned.   Chief among these is a change in the anterior connections of the anterior abdominal vein.   Whereas in the lungfish the anterior abdominal opens directly into the sinus venosus, in amphibians it joins the hepatic portal vein (Figs. 12.30 and 12.31).   Thus the renal and hepatic portal systems are brought into close association, since blood from the legs must pass through one or the other.

Pulmonary veins from the lungs enter the left atrium as in the Dipnoi. In lungless salamanders, of course, pulmonary veins are absent and the left atrium is reduced in size.

The ducts of Cuvier which originally receive the subclavian, jugular, and postcardinal veins are further consolidated in amphibians and are now called the *precaval* veins which enter the sinus venosus on each side.   The jugular vein now has *internal* and *external* tributaries.   Since cutaneous

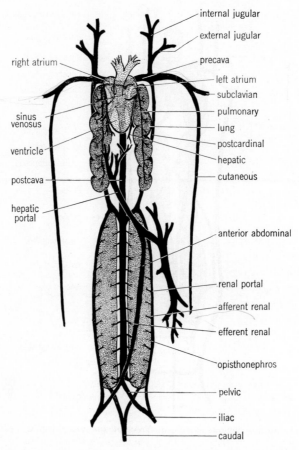

Fig. 12.30.   Diagram of venous system of a typical caudate amphibian, ventral view.

respiration has developed to a high degree in amphibians, exceptionally large cutaneous veins are present which join the subclavians to enter the sinus venosus.

The postcava in amphibians differs from that of *Neoceratodus* in that its anterior portion is derived from the sinus venosus and portions of the original vitelline veins, rather than from the right postcardinal.   The posterior part, however, like that of *Neoceratodus*, comes from the old subcardinals.

Although both caudates and salientians are similar in the above respects, they exhibit certain differences in regard to the arrangement of the post-caval-postcardinal complex.   In most caudates and in a few salientians such as *Bombina* and *Ascaphus*, the anterior portion of each postcardinal persists in reduced form, connecting the middle portion of the postcava with the duct of Cuvier on each side.   In adult salientians, however, the anterior portions of the postcardinals usually disappear and the postcava furnishes the only route through which blood from the kidneys and gonads can be returned to the heart.

Reptiles. Generally speaking, the venous system of reptiles shows little change over the condition in amphibians. The large veins entering the heart gradually shift to the right side, following the further partitioning of the heart into right and left sides.

Two precavae and one postcava enter the sinus venosus. The precavae are the original ducts of Cuvier which receive the jugular, subclavian, and postcardinal veins. The anterior portions of the postcardinals have degenerated into two small *vertebral* veins, which receive small segmental branches. In snakes the subclavians are lacking.

More blood from the posterior part of the body now courses through the anterior abdominal vein, which joins the hepatic portal vein anteriorly. The importance of the renal portal system is diminish-

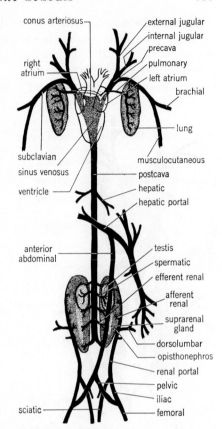

Fig. 12.31. Diagram of venous system of a typical saliention amphibian, ventral view.

ing, and in some forms direct channels may even pass through the kidneys, connecting renal portal and postcaval veins. As in amphibians, blood in the hindlimbs and tail reaches the heart either by the renal portal-kidney-postcaval route or by the pelvic-anterior abdominal-hepatic portal pathway.

Cutaneous respiration does not exist in reptiles, and the pulmonary circulation assumes greater importance. The pulmonary veins from the two lungs show discrepancies in size in various forms, depending upon the degree of asymmetrical development of these respiratory organs. One pulmonary vein may even be entirely absent in certain snakes in which the left lobe of the lung is not present.

The reptilian postcava, as in amphibians, is derived partly from the subcardinals and partly from the vitelline veins. It furnishes the main venous channel from the posterior part of the body, since the postcardinals have practically disappeared.

Birds. The reptilian character of the venous system is clearly indicated in birds. The sinus venosus has been incorporated in the wall of the right atrium, so that caval veins enter the right atrium directly. There are two precavae and a single postcava. The precavae, as in reptiles, are formed by a confluence of subclavian and jugular veins. The original postcardinal connection is no longer in existence. Right and left jugular veins are joined, up in the neck, by an anastomosing vessel, and the right is larger than the left, which, in certain cases, is practically obliterated.

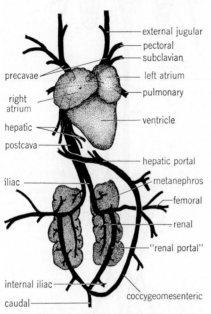

Fig. 12.32. Diagram of venous system of bird, ventral view.

The postcava assumes an even greater importance than does that of reptiles and is the chief pathway for the return of blood from the posterior part of the body. It is derived in the same manner as previously described for amphibians and reptiles. The posterior end of the postcava receives blood directly from the limbs (Fig. 12.32) via the "renal portal" veins (old posterior cardinals). The name "renal portal" is scarcely appropriate in birds, for although these vessels pass through the kidneys, the passage is, for the most part, direct and not interrupted by a capillary network. The hepatic veins of birds join the postcava as it nears the heart.

The caudal vein in birds is greatly reduced in correlation with the decrease in size of the tail. A vein, variously known as the *inferior mesenteric*, *coccygeomesenteric*, and *caudal mesenteric*, connects the caudal vein with the hepatic portal vein. Since this vessel connects the two "portal" systems, it may be homologous with the anterior abdominal vein of amphibians and reptiles, although this homology is questioned by some. Others consider a small *epigastric* vein of birds to be the homologue of the anterior abdominal vein of lower forms. This vessel carries blood from the great omentum to one of the hepatic veins and is not located in the ventral body wall.

It should be recalled that the heart of birds is completely separated into right and left halves, the right half containing only unoxygenated blood and the left only oxygenated blood brought to the left atrium by the pulmonary veins. In birds the double type of circulation is fully developed.

Mammals. The shifting of the main venous channels to the right side is more clearly indicated in the class Mammalia than in others (Fig. 18.26).

As in birds pre- and postcaval veins enter the right atrium directly since the sinus venosus has been gathered into its walls. In some mammals two precavae are present, but in others, as in man, an anastomosis develops between the two through which blood from the left jugular and subclavian veins is shunted to the right side. The combined jugular and subclavian veins of the two sides are called the right and left innominate veins, respectively. The original basal portion of the left precava is modified to form the *coronary sinus*. In such cases, then, only a single precava is present. The internal jugular vein of mammals is the original anterior cardinal vein. It is usually smaller than its external jugular tributary.

In mammals a portion of the anterior end of the right postcardinal persists as the *azygos* vein. This vessel drains the intercostal muscles and enters the precava. It is homologous with the vertebral veins of reptiles. Considerable variation is to be found in the azygos vein in different mammals.

The greatest change in the mammalian venous system occurs in the postcava which appears to have become considerably simplified. No trace of renal portal system exists in the adult, and all blood from the posterior part of the body is collected by the postcava. The embryonic development of the mammalian postcava is complicated by the appearance of new vessels called *supracardinal* veins, which contribute to its formation. In other respects, however, its homologies to the postcavae of lower forms are clear.

The anterior abdominal vein has disappeared in mammals, being found only in *Echidna*. The allantoic, or umbilical, veins of mammalian embryos, returning blood from the placenta, are homologous with the lateral abdominal veins of elasmobranch fishes and to the anterior abdominal vein of amphibians and reptiles. Usually only the left umbilical vein persists, passing through the liver as the *ductus venosus* to join the postcava before it enters the heart (Fig. 12.33). The umbilical vessels degenerate when they cease to function after birth.

The hepatic portal vein of mammals, now simply known as *the* portal vein, is in every respect similar to the hepatic portal vein of lower forms.

FETAL CIRCULATION

The allantoic, or umbilical, circulation is of great importance to the embryos of amniotes. In reptiles and birds, with their large-yolked eggs, the vitelline circulation is used in obtaining nutritive substances from the yolk. Although during early development the vitelline circulation is also used in respiration, it is soon superseded by the allantoic circulation, which, along with the developing allantois, has grown out to the periphery of the egg, beneath the porous shell. Here an exchange of oxygen and carbon dioxide takes place.

In mammals, the eggs of which contain little or no yolk, the vitelline circulation is comparatively of negligible importance. The chief role of

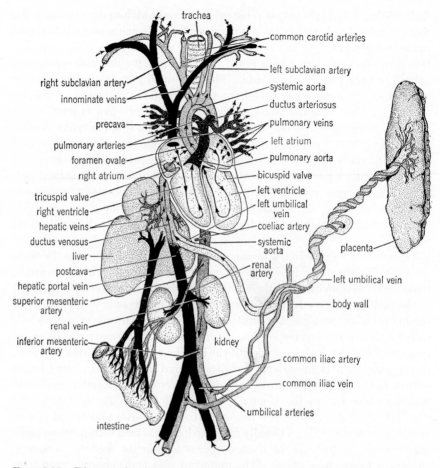

Fig. 12.33. Diagram showing arrangement of the fetal blood vessels of man, ventral view. Arrows indicate the direction of blood flow. Black represents unoxygenated blood; light stippling, oxygenated blood; intermediate stippling, mixed blood.

the vitelline arteries is the establishment of the superior mesenteric artery; that of the vitelline veins lies in the formation of the hepatic portal vein. The placenta usually develops in association with the allantois. Allantoic, or umbilical, arteries carry blood from the embryo to the placenta, and similarly named veins are employed in its return. The placenta is the organ in which exchange of gases, nutrient materials, and wastes takes place between the mother and her developing young.

A pair of umbilical arteries arises from the dorsal aorta and passes out the umbilical cord to the placenta (Fig. 12.33). At first a pair of umbilical veins returns oxygenated blood to the embryo. Later, in birds, the right artery degenerates, but in mammals both persist. In both birds and mammals the right umbilical vein degenerates and the left one alone continues to function. From the umbilical cord it courses through the body wall for a short distance and then enters the liver through a large channel, the *ductus venosus*, finally to join the postcava.

The lungs do not function during embryonic life, and the umbilical circulation is used for respiration. Conditions, therefore, are totally different during the developmental period from those existing after birth has taken place.

In a typical mammalian fetus blood enters the right atrium through pre- and postcaval veins. A portion of it then goes to the right ventricle, past the tricuspid valve. Instead of being pumped to the nonfunctional lungs, however, much of this blood is shunted to the systemic aorta via the ductus arteriosus. It will be recalled that the ductus arteriosus is a portion of the sixth aortic arch which connects the pulmonary and systemic aortae during embryonic life. The rest of the blood in the right atrium passes through an opening in the interatrial septum (*foramen ovale*) into the left atrium. Joined by a relatively small quantity coming from the pulmonary veins, it passes over the bicuspid valve into the left ventricle, from which it is pumped into the systemic aorta. This blood, together with that coming from the ductus arteriosus, is then distributed to all parts of the body, and a representative portion is sent out the umbilical arteries to the placenta.

From the above description it would seem as though a mixing of unoxygenated blood from pre- and postcaval veins, and oxygenated blood from the left umbilical vein, which joins the postcava, would occur in the right atrium. Although this matter has been the subject of much controversy and investigation for over a century, it now seems fairly clear that probably but little mixing occurs. The greater part of the blood from the postcava, carrying a large proportion of oxygenated blood from the left umbilical vein, crosses the dorsal part of the right atrium to enter the left atrium through the foramen ovale. A smaller amount passes into the right ventricle. The stream of unoxygenated blood from the precava(e) passes, for the most part, along the ventral portion of the right atrium into the right ventricle. Although different species vary somewhat in this respect, there is actually a moderately complete separation of oxygenated and unoxygenated blood in the fetal heart.

Changes occurring at birth. At the time of birth when the placenta is loosened from its moorings, the umbilical circulation ceases to function. The umbilical arteries no longer pulsate and gradually constrict. Blood in the umbilical vein drains from the placenta into the body. The stumps of the umbilical arteries become the *hypogastric*, or *internal iliac*, arteries which supply the posterior body wall and portions of the urogenital organs. The umbilical vein disappears, its former course being marked by a fibrous cord, the *ligamentum teres*, extending from the umbilicus (navel) to the undersurface of the liver. The remnant of the ductus venosus is found in the liver as a slender fibrous cord, the *ligamentum venosum*.

When the atrium is first partitioned, a membrane, the *septum primum,* grows down and divides it into left and right chambers. An opening, the *interatrial foramen,* appears in the septum primum, so that the cavities of the atria are in communication. Later a second septum, the *septum secundum,* semilunar in shape, grows down parallel to the septum primum on its right side. An oval aperture in the septum secundum is the *foramen ovale.*

With the cessation of the umbilical circulation, the amount of blood entering the heart through the postcava is materially decreased, since flow through the umbilical vein has stopped. At birth the lungs expand and pulmonary respiration begins. The ductus arteriosus is gradually occluded and becomes a fibrous rudiment, the *ligamentum arteriosum.* Blood from the right ventricle is no longer shunted to the systemic aorta but is sent to the lungs instead. The pulmonary veins now send a greatly increased amount of blood to the left atrium. The foramen ovale then closes. This is brought about by a decrease in pressure in the right atrium, which is now receiving less blood, and an increased pressure in the left atrium due to the increased flow through the pulmonary veins. The septum primum and septum secundum are pushed close together, causing the foramen ovale to be obliterated. A thin area, the *fossa ovalis,* in the interatrial septum indicates the former position of the foramen ovale.

Other factors may also play a part in the changes in circulation occurring at birth. Suffice it to say that after the above changes have taken place, a perfect double circulation has been established.

Faulty development of the septum primum and septum secundum, or other abnormalities, may prevent the foramen ovale from closing properly. An open, or patent, foramen ovale is not necessarily fatal or even very harmful in human beings. In some cases, however, a mixture of oxygenated and unoxygenated blood takes place. As a result the child has a purplish color and is known as a "blue baby." In severe cases this will result in early death. Other anomalous conditions may result from improper closure of the ductus arteriosus or from a failure of the interventricular septum to develop properly.

LYMPHATIC SYSTEM

Origin. The lymphatic vessels originate during embryonic development quite independently of the blood-vascular system. Venous connections with lymphatic vessels are secondary developments. The first indication of the formation of lymph vessels is to be observed in spaces which appear in the mesenchyme. The bordering mesenchymal cells become flattened and differentiate into endothelial cells which come to line the lymphatic vessels. Various lymph spaces unite and branch in a complex manner, so that ultimately an elaborate system of anastomosing vessels extends throughout the entire body. The first lymph spaces to appear originate in close proximity to the larger veins. Enlargement of the lymphatic network in certain regions, or a union of several vessels, results in the formation of lymph sacs, or sinuses. Later, secondary connections appear between the lymphatic vessels and certain veins. The connection usually, but not always, takes place with the large veins in the vicinity of the heart where blood pressure is at its lowest.

Lymph glands, or nodes, are formed when connective-tissue capsules condense about lymphatic plexuses associated with strands of mesenchymal tissue.

Structure. The smallest units of the lymphatic system are the lymph capillaries. These anastomosing vessels collect tissue juice from between cells. This is called *lymph* after it enters the lymphatic vessels. Lymph capillaries end blindly at their free ends. Their bases unite to form larger vessels, which in turn combine to form vessels of still greater caliber. The largest vessels are the ones which in most cases open directly into the great veins near the heart. Although the lymphatic system is a closed system, it does not in itself form a complete circuit and in this respect differs from the blood-vascular system.

Lymph capillaries are tubules of somewhat greater diameter than blood capillaries. Their caliber, however, is not uniform throughout (Fig. 12.34).

Fig. 12.34. Lymph capillaries.

No valves are present in the lymph capillaries. Their walls are extremely thin, consisting of a single layer of flat, squamous, endothelial cells. The blind ends of the tubules appear as small, distended knobs.

The larger vessels formed by the union of lymph capillaries have thicker walls and contain valves. The walls are covered with a thin layer composed of elastic and collagenous fibers as well as a few smooth muscle cells. In still larger vessels, three layers, comparable to those of small arteries and veins, make up the walls. Like those of blood vessels they are called *tunica intima, tunica media,* and *tunica adventitia.* These layers are not so distinct as those in blood vessels.

The valves, which prevent backflow, are more numerous than venous valves and, when present, occur at close intervals. They are arranged in pairs, and their structure is similar to the valves in veins.

The walls of lymphatic vessels are supplied by tiny blood vessels similar to the vasa vasorum supplying the walls of the larger vessels of the blood-vascular system.   The nerve supply to the lymphatics is abundant.

Lymph nodes are masses of lymphatic tissue composed of collagenous and reticular connective-tissue fibers enclosing large numbers of lymphocytes as well as numbers of fixed macrophages.   Lymphatic vessels ramify throughout the nodes, taking a rather circuitous course.   The nodes are placed at intervals along the lymphatic vessels and are arranged in such a manner that lymph must pass through them on its way to the larger vessels.

The small lymph capillaries of the intestine are called *lacteals*.   Unlike the capillaries of the blood-vascular system, they are concerned with fat absorption.

Several factors are instrumental in propelling the slowly moving lymph through lymphatic vessels and nodes.   These include (1) muscular activity of various parts of the body, tending to squeeze the fluid along, (2) pressure built up in the smaller vessels by osmosis and absorption of tissue fluid, (3) the action of pulsating lymph hearts.

Lymph hearts, when present, consist of enlargements in lymphatic vessels which have contractile walls.   They are generally situated near the point where lymph enters the venous system.   Valves are present which control the direction of flow.   The rhythm of the beating lymph hearts bears no relation to the beat of the heart itself.

Not a great deal is known about the comparative anatomy of the lymphatic system.   The small size and delicate structure of the vessels are barriers to detailed study.   Furthermore the great irregularity of the channels in the various classes of vertebrates precludes a study of evolutionary advance.   Most studies have been carried out on mammals and birds.   Less is known about conditions in the lower classes.

Fishes.   The lymphatic vessels of fishes are extensively developed.   Peripherally located channels extend into head, tail, and fins.   Deeper channels follow the course of some of the larger veins.

Several connections occur between the lymphatic and venous systems in the posterior and middle as well as the anterior part of the body.   Lymph hearts are usually not present, but some have been described in certain forms near the point of junction of lymphatic vessels and veins.   The eel has a lymph heart in the tail.   In the European catfish, *Silurus*, two caudal lymph hearts are present.   Lymph nodes seem to be lacking in fishes.

Amphibians.   In caudate amphibians, two main sets of lymphatic vessels are present.   Superficial vessels, beneath the skin, carry lymph to cutaneous and postcardinal veins.   Fourteen to twenty lymph hearts have been observed along their course in various forms.   The deeper channels follow the dorsal aorta on each side and enter the subclavian veins.

Salientians are characterized by the presence of large lymph sacs, or spaces, beneath the skin.   Most of the lymph flows toward the heart.   Two pairs of lymph hearts are usually present in adult forms. In the frog the first pair lies behind the transverse processes of the third vertebra, pumping lymph into the vertebral vein. A posterior pair, located near the end of the urostyle, pumps lymph into the transverse iliac vein.

Lymph hearts are more numerous in larval and tadpole stages. It has been reported that over 200 lymph hearts are present in caecilians, located along the intersegmental veins beneath the skin.

Reptiles. A well-developed lymphatic system is present in reptiles. A large subvertebral trunk divides anteriorly to enter the precaval veins. In snakes the lymphatic vessels and sinuses are exceptionally large and numerous. Only a posterior pair of lymph hearts is to be found in reptiles. They pump lymph into the iliac veins.

Birds. The lymphatic vessels of birds ultimately enter two thoracic lymph ducts which join the precaval veins. Transitory lymph hearts have been observed, during embryonic development, in the pelvic region. They are not present in adult birds.

Mammals. Lymph hearts are altogether lacking in mammals. A main trunk, the *thoracic duct* (Fig. 18.26), drains all the lymphatic vessels of the posterior part of the body as well as those coming from the left side of the head, neck, and thoracic regions. It lies beneath the vertebral column and courses anteriorly to open into the left subclavian vein just past the latter's junction with the internal jugular vein. The lower end of the thoracic duct is expanded into a conspicuous enlargement, the *cisterna chyli.* A so-called *right lymphatic duct* drains lymph from the right side of the head and neck, the right arm, and the right side of the thorax. It enters the *right* subclavian vein near the angle of junction with the right internal jugular vein.

It is through the lymph capillaries (lacteals) in the villi of the small intestine that fats enter the circulatory system. Since these vessels ultimately drain into the thoracic duct, after a fatty meal the lymph in the thoracic duct contains a much greater amount of fat than at other times. The emulsified fat, carried by the lymph, gives the latter a milky-white appearance. The term *chyle* is used to refer to this milky fluid. The chyle passes into the left subclavian vein, as was previously noted.

In mammals, lymph nodes are particularly abundant in superficial regions of the head and in the neck, axillae, and groin. Within the body cavity great numbers lie in close association with the large blood vessels. They are exceptionally large and numerous in the mesentery of the intestine. In all these localities they serve to prevent invasion of the body by bacteria. The phagocytic action of the fixed macrophages, in particular, is primarily responsible for this phase of bodily protection.

Other lymphatic organs. Among other structures usually considered to belong to the lymphatic system are certain organs of pharyngeal origin, previously discussed in that connection. They include the *tonsils, adenoids,* and *thymus* glands. *Peyer's patches* are nodules of lymphoid tissue in the small intestine, especially numerous in the region of the ileum. In the horse a single patch of Peyer may be 2 in. long and $\frac{1}{2}$ in. wide.

Hemolymph glands. Certain organs of the body closely resemble lymph glands except that they enclose blood vessels rather than lymphatics. Blood, therefore, rather than lymph, filters through them. They are called *hemolymph glands*, or *hemal nodes*. It is believed that they may play a part in the destruction of old and worn-out red corpuscles and may even have a role in erythrocyte formation. Their actual function, however, is not entirely clear. Most hemolymph glands are very small. They are very abundant in retroperitoneal tissue near the points of origin of the superior mesenteric and renal arteries. Hemal nodes are most numerous in ruminating animals. Their occurrence in man is doubtful.

Spleen. The largest lymphoid organ in the body is the spleen. It first appears during development as a localized thickening in the dorsal mesogastrium, the mesentery suspending the stomach. When the stomach later swings over to the left, the spleen is also carried to the left side of the body. The organ itself, derived from mesenchymal cells, continues to grow and ultimately is connected to the stomach by a band, the gastrosplenic ligament, which is a portion of the original mesogastrium. Differentiation of the original mass of mesenchyme is complex and depends mainly on the development and distribution of the blood vessels with which it is supplied.

The spleen is considered by some to be a hemolymph gland, since it is interposed in the blood stream rather than in lymphatic vessels. Blood, therefore, rather than lymph filters through the spleen. Because of the peculiar arrangement of the blood vessels within the spleen, the blood comes in close contact with phagocytes (macrophages). The fragments of disintegrating red corpuscles are engulfed by these cells.

The spleen also serves as a storehouse for erythrocytes. Large numbers may be housed by the spleen, which can return them to the blood vascular system as requirements of the body demand. In addition to the usual capillary network between arteries and veins, there are in the spleen certain direct, sinuslike connections between the two. The presence of these sinuses may account for the blood-storing properties of the spleen. Contraction of the spleen occurs in response to the demand by the body for an increased supply of red blood corpuscles, which are thus forced into the blood stream.

During embryonic development the spleen functions as a blood-forming (*hemopoietic*) organ since erythrocytes and lymphocytes are formed in its tissues. In mammals the production of erythrocytes by the spleen ceases in adult life but it continues to form lymphocytes.

The spleen is also of importance in the production of antibodies and thus serves as a mechanism of defense of the body against certain diseases. Enlargement of the spleen is a feature of malaria and certain other diseases in which the organ may assume relatively enormous proportions.

Among vertebrates, cyclostomes lack a spleen. Some peculiar tissue in the wall of the intestine has, however, been homologized with the spleen by some authorities. Splenic tissue has been described in the stomach wall in *Protopterus*, which also lacks a discrete spleen but possesses a lymphoid mass partially surrounding the stomach.

In other fishes the spleen is usually large and distinct, but variable in shape in different species. It lies in close association with the stomach and is important in the formation of red corpuscles.

The spleens of higher forms, in general, vary but little from those of fishes in their location, usually being compact organs lying toward the left side of the body close to the stomach. Among amphibians it has been reported that the spleen of the newt is the only place in the body where erythrocytes are formed. In salientians the spleen first begins to be less significant in production of red corpuscles, and in the adults of higher forms this property has probably been lost altogether. The spleen continues to form lymphocytes, however.

Blood-forming (hemopoietic) tissues. A regular sequence of blood-cell formation occurs in various organs and regions of the body during development. In early embryonic life blood cells are first differentiated in the wall of the yolk sac, at least in cases where a yolk sac is present. Body mesenchyme then follows as a site of blood-cell formation. With the development of the liver, that organ takes over hemopoiesis for the time being. Then the spleen, thymus, and lymph glands next play a part in blood formation, followed finally by the bone marrow, which, in addition to the lymph glands, functions as the hemopoietic organ of the adult. It is in the salientians that the bone marrow first becomes hemopoietic. In mammals the bone marrow is the chief hemopoietic organ.

Lymphocytes originate in lymphatic tissue mostly by mitotic proliferation of previously existing lymphocytes. The granular leukocytes as well as erythrocytes, on the other hand, are formed in the bone marrow.

In some fishes and in certain amphibian larvae, the opisthonephric kidneys function, at least for a time, as blood-forming organs.

BLOOD

The composition of vertebrate blood has been discussed (pages 74 to 77). Several differences exist in the bloods of various vertebrates, a few of which will be considered. The chemical composition of blood plasma shows great variation, not only in different vertebrate classes but in the species within a class, or even a genus, as well. Dissimilarities are observed in the percentage of water and solids, including proteins and other organic constituents, salts, and other materials. Among the formed elements, too, considerable differences exist.

The blood of amphioxus is practically colorless and contains but few red corpuscles. Apparently no leukocytes are present. Contrary to the condition in red-blooded invertebrates, in which the respiratory pigment hemoglobin is dissolved in the plasma, in vertebrates the hemoglobin is confined to the red corpuscles. The erythrocytes of vertebrates (Fig. 12.35), in all classes except mammals, are oval in shape and flattened. Each contains a conspicuous nucleus which causes the corpuscle to bulge in the center. Considerable variation in size occurs, the erythrocytes of the salamander, *Amphiuma*, being the largest of any animal. Among mammals, only the family Camelidae (camels and llamas) possesses oval corpuscles. Those of other mammals are round and biconcave. The musk deer has the smallest red corpuscles of all, averaging less than 1/12,000 in. in diameter as com-

SHARK   ELECTRIC   SALAMANDER (Proteus)   TOAD
          EEL

SNAKE   CROCODILE   OSTRICH   PIGEON   MAN   MUSK   ELEPHANT
                                             DEER

Fig. 12.35. Relative sizes of red corpuscles of representative vertebrates.

pared with man, in which the average is 1/3,200 in. The erythrocytes of elephants are the largest found among mammals, but they do not exceed those of man by a great deal.

Mammals are unique in that the *erythroblasts*, cells which give rise to erythrocytes, extrude their nuclei before becoming mature erythrocytes. It is not surprising that the red cells should be relatively short-lived since they have lost their nuclei. It has been estimated that red blood cells in man live in the blood stream anywhere from 50 to 100 days before they break down. In the dog, 124 days is reported to be the maximum length of erythrocyte life.

About 10 million red cells are destroyed every second in the human being, and, of course, a comparable number must be formed to replace them. Since the normal number of red corpuscles in man is about 5 million per cubic millimeter, the rate of destruction and formation is not so tremendous as might seem at first glance.

Leukocytes are much less numerous than erythrocytes. They retain their nuclei and may be classified into granular and nongranular types, each type having two or more subdivisions (pages 75 to 77). A sudden increase in their number often indicates the presence of an infection. Leukocytes in mammals are larger than erythrocytes, and their numbers are subject to much variation. An average healthy human being has approximately 7,000 per cubic millimeter of blood. The phagocytic action of certain leukocytes enables the body to combat invasion by bacteria. A localized site of painful swelling and inflammation usually marks an area in which numbers of leukocytes have congregated in an effort to destroy bacteria. Usually the leukocytes destroy the bacteria, and the infected site is once more restored to normal. When pus forms, the bacteria have, at least temporarily, gained the upper hand, pus being composed of large numbers of dead leukocytes. Monocytes and granular neutrophils are the chief phagocytic cells of the body. They are not confined to blood vessels but, through their ameboid movements, are able to migrate throughout the entire body where they function as scavengers. They push between the flat endothelial cells of the capillaries (diapedesis) and in that manner are able to leave or enter the blood stream. Most, if not all, phagocytic action takes place outside the blood stream in the tissue spaces.

Blood platelets are formed elements found only in the blood of mammals. They are small, colorless bodies, round or oval in shape and biconvex. It is not known with certainty where they are formed in the body. Some authors consider them to be fragments of pseudopodia of certain giant cells in the bone marrow, but this theory is questioned by others. Platelets in man number approximately 250,000 per cubic millimeter of blood. It is very difficult to ascertain their exact number, since they disintegrate when exposed to air or to rough surfaces. Blood platelets are lacking in other vertebrates, which, instead, possess nucleated *spindle cells*, or *thrombocytes*, that are believed to serve the same function.

The platelets play an important part in the clotting of blood. The exact manner in which clotting occurs is not known with certainty. Howell's theory, as modified by Ferguson, is the most widely accepted explanation of many that have been advanced.

According to this concept, a substance called *prothrombin* is present in the blood stream but is normally kept inactive by another substance, *anti-prothrombin*. When an injury or break occurs, still another substance called *thromboplastin* is liberated from injured tissues and blood platelets, which disintegrate upon exposure to air. Thromboplastin reacts with antiprothrombin. Prothrombin, now no longer held in check, is acted upon by calcium ions in the blood in the presence of an enzyme, *tryptase*, which becomes activated during the clotting process. The prothrombin changes to *thrombin*. Thrombin then acts on the blood protein *fibrinogen*, changing it to *fibrin*, which is laid down at the site of injury in the form of a fine mesh-work of threads, so closely interlaced that even minute erythrocytes cannot pass through the interstices. The mass of fibrin threads is known as the *clot*. In the condition referred to as *hemophilia*, in which a severe and even fatal hemorrhage may occur after a trivial injury, the blood fails to clot. In such cases one or more links in the above chain of events is apparently lacking. Some believe that there is a deficiency of thromboplastin. Hemophilia is a hereditary condition which is transmitted as a sex-linked, recessive character. It appears only in males and is transmitted through females to their masculine offspring.

SUMMARY

1. The circulatory system of higher metazoans serves to carry substances of physiological utility to all parts of the body and to remove from them the waste products of metabolism. Wastes are carried to appropriate organs for elimination.

2. The vertebrate circulatory system is of mesodermal origin and is composed of two systems of elaborately branched tubes which ramify throughout the body. They are (a) the blood-vascular system, composed of heart, arteries, arterioles, capillaries, venules, and veins, (b) the lymphatic system, made up of lymph capillaries, vessels, sinuses, nodes, and lymphoid organs of various types.

3. The blood-vascular system is subdivided into arterial and venous systems, the former carrying blood away from the heart and the latter returning it. One, two, or three portal systems of veins are present. Each breaks up into a capillary network before reaching the heart. Two of these systems are known as the hepatic-portal and renal-portal systems, ending in liver and kidneys, respectively. The third is associated with the pituitary gland.

4. The walls of arteries, veins, and the larger lymphatic vessels are composed of three layers, the tunica intima, tunica media, and tunica adventitia. The thickness and detailed structure of these three layers vary in the different types of vessels.

5. Both blood and lymphatic vessels first appear in embryonic development as spaces in the mesenchyme which subsequently grow and branch in a complex manner. If a yolk sac is present, the first vessels appear in its splanchnic mesoderm.

6. The heart is primarily a pulsating tube derived from a fusion of two vitelline veins. It becomes divided into chambers called atria and ventricles. In addition, two accessory chambers may be present, called the sinus venosus and conus arteriosus, respectively. Cyclostomes and fishes have two-chambered hearts, with one atrium and one ventricle; Dipnoi and amphibians with three-chambered hearts have two atria and one ventricle; the three-chambered heart of reptiles is like that of amphibians, but an incomplete partition appears in the ventricle. In crocodiles and alligators this becomes complete, forming a four-chambered heart with two atria and two ventricles. Birds and mammals have four-chambered hearts. Valves of various types are present which regulate the direction of blood flow.

7. Animals with two-chambered hearts have the single type of circulation in which only unoxygenated blood passes through the heart which pumps it to the gills for aeration. The double type of circulation exists in three-

chambered and four-chambered hearts through which pass two streams of blood, one oxygenated and the other either unoxygenated or partly oxygenated. These two streams do not mix, at least to any appreciable extent.

8. Vessels which carry blood from the heart to the lungs and back comprise the pulmonary circulation. Unoxygenated blood or partially unoxygenated blood is pumped from the right ventricle (or right side of the ventricle) to the lungs. Oxygenated blood returns from the lungs to the left atrium. The remaining vessels make up the systemic circulation which sends oxygenated blood throughout the body and returns unoxygenated blood to the right atrium. A special coronary circulation supplies and drains the tissues of the heart itself.

9. The arterial systems of vertebrates are essentially similar, at least during developmental stages. Usually six pairs of aortic-arch vessels extend from the ventral aorta to the dorsal side of the pharyngeal region where they fuse to form a vessel on each side. These two vessels combine posteriorly to form a single dorsal aorta. Changes in the aortic arches constitute the chief differences in the arterial systems of the separate vertebrate classes. A progressive reduction in the numbers of aortic arches occurs as the evolutionary scale is ascended. In cyclostomes and fishes which retain the greatest number of aortic arches, each arch is broken up into afferent and efferent portions connected by a capillary network. The gill lamellae through which the capillaries ramify serve as respiratory organs. In teleosts only the last four arches are retained. In remaining vertebrates arches 1, 2, and 5 disappear as does the radix on each side between arches 3 and 4. Arch 3 on each side, together with remnants of the ventral aorta and the anterior portions of the radices, becomes the carotid complex, consisting of a basal common carotid artery with internal and external branches. The fourth pair of arches persists in amphibians and reptiles to become the systemic arches which unite to form the dorsal aorta. The left fourth arch in reptiles splits off the ventral aorta (truncus arteriosus) and establishes a connection with the newly forming right ventricle. In birds the left fourth aortic arch loses its connection with the dorsal aorta and degenerates. Mammals are similar to birds except that the right fourth aortic arch instead of the left degenerates in part. In Dipnoi and the higher classes which use lungs for respiration, pulmonary arteries grow out from the sixth aortic arches to the lungs. The connection of arch 6 to the aorta on each side functions during embryonic life as the ductus arteriosus. This is closed after birth. In reptiles, birds, and mammals the pulmonary arteries come from a separate pulmonary aorta formed by a splitting of the truncus arteriosus which connects with the right ventricle. The rest of the truncus, known as the systemic aorta, leaves the left ventricle.

10. The single dorsal aorta, as it courses posteriorly, gives off many paired somatic arteries to supply the body proper. Paired visceral vessels pass to the derivatives of the embryonic mesomere. Usually three un-

paired visceral vessels, the coeliac, superior, and inferior mesenteric arteries, are distributed to the digestive tract.

11. The primitive venous system arises, in most cases, from several paired veins all of which join the sinus venosus to enter the heart. These consist of (*a*) a pair of vitelline veins, continued posteriorly as the subintestinal veins, (*b*) paired anterior and posterior cardinals which, on each side, join to form a common cardinal vein, or duct of Cuvier, entering the sinus venosus, (*c*) lateral abdominal veins from the body wall which also enter the duct of Cuvier, (*d*) subcardinal veins which appear between the opisthonephric or mesonephric kidneys and which are joined by the caudal vein from the tail.

12. The vitelline and subintestinal veins give rise to the hepatic portal system of veins, which lose their connection with the sinus venosus and, instead, break up in capillaries in the liver.

13. The anterior cardinal veins become the internal jugulars. In fishes and caudate amphibians a pair of inferior jugular veins also enters the sinus venosus, coming from the ventral head region. The latter vessels are without homologues in higher forms.

14. The caudal vein from the tail loses its connection with the subintestinal and subcardinal veins and splits in two at its anterior end, each portion connecting with the posterior part of the postcardinal. The postcardinals break up into two portions. The posterior parts, joined by the caudal vein, bring blood to the kidneys, and these become the renal portal veins. The anterior portion is joined by the subcardinals. In Dipnoi the right postcardinal is larger than the left and is called the postcava. In higher forms, however, the postcava is derived as an outgrowth of the vitelline veins which join the subcardinals. In such cases the postcardinals are reduced. In reptiles they become the vertebral veins. The right postcardinal in mammals contributes to the formation of the azygos vein.

15. A subclavian vein from each forelimb enters the duct of Cuvier on each side, and an iliac vein joins the posterior part of each lateral abdominal vein after it leaves the hindlimb.

16. Beginning with the Dipnoi, the two lateral abdominal veins fuse to form an anterior abdominal vein, which then joins the hepatic portal vein near the liver. This vessel loses its importance in reptiles and birds and is absent in all mammals except *Echidna*. The anterior abdominal vein connects the hepatic-portal and renal-portal systems.

17. The renal-portal system also becomes reduced in reptiles and birds and is absent in mammals, the postcava furnishing the main venous drainage for the posterior part of the body.

18. The ducts of Cuvier, from amphibians on, become the precaval veins which in amphibians and reptiles enter the sinus venosus but in birds and mammals enter the right atrium directly, the sinus venosus having been incorporated in the wall of the right atrium. In several mammals the left

precava loses its connection with the heart and a new vessel shunts blood from the left side of the anterior end of the body to the right precaval vein. The remnant of the left precava becomes the coronary sinus.

19. During fetal life, in amniotes, an umbilical, or allantoic, circulation exists which performs a role in respiration. The pulmonary circulation is inconsequential before birth, at which time it first begins to function and the umbilical circulation ceases. Umbilical arteries are branches of the dorsal aorta. The umbilical vein, formed primarily from the left umbilical vein, is homologous with the lateral and anterior abdominal veins of lower forms. An opening, the foramen ovale, in the interatrial septum, and the ductus arteriosus, connecting pulmonary and systemic aortae, make possible the peculiar routing of blood which is characteristic during fetal life. The umbilical vessels, foramen ovale, and ductus arteriosus do not exist as such after birth.

20. The lymphatic system collects tissue juice from all parts of the body. After the fluid enters the lymphatic system, it is called lymph. The lymphatic vessels connect with the venous system at certain places, usually with the large veins near the heart. Much variation in detailed structure exists in the various groups of vertebrates. Some forms have lymph hearts which help to propel the lymph, but in others, muscular movements and the pressure of newly accumulated lymph cause the fluid to flow slowly through the lymphatic vessels. Lymph nodes, composed of lymphatic tissue and through which lymph slowly filters, interrupt the course of lymphatic vessels. Tonsils, adenoids, thymus glands, and Peyer's patches are lymphoid structures.

21. Many vertebrates have hemolymph glands which interrupt the course of blood vessels in a manner similar to that of lymph nodes interrupting the course of lymphatic vessels.

22. The spleen is the largest lymphoid structure in the body. It functions as a hemolymph gland but, in addition, is able to store and discharge red corpuscles as the needs of the body dictate. The spleen lies in the mesentery of the gut near the stomach. It is absent in cyclostomes and Dipnoi.

23. Blood-forming (hemopoietic) tissues include the splanchnic mesoderm of the yolk sac, body mesenchyme, liver, spleen, lymphoid organs, and bone marrow. Most of these function in this capacity only during embryonic life. In adult mammals only the lymphoid tissues and bone marrow ultimately have a hemopioetic function.

24. The composition of blood varies somewhat in different vertebrate groups. The main difference lies in the erythrocytes which are flattened, oval-shaped cells in all except mammals. Only camels and llamas, among mammals, have oval erythrocytes. The red corpuscles are nucleated except in mammals, in which the erythroblasts, which form erythrocytes, extrude their nuclei.

25. Leukocytes, formed in the bone marrow and lymphoid tissues, can wander about the body outside blood vessels. Certain kinds act as phagocytes, engulfing bacteria and particles of various kinds.

26. Blood platelets, possibly homologous with spindle cells of lower forms, are concerned with blood clotting in mammals. Their origin is not known with certainty.

CHAPTER 13

NERVOUS SYSTEM

Of all the cells in the body, those of which nervous tissue is composed have the property of irritability most highly developed. The detailed structure of nervous tissue has been discussed previously (Chap. 3). It will be recalled that all nervous tissues are of ectodermal origin. They trace their beginning, for the most part, from the embryonic neural tube and neural crests. In some cases, *placodes*, or thickenings of the superficial ectoderm, in certain restricted areas, also give rise to nervous elements.

In addition to nerve cells, or *neurons*, of various types, there are present in the central nervous system (brain and spinal cord) other components referred to as *neuroglia*. These ectodermal cells are interspersed among the nervous elements, providing support and some degree of protection. True connective tissue is not present. Several types of neuroglia cells are recognized. They generally consist of very much branched cells, the processes of which form an interlacing network between neurons. Other nonnervous, supporting, *ependymal cells* of an epithelial nature line the cavities of brain and spinal cord. They are often ciliated.

Gray matter and white matter. Nerve-cell bodies, their dendrites, and the proximal unmyelinated portions of the axons have a grayish appearance and form the greater part of the *gray matter* of the brain and spinal cord. Groups of nerve-cell bodies are called *ganglia*. The term ganglion is generally used to refer to an aggregation of nerve-cell bodies forming a mass or enlargement *outside* the central nervous system. Gray ganglionic masses *within* the brain and cord are usually designated as *nuclei*, or *nerve centers*. *White matter*, on the other hand, is composed chiefly of bundles of glistening-white myelinated, or medullated, fibers. Such bundles, which are possible to trace in prepared sections of brain and spinal cord, are known as *fiber tracts*. In some regions gray and white matter are intermingled to varying degrees, such an arrangement being known as a *reticular formation*.

Primary divisions. The nervous system is extremely complex, and all parts are structurally connected and functionally integrated. It is customary, nevertheless, to speak of two main divisions. These are (1) the *central nervous system*, composed of the *brain*, which lies within the cranial cavity of the skull, and the *spinal cord*, lying within the neural, or spinal, canal formed by the arches of the vertebrae, (2) the *peripheral nervous system*, made up of nerves and ganglia which are connected to the brain and the spinal cord. Part of the peripheral nervous system is composed of autonomic fibers which are distributed to those parts of the body under involuntary control. These, in turn, consist of sympathetic and parasympathetic components which function in an opposite manner in mediating various involuntary activities of the body. The autonomic portion of the peripheral nervous system is sometimes spoken of as a third division of the nervous system and is called the *autonomic nervous system*. However, since autonomic fibers are anatomically associated with spinal nerves and certain cranial nerves, it is most logical to include them under the category of the peripheral nervous system. In the following pages we shall refer to the autonomic components as the *peripheral autonomic system*.

CENTRAL NERVOUS SYSTEM

Early development. The ectodermal neural plate from which the neural tube is formed consists at first of a single layer of epithelial cells. These usually proliferate as the neural folds are developing. By the time that the folds have fused dorsally to form the neural tube, its walls are composed of several layers of cells. The original epithelial cells give rise to two types of daughter cells, *neuroblasts* and *spongioblasts*. Neuroblasts develop into typical neurons with their highly specialized properties of irritability and conductivity. Spongioblasts give rise to the nonnervous supporting ependymal and other neuroglial elements.

Soon after the neural tube has formed, it can readily be discerned that the cells of which it is composed become arranged in three rather definite layers: (1) an inner, epithelial *ependymal layer*, (2) an intermediate, nucleated *mantle layer*, (3) an outer, fibrous *marginal layer*, free of nuclei (Fig. 13.1). It is from the neuroblasts in the mantle layer that the nerve cells forming the gray matter of brain and spinal cord develop. An axon and one or more dendrites grow out from each neuroblast in the development of a typical neuron. The axons of certain cells grow peripherally until they reach the marginal layer of the neural tube. They may then course anteriorly or posteriorly in that layer, ultimately to form the fiber tracts of brain and cord. The axons of other mantle-layer neurons penetrate through the marginal layer primarily in the ventrolateral angles of the neural tube. These become the *ventral*, or *motor*, *roots* of the spinal nerves and the motor components of certain cranial nerves. The ependymal cells form the lining of the *central canal of the spinal cord* and the *ventricles of the brain*, which are derived from the original cavity of the neural tube. Cilia develop from the ends of the ependymal cells in contact with the central canal. Although cilia are present during embryonic development, they rarely persist in adult life. The remainder of the ependymal cells may branch into long processes which aid in support of the strictly nervous elements.

Brain and spinal cord develop from the dorsal, hollow, neural tube itself. The anterior end of the neural tube, destined to form the brain, enlarges from almost the very beginning. Two constrictions appear in the enlarged portion so that three *primary brain vesicles* are rather clearly marked off. These are called the *forebrain (prosencephalon), midbrain (mesencephalon)*, and *hindbrain (rhombencephalon)*, respectively. The remainder of the neural tube, which fails to enlarge at the same rate as the brain, becomes the spinal cord, or *myelon*.

Subsequent changes in prosencephalon and rhombencephalon result in a further division of these two portions of the brain, but the mesencephalon

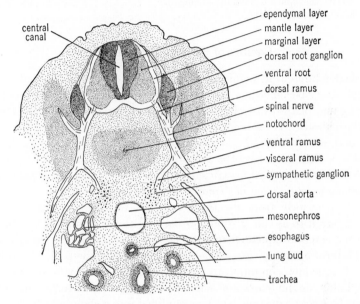

FIG. 13.1. Section through portion of 12-mm. pig embryo, showing differentiation of neural tube and spinal nerves with roots and rami.

undergoes no division. It gives rise to the *optic lobes*. Paired outgrowths from the anterior end of the prosencephalon give rise to the *telencephalon*, destined to form the *cerebral hemispheres;* the remainder constitutes the *diencephalon* (or *thalamencephalon*), which becomes the *'tween brain*. The anteroventral portion of the telencephalon later becomes modified to form the *olfactory lobes*, or *rhinencephalon*. A dorsal projection of the *metencephalon*, or anterior end of the rhombencephalon, gives rise to the *cerebellum*, and the remainder of the hindbrain becomes the *myelencephalon*, or *medulla oblongata* (Fig. 16.17). The floor of the metencephalon in lower vertebrates does not differ from that of the myelencephalon. In higher forms, however, along with the more important role assumed by the cerebellum, the floor in this region becomes thickened by the development of fiber tracts, and in mammals forms the conspicuous *pons*. The posterior end of the myelencephalon is continuous with the spinal cord.

SUMMARY

I. Prosencephalon (forebrain)
   A. Telencephalon
      1. Rhinencephalon (olfactory lobes)
      2. Cerebral hemispheres
   B. Diencephalon ('tween brain)
II. Mesencephalon (midbrain)
III. Rhombencephalon (hindbrain)
   A. Metencephalon (cerebellum, and pons if present)
   B. Myelencephalon (medulla oblongata)
IV. Myelon (spinal cord)

Cavities of Brain and Spinal Cord

With the differentiation of the neural tube into brain and spinal cord, its original cavity becomes modified to form the ventricles of the brain and the central canal of the cord (Fig. 16.19). When the telencephalon develops into the paired cerebral hemispheres, the cavity extends into those structures as the *lateral ventricles*, or *ventricles I* and *II*. The cavity of the diencephalon is then known as the *third ventricle*. Each lateral ventricle communicates with the third ventricle by means of an opening, the *interventricular foramen*, or *foramen of Monro*. In higher vertebrates a narrow canal extends posteriorly from the third ventricle through the mesencephalon and is referred to as the *cerebral aqueduct*, or *aqueduct of Sylvius*. In lower forms the cerebral aqueduct may be considerably expanded on either side and the term *optic ventricle*, or *mesocoele*, is then applied. Posteriorly the cerebral aqueduct communicates with the enlarged cavity of the rhombencephalon, or the *fourth ventricle*. In numerous lower forms the anterior part of the fourth ventricle becomes modified into a chamber, the *metacoele*, extending into the cerebellum. The portion of the fourth ventricle within the medulla oblongata is then referred to as the *myelocoele*. It is continued posteriorly as the *central canal* of the spinal cord.

As development of the brain continues, its walls become thickened with nervous tissue except in two regions where only the epithelial ependymal layer is retained. These regions include the anterior part of the roof of the diencephalon and the roof of the medulla oblongata. In each region a fusion of the roof with a highly vascular membrane, the *pia mater* (page 581), forms a *tela choroidea*. Folds from the tela choroidea project into the third and fourth ventricles and are known, respectively, as the *anterior* and *posterior choroid plexuses*.

Lymphlike cerebrospinal fluid is contained within the cavities of brain and spinal cord and circulates through the ventricles and central canal. It passes out of these cavities through openings, to be mentioned later, to bathe the entire central nervous system. The choroid plexuses are important in forming the cerebrospinal fluid.

The Spinal Cord

The portion of the neural tube which forms the spinal cord undergoes considerably less modification than that forming the brain. It generally assumes the shape of a more or less cylindrical, but slightly flattened, tube. It widens at the anterior end, where it is continuous with the medulla oblongata. The posterior end usually tapers down to a fine thread, the *filum terminale* (Fig. 13.2).

In cyclostomes and fishes, the spinal cord is of fairly uniform diameter throughout its length, but in most tetrapods two conspicuous swellings, or enlargements, occur at points where the nerves going to the limbs arise. Since, with the development of limbs, the nerve supply to these structures is increased, the enlargements are actually places in which greater numbers of nerve-cell bodies are situated than are present at other levels of the cord. The *cervical enlargement* is the more anterior of the two. It is the region where the large nerves supplying the forelimbs arise. The *lumbar enlargement*, near the posterior end of the spinal cord, marks the point of origin of nerves supplying the hindlimbs. The difference in degree of development of forelimbs and hindlimbs in various tetrapods accounts for the fact that in some forms the cervical enlargement exceeds the lumbar

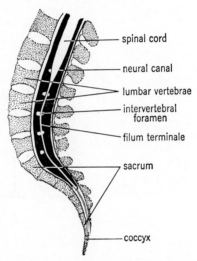

FIG. 13.2. Diagram of sagittal section of lower end of vertebral column of man, showing its relation to spinal cord and filum terminale.

enlargement in size, whereas in others, the reverse condition obtains. In such limbless forms as snakes, neither enlargement is present. It is probable that in certain extinct dinosaurs, which possessed enormous limbs but had relatively little cranial capacity, the nervous tissue composing the cervical and lumbar enlargements exceeded that of the brain itself in size. Casts of the spinal canal of the dinosaur *Stegosaurus* indicate that the lumbar enlargement may have been twelve times as large as the brain.

The spinal cord in higher forms (Fig. 13.3) has a conspicuous *ventral fissure* on its undersurface. A slight median depression, or *sulcus*, may be present on the dorsal side. From the sulcus a *dorsal septum* extends toward the interior of the cord. The dorsal septum and ventral fissure incompletely divide the spinal cord into symmetrical halves, connected across the middle by *commissures* of nervous tissue. The central canal, lined with a single layer of ependymal cells, is very small and lies in the center of the nervous mass connecting the two halves of the cord.

Length of cord. At first, during embryonic development, the spinal cord and vertebral column are of approximately the same length. During subsequent development in many vertebrates, the growth of the cord fails to keep pace with that of the spinal column. As a result, the spinal cord of the adult may be considerably shorter than the backbone. In man it averages slightly less than 18 in. in length and reaches down only to the upper border of the second lumbar vertebra. The filum terminale, however, continues on to the first segment of the coccyx. In other vertebrates,

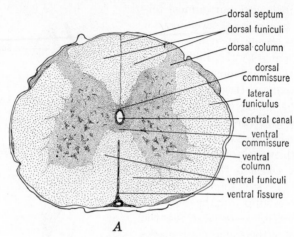

dorsal septum
dorsal funiculi
dorsal column
dorsal commissure
lateral funiculus
central canal
ventral commissure
ventral column
ventral funiculi
ventral fissure

A

B

Fig. 13.3. Cross sections of spinal cords of *A*, cat, and *B*, frog, shown at same magnification. Gray matter is heavily stippled; white matter is lightly stippled.

the spinal cord may be relatively much longer than in man, but within the entire group there is a very definite tendency toward a reduction in length.

Gray and white matter of cord. In cross section the spinal cord is seen to be composed of gray and white matter, the former being almost completely surrounded by the latter (Fig. 13.3). The gray matter in amniotes is arranged somewhat in the form of a butterfly, or in the shape of the letter H. The portions corresponding to the upper bars of the H extend dorsally and are known as *dorsal columns*. The lower bars are the *ventral columns*, and the connecting bar, in which the central canal lies, forms the *dorsal* and *ventral gray commissures*, above and below the central canal, respectively. Considerable variation exists in the arrangement of the gray matter within the spinal cords of different vertebrates, the H-shaped distribution being more typical of higher forms.   The cell bodies in the dorsal columns are, for the most part, those of *association neurons*.   Their dendrites form synapses with the axons of sensory, or afferent, nerve fibers which enter the spinal cord via the dorsal roots of spinal nerves.   The axons of the association neurons, which are of variable length, course up or down the spinal cord, cross to the opposite side, or pass ventrally on the same side, to form synapses with the dendrites of motor, or efferent, neurons, the cell bodies of which are located in the ventral columns.   The axons of the motor neurons in higher forms typically emerge via the ventral roots of the spinal nerves (Fig. 13.13*B*).

Neurologists have discovered that the cells in the dorsal and ventral columns show a rather definite arrangement into areas, each of which is associated with a certain type of function.   All functions carried on by the body can be resolved into two main categories, *somatic* and *visceral*.   Somatic functions are those carried on by the skin and its derivatives, the voluntary musculature and skeletal structures.   Visceral functions are those performed by the other organ systems of the body, i.e., digestive, respiratory, excretory, reproductive, endocrine, and circulatory systems. Somatic sensory fibers carry impulses from the somatic tissues to the central nervous system.   They form synapses with cells in the *upper* portion of the dorsal columns.   Visceral sensory fibers are those carrying impulses from the visceral organs.   They form synapses with cells in the *lower* portion of the dorsal columns.   The motor neurons, the cell bodies of which are located in the ventral columns, are likewise of two types, somatic and visceral.   The cell bodies of somatic motor neurons are located primarily in the *lower* portions of the ventral columns, whereas visceral motor neurons have their origin in the *upper* and *lateral* portions of the ventral columns. There are thus four areas in the gray matter on each side of the spinal cord, arranged in a dorsoventral sequence as follows: somatic sensory, visceral sensory, visceral motor, somatic motor (Fig. 13.4*A*).   The visceral areas are, in general, smaller than the somatic areas.   A similar arrangement is present in the gray matter of the medulla oblongata (Fig. 13.4*B*).

The white matter of the cord is arranged in longitudinal columns called *funiculi* which lie outside the gray matter.   The funiculi are in turn divided into *fasciculi*, or *fiber tracts*, composed of medullated fibers that carry impulses up and down the cord and to and from the brain.   A *lateral funiculus* is present on each side between dorsal and ventral columns.   A *dorsal funiculus* lies between the dorsal septum and the dorsal column on each side, and a ventral funiculus is located between the ventral fissure and the ventral column of gray matter.   The two ventral funiculi are in communication through the *white commissure* which lies just below the ventral gray commissure.   This serves as a bridge between the white matter of the two sides.

It is beyond the scope of this book to discuss the detailed arrangement of fiber tracts in which nerve fibers ascend and descend the spinal cord.   Suffice it to say that those in the dorsal funiculi, for the most part, carry sensory nerve impulses *up* the cord and *to* the brain. Those in the ventral funiculi are primarily motor, carrying impulses *down* the cord and *from* the brain. The lateral funiculi carry both ascending (sensory) and descending

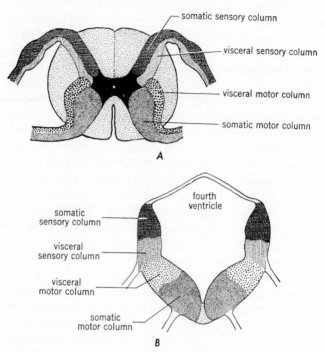

Fig. 13.4. Diagrams indicating the relative positions of the four columns of gray matter in mammals on each side of *A*, the spinal cord, *B*, the medulla oblongata.

(motor) fibers. In general, the lower vertebrates do not show so elaborate an organization or arrangement of the columns, funiculi, and fasciculi in the spinal cord as do the higher forms.

Comparative anatomy of the spinal cord. *Amphioxus.* The spinal cord of amphioxus is of uniform diameter throughout except for a gradual tapering toward the end of the tail. It appears to be somewhat triangular in shape when viewed in cross section. The central canal is slit-shaped. There is no clear-cut distinction between gray matter and white matter, since in amphioxus medullated fibers have not as yet made their appearance. Only in a very general way does a cross section of the spinal cord of amphioxus bear a resemblance to that of the typical vertebrate. Nerve-cell bodies, some of exceptional size, lie in the central region in the vicinity of the central canal. The canal is not lined with a continuous layer of ependymal cells. Some of the giant cells even cross the slitlike central canal.

Cyclostomes. A truly tubular spinal cord first appears in cyclostomes. The cord is considerably flattened and is ribbon-shaped. The dorsal side is more or less convex, and the ventral side concave. Of fairly uniform diameter, the cord tapers gradually to the posterior end. Gray and white matter are not sharply differentiated, the gray matter being in the form of a broad longitudinal band surrounded on all sides by white matter, except where the roots of spinal nerves emerge. Dorsal septum and ventral fissure are lacking.

Fishes. A dorsal fissure is present in the spinal cords of most fishes, but a ventral fissure is absent. Gray matter is arranged in the form of a triangle, the apex of which points dorsally. Paired ventral columns of gray matter are present for the first time. In most fishes the cord tapers gradually to the end of the tail, but in certain teleosts there is a marked shortening and the spinal cord terminates at some distance from the end of the vertebral column. Thus the position of the posterior end is considerably anterior to the parts of the body which it supplies with nerves. The spinal cord of the marine sunfish, *Orthagoriscus*, has been reduced to almost ridiculous proportions. In this large fish, which may reach a length of 8 ft. and weigh a ton or more, the spinal cord is less than $3/4$ in. long and is even shorter than the brain.

Amphibians. In salamanders the spinal cord extends to the posterior end of the vertebral column, but in frogs and toads it has been considerably shortened. The filum terminale in these forms extends into the urostyle. Cervical and lumbar enlargements appear for the first time, since these are the first forms in which the appendages have been modified into true limbs. A dorsal sulcus may be present, and a ventral fissure appears for the first time. Gray matter may appear in the form of an oval in cross section, but dorsal and ventral columns are usually present (Fig. 13.3*B*) and the beginning of the typical H-shaped arrangement found in higher forms is apparent. Fasciculi, or fiber tracts, in the white matter are more clearly indicated than in lower forms.

Reptiles. The reptilian spinal cord extends the entire length of the vertebral column. Cervical and lumbar enlargements are absent in snakes and limbless lizards but are present in other forms. They seem to be unduly conspicuous in turtles, however. The trunk muscles in turtles have been reduced, and their nerve supply is correspondingly less. Therefore, the portion of the spinal cord between the two enlargements is more slender than usual. The H-shaped arrangement of gray matter is typical of the condition found in other amniotes.

Birds. The spinal cord of birds extends the full length of the vertebral column, and a filum terminale is absent. The most conspicuous feature which distinguishes the spinal cord of birds from that of other vertebrates is the separation of the two halves of the cord on the dorsal side of the lumbar enlargement. An elliptical space, the *sinus rhomboidalis*, is present, filled with neuroglia cells of a gelatinous character. The relative sizes of cervical and lumbar enlargements depend upon the degree of development of wings and legs. The ostrich is notable for the large size of its lumbar enlargement.

Mammals. In the duckbill platypus and a few rodents the spinal cord extends to the sacral region of the vertebral column, but in other mammals it has been shortened. Even in mammals with well-developed tails, the cord fails to extend into the caudal region. Such tails are moved primarily by means of longitudinal muscles and ligaments which are innervated by nerves at their bases. In addition to the median dorsal sulcus, dorsolateral and ventrolateral sulci are frequently present. The ventral fissure is conspicuous. A marked discrepancy exists in the size of cervical and lumbar enlargements in bats, which have an unusually large cervical enlargement associated with the large wing muscles used in flight.

The Brain

With the development of bilateral symmetry in the animal kingdom and the necessity that one end of an animal precede the other in locomotion, the end first coming in contact with the environment developed a concentration of nervous tissue as well as sense organs. These structures better enabled animals to cope with their environment in such a manner that they could survive. The term *cephalization* is used in referring to such localization of structures and functions in the head region.

The brain of chordates, which is basically an enlargement of the anterior end of the neural tube, appears in its simplest form in amphioxus where it is but slightly larger in diameter than the spinal cord. In higher forms it becomes more complex as the evolutionary scale is ascended. *Latimeria* has the smallest brain, in relation to the size of the animal, of any vertebrate. In the primitive condition the cell bodies of the neurons comprising the central nervous system are aggregated around the central canal or original cavity of the neural tube. This arrangement persists in the spinal cords of higher forms. In the brain region, however, a movement or migration of cells to peripheral areas has occurred so that gray matter and white matter differ in their spatial relations from the arrangement observed in the spinal cord. The degree of development of the various parts of the brain of vertebrates is correlated with their position in the evolutionary scale and with certain special requirements related to the particular environments in which they live. As the brain has developed it has gradually become the center of control over most body activities, aside from certain simple reflexes (page 610). Various nerve centers in the brain serve to integrate and correlate the impulses brought to it by afferent fibers from all parts of the body.

The three primary divisions of the brain previously mentioned—prosencephalon, mesencephalon, and rhombencephalon—make up what is often referred to as the *brain stem.* Each of these divisions may originally have developed in association with one of the three major sense organs, an arrangement which still persists in all vertebrates. Generally speaking, the sense of smell is related primarily to the prosencephalon, the sense of sight to the mesencephalon, and the sense of hearing to the rhombencephalon. Further developments from the brain stem such as the cerebral hemispheres, roof of the midbrain, and cerebellum appeared later as dorsal outgrowths into which nerve cells migrated, so that gray matter appears in the peripheral areas in these regions.

Such variations from the previously described ground plan of the brain as are to be found in the different classes of vertebrates are the result of certain mechanical factors which should be understood before details of brain structure are considered. These consist of (1) outpocketings or inpocketings (evaginations or invaginations) of various portions of the primitive brain vesicles, (2) folding or plaiting of the walls of different parts of the embryonic brain, thus bringing about an increased surface area of the folded region, (3) thickening of the walls in certain regions as a result of an increase in amount of nervous tissue, (4) failure of the thin-walled embryonic area to differentiate into nervous tissue, (5) bending or folding of the brain along its longitudinal axis, such bends being called *flexures*.

Flexures.   Only in amphioxus are "brain" and spinal cord arranged in a straight line. In vertebrates, however, owing to unequal rates of growth of various components, certain flexures occur during embryonic development which modify the original condition temporarily or permanently. Since the brain lengthens more rapidly than other head structures, the bending is apparently influenced by space limitations.

In all vertebrates a *cephalic*, or *cranial*, *flexure* occurs in the region of the mesencephalon in such a manner that the derivatives of the forebrain are bent downward at right angles to the rest. This is more pronounced in some forms than in others and is least conspicuous in fishes. Later there is a tendency for the brain to straighten out once more, and only in birds and mammals, particularly in primates, is the cephalic flexure permanently retained. The second flexure to appear is the *cervical*, or *nuchal*, *flexure*, occurring near the junction of medulla oblongata and spinal cord. The bend is in the same direction as the cephalic flexure. The third, or *pontine*, *flexure* is found in the region of the metencephalon and is opposite in direction to the other two (Fig. 13.5). Cervical and pontine flexures practically never even appear in anamniotes but may be quite evident in the embryonic stages of amniotes. However, as development progresses, these two posterior flexures tend to straighten and either diminish or disappear. In birds and mammals the front part of the brain (cerebral hemispheres and diencephalon) comes to lie, at least partially, on top of, or over, the posterior portions.

Gray and white matter of brain.   The posterior end of the medulla oblongata merges imperceptibly with the anterior end of the spinal cord. A point just anterior to the first pair of spinal nerves is generally considered to be the level at which brain and spinal cord are joined. The spinal cord lies posterior to the foramen magnum. The structure of the medulla oblongata at its posterior end differs but little from that of the spinal cord. In this region the gray matter is on the inside and the white matter surrounds it peripherally. Farther forward in the brain, gray and white matter lose their original relationship and are more or less irregularly intermingled in a reticular formation. In the cerebral hemispheres, roof of the midbrain (*optic tectum*), and cerebellum, however, the positions of these layers are reversed, so that the gray matter forms a sort of cap over the

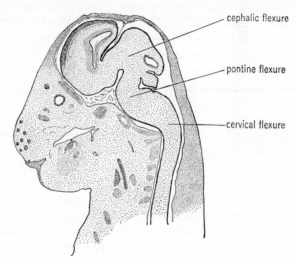

cephalic flexure

pontine flexure

cervical flexure

Fig. 13.5. Sagittal section through head of 18-day rat embryo, showing flexures of the brain.

underlying white matter. The gray matter of the brain, like that of the spinal cord, consists of nerve-cell bodies with their dendrites and proximal portions of their axons. They are usually grouped together in the form of nuclei. The white matter consists of tracts of myelinated fibers connecting various parts of the brain and of ascending and descending fibers carrying impulses to and from the spinal cord.

Myelencephalon. The lateral and ventral walls of the medulla oblongata thicken markedly, but the dorsal wall retains its epithelial character. The *pia mater*, a vascular membrane surrounding the brain, fuses with this thin layer of ependymal cells, the two together being called a *tela choroidea*. This membrane forms the roof of the large, triangular-shaped fourth ventricle of the brain. The fourth ventricle narrows posteriorly, where it is continuous with the central canal of the spinal cord. Vascular folds of the tela choroidea extend into the fourth ventricle to form the *posterior choroid plexus*. In lampreys the posterior choroid plexus forms an everted sac.

The thickened ventral and lateral walls of the medulla contain large white fiber tracts as well as several columns of gray matter. The gray matter is arranged in columns similar to those in the spinal cord, consisting of somatic sensory, visceral sensory, visceral motor, and somatic motor components (Fig. 13.4*B*). A longitudinal groove on the inner wall of each side marks the division between dorsal sensory and ventral motor portions. In higher vertebrates the integrity of the columns of gray matter is lost and a separation into various nuclei has occurred.

Cranial nerves V to XII form connections with the medulla. The points of origin of the purely somatic motor cranial nerves VI and XII lie in the most ventral or somatic motor column of gray matter of the medulla. The visceral motor components of the branchial cranial nerves, V, VII, IX, X, and XI, originate in the visceral motor column. The special sensory fibers of nerve VIII and the somatic sensory constituents of nerves V, VII, IX, and X enter the dorsal somatic sensory column. The visceral sensory components of nerves VII, IX, and X are associated with the visceral sensory column.

Cyclostomes, fishes, and amphibians possess only 10 pairs of cranial nerves. In these animals only cranial nerves V to X are associated with the myelencephalon.

Several fiber tracts in the medulla cross over (decussate) to the opposite side of the brain. This crossing occurs in the posterior region of a swollen part of the myelencephalon composed of paired *pyramids.*

The myelencephalon is sometimes referred to as the oldest part of the brain, since it is well developed in all vertebrates, even though other portions may be rudimentary or lacking.

FIG. 13.6. Dorsal view of brain of buffalo fish, *Carpiodes tumidus*, showing conspicuous vagal lobes. (*After Herrick.*)

It contains important nerve centers which control such vital physiological processes as regulation of heartbeat, respiration, and metabolism. They represent portions of the visceral motor column.

In cyclostomes the medulla oblongata is the only part of the brain that can be said to be really well developed. In these forms, as well as in fishes and caudate amphibians, certain giant cells are located in the medulla. Their axons extend posteriorly to the muscles of the tail and are apparently concerned with execution of muscular contractions involved in swimming.

In some fishes a pair of prominent *vagal lobes* (Fig. 13.6) is present on the sides of the medulla oblongata. They represent enlargements of the visceral sensory area and are centers for the sense of taste, which is very well developed in these fishes. Vagal lobes are not to be found in adult amphibians or in higher vertebrates.

The dorsal anterior portion of the medulla oblongata is referred to as the *acousticolateralis area*. It is actually a development of the somatic sensory column and is continuous with the auricles of the cerebellum (see below). This area contains nuclei associated with nerves from the lateral-line system and the inner ear. With the disappearance of the lateral-line system, in terrestrial vertebrates, the area contains nuclei concerned only with the equilibratory and auditory functions of the ear.

Metencephalon. The dorsal part of the metencephalon, contrary to that of the myelencephalon with its thin epithelial covering, becomes the elevated and thickened cerebellum. The function of this portion of the brain is to coordinate the neuromuscular mechanism of the body. It is concerned with the proprioceptive muscle sense and with the sensory nerves connected with the equilibratory portion of the inner ear. One finds, as would be expected, that the cerebellum is much more highly developed in animals that are active, whether such activity occurs in water, on land, or in the air. In cyclostomes, sluggish fishes, and amphibians the cerebellum is poorly developed and consists of little more than a transverse shelf or ridge bordering the anterior edge of the tela choroidea of the myelencephalon. In such active fishes as most elasmobranchs and certain teleosts, the cerebellum becomes a prominent structure (Fig. 16.17) extending dorsally and partially overlapping the mesencephalon anteriorly, and the medulla oblongata posteriorly. Its cavity, the *metacoele*, or *cerebellar ventricle*, connects below by a narrow aperture with the myelocoele near the point where the latter is joined by the cerebral aqueduct. A shallow, median, longitudinal depression on its dorsal surface, as well as a transverse groove, gives a lobed appearance to the cerebellum in certain elasmobranchs. The ventral portion of the metencephalon in the lower vertebrates is composed of heavy fiber tracts which merge with those of the medulla oblongata.

Prominent, irregular projections called the *auricular lobes*, or *restiform bodies*, continuous with the medulla oblongata, are actually parts of the cerebellum although some authorities consider them to belong to the medulla. They are situated at the anterior lateral angles of the medulla in certain fishes (Elasmobranchii, Paleopterygii, Dipnoi, and a few others). Each auricle contains a cavity, or *auricular recess*, continuous with the fourth ventricle. The auricles are centers of equilibration. They serve to correlate muscular movements of the body in relation to impulses arising in the sensory nerves connected with the inner ears. The inner ears of these fishes are primarily organs of equilibration.

The cerebellum of reptiles is not so highly developed as that of elasmobranch fishes. It is rather simple in structure, in keeping with the sluggish life and poikilothermous nature of these animals. Swimming reptiles have a better-developed cerebellum than do others. The greatest advance in the reptilian cerebellum is seen in such higher forms as crocodilians, in which a pair of small, lateral, *floccular lobes* first appears near the ventral side of the cerebellum. These correspond to the auricles, or restiform bodies, of the fishes mentioned above.

In birds, the cerebellum shows considerable advance over the reptilian condition. It consists of a prominent middle portion called the *vermis*, which is indistinctly divided into anterior, middle, and posterior portions. The vermis bears a number of transverse furrows. Lateral floccular lobes are much more highly developed than those of reptiles and lie on either side of the vermis. The cerebellum of birds extends quite far posteriorly and entirely covers the tela choroidea of the medulla oblongata. The *cerebellar cortex*, or gray matter of the cerebellum, covers the white matter which, in birds, shows a complexly branched arrangement called the *arbor vitae*. A small cavity, a projection of the fourth ventricle, extends into the cerebellum. In some birds there appears for the first time a sort of bridge of nerve fibers called the *pons* on the ventral side of the cerebellum and below the medulla oblongata. The fiber tracts of the pons connect the cerebral cortex with the cerebellum. They decussate, crossing to the opposite side, as they pass to the cerebellum.

The mammalian cerebellum (Figs. 18.32A and 18.33) is more highly developed than in other vertebrates. The middle portion, or vermis, is divided into anterior, middle, and posterior lobes. The anterior and posterior lobes are entirely median, but the middle lobe has bilateral extensions, the *cerebellar hemispheres*. The floccular lobes on either side of the posterior lobe of the vermis are much larger than those of reptiles and birds. The whole surface of the cerebellum is thrown into numerous folds, or *gyri*, separated from one another by deep grooves, or *sulci*. Branches of the arbor vitae extend into the cerebellar folds. The ventral part of the mammalian metencephalon is marked by a conspicuous *pons*. This is composed of a prominent mass of transverse nerve fibers, conspicuously arched. In its center is a median longitudinal groove, the *basilar sulcus*, where the basilar artery lies. In mammals, control of body movement has been shifted to the cortex of the highly developed cerebral hemispheres. Motor fibers from the cerebral cortex pass to the cerebellum via the pons. The ventral portion of the pons consists mostly of nerve fibers interspersed with small amounts of gray matter; its dorsal portion is largely a reticular formation continuous with that of the myelencephalon and containing several large nuclei. In lower mammals the cerebellum shows a simpler form of organization than does that of higher forms. Advancement is shown primarily by an increase in number and complexity of the cerebellar folds.

The cortex of the cerebellum consists of three layers: (1) an outer, or *molecular, layer,* (2) a middle, or *granular, layer,* (3) an internal *medullary layer* composed of white, medullated nerve fibers. Between the molecular and granular layers lie the large complexly branched *Purkinje cells* (Fig.

13.7), which are characteristic of the minute structure of the cerebellum. They are believed to play an important part in correlating nerve impulses with equilibratory muscular movements.

Mesencephalon. The embryonic midbrain undergoes relatively less differentiation than other portions of the brain. It is marked off from the hindbrain very early in development by a conspicuous constriction, the *isthmus.* The floor and walls of the mesencephalon are thick and composed of fiber tracts, the *cerebral peduncles,* connecting forebrain and hindbrain. The roof consists of a thick layer of gray matter, the *optic tectum.* Here the nerve cells become organized in layers somewhat similar to those of the cerebellar cortex. In lower vertebrates two dorsal prominences develop in the roof of the mesencephalon. They are the *optic lobes,* or *corpora bigemina,* which serve as centers for the visual sense. In lower forms each optic lobe contains a large cavity, the *optic ventricle,* the two ventricles together forming the *mesocoele* (Fig. 16.19). In higher forms, however, the lobes are practically solid structures and only the narrow cerebral aqueduct passes through the center of the mesencephalon. A definite transverse fissure divides the optic lobes of snakes and mammals into four prominences, the *corpora quadrigemina.*

FIG. 13.7. Purkinje cell from cerebellar cortex.

As the name implies, the optic lobes are primarily receptive centers for sensory nerve impulses coming from the eye. When corpora quadrigemina are present, as in mammals, the anterior pair, called the *superior colliculi,* contains receptive centers for the visual sense and the posterior pair, or *inferior colliculi,* serves to integrate auditory impulses. The superior colliculi in mammals have become less important as visual centers with the great development of the cerebral cortex, which seems to have taken over much of the integration and coordination of visual impulses.

At the anterior end of the roof of the mesencephalon is located the *posterior commissure* consisting of fiber tracts which connect the two sides of the brain. Some of the fibers are probably derived from the diencephalon.

Nuclei for the oculomotor, or third cranial nerve, lie in the floor of the mesencephalon near the midventral line. They are actually portions of the somatic motor column of gray matter which is continued forward into the midbrain. Nuclei for the trochlear, or fourth, cranial nerve are more posteriorly located and lie near the junction of mesencephalon and metencephalon. The fibers of the trochlear nerve course through the lateral walls of this portion of the brain to emerge from the dorsal side. The oculomotor and trochlear nerves supply certain muscles which move the eyeball (pages 477 to 478).

The optic lobes are more conspicuous features of the brains of lower vertebrates than of higher forms. In birds, however, the lobes are unusually well developed in correlation with the highly organized visual-sensory system which is so necessary to these animals in flying and feeding.

It is noteworthy that a vascular choroid plexus is present in the mid-dorsal portion of the mesencephalon in cyclostomes.

Diencephalon. The 'tween brain is bounded posteriorly by the posterior commissure, mentioned above, and anteriorly by a thin, membranous structure, the *lamina terminalis*. An *anterior commissure*, connecting the olfactory regions of the brain, is located in the lamina terminalis. The latter is usually considered to belong to the telencephalon. Its ventral termination is marked by a small recess just anterior to the optic chiasma. A fold, the *velum transversum*, marks the anterior end of the diencephalon on the dorsal side of the brain. It will be recalled that the third ventricle lies within the diencephalon. The optic vesicles, from which the sensory portions of the eyes develop (page 624), arise from the embryonic diencephalon. The original diencephalon undergoes considerable modification. It is composed of a dorsal *epithalamus*, a middle, very much thickened *thalamus*, and a thinner ventral portion, the *hypothalamus*. The thalamus in turn is divided into dorsal and ventral regions.

Epithalamus. The anterior portion of the dorsal roof plate covering the third ventricle retains its original epithelial, ependymal character and, together with the pia mater, forms a tela choroidea similar to that covering the fourth ventricle. Vascular folds of the tela choroidea extend into the third ventricle forming the *anterior choroid plexus*. Portions of the plexus may pass through the interventricular foramina into the lateral ventricles of the cerebral hemispheres. During early development, a prominent irregular fold of the tela choroidea, the *paraphysis*, extends dorsally from its very anterior end, overlapping the cerebral hemispheres to some extent. The paraphysis is actually a part of the roof of the telencephalon since it lies anterior to the velum transversum. Its cavity, however, is considered to be a part of the third ventricle. The function of the paraphysis is unknown. It usually disappears in adult life. In certain lower vertebrates large external folds of the anterior choroid plexus may be present in addition to the paraphysis.

Posterior to the tela choroidea the roof of the diencephalon consists largely of what has been termed the *epiphyseal apparatus*. This is composed, in several lower forms, of two median dorsal projections: an anterior *parietal body* and a posterior *pineal body*, or *epiphysis*. Both these structures are present in cyclostomes and in many fishes and reptiles. The two apparently fuse in amphibians. In most vertebrates, however, the parietal body has disappeared and only the pineal body persists.

The parietal body, when well developed, forms a small median eye. In lampreys a pigmented but rudimentary sort of retina is present at the distal end of the parietal stalk. The highest degree of development of this organ is found in the peculiar reptile *Sphenodon punctatum* and to a lesser degree in certain lizards. An *interparietal foramen* in the skulls of these and certain other forms provides a passage for the nerve connecting the parietal eye and brain. In no case is the parietal eye so well developed as to be comparable to the usual vertebrate eye, but it may well be capable of distinguishing light from dark.

The pineal body, which lies posterior to the parietal body when the latter is present, is thought by some to represent what may originally have been still another eye. This, together with the parietal eye, presumably formed a second, but median, pair of visual organs. Only in cyclostomes, however, does the epiphysis actually form an eyelike structure. The pineal body is present in all vertebrates and appears to be glandular in nature. Whether it is an endocrine gland or merely an interesting vestigial structure is still a matter for conjecture. There is no clear-cut proof that it is a functional endocrine organ. There are numerous reports in the literature that a condition known as precocious puberty (*macrogenitosomia praecox*) is associated with abnormalities of the pineal body.

The *brow spot*, commonly observed in the frog by students in elementary zoology courses, marks the location of the pineal organ. It apparently is a vestige of what may at one time have been a third, median eye.

A pair of *habenular bodies* lies just in front of the pineal body in the roof of the diencephalon. These structures are connected by means of a delicate *habenular commissure*. The habenular nuclei serve as olfactory centers.

The epithalamic portion of the diencephalon is of relatively little significance as a nerve center.

Thalamus. The thickened lateral portion of the diencephalon, known as the thalamus, which is divided into dorsal and ventral parts, contains important relay centers and consists largely of numbers of important nuclei of gray matter. They are integrating centers for impulses passing to and from the cerebral hemispheres. The dorsally located nuclei are concerned primarily with sensory impulses, and the ventral nuclei with motor impulses. Important sensory centers are the *lateral* and *medial geniculate bodies* which relay optic and auditory impulses, respectively. In reptiles the walls of the thalamus are thickened inwardly so as to meet in the center of the third ventricle. This condition is also found in mammals, the mass of gray matter connecting the two sides being termed the *intermediate mass,* or *soft commissure* (Fig. 18.33).

Hypothalamus. The ventral portion of the diencephalon is of great physiological importance, for both sympathetic and parasympathetic centers are located here. In other words, it is in the hypothalamus that the functions of the peripheral autonomic system are integrated with those of other nervous tissues of the body. The hypothalamus is the control center for such involuntary mechanisms as water, fat, and carbohydrate metabolism; temperature regulation; genital functions; and the rhythm of sleep. It is a conspicuous feature of the brains of fishes. The hypothalamus is less noticeable in amphibians, but in higher forms it becomes increasingly well developed. An important hormonal substance which has been tentatively named *hypothalamic D,* or the ACTH-hypophysiotropic factor, has been extracted from the hypothalamus (page 357).

The hypothalamus is composed of four main parts. The *optic chiasma,* or most anterior portion, is the point at which the two optic nerves cross as they pass from the eyes to the brain. Behind the chiasma is the *tuber cinereum* in which are located several nuclei thought to make up the parasympathetic center. Posterior to the tuber cinereum lies a pair of *mammillary bodies* containing nuclei for the integration of the olfactory sense in relation to other parts of the body. The *infundibulum* is an evagination of the hypothalamus at the level of the tuber cinereum. It grows ventrally to establish a connection with a diverticulum (*Rathke's pocket*) which arises from the roof of the embryonic mouth (stomodaeum). From the distal portion of the infundibulum is derived the *posterior lobe,* or *pars nervosa,* of the *pituitary gland.* Rathke's pocket, it will be recalled, gives rise to the anterior and intermediate lobes of that structure. A portion of the third ventricle frequently extends into the infundibulum.

In fishes and amphibians a pair of *inferior lobes* is present on either side at the base of the infundibulum. In these vertebrates the distal end of the infundibulum expands into a thin-walled, vascular sac, the *saccus vasculosus* (Fig. 16.18), of unknown function. Inferior lobes and saccus vasculosus are absent from the hypothalmic region in higher vertebrates.

Telencephalon. It is in the degree of development of the telencephalon that the greatest differences in the brains of vertebrates are to be found. In higher forms, the cerebral hemispheres, derived from the telencephalon, cover over the greater part of the remainder of the brain. The seat of consciousness lies in the cerebral hemispheres. Here are located the nerve centers controlling the activities which characterize the highly developed psychic life of man, such as intelligence, thought, and sensation.

Early in embryonic life two lateral swellings, or evaginations, appear at the anterior end of the prosencephalon. These grow anteriorly and dorsally. In some animals the two vesicles become fused secondarily along the median line. A longitudinal fissure between the two hemispheres is a conspicuous feature of most vertebrates but is only slightly indicated in fishes. The original anterior end of the neural tube remains practically unchanged in its position and becomes the lamina terminalis, mentioned above, which later marks the posterior border of the telencephalon on the ventral side of the brain. An *anterior commissure*, previously mentioned, connecting the olfactory regions of the two halves of the brain, is later located in the lamina terminalis.

At the anterior end of each hemisphere is an outgrowth called the *olfactory lobe*, or *rhinencephalon*. Projections of the lateral ventricles may or may not extend into the rhinencephalon. The olfactory lobes may come in contact with the posterior part of the nasal apparatus. In some forms in which the nares are located at some distance from the brain, the olfactory lobes are drawn out to a considerable length. In such cases each lobe becomes subdivided into an anterior, expanded *olfactory bulb*, which borders upon the olfactory apparatus, and a narrow *olfactory stalk*, or *tract*, connecting the bulb with the remainder of the brain (Fig. 16.17). The comparative size of the olfactory lobes is closely correlated with the extent to which the sense of smell is developed.

The anterior paired telencephalic swellings, or cerebral hemispheres, enlarge to an increasing degree as the vertebrate scale is ascended and undergo the greatest change of any of the brain regions. In the lowest living vertebrates, the cyclostomes, each hemisphere is divided into an anterior *olfactory bulb* and a posterior olfactory lobe, sometimes called the cerebral hemisphere. This part of the brain is concerned mainly with receiving olfactory impulses from the olfactory apparatus and relaying them to the diencephalon. In all vertebrates the floor of each hemisphere early differentiates into a thickened *corpus striatum*, a reticular formation, which receives its name from the fact that it has a striated appearance when viewed in microscopic section. The gray regions of the corpus striatum are often referred to as *basal nuclei*. The function of the corpus striatum is rather obscure. It is poorly developed in cyclostomes. The remainder of the hemisphere consists of a *pallium* which roofs over the lateral ventricles. It is the pallium that has become so highly developed and modified in the evolution of the higher groups of vertebrates (Fig. 13.9).

The pallium is at first relatively thin walled, and the gray matter is present only on its inner walls adjacent to the ventricle. In teleost fishes a thin, nonnervous layer forms the roof of the ventricle (Fig. 13.8). Here the gray matter of the pallium has pushed laterally and downward toward the corpus striatum, which is very large and well developed, bulging upward into the lateral ventricle on each side. The cerebral hemispheres of teleosts are usually small. The two halves are incompletely separated by a shallow median fissure. In elasmobranch fishes the cerebral hemispheres become more pronounced (Fig. 16.17). A shallow median groove on the dorsal side indicates a partial separation into two halves. The olfactory lobes in these

fishes are large and drawn out into bulb and stalk, as previously described.
In elasmobranchs and Dipnoi the pallium is fairly thick but is nevertheless
chiefly related to the sense of smell.   The gray matter is still undifferentiated and lines the cavities of the ventricles, white matter forming the
outer surface.   The corpus striatum is well developed.   In fishes, in general,
the telencephalon has not progressed beyond serving as an olfactory center.
In certain species some cells migrate from the gray matter into the outer
white region.

As the vertebrate scale is ascended there is an increasing tendency for
nerve cells from the inner gray layer to migrate out into peripheral areas.
In amphibians the arrangement differs but little from that of fishes except
that the pallium is thicker and more cells from the gray matter have moved
to peripheral positions.   The pallium can now be divided into two general
regions, a dorsal, medial *archipallium* and a more lateral *paleopallium* (Fig.
13.9).   The latter represents the olfactory region and lies above and adja-

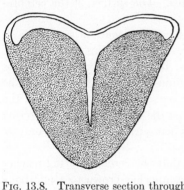

Fig. 13.8.   Transverse section through
cerebral hemispheres of teleost fish,
showing thin-walled roof.

Fig. 13.9.   Diagrams indicating evolutionary progress in development of
pallium.

cent to the corpus striatum.   The archipallium is also still associated with
olfactory nerve fibers.   The cerebral hemispheres of amphibians are relatively larger than those of fishes.   Olfactory lobes merge almost imperceptibly with the anterior ends of the cerebral hemispheres.   It is question-

able whether the telencephalon in amphibians functions in other than an olfactory capacity.

The first really marked change to be observed in the telencephalon of vertebrates occurs in reptiles. Most conspicuous is an increase in size of the cerebral hemispheres, which have grown backward to some extent and partially cover the diencephalon. The hemispheres are separated by a deep dorsal fissure. The corpus striatum is well developed but has assumed a more medial position. An increased amount of gray matter has migrated toward the peripheral surface. In certain reptiles, however, a new area, the *neopallium*, has appeared on the outer portion of each cerebral hemisphere at its anterodorsal end, between archipallial and paleopallial areas (Fig. 13.9). It is the growth and development of the neopallium that accounts for the large size of the cerebral hemispheres of the amniote vertebrates. In crocodilians, for the first time, nerve cells migrate into the neopallium and become arranged along its outer surface, thus forming a true cerebral cortex which serves as an association center. The surface of the cerebral hemispheres is smooth.

In birds, in correlation with the poorly developed sense of smell, the olfactory lobes are practically rudimentary. Archipallium, paleopallium, and neopallium are present as in reptiles, but a true cerebral cortex is poorly developed. The corpus striatum is unusually large and thick. The cerebral hemispheres in birds are so large, because of the great size of the corpus striatum, that they push back against the cerebellum, thus covering over the diencephalon and optic lobes. Their surface is smooth, and the outer wall rather thin.

It is in mammals, particularly in man, that the cerebral cortex reaches the height of its development. The neopallium has grown to a relatively enormous degree (Fig. 13.9), pushing the archipallial area medially and ventrally so that it becomes folded and lies in the ventromedial portion of the cerebral hemisphere, where it is known as the *hippocampal lobe*. This continues to serve as an olfactory center. Likewise, with the development of the neopallium, the paleopallium, originally in a lateral position, is pushed ventrally where it becomes the *pyriform lobe*, a portion of the olfactory lobe. The gray nerve-cell bodies in the neopallium become so numerous that they form a layer of gray matter, the cerebral cortex, in the outer part of the cerebral hemispheres. This layer, however, even in man, where it is most highly developed, is only a few millimeters thick, the thickness varying somewhat in different portions of the cerebral hemispheres. The corpus striatum in mammals is less conspicuous than in some lower forms.

The cerebral cortex is actually composed of six layers of cells, the detailed structure and arrangement of which varies from region to region. As a result of the expansion of the cerebral hemispheres, the number of cells in the cortical layer increases accordingly. It has been estimated that the number of cells in the human cerebral cortex is between 90 billion and 100 billion. The total mass of gray matter is small nevertheless.

In all vertebrates below mammals the cerebral hemispheres are smooth. In many mammals, however, the surface becomes folded or convoluted so that ridges and depressions appear (Fig. 18.32). The folding is caused by the more rapid multiplication of cells in the cortex than occurs in the underlying structures. The ridges of the folds are called *gyri*, and the depressions *sulci*. Since the cortical gray matter follows the convolutions, there is a considerable increase in surface area and the total amount of gray matter. The area of gray matter in the cerebral cortex of man is approximately 18 in. square. The extent to which the cerebral cortex is convoluted is not necessarily a criterion of intelligence, since some apes, with obviously highly developed mental faculties, have fewer convolutions than do certain other mammals with less well developed intellects. Large mammals generally have more convolutions than smaller species.

The presence of convolutions serves to divide the cerebral hemispheres into certain regions called *lobes*, among the most prominent of which are the temporal, occipital, frontal, and parietal lobes, named according to their position in relation to similarly named bones of the cranium. Each lobe is secondarily divided into numerous gyri. In the brains of primates the olfactory-lobe region shows a pronounced reduction, correlated with the poorly developed sense of smell of these animals.

Beginning with marsupials, a broad, white mass, the *corpus callosum*, or *anterior pallial commissure*, appears in mammals between the two hemispheres (Fig. 18.33). It is composed of a band of white medullated fibers which connect nearly all parts of the neopallial cortical regions of the two sides. Lying ventral to the corpus callosum is a similar band of white fibers, the *fornix*, which connects the hippocampal lobes with the hypothalamus.

The cerebral hemispheres in man are so large that they cover over all the other portions of the brain. A description of their detailed structure is beyond the scope of this book, and special treatises on neurology should be consulted by the interested student. The numerous neurons in the cerebral cortex communicate with one another in an intricate manner by means of their processes. Beneath the outer layer of gray matter is the *medulla of the cerebral hemisphere*, composed of white medullated fibers which either originate in cortical cells and carry outgoing impulses from the cortex or else come from other parts of the brain and bring impulses to the cortex. In addition, there are commissural fibers in the cerebral medulla which form complex connections between the two cerebral hemispheres.

Localization of functions. There is no evidence that certain portions of the cerebral hemispheres possess functions which correspond to various faculties of the mind. There is, for example, no particular area for mathematical reasoning, logic, honesty, etc. The practice of phrenology, which seeks to determine facts about the mind and character by studying the contours of the cranium, which fits so closely to the cerebral hemispheres, belongs in the realm of quackery. Much has been learned, however, about localization of various body functions in the cerebral cortex by study of persons who by accident have had portions of the cerebral hemispheres destroyed. The facts learned have been substantiated by experimental removal or electrical stimulation of areas in the cerebral hemispheres of laboratory animals. There is now a large body of evidence showing that there are definite areas in the cerebral cortex which mediate various functions of the body such as speech, sight, smell, and movements of certain muscles. Both sensory and motor areas are present. These areas are not clearly circumscribed, however. The different regions are so closely connected anatomically and physiologically that injury to one may bring about changes in others located in a distant portion of the brain.

Decussation. The presence of a number of commissures in the brain and spinal cord has frequently been alluded to in the previous pages. They serve to connect similar regions in the two sides of the central nervous system and make bilateral integration possible. There are also fiber tracts in the brain which, in their course, cross over, or *decussate*, to the opposite side.

It is a well-known fact that injury to the brain on one side of the body often results in paralysis of muscles on the opposite side. Impulses set up in certain *pyramidal cells* in the cerebral cortex travel down fibers leading to the nuclei of various cranial and spinal nerves. The fibers which course through the pyramids of the medulla oblongata, as previously mentioned, cross to the opposite side. In other words, injury anterior to the pyramidal decussation will affect structures on the opposite side of the body. Damage to fiber tracts posterior to the decussation, in the main, affects only the same side of the body as that on which the damage occurred. Conversely, nerve impulses, entering the body, travel up the spinal cord to the brain, crossing over to the opposite side of the body en route.

Meninges. Both brain and spinal cord are surrounded by membranes, or *meninges* (singular, *meninx*), the complexity in arrangement of which increases according to advance in the evolutionary scale. These membranes protect and give support to the central nervous system. The blood vessels, with which they are richly supplied, bring nourishment to the underlying nervous structures.

Cartilage and bone are covered with a tough, vascular membrane known as the *perichondrium* or *periosteum*, as the case may be. The cavities of the cranium, and the spinal canal of the vertebral column, are thus lined with perichondrium or periosteum, depending upon whether the skeleton is composed primarily of cartilage or of bone. In either case the lining membrane is called the *endorachis*. It is not considered to be a true meninx.

In cyclostomes and fishes (Fig. 13.10*A*) a single membrane, the *meninx* *primitiva*, forms a close union with brain and spinal cord, which it covers. Between the meninx primitiva and the endorachis is a space, the *perimeningeal space*, filled with lymphlike, cerebrospinal fluid. Delicate strands of connective tissue cross the perimeningeal space, connecting the meninx with the endorachis.

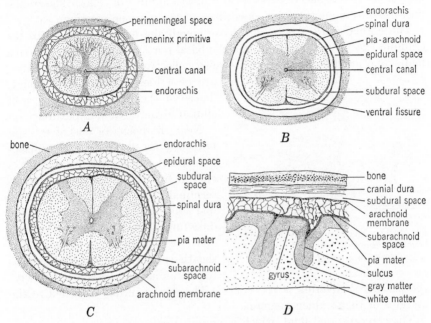

FIG. 13.10.   Diagrams illustrating the relations of the meninges to the spinal cord and brain.   *A* and *B*, cross sections through spinal cords of dogfish and salamander, respectively; *C* and *D*, sections through spinal cord and brain of mammal, respectively.

Beginning with caudate amphibians (Fig. 13.10*B*), instead of a single meninx, two more or less distinct layers are present, an inner *pia-arachnoid layer* and an outer *dura mater*. The pia-arachnoid layer apparently has its origin from neural-crest cells, whereas the dura mater is composed, for the most part, of connective tissue. The pia-arachnoid is a very vascular membrane in intimate contact with the surface of brain and cord. Between pia-arachnoid and dura mater is the *subdural space*. The cavity between the dura mater and the endorachis is the *epidural space*. Cerebrospinal fluid is present in both subdural and epidural spaces.

In mammals (Figs. 13.10*C* and *D*) the pia-arachnoid membrane differentiates further into two layers, an inner *pia mater* and an outer *arachnoid membrane*. A *subarachnoid space*, filled with cerebrospinal fluid, makes its appearance between the two. In the brain region the *cranial dura mater* fuses with the endorachis and the epidural space thus disappears. The *subdural space* between the dura and arachnoid membrane is shallow and contains only a minimum of fluid. Melanoblasts are usually present in the portion of the pia mater of mammals on the ventral side of the medulla oblongata.

About the spinal cord a fusion of *spinal dura* and endorachis does not occur, and the epidural space, which thus persists in this region, contains fatty and other connective tissues as well as a number of veins. The cranial dura is continuous with the spinal dura at the foramen magnum.

The cranial dura is a tough, dense membrane loosely attached to the cranium except at the sutures and the basal portion of the skull. The pia mater and arachnoid membrane, known collectively as the *leptomeninges,* are of a loose, delicate consistency. Those of the brain and cord are of similar structure and appearance.

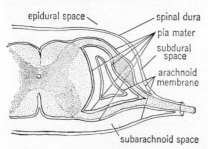

FIG. 13.11. Diagram illustrating the relations of the meninges to the roots of a spinal nerve in a mammal.

Near the posterior end of the spinal cord the subdural space disappears and the spinal dura forms a close-fitting sheath around the filum terminale. At the points where cranial and spinal nerves emerge, the dura forms sheaths around the nerves and their roots (Fig. 13.11). The sheaths pass through the intervertebral foramina and are continuous with the periosteal covering of the bones. The dura is firmly attached to the margins of the foramen magnum.

The cerebrospinal fluid, which is present in the ventricles of the brain, central canal of the spinal cord, and the subarachnoid space, circulates slowly through these various cavities and spaces. Elaborated, for the most part, by the anterior choroid plexus, the fluid passes into the lateral ventricles, through the interventricular foramina to the third ventricle, and thence through the cerebral aqueduct to the fourth ventricle. Three openings in the roof of the medulla oblongata—a single, median *foramen of Magendie* and two lateral *foramina of Luschka*—serve for the passage of cerebrospinal fluid into the subarachnoid space. Thus the surfaces of brain and cord are constantly bathed by cerebrospinal fluid. The fluid is continually being absorbed by blood vessels present in the arachnoid membrane.

Certain modifications of the meninges are to be observed in mammals. The cranial dura sends a process, or fold, the *falx cerebri,* down into the fissure separating the two cerebral hemispheres. A similar process, the *tentorium,* pushes down between the cerebral hemispheres and cerebellum. In some forms, as in the cat, the tentorium becomes ossified and fused to the parietal bones. On the ventral side of the brain, the dura encapsulates the pituitary gland but forms a fold, the *diaphragma sellae,* over the sella turcica, or depression in the dorsal face of the sphenoid bone, in which the pituitary gland lies. The stalk of the infundibulum penetrates the diaphragma sella.

PERIPHERAL NERVOUS SYSTEM

The nerves and ganglia which form connections with the central nervous system, and which are distributed to all parts of the body, comprise the peripheral nervous system. The autonomic portion of the peripheral nervous system is composed of those nerve fibers distributed to structures under involuntary control. Connection with the central nervous system is mediated via spinal and cranial nerves. Spinal nerves, which form connections with the spinal cord, are paired, metameric structures. The paired cranial nerves, on the other hand, are connected with the brain, all but the first four being joined to the medulla oblongata. Metamerism is not so clearly indicated in the arrangement of the cranial nerves.

Spinal Nerves

Each spinal nerve connects to the spinal cord by means of two roots, *dorsal* and *ventral*. Except in amphioxus and the petromyzont cyclostomes, the two roots unite a short distance lateral to the cord to form the spinal nerve proper. The two roots have different embryonic origins.

Dorsal roots. The dorsal roots originate from neural crests which form in the crevice between neural tube and superficial ectoderm on each side. A band of neural-crest cells is, therefore, at first present on either side of the spinal cord and extends in a longitudinal direction. At metameric intervals in each band, enlargements occur and the parts of the band between enlargements gradually disappear. Each neuroblast in these thickenings sends out two processes: (1) an axon, which grows toward the spinal cord and enters it in the region of the dorsal column, and (2) a dendrite, which grows peripherally to the skin, voluntary muscles, skeleton, or some visceral structure. The axon may pass up or down the cord for some distance. The dorsal root contains a rather conspicuous swelling, the *dorsal root ganglion*, which represents the location of the cell bodies of the sensory neurons present in the dorsal root. Experiments have demonstrated that sensory nerve impulses travel through the spinal nerves *toward* the spinal cord and in doing so pass through the dorsal roots which, except in some of the lower forms, are strictly *sensory roots*. The sensory components of spinal nerves are therefore found in the dorsal roots and are spoken of as *afferent fibers*. The dorsal roots in certain lower vertebrates are not composed entirely of sensory fibers since some motor fibers (visceral efferent fibers) course through them.

When sensory nerve fibers enter the spinal cord they form synapses with dendrites of nerve cells located in the gray matter of the cord. Sensory fibers are said to be either somatic or visceral. *Somatic sensory fibers* are

those coming from the skin and its derivatives, voluntary muscles, and
skeletal structures. They form synapses with cells in the somatic sensory
column of gray matter. *Visceral sensory fibers* from visceral structures
(page 563) terminate in the visceral sensory column of gray matter.

Ventral roots. The cell bodies of the neurons making up the ventral, or
motor, roots lie in the gray matter of the ventral columns of the spinal cord.
Their dendrites, therefore, lie within the cord itself, but their axons emerge,
at metameric intervals, from the ventrolateral angles of the cord from which
they pass to peripheral voluntary muscles or to autonomic ganglia. In
motor fibers, impulses are conveyed *away from* the spinal cord. Motor
fibers are therefore referred to as *efferent fibers*. *Somatic motor fibers* arise in
the somatic motor column of gray matter in the spinal cord and are distributed to somatic structures. *Visceral motor fibers*, the cell bodies of
which are located in the visceral motor column of gray matter, pass to
autonomic ganglia where they form synapses with motor autonomic
neurons.

In amphioxus and lampreys visceral motor fibers emerge from the spinal
cord and pass out the *dorsal* roots which are thus composed of both afferent
and efferent fibers. This undoubtedly represents the primitive condition.
In fishes and amphibians, visceral efferent fibers are found in both dorsal
and ventral roots. Only in amniotes, therefore, is the dorsal root strictly
sensory.

According to the above description the spinal nerve proper, formed by
the union of dorsal and ventral roots, is composed partly of dendritic processes of sensory cells, located in the dorsal root ganglion, and partly of
axons of efferent motor neurons, the cell bodies of which are situated in the
ventral column of gray matter in the cord. The axons of the sensory cells
are short, being confined to the proximal portion of the dorsal root. They
pass to the somatic sensory or visceral sensory columns of gray matter
in the cord, as the case may be.

Rami. Not far from the point where dorsal and ventral roots unite to
form the spinal nerve, three branches, or rami (Figs. 13.12 and 13.13), are
usually given off. These include (1) a *dorsal ramus* supplying the skin and
epaxial muscles of the dorsal part of the body, (2) a *ventral ramus* distributed to the hypaxial ventral and lateral regions, and (3) a *visceral ramus*, or
ramus communicans, which courses medially and, in most cases, forms connections with one of the chain ganglia of the peripheral autonomic nervous
system (Figs. 13.12 and 13.13). Both dorsal and ventral rami are composed
of somatic sensory and somatic motor fibers. Some autonomic fibers going
to the periphery are also included in these rami (page 585). A typical
visceral ramus consists of two parts, a *white ramus* and a *gray ramus*. The
white ramus is made up of visceral sensory and visceral motor fibers, mentioned above. Both visceral sensory and visceral motor fibers are medul-

lated, giving this ramus a glistening-white appearance. The axons of the visceral motor fibers are distributed to ganglia of the peripheral autonomic system. The fibers may go to the chain ganglia or pass through them to terminate in other peripheral ganglia. In either case they form synapses with nonmedullated fibers of the peripheral autonomic system. The medullated visceral motor fibers are also referred to as *preganglionic fibers* since they terminate in autonomic ganglia. They form relays with nonmedul-

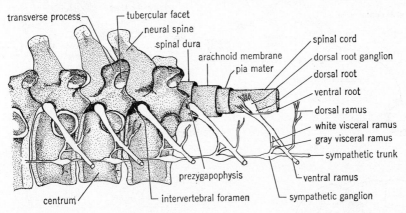

FIG. 13.12.   Diagram showing relation of spinal nerves to spinal cord, meninges, vertebrae, and sympathetic trunk.

lated *postganglionic fibers* which originate in the autonomic ganglia. The gray ramus communicans, composed of nonmedullated, gray, postganglionic fibers, runs parallel to the white ramus. The cell bodies of these fibers are located in chain ganglia. The fibers of the gray ramus join the spinal nerve and travel out either dorsal or ventral rami where they supply structures under involuntary control such as blood vessels, arrector pili muscles, and glands of the skin.

To summarize: dorsal and ventral rami carry medullated somatic sensory fibers, medullated somatic motor fibers, and nonmedullated postganglionic motor autonomic fibers; the white visceral ramus carries medullated visceral sensory and medullated preganglionic motor fibers; the gray visceral ramus carries only nonmedullated postganglionic autonomic motor fibers.

Plexuses. In the regions of the appendages the ventral rami of certain spinal nerves are drawn out into the appendages. In such cases a more or less complicated network, or *plexus*, may be present, formed by the connection of branches of certain nerves with those of others (Fig. 13.14). In lower forms an anterior *cervicobrachial plexus* is present for each pectoral appendage and a posterior *lumbosacral plexus* for each hindlimb. In higher vertebrates a further differentiation takes place, so that separate cervical, brachial, lumbar, and sacral plexuses may be present. In mammals

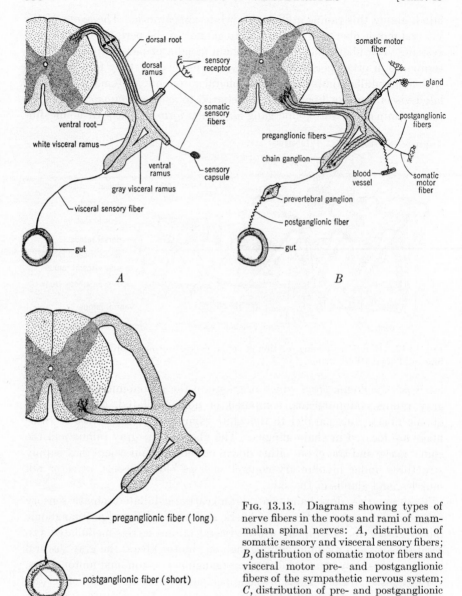

Fig. 13.13.   Diagrams showing types of nerve fibers in the roots and rami of mammalian spinal nerves: *A*, distribution of somatic sensory and visceral sensory fibers; *B*, distribution of somatic motor fibers and visceral motor pre- and postganglionic fibers of the sympathetic nervous system; *C*, distribution of pre- and postganglionic fibers of parasympathetic nervous system as found in certain sacral spinal nerves.

such large nerves as the *ulnar* and *median nerves* of the forelimbs and the *femoral* and *sciatic nerves* of the hind legs represent convergences of portions of the above-named plexuses.

Cauda equina.   Since the spinal cord lies in the canal formed by the neural arches of vertebrae, the spinal nerves must pass out of the vertebral column in order to reach their destination. Dorsal and ventral roots, except in certain lower forms, lie within the neural canal. Openings, known as intervertebral foramina, are present between adjacent vertebrae, providing for the passage of spinal nerves. At first, during embryonic development, each spinal nerve passes through an intervertebral foramen located

5th cervical spinal nerve

6th cervical spinal nerve

7th cervical spinal nerve

phrenic nerve

8th cervical spinal nerve

radial nerve

1st thoracic spinal nerve

ulnar nerve

FIG. 13.14. Diagram of right brachial plexus of cat, ventral view. (*After Reighard and Jennings, "Anatomy of the Cat," Henry Holt and Company, Inc. By permission.*)

at the same level as the part of the cord from which the nerve arises (Fig. 13.15*A*). Later, however, growth of the cord fails to keep pace with that of the vertebral column. As a result, the spinal nerves, particularly those toward the posterior end, are drawn posteriorly so that they emerge through foramina which may be a considerable distance posterior to the point at which the spinal nerve leaves the cord (Fig. 13.15*B*). These nerves, therefore, must course for some distance through the neural canal, running obliquely or else parallel to the spinal cord, before they finally emerge. The more posterior the spinal nerve, the greater distance must it travel before reaching the foramen through which it passes. Because of the brushlike appearance of the posterior spinal nerves of higher forms and their fancied resemblance to a horse's tail, early anatomists gave to these nerves the name *cauda equina*.

Comparative anatomy of spinal nerves. *Amphioxus.* The roots of the spinal nerves of amphioxus do not arise from the spinal cord in symmetrical pairs as do those of higher forms. Instead, those of one side alternate with those of the other in a manner similar to that of the myotomes, or muscle segments. Dorsal and ventral roots do not unite. Furthermore, they do not arise from the same level, the dorsal roots emerging opposite the myocommata and the ventral roots opposite the myotomes. The dorsal roots are composed of compactly arranged fibers, and dorsal root ganglia are lacking. The cell bodies of the sensory neurons in the dorsal roots lie

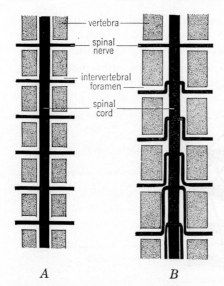

A   *B*

Fig. 13.15. Diagram illustrating the formation of cauda equina: *A*, the spinal nerves emerge through the vertebral column at right angles to the spinal cord; *B*, because of disproportionate growth of vertebrae and spinal cord, the nerves emerge at some distance posterior to their point of origin.

within the spinal cord itself. The ventral roots are less compact, each arising from the cord by a number of loosely arranged bundles. The dorsal roots of the spinal nerves in amphioxus carry somatic sensory, visceral sensory, and visceral motor fibers, the ventral roots being composed of somatic motor fibers alone. Each dorsal root branches into dorsal and ventral rami soon after leaving the cord. The ventral ramus gives off a visceral branch.

Cyclostomes. As in amphioxus, the dorsal and ventral roots of the spinal nerves of cyclostomes alternate with each other as they arise from the cord, the dorsal root coming off somewhat posterior to the ventral root. In lampreys the roots do not join each other, but in hagfishes such a union is usual except in the caudal region. In either case each dorsal root bears a ganglion.

In the gill region of lampreys, fibers from adjacent dorsal roots unite as do fibers from adjacent ventral roots, so as to form two nerves, one sensory and the other motor. These together form the *hypobranchial nerve*, which supplies the ventral part of the gill region. The motor components of this nerve presage the appearance of the hypoglossal nerve of amniotes.

Since paired appendages are lacking in cyclostomes, no spinal nerve plexuses are present.

Fishes. Dorsal and ventral roots unite in fishes, but the union occurs *outside* the vertebral column. In elasmobranchs the components form a looser union than is commonly the case. Also in elasmobranchs the roots do not arise from the cord in the same transverse plane, the dorsal roots coming off a short distance posterior to the ventral roots. A separate foramen is present for each root, that for the dorsal root being located in the intercalary plate and that for the ventral root in the neural arch proper (Fig. 16.2).

In some of the anterior spinal nerves the dorsal roots have disappeared and only the ventral, motor roots of the original spinal nerves persist. They are called *spino-occipital nerves.* Fibers from these nerves contribute to the formation of a hypobranchial nerve (Figs. 16.17 and 16.18) similar to that described for cyclostomes except that it is composed of efferent fibers alone.

There is much variation in the complexity of the cervicobrachial and lumbosacral plexuses in fishes. The most complicated condition is found in skates, with their highly developed pectoral fins. As many as 25 spinal nerves may contribute to the formation of the cervicobrachial plexus in these fishes.

Amphibians. In amphibians, as in previous forms, the dorsal roots of the spinal nerves arise somewhat posterior to the level at which the ventral roots come off. The two roots unite as they pass through the intervertebral foramen. A swelling, the dorsal root ganglion, is located at the point of junction just outside the foramen. It is protected anteriorly by the transverse process of the vertebra and dorsally by the articular processes. From the spinal ganglion arise a dorsal ramus, in the form of a number of twigs, and a large ventral ramus. The visceral ramus comes off the ventral ramus.

In salientians, chalky masses known as *calcareous bodies*, apparently of lymphatic origin, surround the spinal ganglia. They are believed to serve as reserve supplies of calcium. In caudates there are no calcareous bodies but the ganglia are surrounded by spongy, fatty tissue.

Between the occipital condyles and the first, or atlas, vertebra, the ventral root of a small *suboccipital nerve* emerges on each side. Some authorities consider it to be the first spinal nerve, but there is disagreement on this point. Usually the nerve emerging between the first and second vertebrae is called the first spinal nerve, at least in the anamniota. It, also, consists only of a ventral root, the dorsal root and ganglion having disappeared at the time of metamorphosis. The nerve is purely motor and may represent the hypoglossal cranial nerve of higher forms. The remaining spinal nerves are typical. In caudates the number varies with the number of segments in the body. At the time of metamorphosis in salientians there is a reduction in number of spinal nerves, so that in most cases only 10 or 11 remain. Cervicobrachial and lumbosacral plexuses are present, the latter being more complex in salientians in accordance with the greater degree of development of the hindlimbs. A conspicuous cauda equina is present in frogs and toads.

Reptiles. In the amniota there are 12 pairs of cranial nerves in contrast to the condition in lower forms in which there are but 10. It is generally believed that the eleventh cranial nerve (spinal accessory) represents a separation of a visceral motor component of cranial nerve X (vagus) together with certain fibers contributed by spino-occipital nerves. The twelfth cranial nerve (hypoglossal) represents a union of two or three spino-occipital nerves which have been incorporated within the skull and, therefore, arise from the medulla oblongata. The hypoglossal is a motor nerve which lacks a dorsal root, as is the case with the spino-occipital nerves which contain only efferent fibers. The probable homology of the hypoglossal nerve with the hypobranchial nerve of lower forms has already been alluded to. With the appearance of the hypoglossal nerve in amniotes, spino-occipital nerves are no longer present.

The spinal nerves of reptiles show no peculiarities. As in other amniotes, dorsal roots contain only sensory fibers. Both visceral motor and somatic motor fibers are confined to the ventral roots. It is of interest that in certain snakes and limbless lizards a distinct, although poorly developed, lumbosacral plexus is present, indicating that these limbless forms arose in evolution from ancestors with limbs.

Birds. The arrangement of spinal nerves in birds is typical. In certain long-necked forms, the nerves making up the cervicobrachial plexus arise from the cord much farther posteriorly than is usually the case. The lumbosacral plexus may be composed of two or three distinct components, in which case the names *lumbar, sacral,* and *pudendal plexuses* are applied. The lumbar plexus supplies the thigh. The nerves of the sacral plexus unite to form the sciatic nerve passing through the thigh to the lower leg. The pudendal plexus sends branches to the cloacal and tail regions.

Mammals. The spinal nerves of mammals are named according to their relation to the vertebral column. There are, therefore, cervical, thoracic, lumbar, sacral, and caudal or coccygeal spinal nerves. Each is numbered according to the number of the vertebra which lies anterior to it except in the case of the cervical spinal nerves, the first of which emerges between the occipital bone and the atlas. In man there are 31 pairs of spinal nerves: 8 cervical, 12 thoracic, 5 lumbar, 5 sacral, and 1 caudal. The number varies a great deal in different mammals. The horse, for example, has the following numbers: 8 cervical, 18 thoracic, 6 lumbar, 5 sacral, and 5 caudal.

As a general rule, the somatic motor fibers of each spinal nerve supply a single myotome, or muscle segment. In each case the myotome supplied is the one adjacent to the spinal nerve during early embryonic development. No matter how the muscles derived from a certain myotome change or shift in position later on, the original nerve supply is maintained. This is the basis for determining muscle homologies which otherwise might be quite obscure.

The limb plexuses of mammals may be very complicated (Fig. 13.14). They are commonly divided into cervical, brachial, lumbar, and sacral divisions. The *phrenic nerve,* which supplies the diaphragm, arises from the cervical plexus, indicating that the musculature of the diaphragm has been derived from myotomes in the cervical region.

Cranial Nerves

The peripheral nerves which form connections with the brain are called *cranial nerves* (Figs. 16.17, 16.18, and 18.32*B*). They are much more specialized than spinal nerves and in many cases show but little similarity to the latter in origin and distribution. Early human anatomists, not appreciating the functional characteristics of the various cranial nerves nor their homologies in lower vertebrates, assigned numbers to them in an anterior-posterior sequence, a system of classification which, in the light of modern research, has been shown to be very superficial and artificial. Nevertheless, the original terminology has persisted, making it rather difficult for the student to appreciate the complexity of the component parts of the various cranial nerves.

It will be recalled that dorsal and ventral roots of the spinal nerves in amphioxus and lampreys fail to join each other. It is believed that certain cranial nerves may originally have had a similar arrangement. If the two roots of a cranial nerve unite, they do so before emerging from the medulla oblongata. In some cases the dorsal roots and ganglia have apparently been lost, and in others the original ventral roots seem to have disappeared. For example, the *hypoglossal nerve*, or cranial nerve XII, when first formed, has two roots, the dorsal root bearing a ganglion; but the dorsal root and ganglion disappear during subsequent development. The hypoglossal nerve, as mentioned before, has been homologized with the hypobranchial nerve of lower forms. It is a purely motor nerve.

As in the case of spinal nerves, ganglia of the sensory portions of the cranial nerves are located *on* the nerves, in this instance close to the brain. Some of the purely sensory nerves are special structures, not at all comparable in any way to the sensory components of spinal nerves.

It has already been mentioned that there are 10 pairs of cranial nerves in anamniotes and 12 in amniotes. Some are entirely sensory, composed of afferent fibers alone; others are purely motor. Still others are mixed nerves consisting of both motor and sensory fibers. The cranial nerves are usually listed as follows:

I	Olfactory	Sensory
II	Optic	Sensory
III	Oculomotor	Motor
IV	Trochlear	Motor
V	Trigeminal	Mixed
VI	Abducens	Motor
VII	Facial	Mixed
VIII	Auditory	Sensory
IX	Glossopharyngeal	Mixed
X	Vagus	Mixed
XI	Spinal accessory	Motor
XII	Hypoglossal	Motor

In 1894 a new cranial nerve was discovered connecting to the anterior end of the cerebral hemispheres. This nerve was first identified in *Protopterus* and has since been found in all gnathostomes except birds. In order to avoid the confusion which would result if the long-established nomenclature and symbols of the other cranial nerves were changed, the new nerve was called nerve O, or the *terminal nerve*. Some authorities are of the opinion that nerve O is a ganglionated remnant of the first of a series of branchial nerves (page 594). It apparently is unrelated to the olfactory nerve or olfactory sense.

We shall see in the following discussion that merely stating that a nerve is sensory, motor, or mixed has but little meaning so far as functional attributes are concerned. Not all sensory nerves have similar origins, nor are the motor cranial nerves all made up of similar components. We must take into consideration the fact that, like spinal nerves, we have somatic sensory, visceral sensory, visceral motor, somatic motor, and autonomic fibers to consider. Furthermore, associated with certain cranial nerves of lower forms we have, in addition, sensory nerve fibers associated with the *lateralis*, or *lateral-line, system*, a system of sense organs and nerves, of importance in the aquatic mode of life, which has no counterpart in the higher vertebrate classes (page 677).

The sensory neurons of some of the cranial nerves originate, for the most part, from neural-crest cells in the head region. In other cranial nerves some of the sensory neurons may arise from thickenings in the superficial ectoderm which are known as *placodes*. The motor neurons, whether visceral or somatic, like those in the ventral roots of spinal nerves, arise within the neural tube itself. Postganglionic autonomic motor neurons are derived originally from neural-crest cells.

The acousticolateralis system. The lateral-line system consists of certain sense organs found in cyclostomes, fishes, and aquatic amphibians. The receptor organs for this system are called *neuromasts* and are composed of sensory cells and supporting cells. The neuromasts have definite connections with sensory branches of certain cranial nerves. The ganglia of these nerves, however, differ from other sensory nerves in that they arise in the embryo from placodes. The inner ear also arises from a placode in the same general vicinity, and its sensory cells rather closely resemble those making up the neuromasts of the lateralis system. The auditory, or acoustic, nerve and the acoustic ganglion, which lies close to the ear, are, however, derived from neural-crest cells rather than from a placode. Because of the similarity in origin of the inner ear to that of the sensory receptors, nerves, and ganglia of the lateralis system, it is customary to group these structures into what is called the *acousticolateralis system*. As development progresses, the ganglia of the lateralis system move inward and come to lie within the cranium close to the acoustic ganglion alongside of the medulla oblongata. The nerve fibers of the lateralis system become associated or fused with certain cranial nerves, namely, VII (facial), IX (glossopharyngeal), and X (vagus), of which they appear to be branches. Such fibers are entirely sensory and form connections with the somatic sensory column of gray matter near the anterior end of the medulla oblongata in the acousticolateralis area (page 570) close to the auricles, or restiform bodies, of the metencephalon. The lateralis nerves and their ganglia disappear in amniotes and are lost in amphibians at the time of metamorphosis. The nerve fibers of the lateralis nerves are classified as somatic sensory fibers.

The branchial nerves. Four of the cranial nerves are spoken of as branchial nerves, originally supplying the gill region with sensory and motor fibers. Each is primarily associated with a visceral arch. The branchial nerves include (1) the trigeminal nerve (V), which is the nerve of the mandibular arch, (2) the facial nerve (VII), supplying the hyoid arch, (3) the glossopharyngeal nerve (IX), associated with the third arch, and (4) the vagus nerve (X), which takes care of the remaining arches. Each branchial nerve has three main branches: pharyngeal, pretrematic, and posttrematic (Fig. 13.16). Occasionally a fourth, or dorsal, branch is

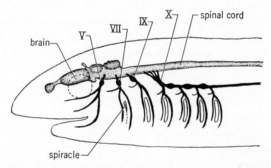

FIG. 13.16. Diagram showing relationship of the branchial cranial nerves (V, VII, IX, and X) to the visceral arches and gill slits. (*Modified from Johnston.*)

present. The branchial muscles of the gill region are considered to be visceral muscles, despite the fact that they are voluntary and striated, because they are originally derived from the splanchnic mesoderm of the hypomere. Hence the motor nerves supplying them directly are composed of visceral motor fibers. These are confined to the posttrematic branches of the branchial nerves. Visceral sensory fibers are found in all except the dorsal branch, the pretrematic and pharyngeal branches being made up only of such fibers. Somatic sensory fibers from the skin above the gill region are confined to the dorsal branch when this branch is present. The ganglia of the branchial nerves are located close to those of the lateralis nerves.

Special sensory nerves. Three of the cranial nerves are of a special nature. They are purely sensory nerves carrying impulses from the three major sense organs: nose, eye, and ear. These nerves are considered to be somatic sensory nerves although there is some dispute as to whether the olfactory nerve (I) is somatic sensory or visceral sensory. The cell bodies of the olfactory nerve are not derived from neural crests, but rather from a placode in the superficial ectoderm of the anterior head region. Those of the optic nerve (II) have a still different origin since they actually come from an outpocketing of the diencephalic region of the brain. The fibers of the auditory nerve (VIII), however, like the sensory fibers of the spinal nerves, originate from neural-crest cells.

Terminal nerve (O). Leaving the anterior, ventral portion of the cerebral hemisphere, although apparently originating in the diencephalon, the *terminal nerve* passes to the olfactory mucous membrane. It is a sensory nerve and bears one or more ganglia. This nerve is best developed in elasmobranch fishes. In amphibians, reptiles, and mammals, it is associated with the vomeronasal, or Jacobson's, organ, which seems to be an accessory olfactory structure. The function of the terminal nerve is not clear. It has been suggested that it may represent the remains of an anterior branchial nerve which long ago lost its significance.

Olfactory nerve (I). The first cranial nerve is composed of nonmedullated fibers. They are outgrowths of neurosensory cells derived from a placode in the anterior head region. The olfactory nerve is considered by most authorities to be a somatic sensory nerve. The cell bodies of this nerve lie in the olfactory epithelium. Their axons grow toward the brain where they form synapses with neurons in the olfactory lobes. The terminal arborizations of several olfactory nerve fibers may synapse with the brushlike dendrites of a single cell in the olfactory bulb. The interlacing of these processes forms the so-called *olfactory glomeruli* of the bulb. No ganglia are present.

In those vertebrates in which the olfactory lobe is drawn out into bulb and tract, the olfactory tract is sometimes mistaken for the olfactory nerve. Actually the nerve proper usually consists of many separate fibers which are not gathered together in a sheath. In some forms, however, as in certain teleosts, amphibians, and lizards, the olfactory nerve is rather long and joins the olfactory lobe, which is not differentiated into a clear-cut bulb and tract. In mammals as many as 20 separate nerve branches on each side pass through openings (olfactory foramina) in the cribriform plate of the ethmoid bone on their way to the brain.

That the single, median, olfactory organ found in cyclostomes is originally of bilateral origin is indicated by the presence of paired olfactory nerves passing from the olfactory mucous membrane through the olfactory capsule to the olfactory bulb of the brain.

A branch of the olfactory nerve is distributed to Jacobson's organ in those vertebrates possessing this structure.

Optic nerve (II). The second cranial nerve shows certain peculiarities for an understanding of which the reader is referred to a description of the embryonic development of the eye (page 624). The optic nerve consists of a bundle of sensory nerve fibers, the cell bodies of which are located in the retina of the eye. The fibers grow down through the walls of the optic

stalk, reaching the brain at the level of the diencephalon.   The fibers of
each optic nerve then cross beneath the diencephalon and pass to the lateral
geniculate bodies or to the optic tectum in the roof of the optic lobes of the
mesencephalon.   In mammals, impulses set up by optic stimuli are relayed
from the optic tectum to the cerebral hemispheres.   The point at which
the nerves cross is called the *optic chiasma*.   In
cyclostomes the chiasma lies *within* the brain.
Crossing is complete in all vertebrates except in
those mammals having binocular vision.   In these
forms only about half the fibers in each optic
nerve pass to the opposite side.   Fibers from the
nasal side of the retina are the ones which decussate, those from the temporal side of the retina
going to the optic tectum on the same side of the
brain as that from which they come.   The term
optic tract is applied to the portion of the optic
nerve which passes from the chiasma to the optic
lobe.   A *commissure (of Gudden)* is located at the
posterior border of the chiasma, its fibers sometimes being confused with those of the optic
nerves.   It connects the two sides of the brain
(medial geniculate bodies), but its fibers are not
derivatives of the optic nerves.   Various optic
chiasmas show unusual structural complications,
a few of which are indicated in Fig. 13.17.

Actually the optic nerve should not be considered in the category of cranial nerves but rather
as a fiber tract of the brain, since it merely grows
from one portion of the brain (optic cup) to another (mesencephalon).   The optic nerve, however, is usually grouped in the category of special
somatic sensory cranial nerves.

Oculomotor nerve (III).   The eyeball is moved
by six muscles, so arranged as to permit a maximum amount of rotary movement.   These muscles
are disposed in two groups consisting of two oblique and four rectus muscles, respectively, arranged as indicated in Fig. 11.11.   Four of these
muscles are derived from the myotome of the first,
or premandibular, pro-otic somite (page 477) and
are all supplied by the same nerve, the oculomotor.
The somatic motor fibers, of which this nerve is
chiefly composed, leave the ventral side of the
mesencephalon and are distributed to the inferior

DOGFISH

MOST
TELEOSTS

HERRING

LIZARD

AGAMID
LIZARD

MAMMAL
with
binocular
vision

Fig. 13.17.   Various types
of optic chiasmas.   (*Those
of herring and agamid lizard, after Wiedersheim,
from Kingsley, "Compara-
tive Anatomy of Verte-
brates,"   The   Blakiston
Division,   McGraw-Hill
Book Company, Inc.   By
permission.*)

oblique, superior rectus, inferior rectus, and internal rectus eye muscles. Some fibers also pass to the muscle (*levator palpebrae*) elevating the upper eyelid. Preganglionic autonomic fibers accompanying the somatic motor fibers are distributed to the ciliary ganglion. Postganglionic fibers then lead to the ciliary apparatus, which is concerned with accommodation, and to the sphincter muscles of the iris, which regulate the size of the pupil. A few somatic sensory proprioceptive fibers are borne by the oculomotor nerve.

In the lamprey the oculomotor nerve innervates only the superior rectus, internal rectus, and inferior oblique. The inferior rectus is supplied by the abducens nerve. For a possible explanation of this peculiar state of affairs the reader is referred to page 477.

Trochlear nerve (IV). The somatic motor trochlear nerve is the smallest of all the cranial nerves. Its nucleus lies near the floor of the mesencephalon. From here, fibers pass upward to the dorsal side where they decussate. The nerve leaves the dorsal side of the mesencephalon near its posterior end. It then enters the orbit to supply the superior oblique eye muscle derived from the mandibular, or second, pro-otic somite. The word *trochlear* comes from a Greek term meaning pulley. The word is applicable because of the pulleylike arrangement of the superior oblique eye muscle in man. Like the oculomotor, a few proprioceptive sensory fibers are carried by the trochlear nerve.

Trigeminal nerve (V). The trigeminal nerve is a large nerve arising from the lateral side of the anterior end of the medulla oblongata. Near its point of origin it bears a large *Gasserian*, or *semilunar, ganglion* which sends fibers to the somatic sensory column of gray matter in the medulla. The trigeminal is characteristically divided into three main branches, the *ophthalmic, maxillary*, and *mandibular nerves*. The first two of these branches bear somatic sensory fibers alone, but the mandibular branch is composed of both somatic sensory and visceral motor fibers. Visceral sensory and somatic motor fibers are lacking in the trigeminal nerve. The trigeminal is usually considered to be the first of the branchial nerves and is the nerve of the mandibular arch. It differs somewhat from the others in that its pretrematic (maxillary) and posttrematic (mandibular) branches bear somatic sensory rather than visceral sensory fibers.

In fishes the ophthalmic branch is composed of *superficial* and *deep* (*profundus*) portions, the latter possibly representing what originally may have been a separate branchial nerve. The superficial branch supplies the skin on the dorsal side of the head and snout with sensory fibers. A similarly named branch of the seventh nerve accompanies the superficial ophthalmic branch of the trigeminal, but is distributed to portions of the lateral-line system in this region. The trigeminal does not supply any of the lateral-line organs. The deep ophthalmic, composed solely of fibers of the fifth nerve, courses separately behind the eyeball, which it supplies with some small ciliary nerves, and then joins the superficial ophthalmic and, along with that branch, is distributed to the skin in the dorsal and lateral regions of the snout. In higher vertebrates the two portions of the ophthalmic branch are not distinct and but a single ophthalmic nerve is present. It is the smallest of the three branches and supplies sensory fibers to the conjunctiva, cornea, iris, ciliary body, lacrimal gland, part of the mucous membrane of the nose, and the skin of the forehead, nose, and eyelids. The *ciliary ganglion* of the autonomic nervous system lies in close relationship to the ophthalmic branch.

The maxillary branch is the main nerve to the upper jaw, supplying the upper lip, side of the nose, lower eyelid, teeth of the upper jaw, and, when present, Jacobson's organ. The *sphenopalatine ganglion* of the autonomic nervous system lies close to the maxillary branch.

The somatic sensory portion of the mandibular branch is distributed to the lower lip and the teeth of the lower jaw. In mammals it also supplies the skin of the temporal region, external ear, and lower part of the face. A *lingual branch* goes to the mucous membrane of the anterior part of the tongue in mammals and certain reptiles. The visceral motor fibers of the mandibular branch go directly to the muscles used in chewing. *Otic* and *submaxillary ganglia*, belonging to the autonomic nervous system, are in close proximity to the mandibular nerve.

It should not be inferred from the above that the trigeminal nerve is part of the peripheral autonomic nervous system because of the close relationship of its branches to certain autonomic ganglia.

Abducens nerve (VI). The small abducens nerve arises from the ventral part of the medulla oblongata close to its anterior end, courses anteriorly in an oblique direction, and is distributed to the external rectus eye muscle which has its origin from the third, or hyoid, pro-otic somite. Like the other nerves supplying the eye muscles, it is a somatic motor nerve which carries a few proprioceptive sensory fibers. In the lamprey, the inferior rectus muscle, in addition, is supplied by the abducens nerve (page 596). A branch of the abducens goes to the nictitating membrane if such a structure is present.

Facial nerve (VII). In lower aquatic vertebrates the large, somatic sensory components of the facial nerve are distributed to the lateral-line system. In fishes these include a *superficial ophthalmic branch*, which accompanies the superficial ophthalmic branch of the trigeminal nerve on the dorsal side of the snout, and a *buccal branch*, which, with the maxillary branch of the trigeminal, courses along the floor of the orbit as the *infraorbital nerve*. The buccal and superficial ophthalmic branches supply the lateral-line organs on the snout. A third branch, the *hyomandibular*, represents the posttrematic branchial portion of the seventh nerve, which is the nerve of the hyoid arch. It contains visceral sensory, visceral motor, and somatic sensory fibers, the latter being lateralis components distributed to parts of the lateral-line system in the region of the hyoid arch. A *geniculate ganglion*, containing the cell bodies of the sensory neurons of the facial nerve, is located at the point where the hyomandibular branch leaves the medulla oblongata.

In elasmobranchs, the hyomandibular nerve lies just posterior to the spiracle. Near the geniculate ganglion it gives off a palatine branch composed of visceral sensory fibers alone. It represents the pharyngeal branch of this branchial nerve. The palatine branch passes to the roof of the mouth. A small twig from the palatine passes to the anterior side of the spiracle. This and other visceral sensory fibers, probably representing the pretrematic portion of the facial nerve, supply the taste buds and mucous membrane of the mouth. The visceral motor fibers of the hyomandibular innervate muscles of the hyoid region directly.

With the loss of the lateral-line system in terrestrial forms, the somatic sensory part of the facial nerve becomes relatively unimportant. Visceral sensory fibers in mammals supply the taste buds of the anterior two-thirds of the tongue. These fibers form part of the *chorda tympani*, a branch of the facial nerve which passes through the middle ear. After leaving the middle ear its fibers course along with those of the lingual branch of the trigeminal nerve on their way to the tongue.

The visceral motor components of the facial nerve are more widely distributed. They pass to the muscles of the face, scalp, and external ear and to a few superficial neck muscles. Preganglionic visceral motor fibers, of the peripheral autonomic system, accompany the chorda tympani branch of the facial nerve and pass to the *submaxillary ganglion*. From this ganglion arise postganglionic fibers leading to the submaxillary and sublingual salivary glands. Other preganglionic fibers of the facial nerve pass to the *sphenopalatine ganglion*, where they relay with postganglionic fibers which are distributed, in turn, to the lacrimal gland and mucous membrane of the nose.

Auditory nerve (VIII). The purely somatic sensory auditory nerve bears an *acoustic ganglion* closely associated with the geniculate ganglion of the facial nerve. It arises from neural-crest cells, although possibly some cells may be contributed by the auditory placode from which the inner ear is derived. For a number of reasons (page 592) the inner ear is believed to have arisen in evolution in the same manner as the organs and nerves of the lateral-line system. The term *acousticolateralis system* is frequently used to designate the close relationship of the two. The auditory nerve comes from the lateral side of the medulla oblongata. Its ganglion is often inseparably fused with those of the trigeminal and facial nerves.

In higher forms, in which the inner ear serves both as an organ of hearing and of equilibration, the auditory nerve is divided into two main branches, a *vestibular branch*, which carries equilibratory impulses from the vestibular portion of the inner ear, and a *cochlear branch* for auditory impulses arising in the cochlea. In such cases the acoustic ganglion is divided into *vestib-*

ular and *spiral* (*cochlear*) *portions.* In lower forms, in which the auditory function has not developed, the vestibular part of the nerve is the only portion that is present.

Strong fiber tracts in the brain pass from the eighth nerve to the cerebellum, where the center for equilibration is located. Impulses set up by auditory stimuli pass to the inferior colliculi of the optic tectum (roof of mesencephalon) and to the medial geniculate bodies in the roof of the diencephalon. In mammals, auditory impulses are relayed to centers in the cerebral hemispheres.

Glossopharyngeal nerve (IX). The ninth cranial nerve, arising from the medulla oblongata, is the nerve of the third visceral arch and the second gill pouch. Most typical of all the branchial nerves, in fishes its pretrematic, or hyoid, branch, made up of visceral sensory fibers, passes to the anterior side of the first *typical* gill slit.* Its posttrematic, or branchial, branch, composed of visceral sensory and visceral motor fibers, supplies the hemibranch on the posterior border of this gill slit. A small pharyngeal branch, containing visceral sensory fibers alone, goes to the pharynx, where it supplies taste buds and other receptors. In some lower aquatic vertebrates the glossopharyngeal sends a small dorsal somatic sensory branch to the anterior part of the lateral line proper. A prominent *petrosal ganglion* lies near the base of the glossopharyngeal nerve. It is situated close to the ganglia of the tenth cranial nerve and, in amphibians, actually fuses with them.

Two ganglia are present on the ninth nerve in higher forms. These are (1) a small, *superior ganglion,* close to the medulla, and (2) a *petrosal ganglion,* a short distance away. In these vertebrates some visceral motor components of the glossopharyngeal are distributed directly to muscles of the pharynx derived from the third visceral arch region. Preganglionic visceral autonomic motor fibers are also present, passing to the *otic ganglion.* Postganglionic fibers then relay impulses to the parotid salivary gland. In mammals the visceral sensory fibers of the ninth nerve pass to the taste buds of the posterior one-third of the tongue, to the mucous membrane of the pharynx, and to the palatine tonsils.

Vagus nerve (X). The vagus nerve is perhaps the most important of all the cranial nerves because of the preganglionic fibers of the parasympathetic portion of the peripheral autonomic nervous system which it contains. Through these the vagus controls such vital activities as heartbeat, respiratory movements, and peristalsis.

The tenth cranial nerve arises from the medulla oblongata by a number of roots. In lower aquatic vertebrates it bears a *lateralis ganglion* and a *jugular ganglion* near its base. A large, somatic sensory, lateralis compo-

---

* The spiracle, found in elasmobranchs and a few other fishes, actually represents the first gill pouch. It disappears in teleost fishes. The first gill pouch as found in teleosts, therefore, really represents the second pouch of elasmobranchs.

nent, the *lateral nerve,* branches off the vagus near its proximal end and extends the length of the body to nearly the end of the tail, lying underneath the lateral-line canal and located between the epaxial and hypaxial muscles of the body wall. The lateral nerve may be several feet long. It is not present in the amniota. In amphibians, with the exception of the perennibranchiates, it disappears at the time of metamorphosis. The lateralis ganglion is also lost.

In addition to the lateral nerve there is a large *branchiovisceral branch* with the jugular ganglion at its base. It is composed of visceral sensory and visceral motor fibers, together with a negligible number of somatic sensory fibers which are distributed to the skin in the area about the ear. Some sensory proprioceptive fibers are also present. Part of the branchiovisceral branch of the vagus serves as a branchial nerve supplying the visceral arches posterior to the third and the remaining gill pouches. In the gill region of fishes this branch gives off twigs, each of which in elasmobranchs (and lampreys) bears a small *epibranchial ganglion.* In teleosts the epibranchial ganglia fuse into a single mass located on the main trunk. Each twig in turn gives off a pharyngeal branch and then divides into pretrematic and posttrematic branches supplying the anterior and posterior hemibranchs, respectively, of each of the gill pouches posterior to that supplied by the glossopharyngeal nerve. As in the similarly named branches of the glossopharyngeal nerve, the pretrematic branches bear visceral sensory fibers alone, the posttrematic branches being composed of visceral sensory and visceral motor fibers distributed to the branchial muscles in this region. The pharyngeal branches pass to the pharynx where they supply taste buds and other sensory receptors. Posterior to the gills the vagus courses caudally, giving off a branch to the heart, and then distributes its visceral sensory and visceral motor preganglionic fibers to the coelomic viscera, except those at the posterior end. The preganglionic autonomic motor fibers borne by the vagus terminate in small autonomic ganglia in, or close to, the walls of these organs, where they form synapses with very short postganglionic fibers (page 607).

With the disappearance of gills in amniotes and after metamorphosis in amphibians, the branchial branches of the vagus are lost for the most part. The visceral motor remnants of the posttrematic branches persist to supply directly certain muscles of the pharyngeal and laryngeal regions derived from this part of the gill region. Visceral sensory fibers pass to the taste buds and other receptors in the posterior pharyngeal region. In tetrapods preganglionic, visceral motor, vagal fibers supply the larynx, trachea, lungs, and abdominal viscera except those at the posterior end. In mammals a large *nodosal ganglion* is present at the base of the vagus a short distance distal to the jugular ganglion. It may possibly be homologous with the epibranchial ganglion of teleost fishes.

The fact that a *cranial* nerve supplies organs so far removed from the brain indicates that these structures must have migrated posteriorly from an originally more anterior position.

Spinal accessory nerve (XI). An eleventh cranial nerve is found only in amniotes. It bears a very close relation to the vagus. The spinal accessory is apparently composed of a cranial portion, derived from certain posterior visceral motor fibers of the vagus, and a spinal portion, representing somatic motor fibers of some of the most anterior cervical spinal nerves (spino-occipital nerves). Fibers of the cranial portion accompany branches of the vagus to pharynx and larynx and should be considered to belong to the category of branchial nerves. Those of the spinal portion supply the sternocleidomastoid and trapezius muscles, which thus may be derivatives of myotomes. Their exact homologies are uncertain.

In lower vertebrates having but 10 cranial nerves in addition to the terminal nerve (O), the cranial portion of the spinal accessory is already indicated by a posterior branch of the vagus.

Hypoglossal nerve (XII). The twelfth cranial nerve, also found only in amniotes, is a purely somatic motor nerve which arises from several roots and supplies the intrinsic muscles of the tongue, as well as a number of muscles below the tongue in the lower jaw. As has been previously suggested, the hypoglossal is represented in lower forms by the hypobranchial nerve, formed by the union of two or three spino-occipital nerves and which, in amniotes, has acquired cranial connections. The nerve has assumed greater importance with the appearance of muscles which move the tongue, and for this reason the twelfth nerve is best developed in mammals.

Autonomic Nerves

The autonomic portion of the peripheral nervous system is closely related anatomically to the spinal nerves and certain cranial nerves. Furthermore, nerve centers controlling the activity of autonomic neurons are located in the central nervous system. Consequently, all parts of the nervous system are so intimately bound together both structurally and functionally that none of its major constituents can be considered independently of the others.

The autonomic portion of the peripheral nervous system is composed of efferent neurons which send impulses to smooth muscles and glands in all parts of the body. It regulates the function of structures which are under involuntary control. The muscle of the heart, although striated, is not subject to voluntary control, and it, too, is innervated by autonomic fibers. The proper functioning of this part of the nervous system is necessary for regulating such activities as rate of heartbeat, respiratory movements, composition of body fluids, constancy of temperature, secretion of various glands, peristalsis, and other vital processes.

The complex connections of the autonomic neurons add to the difficulties embodied in an understanding of its structure. Most investigations have been carried out in mammals, and in man in particular. It will best serve our purpose first to discuss the autonomic system in man and then to make comparisons with other vertebrates.

It will be recalled that the cell bodies of the somatic motor neurons of cranial and spinal nerves are located in the ventral somatic motor column of gray matter of brain or spinal cord. Their medullated axons continue without interruption to the effector organ. A different pattern obtains in the autonomic system in which efferent impulses must travel through *two* neurons, *preganglionic* and *postganglionic*, before they can bring about an effect (Figs. 13.13*B* and *C*).

The system is composed of these two types of neurons and a number of ganglia which serve as relay centers. The cell bodies of the preganglionic neurons are located in the visceral motor column of gray matter in the central nervous system. Their medullated fibers pass to outlying ganglia. These fibers make up some visceral motor components of certain cranial nerves and of spinal nerves. In the latter they are constituents of the white visceral rami. Postganglionic neurons have gray, nonmedullated axons. The cell bodies of these neurons, which are derived from neural-crest cells, lie in outlying ganglia which are often located at some distance from the central nervous system. It is here that the preganglionic fibers form synapses with the dendrites of postganglionic neurons. The axons of the postganglionic neurons are the ones which are distributed to smooth muscles, cardiac muscle, and glands in various parts of the body.

Although the peripheral autonomic system is essentially an efferent system, some authorities claim that certain visceral afferent fibers should be included. Such fibers pass from visceral organs up the dorsal roots of the spinal nerves to connect with the central nervous system.

Three large masses of nervous tissue, called ganglionated plexuses, are located near the vertebral column in the thoracic, abdominal, and pelvic regions. They are known, respectively, as the *cardiac, coeliac*, or *solar*, and *hypogastric plexuses*. Each is composed of an intricate meshwork of nerves and ganglia containing visceral afferent fibers and visceral efferent fibers of the autonomic system. The cardiac plexus is situated near the base of the heart. The large coeliac, or solar, plexus is located at the upper level of the lumbar region and surrounds the roots of the coeliac, superior mesenteric, and inferior mesenteric arteries. A heavy blow stimulating the solar plexus affects almost all parts of the body. The hypogastric plexus, in the region where the sacrum joins the last lumbar vertebra, is composed of fibers distributed to the pelvic viscera.

The autonomic portion of the peripheral nervous system is divided into two main parts, the sympathetic and parasympathetic systems (Figs. 13.18 and 13.19). The postganglionic fibers of both are, in most cases, distributed to all the involuntary structures of the body. The two systems, in general, work antagonistically. Whereas the one system functions in such a manner as to strengthen an animal's defenses against adverse conditions by an expenditure of energy, the other is concerned with processes which tend to conserve and restore energy. Moreover, the manner in which these two systems bring about their effects differs for the most part. In both cases the postganglionic fibers give off chemical substances which, in the last analysis, bring about the effects. Postganglionic sympathetic fibers, except those going to the sweat glands and uterus, and which cause vasodilatation, produce a substance similar to or identical with epinephrine, or adrenalin. They are, therefore, usually spoken of as *adrenergic fibers*. Postganglionic parasympathetic fibers, and those postganglionic sympathetic fibers supplying the sweat glands and uterus, liberate a chemical called acetylcholine and are frequently referred to as *cholinergic fibers*. Preganglionic fibers of both sympathetic and parasympathetic nerves are also considered to be cholinergic since they liberate acetylcholine at the synapse (page 85). Adrenalin and acetylcholine have opposite effects upon smooth muscles and glands. This further emphasizes the dual nature of the autonomic portion of the peripheral nervous system.

Sympathetic nervous system (Fig. 13.18). Since the preganglionic fibers of the sympathetic nervous system connect to the spinal cord only in the thoracic and lumbar regions, the term *thoracolumbar outflow* is often applied to this portion of the autonomic system.

On either side of the ventral part of the vertebral column lies a long *sympathetic trunk*, extending from the foramen magnum to the coccyx. The trunk even enters the cranial cavity through the carotid canal in the temporal bone. At fairly regular intervals each sympathetic trunk bears enlargements known as the *chain ganglia* (Figs. 13.12 and 13.18). Groups of these ganglia at the anterior end of the sympathetic trunk have fused, forming three large masses, the *superior, middle*, and *inferior cervical ganglia*. The latter is located near the point of junction of the last cervical and first thoracic vertebrae. The chain ganglia are numbered according to the vertebrae opposite which they lie, but fusions may occur which obscure their segmental character.

The white visceral rami of all the thoracic spinal nerves and the first, second, and third lumbar are partly composed of preganglionic fibers which connect with the corresponding chain ganglia. They may terminate in the ganglion at the point where they enter, or send fibers up or down the sympathetic trunk for some distance. Other preganglionic fibers pass without synapses *through* ganglia of the sympathetic trunk and form connections with one or more of three large, *prevertebral ganglia* of the coeliac plexus, located in the abdominal region in front of the lumbar vertebrae. According to definition, prevertebral ganglia are sympathetic ganglia of the thorax and abdomen other than those of the sympathetic trunk. The prevertebral ganglia of the coeliac plexus include the *coeliac, superior*

SPINAL CORD

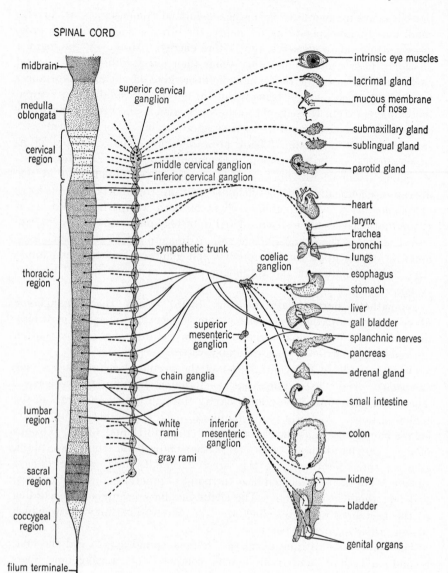

Fig. 13.18. Diagram of essential parts of sympathetic nervous system of man. Preganglionic fibers are shown in solid lines; postganglionic fibers in dotted lines.

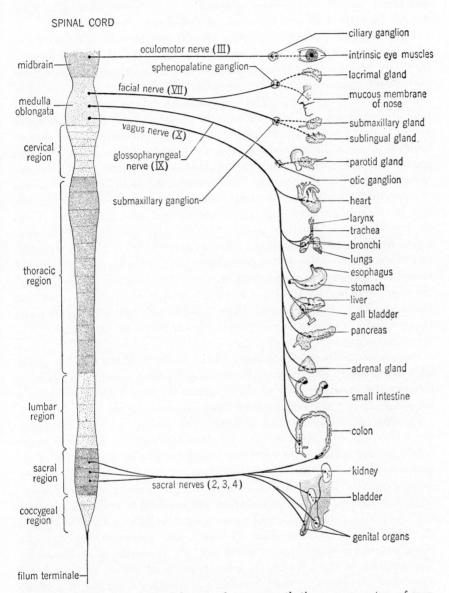

FIG. 13.19. Diagram of essential parts of parasympathetic nervous system of man. Preganglionic fibers are shown in solid lines; the very short postganglionic fibers in dotted lines.

mesenteric, and *inferior mesenteric ganglia.* The nerves leading to these ganglia from the sympathetic trunk are called the *splanchnic nerves.*

From the chain ganglia and prevertebral ganglia arise nonmedullated postganglionic fibers which are distributed to the various structures in the body under involuntary control. A *gray visceral ramus* comes from each chain ganglion of the sympathetic trunk whether or not a white visceral ramus is present. The postganglionic fibers of which the gray rami are composed are distributed via the dorsal and ventral rami of spinal nerves to the skin of the head, trunk, and limbs, where they supply smooth muscles in the walls of blood vessels, the arrector pili muscles, and skin glands. Other postganglionic fibers from the cervical ganglia at the anterior end of the sympathetic trunk pass to the intrinsic muscles of the eye, lacrimal glands, mucous membrane of the nose, palate, and mouth, and to the submaxillary, sublingual, and parotid salivary glands. From the inferior cervical ganglion and the first few chain ganglia in the thoracic region arise postganglionic fibers going to heart, larynx, trachea, bronchi, and lungs. The coeliac and superior mesenteric ganglia are the points of origin of postganglionic fibers which supply esophagus, stomach, small intestine, first part of the large intestine, as well as liver, pancreas, and blood vessels of the abdomen. The inferior mesenteric ganglion sends postganglionic fibers to the remainder of the large intestine and to the urogenital organs.

Preganglionic fibers pass *directly* to the medulla of the adrenal gland. This ectodermal, glandular structure, derived from neural-crest cells, is composed of specialized, or modified, sympathetic ganglionic cells which are homologous with postganglionic sympathetic neurons.

Function of the sympathetic system. The action of the sympathetic neurons on the structures supplied by them has been the subject of many investigations. Among the reactions brought about by stimulation of the sympathetic system are (1) constriction of cutaneous blood vessels, causing pallor, (2) contraction of arrector pili muscles, causing "goose flesh" and making the hair stand erect, (3) secretion of sweat glands (cold sweat), (4) dilatation of the pupil, permitting more light to enter the eyeball, (5) reduction in amount of saliva secreted so that but small quantities of a thick, mucinous secretion are given off, (6) acceleration of heartbeat, (7) dilatation of the bronchi, (8) relaxation, or inhibition, of the smooth muscles of the digestive tract, causing a temporary cessation of peristalsis, (9) relaxation of bladder musculature, (10) contraction of the sphincter muscle of the bladder, (11) increase in blood sugar, (12) rise in blood pressure, (13) increase in number of red corpuscles in the blood stream, (14) decrease in clotting time of blood.

The above reactions, when considered together, are those usually associated with pain, fear, and anger. They serve the body in a beneficial capacity in times of danger or when it is in an "aggressive" state. Many individuals, under conditions of extreme fear, may void urine involuntarily. This would seem to be paradoxical in light of the above. In such cases, however, certain reflexes, referred to as *conditioned reflexes*, usually established in early life, may bring about a reversal of reactions which normally occur in the aggressive state. Punishing or hurting a child in an effort to train it in toilet habits may be basically responsible for such poor conditioning.

Injection of adrenalin (epinephrine), the hormone of the medulla of the adrenal gland, causes effects which appear to be identical with those brought about by stimulation of the nerves of the sympathetic system. The hormone presumably acts upon the structures supplied by sympathetic nerve endings. Under normal circumstances the adrenal medulla secretes only insignificant amounts of epinephrine into the blood stream. In times of stress, however, significant amounts may be liberated and the action of the hormone reinforces that of the sympathetic system so that maximal efficiency results. This action of epinephrine has been called the "emergency mechanism" of the body, for during times of stress the body is thus better adapted for self-preservation.

The adrenal medulla and its secretion are not essential to life. Sympathetic effects may be secured after removal of the adrenal medulla. It has been postulated that sympathetic stimulation induces the postganglionic sympathetic nerve endings to secrete a substance very similar to, if not identical with, epinephrine. This substance has been called *sympathin*.

Epinephrine and sympathin are relatively stable compounds which, circulating in the blood stream, will simultaneously stimulate *all* structures supplied by the sympathetic system. Although these substances act rapidly, the effect lasts only a short time.

Other tissues known as *chromaffin tissues*, located in certain other parts of the body, also secrete epinephrine or sympathin. They are actually modifications of sympathin-producing nerves.

Parasympathetic nervous system. The term *craniosacral outflow* is frequently used to designate the complex of preganglionic fibers of the parasympathetic nervous system (Fig. 13.19). The term is appropriate, since only certain cranial and sacral spinal nerves are involved.

Four cranial nerves are composed, at least in part, of preganglionic parasympathetic fibers. They are the oculomotor (III), facial (VII), glossopharyngeal (IX), and vagus (X) nerves. The ganglia in which they terminate are situated close to, or in, the organs supplied by this system. Hence the preganglionic fibers are rather long, and the postganglionic fibers are very short.

The preganglionic parasympathetic components of the oculomotor nerve terminate in a *ciliary ganglion*, about the size of the head of a pin, situated in the back part of the orbit. Here they synapse with postganglionic fibers which pass to the eyeball, supplying the sphincter muscle of the iris as well as the ciliary muscles.

The facial nerve contains preganglionic fibers which pass either to the *sphenopalatine* or to the *submaxillary ganglion* in the head region. In the sphenopalatine ganglion, located close to the sphenopalatine foramen, certain fibers of the facial nerve synapse with postganglionic neurons, the fibers of which pass to the lacrimal gland, mucous membrane of the nose, palate, and upper part of the pharynx. Certain fibers of the chorda tympani branch of the facial nerve are preganglionic fibers which pass to the small submaxillary ganglion situated just above the submaxillary salivary gland. Short postganglionic fibers arising in the submaxillary ganglion are distributed to the submaxillary and sublingual glands.

An *otic ganglion,* located close to the foramen ovale of the sphenoid bone, receives preganglionic fibers of the glossopharyngeal nerve. Postganglionic fibers pass to the parotid gland and mucous membrane of the mouth.

The preganglionic fibers of the vagus nerve, like those of the other three cranial nerves forming part of the parasympathetic system, terminate in ganglia, but the ganglia are very small and are located in the walls of the structures which they supply. It is believed that those of the esophagus, stomach, small intestine, and upper part of the large intestine connect with the *plexuses of Auerbach* and *Meissner.* From these plexuses postganglionic fibers are distributed to the smooth muscles and glands of the alimentary tract. Other parasympathetic fibers of the vagus innervate the heart, larynx, trachea, bronchi, lungs, blood vessels of abdomen, liver, gall bladder, and pancreas.

The part of the parasympathetic system known as the *sacral outflow* is composed of efferent fibers which course through the white visceral rami of the second, third, and fourth sacral nerves which together form the *pelvic nerve.* These preganglionic fibers, like those of the vagus, pass directly to the structures which they supply, to terminate in ganglia in, or very near, the organs. The pelvic nerve supplies the lower part of the large intestine, kidneys, bladder, and reproductive organs. Postganglionic fibers within these organs are relatively short.

Function of the parasympathetic system. Stimulation of the various components of the parasympathetic system brings about effects which are, in general, opposite to those secured by stimulating the sympathetic nerves supplying the same organs. Among these reactions are (1) dilatation of blood vessels (except the coronary vessels of the heart), (2) constriction of the pupil, (3) increase in salivary and gastric secretion, (4) constriction of bronchi, (5) contraction of walls of the digestive tract, bringing about peristalsis and other types of contractions, (6) contraction of bladder musculature, (7) relaxation of the sphincter muscle of the bladder, (8) dilatation of blood vessels of the external genital organs.

The above reactions, when considered as a group, are those associated with comfortable or pleasurable sensations in the body and conserve energy. They form the mechanism of normal functions when the body is in a "receptive" state.

It has already been mentioned that the parasympathetic system brings about its effects by the liberation of a chemical substance, *acetylcholine*, at the terminal nerve endings of the postganglionic fibers. Acetylcholine may also be produced in other parts of the body besides the parasympathetic nerve endings. It is an unstable chemical substance, quickly rendered inactive in the body. Hence its effect is limited to the immediate region in which it is produced. It cannot affect parts of the body at any distance from the point of secretion or liberation. For example, when a savory odor induces the parasympathetic system to bring about muscular contractions of the stomach, it does not at the same time cause a desire to void, nor does it cause the pupils to constrict. The changes in the body associated with sexual stimulation, such as erection and glandular secretion, are the result of stimuli affecting the parasympathetic fibers of the sacral outflow which are distributed to the genital organs.

Hypothalamus. It has been amply demonstrated that the hypothalamus is a region of great importance in connection with the proper functioning of the autonomic nervous system. It is here that the nerve centers controlling the sympathetic and parasympathetic systems are located. Nerve fibers supplying the posterior lobe of the pituitary gland are also connected with this portion of the diencephalon. It is in the hypothalamus that the autonomic system forms connections with all the other nervous tissues of the body and is thus influenced by every external and internal change. The possible role of the hypothalamus as an endocrine organ has already been mentioned (pages 357 and 575).

The stable nature of the internal environment of the body, referred to as *homeostasis*, is controlled by hypothalamic nuclei. Such phenomena as constancy in amount of blood sugar, the part played by the sweat glands in regulating body temperature, composition of body fluids, and rate of heartbeat under different conditions are regulated and integrated in the hypothalamus.

Lesions of the hypothalamus are believed to be associated with such abnormal conditions as *diabetes insipidus* and *adiposogenital dystrophy*.

Autonomic system of lower chordates. The general scheme of arrangement of the autonomic system in tetrapods is similar to that of man. The lower vertebrates show a progressive complexity of the autonomic system as the evolutionary scale is ascended.

In amphioxus only the sympathetic system is represented. Here the visceral motor neurons course through the dorsal spinal nerves. It will be recalled that in amphioxus dorsal and ventral spinal nerve roots remain separate. Since there is no true brain and no cranial nerves are present, a parasympathetic system is lacking. In cyclostomes segmental sympathetic ganglia are present, but these are not connected, nor are sympathetic trunks to be found. In lampreys, as in amphioxus, the dorsal and ventral spinal nerves do not unite. Preganglionic sympathetic fibers emerge from the spinal cord through the dorsal spinal nerves. In the hagfishes, in which the roots do unite, these fibers apparently pass through the ventral roots. A parasympathetic system appears for the first time in cyclostomes since visceral motor branches of the vagus nerve (X) terminate in the walls of the heart and gut. The autonomic system is much better developed in elasmobranchs. Sympathetic and parasympathetic components are clearly demarcated. The sympathetic elements are confined to the abdominal region, there being no cranial sympathetic nerve fibers. The consecutive sympathetic ganglia are sometimes joined by lateral connectives, but, in general, the sympathetic strands dorsal to the body cavity have a rather diffuse arrangement. All sympathetic ganglia connect with spinal nerves by white visceral rami, and each ganglion is closely associated with a small mass of chromaffin tissue. Parasympathetic fibers of the vagus pass to esophagus and stomach but do not seem to go the the intestine or urogenital organs. Parasympathetic fibers are also present in the oculomotor (III), facial (VII), and glossopharyngeal (IX) nerves. In teleosts, the autonomic system shows a still greater advance and considerable similarity to that of tetrapods. The sympathetic ganglia on each side are connected by a longitudinal trunk, forming a chain. This extends from the first spinal nerve to the first hemal arch. The two trunks come together and fuse into a single strand between the kidneys, but diverge again posteriorly, becoming paired in the first hemal arch. Parasympathetic components seem to be confined to the oculomotor and vagus nerves. The Dipnoi also have a pair of longitudinal sympathetic trunks, but segmental swellings, or ganglia, are inconspicuous or absent, although they are joined by metameric white visceral rami. The oculomotor and vagus nerves apparently contain parasympathetic fibers. In caudate amphibians the condition is similar to that of teleosts except that the sympathetic system is divided into cephalic, cervical, abdominal, and caudal regions. White visceral rami form connections in all but the cephalic region. Only cranial parasympathetic fibers are present, and these seem to be confined to the oculomotor and vagus nerves. In salientians, for the first time, a sacral outflow appears, in addition to the usual cranial parasympathetic fibers. The autonomic system in the Gymnophiona has not been extensively studied. A typical sympathetic system is present, but little is known about the parasympathetic system. For further information on the autonomic nervous system of lower chordates, the interested student should consult a paper by J. A. C. Nicol which gives a comprehensive description and discussion of this system (1952, *Biol. Revs. Cambridge Phil. Soc.*, **27**:1–49).

REFLEXES

The term *reflex action* refers to an immediate involuntary response to a sensory stimulus. The so-called "knee jerk" is a familiar example of reflex action. If the knees are crossed and the patellar ligament is tapped, the lower leg jerks forward involuntarily because of sudden contraction of the *quadriceps femoris muscle*. In this case impulses set up in sensory fibers in the patellar ligament travel from the knee to the spinal cord, where they form synapses with motor fibers leading to the quadriceps femoris muscle. The pathway through which such impulses travel is known as a *reflex arc* (Fig. 13.20).

Reflex arcs make up the *functional units* of the nervous system. A reflex

FIG. 13.20.   Diagram showing arrangement of simple reflex arc.

arc consists of two or more neurons together with a nonnervous component, called the *effector*, which in most cases is either a muscle cell or a glandular cell. A *receptor* element is present which receives stimuli and transmits impulses thus set up in the neuron. Receptors are sensory neurons, the dendritic ends of which are frequently associated with special accessory structures which facilitate the reception of stimuli. The terminal arborization of the axon of the receptor makes direct or indirect connections with the dendrites of a motor neuron within brain or spinal cord. The axons of the motor neuron terminate in the effector, the action being mediated by means of a neurohumor, in all probability. The simplest type of reflex arc consists of a sensory neuron synapsing directly with a motor neuron which leads to an effector.

In most cases one or more *intermediate neurons* are present between receptor and effector neurons. Through these, impulses are transmitted from sensory neurons to other neurons in brain or cord. Intermediate neurons on the same side of the central nervous system are called *association neurons*. If they cross to the opposite side, they are known as *commissural neurons*. The presence of intermediate, association, or commissural fibers determines whether a reflex will occur on the same side or on the opposite side to that in which the sensory impulse travels.

Reflexes are commonly thought of as taking place only in the central nervous system, but they occur in the outlying ganglia of the autonomic nervous system as well.

Two types of reflexes, unconditioned and conditioned, are recognized.

Unconditioned reflexes are those which are present at birth and which do not depend upon previous experience. They are characteristic of the species and are inherited as such. For example, the mere sight of food has no effect upon a newborn puppy, but placing food in the mouth will bring about a copious secretion of saliva. Later the sight or smell of food even at some distance may cause saliva to flow freely. Previous experience has established a *conditioned reflex*. The past association of the sight or odor of food with the secretion of the salivary glands has brought it about.

Much of the behavior of animals and human beings is due to conditioned reflexes, which often show a high degree of complexity. The more often certain reflexes occur, the more firmly do they become established and the more difficult are they to overcome or break.

The building up of proper reflexes is of utmost importance in the training of children. Among the earliest autonomic reflexes that take place in a child are those concerned with emptying the rectum and bladder. These are unconditioned reflexes. Reflex activity consists of contraction of the muscular walls in response to tension of the organ which stimulates sensory receptors. Evacuation of rectum and bladder results in a feeling of comfort. In these examples, the effectors, or muscles involved in the reflexes, are those supplied by parasympathetic nerve fibers. It may well be that the early association of comfort with contractions of these hollow organs and relaxation of the sphincters accounts for the feeling of pleasure with which the parasympathetic system is associated in later life. On the other hand, the discomfort felt by the child when the sphincters do not relax and when the organs are distended may be associated with feelings of anger, pain, and fear, with which the sympathetic system is later associated.

It is quite possible to reverse the action of these mechanisms by the establishment of the wrong kinds of conditioned reflexes during the early training period of a child. It has been already pointed out that unwise procedures, such as spanking or hurting a child in an effort to train it in toilet habits, must be considered in persons who later in life demonstrate abnormal reactions to certain stimuli. Poor conditioning of this sort may well explain why some adults have a tendency to urinate or defecate involuntarily when anxious or frightened, whereas the usual tendency is to do so during periods of uncontrollable laughter. The aim of modern education and habit training is to establish the association of desirable activities with parasympathetic reactions and undesirable activities with sympathetic responses.

SUMMARY

1. Almost all the nervous system is derived from the neural tube and from neural crests, structures that appear very early in embryonic development.

2. The cells making up nervous tissue have the property of irritability

more highly developed than do those of other tissues in the body. They are derived from ectoderm.

3. Nerve fibers are of two types: medullated or nonmedullated, depending upon whether or not they are surrounded by myelin sheaths. Medullated fibers are white in appearance; nonmedullated fibers are gray.

4. Bundles of nerve fibers are called fiber tracts or nerves, depending upon their location. Fiber tracts are found in the brain and spinal cord; nerves are peripheral structures. Aggregations of nerve-cell bodies are referred to as nuclei or ganglia, again depending upon where they are located, nuclei being confined to the brain or spinal cord. A ganglion is an enlargement in the course of a nerve.

5. The nervous system is divided into two main parts: (1) the central nervous system, composed of brain and spinal cord, and (2) the peripheral nervous system, made up of cranial and spinal nerves. An important part of the peripheral nervous system, and often referred to as the autonomic system, consists of portions of certain cranial and spinal nerves, as well as numbers of outlying ganglia, connected with those structures of the body under involuntary control.

6. The central nervous system is composed of gray matter and white matter. Gray matter consists of nerve-cell bodies together with non-nervous ependymal and neuroglia cells. White matter is made up of bundles of medullated fibers.

7. Early in development the anterior end of the neural tube enlarges to form the brain. Two constrictions occur, forming three primary vesicles: the forebrain, or prosencephalon; midbrain, or mesencephalon; and hindbrain, or rhombencephalon. The first and third become secondarily divided, but the midbrain undergoes no division. The remainder of the neural tube becomes the spinal cord.

8. The prosencephalon differentiates into two regions: the telencephalon, consisting of olfactory lobes (rhinencephalon) and cerebral hemispheres, and the diencephalon, or 'tween brain. The rhombencephalon gives rise to an anterior metencephalon, the dorsal part of which forms the cerebellum, and posterior myelencephalon, or medulla oblongata.

9. The original cavity of the neural tube forms the ventricles of the brain and the central canal of the spinal cord. A pair of lateral ventricles (I and II) is present in the cerebral hemispheres. These open into the third ventricle, located in the diencephalon, through the interventricular foramina, or foramina of Monro. The fourth ventricle lies in the medulla oblongata. It is connected with the third ventricle by the cerebral aqueduct. Expansions of the aqueduct in the optic lobes of lower forms make up the mesocoele. A cavity, the metaceoele, may extend from the fourth ventricle into the cerebellum.

10. The spinal cord in tetrapods bears two enlargements at the levels where nerves going to the limbs arise. These are the cervical and lumbar

enlargements opposite the forelimbs and hindlimbs, respectively. In most forms the posterior end of the spinal cord tapers down to a fine thread, the filum terminale. There is a tendency toward a shortening of the spinal cord, and it rarely extends throughout the length of the vertebral column. In the spinal cord, gray matter is centrally disposed and almost completely surrounded by white matter. The gray matter is arranged in the form of a pair of dorsal, or sensory, columns and a pair of ventral, or motor, columns. The dorsal column has upper somatic sensory and lower visceral sensory regions. The ventral column, in turn, is composed of upper visceral motor and lower somatic motor regions. Sensory neurons, the cell bodies of which lie outside the central nervous system, form connections with cells in the dorsal column. The cell bodies of motor neurons lie within the ventral column of gray matter.

11. Because of the unequal rate of growth of various components during embryonic development, certain bends or flexures occur. There are three of these: (1) a cephalic flexure between forebrain and midbrain, (2) a cervical flexure near the junction of medulla oblongata and spinal cord, (3) a pontine flexure in the region of the metencephalon. Later the brain tends to straighten out and the flexures diminish or disappear, but in birds and mammals the cephalic flexure is retained. Thus in these forms the front part of the brain comes to lie on top of the posterior portions.

12. It is in the development of the telencephalon that the greatest changes appear in the brains of vertebrates. In lower forms, the dorsal part, or pallium, is thin-walled, the ventral portion becoming the thickened corpus striatum. An outgrowth of the anterior portion of each cerebral hemisphere becomes the olfactory lobe, or rhinencephalon, concerned with the sense of smell. In higher forms the cerebral hemispheres have become the more significant part of the telencephalon and the olfactory lobes are of secondary importance. As the vertebrate scale is ascended there is an increasing tendency for nerve cells from the inner layer of gray matter in the pallium to migrate out to the periphery. A new area, the neopallium, first appears in reptiles in the outer, anterodorsal part of each cerebral hemisphere. The growth and development of the neopallium account for the large size of the cerebral hemispheres in amniote vertebrates. Its outer surface, into which nerve cells have migrated, forms a gray layer, the cerebral cortex. The cerebral hemispheres are usually smooth, but in most mammals folds, called gyri, are present, separated by depressions, known as sulci. These increase the surface area of the cerebral cortex. In mammals, a white mass, the corpus callosum, contains nerve fibers connecting the cortical areas of the two cerebral hemispheres. The well-developed cerebral cortex of man is responsible for those phenomena which characterize the high degree of his psychic development.

13. The thickened lateral portion of the diencephalon on each side makes up the thalamus. This portion contains important relay centers and con-

sists largely of numbers of nuclei of gray matter. The floor, or hypothalamus, contains centers which integrate the activities of the peripheral autonomic nervous system with those of other nervous tissues. A ventral evagination of the hypothalamus forms the infundibulum, the distal portion of which gives rise to the posterior lobe of the pituitary gland. The anterior part of the roof of the diencephalon remains epithelial and, together with the pia mater, forms a tela choroidea. Vascular folds of the tela choroidea become the anterior choroid plexus where cerebrospinal fluid is liberated. A prominent fold at the anterior end, present during early development, is actually a portion of the telencephalon. It is called the paraphysis. The epithalamus, or roof of the diencephalon, posterior to the tela choroidea consists largely of the epiphyseal apparatus. In numerous forms this gives rise to parietal and pineal outgrowths originally associated with additional eyes. In higher forms only the pineal body persists. This may be nothing more than a rudiment.

14. The floor and walls of the mesencephalon are thick and composed of fiber tracts connecting forebrain and hindbrain. The roof consists of a thick layer of gray matter, the optic tectum. Two prominences are present in the roof of the mesencephalon of lower forms. They are the corpora bigemina, or optic lobes, which serve as visual centers. In snakes and mammals there are four prominences, the corpora quadrigemina. The anterior pair serves as visual centers, and the posterior pair as auditory centers.

15. The dorsal part of the metencephalon becomes the cerebellum, the function of which is to coordinate the neuromuscular mechanism of the body. It is poorly developed in sluggish forms but is well developed in the more active vertebrates. In a few birds and in mammals there appears on the ventral side of the metencephalon a sort of bridge of nerve fibers, the pons. These fibers connect the cerebral hemispheres with the cerebellum in those forms in which certain areas of the cerebral cortex have assumed control of body movements.

16. The myelencephalon forms the medulla oblongata. The lateral and ventral walls are markedly thickened, but the dorsal wall retains its epithelial character. Together with the pia mater it forms a tela choroidea and posterior choroid plexus. The ventral and lateral walls contain large white fiber tracts as well as columns of gray matter similar to those of the spinal cord. Certain nuclei of the visceral motor column serve as centers for such vital functions as heartbeat and respiration. The anterodorsal portion of the medulla oblongata, referred to as the acousticolateralis area, is a development of the somatic sensory column. It contains nuclei associated with nerves from the lateral-line system, if present, and from the inner ear. Cranial nerves V to X (or XII) form connections with the medulla. Paired pyramids in the posterior portion mark the region where several fiber tracts cross (decussate) to the opposite side of the brain.

17. Brain and spinal cord are surrounded and protected by membranes

called meninges. A single meninx primitiva is present in fishes. Two membranes, an inner pia-arachnoid membrane and an outer dura mater, exist in amphibians, reptiles, and birds. In mammals, however, a further differentiation of the pia-arachnoid membrane occurs, forming an inner pia mater and an outer arachnoid membrane.

18. The peripheral nervous system, made up of cranial and spinal nerves, consists of several kinds of fibers, each mediating a different type of function. Somatic sensory fibers, from peripheral parts of the body, lead to the somatic sensory column of gray matter in the central nervous system. Somatic motor fibers lead directly from the somatic motor column of gray matter to the periphery, where they supply voluntary muscles, except those in the gill region. Visceral sensory fibers bring impulses from the viscera to the visceral sensory column. Visceral motor fibers of certain cranial nerves pass from the visceral motor column directly to gill muscles, at least in aquatic forms. Preganglionic visceral motor fibers go to outlying ganglia where they synapse with autonomic neurons, the gray, nonmedullated fibers of which go to smooth muscles and glands in the viscera and skin.

19. Spinal nerves are paired and segmentally arranged. They arise from the spinal cord by two roots, a dorsal root bearing a ganglion and a ventral root which lacks a ganglion. In higher forms these roots lie within the spinal canal, and the spinal nerves, formed by their union, pass out of the vertebral column through intervertebral foramina. Most spinal nerves give off three branches, or rami, a short distance beyond the point where they emerge. Dorsal and ventral rami are usually present, but a white visceral ramus is lacking in some. In the regions of the limbs, cross connections between certain spinal nerves form plexuses.

20. The cranial nerves, arising from the brain, number 10 in anamniotes and 12 in amniotes. The twelfth nerve and part of the eleventh nerve represent spinal nerves which have been taken over by the brain. Some cranial nerves are purely sensory (I, II, and VIII), and others are purely motor (III, IV, VI, XI, and XII). The remainder (V, VII, IX, and X) are mixed sensory and motor, but even these differ from spinal nerves in that if their roots unite they do so before emerging from the medulla oblongata. In lower vertebrates, nerves VII, IX, and X have branches related to the lateral-line system, a system peculiar to the aquatic mode of life. These branches disappear in terrestrial forms. Cranial nerves III, VII, IX, and X bear preganglionic visceral motor fibers which make up part of the parasympathetic nervous system. Another cranial nerve called the terminal nerve (O), discovered in 1894, is a sensory nerve bearing one or more ganglia and passing to the olfactory mucous membrane from the cerebral hemispheres. Its function is not clear.

21. The olfactory nerve (I) is a somatic sensory nerve passing from the olfactory epithelium to the olfactory lobe of the brain.

22. The optic nerve (II) is not actually a nerve, but rather a fiber tract of the brain, passing from the retina of the eye to the optic lobes. The optic nerves of the two sides cross beneath the diencephalon to form the optic chiasma.

23. The oculomotor nerve (III) is a somatic motor nerve arising from the midbrain and supplying the superior, inferior, and internal rectus muscles, the inferior oblique eye muscle, and the muscle elevating the upper eyelid. It also contains preganglionic autonomic fibers which go the the ciliary ganglion. Postganglionic fibers then lead to the iris and to the muscles of accommodation.

24. The trochlear nerve (IV), coming from the posterodorsal side of the midbrain, is a somatic motor nerve which supplies the superior oblique eye muscle.

25. The trigeminal nerve (V) is the nerve of the mandibular arch. It arises from the medulla oblongata and has three branches: ophthalmic, maxillary, and mandibular. The first two contain somatic sensory fibers; the last consists of both somatic sensory and visceral motor fibers. In fishes the ophthalmic is composed of superficial and deep (profundus) portions. In higher forms the two portions are not distinct and a single opthalmic nerve is present. It supplies somatic sensory fibers to the conjunctiva, cornea, iris, ciliary body, lacrimal gland, mucous membrane of the nose, and the skin of the forehead, nose, and eyelids. The maxillary branch is the sensory nerve to the upper jaw. The mandibular branch sends somatic sensory fibers to the lower jaw and visceral motor fibers directly to the muscles used in chewing. The trigeminal nerve bears a Gasserian ganglion.

26. The abducens nerve (VI) is a somatic motor nerve, arising from the ventral part of the medulla and supplying the external rectus eye muscle and the nictitating membrane if present. In lampreys it also supplies the inferior rectus.

27. The facial nerve (VII), arising from the medulla, is a mixed nerve supplying the second visceral, or hyoid, arch. In lower aquatic forms it has large somatic sensory components supplying structures of the lateral-line system. In mammals its visceral sensory portion supplies the taste buds of the anterior two-thirds of the tongue. The major part of the nerve is visceral motor and is distributed directly to the muscles of the face. Preganglionic visceral motor fibers of the facial pass either to the submaxillary or to the sphenopalatine ganglion. From the submaxillary ganglion arise postganglionic fibers leading to the submaxillary and sublingual salivary glands; those from the sphenopalatine ganglion go to the lacrimal gland and mucous membrane of the nose. The facial nerve bears a geniculate ganglion at its base.

28. The auditory nerve (VIII) is purely somatic sensory. It connects with the medulla oblongata and carries impulses from the inner ear to the

brain. The auditory nerve supplies the organs of equilibrium and those for sound reception.

29. The glossopharyngeal nerve (IX), arising from the medulla, carries visceral sensory and visceral motor fibers and in fishes sends some somatic sensory fibers to the lateral-line system. It is the nerve of the third visceral arch and the second gill pouch. In lower forms, it bears a petrosal ganglion near its base. In higher forms, two ganglia, superior and petrosal, are present. In higher vertebrates, visceral motor fibers pass directly to the muscles of the larynx derived from the third gill arch. In mammals, visceral sensory fibers pass to taste buds on the posterior one-third of the tongue and mucous membrane of the pharynx. Preganglionic autonomic fibers go to the otic ganglion, synapsing with postganglionic fibers which supply the parotid gland.

30. The vagus nerve (X), coming from the medulla by several roots, is a mixed nerve. In lower aquatic forms, a somatic sensory branch supplies the lateral line proper. Visceral sensory and visceral motor fibers are distributed to the remaining visceral arches and to the pharynx. Visceral sensory fibers and visceral motor autonomic preganglionic fibers also pass to the heart, lungs (in higher forms), and all parts of the digestive system except those at the posterior end. Two ganglia, jugular and nodosal, are borne by the vagus nerve in higher forms.

31. The spinal accessory nerve (XI), arising from the medulla in amniotes, bears visceral motor fibers, some of which accompany the vagus to larynx and pharynx. Other somatic motor fibers pass to neck muscles which are possibly derived from myotomes. The nerve apparently is made up of a branch of the vagus which has become separated from that nerve, as well as of fibers from certain anterior cervical spinal nerves.

32. The hypoglossal nerve (XII), also arising from the medulla in amniotes, is a somatic motor nerve carrying fibers to the intrinsic muscles of the tongue and to certain muscles of the lower jaw. It actually represents the motor portions of two or three anterior spinal nerves which have been taken over by the brain.

33. The sympathetic components of the peripheral autonomic nervous system in man consist of medullated, visceral motor, preganglionic fibers leading from the spinal cord to outlying ganglia and of nonmedullated postganglionic fibers leading from outlying ganglia to all muscles and glands of the body under involuntary control. Preganglionic fibers course through the visceral rami of all the thoracic and the first, second, and third lumbar spinal nerves. They are referred to as the thoracolumbar outflow. On either side of the vertebral column a sympathetic trunk courses longitudinally. Each trunk bears metameric chain ganglia with which the visceral rami of the above-mentioned spinal nerves connect. Other sympathetic ganglia—coeliac, superior mesenteric, and inferior mesenteric—lie among the viscera and are known collectively as the prevertebral ganglia.

34. The parasympathetic portion of the autonomic nervous system in man is composed of portions of cranial nerves III, VII, IX, and X and of the visceral rami of sacral nerves 2, 3, and 4. These consist of long preganglionic fibers, frequently referred to as the craniosacral outflow. They terminate in ganglia close to, or in, the organs which they supply. Postganglionic fibers are therefore very short. Four ganglia in the head region are associated with cranial nerves III, VII, and IX. They are called the ciliary (nerve III), submaxillary, sphenopalatine (nerve VII), and otic (nerve IX) ganglia, respectively. The ganglia associated with the vagus (X) lie within the walls of the structures which this nerve supplies. In the digestive tract connections are formed with the plexuses of Auerbach and Meissner.

35. The two parts of the autonomic system work antagonistically, thus serving to control the functions of all involuntary mechanisms in the body.

36. In other tetrapods the structure of the autonomic portion of the the nervous system is, in general, similar to that of man, but in lower forms it is less complicated. Sympathetic ganglia in cyclostomes are not connected. In elasmobranchs delicate nerve strands connect certain sympathetic ganglia, but true sympathetic trunks are lacking. In teleosts the sympathetic ganglia are connected for the first time by a longitudinal trunk. A parasympathetic system first appears in cyclostomes. In fishes and amphibians the cranial outflow seems to be confined to the oculomotor and vagus nerves. A sacral outflow first appears in salientian amphibians.

CHAPTER 14

RECEPTOR ORGANS

Closely associated with the nervous system are certain sensory receptor organs. They are so constructed as to be capable of responding to various stimuli by setting up impulses which are in turn transmitted by nerve fibers to the central nervous system. In the higher centers of the brain such impulses are interpreted as *sensations*. The thalamus serves as such a center in most vertebrates, but a well-developed cerebral cortex, if present, may be the seat of further sensory integration. The receptor organs themselves do not perceive anything but merely serve as a means of access to the nervous system.

In lower forms of animal life the entire integument may possess a sensory function. Sensory receptors, in such forms, are of a generalized character but are invariably derived from ectoderm. This is what one would expect, since the ectoderm is primitively the outer layer of the body and most likely to be affected by environmental change. Even though most vertebrate sense organs have been modified greatly in the course of evolution into structures of considerable complexity, nevertheless the actual receptor cells, with rare exceptions, are in each case derived from ectoderm.

Most of what is known about sense organs has been gathered from studies of man. In other animals little can be determined concerning their sensations. Investigators are therefore confined, for the most part, to studies of muscular and glandular responses to stimuli. Behavioral responses are usually analyzed in terms of human reactions under similar conditions. Much caution must be exercised, however, in interpreting the results of behavior experiments. Nevertheless, similarity in structure of the sense organs of man and other vertebrates leads us to assume that similar functions and even sensations are experienced by all.

The receptor organs with which we are most familiar are those for the senses of sight, hearing, smell, taste, and touch. However, numerous other sense organs are also present in the body. They include receptors for such senses as pain, heat, cold, equilibrium, hunger, thirst, fatigue, sex, and muscle position. Most of the sense organs are stimulated by environmental disturbances of various kinds. They are therefore spoken of as *external sense organs*. The receptors for the external sense organs are called *exteroceptors*. *Internal sense organs*, on the other hand, are affected by stimuli originating within the body itself. Certain internal sensory receptors are located in tendons, joints, skeletal muscles, heart, and other areas. The structures in which they lie are not in direct contact with the environment but may, nevertheless, be affected by factors of environmental origin. Receptors located in the walls of the digestive organs are known as *interoceptors*. They are responsible for such internal sensations as hunger, thirst, nausea, and others. No specific receptor organs have been discovered for some of these senses, the nerve endings themselves probably serving as receptors. Yet it would seem obvious that some sort of differentiation must exist at the ends of dendrites of the nerves in question. Some authorities list over 30 different senses. The actual number enumerated by a particular author depends largely upon the manner in which the various senses are classified.

Terminology. The different kinds of receptors are named according to the nature of the stimulus by which they are affected. The following list includes the names of those more commonly known:

External senses	Exteroceptors
Sight	Photoreceptors
Hearing	Phonoreceptors
Smell	Olfactoreceptors
Taste	Gustatoreceptors
Touch (transient contact)	Tangoreceptors
Pressure (sustained contact)	Tangoreceptors
Temperature	Thermoreceptors
Heat	Caloreceptors
Cold	Frigidoreceptors
Pain	Algesireceptors
Currents of water	Rheoreceptors
Internal senses	
Muscle position	Proprioceptors
Equilibrium	Statoreceptors
Hunger, thirst, etc.	Interoceptors

The term *teloceptor* is sometimes used to distinguish those exteroceptors which are able to detect stimuli coming from a distance. The olfactory, auditory, and visual receptors are examples. Caloreceptors might even be included under this category.

Each sense organ functions only within circumscribed limits. The limits, however, vary in different species of animals. Sounds of high frequency, for example, which can be detected by some mammals may be inaudible to man. The visible portion of the spectrum, produced when ordinary light passes through a prism, is in man confined to red on one hand and violet on the other. It has been demonstrated that certain insects can perceive ultraviolet light, which is invisible to man. The olfactory sense of the dog is clearly superior to that of man.

In some cases the application of a different kind of stimulus to an exteroceptor will affect it in a manner similar to that produced by the usual type of stimulus. Thus, mechanical or electrical stimulation of the retina of the eye, even if performed in total darkness, gives a sensation of light. Similarly, mechanical stimulation of the tympanic membrane gives a sensation of sound. When a certain chemical called menthol is applied to the skin, it produces an impression of cold.

The nerve fibers which convey impulses from receptor organs to the central nervous system are called sensory fibers. In the previous chapter it was emphasized that these may be grouped in two categories: somatic sensory and visceral sensory nerves. Somatic sensory nerves are those which are associated with exteroceptors, proprioceptors, and statoreceptors. Visceral sensory nerves, from the visceral organs, are associated with interoceptors.

SENSE OF SIGHT

Eyes are complicated photoreceptors, but not all photoreceptors are eyes. In certain protozoans a restricted area of the cell may serve as a photoreceptor. The eyespot of *Euglena* is an example. Scattered photosensory cells are frequently present in the integument of invertebrates. In some forms, aggregations of such sensory cells may form "eyes" of various types.

The eyes of vertebrates are highly specialized structures which have no true homologues in animals belonging to other phyla. They appear for the first time in cyclostomes, their evolutionary history being obscure. The unpaired, median eyes of certain vertebrates have been referred to in Chap. 13, Nervous System.

Photoreceptors of Protochordates

The larval ascidian has a single eye with a retina and lens. It lies within a dilatation of the anterior end of the neural tube, the *cerebral vesicle*. The eye is situated slightly off the midline and is apparently the persistent member of a pair of structures, the other degenerating very early during development and being represented only by a small vestigial mass of tissue. Several reasons have been advanced for not homologizing the ascidian eye with those of vertebrates.

The *anterior pigment spot* of amphioxus, frequently referred to as an *eyespot*, has been shown to lack any sensory function. The so-called *infundibular organ*, composed of flagellated, ependymal cells, the long processes of which extend into the cerebral vesicle, is thought by some to function as a crude sort of eye which can detect shadows cast when light strikes the anterior pigment spot. Certain photosensory, ganglionic *cells of Joseph* are present on the dorsal side of the head region of amphioxus. Other photosensory cells, partially surrounded by pigment capsules, are located along the ventral side of the spinal cord.

Vertebrate Eye

As an introduction to the discussion of the vertebrate eye we shall first consider that of man, since its structure and function are better understood than are those of other vertebrates. The human eyeball (Fig. 14.1) is almost spherical in shape. It is composed of three coats, or layers, of which only the outer one is complete. The others are modified near the exposed portion of the eyeball.

The outermost coat protects and gives shape to the eyeball. It is called the *fibrous tunic.* This thick, tough layer is divided into two regions: a transparent exposed portion, the *cornea,* and a larger, opaque, posterior section, the *sclera,* or *sclerotic coat,* the anterior part of which is commonly referred to as the "white" of the eye. The muscles which move the eyeball are attached to the sclera. A thin membrane, the *conjunctiva,* which is

FIG. 14.1. Diagram of sagittal section of human eyeball.

continuous with the inner surface of the eyelids, covers and is fused to the outer surface of the cornea, constituting the *epithelium* of the latter. The cornea is practically circular in outline. It is somewhat thicker than the sclera and bulges out in front of it. The curved surface of the cornea is of importance in focusing light rays, thus supplementing the lens in this respect. Irregularities in the shape of the cornea are often responsible for the condition known as *astigmatism,* an optical defect causing imperfect images or indistinctness of vision.

The middle coat is called the *uvea.* It is divided into three regions: (1) a vascular, pigmented *choroid coat,* closely adherent to the sclera, (2) a portion which forms part of the thickened *ciliary body,* composed of *ciliary muscles* and *ciliary processes,* located anteriorly near the region where sclera and cornea join, (3) a portion which forms part of the *iris,* a thin, circular disc, located at the anterior end of the ciliary body where the uveal coat turns sharply inward and away from the fibrous tunic. An opening in the center of the iris is spoken of as the *pupil* of the eye.

The innermost coat of the eyeball is the retina. It lies against the entire extent of the uvea. The portion in contact with the choroid coat is thickened and is sensitive to light. The remaining part of the retina is thin and nonsensory. It contributes to the ciliary body and iris and terminates at the rim of the pupil. The light-sensitive part of the retina ends abruptly at the ciliary body, its irregular, serrated margin being referred to as the *ora serrata*, or *ora terminalis*.

A biconvex, *crystalline lens* lies immediately behind the iris, pushing the latter forward so as to cause a slight bulge. The lens has a clear, glassy appearance during life, but in preserved specimens it is frequently opaque. Its posterior side is more convex than its anterior surface. A thin *lens capsule* invests the lens closely. From the ciliary body arise numerous radially arranged fibers (Fig. 14.10) which are attached to the lens capsule. They form the *suspensory ligament* (*zonula of Zinn*) which keeps the lens in place. The shape of the lens is not fixed. *Accommodation*, or the adjustment of the eye which enables it to focus on objects at various distances, is accomplished by changing the shape of the lens (page 632).

The cavity of the eye in front of the lens is partially divided by the iris into *anterior* and *posterior chambers*. A clear watery fluid, the *aqueous humor*, fills these cavities, which are continuous with each other at the pupil. The large cavity of the eye in back of the lens is called the *vitreal cavity*, or *chamber of the vitreous humor*. It contains a transparent semi-gelatinous substance, the *vitreous body*, or *vitreous humor*.

The optic nerve leaves the eye from behind, piercing the retina, choroid, and sclerotic coats. The point at which it emerges from the retina is the *blind spot*.

When light enters the eye, it passes first through the thin conjunctival epithelium covering the cornea, then through the cornea proper, aqueous humor, pupil, lens, and vitreous humor, finally to impinge upon photoreceptors in the retina.

Early development. The various structures which, in their aggregate, form the eye, arise from three rudiments: (1) the retina and optic nerve are derivatives of the diencephalon; (2) the lens differentiates from the superficial ectoderm of the head; (3) the other portions come from neighboring mesenchyme.

The first indication of eye formation (Fig. 14.2) is to be observed in the appearance of a pair of lateral expansions, the *optic vesicles*, arising from the forebrain in the region which is later to become the diencephalon. The distal end of each optic vesicle soon enlarges and comes in contact with the superficial ectoderm of the head, but the proximal portion remains relatively unchanged. It is referred to as the *optic stalk*. The distal portion of the swollen vesicle next becomes indented in such a manner as to form a temporarily imperfect (see below), double-walled *optic cup*. Pigment granules appear in the cells forming the outer layer of the optic cup which now is called the *pigment layer of the retina*. The inner layer gives rise to the *sensory*, or *nervous, portion of the retina*. The two layers later fuse.

In the meantime a thickening of the superficial ectoderm occurs at the point where the optic cup established contact with it. This is the *lens placode*, which gives rise to the crystalline lens of the eye. It invaginates at the same time as the optic cup is forming and soon becomes a closed

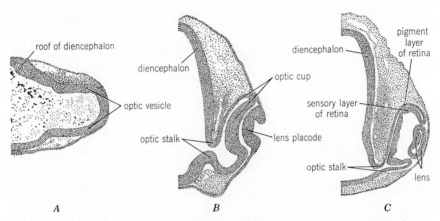

FIG. 14.2. Successive stages *A, B,* and *C* in the development of optic cups in chick embryo: *A,* 33-hour embryo; *B,* 48-hour embryo; *C,* 72-hour embryo. (*Drawn by R. Speigle.*)

vesicle which comes to lie within the optic cup, almost filling the latter during the early stages of development (Fig. 14.3). Experiments have shown that in some animals the developing optic vesicle actually induces the superficial ectoderm in this region to undergo the changes necessary to lens formation. As the optic cup increases in size, the lens fails to grow at the same pace. It ultimately comes to lie at the mouth of the optic cup. The outer wall of the lens vesicle retains its epithelial character, but the inner wall thickens, its cells giving rise to *lens fibers*.

The indentation which formed the optic cup is continued along the ventral side of the cup as well as along the ventral border of the optic stalk. This forms the *choroid fissure*, which appears as a gap, extending from the optic cup toward the brain (Fig. 14.4). For a time the embryonic choroid fissure remains open, furnishing a pathway for blood vessels (*hyaloid artery, hyaloid vein*) which are of particular importance in connection with the development of the lens. Before long, however, the edges of the choroid fissure come together and fuse, thus forming a small and narrow tube within the already tubular optic stalk. Later the hyaloid vessels atrophy within the optic cup proper, but the vessels within the optic stalk are retained as the *central artery* and *vein* of the retina, supplying the retina proper. A lymphatic channel, the *hyaloid canal*, coursing through the vitreous humor from blind spot to lens, marks the former location of the hyaloid artery. The axons of nerve cells which develop in the sensory layer of the retina later converge toward the optic stalk and grow through the wall, or substance, of the optic stalk to the brain, thus forming the optic nerve (II). The optic canal, representing a portion of

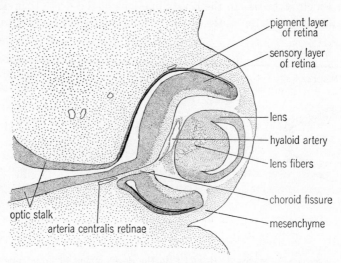

Fig. 14.3. Sagittal section through optic cup of 12-mm. pig embryo.

the original cavity of the brain, persists for a time but is gradually obliterated. The optic nerve, therefore, is actually the transformed optic stalk through which numerous nerve fibers pass to the brain. The central artery and vein of the retina actually course *through* the optic nerve. The optic nerve thus differs from other cranial nerves in that it is a composite of nerve fibers which grow from one part of the brain to another. It is, therefore, properly termed a *fiber tract*, rather than a peripheral nerve.

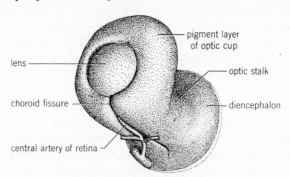

Fig. 14.4. Developing optic cup showing choroid fissure through which the central artery of the retina courses. (*Drawn by R. Speigle.*)

In any event, it is usually classified under the category of special somatic sensory nerves.

The inner layer of the retina near the rim of the optic cup remains thin, whereas the remainder thickens as its cells become differentiated to form the nervous, or sensory, portion. The irregular line which marks the boundary of the two areas is the ora serrata. The thin portion of the inner layer fuses with the pigment layer overlying it, and these two, together with a part of the uveal coat, form the ciliary body and iris.

The mesenchyme surrounding the original optic cup differentiates into the uveal and fibrous coats of the eyeball. The cornea is derived from mesenchyme which grows in between the optic cup and superficial ectoderm, the latter forming the epithelial layer of the cornea.

Fibrous tunic. In numerous lower vertebrates both sclera and cornea may be transparent. The opacity of the sclera is a secondary phenomenon. The tissue of which the sclera is composed consists of interlacing, tough, inelastic, tendinous, connective-tissue fibers, so arranged as to provide equal strength in all directions, thus keeping the eyeball constant in shape and causing it to be highly resistant to external or internal pressure. The sclera is practically noncellular and is not furnished directly with blood vessels. In certain reptiles, and in birds, a ring of bony plates, the *scleral ossicles*, or *sclerotic bones*, lies embedded in the portion of the sclera near the cornea. These provide further protection to the eye. Scleral ossicles appeared early in evolutionary history since they have been identified in many fossil "ancestral" vertebrates. They are not present in mammals. In the region of the cornea the connective-tissue fibers are arranged parallel to each other. Cells are present in small numbers, connecting with each other by long, thin, protoplasmic strands by means of which nutrient materials and wastes may be transferred from blood vessels located at the margins of the cornea. The cornea itself is devoid of blood vessels which, of course, would interfere with the transmission of light. It is possible that the cornea is nourished to some extent by the tears, or secretions of the lacrimal glands, which contain nutrient materials. Lacking blood vessels and lying in an exposed position, together with the fact that there is evaporation from its surface, the temperature of the cornea is somewhat lower than that of the body. Sensory receptors for pain are numerous in the corneal epithelium, but other sensory receptors are apparently lacking. One noteworthy feature of the cornea is the rapidity with which it is repaired after injury.

Uvea. *Choroid coat.* The portion of the uvea which is adherent to the sclerotic coat consists of a thin, soft, dark brown, vascular membrane. Large and medium-sized arteries and veins, as well as numerous capillaries, form a rather rich plexus of blood vessels throughout the choroid coat. The pigment serves to keep light from entering the eyeball at random and also prevents internal reflections from occurring.

Ciliary body. At the point where the choroid portion of the uvea merges with the ciliary body, the uveal membrane becomes thicker, less vascular, and less heavily pigmented. Numerous involuntary, *ciliary muscle fibers* are present in this layer. The inner face of the ciliary body is characterized by numerous radiating folds, the *ciliary processes*. These are formed partly from the uvea and partly from the nonnervous border of the retina, mentioned above, lying beyond the ora serrata.

Iris. The iris is composed of an outer layer, which is part of the uvea, and an inner layer derived from the nonnervous portion of the retina. In the latter region it is the *inner* of the two retinal layers (that nearest the lens) which is heavily pigmented, a condition just opposite to that obtaining in the remainder of the retina. The outer part of the retinal portion of the iris, as well as the uveal portion, contains relatively little pigment. The dark pigment in the inner portion of the iris is the only pigment present in individuals with blue eyes. This pigment as seen through the colorless tissue covering it, because of a physical effect known as the Tyndall-blue phenomenon, involving interference of light rays, gives the impression that the iris is blue. In brown and black eyes additional pigment is present in the outer, or uveal, region. The pink eye of the albino is devoid of all pigment, even in the retinal portion. It owes its color to blood in the numerous vessels of the iris. Although the albino condition is frequently encountered among vertebrates, true albinism rarely occurs in man.

The iris contains two groups of involuntary, ectodermal muscle fibers called *sphincter* and *dilator muscles*, respectively. The sphincter muscle fibers are arranged in concentric bundles about the margin of the pupil. Contraction of these elements results in a diminution in size of the pupil. The dilator muscles are arranged in a radial manner, their contraction causing a dilatation of the pupil. The involuntary contraction of these two sets of muscle fibers regulates the amount of light that enters the eyeball under varying conditions of illumination. The dilator muscles are innervated by postganglionic fibers of the sympathetic nervous system which arise in the upper thoracic segments of the spinal cord and emerge from the superior cervical ganglion (Fig. 13.18). They accompany the internal carotid artery into the cranial cavity, finally entering the trunk of the nasociliary branch of the trigeminal nerve and terminating in the iris. The sphincter muscles of the iris are innervated by postganglionic fibers of the parasympathetic system, the cell bodies of which are located in the ciliary ganglion.

Retina. The pigment layer of the retina is closely applied to the uveal layer throughout its entire extent. The retina consists of three regions: (1) the *optic region* is the thickened portion in contact with the choroid coat, sensitive to light and terminating at the ora serrata; (2) the *ciliary region*, which together with the ciliary portion of the uvea forms the ciliary body; (3) the *iridial portion*, contributing to the structure of the iris. It is in the iris that the uvea and nonnervous portion of the retina are most closely associated. We are chiefly concerned with the optic region, since it is here that the photoreceptors of the vertebrate eye are situated.

The term *optical axis* is used to refer to an imaginary line passing through the center of the cornea, pupil, and lens to the posterior pole of the eye. A small area of the optic portion of the retina in direct line with the optical axis is the *area centralis*, often called the *macula lutea* because of the yellow pigment which it contains. In the center of the macula lutea is a shallow depression, the *fovea centralis*, which is the area of most acute vision. The remainder of the retina in a fresh specimen is practically transparent.

The structure of the optic portion of the retina is highly complex. It

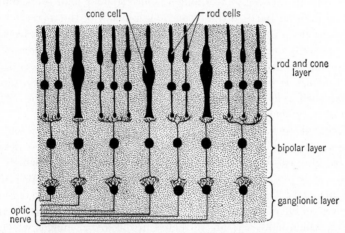

FIG. 14.5. Simplified diagram showing relation of rod and cone cells to bipolar and ganglionic layers of retina. Note "convergence" of several rod cells onto a single bipolar cell. Bipolar cells may converge in a similar manner onto a single ganglionic cell.

consists of seven layers of nervous elements and two supporting membranes, the detailed discussion of which is beyond the scope of this book. Neurosensory photoreceptors called *rods* and *cones* are located in the *outermost* part of the retina, *i.e.*, that which is farthest from the source of light and nearest the choroid coat. Rods and cones differ as to shape, the rods being slender and filamentous and the cones short and thick (Fig. 14.5). Rods are believed to distinguish different degrees of light and darkness, whereas cones, in man and other higher primates, are chiefly concerned with both visual acuity and color vision. In the human eye, rods far outnumber the cones, the proportion being about 20 to 1. From the rod and cone cells, slender nerve fibers extend toward the vitreous humor, forming synapses with dendrites of *bipolar neurons*. The axons of the bipolar cells synapse in turn with the dendrites of neurons forming the *ganglionic layer* of the retina. This is the layer nearest the vitreous humor. The axons of the ganglionic layer course over the inner surface of the retina next to the vitreous humor. They converge at a single point a short distance from the fovea centralis, bend sharply, and then run parallel to each other to form the optic nerve. The nerve then passes through the retina, choroid, and sclerotic coats on its way to the brain. At the point where the fibers converge to form the optic nerve, neurosensory receptors are lacking. This area, therefore, is called the *blind spot*, since its presence is responsible for a gap in the visual field.

Macula lutea and fovea centralis. A true macula lutea, or yellow spot, is found only in man and some other primates. In other vertebrates the term *area centralis* is more appropriate. In the macula lutea rod cells have been practically eliminated and only cone cells are present. Furthermore, the cone cells in this region are longer, more slender, and more numerous than those in other parts of the retina. As a result of the increase in number of cones, the number of bipolar and ganglionic cells is increased in this area since here a single cone cell usually synapses with a bipolar cell and a single bipolar cell connects with a ganglionic cell. Each cone cell thus has its own line of access to the brain and is individually more important than if several such cells connected to a single bipolar cell. The latter arrangement is typical of rod cells.

A depressed fovea centralis is present in man and numerous other vertebrates but does not occur in all forms. Birds have the best-developed foveas of all. In the foveal region retinal blood vessels, which would interfere with visual acuity, have been eliminated. According to G. L. Walls (1942, "The Vertebrate Eye," Cranbrook Institute of Science), the fovea is an effective magnifying device. Because of its shape, and the manner in which light rays are refracted in the fovea, images which come to a focus on the fovea are magnified to a considerable extent and thus perceived more clearly than those in other portions of the retina. In the fovea the cone cells are arranged obliquely rather than perpendicularly. This also may be a factor in bringing about greater visual acuity. In order to see things more distinctly, we are constantly changing the position of the eyeball so as to focus the image of the object we wish to observe upon the fovea.

Rhodopsin. The outer segment of each rod cell contains a reddish pigment called *rhodopsin*, or *visual purple*. Its chemical structure is not yet completely known. Vitamin A seems to be an important constituent. The presence of rhodopsin is necessary for any rod vision in dim light. In bright light it disappears or is reduced so that the threshold for vision is raised. In going from bright light into darkness or semidarkness it again makes its appearance, apparently being built up again, or regenerated, by the rod cells. This decreases the threshold for vision since much less light is required to stimulate the rods. Several minutes must elapse, however, before the eyes become adapted to such changed conditions. During this interval the concentration of rhodopsin is restored to a higher level. When emerging from darkness into bright light, we may be temporarily blinded until the rhodopsin has been depleted sufficiently to enable us to see normally. *Destruction* of rhodopsin, therefore, is important in *light* adaptation, whereas its *formation* is necessary in *dark* adaptation. Rhodopsin is not present in cone cells.

It has been determined that sufficient quantities of vitamin A must be available in order that the body can synthesize rhodopsin. The importance of supplying adequate amounts of vitamin A in the diet was emphasized in World War II, in which nocturnal activities of various kinds played so important a part.

If a fresh mammalian eye which has been kept for a time in total darkness is exposed to a bright object and then fixed immediately in a solution of alum, a photographic image of the object can be observed on the retina upon dissection. The formation of the image is brought about by bleaching or destruction of the rhodopsin in the rods upon which the bright portion of the image fell, the surrounding parts retaining their dark coloration. The fact that rhodopsin fades upon exposure to light is responsible for this phenomenon.

Inversion of the retina. In the vertebrate eye light must pass *through* the various *layers* of the transparent retina before it can stimulate the sensory rod and cone cells. Impulses thus set up must then pass back through the *cells* comprising these layers to reach the optic nerve. Such an arrangement is certainly not what one would expect, nor can it be considered an efficient plan. This peculiar state of affairs is encountered only in the vertebrates which are said to possess an "inverted" eye.

Several theories have been advanced which seek to explain the inversion of the retina and its evolutionary origin, but none seems wholly adequate. The most satisfactory explanation for the origin of the photoreceptive elements of the retina and their inverted position was advanced by Studnicka in 1912 and later elaborated by Walls (1942). According to their idea, rods and cones are actually modified ependymal cells which line the cavity of the neural tube. The position of the sensory cells in the optic cup and optic stalk can be traced through the configurations of cup and stalk and are found to be continuous with the ependymal layer of the neural tube proper. Ependymal cells, at least during embryonic stages, are frequently flagellated, the flagella assisting in the circulation of cerebrospinal fluid in the central canal of the cord and the ventricles of the brain. If the flagella of ependymal cells are photosensitive, as indeed they are in the infundibular organ of amphioxus, then according to Walls' conception, the receptive elements of the rod and cone cells are homologous with the flagella of ependymal cells and, therefore, lie in a reversed position in the fully formed vertebrate retina (Fig. 14.6). The fact that the receptive portions of rod and cone cells differentiate during development, in a manner strikingly similar to that of flagella, lends further support to this view.

Many authorities have sought to explain the evolutionary appearance of the vertebrate lens which in some vertebrates develops under the organizing influence of the optic cup. No really satisfactory explanation has been offered which accounts for all the factors involved.

A B C

Fig. 14.6.   Diagram illustrating Studnicka's and Walls' theory of retinal inversion.

Accommodation.   Stimulation of the photoreceptive rods and cones may produce several sensations: light, various colors, form, perspective, and motion.   In order to perceive objects and patterns in detail, it is essential that a picture of the object or pattern to be perceived fall upon the retina in perfect focus so that the photoreceptive rods and cones are stimulated in the correct manner.   Practically all parts of the eye play a part in bringing this about, but the curved surfaces of the cornea and lens are of primary importance.   The cornea is responsible for placing the image on the retina; the lens makes minor adjustments in sharpening the focus.

The eye must adapt itself in order to bring objects at various distances into focus.   This is known as *accommodation*.   In higher vertebrates accommodation is brought about by changing the shape of the lens.   In some, as in birds and possibly in certain reptiles, changing the degree of curvature of the cornea is employed as well.   To appreciate the necessity of altering the shape of the lens in focusing, it is advisable at this point to review certain fundamental physical principles dealing with light and its passage through transparent media.

Refraction.   Light, which is responsible for the various aspects of the sensation of sight, travels in straight lines through transparent media at incredible speeds.   Whenever a ray of light passes obliquely into a transparent medium which differs in density from the one in which it is traveling (*e.g.*, from air through water or glass), it is bent, or refracted (Fig. 14.7). In going from a rarefied medium into a more dense medium the ray is said to be bent *toward* the normal or perpendicular.   Conversely, in passing from a dense to a more rarefied medium it is bent *away from* the perpendicular.   If the second medium is surrounded by the first, as in the case of a pane of glass surrounded by air, the light ray is bent twice, once when it enters the glass and again when it leaves it (Fig. 14.8). When it passes through two such plane, parallel surfaces, it is found, upon emerging, to be displaced laterally to some extent but it proceeds in a direction parallel to the original. Rays which strike the surface between two media per-

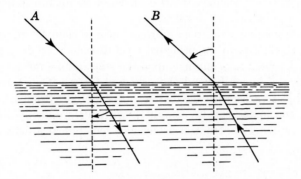

FIG. 14.7.   Refraction of light: *A*, passing from rarefied to a more dense medium; *B*, passing from dense to more rarefied medium.

pendicularly are not refracted. The more oblique the angle at which they strike, the greater is the angle of refraction.

When light passes through a lens or a refracting medium in which at least one of the surfaces is curved, its behavior is somewhat different from that just described for plane surfaces. In convex lenses, light rays are bent to such a degree that they meet at a certain point, or are said to come to a focus.

Image formation by lenses. A biconvex lens such as that found in the eye is a transparent refracting medium bounded by two spherical surfaces facing each other. In such lenses there is a point called the *optical center* so situated that any ray of light passing through it undergoes no angular deviation. A biconvex lens possesses what is known as a *principal axis*.

FIG. 14.8.   Refraction of light in passing through a medium with two plane, parallel surfaces.

This is a line passing through the center of the lens. Diagonal lines which intersect the principal axis at the optical center are referred to as *secondary axes* (Fig. 14.9). Rays of light traveling along the principal or secondary axes pass through the lens without changing their direction, but those passing through other parts are refracted. The farther a ray is removed from the principal axis, the greater will be its angle of refraction.

Light rays coming from objects at a distance of 20 ft. or more may be considered as parallel, at least so far as the eye is concerned. When such parallel rays pass through a biconvex lens, all except those on the principal axis are first refracted and then meet at a point called the *principal focus*. The distance on the principal axis between the center of the lens and this point is known as the *focal distance* of the lens. The focal distance of a biconvex lens depends upon its degree of curvature as well as upon its refractive properties. A small, *inverted* image of the distant object appears in perfect focus beyond the focal point.

Light rays coming from near objects (nearer than 20 ft. but farther away from the lens than the principal focal distance) are divergent rather than parallel. Such rays impinge upon the lens and are refracted, forming a small, *inverted* image beyond the principal focus. The image distance of a near object varies with the distance of the object from the lens. The location of the image can be computed with little difficulty (Fig. 14.9). Let *AB* be an object in front of a biconvex lens but at a distance greater

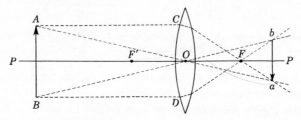

Fig. 14.9. Diagram illustrating image formation by lens: *AB*, object; *ab*, inverted image; *O*, optical center; *PP*, principal axis; *Aa*, *Bb*, secondary axes; *F*, principal focus; *OF*, focal distance.

than its focal length. From point *A* one ray and only one, *AC*, will travel parallel to the principal axis. This will be refracted and pass through the principal focus *F*. The image of point *A* will be found somewhere on the line *CF*. In addition, from point *A* one ray and only one will impinge upon the lens so as to pass through its optical center *O*, and this ray will pass through the lens without undergoing any angular deviation. The image of point *A* will be found somewhere on the line *AO*. Actually the image of point *A* will be found where lines *CF* and *AO* intersect at *a*.

In the same manner the ray *BD* is parallel to the principal axis. It is refracted and passes through the principal focus *F*. Another ray, *BO*, travels along a secondary axis through the optical center. The point of intersection of lines *DF* and *BO* is at *b*, and it is here that the image of *B* will fall.

The line *AB* is made up of innumerable points, each of which gives off rays independently. For each point in the object there will be a corresponding point in the image *ab*. Because each image point appears on the opposite side of the principal axis from that of its corresponding object point, the image is inverted.

The image points for distant objects, *e.g.*, those anywhere from 20 ft. to *infinity* away from the lens, differ so little in position (no more than a fraction of a millimeter) that they are actually the same for all practical purposes. In the perfectly normal eye, the image point for distant objects falls upon the retina.

If an object is nearer the lens than its principal focal distance ($F'O$), its divergent rays, after being refracted, are still divergent and a *virtual, enlarged image* is formed. This is of no practical importance so far as the eye is concerned.

It should be understood from the above account that if a lens is rigid, as is true of all lenses made of glass, the image points for distant objects coincide. Each near object, however, has its own image point, depending upon its distance from the lens. Since the retina of the eye is the screen upon which both near and far objects form images, it is apparent that a rigid lens in the eye would be unsuitable. In such cases an image would fall exactly upon the retina only when the object was at a certain fixed distance away. Only at this distance would the image be sharply defined.

Image formation by the lens of the eye. A remarkable characteristic of the eye is that it has the power of accommodating itself to objects at various distances by changing the convexity of the crystalline lens. Altering the shape of the lens changes its focal distance so that images of objects at various distances can be brought to a focus on the retina. The only variable lenses in existence are those in the eyes of certain living vertebrates.

If the eye follows a moving object, the lens changes its curvature, always in such a manner as to form a sharply focused image upon the retina. As the object approaches the eye the lens becomes more convex. Conversely, as an object moves away from the eye the lens tends to flatten out. Thus when our eyes are focused upon distant objects the lens is flattened and said to be at rest. Focusing upon near objects requires some effort in order to increase the curvature of the lens. The ciliary body is the structure in the eye which is responsible for accommodation in mammals.

Ciliary body. If a mammalian eye is cut into anterior and posterior halves and the anterior half viewed from its cut surface, the ciliary body appears as a concave bowl with the transparent crystalline lens in its center (Fig. 14.10). Its outer edge is bounded by the ora serrata. Thus the ciliary body extends from the ora serrata to a point near the circumference of the lens. It is attached to the lens capsule by numerous fine fibers which form the *suspensory ligament.*

The ciliary body, as previously mentioned, is derived from both the uveal coat and the nonnervous portion, or border, of the retina beyond the ora serrata. The greater part, however, is of uveal origin and is thus continuous with the choroid coat. It is made up of three main parts: (1) an outer rim, the *orbicularis ciliaris,* directly continuous with the choroid, (2) a large number of radiating folds, the *ciliary processes*, to which the fibers of the suspensory ligament are attached on the inner face, (3) the involuntary *ciliary muscles*, on the outer face, lying between uvea and sclera at the point where the latter passes into the cornea and the former forms the ciliary body. Some of the ciliary muscle fibers are arranged circularly, but most are meridional or radial.

The capsule enclosing the lens is an elastic membrane which varies in thickness, being thinner on the posterior than on the anterior surface. The posterior face of the lens, therefore, bulges out farther and possesses

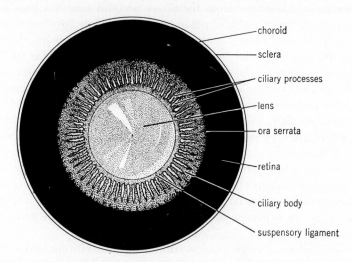

choroid

sclera

ciliary processes

lens

ora serrata

retina

ciliary body

suspensory ligament

Fig. 14.10. Anterior section of mammalian eye as viewed from behind after cutting the eyeball into anterior and posterior halves.

a greater degree of curvature than does the anterior face. Any pull on the lens capsule would tend to flatten the elastic lens. When the eye is at rest, *i.e.*, focused for distant objects, the ciliary muscles are relaxed. Under such conditions the pull upon the suspensory ligament is greatest and the lens is flattened. The ciliary muscles are controlled by sympathetic and parasympathetic nerve fibers, the preganglionic fibers of the latter being associated with the oculomotor nerve. When the muscles contract, as they do when the eye focuses for near objects (those within the critical distance of 20 ft.), they tend to pull the choroid coat forward. This relieves the tension on suspensory ligament and lens capsule, and the lens tends to bulge and become more rounded. The greater part of the bulging occurs in the center of the anterior face. Pressure of the vitreous humor against the posterior surface prevents the latter from changing its shape to more than a slight degree. At any rate, the increase in curvature of the anterior face of the lens increases its refracting power, so that the image of the object is thrown into focus on the retina rather than at a point posterior to it.

Images which appear on the retina are inverted in the same manner as those formed by rigid lenses (Fig. 14.9). Actually we see them as though they were erect. Nerve centers for the sense of sight, located in the thalamus and cerebral cortex, are responsible for the fact that we see things right side up instead of upside down. This is a secondary phenomenon learned by experience.

The various transparent media of the eye play an important part in the refraction of light rays. They include the cornea, aqueous humor, lens, and the vitreous body. These media are of different densities, and each has its own refractive index. Actually the greatest amount of refraction occurs in the cornea, which is even more important than the lens in this respect. Since in most vertebrates the curved surface of the cornea is in a fixed position, it is of little importance in accommodation as compared with the variable lens.

Accessory structures of the eye. Numerous structures associated with the eye play an important part in the efficient functioning of this receptor organ. Of greatest significance are the muscles which move the eyeball, the eyelids, eyebrows, and the various parts of the lacrimal apparatus.

Muscles. Six broad, strap-shaped muscles are inserted on the sclerotic coat and are so arranged that, when they contract, they cause the eyeball to rotate for a variable distance, depending upon the degree of contraction. These extrinsic muscles are arranged in two groups (Fig. 11.11). The first group, known as the *rectus muscles*, is composed of four elements named the superior rectus, inferior rectus, internal (medial) rectus, and external (lateral) rectus, respectively. Each derives its name from the region of the eyeball on which it inserts, the points of insertion being rather evenly spaced around the equatorial region of the eyeball. All four muscles converge to their point of origin in the posteromedial portion of the orbit, near where the oculomotor nerve emerges. The second, or *oblique, group of muscles* is made up of two elements, the superior oblique and inferior oblique. They insert on the sclera very near the insertions of the superior rectus and inferior rectus, respectively, but their points of origin are at the anteromedial wall of the orbit. These extrinsic muscles are innervated by three motor cranial nerves, the oculomotor, trochlear, and abducens. The oculomotor supplies four muscles: superior rectus, inferior rectus, and internal rectus, and inferior oblique. The superior oblique is innervated by the trochlear nerve, and the external rectus by the abducens. The common origin of the four muscles supplied by the oculomotor, from a single pro-otic myotome, is discussed on page 595.

Eyelids. Two transverse folds of skin, the upper and lower eyelids, lie in front of the eye, serving to protect it from injury. Each eyelid is lined on the inside with conjunctiva continuous with that reflected over the surface of the cornea. The opening between the lids is spoken of as the *palpebral fissure*. Both lids are movable in most vertebrates, but the upper lid in man and some other forms has a greater range of movement than the lower. A muscle, the *levator palpebrae superior*, functions in elevating the upper eyelid. It is innervated by the oculomotor nerve.

In many vertebrates a third eyelid, or *nictitating membrane*, is present. This lies beneath the other two and passes from the inner angle out over the surface of the eye. It is usually transparent. In most mammals the nictitating membrane is reduced. In man a small fold, the *plica semilunaris*, in the inner corner of the eye, is believed by some to be a homologue of the nictitating membrane. If a nictitating membrane is present, it is supplied by the abducens nerve. The so-called "nictitating membrane" of amphibians is not homologous with those of higher vertebrates (page 644).

In man the edges of each eyelid are provided with two rows of hairs called *eyelashes* which give added protection to the eyes. Modified sweat glands, the *glands of Moll*, open into the follicles of the eyelashes. On the margins of the eyelids just inside the lashes are the openings of the *Meibomian*, or *tarsal*, *glands*.

Eyebrows. In mammals, thickened areas of the integument may be situated above the upper edge of the orbit and provided with numerous thick, stiff hairs. These furnish added protection to the eyes.

Lacrimal apparatus. The lacrimal apparatus of each eye consists of a *lacrimal gland*, which secretes a watery fluid, and a system of small canals by means of which the fluid is conveyed from the medial corner of the eye to the nasal passage.

In mammals the lacrimal gland lies beneath the lateral portion of the upper eyelid where several small ducts penetrate the conjunctiva. The tears, or *lacrimal fluid*, moisten the surface of the eyeball and provide nourishment for the nonvascular cornea. They are secreted continuously, even when the eyelids are closed, passing to the inner corner of the eye. A small opening, the *lacrimal punctum*, is present on the margin of each eyelid near its median border. Each punctum opens into a small *canaliculus*. These, after coursing a short distance, unite to form the *lacrimal duct*, which in turn opens into the nasal passage, passing through an opening between the maxillary and lacrimal bones en route. Tears pass through the puncta, canaliculi, and lacrimal duct into the nasal passage. The constant flow of tears over the surface of the eyeball serves to keep it clean by washing away dirt and other foreign particles which might otherwise accumulate. When lacrimal fluid is secreted in excess, the tears cannot drain away fast enough through the lacrimal duct. In such cases they break through the "dam" formed by the oily secretion of the Meibomian glands and overflow onto the lower eyelids and cheeks.

Occasionally, accessory lacrimal glands are present in mammals beneath the lower eyelid. This condition is reminiscent of that encountered in amphibians and reptiles, in which such glands lie under the lower lid. In these forms the lower eyelid is the more movable of the two.

Miscellaneous structures. OPTIC PEDICEL. In most elasmobranch fishes a cartilaginous rod, the *optic pedicel* (Fig. 11.11), connects the eyeball to the skull. It is situated in such a manner as to be surrounded by the converging rectus muscles. The eyeball end is frequently expanded and is loosely attached to the sclera. The optic pedicel gives support to the eyeball. Higher fishes do not have an optic pedicel. A ligamentous *tenaculum* is frequently present, however, helping to keep the eyeball in place. The tenaculum is not considered to be a homologue of the optic pedicel since in certain rays both structures are present. These supporting elements have no counterpart in terrestrial vertebrates.

HARDER'S GLAND. A sebaceous gland known as the Harderian, or Harder's, gland is associated with the eye in many amphibians, reptiles, and birds, as well as in some mammals. It generally lies behind the eyeball and secretes an oily fluid which serves to lubricate the nictitating membrane.

MUSCLES. In some vertebrates, in addition to the usual rectus and oblique muscles, other muscles may be present. These include (1) a *retractor bulbi*, derived from the external rectus and used to draw the eyeball into its socket, (2) a *levator bulbi*, which raises the eyeball back to its original position.

SCLERAL OSSICLES. In birds and reptiles, with the exception of snakes and crocodilians, the exposed portion of the sclera, adjacent to the cornea, is covered by a circle of thin, overlapping bones, the *scleral ossicles*, or *sclerotic bones*. The number varies in different forms, some birds having as many as 18 separate bones. They arise during embryonic development as dermal bones which sink down into the sclera. They afford protection to the eye and are of some importance in accommodation in the forms in which they occur. Some modern fishes possess sclerotic bones, but no more than two are present. In some species they are fused to form a single ring. It is not clear whether these are homologues of the numerous small ossicles of reptiles and birds. A circlet of small *circumorbital* skull bones surrounds the eye in many fishes. These are sometimes homologized with the sclerotic bones of reptiles and birds, but in some fishes both types of bones are present, thus raising doubts concerning such homologies. Numerous so-called "scleral" ossicles were present in extinct stegocephalian amphibians, usually in the form of an incomplete dorsal ring. It is possible that they were located in the upper eyelid and in this way offered protection to the eye. Their homologies are also questionable. Scleral ossicles are not present in mammals.

Comparative anatomy of the vertebrate eye. The eyes of all vertebrates are constructed on the same fundamental plan, but many variations are to be found. In some forms the eyes are primitive; in others they are degenerate and functionless. The most important differences in the highly complex eyes of most forms are to be found in methods of accommodation, degree of development of the retina, and the shape of the pupil.

Cyclostomes. In members of the class Cyclostomata two conditions are to be found. In hagfishes the eyes are degenerate and functionless, whereas those of adult lampreys are excellent visual organs showing no signs of degeneracy.

The hagfish eye is extremely small, being scarcely more than a millimeter in diameter. It lies entirely beneath the skin and is insensitive to light. The optic nerve is degenerate. Other nerves, as well as muscles and lens, are lacking. Cornea, sclera, and choroid are not differentiated, and pigment is absent. The retina is folded so as to fill entirely what would ordinarily be considered to be the chamber of the vitreous humor. A lens placode begins to form in the embryo, but it soon flattens out and disappears.

The eye of the lamprey, although primitive, is nevertheless a well-developed structure. It offers no clue as to the possible evolutionary origin of the vertebrate eye. From the time that the ammocoetes larva burrows into the mud, until metamorphosis, the eyes are undeveloped and functionless. At the time of metamorphosis the eye develops markedly and the skin covering it becomes transparent. Among the important features are a flattening of the outer surface of the eyeball, a thin membranous sclera, thin cornea *not* fused to the skin, lack of suspensory ligament and ciliary apparatus, fixed size of the pupil, and a permanently spherical lens, held in place by the vitreous humor. Eyelids are lacking. In the lamprey the abducens nerve supplies both the external and inferior rectus muscles (page 477), whereas in other forms the latter is controlled by the oculomotor nerve which also supplies the superior rectus, internal rectus, and inferior oblique. Accommodation is brought about by flattening the cornea, which then pushes the lens toward the retina. This is accomplished by contraction of a special *corneal muscle.* Although both rod and cone cells are present in most forms, the rods far outnumber the cones. Both rods and cones are cone-shaped but differ in certain other respects. Walls (1942) is of the opinion that cones are phylogenetically older than rods and that the rods of lampreys are not related to the rods found in other vertebrates. Whether or not lampreys have color vision has not been established.

A cross section of the optic nerve reveals its primitive character. A core of ependymal cells is present, bearing the same relation to the fibers of the optic nerve as the ependymal cells of the neural tube bear to the brain wall. This relationship emphasizes the fact that the retina is actually an evagination of the brain.

Elasmobranchs. The eyes of the cartilaginous fishes are exceptionally large, those of the deep-sea-dwelling holocephalians being largest of all in relation to body size.

Eyelids consist of mere folds of skin which have but little power of movement. The presence of an optic pedicel is characteristic, although lacking in a few forms. The eyeball is usually elliptical in shape with a short anterior-posterior axis. Conspicuous features include the presence of cartilage in the sclera, lack of intrinsic muscles in the ciliary body, and a large, permanently spherical lens which pushes the iris far forward so that it almost touches the cornea (Fig. 16.20). The pupil is round in most forms but is slitlike in a few species. Muscles in the iris are poorly developed and are altogether lacking in deep-sea forms. The presence of a core of ependymal cells in the optic nerves of a few elasmobranchs is indicative of a relationship to the condition found in the lamprey.

In most elasmobranchs the surface of the choroid coat adjacent to the retina contains a layer of light-reflecting crystals composed of a chemical substance known as *guanin*. The layer is called the *tapetum lucidum*. Light rays striking the tapetum lucidum are reflected back, causing the eyes to "shine." This is, of course, most noticeable at night, and the presence of a tapetum in the many higher forms in which it occurs is generally restricted to those animals of nocturnal habit. Visibility is thought to be enhanced under such conditions. The tapetum lucidum of elasmobranchs is exceptionally well developed.

Cones are absent from the elasmobranch retina except in members of the genus *Mustelus* and perhaps one or two other species. It is probable that color vision is lacking. Here, for the first time, an *area centralis* is present, somewhat comparable to the macula lutea of primates except that it is devoid of pigment. No fovea is to be found.

The suspensory ligament which holds the elasmobranch lens in place consists of a washer-shaped gelatinous membrane. The peripheral portion is fastened over the inner surface of the ciliary body and its center border to a restricted, equatorially placed band on the surface of the lens. A portion of the ciliary body in the middorsal region extends downward and helps to support the lens. The ventral side of the lens is supported by a papilla-like projection of the ciliary body, which is attached anteriorly to the iris. A small muscle, the *protractor lentis*, of ectodermal origin, is located on the lens side of the papilla. It is so arranged that contraction of its fibers causes the lens to swing forward, somewhat in the manner of a pendulum. The protractor lentis thus serves as a muscle of accommodation, moving the lens forward, rather than changing its shape, when focusing for near objects. The distance through which the lens can move is restricted by the shallowness of the space between iris and cornea, thus limiting accommodatory efforts to a rather narrow range.

Other fishes. A great many interesting variations are to be observed in the eyes of fishes. Only certain general features will be considered here. Typically there is a flattening of the anterior surface of the eyeball. Cartilage is present in the sclera, and in some forms bony plates may replace or supplement the cartilaginous elements. The cornea is composed of four layers, a *dermal layer* being interposed between conjunctival and scleral layers and a fibrous *autochthonus layer* lying inside the scleral portion. A tapetum lucidum is usually present in the choroid coat. The outer portion of the uvea in fishes is surrounded by a layer, the *argentea*, composed of silvery guanin crystals. This layer covers the dark pigment of the uvea and, by reflecting light, aids in rendering the almost transparent young fish inconspicuous. The argentea loses its significance during later life. A silvery *retinal tapetum* is present in a number of fishes. The light-reflecting crystals are located in the pigment layer of the retina. The visual cells of the retina consist of exceptionally long rods and two kinds of cones, single and "twin." The latter are to be found only in teleost fishes. Color vision seems to be widespread among teleosts. An area centralis is present in the retinae of many bony fishes. A number of teleosts possess a fovea. Ciliary and functional iris muscles are lacking. Accommodation in the eyes of fishes is usually accomplished by changing the position of the spherical lens. In most cases a sickle-shaped, *falciform process* is present in the form of a ridge of the choroid coat on the floor of the eyeball, projecting through the choroid fissure which, in teleosts, remains open. Beginning at the blind spot, its distal end extends forward and upward into the chamber of the vitreous humor. This end is attached to the lower border of the lens by a structure called the *campanula Halleri*, or *retractor lentis*. Small muscle fibers of ectodermal (retinal) origin located in the retractor lentis pull upon the lens (which is suspended from above, like a pendulum), drawing it backward.

Deep-sea fishes which live in a realm of total darkness have relatively enormous eyes. Most of these forms possess luminescent photophores which furnish the only source of light that may affect their eyes. Recognition of enemies, of prey, of members of the same species, and of members of the opposite sex is thus possible in these abyssal regions. The eyes have undergone modifications, all of which are conducive to increasing their sensitivity to light. Pupil and lens are extraordinarily large. Rod cells are extremely long and numerous, whereas cone cells are almost altogether lacking. In many forms the eyeball has assumed a tubular shape, its greatest diameter being in the region where the lens is situated.

Surprisingly enough, relatively few deep-sea fishes are blind. In some species, however, the eyes are degenerate. In others they are covered with a thick, opaque layer of skin. Only one fish (*Ipnops murrayi*) is known in which the eyes have disappeared altogether. This is the only vertebrate in which such a condition is known to exist. Better-known blind fishes,

such as those found in certain caves, have degenerate, microscopic, functionless eyes. There has been much speculation as to the reason for the
degenerate eye condition in so many cave-dwelling forms. The concensus
is that the fish did not become blind because they lived in darkness but
rather that those with degenerate eyes found refuge in caves and became
adapted to such an environment. In such fishes, eyes begin to develop
during embryonic life but they fail to differentiate further after a certain
developmental stage is reached.

In flat fishes, as in the flounder and halibut, both eyes in an adult are on
the same side of the head. These fishes lie on the bottom of the ocean. The
underside may be either the right or left, depending upon the species.
Early in life the eye on the side on which the animal will lie migrates over
or even through the head, bringing about the curious condition observed
only in these fishes.

The eyes of certain teleosts are adapted for vision in both air and water.
Those of the mudskippers, *Periophthalmus* and *Boleophthalmus*, are set in
the ends of retractible stalks. The
four-eyed fish *Anableps* of Central
America has two pupils in each eye.
A horizontal partition, which appears
in the iris during larval life, divides
the original pupil in two, the upper
one being the larger. The upper pupil
is usually out of water and is used in
air vision. Another fish, *Dialommus*,
also appears to have two pupils in
each eye, but these are actually circular, transparent areas in the otherwise pigmented, opaque cornea (Fig.
14.11). The use to which these areas
is put is not understood.

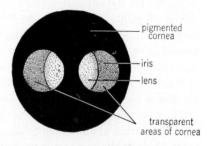

FIG. 14.11. Front view of eye of the
blenny, *Dialommus*, showing two transparent areas in the opaque, pigmented
cornea. (*After Breder and Gresser, from
Walls, "The Vertebrate Eye." By permission of the author.*)

Amphibians. Among amphibians are to be found strictly aquatic types
which never leave the water, as well as terrestrial forms which return to the
water only for breeding purposes. Most of the latter, however, spend their
larval lives in ponds or streams, but a few make use of tiny temporary pools
formed when rain water collects between leaves. It is probable that no
amphibians possess both air and water vision comparable to that of the
peculiar fishes mentioned above.

Aquatic amphibians have no problem to contend with in keeping their
corneas moist, but terrestrial forms have been forced to make adjustments
to keep the surface of the eye from drying in order that it may function
efficiently. In such forms movable eyelids, moistened with glandular
secretions, appear for the first time. The eyelids consist of a thick upper
lid and a thinner, more movable lower lid. The upper border of the lower

lid is transparent and is moved upward in closing the eye. This portion is particularly well developed in salientians, in which it is frequently referred to as the "nictitating membrane" although it is probably not homologous with the true nictitating membranes of other forms. When the eye is open, this transparent structure is folded inside the remaining portion of the lower lid. Closure of the eye is not accomplished merely by moving the eyelids but is brought about by retracting the entire eye within the orbit by means of the *retractor bulbi* muscle. This has its origin from the undersurface of the parasphenoid bone and its insertion on both upper and lower surfaces of the eyeball. It is believed to represent a bifurcation of the external rectus. Contraction of the retractor bulbi causes the nictitating membrane to be pulled upward. Conversely, protrusion of the eyeball is effected by means of the *levator bulbi*, which lies ventral to the orbit, together with contraction of a small muscle, the *depressor membrane nictitans*, which pulls the lower lid downward. The levator bulbi originates from the frontoparietal, parasphenoid, pterygoid, sphenethmoid, and palatine bones. It inserts on the superior border of the upper jaw.

The elements responsible, in terrestrial forms, for keeping the cornea moist first appear in land salamanders and consist, in these more primitive amphibians, of a row of glands in the lining of the lower lid. A group of these glands, located at the inner angle of the eye, may be the forerunner of Harder's gland. Another group in the outer angle of the eyelid may have given rise to the lacrimal glands of higher forms.

The eyes of salientians are best developed among amphibians. A prominent Harderian gland develops during metamorphosis. It is located at the inner angle of the eye and is pear-shaped. The gland is bound together by a capsule of connective tissue and is packed about the eyeball in the orbit. No true lacrimal gland is present, but a small "lacrimal" duct opens into the nasal passage behind and below the eye. Its outer end connects by a number of tubules to the outer angle of the eye. The duct is lined with ciliated columnar epithelium. The eyeball is almost spherical. Its anterior chamber is rather deep, the increased depth being brought about by the greater curvature of the cornea and the deeper position of the lens. Cartilage appears in the sclera during or after metamorphosis.

One of the most interesting features of the salientian eye is the ciliary body, which is more complex than in any of the lower vertebrates. It is triangular in cross section, with the base of the triangle attached to the sclera. Numerous folds join the posterior surface of the iris. From the ciliary body come many fibers which are joined to the lens capsule, thus forming a suspensory ligament. These fibers lie entirely in the vitreous humor. Two small muscles of mesodermal origin, one dorsal and the other ventral, are responsible for accommodation. Each courses from the cornea to the inner part of the ciliary body. When these *protractor lentis* muscles contract, they draw the lens more closely toward the cornea. In doing so, the outer face of the lens may become slightly flattened.

No argentea is present in the outer layer of the choroid coat in amphibians, nor is a true tapetum lucidum present, despite the fact that the eyes of certain salientians "shine."

The photoreceptor cells in the retina consist of four types: red rods, green rods, and single and double cones. Red rods are more numerous than green rods, the two differing considerably in shape. Red rods contain the reddish pigment, rhodopsin (*visual purple*), whereas green rods are reported to contain a greenish substance sometimes called *visual green*. The latter may function in the same manner as visual purple. It has not been demonstrated that amphibians have any color vision whatever. Frogs possess an area centralis, but no fovea is present.

The beautiful colors of the iris observed in many salientians are noteworthy. The shape of the pupil shows many variations and is frequently used as an aid in classification. Vertical, horizontal, oval, and elliptical-shaped pupils are to be found, and in some forms the opening may even have an irregular, rhomboid shape.

The eyes of caudate amphibians are, on the whole, smaller and less complex than those of salientians. The lids are absent in permanently aquatic forms and are poorly developed in others. A nictitating membrane never develops beyond the rudimentary stage. The *retractor bulbi* muscle is present and is used in pulling the eye downward in its orbit. Such action aids in swallowing by compressing the mouth cavity. The beginning of differentiation of lacrimal and Harderian glands is discernible in certain members of the group. In the more terrestrial caudates the eyes, in some respects, approach the degree of development found in salientians. In some permanently aquatic forms, such as *Necturus*, the cornea is fused to the skin, and the eyes, therefore, are capable of little, if any, movement. Generally speaking, the caudate lens is exceptionally large, the anterior chamber is shallow, cartilage is present in the sclera, and only a ventral *protractor lentis* muscle is present. The entire ciliary body is less highly developed than in salientians. The visual cells in the caudate retina include both red and green rods and single and double cones. Green rods, however, are not uniformly present. The red rods of *Necturus* are the largest rod cells that are known.

The eyes of some of the blind, cave-dwelling salamanders indicate that arrested development has occurred. Others show signs of secondary degeneration. Eye muscles and lens may be lacking, and retina and vitreal chamber are modified or degenerate.

The tropical, limbless caecilians, considered by many to be blind, actually have very small, almost microscopic eyes which can be utilized to some extent. The eyeball, which is only a fraction of a millimeter in diameter, lies beneath a transparent area of skin to which it may be fused. The lens protrudes through the pupil. No mechanism for accommodation is present. Rod cells alone are to be found in the surprisingly well developed retina. A large Harderian gland almost completely fills the orbit. Its secretion, instead of affecting the eye, is utilized in lubricating the *tentacle*, a structure with highly developed olfactory and tactile properties.

Reptiles. The eyes of reptiles, with the exception of snakes, show a marked similarity in structure. In these animals, which have adopted a terrestrial mode of life, the chief changes to be observed over amphibians are found in perfections of structures first developed by the latter when making their transition from water to land. Among these features in the eyes of reptiles other than snakes and a few others are the increasingly movable eyelids, the lower lid still being the larger and more movable of the two. A true, transparent nictitating membrane is present, lying between the other eyelids and the eyeball. This membrane is lubricated by the secretion of a well-developed Harderian gland in the inner angle of the palpebral fissure. Except in *Sphenodon*, chameleons, and snakes, a lacrimal gland in the outer angle of the eye makes its appearance. A lacrimal duct drains the secretions of lacrimal and Harderian glands into the nasal passage. Turtles lack a nasolacrimal duct. One of the most important differences in the reptilian eye is the modification of the ciliary apparatus which alters the shape of the lens and cornea by a peripheral squeezing action. The curvature of the cornea and that of the outer surface of the lens are increased by this process. The scleral ossicles are so arranged as to form a rigid, concave area, the function of which seems to be to resist the intraocular pressure which squeezes the lens. Of all vertebrates the lens of the turtle is most flexible. A *conical papilla* extends from the blind spot into the vitreal chamber in most reptiles, but this is lacking in *Sphenodon* and is poorly developed in crocodilians. It is composed, for the most part, of ectodermal neuroglia tissue enclosing numerous small blood vessels which nourish the inner part of the retina by diffusion of substances through the vitreous humor. A relative increase in the number of cones is apparent in reptilian eyes, and in one turtle, *Amyda*, rods seem to be lacking. A central area for more acute vision is present in the retinae of most reptiles. A conspicuous fovea appears in *Amyda*, *Sphenodon*, and several snakes and lizards. In some chameleons it may be even larger than that of man. Color vision is believed to exist in turtles and lizards but is of doubtful occurrence in crocodilians and snakes.

The eyes of snakes present several features which cause them to differ markedly from those of other reptiles. One of the chief differences lies in the lack of eyelids, the skin over the eye forming a transparent window, or "*spectacle*," which is responsible for the fixed stare characteristic of these animals. In some of the limbless lizards and in a group of small lizards, the geckos, eyelids are also lacking. In snakes true lacrimal glands are absent.

Instead of lacrimal fluid the oily secretion of Harder's gland flows in the space between cornea and spectacle. It drains through a duct into nose and mouth where it is added to the salivary secretion. In snakes a fine plexus of blood vessels ramifies over the retinal surface, thus providing nourishment to that structure as well as supplying the conical papilla. This structure in snakes is entirely of mesodermal origin and therefore is not homologous with the similarly named structure in the eyes of other reptiles which has a neuroglial framework of ectodermal origin. For these reasons, as well as others, some authorities are of the opinion that the snake eye has arisen along different evolutionary lines from those followed by other reptiles.

Birds. Just as is true of other anatomical features, the eyes of birds are strikingly uniform in structure. There is but little deviation in essential features from the condition found in reptiles. The eyeball of the bird is very large in proportion to body size, a fact undoubtedly correlated with aerial life and the necessity for seeing with precision over considerable distances. The actual size of the bird's eye is usually unsuspected, since only the cornea is visible externally. A medium-sized hawk may have an eyeball as large as that of man.

The eyeball is never spherical, but is partly concave. The concave area is pronounced to varying degrees and is caused by the presence of a ring of scleral ossicles which surrounds the eyeball in the region of the ciliary apparatus. The portion in front of the ossicles is more or less conical in shape, whereas the posterior part is expanded and somewhat flattened. Flat, globular, and tubular shapes are recognized, depending upon how far back on the eyeball the concave area is located (Fig. 14.12).

A highly developed nictitating membrane is present in birds. It is well lubricated and cleans the lining of the other lids as well as the corneal sur-

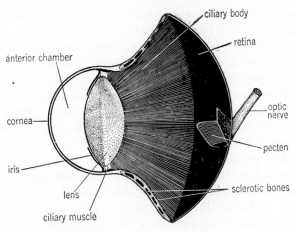

Fig. 14.12. Diagrammatic sagittal section through eye of bird of prey.

face. In many birds the nictitating membrane moves independently of the upper and lower lids, which remain open during waking hours without blinking. During flight the nictitating membrane is said to be closed, offering protection to the delicate cornea. Harderian glands and lacrimal glands are well developed and situated in the usual positions. Accommodation in the bird's eye is controlled by the ciliary apparatus, as in reptiles. It involves deformation of the cornea and increasing the curvature of the anterior surface of the lens by a squeezing action.

Rods and two kinds of cones, single and double, are present in the retina of the bird. Cones predominate in birds of diurnal habit, and rods in nocturnal forms. A conspicuous depressed fovea centralis is present in the area centralis. In certain birds more than one fovea may be present, a fact which helps explain the great visual acuity of birds. Color vision seems to be widespread in this class of vertebrates.

Perhaps the most interesting feature of the bird's eye is the *pecten*, a serrated, fan-shaped structure, which extends into the vitreal cavity. The base of the pecten is attached to the blind spot and along the line formed by the fusion of the lips of the choroid fissure from which it is derived. Many variations in shape are to be noted. The best-developed pectens are found among diurnal birds, and the most poorly organized structures occur in nocturnal forms. The function of the pecten has long been the subject of speculation. Even today no well-authenticated explanation has been forthcoming. Among the most plausible suggestions are (1) that the pecten is an erectile organ of accommodation which, by varying the intraocular pressure, can cause the lens to change its shape, (2) that a shadow of the pecten falls upon the retina, thus aiding in the perception of movement, (3) that the pecten is a supplemental nutritive device which supplies the retina with necessary substances by diffusion through the vitreous humor. If this last suggestion is accepted, it would indicate that the highly vascular pecten is an elaboration of the vascular conical papilla found in the eyes of numerous reptiles. The bird's eye lacks an arteria centralis retinae.

In many birds, as in numerous other vertebrates, the eyes are laterally located, each covering a different visual field. The term *uniocular vision* refers to this arrangement. Even in such animals, however, the two visual fields usually overlap to some extent. Birds of prey, such as owls, and, to a lesser degree, hawks and eagles, have *binocular vision*. Both eyes can be focused upon the same object, and the two visual fields overlap to a much greater degree than in animals having uniocular vision. Binocular vision is of advantage in judging distance and, therefore, in capturing prey. In uniocular vision a greater visual field is covered, enabling its possessor to detect danger coming from almost any direction.

Mammals. Although the eye of man, as previously described, is a more or less typical mammalian eye, there are, among members of the class Mammalia, certain deviations which are worthy of special mention. The upper eyelid in mammals is larger and more movable than the lower. Eye-lashes and Meibomian glands are usually present. Lacrimal glands in mammals are located under the upper lid at the outer angle. Harderian glands are lacking in most forms but are present in whales and certain semi-aquatic forms, as well as in mice and shrews.

PROTOTHERIA. A well-developed nictitating membrane is present in *Ornithorhynchus* but altogether lacking in *Echidna*. The eyes of these lower mammals show unmistakable reptilian affinities. There is little, if any, accommodation, however, and no trace of a conical papilla can be found. Cartilage is present in the sclera. The photoreceptors of the duck-bill include rods and single and double cones. In *Echidna*, cones are lacking.

METATHERIA. Among marsupials the nictitating membrane is reduced but a Harderian gland is still present. No cartilage appears in the sclerotic coat, and with its elimination the eyeball has assumed a spherical shape. Ability to accommodate has not been definitely verified for the group, although the presence of a small ciliary muscle suggests that it is possible to change the shape of the lens. A vestigial conical papilla may occur in marsupials, but all traces of this structure are lost in higher forms.

EUTHERIA. In the large group of eutherian, or placental, mammals many variations are encountered but none is of primary importance. Numerous adaptations correlated with aquatic, terrestrial, or aerial life are to be found, as well as those fitting animals for nocturnal or diurnal existence. The eyes of moles are tiny, degenerate structures embedded in the skin. The smallest normal eyes are those of the shrews and certain bats, in which they are scarcely more than a millimeter in diameter. At the other extreme are the eyes of the blue whale, which measure between 4 and $5\frac{1}{2}$ in. across, although much of the size is due to the presence of an exceptionally thick sclera. No cartilage is to be found in the eutherian sclera, however. A tapetum lucidum is present in many night-active forms. Hoofed mammals possess a *tapetum fibrosum*. This differs from the tapetum in elasmo-branchs in that a portion of the choroid coat is composed of a tendinous type of connective tissue which glistens in a manner similar to a fresh tendon. Certain marsupials, elephants, and whales also have fibrous tapeta. Another type of tapetum, the *tapetum cellulosum*, is found in carnivores, seals, and lower primates. It is composed of several layers of cells which are filled with little rods or threads composed of some unknown organic material. It does not seem to be related to guanin. One or two other types of tapeta are recognized. The mechanism for accommodation is essentially similar to that described for man. There are many variations in shape of the mammalian pupil. The round pupil is most common. A vertical, slit-shaped pupil is characteristic of the cat family and certain others. The vertical slit, which assumes a rounded shape under nocturnal conditions, may be closed almost entirely in bright light. A wide, transversely arranged opening is met with among many ungulates, whales, and other mammals. A modification of the portion of the iris bordering the pupil and referred to as the *umbraculum* is encountered in the cony, gazelle,

camel, and a few other species. This consists of an irregular, pigmented sort of fringe (Fig. 14.13) which is thought to protect the retina from excessive glare coming either from above or below. Well-developed nictitating membranes appear only sporadically among eutherian mammals. Among those possessing such membranes are the aardvark, horse, scaly anteater, caribou, and panda. In carnivores it may be fairly well developed but cannot be drawn over the entire cornea. The retinae of most eutherians

Fig. 14.13. Umbraculum of iris in the camel. (*After Lindsay Johnson, from Walls, "The Vertebrate Eye." By permission of the author.*)

contain both rods and cones of the single type, but in members of the lowest orders cones are apparently lacking. This is true of most of the Edentata and Chiroptera as well as of certain shrews, hedgehogs, and rodents. Pure cone retinae are not found among mammals except in squirrels. Capacity for color vision among mammals seems to be limited to the higher primates. Many mammals possess binocular vision, but this is best developed in man and other primates. Furthermore, because of the partial decussation of fibers in the optic nerves of mammals having binocular vision, the images observed by the two eyes are stereoscopically superimposed in the brain, giving third-dimensional effects not possible to obtain otherwise.

SENSES OF EQUILIBRIUM AND HEARING

The vertebrate ear, which is commonly thought of only as an organ of hearing, usually functions in a dual capacity, serving, at least in higher forms, both as an organ of hearing and of equilibration. The equilibratory function of the ear is more fundamental. The structures responsible for this are to be found in all vertebrates with but little variation in different forms. The portion of the ear which is concerned with hearing first begins to differentiate in fishes and becomes more and more complex as the evolutionary scale is ascended.

When referring to the ear our attention is usually directed to the special apparatus found in higher vertebrates for reception of sound waves and their transmission to sensory receptors located in the head. This apparatus, as it occurs in man and other mammals, is composed of three portions referred to, respectively, as the *outer*, *middle*, and *inner ears*. The outer and middle ears are concerned only with receiving and transmitting sound waves. They are totally lacking in cyclostomes and fishes. The inner ear, present in *all* vertebrates, is the portion in which the sensory receptors are located, whether it serves only for equilibration or for both equilibration and hearing.

Inner Ear

The epithelium lining the inner ear is of ectodermal origin. It first arises in the embryo as a thickened placode in the superficial ectoderm of the head. Each of the paired placodes invaginates in the form of an *auditory pit*, which soon closes over to form a hollow *auditory vesicle*, or *otocyst*. It loses its connection with the superficial ectoderm (Fig. 14.14), lies close to the brain, and is entirely surrounded with mesenchyme.

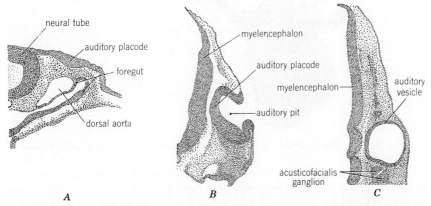

FIG. 14.14. Successive stages, *A*, *B*, and *C*, in the development of auditory vesicles in chick embryo: *A*, 33-hour embryo; *B*, 48-hour embryo; *C*, 72-hour embryo. (*Drawn by R. Speigle.*)

Extensive changes occur as the otocyst develops further. When it has become fully differentiated, its various divisions together with their supporting elements of fibrous connective tissue make up a delicate and complex structure, the *membranous labyrinth*. This consists of a closed series of tubes and sacs lined with epithelium of ectodermal origin.

Equilibrium. The typical membranous labyrinth of vertebrates consists of two chamberlike enlargements, an upper *utriculus* and a lower *sacculus*. These chambers are connected by a constricted area, the *sacculoutricular duct*. The degree of constriction in this region varies considerably in different forms. A narrow *endolymphatic duct*, a dorsomedial evagination of the otocyst, joins either the sacculus or the sacculoutricular duct. It terminates in a saclike swelling, the *endolymphatic sinus*. Three long narrow tubes, the *semicircular ducts*, connect at both ends with the utriculus (Fig. 14.15). They are arranged in planes approximately at right angles to each other and are called the *external, anterior,* and *posterior* semi-

circular ducts.   The external duct lies in a horizontal plane, the other two
being vertical.   At its lower end each duct bears an enlargement, or *ampulla*.   The ampulla of the horizontal duct is situated anteriorly, close to
that of the anterior duct.   In lower forms, a slight projection of the ventral
wall of the sacculus may be present.   It is referred to as the *lagena*.   The
lagena is the forerunner of the auditory portion of the ears of higher forms.

FIG. 14.15.   Right membranous labyrinth of rabbit.   (*Modified from Retzius.*)

   The membranous labyrinth is filled with a fluid, the *endolymph*, the exact
origin of which is not understood.   Its viscosity is two to three times that
of water.   Almost completely surrounding the membranous labyrinth is
the perilymphatic space, filled with fluid *perilymph*.   The perilymph is
actually cerebrospinal fluid, the perilymphatic space being in communication with the subarachnoid space.   Surrounding the perilymphatic space
is cartilage or bone, depending upon the species.   In higher forms a *bony
labyrinth* (Fig. 14.16), situated in the petrous region of the temporal bone,
encloses the membranous labyrinth and follows all its configurations.   The
membranous labyrinth remains attached to the bony labyrinth in certain
places (page 658).   Perilymph fills the spaces between the membranous and
bony labyrinths.   The *semicircular canals* are those portions of the *bony*
labyrinth which surround the semicircular ducts.

   The actual receptors for the sense of equilibrium consist of elevated
patches of sensory cells, the *cristae ampullares* (*acusticae*) and the *maculae
acusticae*.   The former are located in the ampullae of the semicircular ducts.
They are made up of supporting cells and *hair cells* provided with long processes.   The maculae, of which there are typically two, are also composed of
supporting cells and hair cells, the latter bearing short, bristly, hairlike processes.   One, the *macula utriculi*, lies in the wall of the utriculus;
the other, the *macula sacculi*, is located in the wall of the sacculus.   In those

vertebrates having a lagena, a third macula, the *macula lagenae*, lies at its base. Both cristae and maculae are supplied with fibers from the vestibular branch of the auditory nerve (VIII). A thickened mass forms in connection with each macula and covers its surface. This *otolithic membrane* is composed of gelatinous material into which groups of "hairs" from the hair cells penetrate. Each tuft is surrounded by a small space filled with

semicircular canals

cochlea

FIG. 14.16. Bony labyrinth of left ear of man exposed after a portion of the petrous region of the temporal bone has been removed. (*Drawn by G. Schwenk.*)

endolymph. Small crystalline bodies called *otoconia* are deposited in the outer part of the otolithic membrane. They are composed of a mixture of calcium carbonate and a protein. These deposits may be rather extensive, each forming a compact mass referred to as an *otolith*.

The supporting cells of each crista apparently secrete a gelatinous material which, in fixed preparations, appears in the form of a *cupula* into which the sensory hairlike processes extend. The cupula is probably merely an artifact and may not exist as such during life. It has been observed that when the cristae of fishes are being fixed for sectioning, the hairlike processes gradually shorten. Coagulated material appears in the space from which the "hairs" have withdrawn. This shrinks slowly and becomes the cupula.

Movements of the endolymph are believed to affect the cristae, stimulating the sensory hair cells, thus setting up impulses transmitted to the brain by branches of the auditory nerve. The cristae in the ampullae of the semicircular ducts are believed to be the receptors which give an awareness of movement (kinetic sense). They seem to be affected by rotational movements.

Changes in position of the otoliths associated with the maculae, in response to gravitational forces, affect the hair cells and give information regarding the position of the body when at rest (static sense) or of changes in velocity.

Comparative anatomy of the inner ear. *Cyclostomes.* The membranous labyrinth in cyclostomes is atypical and is considered to be degenerate. In the hagfish, *Myxine*, only one semicircular duct is present (Fig. 14.17*B*). It lies in a vertical plane and bears an ampulla at either end. There is no distinction between sacculus and utriculus. A small endolymphatic duct is present, with an enlarged sinus at its dorsal end. The lamprey, *Petromyzon*, has two vertical semicircular ducts (Fig. 14.17*A*), each

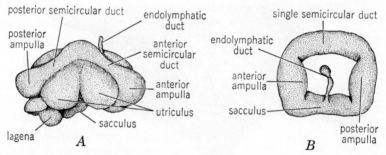

FIG. 14.17. *A*, Membranous labyrinth of lamprey (*modified from Krause*); *B*, membranous labyrinth of hagfish (*modified from Retzius*.)

having an ampulla containing a crista ampullaris. An external, horizontal duct is lacking. A slight constriction is indicative of a separation into sacculus and utriculus. A *macula communis* lies at the bottom of the saccular region.

In all forms above the cyclostomes the typical three semicircular ducts are present without any basic modification.

Fishes. The membranous labyrinth of the elasmobranch fishes shows certain structural peculiarities (Fig. 16.21). The anterior vertical and the horizontal ducts join the utriculus dorsally. Their ampullae lie close together toward the anterior end. Where the posterior vertical duct lies in close proximity to the sacculus, it is somewhat enlarged to form what is sometimes considered to be a second, or posterior, utriculus. The cavity of each "utriculus" connects near its base with that of the sacculus. A small projection from the ventral portion of the sacculus extends posteriorly for a short distance, forming the lagena. From the dorsal side of the sacculus in many elasmobranchs a small tube extends upward, opening on the surface of the head. It is frequently called the endolymphatic duct, although the term *invagination canal* is more appropriate. It is not homologous with the endolymphatic duct of higher forms. Fine sand grains enter the cavity of the sacculus through the openings of the invagination canals and serve as otoconia. They are clumped together in a large mass, the otolith. Sea water, rather than endolymph, in all probability fills the membranous labyrinth.

In other fishes the original invagination canal disappears and a new duct, the endolymphatic duct, forms as an outgrowth from the saccular region. Both utricular and saccular otoliths are present, the latter being more prominent and in some cases so large as almost to fill the saccular chamber. The utricular otolith is called the *lapillus;* that of the sacculus is the *sagitta.* It is possible that the saccular macula is stimulated by low-frequency vibrations and thus may exhibit the beginning of an auditory function. In teleosts an otolith, the *asteriscus,* is also present in association with the macula lagenae. In many fishes a small, sensory patch, the *macula neglecta,* is located in the wall of the utriculus. There is some possibility that the macula lagenae and the macula neglecta may serve as phonoreceptors in fishes. The cavity of the bony labyrinth connects with the cranial cavity, thus providing a means by which perilymph (cerebrospinal fluid) can reach and surround the membranous labyrinth.

In teleost fishes of the order Ostariophysi a chain of small bones, the *Weberian ossicles,* derived from the four most anterior vertebrae, is interposed between the swim bladder and the perilymphatic space, thus relating the function of the swim bladder with the equilibratory and possibly the auditory senses. The separate Weberian ossicles, proceding from the ear to the swim bladder, are known, respectively, as the *scaphium, claustrum, intercalarium,* and *tripus.* Scaphium and claustrum are derived from the neural arch of the first vertebra, the claustrum in some cases being absent or nonfunctional. The intercalarium represents the neural arch of the second vertebra. It lies within a fibrous ligament connecting scaphium and tripus. The latter is the main element and is actually a modified rib of the third vertebra. A contribution from the fourth vertebra is used for support. In other fishes which lack Weberian ossicles, direct connections may exist between the swim bladder and the inner ears.

Amphibians. The membranous labyrinth in amphibians lies entirely within a closed, bony, *auditory,* or *otic, capsule.* The three semicircular ducts are arranged in the manner characteristic of all gnathostomes. A constriction partially separates utriculus and sacculus, the former being the larger of the two chambers and the portion to which the semicircular ducts connect (Fig. 14.18). A small endolymphatic duct extends dorsally from the sacculus and terminates in an expanded endolymphatic sac. In some frogs the sacculus is partially divided into a small upper and a larger lower portion. A small lagena projects from the posterior portion of the sacculus.

This is destined to give rise to the *cochlear duct* of higher forms. A sensory crista is located in each of the three ampullae. The utriculus is equipped with a macula utriculi and, in most amphibians, with an additional, smaller, sensory patch, the macula neglecta. There are two of the latter

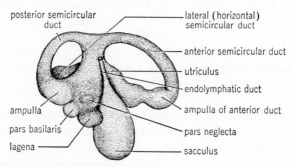

posterior semicircular duct — lateral (horizontal) semicircular duct — anterior semicircular duct — utriculus — endolymphatic duct — ampulla of anterior duct — ampulla — pars basilaris — pars neglecta — lagena — sacculus

FIG. 14.18. Medial view of membranous labyrinth of frog, *Rana esculenta*. (*Modified from Gaupp.*)

in caecilians. A prominent macula sacculi is present in the wall of the sacculus, and a *macula (papilla) lagenae* is located in the lagena. An additional sensory patch, the *papilla basilaris*, apparently derived from the papilla lagenae, is present in the lagena in many amphibians. Others lack a basilar papilla but possess a small *papilla amphibiorum* in the wall of the sacculus near its junction with the utriculus. Caudate amphibians usually have both types of papillae. The papilla amphibiorum seems to function as a hearing device in amphibians but is of little or no significance as a forerunner of the auditory organs of amniotes. Because of certain structural peculiarities, the opinion is generally held that the papilla basilaris and possibly the macula neglecta serve as phonoreceptors, the former being of special significance in the phylogenetic development of the more elaborate hearing organs of reptiles, birds, and mammals. The further development of the acoustic organs is the chief advance made by the ears of amphibians over the condition in fishes, but the main function of the inner ear remains that of equilibration.

Reptiles, birds, and mammals. The significant changes in the membranous labyrinth in reptiles, birds, and mammals involve further development and lengthening of the lagena and an elaboration of the basilar papilla. These structures are concerned with the sense of hearing. The equilibratory portion of the inner ear remains relatively unchanged. The macula lagenae persists in reptiles, birds, and prototherians but is lacking in higher mammals.

Hearing. As mentioned above, it is in fishes that the membranous labyrinth first becomes involved in hearing which, at best, must be of a rather low order. The macula sacculi, macula neglecta, and the macula lagenae have all been considered as possible phonoreceptors, but this has

not been indisputably demonstrated. Sound vibrations in the water may
directly affect skeletal structures in the head which transmit them to the
inner ear. In some fishes the compressible swim bladder may receive vibrations which are transmitted to the ear directly or else indirectly via the
Weberian ossicles.

In amphibians the papilla amphibiorum may function as a phonore-
ceptor, but this structure is apparently without homologues in higher forms.
The papilla basilaris, derived from the macula (papilla) lagenae and present
in many amphibians, alone seems destined for further phylogenetic specialization.

Although a macula neglecta is present in reptiles and birds, it disappears
altogether in mammals. It is of doubtful significance in regard to the sense
of hearing. In amniotes the lagena is drawn out, or lengthened, to form the
cochlear duct, and the sensory, basilar papilla is elaborated into the *organ of
Corti,* which is the actual receptor organ for the sense of hearing. The
cochlear duct begins to assume a spiral form in crocodilians and birds. In
mammals (Fig. 14.19), however, the spiral becomes more complicated,
reaching its epitome in the alpaca in which it makes five distinct turns. In
man only $2\frac{3}{4}$ turns are present. The cochlear duct is fastened to the bony

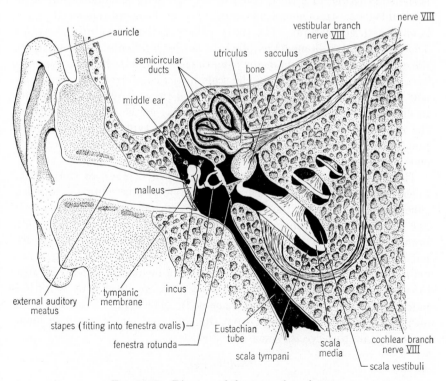

Fig. 14.19. Diagram of the ear region of man.

labyrinth on either side but is free from it above and below. Thus the *cochlea proper* is divided into three longitudinal spaces, or chambers, called the *scalae* (Fig. 14.20). The upper one is the *scala vestibuli*, and the lower

Fig. 14.20. Semidiagrammatic section through mammalian cochlea, showing the three scalae surrounded by the bony labyrinth.

the *scala tympani*. These are filled with fluid perilymph. Between the two is the *scala media*, or *cochlear duct*, which represents a modification of the original lagena. It, of course, like other parts of the membranous labyrinth, is filled with endolymph. The three scalae together make up the *cochlea*. The floor of the scala media is called the *basilar membrane*. This separates the endolymph in the scala media from the perilymph in the scala tympani. The thin-walled sloping roof of the scala media is referred to as the *vestibular*, or *Reissner's, membrane*. It separates the endolymph in the scala media from the perilymph in the scala vestibuli. At the apex of the cochlea, the scala vestibuli is continuous with the scala tympani. The point of junction is known as the *helicotrema*. The scala media comes to a point and ends blindly at the helicotrema.

The basilar membrane supports the complicated organ of Corti, a detailed description of which is beyond the scope of this volume. Stated in general terms, however, the organ of Corti is composed of numerous hairlike cells which have connections at their bases with fibers of the cochlear branch of the auditory nerve. These reach their destination via the basilar membrane. The hairlike cells are very numerous and are arranged in a definite pattern from apex to base of the scala media. The hairlike processes extend out into the endolymph where they are affected by vibrations in a manner to be described later (page 662). The organ of Corti in birds, although structurally different from the similarly named organ in mammals, appears to serve the same function.

Middle Ear

Caudate amphibians and some salientians lack a middle ear. This is a specialized or degenerate condition and not primitive. Beginning with the majority of salientians, however, a special mechanism is present in most vertebrates by means of which sound waves are transmitted to the auditory portion of the membranous labyrinth. The *middle ear,* or *tympanic cavity,* as this portion of the ear is called, is concerned only with the auditory function of the ear and bears no relation to the sense of equilibrium. The middle ear is a modification of the first pharyngeal pouch. It traces its origin to the spiracular (hyomandibular) cleft which opens onto the surface of the head in elasmobranch and a few other fishes.

Formation. During development, in those forms in which a middle ear occurs, the first pharyngeal pouch elongates and comes in contact with the superficial ectoderm. The pouch fails to break through. A membrane, at first composed only of a layer of ectoderm and a layer of endoderm, thus separates the pouch from the outside. Later a small amount of mesodermal tissue pushes in between the two original layers. The membrane becomes the *tympanic membrane,* or *"eardrum,"* upon which sound waves impinge. The outer portion of this pharyngeal pouch becomes expanded to form the tympanic chamber. The portion nearest the pharynx becomes constricted so as to form a narrow *Eustachian tube,* which opens into the pharynx through a small aperture. The Eustachian tube provides a means by which atmospheric pressure on the two sides of the tympanic membrane can be equalized, thus permitting the membrane to vibrate freely. Both middle ear and Eustachian tube are lined with endoderm.

Structure. In most tetrapods two openings are present between the tympanic cavity and the cochlea. The upper one, or *fenestra ovalis* (*vestibular window*), connects with the scala vestibuli. A small bone, the *stapes,* generally serves as a plug which fits into the fenestra ovalis. The lower opening, or *fenestra rotunda* (*cochlear window*), lies between the tympanic cavity and the scala tympani. A delicate membrane over the opening separates the two cavities.

In the majority of salientians a small rod-shaped bone, the *columella* (stapes), extends across the cavity of the middle ear from the center of the tympanic membrane directly to the fenestra ovalis. The rounded base of the columella, referred to as the *stapedial plate,* fits into the fenestra ovalis. In reptiles and birds the columella is usually divided into two parts, a basal portion, the *stapes proper* (sometimes called the *plectrum*), filling the fenestra ovalis, and an *extracolumella,* which is attached to the tympanic membrane. It should be recalled that the columella, or stapes, is derived from the hyomandibular cartilage of elasmobranch fishes along with the shift from the hyostylic to the autostylic method of jaw suspension (pages 397 to 404).

In mammals (Fig. 14.19) two additional bones, the *malleus* and *incus,* make their appearance between the tympanic membrane and the stapes. Malleus, incus, and stapes are referred to as *auditory ossicles.* The malleus, which is derived from the *articular* bone of lower forms, connects at one end with the tympanic membrane and with the incus on the other. The incus, which is homologous with the *quadrate* bone of lower vertebrates, lies between the malleus and stapes. The three auditory ossicles serve to transmit sound vibrations from tympanic membrane to perilymph in the scala vestibuli.

Whether transmission of vibrations is accomplished by columella, extracolumella, and plectrum or by malleus, incus, and stapes, vibrations of the perilymph travel up the scala vestibuli to the helicotrema at the apex of the cochlea. They then pass down the scala tympani. The membrane over the fenestra rotunda moves in and out with corresponding movements of the incompressible perilymph, this serving to damp the vibrations.

Comparative anatomy of the middle ear. *Amphibians.* No middle ear is present in caecilians, caudate amphibians, and a few salientians. Although tympanic membrane, tympanic cavity, and Eustachian tube are lacking, a columella is present. Often it is a vestigial structure. It lies within a ligamentous band, the *suspensor-stapedial ligament*, which extends from the fenestra ovalis to the ends of the squamosal and quadrate bones. In most amphibians, at the time of metamorphosis, another bony or cartilaginous element, the *operculum*, appears, fitting into the fenestra ovalis along with the columella. It is not represented in other vertebrates. In *Amphiuma* and *Necturus* columella and operculum are fused. The operculum is furnished with an *opercular muscle* which is attached to the suprascapula. In strictly aquatic forms it is believed that vibrations are transmitted to the ear via the jaws, suspensory apparatus, columella, fenestra ovalis, to the perilymph. In those terrestrial species lacking a middle ear the pathway is via the forelimbs, shoulder girdle, operculum, fenestra ovalis, to perilymph. In either case the auditory sense must be of a rather low order and confined to the reception of deep vibrations.

Although most salientians have a middle ear of the type previously described, there are some, *i.e.*, certain burrowing toads, which lack a tympanic membrane and middle ear. In some forms, notably the tongueless toads, the two Eustachian tubes open by a single median aperture into the pharynx. In most species, however, two separate openings are present and the tympanic membrane is flush with the surface of the head. In one frog from Siam the tympanic membrane is located at the bottom of a pit corresponding to the external ear passage of mammals (page 661).

Reptiles. Middle ear, Eustachian tube, and tympanic membrane are altogether lacking in snakes, yet the sense of hearing appears to be acute in these reptiles. The extracolumella is attached at its outer end to the quadrate bone. Hence the path of sound vibrations is via the jaws, extracolumella, plectrum, fenestra ovalis, to perilymph. In turtles the tympanic membrane is thin and delicate in aquatic forms but thick and covered with skin in terrestrial species. The two Eustachian tubes in crocodilians open into the pharynx by a single median aperture.

In most reptiles the tympanic membrane is flush with the surface of the head, as in salientian amphibians. However, in certain lizards it lies at the base of an ear pit, which is a slightly depressed area on the surface of the head. It may be partially covered by a fold of integument. Similarly in crocodilians a movable integumentary fold covers and protects the depressed tympanic membrane.

Birds. Well-developed tympanic chambers are present in birds. The Eustachian tubes open by a single, median outlet into the pharynx. The tympanic membrane is located some distance from the surface of the head at the end of a narrow passage.

Mammals. The tympanic cavity in many mammals is surrounded by a bony structure, the *tympanic bulla*, which forms part of the temporal bone. It connects with the pharynx by means of the Eustachian tube. The Eustachian tubes of mammals open separately into the pharynx. The mammalian tympanic membrane is situated at the end of a fairly deep passageway called the *external auditory meatus*. In this respect it differs from most members of the lower classes. The external auditory meatus in man is an inch or more in length.

External Ear

The outer portion of the external auditory meatus, or auditory canal, is supported by cartilage, but the remainder has bony walls. A true external ear, which catches and directs sound waves into the auditory canal, is found only in mammals. Tufts of feathers, present in some birds near the opening of the auditory canal, may possibly function in a similar manner, but these do not constitute a *pinna*, or *auricle*, as the true external ear is called.

There seems to be a tendency to eliminate the external ear in aquatic mammals. Whales, sirenians, and certain seals lack a pinna. In other forms the opening of the external auditory meatus may be hidden in the pelage. Aquatic mammals must be able to close the ear passage so as to prevent the entrance of water. Various types of valvular arrangements are used by different aquatic mammals to effect such a closure. A degeneration of the pinna has also occurred in most burrowing mammals. Loose soil is kept out of the auditory canal by contraction of auricular muscles.

The pinna develops, for the most part, posterior to the opening of the external auditory meatus. Its size and structure show much variation among mammals. The deep cavity within the pinna is referred to as the *concha*. A pinna is lacking in the platypus, but the animal is nevertheless capable of changing the position of its external ear openings by the use of certain muscles. In some mammals, as in man, the pinna is capable of little, if any, movement. In others it is provided with well-developed voluntary muscles and can be moved in various directions so as to receive as many sound waves as possible from their source of origin. The large, flaplike external ears of elephants are probably not so effective in receiving sound waves as their size would indicate.

The external auditory meatus is lined with skin continuous with that covering the pinna. *Ceruminous*, or *wax, glands*, as well as protective hairs, are integumentary derivatives found in the auditory canal.

Mechanism of Auditory Function

Sound waves are caught by the pinna, concentrated by the concha, and directed into the external auditory meatus, finally to impinge upon the tympanic membrane. Vibrations of the tympanic membrane are transmitted to the malleus, and thence to incus and stapes. The stapes, situated in the fenestra ovalis, sets up vibrations in the perilymph of the scala vestibuli. They travel up to the helicotrema at the apex of the cochlea and then down the perilymph in the scala tympani, ultimately to be damped by the membrane covering the fenestra rotunda. Some vibrations are transmitted through the vestibular membrane to endolymph in the scala media and thence through the basilar membrane to the perilymph of the scala tympani.

There is some question as to whether the sensory receptors of the organ of Corti are stimulated by movements of the endolymph caused by vibration of the vestibular membrane or are affected directly by vibrations of the basilar membrane. In either case stimulation of the hairlike cells of the organ of Corti sets up impulses in the endings of the cochlear branch of the auditory nerve, which then travel to the brain where they are interpreted as sound.

OLFACTORY SENSE

The close association between the olfactory and respiratory organs of air-breathing vertebrates has been discussed previously. In lower aquatic vertebrates with the gill type of respiration, the olfactory and respiratory mechanisms bear no relation to one another.

The *olfactoreceptors* consist of individual bipolar neurons derived from thickenings of the superficial ectoderm (olfactory placodes). They are located in the *olfactory epithelium*, or *Schneiderian membrane*, which, in addition to the olfactory neurons themselves, is composed of *basal cells* and *supporting cells*. The relationship of the olfactory nerve to the brain is discussed in Chap. 13.

The exposed ends of the olfactoreceptors are brushlike in appearance, each cell bearing from 5 to 12 delicate *olfactory hairs* at its tip. The number of olfactory hairs varies with the species. They are covered with mucus produced by *Bowman's glands*, the ducts of which pass through the olfactory epithelium. The mucus, in addition to being protective, serves as a moist medium in which volatile substances are dissolved before stimulating the olfactoreceptors. In both chemical senses, smell and taste, it is necessary that substances be in solution before they can be detected.

Comparative anatomy of olfactory organs. *Amphioxus.* Near the pigment spot at the anterior end of amphioxus, but slightly to the left of the
middorsal line, is a small *flagellated pit.* It has been suspected of possessing
an olfactory function, but no nervous connections between it and the brain
vesicle have been discovered, so that its actual function remains in doubt.
The fact that the flagellated pit of amphioxus is unpaired is sometimes used
as an argument in homologizing it with the median olfactory apparatus in
cyclostomes. In the latter group, however, unmistakable evidence indicates a dual origin of the olfactory sac.

Cyclostomes. In the lamprey a single, median, nasal aperture opens onto
the surface of the head. It leads, by means of a short passageway, to the
blind *olfactory sac,* which undoubtedly represents a fusion of two since it is
bilobed in the ammocoetes larva. The olfactory sac is lined with numerous
folds covered with olfactory epithelium. Paired olfactory nerves, which
also indicate a bilateral origin of the olfactory apparatus, pass through a
fibrocartilaginous *olfactory capsule* which surrounds the olfactory sac (Fig.
15.3) and which is situated immediately anterior to the brain. From the
anterior edge of the olfactory sac a long tube extends ventrally and posteriorly, passing beneath the anterior tip of the notochord to the level of
the second gill pouch where it ends blindly. This is the *nasopharyngeal
pouch.* Between the ventral part of the diencephalon of the brain and the
nasopharyngeal pouch lies the small pituitary gland. It has been suggested
(W. J. Leach, 1951, *J. Morphol.*, **89**:271) that the nasopharyngeal pouch,
which has no counterpart in higher vertebrates, may actually represent a
portion of the embryonic stomodaeal cavity which has separated off from
the main part of the stomodaeum. The peculiar position of the nasal
aperture and its unusual relation to the nasopharyngeal pouch, as compared with other vertebrates, are due to a shifting of these organs from
their original ventral position during embryonic development (Fig. 14.21).
Water is alternately forced in and out of the nasopharyngeal pouch and
olfactory apparatus, the intake and outflow coinciding with respiratory
movements in the gill region. In this manner water in contact with the
olfactory mucous membrane is constantly replaced, enabling the animal
to detect chemical substances in solution in the water. In the lamprey
neither olfactory sac nor nasopharyngeal pouch has any connection with
the pharynx.

In the hagfish the condition is somewhat similar to that found in the
lamprey, but the single, median nostril is more anterior in position and the
end of the nasopharyngeal pouch establishes a connection with the pharynx
during late embryonic life. Since *Myxine* frequently lies buried in mud, it
is possible for the respiratory current of water to pass to the pharynx and
gills via the passage furnished by the nasopharyngeal pouch.

Fishes. Among fishes the olfactory organs are paired. They may be
nothing more than blind pits lined with olfactory epithelium. In the bony
fishes the nostrils are usually situated on the dorsal aspect of the head at

some distance from the mouth. In some, as in the perch, there are two nostrils on each side. The pits are so constructed as to have incurrent and excurrent openings which are sometimes quite far apart and connected to each other by a tube. Ciliary currents as well as movements of muscles of gills and jaws are responsible for the passage of water in and out the nostrils.

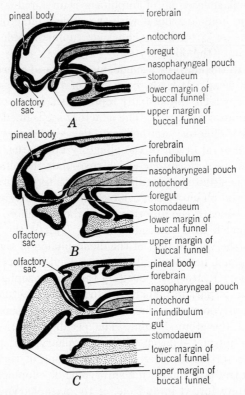

FIG. 14.21. Diagrams showing three stages, *A*, *B*, and *C*, in the development of the olfactory sac and nasopharyngeal pouch of the lamprey. Note how the nasal aperture has shifted to the top of the head. (*Based on Kuppfer and Dohrn.*)

The nostrils of elasmobranchs are located on the ventral side of the snout. A flap of skin extends across the middle of each nostril, partially separating it into two divisions (Fig. 6.1). The flap is so arranged as to direct water in one side and out the other. In many elasmobranchs a prominent *oronasal groove* leads from each nostril to the corresponding corner of the mouth. The presence of an oronasal groove anticipates the condition first found in the Choanichthyes, in which a true connection between the nostrils and the mouth is to be found. In the latter the olfactory epithelium, consisting of a few large folds, is located in the dorsal part of the nasal passage, which connects the internal and external nares.

Among fishes the olfactory epithelium is commonly thrown into numerous *Schneiderian folds*, which greatly increase the epithelial surface. The folds are particularly well developed in elasmobranchs, in which, of all the senses, the olfactory sense is probably of most importance to the animal. The fact that the folds are immersed in water prevents them from collapsing and adhering to one another.

Amphibians. The short olfactory passage in amphibians usually arises as an oronasal groove which sinks into the upper lip and connects the external naris with the mouth at a point just inside the upper jaw. In purely aquatic forms the nasal passage is lined with folds. Olfactory sense cells lie in the depressions between the folds, and ciliated epithelium covers the ridges. In larvae the cilia create a current which causes water to flow through the respiratory passage. During larval life *choanal valves*, consisting of simple folds of mucous membrane, regulate the direction in which the current of water flows. These are lost at metamorphosis, and new valves appear at the external ends of the nasal passages.

In terrestrial amphibians the olfactory epithelium is located in the upper medial portion of the nasal passages. Its surface is not folded to any extent. In some forms a shelflike fold from the lateral wall foreshadows the appearance of the conchae, or turbinal folds, which become highly developed in more advanced vertebrates. Glandular masses within the nasal passages serve to keep the olfactory epithelium moist. The secretion of the glands is of a mucous nature and covers the sensory epithelium. Olfactory hairs pass through the mucous layer, so that their free ends are exposed. During inspiration the air passes toward the medial side of the nasal passage. Expired air passes along the lateral border in which the olfactory epithelium is poorly developed or lacking.

A new structure, the *vomeronasal*, or *Jacobson's, organ,* first makes its appearance in amphibians. In frogs it arises as an anterior, ventromedial evagination of the nasal passage to which it ultimately connects by means of a short duct. In salamanders it is more lateral in position. Jacobson's organ is believed to be used in testing food substances held in the mouth. It is supplied with branches of the terminal (O), olfactory (I), and trigeminal (V) cranial nerves.

The olfactory organ in caecilians is particularly well developed in correlation with their poorly developed eyes and habit of burrowing underground.

The sense of smell seems to play an important role in mating behavior among salamanders. Hedonic glands in the skin apparently secrete odoriferous substances which serve as sexual excitants.

Reptiles. With the development of palatal folds in most reptiles and of a complete secondary palate in crocodilians, the choanae come to open in the posterior portion of the roof of the mouth and the nasal passages become considerably elongated. A single concha is present in the lateral wall of each nasal passage. It consists of a projection of the ethmoid bone and brings about an increase in the olfactory surface. The concha is poorly developed in turtles but is quite large in crocodilians in which it divides anteriorly. A so-called *pseudoconch*, of questionable homology, lies posterior to the concha. The nasal passages in reptiles show, to an increasing extent, a tendency to become divided into anterior respiratory and posterior olfactory regions.

Jacobson's organ is insignificant in turtles and crocodilians but is highly developed in *Sphenodon*, snakes, and lizards (Fig. 6.4). In these reptiles it has lost its connection with the nasal passage and opens directly into the mouth cavity, where it aids in distinguishing various types of food substances (pages 150, 193–194).

Birds. The main advance to be observed in the nasal passages of birds is in the greater elaboration of the conchae. Three conchae are present in the lateral wall of each nasal passage. An anterior *vestibular concha* is located in the vestibular region. Smaller *middle* and *superior conchae* are located more posteriorly and are supported by *maxilloturbinate* and *nasoturbinate* bones, respectively. No olfactory epithelium is to be found covering the vestibular concha. Although the middle concha bears olfactory epithelium for a time after hatching, it soon disappears, so that only the superior concha is finally used to support the Schneiderian membrane. The olfactory sense in birds is thus rather poorly developed. Jacobson's organ exists only as a transitory embryonic rudiment.

Mammals. It is among mammals that the olfactory sense reaches the epitome of development. There are mammals, however, in which the sense of smell is poorly developed or altogether lost. Toothed whales, for example, lack a sense of smell, and in primates, seals, and whalebone whales it is but slightly developed.

In most mammals the elongated nasal passage contains a complicated mass of folds derived from three conchae. The folds may assume the shape of scrolls and greatly increase the surface of olfactory epithelium exposed in each nasal passage. This labyrinth is supported by cartilages or by turbinate bones. They are called the *ethmoturbinate, maxilloturbinate,* and *nasoturbinate,* since they arise from the ethmoid, maxillary, and nasal bones, respectively. Each turbinate bone may have secondary divisions. The epithelial covering of the maxillo- and nasoturbinates is not sensory but is concerned with warming and moistening the air on its way to the lungs. The ethmoturbinates are the chief support for the Schneiderian membrane. The more complicated they are, the keener the sense of smell. Man has three rather poorly developed conchae. Turbinate bones, present during early development, disappear, for the most part. The Schneiderian membrane of the human being consists of a small area extending from the roof of the nasal cavity down both sides of the nasal septum for a short distance. It also covers part of the surface of the superior concha. The total surface area is about 250 sq. mm. on each side. The limited size of this sensory area accounts for the restricted olfactory sense of the human being.

Fibers of the olfactory nerve pass through small *olfactory foramina* in the cribriform plate of the ethmoid bone before establishing connection with the olfactory lobes of the brain.

Large air spaces called *sinuses* are located within certain bones of the skull of eutherian mammals. They are lined with an epithelium which is an extension of the nasal mucosa, but here the mucous glands are smaller and fewer in number. The mucosa is tightly adherent to the periosteal covering of the bones. The sinuses communicate with the nasal passages but are not concerned with the olfactory sense. Their function, if indeed they have any, is obscure. The presence of sinuses makes the skull lighter in weight and, at least in man, adds resonance to the voice. The principal sinuses are those in the frontal, ethmoid, sphenoid, and maxillary bones. The maxillary sinus (antrum of Highmore) is the largest of the sinuses. It is frequently the seat of infection.

In mammals the nasal passage is composed of three or more distinct regions. The first, or *vestibular, portion* is lined with skin and leads to the mucous membrane inside. Hairs and sebaceous glands are present. The second portion is the *respiratory region.* It comprises the greater portion of the nasal passage and is lined with pseudostratified, ciliated, columnar epithelium (respiratory epithelium). Here air is warmed and moistened. The innermost portion is the *olfactory region,* where the Schneiderian membrane is located.

Snouts or noses, commonly observed in mammals, have little if anything to do with the sense of smell. They are primarily tactile organs. The snouts of several forms have become adapted for usages quite divorced from respiration and olfaction. Thus the trunk, or proboscis, of the elephant, representing the enormously elongated nose and upper lip, is used for many purposes. The external nares open at the end of the trunk. The snouts of some forms are used in digging and for sundry other purposes.

A well-developed, but small, Jacobson's organ is present in certain mammals belonging to the lower groups. In most, however, it appears only for a short time during early development.

The sensory receptors for smell differ from those of other organs of special sense in that the *cell bodies* are located in the periphery or in the sensory organ itself. They receive stimuli, and their fibers carry impulses directly to the olfactory lobes of the brain.

The sense of smell is much more acute than the allied chemical sense of taste. Even man, with his relatively poorly developed olfactory organs, can detect certain substances in the air at extreme dilutions. Artificial musk and mercaptan may, for example, be distinguished at a dilution of one part to several billion parts of air.

Odors are caused by the emanation of volatile substances of molecular dimensions which reach the olfactoreceptors in the Schneiderian membrane through air or water. The diffusion of volatile substances through water is slower than in air but is effective, nevertheless. Substances with the strongest odors are those which pass readily into a gaseous state, although not all gaseous substances have odors. Nonvolatile substances lack odors. Volatile substances must be dissolved in the moist surface of the olfactory epithelium before they are capable of stimulating the sensory receptors. It is believed that they may even dissolve in the olfactory hairs themselves before actually acting as stimuli.

Attempts to classify odors have proved to be very difficult, and no truly satisfactory classification has been brought forth. The infinite variety of odors makes efforts at studying the mechanism of olfaction almost impossible of solution, although several explanations have been proposed for such variations.

SENSE OF TASTE

The receptors for the sense of taste are spoken of as *gustatoreceptors*, or *taste buds*. The latter term is descriptive because of the resemblance of these structures to the unfolded leaf buds of plants. Taste buds are composed of two kinds of cells: *supporting cells* and *neuroepithelial cells*. The cellular elements are arranged in such a manner as to give the taste bud a sort of barrel shape, swollen in the middle and tapering at the base and tip (Fig. 14.22). The long axes of the cells extend from the base to the surface of the taste bud, reaching through the entire thickness of the epithelium. The number of taste cells in a taste bud is subject to much variation. Estimates in man range from 4 to 20. The supporting cells form the outer covering of the taste bud, the neuroepithelial cells lying in the interior. Some supporting cells, however, are interspersed among the taste cells.

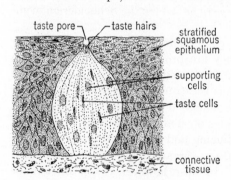

Fig. 14.22. A taste bud.

Each neuroepithelial cell bears a minute *taste hair* at its tip. The taste hairs project into a small, pitlike depression, the *taste pore*. Taste pores are found only in mammals.

Although it is rather difficult to differentiate between the chemical stimuli resulting in smell and from those giving rise to the sensation of taste, it has been established that only four fundamental sensations of taste exist: bitter, sweet, salty, and sour, or acid. Sometimes two additional tastes, alkaline and metallic, are added to the list, but there is no uniform agreement on this. Variations from the above are chiefly due to combinations of two or more of the fundamental tastes and to complications which arise from the part played by the olfactory nerve endings.

The various taste sensations evoked by different chemicals have been the subject of careful study. Bitter taste is related chiefly to certain organic compounds, especially such alkaloids as morphine, quinine, and caffein. Glucosides, picric acid, and bile salts are additional organic substances which give a bitter taste. A few inorganic compounds such as calcium and ammonium salts induce the same sensation. Sweet taste is likewise evoked by a variety of organic and inorganic compounds. Among the former are sugars (glucose, maltose, sucrose, lactose, etc.), alcohols, saccharin, and chloroform. Lead acetate, which is sometimes called sugar of lead, is an inorganic compound giving a sweet taste. Salty taste is brought about chiefly by inorganic salts, especially the chlorides of sodium, potassium, magnesium, lithium, and ammonium. Some iodides, bromides, nitrates, and sulfates are also salty to the taste. Sour, or acid, taste is produced by acids and acid salts.

It is of interest that certain drugs have a specific action upon the various taste sensations, blocking some but leaving others to function normally. The drug cocaine completely blocks all taste sensations as well as those of touch and pain. When cocaine is applied, the various tastes are abolished in definite order, each apparently having its own threshold of response. Bitter disappears first, followed by sweet, salty, and sour in the order given.

Distribution of taste buds. In certain fishes the skin covering the entire body is abundantly supplied with taste buds. However, in most forms the gustatory receptors are confined to the oral region, being particularly numerous on the tongue. Here they are usually associated with certain small elevations of the surface epithelium, the *lingual papillae*. In mammals (Fig. 5.6) four types of papillae are recognized: filiform, or conical; fungiform; foliate; and circumvallate.

Filiform papillae are small, conical elevations scattered over the upper surface of the anterior two-thirds of the tongue. They practically never have taste buds associated with them. In many forms, particularly in the cats, their free surface is highly cornified. This is of advantage to the animal in holding and in rasping minute particles of flesh from bones. *Fungiform papillae* are knoblike, rounded elevations, the free ends of which may bear a few taste buds (Fig. 14.23*B*). These papillae are few in number as compared with filiform papillae. *Foliate papillae* are leaflike structures running in three to eight parallel rows on either side of the tongue toward the base. They may be very much reduced in certain species, as in man. Taste buds are present along the sides of foliate papillae (Fig. 14.23*C*). The most prominent but fewest in number of all are the *circumvallate papillae*. These are rounded, somewhat elevated structures situated near the base of the tongue and arranged in the form of a V, with the apex pointing toward the esophagus. The *foramen caecum*, marking the point of origin of the thyroid gland, lies just posterior to the apex. Each circumvallate papilla is completely surrounded by a trenchlike depression. Taste buds are present in the epithelium which forms the walls of the trench (Fig. 14.23*A*). The circumvallate papillae and the taste buds associated with them are apparently of endodermal origin. This is an exception to the general concept that all sense organs and nervous structures are derived from ectoderm.

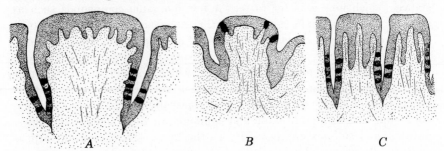

FIG. 14.23. Location of taste buds (shown in black) on *A*, circumvallate papillae; *B*, fungiform papillae; *C*, foliate papillae.

The discrepancy would indicate that the potencies of germ layers, according to the germ-layer concept, are not so fixed as is generally supposed. *Von Ebner's glands* are small structures in the tongue, the ducts of which open into the bottom of the depression surrounding circumvallate papillae. They secrete an albuminous substance.

Comparative anatomy of gustatoreceptors. *Amphioxus.* In the velum and buccal cirri of amphioxus are groups of *hair cells* which may serve as gustatoreceptors or olfactoreceptors. They are supplied with branches of sensory nerves. Similar structures are not to be found over the general body surface. It is of interest that this primitive animal shows an aggregation of sensory receptors at the anterior end of the body.

Cyclostomes. In adult cyclostomes, taste buds are present on the surface of the head in addition to those present in the pharyngeal region. In larval forms they are confined to the pharyngeal lining.

Fishes. In the elasmobranch fishes taste buds are associated with papillae located in the epithelium lining mouth and pharynx.

Higher fishes show a greater diversity in taste-bud distribution. In some they are present on the surface of the head as well as on the pharyngeal epithelium. In such scavenger fishes as carp, suckers, and catfish, taste buds are present over the entire body surface, including fins and tail. It has been estimated that about 100,000 taste buds may be found in the integument of a single catfish. The barbels extending from the head are particularly well supplied.

Beginning with the Dipnoi in the evolutionary scale, the location of taste buds is limited to the lining of the mouth, pharynx, and tongue.

Amphibians. Taste buds of amphibians are present on the roof of the mouth, tongue, and lining of the jaws. In the frogs they occupy a position on the free surfaces of fungiform papillae. Only two kinds of papillae are present: filiform and fungiform. The latter are larger and fewer in number than the former, which do not have taste buds associated with them. A distinction has been made between the responses of amphibians to olfactory and gustatory stimuli. Reaction to taste is indicated by snapping and swallowing movements; olfactory stimuli evoke head and body movements. It has been reported that newts are able to distinguish different tastes.

Reptiles. In the reptiles there is a more distinct localization of taste buds than is to be found in any preceding group. In lizards, snakes, and crocodilians they are practically confined to the pharyngeal region with few or none present on the tongue.

Birds. The horny tongues of most birds are lacking in taste buds which are situated mainly in the lining of the mouth and pharynx. The actual distribution of taste buds, however, shows some correlation with the shape of the tongue. If the tongue is rather broad, the taste buds are located mainly on the lining of the upper beak or pharynx. If the tongue is long and narrow, they are generally confined to the mucous lining of the mandible. The large, rather fleshy tongue of the parrot bears numerous taste buds.

Mammals. The number of taste buds in various species of mammals varies from a few hundred to over 10,000. The arrangement of the papillae on the mammalian tongue has already been referred to. Taste buds are also present on other parts of the mouth as well as in the pharynx. In man, for example, they are found on the mucous membrane covering the soft palate, the passage (fauces) between mouth and pharynx, posterior surface of the epiglottis, and vicinity of the arytenoid cartilages, and even on the vocal cords. Although taste buds on the tongue are almost always associated with papillae, those in other regions merely lie in the mucous membrane of the area in question.

In children the distribution of taste buds differs somewhat from that of adults, especially as regards the number at the tip of the tongue. During childhood many more are present in this area than in adult life.

Variations in arrangement of the papillae in mammals are of some interest. Two rows of circumvallate papillae are found in monotremes, bats, rabbits, and certain others. Three rows occur in marsupials, some insectivores, and apes. Some monkeys have four rows. In man and certain carnivores the number has been reduced to a single row. Hyracoideans and guinea pigs lack circumvallate papillae. Foliate papillae are particularly well developed in rodents, but in many forms, as in man, they are almost rudimentary. In whales the gustatory sense is practically wanting.

Investigations have shown that each of the four tastes predominates in a different area of the surface of the tongue. Sweet prevails at the tip, bitter near the base, sour along the sides, and salty at both edges and the tip.

Nerve supply. Taste buds are innervated by branches of several cranial nerves, but there are no separate nerves for the sense of taste as there are for other senses. From subepithelial nerve plexuses in the vicinity of the taste buds, free nerve endings may penetrate into the taste buds themselves, terminating between the cells. Others may end in arborizations between adjacent taste buds. The manner in which the various types of nerve fibers function has not as yet been determined.

The cranial nerves for the sense of taste are the facial (VII), glossopharyngeal (IX), and vagus (X). In mammals a portion of the chorda tympani branch of the seventh nerve supplies taste buds in the anterior two-thirds of the tongue, those located in the fungiform papillae in particular. The glossopharyngeal furnishes fibers to the foliate and circumvallate papillae on the posterior third. The vagus is much less important in this respect, sending but a few fibers to the epiglottis and laryngeal region.

Visceral sensory branches of the ninth and tenth nerves supply the pharyngeal taste buds of fishes. Those in the mouth and on the surface of the head receive visceral sensory branches of the seventh nerve. In such forms as the catfish and buffalofish, with a general cutaneous distribution of gustatoreceptors, the visceral sensory area on either side of the medulla oblongata is expanded markedly. These prominences are spoken of as *vagal lobes* (Fig. 13.6).

The development as well as the function of the taste buds is dependent upon the nerves with which they are supplied. Experiments have shown that if the nerves of taste are cut, degeneration of the taste buds ensues. In the catfish they begin to degenerate shortly after the tenth day and have completely disappeared by the thirteenth day. After the nerve fibers have regenerated, the buds once more make their appearance. It has been suggested (J. M. D. Olmsted, 1920, *J. Comp. Neurol.*, **31**:465) that the organizing effect of the nerve fiber is mediated through hormonelike chemical substances given off by the fiber.

Development. Filiform and fungiform papillae first make their appearance as elevations of the tongue epithelium. Foliate papillae appear somewhat later as parallel folds along the lateral sides. Circumvallate papillae undergo the most complex development of all. Not only do slight elevations appear, but a circle of epithelial cells grows down into the mass of the tongue. Later this ring of cells splits to form the characteristic sulcus which surrounds the papilla. The glands of von Ebner are at first solid masses of cells which develop from the epithelium at the bottom of the sulcus. These masses later hollow out. Not long after the lingual papillae have formed, taste buds begin to appear. If Olmsted's conception is correct, the appearance of taste buds should coincide with the development of gustatory nerve fibers. Taste cells may be recognized as distinct from surrounding cells by their differential staining properties. Taste buds which are at first present on the crown of the circumvallate papillae later degenerate and disappear, so that only those in the walls of the surrounding trench persist. The taste pores do not appear until relatively late in development.

In such forms as elasmobranchs with pharyngeal taste buds, the latter seem to be of endodermal origin.

COMMON CHEMICAL SENSE

In the lower aquatic vertebrates the entire surface of the body is sensitive to mildly irritating chemicals. The moist integument of amphibians also comes under this category. In terrestrial forms, however, only those surfaces normally kept moist are sensitive to chemical irritants. The conjunctiva, lining of the mouth, nasal mucosa, lining of the anal canal, and genital apertures are all sensitive areas. Free nerve endings of spinal nerves and certain cranial nerves are the receptors concerned with receiving information regarding chemical irritants. The sense has no relation to the chemical senses of taste and smell. Ammonia fumes, for example, can be detected by the olfactory nerves but at the same time have a decidedly irritating effect on the nasal mucosa and conjunctiva.

OTHER SENSORY RECEPTORS

Cutaneous Receptors

In addition to the sense organs already referred to, other external sensory receptors affected by environmental stimuli are abundantly distributed in the skin over the entire surface of the body. The sensations which result from the stimulation of these receptors are referred to as *cutaneous sensations*. They include touch, heat, cold, and pain. All sensory nerve endings in the skin are external receptors of one kind or another. Some consist only of the free endings of nerve fibers. These probably serve as pain receptors and possibly for touch as well. Others are encapsulated nerve endings, and still others, in mammals at any rate, terminate in hair follicles. The skin of man contains a great number of extremely small sensory areas each of which is responsive to one or more of the cutaneous sensations. Areas concerned with one sensation overlap others to some extent. The difficulty confronting investigators in assigning definite functions to the cutaneous receptors can be appreciated when one considers how much the sensory areas overlap and that interpretation depends so largely on the degree of stimulation.

Sense of touch. Touch is the sense by which contact with objects gives evidence of certain of their qualities. The sensory endings for the sense of touch are called *tangoreceptors*. Branches of the dendritic processes of sensory nerve cells penetrating among the epithelial cells of the skin, cornea, and mucous membranes (Fig. 14.24*A*) are considered to be tangoreceptors. The nerve endings for the sense of pain (*algesireceptors*) also terminate freely in the skin. It is therefore very difficult to distinguish between these two types of receptors. In the skin of the pig's snout, nerve fibers which penetrate into the epidermis terminate in small expanded discs which are in contact with special epithelial cells (Fig. 14.24*B*). They are called *Merkel's tactile discs*, or *corpuscles*, and are believed to be tangoreceptors.

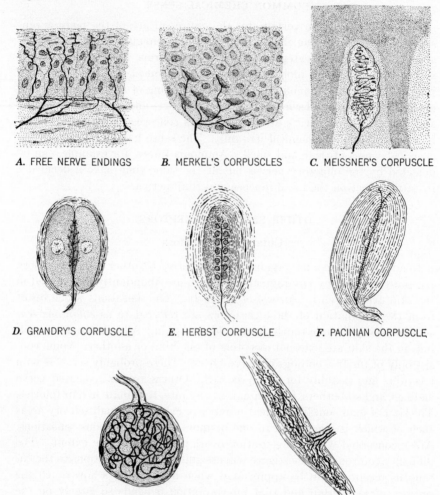

A. FREE NERVE ENDINGS *B.* MERKEL'S CORPUSCLES *C.* MEISSNER'S CORPUSCLE

D. GRANDRY'S CORPUSCLE *E.* HERBST CORPUSCLE *F.* PACINIAN CORPUSCLE

G. END BULB OF KRAUSE *H.* END ORGAN OF RUFFINI

Fig. 14.24. Various types of cutaneous receptors found in vertebrates. Those depicted here are *not* drawn to the same scale.

Several types of tangoreceptors consisting of encapsulated nerve endings have been recognized. They are located for the most part in the dermis of the skin or in the subepidermal connective tissue. Among these are *Meissner's corpuscles* (Fig. 14.24*C*), found in the skin of primates, particularly in areas which normally undergo friction. They are most abundant in the papillae of the corium of the dermis of the palms and soles. *Genital cor-*

puscles are special nerve endings in the skin of the external genitalia and of the nipples. *Grandry's corpuscles,* found on the beaks of certain birds, consist of two encapsulated tactile cells between which a nerve fiber terminates (Fig. 14.24D). *Herbst corpuscles* (Fig. 14.24E) are also found in the mouth parts of birds as well as in areas of the skin where feathers are few in number. They are composed of a capsule enclosing a double-rowed core of cells which surround the terminal nerve fiber. Rather large *Pacinian (Vater-Pacinian) corpuscles* (Fig. 14.24F) are to be found in the deep layers of the dermis as well as in such internally located parts as the tendons and periosteum. It is believed that these encapsulated nerve endings in the skin are stimulated by pressure. The sense of pressure is interpreted as being evoked by a stimulus greater in degree than that which causes the sensation of touch. It is not a true cutaneous sensation. *Corpuscles of Golgi and Mazzoni,* found in the subcutaneous tissues of the fingers, are similar to Pacinian corpuscles but have thicker cores and thinner capsules.

Tactile nerve endings terminating in hair follicles are, of course, found only in mammals. The branching nerve endings are confined to the root of the hair and base of the follicle. Hairs are tactile organs with a fine degree of sensibility. When the hair is removed, hairy areas lose much of their sensitivity. Noteworthy among sensory hairs are the specialized vibrissae which are so well developed in mammals of nocturnal habit.

It is believed that touch or pressure causes a deformation of the surface of the skin with a consequent alteration in shape of the sensory endings. This is the important factor involved in the stimulation of tangoreceptors.

Temperature senses. Sensory thermoreceptors are confined for the most part to the skin. They are almost entirely lacking from the exposed surface of the eyeball. There is some disagreement concerning the specific end organs for temperature sensations. Some authorities believe that free nerve endings in the skin may serve as thermoreceptors, but it is more likely that specific encapsulated endings are responsible for receiving thermal stimuli.

Cold. The *end bulbs of Krause* (Fig. 14.24G) are usually considered to be *frigidoreceptors.* Each consists of a rounded meshwork of nerve terminations. A thin layer of connective tissue encloses the mass.

Heat. The *end organs of Ruffini* (Fig. 14.24H) are generally believed to serve as *caloreceptors* for the sensation of warmth or heat. The endings for this sense lie somewhat deeper in the dermis than do those for cold. The pit organs of the pit vipers are apparently heat receptors (page 31).

Sense of pain. *Algesireceptors,* which mediate pain sensations, consist of naked nerve endings lying in the deeper layers of the epidermis. They are also present in the cornea and internal serous membranes and mesenteries, where tangoreceptors are lacking.

Distribution of cutaneous receptors. Mapping out the sensory spots in the skin of the human being has been the subject of much careful study.

This has been accomplished chiefly in reference to cold and warm spots by moving hot and cold metallic points over the skin. Tactile or pressure points as well as those for pain have been studied mainly by applying fine hairs of various diameters to the skin. Each of the cutaneous senses seems to have its own spots distributed through the skin. It has been estimated that there are in the entire cutaneous surface of man about 16,000 to 30,-000 warm points, 150,000 to 250,000 cold points, 500,000 tactile or pressure points, and from 3 million to 4 million pain points. In certain areas some types of points are much more abundant than in others. The lips and the tips of the fingers are particularly well supplied with receptors for all four of the cutaneous senses.

Little is definitely known concerning cutaneous sense organs in vertebrates other than man.

Internal Receptors

Proprioceptive sense. Receptors located in tendons, joints, and skeletal muscle give information to the central nervous system regarding the position and movements of various parts of the body. These *proprioceptors* may consist of free nerve endings or of spindles and corpuscles of various kinds.

Free nerve endings are found lying between individual muscle fibers. Deep pain sensations are believed to arise from their stimulation. *Pacinian corpuscles*, mentioned previously as being located in the deep layers of the corium, are also found in tendons, joints, and periosteum. Sensory *neuromuscular spindles* may be located in muscular tissue or on tendons but are to be found chiefly at the junction of muscle and tendon. They are long, narrow structures consisting of small bundles of peculiar muscle fibers surrounded by a capsule in which sensory fibers terminate. *Golgi organs*, somewhat similar to neuromuscular spindles, also lie at the junction of tendon and muscle. Each is enclosed in a capsule containing several tendinous fasciculi and into which one or more nerve fibers penetrate. Pacinian corpuscles located in the mesenteries, omenta, and visceral peritoneum are believed to give information concerning stretching of mesenteries, distension of the colon, and the like.

Sense of equilibrium. Although, as mentioned on pages 650 to 656, a portion of the inner ear is chiefly concerned with the sense of equilibrium, other sensory organs may also be involved. Proprioceptors and tangoreceptors, particularly those on the soles of the feet, are important in furnishing information to the central nervous system regarding the position of the body.

Other senses. Such sensations as appetite, thirst, hunger, and nausea, arising from within the body itself, may be mediated by so-called *interoceptors*. No specific endings or corpuscles have been described for these sensations.

Little is known concerning the sensations involved in what is commonly referred to as sexual desire. Certain *genital corpuscles*, present in the dermis of the external genitalia and of the nipples, are thought to be associated with sexual sensations.

LATERAL-LINE ORGANS

The lateral-line system of sense organs occurs only in cyclostomes, fishes, and aquatic amphibians. It is difficult to ascertain the function of these structures with accuracy. Reception of deep vibrations in the water and of stimuli caused by currents or movements of water, including those minor local currents produced by the animal itself, are among the functions ascribed to the lateral-line organs, which are sometimes referred to as *rheoreceptors*. They may thus be functionally equivalent to proprioceptors since they furnish information regarding the position of the body in relation to the environment.

In their most primitive condition the organs consist of sensory papillae called *neuromasts* composed of groups of sensory cells surrounded by supporting cells. Each sensory cell has a hairlike process at its free end. The neuromasts are usually arranged in rows or lines which follow the paths of nerves. In cyclostomes, certain fishes, aquatic amphibians, and amphibian larvae, the neuromasts are located on the surface of the skin, particularly in the head region. In other fishes they sink down into the skin in depressions or grooves which in most forms become closed over to form tubes or canals (Fig. 14.25). In the Holocephali, however, the grooves re-

Fig. 14.25. Diagram showing relation of neuromasts to lateral-line canal and lateral branch of vagus nerve, as found in most fishes.

main open (Figs. 2.10 and 14.26). The closed tubes of most fishes open to the surface of the skin through minute pores which, in bony fishes, penetrate through the scales (Fig. 4.13). The canals are filled with a mucous secretion. In embryonic and larval stages there are typically three longitudinal lateral-line canals, dorsal, ventral and lateral, extending the length of the body. The dorsal and ventral canals disappear in the trunk region, so only the lateral canal persists. On the head, however, the original arrangement remains in the form of three main branches of the lateral-line canal proper (Fig. 14.26). The specific arrangement of the canals varies considerably in different fishes, but in general a large *supraorbital canal* courses forward above the eye and an *infraorbital canal* lies below the eye. Other canals are given such names as *mandibular, hyomandibular,* and *opercular,* according to their position on the head. A *supratemporal,* or

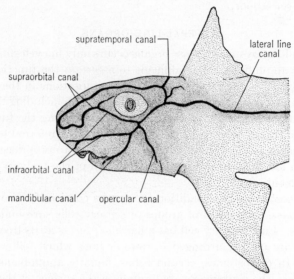

Fig. 14.26. Semidiagrammatic lateral view of head of *Chimaera monstrosa,* showing arrangement of grooves of lateral-line system in the head region.

occipital, canal passes across the posterior part of the head, serving to connect the system on one side with that of the other. The canals are usually, but not necessarily, continuous with each other.

Of interest is the fact that in the newt, *Triturus viridescens,* the lateral-line organs disappear when the animal takes to terrestrial existence, only to reappear when it later returns to water for breeding. Aquatic reptiles and mammals have no trace of a lateral-line system.

The lateral-line system is a somatic sensory system, supplied by branches of three cranial nerves, the seventh, ninth, and tenth. The seventh nerve is associated with the canals in the head region, the ninth with a restricted area at the base of the supratemporal canal, and the tenth with the lateral line proper. Even the portion of the lateral line near the end of the tail is supplied by the lateral branch of the vagus nerve, which in some cases may be many feet long. All three nerves bear sensory ganglia derived in part from thickened placodes in the skin. Because the inner ear arises from a similar placode and the sensory cells of the inner ear are similar in structure to neuromasts of the lateral-line system, the term *acousticolateralis system* is frequently used to embrace both systems. The two are believed to have a common evolutionary history.

Other peculiar sense organs found only in fishes are closely related to the lateral-line system and have a similar innervation. *Pit organs* consist of individual neuromasts which have sunken into small pits in the skin. They may be scattered about in no particular order or else occur in short rows.

Ampullae of Lorenzini, found only in elasmobranchs, are present in large numbers on the surface of the head. Each consists of a lobulated, bulblike enlargement containing sensory cells, supplied by the facial nerve, lying at the base of an elongated, mucus-filled tube or canal which connects to the surface by means of a small pore (Fig. 14.27). Certain studies indicate that the ampullae of Lorenzini are concerned with thermoreception. *Vesicles of Savi*, found only on the ventral surface of the electric ray, *Torpedo*, are closed sacs separated from the rest of the epidermis. Their function is unknown.

FIG. 14.27. A group of sensory ampullae of Lorenzini.

The importance of the lateral-line organs in connection with the aquatic mode of life is indicated by their highly developed supply of branches of cranial nerves and by the fact that they have disappeared entirely in terrestrial forms.

SUMMARY

1. Receptor organs are structures capable of responding to certain types of stimuli by setting up impulses which are in turn transmitted by nerve fibers to the central nervous system. In the higher centers of the brain such impulses are interpreted as sensations. The actual receptor cells, with few exceptions, are of ectodermal origin.

2. Receptor organs are classified as external and internal sense organs. External sense organs, or exteroceptors, are those which are stimulated by environmental disturbances of various kinds. They include those for the senses of sight, hearing, smell, taste, touch, pressure, temperature, and pain. Internal sense organs, affected by stimuli arising within the body, include statoreceptors which, in response to gravitational forces, are concerned with equilibrium, proprioceptors for the sense of muscle position, and interoceptors for such internal sensations as hunger, thirst, and nausea. The lateral-line organs of lower aquatic vertebrates are exteroceptors.

3. The vertebrate eye has no true homologue among other phyla and appears for the first time in cyclostomes. Its evolutionary history is obscure. The retina, or sensory portion, develops as a cuplike outgrowth of the diencephalic region of the forebrain. The lens is derived from the superficial ectoderm which invaginates under the organizing influence of the optic cup

in certain forms. Mesenchyme surrounding the optic cup differentiates into the uveal and fibrous coats of the eyeball.

In the vertebrate eye, light must pass through the various cellular layers of the retina before it can stimulate the sensory receptors, or rod and cone cells. Impulses thus set up must pass back through the cells comprising these layers to reach the optic nerve. The eye is thus said to be inverted. Several theories have been advanced to explain the inversion of the retina.

Accommodation, or adjustment, made by the eye in order to bring objects at various distances into focus, is accomplished in different ways by various vertebrates. Lower forms accommodate by changing the position of the lens. Higher forms change the shape of the lens when accommodating.

The eye is moved by six broad strap-shaped muscles which are supplied by the purely motor third, fourth, and sixth cranial nerves. Other accessory structures are associated with eyes in different vertebrates, in each case serving to adapt the animal better to its own environmental needs.

4. The vertebrate ear, at least in higher forms, functions in a dual capacity as an organ of equilibrium and hearing. The equilibratory function is the more fundamental and primitive. The portion of the ear in which the sensory receptors are located is the inner ear, or labyrinth. The epithelium lining the membranous portion of the labyrinth is derived from an invagination of the superficial ectoderm in the head region, known as the auditory placode, and contains endolymphatic fluid. The portion of the inner ear concerned with equilibrium is to be found in all vertebrates with but little variation in different forms. It consists typically of two chamberlike enlargements, an upper utriculus and a lower sacculus, the two being connected by a canal. An endolymphatic duct joins the sacculoutricular canal. Three long, narrow tubes, the semicircular ducts, arranged at right angles to each other, connect at both ends with the utriculus. Each semicircular duct bears a swelling, or ampulla, at its lower end. The sensory receptors for equilibrium are cristae ampullares and maculae acusticae. They are small, elevated patches of sensory cells located in the ampullae and in the utriculus and sacculus, respectively. An otolithic membrane containing crystalline bodies covers each macula. Movements of the endolymph affect the cristae, whereas changes in position of the otolithic membrane in response to the pull of gravity stimulate the maculae. In cyclostomes the membranous labyrinth is degenerate and only one or two semicircular ducts are present.

A slight projection of the ventral wall of the sacculus, the lagena, is usually present in lower forms. It evolves into the auditory portion of the ear in higher vertebrates. A macula is generally present in the wall of the lagena but is lacking in higher mammals. A basilar papilla, derived from the macula lagenae, first appears in amphibians and is the forerunner of the organ of Corti, the true sensory receptor for hearing in higher forms.

In crocodilians and birds the lagena begins to elongate and spiral to form the cochlear duct, also filled with endolymph. In mammals the cochlear duct (scala media) becomes more complicated. It contains the organ of Corti. Hairlike cells of the organ of Corti are stimulated by vibrations transmitted from the environment.

Beginning with salientian amphibians, a special mechanism is present in most vertebrates by means of which sound waves are transmitted to the auditory portion of the membranous labyrinth. The middle ear, or tympanic cavity, as this portion of the ear is called, is derived from the first pharyngeal pouch. A tympanic membrane, or eardrum, separates the middle ear from the outside. Small bones transmit vibrations from the tympanic membrane to fluid perilymph surrounding the membranous labyrinth. The perilymph in turn affects the endolymph within the membranous labyrinth. A Eustachian tube connects the cavity of the middle ear with the pharynx. It serves to equalize pressure on the two sides of the tympanic membrane. An outer, or external, ear is present only in mammals, although suggestions of such a structure appear in a few lower forms. It serves to catch and direct sound waves, which then impinge upon the tympanic membrane.

5. The receptors for the sense of smell consist of individual bipolar neurons derived from thickened areas in the superficial ectoderm. In aquatic vertebrates these are confined to the olfactory epithelium, or Schneiderian membrane, lining the olfactory sacs. The latter are nothing more than blind invaginations of the outer epithelium. In the crossopterygian fishes a connection between the nares and the mouth first appears. This passage is used in respiration primarily, the olfactory function being secondary. Further advances are to be found in a separation of the respiratory and olfactory regions from the mouth cavity by the development of a palate. Outgrowths from the lateral walls of the nasal passages in the form of folds and scrolls (turbinates or conchae) increase the respiratory and olfactory surfaces. Chemical substances must be in solution before they can stimulate the moist, mucus-covered olfactory epithelium.

6. Taste receptors are arranged in the form of taste buds, small structures composed of neuroepithelial cells and supporting cells. Substances to be tasted must be in solution in order to stimulate the sensory receptors. In some fishes gustatory receptors are distributed throughout the skin covering the entire body, but in most species they are confined to the oral and pharyngeal regions, being particularly numerous on the tongue. Here they are usually associated with small elevations of the epithelium called lingual papillae. The facial (VII) and glossopharyngeal (IX) cranial nerves contain sensory fibers for the sense of taste. The vagus (X) may also play a minor role in mediating taste sensations.

7. The entire surface of the body of lower aquatic vertebrates is sensitive to mildly irritating chemicals. In terrestrial forms, only those surfaces

which are normally kept moist are sensitive to such stimuli. The receptors for this common chemical sense, which is in no way related to smell or taste, consist of free nerve endings of spinal nerves and certain cranial nerves.

8. Cutaneous receptors for the senses of touch, pressure, temperature, and pain consist of free nerve endings in some cases and encapsulated nerve endings of various types in others. No specific nerves are concerned with the cutaneous senses.

9. Internal receptors for the proprioceptive sense consist of free nerve endings or spindles and corpuscles of different kinds. They are located in such places as muscles, tendons, joints, and periosteum. No specific receptors have been found which give rise to such sensations as hunger, thirst, and nausea.

10. Lateral-line organs of fishes and aquatic amphibians are related to the aquatic mode of life. They are believed to receive deep vibrations in the water and also to receive information concerning currents or movements of water, including those produced by the animal itself. The receptors consist of neuromasts made up of sensory cells and supporting cells. They are located either on the surface of the skin or inside grooves or canals in the skin. The lateral-line canal proper usually extends the length of the body but terminates on the head in several branches. The system is innervated by the seventh, ninth, and tenth cranial nerves. Because of the fact that the ganglia of these nerves arise in part from thickened placodes in the embryonic ectoderm similar to those giving rise to the inner ear, and because of the similarity in structure of the sensory receptors of the ear and those of the lateral-line system, the two are often referred to together as the acousticolateralis system. Other structures belonging to the lateral-line system are the scattered pit organs found in fishes and the ampullae of Lorenzini and vesicles of Savi confined to the elasmobranchs.

PART III. REPRESENTATIVE ANIMALS

The following section is included in this volume for those students who wish to gain a more detailed knowledge of the structure of certain representative vertebrates. The animals described are (1) the marine lamprey, *Petromyzon marinus*, an example of the class Cyclostomata, which includes the most primitive living vertebrates, (2) the spiny dogfish, *Squalus acanthias*, which is a member of the most primitive class of living fishes, the Chondrichthyes, and selected here because it typifies the structure of vertebrates in general and because of its availability for dissection, (3) the mud puppy, *Necturus maculosus*, chosen as a representative of the class Amphibia of which it is one of the most primitive and generalized members, embodying a number of features which illustrate changes that occurred in the transition from aquatic to terrestrial life, (4) the common cat, *Felis domestica*, a fairly typical member of the class Mammalia, a knowledge of its structure serving as an introduction to human anatomy.

With a few simple directions from the instructor on methods of procedure, this section may serve in lieu of a laboratory manual. Certain features of these animals have been discussed in previous chapters, and to these appropriate references are made.

CHAPTER 15

THE MARINE LAMPREY (*Petromyzon marinus*)

Although *Petromyzon marinus* is one of the most primitive of living vertebrates, in some respects it shows a high degree of specialization. Among primitive features to be observed are the absence of jaws, true teeth, and paired appendages—structures missing even in the embryo. The brain and skeleton are poorly developed, and the notochord persists throughout life. The little skeleton that is present is entirely cartilaginous, bone being lacking. This, however, may be a degenerate rather than a primitive character since bone is known to have been present in the armor of ostracoderms, the oldest fossil vertebrates on record. The reproductive system in both sexes of the lamprey is also of primitive construction. Although the respiratory system shows a high degree of specialization in some respects, its primitive features are indicated by the large number of gill pouches and the structural arrangement of the gills. Whether the presence of a single median nostril is primitive or specialized is questionable. Most ostracoderms had a single nostril, but in some, apparently, paired ventral nostrils were present. Moreover, during development the bilobed nature of the olfactory sac is evident. The larval form of the lamprey, referred to as the *ammocoetes*, is of rather simple structure and in many ways is similar to amphioxus, one of the protochordates.

EXTERNAL FEATURES

The body of the marine lamprey is long and thin, large specimens attaining a length of about 3 ft. The anterior end is cylindrical, whereas the posterior end is laterally compressed (Fig. 15.1). Numerous small

FIG. 15.1. Lateral view of lamprey.

pores of the lateral-line system can be observed in the head region even though a lateral line proper is absent. A large **buccal funnel,** surrounded

by a fringe of **papillae,** is located at the anterior end. It is beset internally with horny **epidermal teeth** which are definitely arranged (Fig. 15.2). At the apex of the buccal funnel is the **mouth** through which the **tongue** protrudes slightly. The tongue is a very specialized organ not homologous with the tongues of higher verte-
brates. In the lamprey it also bears horny teeth. On the dorsal surface of the head is a single, **median nostril** behind which a light area in the skin indicates the position of the **pineal organ.** The paired **eyes** have no eyelids but are covered with a transparent layer of skin. Seven **external gill slits** appear on each side as small apertures arranged in a row, beginning a short distance behind the eyes. On the ventral side at the junction of trunk and tail is a slitlike depression, the **cloacal pit.*** A **urogenital papilla,** bearing at its tip a small **urogenital aperture,** protrudes through the cloacal pit. The **anus** lies within the cloacal depression immediately

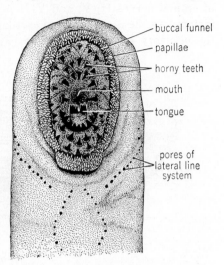

buccal funnel

papillae

horny teeth

mouth

tongue

pores of
lateral line
system

Fig. 15.2. Ventral view of anterior end of lamprey, showing buccal funnel and tongue beset with horny, epidermal teeth.

in front of the urogenital papilla (Figs. 7.7 and 15.4). No paired appendages are present. Two unpaired **median dorsal fins,** supported by slender cartilaginous **fin rays,** are located near the posterior end. The **caudal fin** is posterior to the second dorsal fin, the tail being of the **protocercal** type.

SKELETAL SYSTEM

The **notochord,** a persistent rodlike structure, forms the greater part of the axial skeleton (Figs. 15.3 and 15.6). It terminates anteriorly just underneath the posterior half of the brain. Small, metameric cartilages abut upon the notochord throughout its length. They extend dorsally and partially surround the spinal cord. These incomplete arches represent the rudiments of the **neural arches** seen in the vertebrae of higher forms. Similar cartilages in the tail region extend ventrally to form **hemal arches.** Very slender cartilaginous **fin rays** give support to the median fins.

The part of the skeleton making up the skull and branchial basket,

---

* A cloaca is a common chamber into which the intestinal, urinary, and genital ducts discharge. Strictly speaking, a true cloaca is not present in the lamprey since the anus and urogenital papilla have separate openings.

which supports the gill region, is more complicated. The **cranium** is rather primitive in structure and consists of cartilaginous plates which protect the floor and lateral sides of the brain. The roof of the cranium, except at one point, is membranous in nature. Foramina for the passage of cranial nerves II, V, and VIII pierce the lateral cartilages. The **olfactory capsule** is an unpaired cartilage surrounding the posterior edge of the **olfactory mucous membrane** (Fig. 15.3). It is pierced by two fo-

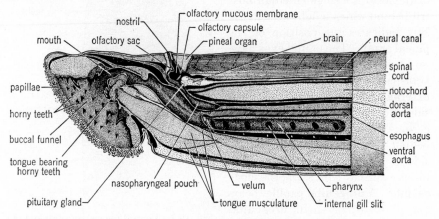

Fig. 15.3. Sagittal section of anterior end of lamprey.

ramina, through which the **olfactory nerves** pass to the brain. It is united to the cranium only by connective tissue. Other cartilages furnish support for the eyes, tongue, and edge of the buccal funnel.

The "visceral skeleton" is commonly known as the **branchial basket** (Fig. 10.28). The cartilage of which it is composed is continuous. Slender irregular cartilaginous bars lie *external* to the gill pouches. They support the gill region. There are several reasons for not homologizing these cartilaginous branchial bars with the typical visceral arches or visceral skeletons of higher forms.

The histological structure of the cartilage of lampreys is somewhat peculiar, there being only a small amount of matrix. It differs in various parts of the body.

MUSCULAR SYSTEM

The muscles of the trunk and tail regions of the lamprey are metameric structures known as **myomeres** or **myotomes** (Fig. 11.6). They are arranged almost vertically but curve forward slightly on both dorsal and ventral sides and become smaller toward the tail. Between adjacent myotomes are **myocommata**. These are tough connective-tissue partitions to which the **muscle fibers** of the myotomes attach and upon which they pull during contraction. The myotomes are practically all alike in structure. Since there is no lateral septum in the lamprey, the myotomes are not divided into dorsal and ventral regions as in higher forms. Only in the region of the head and gills do they become modified as **hypobranchial muscles,** and the superficial metamerism, so easily noted in the trunk and tail regions, loses its identity.

COELOM

The **body cavity,** or **coelom,** in the lamprey is composed of two portions: a small, anterior **pericardial cavity,** containing the heart, and a large **pleuroperitoneal cavity** in which the remaining visceral organs lie. In the adult lamprey these two cavities are completely separated.

DIGESTIVE SYSTEM

The mouth opening at the apex of the buccal funnel leads into a **buccal,** or **mouth, cavity,** which in turn connects posteriorly with two tubes: an upper **esophagus** and a lower **pharynx** (Fig. 15.3). The pharynx is a blind pouch which bears seven **internal gill slits** on each side. A valvelike structure, the **velum,** guards the opening between the mouth cavity and pharynx. The esophagus continues posteriorly as a straight tube and joins the **intestine** which extends directly to the anus (Fig. 15.4). Slight enlargements at either end may be considered to represent the **stomach** and **rectum,** respectively. The single-lobed **liver** surrounds the anterior part of the intestinal, or stomach, region. Its anterior end is concave and partially surrounds the pericardium, inside of which the **heart** is located. No gall bladder or bile duct is present in the adult. A few patches of cells buried in the substance of the liver and in the wall of the intestine may possibly represent **endocrine pancreatic tissue.** This is not macroscopically visible. A conspicuous fold, the **typhlosole,** in the intestinal wall projects into the intestinal lumen. It assumes a slightly spiral course and is sometimes called the **spiral valve.** The typhlosole is believed to increase the digestive and absorptive surface area of the intestine.

The intestine is supported by **mesenteries** only in the region of the rectum. These consist of bands of tissue supporting blood vessels which pass to the intestine from the dorsal body wall (Fig. 7.7). No large continuous membranes, like those of other forms, are present in the lamprey.

The method by which the animal feeds is discussed rather fully on page 198.

RESPIRATORY SYSTEM

The seven **external gill slits** communicate with large, rather spherical spaces, the **gill pouches,** which in turn open into the pharynx by means of **internal gill slits.** The gill pouches are separated from one another by membranous **interbranchial septa.** On either side of a gill pouch is a series of vascular **gill lamellae** arranged in a semicircular manner but forming a

hemibranch, or **half gill.** Each hemibranch is separated from the interbranchial septum by a sinuslike **lymphatic space,** across which extend small **connective-tissue strands** which support the hemibranch. In preserved specimens the lymphatic spaces are usually filled with coagulated lymph. Two hemibranchs enclosing between them an interbranchial septum are termed a **gill,** or **holobranch.** Thus there are **14** hemibranches on each side but only **6** holobranchs, since the first and last hemibranchs do not form parts of a holobranch (Fig. 15.5). The manner in which the lamprey respires is discussed in detail on pages 197 and 198.

UROGENITAL SYSTEM

The **kidneys** of *Petromyzon marinus* (Figs. 7.7, 15.4, and 15.6) are of the **opisthonephric type.** They are long, strap-shaped structures which lie on either side of the middorsal line from which they are suspended by mesenterylike membranes. Running along

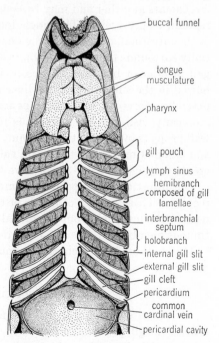

liver

body wall (cut)

skin

vestigial portion of archinephric duct

stomach region

ovary

opisthonephric kidney

intestine

opisthonephric kidney

rectum

archinephric duct

anus

urogenital papilla

cloacal pit

buccal funnel

tongue musculature

pharynx

gill pouch

lymph sinus

hemibranch composed of gill lamellae

interbranchial septum

holobranch

internal gill slit

external gill slit

gill cleft

pericardium

common cardinal vein

pericardial cavity

Fig. 15.4. Ventral view of coelomic viscera of female lamprey. Portions of the ovary have been removed to show details of kidney structure.

Fig. 15.5. Frontal section of anterior end of lamprey, showing arrangement of the gills, as seen from below.

the free edge of each kidney is an **archinephric duct.** Vestiges of the old embryonic **pronephric ducts** can be seen anterior to the functional part of the **opisthonephros.** At the posterior end of the body the archinephric ducts open into the **urogenital sinus,** which is the cavity within the **uro-genital papilla.** This opens by means of a **urogenital aperture** to the outside. A **genital pore** on each side connects the urogenital sinus with the coelom.

In *Petromyzon* the sexes are separate. In both, however, a single **gonad** extends the length of the pleuroperitoneal cavity and is suspended from the middorsal body wall by a membrane: the **mesorchium** in the male and the **mesovarium** in the female. When eggs or sperm are ripe, they break out of the gonad into the body cavity and find their way through the genital pores to the urogenital sinus and thence to the outside. No reproductive ducts are present, and fertilization is external. When spawning is tak-

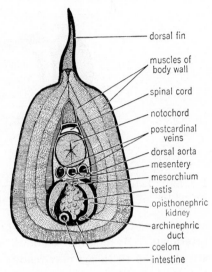

dorsal fin

muscles of body wall

spinal cord

notochord

postcardinal veins

dorsal aorta

mesentery

mesorchium

testis

opisthonephric kidney

archinephric duct

coelom

intestine

FIG. 15.6. Cross section of male lamprey at level of first dorsal fin.

ing place, the male wraps the posterior part of his body about the female and sheds sperm over the eggs as they emerge.

ENDOCRINE SYSTEM

Most of the structures belonging to the endocrine system in the lamprey are extremely small or diffuse and do not lend themselves readily to gross dissection. Each of the endocrine organs of the lamprey is discussed under an appropriate heading in Chap. 9, Endocrine System.

CIRCULATORY SYSTEM

The **heart** (Fig. 15.7) is a two-chambered organ located on the ventral side of the animal just posterior to the last pair of gill pouches. It lies in the **pericardial cavity** (Fig. 15.5) which is enclosed within a thick, tough **pericardium** of a purplish color. This is partially reinforced by cartilage of the posterior end of the branchial basket. The posterior portion of the pericardium is surrounded by the liver. The **atrium** lies on the left side of the **ventricle,** receiving blood from a rather small **sinus venosus.** The sinus venosus is situated in the cleft between atrium and ventricle. Three vessels enter the sinus venosus: a large **common cardinal vein** from the dorsal side, a small **inferior jugular vein** from the anterior ventral side, and a small **hepatic vein** from the liver on the posterior side. A rudimentary **conus arteriosus** carries blood from the ventricle to the **ventral aorta,** which in turn distributes it through **eight pairs** of **afferent branchial arteries** (Fig. 12.16) to the gills where aeration occurs. Where the ventral

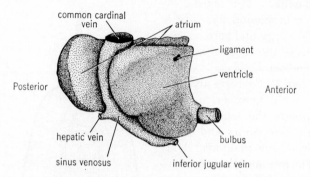

Fig. 15.7. Lateral view of heart of lamprey as seen from the right side. The posterior part of the atrium has been deflected to expose the sinus venosus to view.

aorta leaves the ventricle it is slightly expanded, forming a small **bulbus arteriosus.** By making windows in atrium and ventricle the internal structures of the heart may readily be studied. The sinus venosus communicates with the atrium through a **sinuatrial aperture** guarded by a **sinuatrial valve.** Likewise, an **atrioventricular aperture** with an appropriate valve lies between atrium and ventricle. A single set of two **semilunar valves** in the conus region prevents backflow of blood from ventral aorta to ventricle. Further details concerning the arterial and venous systems of the lamprey are discussed on pages 520 and 533, respectively.

NERVOUS SYSTEM AND SENSE ORGANS

The rather poorly developed **brain** of the lamprey lies just above and anterior to the tip of the notochord (Fig. 15.3). The **telencephalon,** or foremost part of the brain, on each side is divided into an anterior **olfactory bulb** and a posterior **olfactory lobe.** The olfactory lobes are frequently referred to as **cerebral hemispheres.** Posterior to the olfactory lobes two small, median structures, an anterior **parietal body** and a posterior **pineal organ,** project from the roof of the **diencephalon.** They are practically microscopic in size. At the distal end of each in the lamprey an eyelike structure is present. The pineal organ is the better developed of the two. However, it is probably capable of little more than distinguishing light from dark. The **pituitary gland** is attached to the ventral side of the diencephalon. The **optic lobes** of the **mesencephalon** are poorly differentiated in the lamprey. An apparently unique feature is the presence of a vascular, **mesencephalic, choroid plexus** extending from the roof of the mesencephalon in the form of an everted sac. The **cerebellum** is represented only by a slight fold. The **medulla oblongata** is the only part of the brain that is really well developed. Its roof consists of a rather large, everted **posterior choroid plexus.** Ten pairs of **cranial nerves** are present in *Petromyzon.*

The **spinal cord** is a flat, ribbonlike structure of fairly uniform width throughout. **Dorsal roots** of **spinal nerves** are found to alternate with **ventral roots** so far as their origin from the spinal cord is concerned. The roots do not unite to form a common trunk as in higher forms.

The **olfactory apparatus** of the lamprey (Fig. 15.3) is a unique structure. The single dorsal **nostril** leads into a canal which connects posteriorly with a small **olfactory sac.** This lies just anterior to the brain. Its walls are composed of ridges, covered over by a heavily pigmented **olfactory mucous membrane.** The **olfactory capsule,** mentioned above, surrounds the olfactory mucous membrane. The fact that the single median olfactory mucous membrane is supplied by a *pair* of cranial nerves not only gives evidence of its bilateral origin but indicates that the single olfactory organ of lampreys is specialized rather than primitive and probably represents a fusion of paired structures. There is also some evidence from embryology to support this point of view. From the anterior edge of the olfactory sac a long tube extends ventrally and passes underneath the anterior tip of the notochord. This is the **nasopharyngeal pouch.** The pituitary body lies between the nasopharyngeal pouch and the floor of the diencephalon. It is a very small structure, scarcely larger than a pinhead. The homologies and method of functioning of the nasopharyngeal pouch of the lamprey, which has no counterpart in higher vertebrates, are discussed on pages 359 and 663 (Fig. 14.21).

The **eyes** of the lamprey are primitive but well developed. In the ammocoetes larva they are undeveloped and lie hidden under the thick skin, which, however, thins out in the adult and becomes transparent. The **cornea** is not fused to the overlying skin and therefore lacks a corneal epithelium. The **lens** is permanently spherical, and suspensory ligament and ciliary apparatus are lacking. Furthermore, the size of the **pupil** is fixed.

The auditory organs of the lamprey are considered to be degenerate. Only the **membranous labyrinth** of the inner ear is present. Utricular and saccular regions are not distinct, and only the two vertical **semicircular ducts** are present, each with an **ampulla** at its lower end (Fig. 14.17*A*). The inner ear does not lend itself well to ordinary dissection.

CHAPTER 16

THE SPINY DOGFISH (*Squalus acanthias*)

The structure of the spiny dogfish, one of the cartilaginous fishes, is described in some detail in this chapter. It is less highly developed than the rather common, bony, or teleost, fishes, yet shows distinct advances over the cyclostomes. This is most clearly evidenced by the presence of paired pectoral and pelvic appendages (fins) and true upper and lower jaws. Furthermore, the nostrils are paired and the gill slits, which open separately to the outside, are reduced in number.

EXTERNAL FEATURES

The **body** of the spiny dogfish is fusiform in shape (Fig. 16.1). It is of grayish-green color on the dorsal side and yellowish-white on the under-

Fɪɢ. 16.1. Lateral view of female dogfish, *Squalus acanthias*. (*Drawn by R. Schugt.*)

surface. A few irregularly spaced white spots are present in the skin of young dogfish, but these tend to disappear as the animals grow older. Furthermore, they are less obvious in preserved specimens. The **head** is broad and somewhat flattened in a dorsoventral direction. Posteriorly the body tapers gradually from a more or less cylindrical form to the laterally compressed **tail**. The skin is almost entirely covered with minute **placoid scales** which point posteriorly (Fig. 4.14). The presence of these scales may be detected by rubbing the hand from posterior to anterior ends. The subterminal **mouth** is on the ventral side of the head. At the borders of the mouth the placoid scales are enlarged and modified to form **teeth** which are arranged in several rows. At each corner of the mouth a **labial groove,** or **pocket,** extends forward toward the **nostril,** and posteriorly for a short distance. Whether the labial pocket of *Squalus acanthias* is homologous with the oronasal groove of certain other elasmobranchs and of higher vertebrates has been questioned. Each pocket marks the location of a **labial cartilage** which permits a certain degree of movement of the **lower jaw,** or **mandible** (Meckel's cartilage). Each nostril appears to be divided by a flap of skin so arranged as to direct water in one side of the nasal cavity and out the other (Fig. 6.1).

The anterior, paired **pectoral fins** have short bases and flexible surfaces. A cartilaginous **coracoid bar,** forming part of the **pectoral girdle** and lying between the pectoral fins, may be felt through the skin on the ventral side. The posterior paired **pelvic fins** are smaller than the pectoral appendages. They, too, are connected ventrally. A cartilaginous **ischio-pubic bar** forms the **pelvic girdle,** which also may be detected through the skin. In males the median border of each pelvic fin is elongated and modified into a **clasper** (Fig. 8.33) which bears a deep groove along the dorsomedial border. Folds of skin overlap the groove so that only a small portion is actually open to the outside. The claspers serve as copulatory organs. Each is supported by cartilages. Neat the end of the clasper and along its outer edge is a sharp, grooved **spine.** On the inner side is a curved **hook** which presumably aids in making copulatory contact. Two median **dorsal fins** are present, each bearing a strong, sharp, posteriorly directed spine on its anterior border. The **fin spine** is a highly modified placoid scale. The **caudal fin** forms an important part of the **heterocercal tail.** In this type of tail the skeletal axis bends upward to enter the larger dorsal flange. By holding the fins up to the light it may be observed that they are supported by **fin rays.** These are thin rods of dermal origin.

A light-colored **lateral line** extends lengthwise along each side of the body from head to tail. The skin of the lateral line is slightly raised. Coursing through the dermis of the skin of the lateral line is the **lateral-line canal** which opens to the outside at intervals through small, microscopic pores. The lateral-line canal may easily be observed by cutting through the skin across the lateral line and examining the cut edge under a binocular dissecting microscope. The lateral-line system is an organ of special sense related to the aquatic mode of life. It appears only in fishes and aquatic amphibians. Reception of deep vibrations and of pressure stimuli caused by currents or movements of the water, enabling the animals to orient themselves in relation to currents, is among the functions attributed to the lateral line. On the head are numerous **pores of the lateral-line system.** Some of these, arranged in rows, are connected with branches of the lateral-line canal. Numerous other pores on the head represent the openings of an additional set of sense organs, the **ampullae of Lorenzini.** It is believed that they may detect variations in temperature.

The **eyes** are located on the lateral sides of the head. Immovable upper and lower **eyelids** are present.

Five pairs of oblique openings on the sides of the head are the **external gill slits.** They communicate internally with the **pharynx.** Another pair of openings called the **spiracles** actually represents the first pair of gill slits, which has become modified. A **spiracular valve** projects posteriorly from the anterior wall of each spiracle.

Between the spiracles and near the median line are two small openings. They are the external apertures of the **invagination canals** which connect the cavities of the **inner ears** with the outside.

On the ventral surface of the body between the pelvic fins is an opening, the **cloaca,** which is the common exit of the digestive and urogenital systems. Just within each lateral edge of the cloaca is an **abdominal pore** which leads directly into the body cavity. In young specimens they are usually closed. The function of the abdominal pores is obscure. The **anus** opens into the cloaca posteriorly. A cone-shaped papilla (**urogenital papilla** in the male and **urinary papilla** in the female), with a **urogenital** or **urinary pore** at its tip, projects into the cloacal cavity dorsal and posterior to the anus. The **oviducts** of the female also open into the cloaca by means of **genital pores,** located on either side of the urinary papilla.

SKELETAL SYSTEM

The **skeleton** of the spiny dogfish is composed entirely of **cartilage** impregnated to varying degrees with lime salts. No true bone is present. It is made up of two main portions: the axial and appendicular skeletons. As its name implies, the **axial skeleton** is that which forms the main axis of the body. It is divided into (1) the **spinal column,** which surrounds and protects the spinal cord; (2) the **skull,** composed in turn of (*a*) the **cranium,** or that portion which surrounds and protects the brain, (*b*) the **sense capsules,** which enclose and protect the auditory and olfactory organs, and (*c*) the **visceral skeleton,** supporting the jaws and gills. The **appendicular skeleton** is confined to the paired anterior **pectoral** and posterior **pelvic fins,** together with their respective **girdles,** by means of which they are connected indirectly to the axial skeleton by muscles, connective tissue, and ligaments.

Axial Skeleton

Vertebral Column

The **notochord** is the primitive axial skeleton of vertebrates. In the shark the notochord is still present but has been partially replaced and invested by the cartilaginous **vertebral column.** The **vertebrae** do not show extensive modifications such as are to be found in most higher forms. There are only two regions in the vertebral column of the dogfish: a **body,** or **trunk, region** and a **tail,** or **caudal, region.**

A typical body vertebra (Fig. 16.2*B*) consists of a ventral **centrum** both ends of which are deeply concave (*amphicoelous*). A small canal runs through the centrum from one concavity to the other. The remains of

the notochord occupy the canal. The notochord is expanded at each concavity. From each ventrolateral border of the centrum extends a platelike **transverse process (basapophysis),** to the end of which a slender **rib**
is attached.

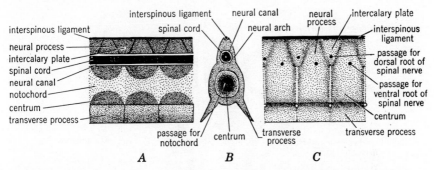

Fig. 16.2. Trunk vertebrae of dogfish: *A*, sagittal section through three vertebrae;
B, end view of vertebra; *C*, lateral view of three intact vertebrae.

The remainder of the vertebra above the centrum consists of a **neural
arch** which encloses and protects the spinal cord. Each neural arch is
made up of a triangular **neural process** on either side, with its broad base
on the centrum. A small **foramen** for the passage of the *ventral root* of a
spinal nerve is present near the base. The two neural processes meet
dorsally, forming the **neural spine.** A triangular **intercalary plate** fills in
the space between two adjacent neural processes (Fig. 16.2*A* and *C*). It
also contains a foramen which, in this case, serves for the passage of the
dorsal root of a spinal nerve. The two intercalary plates of a vertebra
unite dorsally. A strong, tough, continuous **interspinous ligament** runs
along the dorsal edge of the neural arches.

The tail, or caudal, vertebrae differ from the body vertebrae principally
in that there are no transverse processes and a **ventral,** or **hemal, arch** lies
below the centrum. The hemal arch surrounds the caudal blood vessels.
The **caudal artery** is dorsal, and the **caudal vein** lies ventral to it.

Skull

The **cranium** consists of a single piece of cartilage to which the **capsules**
for the olfactory and auditory organs have fused. Openings, or foramina,
for the passage of nerves and blood vessels going to and from the brain
perforate the cranium at various places. The dorsal side is relatively flat
and broad, whereas the ventral side is narrow (Figs. 16.3 and 16.4). At
the anterior end is a scooplike projection, the **rostrum,** which has a large
dorsal opening, the **precerebral cavity,** sometimes incorrectly referred to
as the anterior fontanelle. During life the rostrum is filled with a gelatinous material. At its base are two large openings, the **rostral fenestrae.**
These are continuous with the cavity of the cranium. On either side of

the base of the rostrum is an **olfactory capsule** which partially surrounds and protects the **olfactory sac,** the organ for the sense of smell.   On either side of the cranium is a large **orbit** in which the eye is accommodated dur-

FIG. 16.3.   Dorsal view of skull of *Squalus acanthias.*   (*After Senning, outline drawings for "Laboratory Studies in Comparative Anatomy," McGraw-Hill Book Company, Inc. By permission.*)

ing life.   A prominent **supraorbital crest** marks the lateral edge of the cranium above the orbit.   **Anterior** and **posterior orbital processes** project laterally and mark the ends of the supraorbital crest.   A row of foramina paralleling the supraorbital crest serves for the passage of certain branches of the fifth and seventh cranial nerves.   The large, rounded, posterolateral projections of the cranium are the **postotic processes.**   The **inner ears** lie within these masses.   An opening in the median line just posterior to the precerebral cavity is the **epiphyseal foramen** for the passage of the **epiphysis,** or **pineal body.**   Farther back in the region of the auditory capsules is an **endolymphatic fossa,** or **depression,** in which lie two pairs of openings.   The smaller, anterior ones are for the passage of the **invagination canals;** the larger, posterior openings are referred to as the **perilymphatic fenestrae.**   Each perilymphatic fenestra enters the cavity surrounding the membranous labyrinth.   During life the aperture is closed over by a membrane.   A semifluid material lies over the membrane, above which is the skin. It is possible that this apparatus may transmit sound waves to the cavity below. The membrane thus may serve in the manner of the tympanic membrane of terrestrial vertebrates, but by no means should the two

rostrum

rostral keel

olfactory capsule

rostral fenestra

anterior orbital process

anterior orbital shelf

infraorbital ridge

supraorbital crest

foramina for branches of cranial nerves V and VII

foramen for passage of internal carotid arteries

posterior orbital process

foramen for cranial nerve X

foramen for cranial nerve IX

occipital condyle

FIG. 16.4. Ventral view of skull of *Squalus acanthias*. (*After Senning, outline drawings for "Laboratory Studies in Comparative Anatomy," McGraw-Hill Book Company, Inc. By permission.*)

be considered as homologous structures. A large opening at the posterior end of the cranium is the **foramen magnum** through which the spinal cord passes. Small projections on either side of the foramen magnum are the **occipital condyles** for articulation with the first vertebra. A slight ridge, the **crista occipitalis,** extends between the foramen magnum and the endolymphatic fossa.

On the ventral side of the cranium (Fig. 16.4) an **anterior orbital shelf** marks the anterior boundary of the orbit. Posterior to this the floor of the cranium narrows down to a heavy **infraorbital ridge.** In the median line opposite the posterior edges of the orbit is a foramen through which the **internal carotid arteries** enter the cranial cavity. Conspicuous foramina for the passage of the ninth and tenth cranial nerves are situated at the posterior lateral corners of the cranium.

Several foramina are located in the orbit. The **optic foramen** is a large anteroventral opening for the passage of the optic nerve. Numerous foramina on the dorsal side are for the branches of the fifth and seventh cranial nerves, previously mentioned. In the posteroventral corner of the orbit is another group of foramina. The largest, or **trigeminofacial canal,** is for the exit of nerves V and VII. Smaller openings are for cranial nerves III and VI and for blood and lymphatic vessels. A depression in this region represents the point of attachment of the **optic pedicel** (page 478).

The remainder of the skull is called the **visceral skeleton,** or **splanchnocranium** (Fig. 16.5). In the spiny dogfish there are seven cartilaginous

orbital process
palatopterygoquadrate cartilage
labial cartilage
Meckel's cartilage
basihyal
ceratohyal
ceratobranchial
hypobranchial (2)
basibranchial
hypobranchials (3 & 4)
basibranchial
gill rays
pharyngobranchials (4 & 5)
epibranchials

Fig. 16.5. Ventral view of visceral skeleton of *Squalus acanthias.* The hyomandibular cartilage is not shown.

visceral arches which almost completely surround the anterior end of the alimentary canal and support its walls in the gill region. These arches have been modified to perform various functions. The first, or **mandibular, arch** is somewhat complicated in structure. It has been modified on each side, forming dorsal and ventral portions. The dorsal part is called the **palatopterygoquadrate cartilage,** and the ventral portion is known as **Meckel's cartilage.** These form the upper and lower jaws, respectively. The tissue covering these cartilages bears **teeth.** The angle of the mouth on each side lies at the point where palatopterygoquadrate and Meckel's cartilages join each other posterolaterally by a hinge joint. Each palatopterygoquadrate cartilage bears a dorsally directed **palatine,** or **orbital, process** which extends upward along the inner wall of the orbit. The second, or **hyoid, arch** is also made up of dorsal and ventral portions. The dorsal part is the **hyomandibular cartilage.** It is attached to the **otic region** of the cranium. It serves as a suspensor of the jaws since both palatopterygoquadrate and Meckel's cartilages are joined to it by a ligamentous connection. This type of jaw suspension is known as the **hyostylic method** (Fig. 10.24*B*). Ventral to the hyomandibular cartilage is a **ceratohyal cartilage.** A median

basihyal cartilage connects the ceratohyals of the two sides. It supports the tongue. The hyomandibular and ceratohyal cartilages support the first **half gill,** or **hyoid hemibranch.**

The next four visceral arches support the remaining gills. The seventh, or last, visceral arch, however, is not associated with a gill. Each of the last five visceral arches is made up of several cartilages. Their detailed relations are illustrated in Figs. 10.22 and 16.5. The second, third, fourth, fifth, and sixth visceral arches bear slender cartilaginous **gill rays** which are embedded in the septa of the gills to which they give support. No gill rays are associated with the seventh visceral arch.

Appendicular Skeleton

Pectoral Girdle and Fins

The **shoulder,** or **pectoral, girdle** of the spiny dogfish (Fig. 16.6) is a U-shaped cartilage supporting the anterior paired fins and located just pos-

Fig. 16.6.   Anterolateral view of pectoral girdle and fin of *Squalus acanthias.*

terior to the gill region. It is connected to the axial skeleton only indirectly. The girdle consists of a single **scapulocoracoid cartilage.** The **coracoid bar** makes up the ventral portion. A rather long **scapular process** extends dorsally on each side beyond the **glenoid region,** or point of articulation of the pectoral fin. A distinct **suprascapular cartilage** is attached to the free end of each scapular process. A **foramen** for the passage of nerve fibers going to the fin lies just mediad the glenoid articulation.

The base of the pectoral fin proper consists of three cartilages known as **basalia.** The smallest and most lateral is the **propterygium;** next to it lies the large, triangular **mesopterygium;** last is the medial **metapterygium.** Numerous cartilaginous **radialia** extend beyond the basalia. Each is made up of two or three segments. Fibrous, dermal **fin rays (ceratotrichia)** extend beyond the radialia and give support to the main part of the fin.

Pelvic Girdle and Fins

The **pelvic girdle** is of much simpler structure than the pectoral. It is made up of a transverse **ischiopubic bar,** corresponding to the coracoid bar of the pectoral girdle, and a small **iliac process** which projects dorsally to a slight extent. The iliac process is comparable to the scapular process of the pectoral girdle.

Each **pelvic fin** (Fig. 16.7) consists of two **basal cartilages,** or **basalia,** which join the pelvic girdle at the **acetabular region.** They include a short,

FIG. 16.7. Pelvic girdle and fin of male *Squalus acanthias.*

lateral **propterygium** and a long, medial **metapterygium,** extending posteriorly. Numerous **radialia** extend outward from the basalia. In males, the skeleton supporting the clasper is a continuation of the metapterygium and probably represents a modified radial cartilage. Its distal end is divided into several pieces. Dermal **fin rays** support the remainder of the fin.

MUSCULAR SYSTEM

The muscular system of the dogfish is rather simple compared with that of higher vertebrates. Nevertheless, it shows certain marked advances over the rather primitive arrangement observed in cyclostomes.

Trunk Musculature

Removal of the skin from an area at a level just anterior to the first dorsal fin will expose a series of muscle segments which are rather typical of those making up the greater part of the body wall. These are known as **parietal muscles,** as opposed to the **visceral branchial muscles** which are located in the gill region. The parietal muscles are arranged in zigzag bands around the body (Fig. 11.7). Each muscular band is known as a **myotome,** or **myomere.** The myotomes are separated from each other by connective-tissue septa called **myocommata.** Each myotome is made up of many parallel **muscle fibers** which run from one myocomma to the next. A white band of connective tissue, called the **linea alba,** along the midventral line, separates the myotomes of the two sides of the body. A tough **lateral septum,** lying directly beneath the lateral line, separates the myotomes into dorsal **epaxial** and ventral **hypaxial regions.** Further details concerning the parietal muscles of *Squalus acanthias* are given on pages 469 to 470.

Appendicular Musculature

The muscles which move the fins are derived from myotomes of the trunk. They have been modified to such an extent that their basic metameric arrangement has become obscured. The muscles of the pectoral fins are described on pages 479, 487, and 488, and those of the pelvic fins on page 480.

Hypobranchial Musculature

As in cyclostomes, the first few myotomes posterior to the gill region send out portions in an anteroventral direction to form a series of muscles lying ventral to the gill and pericardial regions. These compose the **hypobranchial muscles** (Figs. 11.17 and 11.18), which are discussed in further detail on pages 470 and 488.

Branchial Musculature

Another series of muscles, referred to collectively as the **branchial musculature,** serves to move the visceral arches, gills, and jaws. These are not derived from myotomes but rather from splanchnic mesoderm. Although most muscle which differentiates from splanchnic mesoderm is of the involuntary, smooth type, the branchial muscles are voluntary, striated structures. Their nerve supply, however, reveals their true identity. The branchial muscles of *Squalus acanthias* and their nerve supply are described rather fully on pages 486 to 489.

COELOM

The **body cavity,** or **coelom,** in *Squalus acanthias*, like that of the lamprey, is actually composed of two cavities: the **pleuroperitoneal,** or **abdominal, cavity,** in which the abdominal viscera are located, and the **pericardial cavity,** in which the heart lies. A muscular and membranous partition, the **septum transversum,** almost completely separates the two.

Inside the pleuroperitoneal cavity it will be noted that the body wall is lined with a smooth, shiny membrane, the **parietal peritoneum.** Reflected over the surface of the viscera is the **visceral peritoneum.** The parietal peritoneum and the visceral peritoneum, which covers the alimentary canal, are connected to each other along the middorsal line of the abdominal cavity by the **dorsal mesentery.** This is actually a two-layered sheet, continuous dorsally with the two halves of the parietal peritoneum. The relationships of these layers are indicated in Fig. 16.8. With the differentiation of the alimentary tract into various regions, appropriate names are applied to certain portions of the dorsal mesentery. Thus, the term **meso-gaster** is used to denote the part of the dorsal mesentery which supports the stomach. A **ventral mesentery** connecting the gut with the ventral body wall is usually present during developmental stages. This, however, dis-

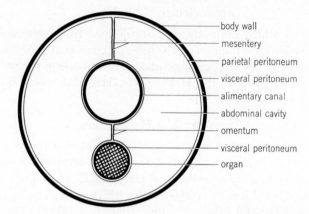

body wall

mesentery

parietal peritoneum

visceral peritoneum

alimentary canal

abdominal cavity

omentum

visceral peritoneum

organ

Fig. 16.8. Diagram showing relationship of a mesentery and an omentum to parietal and visceral peritoneum.

appears before long in most cases. In some regions a part of the alimentary canal is connected to an adjacent organ or part by a mesenterylike band of tissue, called an **omentum.** The names of the various omenta are indicative of the structures which they connect. In the spiny dogfish the following mesenteries and omenta may be noted:

1. The **mesogaster,** suspending the stomach from the middorsal wall of the coelom.
2. The **mesentery proper,** supporting the intestine.
3. The **mesorectum,** supporting the rectal gland and large intestine.
4. The **gastrosplenic omentum,** from stomach to spleen.
5. The **gastrohepatoduodenal omentum,** roughly divided into two parts: (*a*) the **hepatoduodenal** portion, extending from liver to duodenum, and (*b*) the **gastrohepatic** portion, joining stomach to liver. The bile duct and certain blood vessels course through the hepatoduodenal part.

The gonads, which project into the body cavity, are suspended from the dorsal body wall by two-layered membranes similar to the mesentery of the gut. Those supporting the ovaries are called **mesovaria;** those suspending the testes are **mesorchia.**

DIGESTIVE SYSTEM

The **teeth,** previously mentioned, have no roots but are closely united to the tissue covering the jaw cartilages. This is the **acrodont** method of tooth attachment. All the teeth are similar in shape, the dentition, therefore, being of the **homodont** type. The teeth are arranged in rows, each functional tooth having behind it a series of reserve teeth. If a tooth is lost or destroyed, it is replaced by a reserve tooth. Since replacement may take place an indefinite number of times, the dentition is said to be **polyphyo- dont.**

The **mouth, or oral cavity,** lies just within the borders of the jaws. On its floor lies the immovable **tongue,** supported by the cartilaginous **hyoid arch.** Posterior to the mouth is the **pharynx** with six pairs of openings to the outside. The first pair, called the **spiracles,** are rounded openings on the dorsal side. The five pairs of **internal gill slits** open laterally. The **visceral arches,** which support the gills, bear numerous projections, the **gill rakers.** These serve to strain out food particles, which are thus pre- vented from entering the gill chambers.

The posterior end of the pharynx (Fig. 16.9) is constricted and enters the short **esophagus** which leads directly to the **cardiac end** of the **stomach.** This is a large J-shaped structure, the shorter limb of which, known as the **pyloric end,** terminates in a muscular thickening, the **pylorus,** or **pyloric valve.**

The location of the pyloric valve marks the beginning of the **small in- testine.** The first part, called the **duodenum,** is only a short tube which connects posteriorly with the remainder of the small intestine. This is a rather wide, straight structure, the surface of which shows a spiral line which marks the point of attachment of the **spiral valve,** located within this portion of the small intestine.

A finger-shaped **rectal gland** opens into the intestine by means of a duct. Its function is not clear, but it appears to be a mucus-secreting gland. Some authorities homologize the rectal gland with the caecum of higher forms. The point at which the duct of the rectal gland enters the intestine marks the division between **small** and **large intestines.** The narrow large intestine is very short. It opens through the **anus** into the **cloaca.** The terms large and small intestine may seem ambiguous here. They are used, however, because of their homologies with similarly named structures of higher forms in which the large intestine is of greater diameter than the small intestine.

The **liver** of *Squalus acanthias* is very large. It consists of elongated **right** and **left lobes** and a small **median lobe.** The **gall bladder,** easily recognized by its greenish tinge, is embedded along the entire length of the median lobe of the liver on its right side. The **bile duct,** or **ductus choledo- chus,** leaves the gall bladder at its *anterior* end, passes posteriorly through the hepatoduodenal omentum to the dorsal side of the duodenum, and then courses through the duodenal wall for some distance before entering the cavity of the duodenum.

The **pancreas** is a whitish organ composed of two lobes lying in the bend where the stomach joins the duodenum. The **dorsal lobe** is long and nar- row, lies dorsal to the pylorus, and extends as far posteriorly as the spleen. It is connected by a short **isthmus** to the rounded and flattened **ventral**

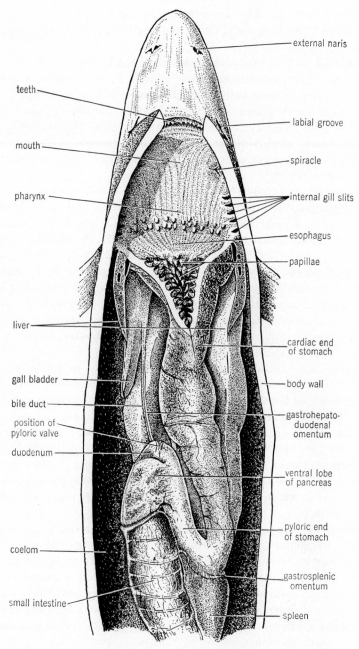

FIG. 16.9. Ventral view of abdominal viscera of *Squalus acanthias*.

lobe, which lies just below the duodenum.   The pancreatic duct is small in diameter.   It leaves the posterior margin of the ventral lobe to enter the wall of the duodenum through which it courses for almost an inch before opening into the duodenal cavity.

Although the **spleen** is an organ belonging to the circulatory system, it forms such a conspicuous part of the abdominal viscera that mention should be made of it here.   It is a dark, triangular structure, loosely attached to the posterior bend of the stomach, where cardiac and pyloric portions join, by means of the **gastrosplenic omentum.**

The lining of the esophagus and upper portion of the stomach, commonly called the **cardiac end,** bears numbers of posteriorly directed **papillae,** which tend to prevent the contents of the stomach from passing back into the pharynx and the mouth.   Farther back, the lining of the stomach is thrown into rather heavy **longitudinal folds.**   The size of the folds varies with the degree to which the stomach is contracted.   In a stomach gorged with food the longitudinal folds may disappear temporarily.

The **spiral valve,** which is located within the small intestine, is arranged in the manner of a spiral staircase (Fig. 5.23).   It serves to retard the passage of food through the small intestine, thus facilitating the completeness of the digestive processes and affording a large surface for secretion of enzymes and for absorption of the products of digestion.   In *Squalus acanthias* the spiral valve takes **14½** turns.

RESPIRATORY SYSTEM

Respiration in the dogfish is carried on entirely by means of vascular **gill lamellae.**   Except for the almost vestigial lamellae of the pseudobranch in the spiracle (page 203), which receives oxygenated blood, the gill lamellae are supplied with unoxygenated blood which takes oxygen from the water bathing them and gives off carbon dioxide.

There are six pairs of **gill pouches,** the **spiracles** being considered as the first pair.   The **gills** are made up of rows of lamellae which radiate from the membranous covering of the cartilaginous bars known as **visceral arches** (Fig. 16.5).   The gills are supported by numerous cartilaginous **gill rays** which extend from the visceral arches into the **interbranchial septa.**   Each interbranchial septum thus contains a single visceral arch at its base with its respective gill rays.   The **hyoid arch** is present anterior to the second gill pouch (first typical gill slit).   It bears gill lamellae on its posterior surface alone.   Just as in the lamprey, such a single set of lamellae, or **half gill,** is termed a **hemibranch.**   An entire gill, or **holobranch,** is made up of two hemibranchs enclosing between them an interbranchial septum.   In *Squalus acanthias* there are nine hemibranchs, but only four holobranchs, on each side.   Thus the last gill pouch bears lamellae only on its anterior wall. Nevertheless, there are five cartilaginous visceral arches posterior to the hyoid arch.   No lamellae are associated with the last visceral arch.   **Gill rakers** project into the pharynx from the inner surfaces of the visceral arches, including the last.

The gill lamellae of the dogfish (Fig. 6.10*A*), unlike those of the lamprey, are closely attached to the interbranchial septa.   However, the septa extend laterally past the outer edges of the lamellae and are continuous with the skin, helping to form the protecting flaps which guard the external openings of the gill pouches.

Water taken into the mouth and pharynx passes through the internal gill slits, bathes the lamellae, and then passes out the external gill slits.   Since the vestigial lamellae in the spiracle receive blood that has already been oxygenated, they form what is sometimes called a **pseudobranch,** or **false gill.**

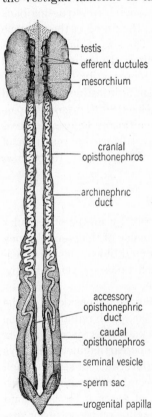

FIG. 16.10.   Ventral view of urogenital organs of mature male dogfish.

*Labels on figure:*
testis
efferent ductules
mesorchium
cranial opisthonephros
archinephric duct
accessory opisthonephric duct
caudal opisthonephros
seminal vesicle
sperm sac
urogenital papilla

UROGENITAL SYSTEM

Since in the dogfish, as in all vertebrates, the organs of reproduction and those for the elimination of nitrogenous wastes are so closely related, they will be considered together.

The Male

The **opisthonephric kidneys** form a pair of long, strap-shaped bodies lying against the dorsal body wall above the parietal peritoneum, on either side of the median line. The dorsal aorta and postcardinal veins lie between them.   The kidneys extend almost the entire length of the body cavity.   Each opisthonephros is composed of an anterior slender portion, the **cranial opisthonephros,** and a posterior, thicker **caudal opisthonephros** (Fig. 16.10).   The posterior part is apparently the chief functional excretory organ of the adult animal.

The **testes** are rather small, pale bodies lying dorsal to the anterior part of the liver, each one being attached to the middorsal body wall by a double peritoneal fold, the **mesorchium.**   A few small delicate ducts, the **efferent ductules,** course through the mesorchium, connecting the tubules of the testis with certain anterior kidney tubules of the cranial opisthonephros.   Since the cranial opisthonephros is concerned more with transportation of sperm than with excretion, it is sometimes referred to as the **epididymis**. It may be homologized with a portion of the epididymis (caput epididymidis) of higher forms.

A large **archinephric duct** extends along the entire ventral face of the kidney. In mature males it is very much convoluted. The tubules of the opisthonephros connect with the archinephric duct. Since it serves for the passage both of urinary wastes and spermatozoa, it has a dual function.

In the region of the caudal opisthonephros the archinephric duct straightens out and is considerably enlarged. This portion is referred to as the **seminal vesicle**. Each seminal vesicle opens at its posterior end into a ventrally situated **sperm sac,** the cavities of the two sperm sacs uniting medially to form the **urogenital sinus**. This is the space inside the small **urogenital papilla** which projects into the cloaca. The urogenital sinus opens to the outside at the tip of the papilla. Seminal vesicles and sperm sac are usually filled with a whitish **seminal fluid** containing great numbers of **spermatozoa**.

Accessory opisthonephric ducts are also present in the caudal opisthonephros. They lie just dorsal to the seminal vesicles and enter the sperm sacs through minute pores near the openings of the seminal vesicles. Two or three of these fine, threadlike ducts are often present.

Squalus acanthias is an ovoviviparous species with internal fertilization. Copulation is accomplished by means of **clasping organs** (Fig. 8.33), which are modifications of the median portions of the pelvic fins of males and used for transport of spermatozoa. Each clasper is provided with a median groove, the middle portion of which actually serves as a closed tube since the edges overlap in the manner of a scroll. The groove connects anteriorly with a **siphon sac** beneath the skin in the posterior, ventral abdominal region. The manner in which siphon sacs and claspers function during copulation is discussed in detail on pages 309 and 310.

The Female

The opisthonephric kidneys of the female are similar to those of the male with narrow cranial portions and larger caudal regions. Since the archinephric duct of the female serves only for the passage of urinary wastes, it is smaller than that of the male. It courses in a straight line along the ventral face of the kidney. An accessory duct is also present in the caudal opisthonephros of the female. The accessory ducts and archinephric ducts course posteriorly to enter the **urinary sinus** within the small, median **urinary papilla** which projects into the cloaca. The accessory duct of the female is very slender and often difficult to find.

The **ovaries** of a mature female are lobulated bodies, located dorsally on either side of the anterior end of the body cavity (Fig. 16.11). The lobulated character of the surface of the ovary is due to the presence of large eggs, located in sacs called **ovarian,** or **Graafian, follicles.** These are not to be observed grossly in young immature females in which the ovaries are small smooth-walled structures. Each ovary is attached to the dorsal body wall by a peritoneal fold, the **mesovarium.** On the midventral line, and near the anterior end of the body, is a folded, rather loose membrane with a single longitudinal slit, the **ostium tubae,** on its *dorsal* aspect. The ostium tubae leads to a short duct which soon divides into right and left portions. These **oviducts, or Müllerian ducts,** extend dorsolaterally and then posteriorly. Vestiges of the ostium and oviducts may even be observed in males of this species. At their anterior ends the oviducts are narrow tubes. A short distance posteriorly they bear a slight enlargement, the **shell gland,** which secretes a thin membrane over the eggs as they pass down the oviduct. The oviducts become narrow again as they pass posteriorly, but then suddenly enlarge to form the **uteri.** The cavity of each uterus opens into the cloaca on either side of the pointed urinary papilla. This region of the cloaca is often termed the **urogenital sinus,** and the openings of the uteri are spoken of as the **genital openings, or pores.** The large mesenterylike membranes which suspend the oviducts and uteri of mature females are known as **mesotubaria.** In immature females the oviducts are slender tubes coursing along the ventral face of the opisthonephric kidneys. No mesotubaria are present during the immature stage.

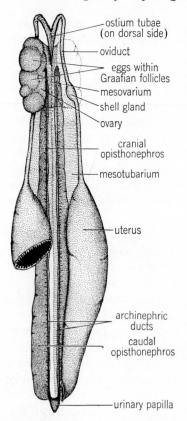

ostium tubae (on dorsal side)

oviduct

eggs within Graafian follicles

mesovarium

shell gland

ovary

cranial opisthonephros

mesotubarium

uterus

archinephric ducts

caudal opisthonephros

urinary papilla

Fig. 16.11. Ventral view of urogenital organs of mature, pregnant female dogfish. One ovary is shown only in outline, and part of one uterus has been removed in order to expose structures lying dorsal to them.

The ovaries are not connected to any duct whatsoever. When the eggs are ripe they break out of the ovarian follicles, pass through the wall of the ovary, and drop into the body cavity. They make their way passively to the anterior end and are engulfed by the ostium tubae. Passage down the right or left oviduct seems to be a matter of chance. Spermatozoa in the upper reaches of the oviduct fertilize the eggs as they pass through this region. Development of the embryos takes place in the uterus. Further details of development are discussed on page 274.

ENDOCRINE SYSTEM

Although several of the endocrine glands of *Squalus acanthias* are too small to lend themselves to gross dissection, a description of these organs is included here for the sake of completeness.

Gonads. The ovaries and testes of the dogfish have already been described in connection with the reproductive system. In addition to their gamete-producing function, the gonads are endocrine glands, secreting **sex hormones** of primary importance in regulating the development and function of the **accessory sex organs** and **secondary sex characters.** The actual endocrine elements of the gonads cannot be discerned in gross dissection. Furthermore, the tissues responsible for secretion of sex hormones in fishes are not known with certainty.

Pancreas. The gross structure of the pancreas was discussed in connection with the digestive system. As in the case of the gonads, the pancreas serves a dual function. In its relation to the digestive tract it functions as an exocrine gland, pouring its secretion, pancreatic juice, which is rich in digestive enzymes, into the duodenal portion of the intestine. The endocrine tissue of the pancreas consists of numerous groups of special cells, the **islands of Langerhans,** scattered throughout its substance. These have no ducts, and the secretion which they produce enters the blood-vascular system directly. It is necessary to study sections of the pancreas under the microscope in order to observe the islands of Langerhans.

Thyroid gland. The thyroid gland of *Squalus acanthias* is a rather dark, flattened mass of tissue lying in the floor of the mouth just posterior to the middle of the cartilage of the lower jaw, or symphysis of the mandible. It is just anterior to the point where the ventral aorta bifurcates into the first pair of afferent branchial arteries.

Parathyroid glands. Some small bodies in the pharyngeal region of the dogfish may represent parathyroid tissue, but this has not been determined with certainty.

Adrenal glands. Two sets of structures in elasmobranchs represent the homologues of the cortical and medullary portions of the adrenal glands of mammals. The first of these, the **interrenal bodies,** homologous with the adrenal cortex of mammals, lie between the posterior ends of the opisthonephric kidneys. In the dogfish they consist of an unpaired mass of tissue which, in the living animal, has a yellowish color. The **chromaffin bodies,** homologous with the adrenal medulla in mammals, are small, paired masses located on the intersegmental branches of the dorsal aorta on either side of the vertebral column. Some of the anterior bodies may be elongated and united. Their close relationship to the sympathetic ganglia is evident in elasmobranchs.

Pituitary gland. The pituitary gland is a conspicuous structure attached to the ventral side of the diencephalon and lying just posterior to the optic chiasma. In the center is the **infundibulum** with its laterally placed **in-**

ferior lobes. A thin, median stalk extends posteriorly from between the inferior lobes and then expands dorsally to form the thin-walled **saccus vasculosus.** This is found only in aquatic animals and may possibly have a sensory function associated with life in the water. Attached to the ventral part of the saccus vasculosus is the small **hypophysis,** or **pituitary gland.** The **posterior lobe** of this structure in the dogfish is diffuse and cannot be identified readily. The pituitary gland lies in a depression of the skull called the **sella turcica.**

Thymus gland. The actual existence of thymus tissue in elasmobranchs is far from clear. Some authorities claim that small masses of tissue derived from all except the first of the pharyngeal pouches represent thymus tissue. It is doubtful whether the thymus possesses an endocrine function.

Pineal body. The **epiphysis,** or **pineal body,** consists of a slender stalk extending upward from the posterior portion of the diencephalon. Whether it is an endocrine organ is doubtful. In specimens of *Squalus acanthias* prepared for dissection by biological supply houses, the pineal body is frequently destroyed when a hole is made in the cranium to permit formaldehyde to enter the cranial cavity in order to harden and preserve the brain.

CIRCULATORY SYSTEM

The Heart

On the ventral side of the head, slightly anterior to the coracoid cartilage of the pectoral girdle, lies the **pericardium.** The **heart** lies within it in the **pericardial cavity.** Dorsal to the posterior end of the heart is a rather large opening which leads into a short passage running along the ventral side of the esophagus for a distance of about 1 in. This is the **pericardioperitoneal canal** connecting pericardial and pleuroperitoneal cavities. The heart itself is made up of a series of parts of which only two, the **atrium** and **ventricle,** are classified as **true chambers.**

The **sinus venosus** is the most posterior portion (Fig. 16.12). It is a thin-walled, triangular structure extending transversely across the posterior wall of the pericardial cavity to which it is attached. On either side, a large **Cuvierian sinus (duct of Cuvier, common cardinal vein)** opens into the sinus venosus. Posteriorly two **hepatic veins** bring blood to the sinus venosus from the liver. The cavity of the sinus venosus connects with the atrium through a **sinuatrial opening** which is guarded by a **sinuatrial valve.** This con-

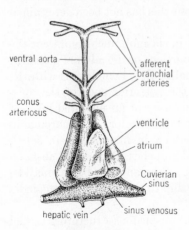

ventral aorta

afferent branchial arteries

conus arteriosus

ventricle

atrium

Cuvierian sinus

hepatic vein   sinus venosus

FIG. 16.12. Ventral view of heart of *Squalus acanthias.*

sists of two folds continuous with the lining of the atrium. They are so arranged that blood may pass freely into the atrium but cannot pass in the opposite direction because of closure of the valve.

The **atrium** is a large, thin-walled sac. It contains but a single cavity which opens ventrally through an **atrioventricular opening** into the ventricle. The opening is guarded by the **atrioventricular valve.**

The **ventricle** is relatively small in size but has heavy muscular walls since it must propel blood to all parts of the body. **Tendinous cords** within the ventricle are attached to the opposite walls. They prevent the ventricle from expanding beyond its capacity.

The cavity of the ventricle is continuous with that of the **conus arteriosus.** This is a short, muscular tube, the cavity of which is triangular in cross section. Inside the conus arteriosus are three sets of **semilunar valves,** each consisting of three pocketlike structures. The anterior set is located at the front of the conus, and its three components are larger than those of the others (Fig. 12.10). Anterior to the conus arteriosus, and continuous with it, is the **ventral aorta** from which arise **afferent branchial arteries** which distribute blood to the gills. The ventral aorta bifurcates at its anterior end a short distance posterior to the mandibular arch. It should be recalled that the thyroid gland lies in this vicinity.

Blood Vessels

It already has been emphasized that blood vessels which carry blood away from the heart are called **arteries** and those bringing it back to the heart are called **veins.** Whether a vessel carries oxygenated or unoxygenated blood has nothing to do with the terminology. Arteries are stronger, and their walls are more muscular than veins. Veins frequently have valves present within them which prevent a backward flow of blood. In the dogfish many of the veins are primitive structures and are more properly called **sinuses.** Arteries and veins are connected by microscopic **capillaries.**

ARTERIAL SYSTEM

Blood passes through the parts of the heart in the following order: sinus venosus, atrium, ventricle, conus arteriosus. When it enters the ventral aorta from the conus arteriosus it has entered the arterial system.

Five pairs of **afferent branchial arteries** leave the ventral aorta. The first two arise from a common trunk formed on each side by the bifurcation of the ventral aorta. The more anterior of the two supplies the hyoid hemibranch, the second going to the first holobranch and supplying the second and third hemibranchs. The third afferent branchial artery comes off the ventral aorta at a point approximately one-third of the distance from the conus. It supplies the second holobranch composed of hemibranchs 4 and 5. The last two afferent branchial arteries arise from the ventral aorta near its junction with the conus. Sometimes they arise independently, but they frequently spring from a common trunk. These arteries are more difficult to find than the others, since they are embedded in the muscular layer just dorsal and lateral to the anterior end of the conus. They supply the third and fourth holobranchs, respectively. Since no gill lamellae are present on the posterior wall of the last gill pouch, no vessel from the ventral aorta supplies this region.

Within the gill lamellae the afferent branchial arteries branch into minute, thin-walled capillaries. It is here that the blood takes oxygen from the water and gives off carbon dioxide. The capillaries within the lamellae of a given hemibranch combine to form a single vessel. This is called a **pretrematic** or **posttrematic artery,** depending upon whether the hemibranch is on the anterior or posterior wall of the **gill pouch.** In this manner each interbranchial septum is found to carry both a pretrematic and a posttrematic artery (Fig. 16.13). Several large **cross connections** are present between these vessels. The pretrematic artery is of smaller caliber than the posttrematic artery. The pretrematic and posttrematic arteries draining each *gill pouch* unite to form an **efferent branchial artery.** There are four pairs of efferent branchial arteries located on the roof of the pharynx just above the lining mucous membrane. Blood in the pretrematic artery draining the ninth hemibranch passes entirely through cross connections into the posttrematic branch of the fourth efferent branchial artery.

The efferent branchial arteries bend posteriorly and then unite in the dorsal midline to form the large **dorsal aorta.** This courses straight backward to the tail where it is continued as the **caudal artery.** Numerous paired and unpaired arteries come from the dorsal aorta. The first paired arteries are the **subclavians,** which arise from the aorta between the junction of the third and fourth pairs of efferent branchial arteries (Fig. 16.13). Each subclavian gives off a small **lateral artery,** which passes posteriorly along the body underneath the lateral line. This artery lies close to the skin. A **ventrolateral artery** comes from the subclavian at a level about halfway between the lateral line and midventral line and extends posteriorly. Beyond the point where the ventrolateral artery comes off, the subclavian continues into the pectoral fin as the **brachial artery.**

Numerous paired **parietal arteries** arise along the whole length of the aorta to supply the body wall. Many small **renal arteries** likewise arise from the aorta in the region of the opisthonephric kidneys to supply these structures with oxygenated blood. At the level of the pelvic fins a pair of **iliac arteries** comes from the aorta. A branch from each iliac extends anteriorly to anastomose with the ventrolateral artery mentioned above.

Four unpaired arteries (Fig. 16.14) arise from the dorsal aorta to supply the abdominal viscera. The first and largest of these is the **coeliac artery,** which comes from the aorta a short distance posterior to the subclavian arteries at a level with the anterior end of the body cavity. Near its origin the coeliac gives off branches which supply the esophagus, cardiac end of the stomach, and the gonads. It then continues for some distance before it again branches. The coeliac artery enters the gastrohepatic omentum and

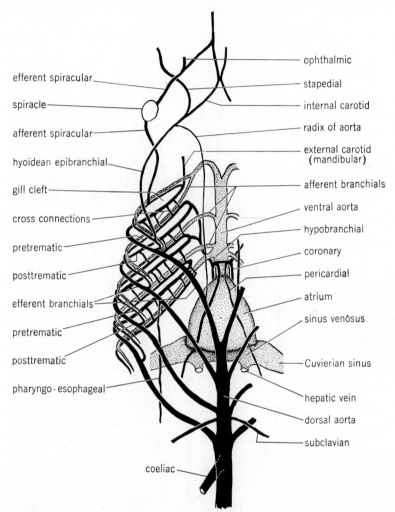

Fig. 16.13. Diagram showing arteries in the left gill region of dogfish as seen from the dorsal side. The length of the arteries at the anterior end has been exaggerated for the sake of clarity. Capillary connections between afferent and efferent arteries have been omitted. (*Modified from Daniel.*)

branches into three main arteries: (1) the **gastric,** which soon divides into **dorsal** and **ventral branches** supplying the stomach, (2) the small **hepatic artery,** which courses anteriorly along the bile duct to supply the liver, (3) the large **pancreaticomesenteric artery,** which passes along the dorsal side of the pyloric valve, giving off branches to the pyloric region of the stomach and to the pancreas. A **duodenal branch** supplies the duodenum, but the main vessel continues along the right side of the small intestine, where it is known as the **anterior intestinal artery.** This vessel

Fig. 16.14. Diagram showing portion of the dorsal aorta and its unpaired branches which supply the viscera of the dogfish, ventral view.

gives off branches corresponding to the places of attachment of the spiral valve.

The second and third unpaired arteries arise from the aorta close together just posterior to the level of the spleen. The more anterior is the **superior mesenteric artery,** which courses along the left side of the small intestine as the **posterior intestinal artery** and gives off branches at the points of attachment of the spiral valve. The **gastrosplenic artery** lies just posterior the point of origin of the superior mesenteric. It crosses the latter and extends anteriorly to supply the spleen and lower end of the stomach. The last unpaired branch of the aorta is the **inferior mesenteric artery,** which arises somewhat anterior to the iliac arteries to supply the rectal gland. Occasionally two inferior mesenteric arteries are encountered.

The arteries supplying the head region (Fig. 16.13) are more complex in their arrangement. From about the middle of the first pretrematic artery arises a large **afferent spiracular artery** which courses dorsally under the skin to supply the pseudobranch, or rudimentary gill lamellae, of the spiracle. This artery may best be found by removing the skin from an area immediately posterior to the spiracle where it occupies a rather superficial position. For some reason or other the afferent spiracular arteries often remain uninjected. An **efferent spiracular (spiracular epibranchial) artery** carries blood away from the spiracle. It courses in an anteromedial direction, giving off an **ophthalmic (optic) artery** to the eyeball, and then joins the **internal carotid artery,** described below.

From the *ventral* end of the first efferent branchial loop, or the point where the pretrematic and posttrematic branches of the first efferent branchial artery join each other ventrally, a small vessel arises and passes for a short distance forward in the lower jaw. This is the **external carotid artery,** sometimes referred to as the **mandibular artery.**

Just before the pretrematic and posttrematic branches of the first efferent branchial artery unite *dorsally*, the pretrematic artery gives off a conspicuous **hyoidean epibranchial artery.** This passes toward the midline. It is joined by a slender vessel, the **radix of the aorta,** which springs from the first efferent branchial artery near its junction with the dorsal aorta. Soon after receiving the radix the hyoidean epibranchial gives off a branch, the **stapedial artery,** which passes to the region where the hyomandibular cartilage (future stapes) joins the otic region of the cranium. The continuation of the hyoidean epibranchial is the **internal carotid artery.** The internal carotids of the two sides come together in the midline, penetrate the skull through a foramen, and then diverge. Each internal carotid is soon joined by the efferent spiracular artery, mentioned above, and continues forward to the brain.

On each side of the roof of the mouth and pharynx is a **pharyngo-esophageal artery.** It arises from the second efferent branchial artery, not far from the point where the pretrematic and posttrematic branches join, and supplies the dorsal region of the pharynx and esophagus.

From the ventral ends of the second and third efferent branchial loops, where pretrematic and posttrematic arteries join, vessels are given off which soon unite to form a **hypobranchial artery** on each side. There is some variation in this region among different specimens. Each hypobranchial courses posteriorly, ventral to the pharynx and visceral arches. As it reaches the level of the anterior end of the conus arteriosus, it divides into two branches. The more dorsal branch, the **pericardial artery,** courses through the pericardium, supplying its walls, and continues on to the esophagus and adjacent tissues. The proximal parts of the pericardial arteries of the two sides are united dorsal to the conus arteriosus by a transverse vessel. The ventral branch of the hypobranchial artery on each side is the **coronary artery** which supplies the wall of the ventricle of the heart itself.

Venous System

Systemic veins. All the systemic veins of the dogfish ultimately drain into the **Cuvierian sinuses** which in turn enter the sinus venosus. The systemic veins are, for the most part, large spaces in the tissues without definite walls. They are more properly called **sinuses.**

inferior jugular
anterior cardinal
sinus venosus
Cuvierian sinus
subclavian
hepatic
esophageal
postcardinal sinus
genital sinus
postcardinal
lateral
efferent renal
afferent renal
renal portal
iliac
cloacal
caudal

Fig. 16.15. Diagram of systemic veins and renal portal system of dogfish, ventral view.

From the head region on each side come two main sinuses: a smaller, median, ventral, **inferior jugular sinus** and a large, dorsolateral **anterior cardinal sinus** (Fig. 16.15). The inferior jugular drains blood from the floor of the mouth, the region ventral to the visceral arches, and the pericardial region. The anterior cardinal sinus lies dorsal to the visceral arches. It receives blood from the **postorbital sinus** which lies between the posterior border of the eye and the first hemibranch. The postorbital sinus is in communication with the large **orbital sinus** which encircles the eye. An **interorbital canal,** which lies in the floor of the skull, connects the posterior borders of the two orbital sinuses. It does not lend itself well to dissection. A **hyoidean sinus,** located just in front of the hyoidean hemibranch, connects the anterior cardinal and inferior jugular sinuses.

Between the kidneys lies a pair of **postcardinal veins** which receive

blood from the **efferent renal veins** in the kidneys. Each postcardinal
courses straight forward, receiving small intersegmental **parietal veins** from
between the myotomes en route, to enter a very large, saclike, **postcardinal
sinus.** Each postcardinal sinus enters the posterior part of the Cuvierian
sinus on its respective side through a large opening. The postcardinal
sinuses communicate with each other by means of a large aperture. The
anterior cardinal sinus on each side opens posteriorly into the postcardinal sinus, the point of junction marking the beginning of the Cuvierian
sinus. A large **genital sinus,** which drains the gonad on each side, communicates with the postcardinal sinus by means of **genital** (ovarian or spermatic) **veins** along its ventrolateral aspect.

On the inner surface of the body wall on either side a large **lateral vein**
courses anteriorly, receiving small intersegmental **parietal veins** from between the myotomes along its length. Each lateral vein is formed posteriorly by the union of a **cloacal vein,** from the cloacal region, and an **iliac
vein,** from the pelvic fin. The cloacal veins from the two sides join each
other in the midline. Anteriorly each lateral vein is joined by a **brachial
vein** from the pectoral fin which receives a **subscapular branch** from the
pectoral girdle. The vessel formed by the union of brachial and lateral
veins is the **subclavian vein.** This joins the Cuvierian sinus at about the
level where the inferior jugular vein enters.

Portal systems. A portal system of veins is one which begins in capillaries and again breaks up into capillaries before the blood which it contains reaches the heart. In *Squalus acanthias* there are two portal systems,
the renal portal and the hepatic portal.

Renal portal system. In the renal portal system the venous blood collected from the tail passes through a network of capillaries in the opisthonephric kidneys. Blood in the tail is collected by a **caudal vein** which
lies ventral to the caudal artery in the hemal arch. The two are separated
by a septum. At about the middle of the cloacal region the caudal vein
divides into right and left **renal portal sinuses** (Fig. 16.15). These course
forward dorsolateral to the opisthonephric kidneys, giving off small **afferent renal veins** to these structures. **Efferent renal veins,** which join the
postcardinal veins, collect the blood after it has passed through the capillaries in the kidneys.

Hepatic portal system. The hepatic portal system of veins drains the
various parts of the digestive tract and the spleen. The hepatic portal vein
of the dogfish is formed by the converging of four vessels (Fig. 16.16). The
first of these is the very small **duodenal vein,** often poorly injected. It
courses along the lower end of the bile duct, draining the duodenum, anterior part of the small intestine, and the ventral lobe of the pancreas. A
large **gastric vein** on the left drains the main part of the stomach by means
of **dorsal** and **ventral gastric branches.** The large **lienomesenteric vein**
drains the rectal gland and the left side of the small intestine where it is

known as the **posterior intestinal vein.** This vessel receives branches from the places of attachment of the spiral valve. It is joined by a **posterior lienogastric vein (posterior splenic)** from the posterior end of the spleen and

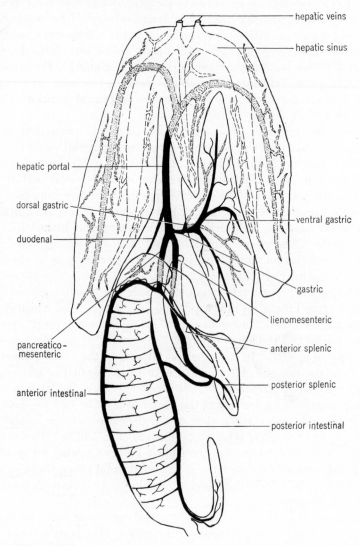

Fig. 16.16. Diagram of hepatic portal vein and its tributaries in *Squalus acanthias*, ventral view.

adjacent stomach region. The main part of the lienomesenteric vein passes through the dorsal lobe of the pancreas, receiving **pancreatic veins** en route. The large **pancreaticomesenteric vein** is formed by an **anterior intestinal vein** draining the right side of the small intestine and points of attachment of the spiral valve and an **anterior lienogastric vein (anterior splenic)** from the anterior end of the spleen and gastrosplenic omentum.

NERVOUS SYSTEM

Dorsal Aspect of Brain (Fig. 16.17)

The brain of *Squalus acanthias* is made up of three main parts: the **forebrain, or prosencephalon**; the **midbrain, or mesencephalon**; and the **hindbrain, or rhombencephalon.**

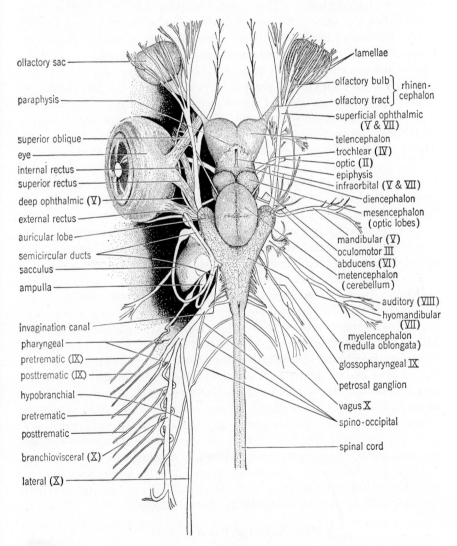

olfactory sac

paraphysis

superior oblique
eye
internal rectus
superior rectus
deep ophthalmic (V)
external rectus
auricular lobe
semicircular ducts
sacculus
ampulla

invagination canal
pharyngeal
pretrematic (IX)
posttrematic (IX)
hypobranchial
pretrematic
posttrematic
branchiovisceral (X)
lateral (X)

lamellae
olfactory bulb ⎫
olfactory tract ⎰ rhinen-cephalon
superficial ophthalmic (V & VII)
telencephalon
trochlear (IV)
optic (II)
epiphysis
infraorbital (V & VII)
diencephalon
mesencephalon (optic lobes)
mandibular (V)
oculomotor III
abducens (VI)
metencephalon (cerebellum)
auditory (VIII)
hyomandibular (VII)
myelencephalon (medulla oblongata)
glossopharyngeal IX
petrosal ganglion
vagus X
spino-occipital
spinal cord

FIG. 16.17. Dorsal view of brain, sense organs, and cranial nerves of *Squalus acanthias.*

The prosencephalon has two main divisions. The first is the **telenceph-alon,** the anterior part of which is the **rhinencephalon,** composed of **ol-factory lobes.** These lie immediately behind the **olfactory sacs.** The cavity of each olfactory sac opens to the outside through the **nostril,** or **naris.** Its inner wall contains a number of folds called **lamellae.** The rhinencephalon on each side is composed of an **olfactory bulb,** connected at its anterior end with the olfactory sac, and a narrow **olfactory tract,** which extends pos-teriorly to the cerebral hemisphere. The bulb and tract together con-stitute the **olfactory lobe.** The paired **cerebral hemispheres** make up the rest of the telencephalon. The rounded anterior portion of each is some-times called the olfactory lobe. Posterior to the telencephalon lies the second portion of the forebrain, the **diencephalon,** or **thalamencephalon.** It is roofed over by a thin vascular membrane, the **tela choroidea.** Vascular folds of the tela choroidea extend into the cavity, or third ventricle, below, forming the **anterior choroid plexus.** A flattened fold, the **paraphysis,** an-terior to the anterior choroid plexus, extends dorsally, overlapping the cerebral hemispheres to some extent. Its function is unknown. From the posterior dorsal portion of the diencephalon a slender stalk extends upward. This is the **pineal body,** or **epiphysis.** In specimens secured from biological supply houses an opening has been made deliberately on the top of the head to permit formaldehyde to enter the cranial cavity in order to harden and preserve the brain. If this has been done the pineal body has probably been destroyed.

The **mesencephalon** comes next in order behind the diencephalon. Its roof is called the **optic tectum.** This appears in the form of two rounded **optic lobes,** or **corpora bigemina,** which are centers for the visual sense.

The anterior part of the rhombencephalon is referred to as the **meten-cephalon.** Its dorsal part consists of a rather large, oval-shaped structure, the **cerebellum.** This partially overlaps the mesencephalon in front. The remaining portion of the hindbrain, which is also partly covered by the cere-bellum, is the **myelencephalon,** or **medulla oblongata.** A pair of prominent, irregular projections, the **auricular lobes (restiform bodies),** is present at the anterior end of the medulla oblongata on the dorsal side. These are actually parts of the metencephalon although several authors regard them as parts of the medulla oblongata. They serve as equilibratory nerve cen-ters, correlating muscular movements in relation to impulses arising in sen-sory nerves connected with the inner ears. Posteriorly the myelencephalon tapers down to connect with the **spinal cord,** or **myelon,** which extends back to the tail. The medulla oblongata is roofed over by a thin, vascular tela choroidea. Folds of the tela choroidea extend into the cavity, or fourth ventricle, below, to form the **posterior choroid plexus.**

Ventral Aspect of Brain (Fig. 16.18)

The ventral aspect of the brain of *Squalus acanthias* should not be studied by the student until after the cranial nerves have been identified and traced.   The brain may then be removed and its ventral surface examined.

Certain conspicuous features mark the ventral side of the brain, particularly in the region of the diencephalon.   The **optic chiasma** is an

olfactory sac
olfactory bulb
olfactory tract
deep ophthalmic (Ⅴ)
eye
inferior oblique
optic chiasma
inferior rectus
optic lobe
oculomotor (Ⅲ)
external rectus
abducens (Ⅵ)
ampullae

sacculus

semicircular ducts
petrosal ganglion (Ⅸ)

glossopharyngeal (Ⅸ)

pharyngeal

pretrematic (Ⅸ)

posttrematic (Ⅸ)

pretrematic

posttrematic

superficial ophthalmic (Ⅴ & Ⅶ)
deep ophthalmic (Ⅴ)
telencephalon (cerebral hemisphere)
trochlear Ⅳ
infraorbital (Ⅴ & Ⅶ)
optic Ⅱ
lobi inferiores
infundibulum
hypophysis   } hypothalmus
saccus vasculosus

mandibular (Ⅴ)
auditory (Ⅷ)
myelencephalon
(medulla oblongata)
hyomandibular (Ⅶ)

vagus Ⅹ
occipital
hypobranchial
spinal nerves
spinal cord

branchiovisceral (Ⅹ)

lateral (Ⅹ)

FIG. 16.18.   Ventral view of brain, sense organs, and cranial nerves of *Squalus acanthias*.

X-shaped structure where the two **optic nerves** cross each other on the ventral side of the diencephalon.   Fibers from the chiasma pass posteriorly and dorsally to enter the optic lobes.   They form the **optic tracts.**   Posterior to the chiasma the ventral portion of the diencephalon forms a large projection, the **hypothalamus.**   In its center is the **infundibulum** with its **inferior lobes** on either side.   The narrow infundibulum, which appears as a thin, median stalk, extends posteriorly between the inferior lobes and expands on its dorsal side to form a saclike structure, the **saccus vasculosus.**   The ventral part of the saccus vasculosus is attached to the small **hypophysis,** or **pituitary gland,** which often breaks off and remains in the **sella turcica** of the skull when the brain is removed.

The points of origin of two pairs of slender cranial nerves, the **oculomotor (III)** and **abducens (VI)** arising from the ventral side of the brain, may be clearly seen on the ventral aspect. The oculomotor nerves emerge from the ventral part of the mesencephalon posterior to the hypothalamus and pass laterally. The abducens nerves emerge from the ventral side of the medulla oblongata near the median line, coursing in an anterolateral direction.

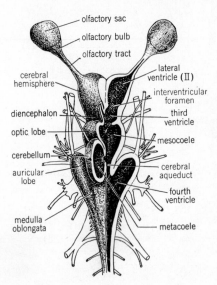

Fig. 16.19. Dorsal view of brain of dog-fish with part of wall removed to show the cavities of the brain.

Cavities of Brain and Spinal Cord

In the region of the brain the original cavity of the hollow dorsal nerve cord is conspicuously modified to form the large cavities, or **ventricles,** of the brain (Fig. 16.19). The **lateral,** or **first** and **second,** **ventricles** are in the telencephalon. They extend forward as narrow channels through the olfactory tracts into the olfactory bulbs. Posteriorly each lateral ventricle opens by an **interventricular foramen (foramen of Monro)** into the **third ventricle,** which is the cavity within the diencephalon. The third ventricle, as previously noted, is covered by a tela choroidea, vascular folds of which make up the anterior choroid plexus. The cavity within the medulla oblongata is the **fourth ventricle.** It, also, is covered by a tela choroidea, folds of which form the posterior choroid plexus. In higher vertebrates a narrow canal, the **cerebral aqueduct (aqueduct of Sylvius),** connects the third and fourth ventricles. In *Squalus acanthias* the cerebral aqueduct is much expanded on either side, forming large cavities in the optic lobes. These are known as the **optic ventricles,** or, together, as the **mesocoele.** A large cavity in the cerebellum of the dogfish is called the **metacoele.** It is actually a dorsal continuation of the fourth ventricle. The portion of the fourth ventricle in the medulla oblongata is often referred to as the **myelocoele.** It is continuous posteriorly with the minute **central canal** of the spinal cord.

Cranial Nerves (Figs. 16.17 and 16.18)

Although it is usually stated that there are ten **cranial nerves** in the dogfish, there are actually *eleven.* The most anterior of these, the **terminal**

nerve (0), is often omitted from descriptions. The distribution of the
cranial nerves is of interest since it is similar to that of higher vertebrates
except for certain portions which are associated with the aquatic mode of
life.

The **terminal nerve (0)** in *Squalus acanthias* is found with some difficulty.
It is a very small nerve coursing along the entire medial side of the olfactory
tract. Although a pair of terminal nerves has been found in representatives
of all classes of vertebrates except cyclostomes and birds, it is best developed in the elasmobranch fishes. It is a sensory nerve bearing one or more
ganglia. Its function is not clear.

The **olfactory nerve (I)** on each side is composed of a great number of
separate fibers, so small that they can scarcely be seen by the unaided eye.
In their aggregate they are known as the olfactory nerve. The fibers are
located in the lamellae of the olfactory sac and terminate in the olfactory
bulb, mentioned previously. The olfactory nerve is a **somatic sensory
nerve.**

The **optic nerve (II)** is a large white cord which has its origin in the retina
of the eye. It passes through the various coats of the eye to the ventral
side of the diencephalon. The fibers of each optic nerve cross to the opposite side of the brain. In doing so they form an X-shaped figure, the
optic chiasma. The fibers terminate in the optic lobes. The term **optic
tract** is the name given to the portion of the nerve between the chiasma and
the optic lobe. The optic nerve is generally referred to as a **special somatic
sensory nerve.** Since the retina of the eye is derived in the embryo from a
lateral extension of the diencephalon, the optic nerve really should not be
included in the category of cranial nerves. Unlike other cranial nerves it
grows from one part of the brain to another and thus is actually a **fiber
tract** of the brain.

The **oculomotor nerve (III)** is usually thought of as a **somatic motor
nerve.** Actually it carries some **preganglionic autonomic fibers** as well as a
few **somatic sensory proprioceptive fibers.** The nerve arises from the ventral surface of the mesencephalon. It passes into the orbit, where it divides
into four branches going to the inferior oblique and superior, inferior, and
internal rectus eye muscles. Its distribution is indicated in Fig. 11.11. The
autonomic fibers enter the eyeball via a small **ciliary nerve.**

The **trochlear nerve (IV)** is primarily a **somatic motor nerve** which, like
the oculomotor, bears a few **proprioceptive somatic sensory fibers.** It
emerges from the posterodorsal side of the mesencephalon where that part
of the brain joins the cerebellum. The trochlear nerve passes into the orbit
to innervate the superior oblique eye muscle.

The **trigeminal nerve (V)** is a **mixed** nerve, being composed of **somatic
sensory** and **visceral motor fibers.** It comes from the lateral side of the
medulla oblongata along with the seventh and eight cranial nerves. These
nerves at their bases are inextricably fused. The trigeminal nerve has three

main branches: **ophthalmic, mandibular,** and **maxillary.** The ophthalmic branch is divided into **superficial** and **deep** portions.

The fibers of the **superficial ophthalmic** and those of the similarly named branch of nerve VII are inseparably intermingled. They pass forward along the inner wall of the eye socket, or orbit, above the muscles of the eyeball. The trigeminal nerve supplies sensory fibers to the skin. The facial fibers innervate the ampullae of Lorenzini and pores of the lateral-line system on the dorsal surface of the snout. The superficial ophthalmic nerve bears only **somatic sensory fibers.**

The **deep ophthalmic (profundus)** passes between the superior and external rectus muscles, sending a small **ciliary branch** to the eye, and then continues forward along the inner surface of the eyeball. It leaves the orbit through a foramen and joins the superficial ophthalmic branch, being distributed along with it to the dorsal and lateral surfaces of the snout. The deep ophthalmic is entirely a **somatic sensory nerve.**

The **mandibular branch** of the trigeminal nerve runs along the posterior wall of the orbit. It passes ventrally and innervates the skin of the lower jaw as well as the muscles of the mandibular arch, including the levator maxillae, adductor mandibulae, and the first superficial ventral constrictor. It contains both **somatic sensory** and **visceral motor fibers.**

The fibers of the **maxillary branch** run together with those of the **buccal branch of nerve VII.** Together they form the large **somatic sensory infra-orbital nerve,** a broad white band extending forward on the floor of the orbit. Near the anterior part of the orbit the infraorbital nerve divides into three main branches. The smallest and most lateral of these passes to the skin lateral and anterior to the eye. The largest and most medial branch courses forward toward the tip of the snout. The middle branch, composed of numerous rather short fibers, passes to the angle of the mouth. The easiest way to identify these branches is to remove the skin from the ventral surface of the snout and to note their superficial distribution. The fibers of the maxillary nerve innervate the skin on the ventral side of the snout. Those of the buccal supply the infraorbital lateral-line canal and ampullae of Lorenzini in the same region.

The trigeminal nerve should be thought of as the nerve of the mandibular, or first visceral, arch, from which both upper and lower jaws are derived. The large **Gasserian ganglion** of the trigeminal nerve lies in the mass of tissue from which the trigeminal, facial, and auditory nerves arise lateral to the medulla oblongata.

The **abducens nerve (VI),** like the other nerves going to the eye muscles, is a **somatic motor nerve** carrying a few **proprioceptive somatic sensory fibers.** It emerges from the ventral side of the medulla oblongata and runs forward and laterally to enter the orbit where it supplies the external rectus eye muscle.

The **facial nerve (VII),** part of which in its distribution is closely associated with the trigeminal nerve, contains **somatic sensory, visceral sensory,** and **visceral motor fibers.** It has three main branches, the first two of which are composed only of somatic sensory fibers supplying the lateral-line system and ampullae of Lorenzini. The **superficial ophthalmic branch,** as previously noted, courses with the similarly named branch of nerve V. The **buccal branch,** together with the maxillary branch of nerve V, forms the large **infraorbital nerve.** These branches of the seventh nerve are not present in higher vertebrates, having disappeared in the course of evolution with emergence from water to life on land. A third branch, the **hyomandibular,** which contains fibers of the facial nerve alone, bears a **geniculate ganglion** at its base. It is the nerve of the second, or hyoid, arch, distributed to the side of the head immediately behind the spiracle. It is a mixed nerve supplying somatic sensory fibers to the mandibular and hyomandibular lateral-line canals as well as to the ampullae of Lorenzini in this region, and visceral motor fibers to the superficial constrictor muscles of the hyoid arch. Visceral sensory fibers are also supplied to the lining of the mouth by means of a small **palatine branch** which comes from the geniculate ganglion. It passes to the roof of the mouth, giving off a branch to the spiracle.

The **auditory nerve (VIII),** which is purely **somatic sensory,** connects to the lateral side of the medulla oblongata along with the roots of nerves V and VII. It is a short nerve extending from the internal ear to the brain. Branches come from the ampullae of the semicircular ducts (page 730) as well as from sacculus and utriculus.

The **glossopharyngeal nerve (IX)** is a mixed nerve emerging from the lateral side of the medulla oblongata under the inner ear. It bears a swollen **petrosal ganglion** a short distance from the brain. Beyond the ganglion it divides into three main branches. The first, or **pretrematic (hyoid), branch** is a **visceral sensory nerve** supplying the first hemibranch. The second, or **posttrematic (branchial), branch** is composed of **visceral sensory** and **visceral motor fibers.** The sensory fibers are distributed to the second hemibranch, and the motor fibers to the muscles associated with the third visceral arch. The third, or **pharyngeal, branch,** containing **visceral sensory fibers** alone, goes to the lining of the pharynx. Another small branch, sometimes called the **supratemporal nerve** and composed of **somatic sensory fibers,** passes from the petrosal ganglion through the auditory capsule to the supratemporal lateral-line canal and anterior part of the lateral line proper. The glossopharyngeal is considered to be the most typical of the cranial nerves.

The **vagus nerve (X)** is a **mixed** nerve, consisting of a large trunk which arises from the lateral edge of the medulla oblongata by a number of roots. The vagus soon gives off a large, **somatic sensory lateral (dorsal) branch** which passes under the main lateral-line canal to the tail. The vagus proper continues as the **branchiovisceral nerve** to supply the remaining four gill pouches and the viscera. Four **branchial branches** come off this nerve to supply the last four visceral pouches. They course across the floor of the anterior cardinal sinus. Each branchial branch bears a small ganglion from which arise three branches: a small, **visceral sensory pharyngeal branch,** which goes to the lining of the pharynx; an anterior, **visceral sensory pretrematic branch,** supplying the anterior hemibranch of the gill pouch; and a **posttrematic branch,** composed of both **visceral sensory** and **visceral motor fibers** passing to the posterior hemibranch. The visceral motor fibers of the posttrematic branches of the vagus supply the muscles of the fourth to the seventh visceral arches in succession. Since no hemibranch is present on the posterior wall of the last gill pouch, the last posttrematic passes to muscles in that region. The (branchio) visceral branch continues posteriorly and more deeply to enter the body cavity where it sends branches to the heart, digestive tract, and other viscera.

Spinal Nerves

Paired, metameric **spinal nerves** come from the spinal cord at regular intervals along its entire length. Each spinal nerve arises from the cord by two **roots, dorsal** and **ventral.** In such lower forms as *Squalus acanthias* the dorsal root carries **somatic sensory, visceral sensory,** and **visceral motor fibers**; the ventral root is composed of both **somatic motor** and **visceral motor fibers.** The ventral root passes through a foramen in the cartilaginous neural arch of the corresponding vertebra and is located somewhat anterior to the dorsal root which passes through the intercalary plate. The two roots then join to form a spinal nerve. Between the point of junction and the foramen through which it emerges, the dorsal root bears a swelling, the **dorsal root ganglion.**

In the region of the *pectoral fin* the third, fourth, fifth, and sixth spinal nerves extend posteriorly and ventrally. When they reach the level of the pectoral girdle they join each other by means of cross connections to form the **cervicobrachial plexus** from which branches go to the fins. The seventh to eleventh spinal nerves pass to the level of the fin and then branch. One branch goes to the muscles of the ventral body wall, and the other to the fin.

Each *pelvic fin* is supplied by nine or ten spinal nerves. The most posterior ones may be connected by cross-branches to form the **lumbosacral plexus.**

Between the first typical spinal nerve and the vagus on each side, two or three small roots arise from the medulla oblongata. These are referred to as the **spino-occipital nerves.** Some authorities are of the opinion that they represent the ventral roots of certain anterior spinal nerves the dorsal roots of which have been taken over by, and incorporated within, the vagus nerve. The roots unite to form the **occipital nerve.** This joins the vagus for a short distance and then diverges from it. It is soon joined by the first two spinal nerves. The **hypobranchial nerve,** formed by their union, crosses over the branchiovisceral branch of the vagus and then turns ventrally to supply muscles in the floor of the mouth. It is possible that the hypobranchial nerve is homologous with the twelfth cranial nerve (hypoglossal nerve) of more advanced vertebrates.

Peripheral Autonomic Nervous System

The term *peripheral nervous system* is applied to the nerves and ganglia which are connected with the brain and spinal cord. We have spoken of these as cranial and spinal nerves. Parts of the peripheral nervous system are composed of **autonomic fibers** which are **motor fibers** distributed to those parts of the body under involuntary control. This portion of the peripheral nervous system is often referred to as the **peripheral autonomic system**. Its fibers pass to the heart and to smooth muscles and glands all over the body. In higher forms it has been clearly shown that this part of the nervous system is subdivided functionally and anatomically into **sympathetic** and **parasympathetic portions**. These elicit opposite responses. The hypothalamic region of the diencephalon is believed to be the center of control of the autonomic fibers. It is not practicable for the student to make a gross study of the peripheral autonomic fibers of the dogfish. Investigations have shown that both sympathetic and parasympathetic elements are present, but they do not show complexities as do those of higher forms. The sympathetic portion seems to be confined to the abdominal region, there being no cranial sympathetic nerve fibers. It is represented anteriorly by a series of consecutive **sympathetic ganglia** on either side of the middorsal line of the pleuroperitoneal cavity, embedded in the dorsal wall of the postcardinal sinus and anterior end of the opisthonephric kidney. The ganglia form connections with spinal nerves and are in close association with the chromaffin bodies. The fibers associated with these ganglia have a rather diffuse arrangement, and no true, longitudinal, sympathetic trunks are evident. Preganglionic parasympathetic fibers are present in the oculomotor (III), facial (VII), glossopharyngeal (IX), and vagus (X) nerves. Those of the vagus pass to esophagus and stomach but do not seem to go to the intestine or urogenital organs.

SENSE ORGANS

In addition to such major sense organs as the olfactory apparatus, eye, and ear, fishes possess certain sense organs the functions of which seem to be associated with the aquatic mode of life. These include the lateral-line system and the ampullae of Lorenzini. The latter are to be found only in elasmobranchs.

Ampullae of Lorenzini

Scattered over the surface of the head are numerous small pores which represent the openings of the **ampullae of Lorenzini** (Fig. 14.27). A crystalline mucus may be forced to exude from them if pressure is applied. Each pore leads to a small **canal of Lorenzini** which terminates in a lobulated, bulblike expansion, the **ampulla,** containing sensory cells. These cells are supplied by delicate nerve strands coming from branches of the facial nerve. The ampullae of Lorenzini have, in the past, been believed to be associated with perception of pressure and of vibrations in the water. More recent studies, however, indicate that they may have a thermosensory function.

Lateral-line System

The lateral-line system, previously mentioned, is in *Squalus acanthias* made up of a number of canals which lie beneath the skin. They open to the surface by numerous **pores.** Sensory receptors, called **neuromasts,** are located in the canals. The **lateral-line proper** extends the length of the body from head to tail. It lies over the lateral septum which separates the epaxial and hypaxial muscles of the body wall. At about the level of the spiracles the two lateral canals communicate with each other by a **supratemporal,** or **commissural, canal.** Anterior to this point each canal branches. A **supraorbital canal** runs forward dorsal to the eye; an **infraorbital canal** lies between the eye and the spiracle and runs forward below the eye; a **hyomandibular canal** passes backward from the infraorbital canal to the hyoid arch region and ventral surface of the snout; a **mandibular canal** lies in the lower jaw. It is believed that the lateral-line system functions in making the animal aware of deep vibrations in the water and of currents or movements of the water, including those caused by movements of the animal itself.

The neuromasts of the lateral-line proper are supplied by small twigs coming from the lateral branch of the vagus nerve (X); those of the canals of the head region receive their nerve supply from branches of the seventh and ninth cranial nerves.

Olfactory Apparatus

Each naris on the ventral side of the snout opens into a blind pouch, the **olfactory sac.** A flap of skin over the naris directs water in one side and out the other. Inside the olfactory sac are many small plates, or **lamellae,** which are covered by the sensitive olfactory epithelium. The numerous fibers of the olfactory nerve lie embedded in the lamellae. They form synapses with fibers in the olfactory bulb, previously described.

Eye

The eye lies in a socketlike depression in the side of the skull, referred to as the **orbit.** Six eye muscles are attached to the eye and help to keep it in place (Fig. 11.11). Two of these muscles, located at the anterior end and originating from the anterior part of the orbit, are called **oblique muscles.**

The **superior oblique** is attached to the anterior, dorsal side of the eyeball, the **inferior oblique** being attached to the anteroventral side. Four muscles which have their origin in the posterior part of the orbit are known as the **rectus muscles.** The **superior rectus** is attached to the dorsal side of the eyeball at practically the same place as the superior oblique. The **inferior rectus** passes to the ventral side of the eyeball, inserting at the same point as the inferior oblique. An **external rectus** is attached to the posterior surface of the eyeball at about its center. The **internal rectus** extends most anteriorly of all the rectus muscles. It is attached to the medial side of the eyeball under the superior oblique muscle. A cartilaginous **optic pedicel,** located among the rectus muscles, helps hold the eyeball in place. The various cranial nerves which supply the eye muscles should be recalled at this time.

The **conjunctiva** is the outermost covering of the front of the eyeball (Fig. 16.20). It is continuous with the lining of the immovable eyelids and is not included among the true coats of the eye, being but a modified portion of the epidermal layer of the skin. The outer coat of the eye is the **fibrous tunic.** This is composed of two regions: a posterior, opaque region called the **sclerotic coat,** or **sclera,** and a transparent portion in the front of the eyeball,

FIG. 16.20. Diagrammatic sagittal section through eye of dogfish.

called the **cornea.** The cornea and conjunctiva are fused. By cutting a large window in the dorsal side of the eyeball, preferably under water, the inner structure of the eye may be readily observed.

The three coats making up the wall of the eyeball should be evident, particularly in the posterior portion. The outermost coat is the **sclera,** already alluded to. Next to it is the heavily pigmented **choroid coat.** The innermost, greenish-yellow layer is the **retina,** which is often collapsed in preserved specimens. The retina contains the sensory light-receptor cells and is therefore the actual sensory portion of the eye. A thickened, vascular portion of the choroid coat, called the **suprachoroid layer,** lies between the choroid and sclerotic coats on the medial aspect of the eyeball. It is present only in those elasmobranchs having an optic pedicel.

Toward the front of the eye the choroid coat and a nonsensory part of the retina separate from the sclera and form a curtainlike structure called the **iris.** In the center of the iris is a round hole, or opening, the **pupil.** The choroid coat and the nonsensory portion of the retina immediately in back of the iris form a series of radiating folds which make up the **ciliary body** to which the large **crystalline lens** is attached by means of a **suspensory liga-**

ment. Accommodation in the elasmobranch eye is discussed on page 641.

The sensory portion of the retina extends forward toward the front of the eye as far as the ciliary body. The irregular border of this part of the retina is called the **ora serrata.** The nonsensory portion of the retina already referred to, which cannot be distinguished in gross preparations, continues forward beyond the ora serrata, covering the posterior surface of the ciliary body and of the iris, forming a part of both these structures.

The **blind spot** may be observed in the posteroventral part of the inside of the eyeball. It is the point of origin of the optic nerve. Sensory light-receptor cells, found in other parts of the sensory portion of the retina, are lacking at the blind spot.

When the dogfish is alive the lens is attached both to the ciliary body and to the margin of the pupil. In preserved specimens the attachment is usually broken. The **anterior chamber** of the eye lies between iris and cornea. The small space between the lens and the iris is called the **posterior chamber.** A transparent fluid, the **aqueous humor,** fills the anterior and posterior chambers. The large cavity in back of the lens, the **vitreous chamber,** is filled with a jellylike mass, the **vitreous humor.**

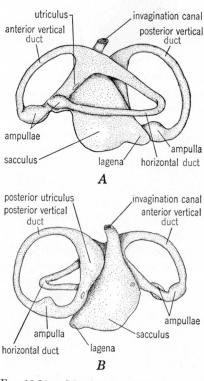

Fig. 16.21.   Membranous labyrinth of dogfish: *A*, lateral view of left ear; *B*, medial view of left ear.

Ear

In fishes there are no external ears or middle ears. Only an **inner ear** is present. In the spiny dogfish (Fig. 16.21*A* and *B*) it is a delicate membranous structure embedded in cartilage in a set of channels and a rather large central cavity, collectively known as the **cartilaginous labyrinth. Anterior, posterior,** and **horizontal semicircular canals** are present in the cartilaginous labyrinth. Within these canals and central cavity lies the **membranous labyrinth** consisting of three **semicircular ducts,** each with an **ampulla** at its lower end, together with a **vestibule** made up of **saccular** and **utricular regions.** The anterior and horizontal ducts join a delicate chamber, the **anterior utriculus,** dorsally. Their ampullae, which are placed close together, also join the anterior utriculus ventrally. Both ends of the posterior canal join a chamber which is considered by some authorities to be a second, or **posterior, utriculus.** The **sacculus** is a pear-shaped structure which lies between the two **utriculi.** It opens to the top of the head by the **invagination canal** which is *not* homologous with the endolymphatic duct of higher vertebrates as often stated. On the ventral side of the sacculus a blunt projection, the **lagena,** extends posteriorly. The cavities of the sacculus and utriculi communicate with each other by small apertures.

The membranous labyrinth is filled with fluid. This is usually referred to as **endolymphatic fluid,** but it is probable that in elasmobranchs it is largely composed of sea water. Sand grains from the exterior may enter the sacculus through the opening of the invagination canal. These, together with crystals of calcium salts, are gathered together in a rather large, loose mass, the **otolith.** The internal ear of the dogfish is primarily an organ of equilibration, but it is possible that it may play a role in sound reception of a sort (page 697). Movements of the endolymph and of the otolith stimulate sensory endings in the ampullae and vestibule, thus informing the animal of its position in the water.

CHAPTER 17

THE MUD PUPPY (Necturus maculosus)

The mud puppy, or water dog, is a caudate amphibian frequently studied in courses in comparative anatomy as an example of a primitive terrestrial vertebrate. Members of the genus *Necturus* are found throughout North America east of the 100th meridian. *Necturus maculosus* is the most widely distributed species. This large salamander, adult specimens of which vary in length from 11 to 18 in., is commonly found in the Mississippi River system from the Arkansas River and northern Alabama northward into Canada and eastward into the mountainous regions of North Carolina, Virginia, West Virginia, and Pennsylvania. Its range includes the Great Lakes and St. Lawrence River and their tributaries in Manitoba, Ontario, and Quebec; the Hudson River drainage system; and the Susquehanna and Delaware rivers. *Necturus* spends its entire life in the water and, unlike most amphibians, does not metamorphose, retaining its external gills throughout life. This condition, in which larval characteristics persist during adult life, is referred to as **neoteny.** The neotenic condition is considered to be degenerate rather than primitive. Amphibians which retain their gills throughout life and fail to undergo metamorphosis are called **perennibranchiates.**

Necturus is frequently caught with hook and line by fishermen, many of whom believe the animal to be poisonous. Actually it is harmless. Even a bite by *Necturus* is of little consequence since the teeth are small and are not apt to cause skin abrasions.

Necturus feeds on crayfish, worms, aquatic insects and their larvae. The animal is of little or no economic value although occasionally used as food for human beings. These amphibians are sluggish creatures which usually forage at night.

Fertilization is internal in *Necturus.* In the autumn gelatinous masses of spermatozoa, the **spermatophores,** are deposited by the male on underwater objects. By movements of the lips of the cloaca of the female, the tips of the spermatophores are taken into the cloacal orifice. A saclike mass of tubules, the **spermatheca,** opens into the posterodorsal wall of the cloaca of the female. Here the spermatozoa are stored. In the following spring, as the eggs pass down the oviducts into the cloaca prior to laying, they are fertilized by the stored spermatozoa. Neither amplexus nor copulation occurs in *Necturus* or other salamanders. The eggs, which appear as pale yellow spheres, are deposited individually on the undersides of stones or

other submerged objects. Sometimes nests are prepared under water in a
sunny place in the sand. As many as 150 eggs may be laid. They take
from 6 to 9 weeks to hatch. At the time of hatching, the larvae measure
approximately ¾ in. in length. It takes from 7 to 8 years for the animals
to reach maturity, and they may live as long as 23 years or more.

EXTERNAL FEATURES

During life *Necturus* is rusty brown in color and has a mottled appearance. Its body is somewhat indistinctly divided into three regions: **head,
trunk,** and **tail** (Fig. 17.1). Head and trunk are flattened in a dorsoventral

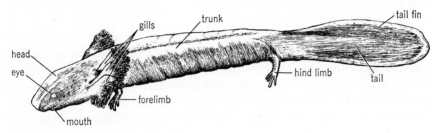

Fig. 17.1. External view of *Necturus maculosus*.

direction, but the tail is laterally compressed. It bears a **tail fin** which,
unlike the fins of fishes, is not supported by fin rays. The **skin** is smooth,
devoid of scales, and very slimy because of the numerous mucous glands
which it contains. In preserved specimens the mucus has coagulated,
giving the animal a grayish appearance. **Lateral-line organs** are present,
even in the adult.

Necturus has two pairs of weak limbs. The **pectoral limbs,** or **forelegs,**
are divided into **upper arm, forearm, wrist,** and **hand**; the **pelvic,** or **hind,
limbs** are made up of **thigh, shank, ankle,** and **foot.** Each limb has but
four **digits** (fingers or toes), although the five-fingered (pentadactyl) condition is considered to be primitive. The first digit is the one which has
disappeared in *Necturus*. The limbs are used effectively in crawling about
on the bottoms of lakes, ponds, and streams. On land, however, they are
of little value, since the decreased buoyancy of the body when surrounded
by air makes it impossible for the weak limbs to support it for any length of
time.

The head contains a terminal **mouth** bordered by **lips.** The upper jaw
extends *over* the lower jaw. A pair of **nostrils,** or **external nares,** lies at the
anterior end of the snout. The nostrils are rather far apart. Each communicates with the mouth cavity through an **internal naris (choana).**
This is an important advance over the condition observed in most fishes in
which the nostrils are nothing more than blind sacs. The **eyes** are relatively small and without lids. No external sign of an ear is present.

Gills are located on either side at the posterolateral border of the head. They are **external gills,** derivatives of the integument, and not homologous with the internal gills of fishes. The gills of *Necturus* number three on each side. Each terminates in a large number of delicate **filaments** which have a plumelike appearance when extended in the water. As mentioned previously, the gills are retained throughout life. Two **gill slits** are present on each side. They are located between the bases of the first and second and the second and third gills and connect the pharynx with the outside. It is doubtful whether water passes through the gill slits of *Necturus*.

Just in back of the hindlimbs on the midventral line is the **cloacal opening** through which the products of digestion, excretion, and reproduction pass.

SKELETAL SYSTEM

The **bony skeleton** of *Necturus* is primitive but, nevertheless, of a much higher level of organization than that of the shark or dogfish. The skeleton is composed of **axial** and **appendicular portions.** The axial skeleton includes the **skull, vertebral column, ribs,** and **sternum;** the **appendicular skeleton** includes the bony framework of the **limbs** and **limb girdles.**

Axial Skeleton

Vertebral Column and Ribs

The **vertebrae** of *Necturus*, like those of fishes, are typically **amphicoelous,** the **centra** being hollow at either end. The **spinal column** is composed of four regions: **cervical, trunk, sacral,** and **caudal.** The cervical portion consists of a single vertebra, the **atlas,** which articulates with the skull. Its anterior face bears a pair of small concavities, the **condylar facets,** for reception of the **occipital condyles.** The atlas does not bear ribs. The trunk vertebrae are all of similar structure (Fig. 17.2). There are usually **17** trunk vertebrae in *Necturus*. Above the centrum is a **neural arch** which encloses the **neural,** or **vertebral, canal** in which the spinal cord lies. The neural arch is composed of two **neural processes** which meet above the neural canal, forming a slight dorsal projection, the **neural spine.** Paired **prezygapophyses** and **postzygapophyses** project from the anterior and posterior ends of the neural arch, respectively. The prezygapophyses of one vertebra articulate with the postzygapophyses of the vertebra immediately anterior to it. **Articular facets** are present on the zygapophyses, those of the prezygapophyses facing upward and those of the postzygapophyses facing downward. A **transverse process** extends laterally from each side of the vertebra. It is composed of two parts: a **diapophysis** coming from the neural arch, and a **parapophysis** from the centrum. Small **ribs** are attached to the transverse processes. Each rib is forked, presenting two surfaces for attachment to the vertebra. The upper limb of the fork constitutes the **tubercular head,** the lower limb being the **capitular head.** These articulate with the diapophysis and parapophysis, respectively.

Only one vertebra is usually present in the sacral region, although the number of sacral vertebrae shows some variation among different specimens. The ribs of the sacrum are stout structures which are united with the pelvic girdle.

The caudal vertebrae (Fig. 17.3) are numerous. Most of them lack ribs. In addition to the usual parts,

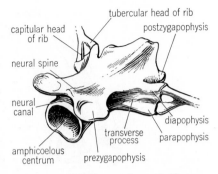

FIG. 17.2. Trunk vertebra of *Necturus*. (*Drawn by R. Archer and G. Schwenk.*)

the caudal vertebrae bear **hemal arches** on their ventral sides. These are comparable to the neural arches on the dorsal side. The caudal vein and artery are enclosed within the hemal arches. The first caudal vertebrae do not possess hemal arches but may carry rudimentary ribs. Toward the end of the tail the caudal vertebrae become very much reduced.

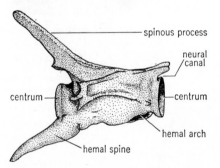

FIG. 17.3. Lateral view of caudal vertebra of *Necturus*.

STERNUM

The origin of the **breastbone,** or **sternum,** in evolution is obscure (page 734). According to one theory, the earliest indication of a sternum is to be found in *Necturus,* in which it is referred to as the **archisternum.** This is rather difficult for the student to identify and is usually lost in ordinary skeletal preparations. It consists of a few cartilages which appear in the intermuscular connective-tissue septa (myocommata) in the ventral thoracic region. Fusion of some of the archisternal elements may possibly explain how the sternum of higher forms may have originated.

SKULL

The **skull** (Figs. 17.4 and 17.5) consists of the **cranium** and **sense capsules,** surrounding and protecting the brain and sense organs, and the **visceral skeleton,** associated in development with the anterior part of the alimentary canal. The skull of *Necturus* is composed partly of cartilage and partly of bone.

During development the cranium is at first cartilaginous and, together with the sense capsules, forms a **chondrocranium** which, although incomplete on the dorsal side, is comparable to the chondrocrania of cyclostomes and elasmobranchs. As development progresses, the cartilage is replaced

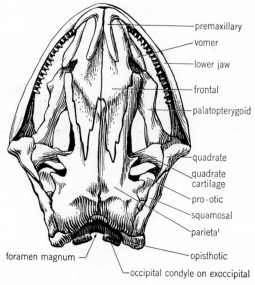

Fig. 17.4. Dorsal view of skull of *Necturus*. (*Drawn by R. Archer and G. Schwenk.*)

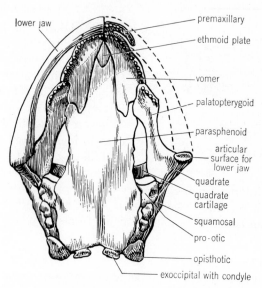

Fig. 17.5. Ventral view of skull of *Necturus*. (*Drawn by R. Archer and G. Schwenk.*)

in part by bones (cartilage bones). Dermal, or membrane, bones, which do not go through a cartilage stage in development, form a roof over the greater part of the chondrocranium. Dermal bones may also cover or invest other parts of the chondrocranium. Such bones are derived from the dermis of the skin and are believed to represent the bony dermal scales of fishes.

The visceral skeleton of *Necturus,* as in *Squalus acanthias,* is at first laid down in cartilage. The first, or **mandibular, visceral arch** becomes divided into an upper **palatopterygoquadrate cartilage** and a lower **Meckel's cartilage.** Although the posterior part of the palatopterygoquadrate bar is replaced by bone (quadrate bone), the remainder becomes invested by membrane bones. This is also true of Meckel's cartilage. The remaining parts of the visceral skeleton of *Necturus* retain their original cartilaginous character or disappear. In adult animals cartilage bones and membrane bones are not readily distinguishable. Furthermore, in dried skulls even the bony and cartilaginous elements are difficult to tell apart. Soaking the skull in water will often reveal which parts are bony and which are cartilaginous. Where bones are joined with one another the lines of fusion are referred to as **sutures.**

At the posterior end of the cranium where it articulates with the vertebral column are two **exoccipital bones,** each bearing on its posterior face a protuberance, the **occipital condyle,** for articulation with the atlas, or first vertebra. Dorsally the two occipitals are separated by a small cartilaginous **synotic tectum** and ventrally by a narrow cartilaginous **basioccipital arch.** The large opening between the two occipital bones is the **foramen magnum** where brain and spinal cord become continuous. Lateral to each exoccipital is an **opisthotic bone,** extending from the dorsal to the ventral side of the skull, articulating dorsally with the **squamosal** and **parietal** and ventrally with the **parasphenoid.** Most of the posterior dorsal part of the skull is covered with a pair of **parietal bones** which meet in the midline. These articulate anteriorly with paired **frontal bones** which partially overlap them. The anterior end of the skull is bordered by two small V-shaped **premaxillary bones** with which the frontals articulate. One limb of the V partly overlaps the frontal. **Teeth** project from the ventral side of the premaxillaries. A **vomer bone** lies posterior to each premaxillary along the lateral margin of the skull. From the anterolateral portion of the opisthotic on each side extends a slender **squamosal bone.** It lies lateral to the parietal and meets the **quadrate** anteriorly. A small pro-otic bone is present on each side between the squamosal and parietal. It is separated from the opisthotic by a small cartilage.

On the ventral side of the skull (Fig. 17.5) an unpaired parasphenoid bone extends forward from the exoccipitals. Anteriorly it is flanked on either side by the vomer bone which lies beneath the nasal capsule. The vomer bones bear teeth. A cartilaginous **ethmoid plate** lies anterior to the parasphenoid between the two vomers. A **palatopterygoid (pterygoid)** passes posteriorly from each vomer. Its anterior portion bears teeth. Posteriorly it articulates with the quadrate. The latter forms a projecting process near the middle of the lateral border of the skull. The quadrate serves as the point of articulation of the lower jaw.

The skull of the mud puppy lacks nasal and maxillary bones. The **orbit,** which accommodates the eye, is *not* surrounded by bony elements in *Necturus*.

The **lower jaw** of the mud puppy consists of three bones on each side arranged about the cartilaginous core called **Meckel's cartilage.** A **dentary bone** bearing teeth forms the greater part of the outer surface of the anterior end. A small **splenial,** also bearing teeth, is located near the middle of the inner surface. The third bone, or **angular,** makes up the greater part of the inner surface. Its posterior end passes below the dentary to the outer surface of the jaw. The posterior end of Meckel's cartilage is expanded. This is the portion of the lower jaw which articulates with the quadrate. The two halves of the lower jaw are rather loosely united in front.

Despite the fact that numerous cartilage and dermal bones are present in the skull of *Necturus*, some of the original chondrocranium persists. It is usually not practicable to study separately the chondrocranial remnants since it involves removal of the membrane bones. Portions already noted, however, include the synotic tectum, the basioccipital arch, the ethmoid plate, the small cartilage lying between the pro-otic and opisthotic bones, and Meckel's cartilage of the lower jaw.

The **nasal** and **otic capsules,** which are originally separate cartilages, contribute to the chondrocranium. The nasal capsules are fragile and usually are destroyed in preparation of skulls. The cartilaginous otic capsules are largely replaced by the pro-otic and opisthotic bones. On the medial side of each otic capsule is a large **foramen** through which blood vessels and nerves pass. A ventrolateral opening is the **fenestra ovalis,** which is plugged by the **stapes bone.** A **columellar process** is attached to the stapes at one end and by means of a suspensorstapedial ligament to the squamosal bone on the other.

For convenience, the remnants of the chondrocranium, as well as the various cartilage and membrane bones of the skull of *Necturus*, are listed below.

Cartilages	*Cartilage bones*	*Membrane bones*
Nasal capsules	Exoccipitals	Parietals
Ethmoid plate	Pro-otics	Frontals
Synotic tectum	Opisthotics	Vomers
Basioccipital arch	Quadrates	Premaxillaries
Meckel's cartilage	Stapes	Squamosals
		Parasphenoid
		Palatopterygoids ?
		Dentary
		Splenial
		Angular

The arches which support the gill region of *Necturus* are cartilaginous. A reduction in number, in comparison with the primitive condition, has occurred. However, the hyoid arch and the three following visceral arches are represented (Fig. 17.6).

The **hyoid arch,** which lies just in back of the lower jaw, consists of two cartilages on each side, a small medial **hypohyal** and a larger, lateral **ceratohyal.** The next visceral arch, often called the **first branchial arch,** is likewise composed of two cartilages, a medial **first ceratobranchial** and a lateral **epibranchial.** Between the ceratobranchials and hypohyals is a single median **copula,** or **basibranchial, cartilage.** A small **second basibranchial** lies posterior to the union of the first ceratobranchials in the midline. Branchial arches 2

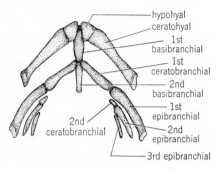

FIG. 17.6. Hyoid apparatus of *Necturus*.

and 3 (visceral arches 4 and 5) are much reduced, since the ceratobranchial elements are very small or are lacking altogether. The second and third epibranchials are represented, however, by small cartilaginous bars lying in succession behind the first epibranchial.

Appendicular Skeleton

PECTORAL GIRDLE AND LIMBS

The **pectoral girdle** (Fig. 17.7) is an arch of cartilage and bone which supports the forelimbs. It is composed of two halves which are not united but overlap each other ventrally. Each half consists of a single skeletal element in which regions may be recognized. The ventral part, which is cartilaginous, has anterior **precoracoid** and posterior **coracoid regions.** A depression, the **glenoid fossa,** on the lateral border, serves as the point of articulation of the arm with the girdle. A narrow, bony region, the **scapula,** projects dorsally. To its distal border is attached a broad **suprascapular cartilage.** The pectoral girdle forms no direct connection with the vertebral column.

The single bone of the upper arm is the **humerus.** It bears a **deltoid crest** on its lower surface for muscle attachment. Two bones, **radius** and **ulna,** are in the forearm. They can be distinguished from each other since the proximal end of the ulna projects beyond the elbow joint as the **olecranon process.** The radius is on the thumb side. Six or seven very small bones arranged in three rows make up the **wrist,** or **carpal, bones.** Two are proximal, consisting of a **radiale** on the side of the radius and an ulnare on the ulnar side. A small **intermedium** is generally fused to the ulnare. Three carpal bones are distal. A single **centrale** lies between the proximal and distal rows. Four **metacarpals** are present in the hand.

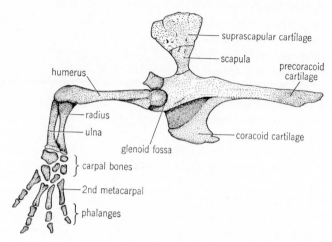

Fig. 17.7. Pectoral girdle and limb of *Necturus*, lateral view.

The first digit, or **thumb (pollex),** is absent. Digits 2, 3, and 5 contain two **phalanges** each. The fourth contains three.

Pelvic Girdle and Limbs

The **pelvic girdle** (Fig. 17.8) is almost entirely cartilaginous. It consists of a **puboischium** and an **ilium**. The puboischium is a flat plate on the ventral side of the animal. Its anterior end represents the **pubis** and the

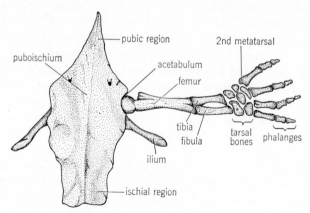

Fig. 17.8. Pelvic girdle and limb of *Necturus*, ventral view.

posterior end the **ischium**. Part of the ischial region may be bony. The puboischium bears a depression, the **acetabulum,** on either side, for reception of the head of the femur. A bony rod extends dorsally from the lateral side of the puboischium. This is the **ilium.** It is fastened to the strong rib of the sacral vertebra. The actual number of sacral vertebrae, as mentioned previously, shows some variation among different specimens.

The pelvic limb is much like the pectoral limb in structure. The upper leg, or thigh, contains a single bone, the **femur.** Two bones, **tibia** and **fibula,** are in the shank. The tibia corresponds to the radius and the fibula to the ulna. Six **tarsal,** or **ankle, bones** are present, arranged in a manner similar to that of the carpals. The terms **tibiale** and **fibulare** are applied to the two bones of the proximal row lying opposite the tibia and fibula, respectively. There are three **distal tarsals** and a **centrale,** the latter lying between the proximal and distal rows. The foot contains four **metatarsal bones,** the first, or **hallux,** being lacking. As in the hand, each digit has two **phalanges,** except the fourth, in which there are three.

MUSCULAR SYSTEM

The muscles of *Necturus* do not deviate very greatly from the primitive condition. This is particularly true of those in the trunk and tail regions. In the pectoral and pelvic regions modifications have occurred in connection with the evolution of tetrapod limbs.

Trunk Musculature

The muscles of the two sides of the body are distinct from each other. A thin connective-tissue partition, the **linea alba,** separates the muscles of the two sides along the midventral line. Toward the dorsal side a horizontal **lateral septum** divides the muscles into dorsal **epaxial** and ventral **hypaxial regions** (Fig. 11.8). The lateral septum is more dorsal in position than that of *Squalus acanthias*. As a result the epaxial musculature is reduced. The muscles consist of a series of metameric, blocklike **myotomes,** or **myomeres,** each extending all the way from the middorsal to the midventral line. The myotomes are separated from one another by connective-tissue partitions, the **myocommata,** or **myosepta.** The greater part of the epaxial region has become modified to form a single muscular unit, the **longissimus dorsi (dorsalis trunci)** on each side. Here the muscle fibers course in a longitudinal direction. The deeper portion of the epaxial region forms a series of short **intersegmental bundles** passing from one vertebra to the next. The hypaxial muscles have differentiated into three layers. The outermost layer is the **external oblique.** Its fibers course obliquely, slanting in a posteroventral direction. Under the external oblique is the **internal oblique** in which the fibers slope in an anteroventral direction. The third layer, or **transversus,** lies under the internal oblique just outside the **parietal peritoneum.** Its fibers are arranged almost in a circular, or vertical, direction. On either side of the linea alba is a thin **rectus abdominis muscle.** It extends from the pubis to the pectoral region. Its longitudinally directed fibers are interrupted at regular intervals by myocommata.

Muscles of the Head and Gill Region

Two superficial muscles are present on the ventral side of the head (Fig. 17.9). Each passes laterally from a midventral raphe to the bone of the lower jaw. These are **branchial muscles.** The more anterior of the

Fig. 17.9.   Muscles of head of *Necturus*, ventral view.

two is the **intermandibular.** The **interhyoid** lies posterior to it. Dorsal to these muscles are the **geniohyoids** which pass from the front of the lower jaw to the second basibranchial cartilage. One is found on either side of the midline. They are **hypobranchial muscles.**

On the dorsal surface of the head (Fig. 17.10) the anterior end of the longissimus dorsi may be observed attached to the skull. A **levator mandibulae** covers the greater part of the top of the skull. It is divided into anterior, external, and posterior portions. The **anterior levator mandibulae** lies near the middorsal line; the **external levator mandibulae** is located behind the eye; the smaller **posterior levator mandibulae** lies under the external levator mandibulae. All three components insert on the lower jaw and function in raising the lower jaw, thus closing the mouth. Two additional branchial muscles lie between the external levator mandibulae and the gills. The more anterior of the two is the **depressor mandibulae.** Its fibers pass from the visceral arch behind the hyoid to the posterior part of the lower jaw near where it articulates with the quadrate. The other is the **branchiohyoid.** This has the same origin as the depressor mandibulae but passes to the ceratohyal. Several small muscles lie above the gill region. These are the **branchial levators.** They pass from the skin to the remaining visceral arches and serve to raise the gills. Several small **subarcual muscles,** passing from one visceral arch to another, lie dorsal to the geniohyoids and branchiohyoids. Three small **branchial de-**

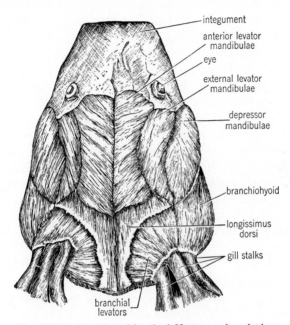

integument

anterior levator mandibulae

eye

external levator mandibulae

depressor mandibulae

branchiohyoid

longissimus dorsi

gill stalks

branchial levators

FIG. 17.10.   Muscles of head of *Necturus,* dorsal view.

pressors which lower, or depress, the gills pass from the ventral portions of the posterior visceral arches to the bases of the external gills.

Muscles of the Pectoral Girdle and Forelimb (Fig. 11.14)

Immediately behind the gills is the **cucullaris muscle.** It originates from fascia and inserts on the scapula near the glenoid cavity. Posterior to the cucullaris lies the **dorsalis scapulae.** It originates on the supra-scapula, covers most of the scapula, and passes to the humerus. Still another muscle, the **latissimus dorsi,** is situated posterior to the dorsalis scapulae. It arises by several small slips from myocommata and fascia in the epaxial region and inserts on the proximal end of the humerus. A small muscle, the **pectoriscapularis,** lies anterior and ventral to the cucullaris and inserts on the scapula. It partially covers another muscle, the **sternohyoid (rectus cervicis),** which is the anterior continuation of the **rectus abdominis.** Deeper muscles in this region include the **levator scapulae** and **serratus anterior.** They originate from the epaxial muscles and insert on the scapula. On the ventral side of the body in the pectoral region three additional muscles may be observed. The first of these, the **pectoralis,** passes from the linea alba to the ventral side of the proximal end of the humerus. A **supracoracoid muscle** lies anterior to the pectoralis which partly overlaps it. It extends from the coracoid cartilage of the pectoral girdle and also inserts on the humerus. The third muscle, the **precoracohumeralis,** is a slender muscle, lateral in position, extending from the precoracoid cartilage to the humerus. Between the two precoracohumeralis muscles lies the **sternohyoid,** previously mentioned.

On the ventral surface of the foreleg proper is the **humeroantibrachialis,** often referred to as the **biceps.** It passes from the proximal end of the humerus to the radial side of the forearm. A larger muscle, the **coracobrachialis,** lies behind the humeroantibrachialis. It passes from the coracoid cartilage to insert on the distal end of the humerus. On the dorsal surface of the upper arm is the **anconeus.** It originates from several slips, or heads, from the coracoid, scapula, and proximal part of the humerus. The anconeus inserts on the ulna. The muscles of the forearm are grouped into two divisions. An **extensor digitorum communis** lies on the dorsal surface, and a **flexor digitorum communis** is found on the ventral side. Both extensor and flexor muscles are separated into various small components which insert on the digits.

Muscles of the Pelvic Girdle and Hindlimb (Fig. 11.15*A* and *B*)

In *Necturus* two separate muscles pass from the midventral line to the hindlimb. The more anterior of the two is the **puboischiofemoralis externus.** It passes from the anterior end of the pubis to the proximal end of the femur. Posterior to the puboischiofemoralis externus lies the **puboischiotibialis.** This muscle originates on the puboischiac plate of the pelvic girdle and inserts along the shaft of the tibia. It lies anterior to a glandular mass, the **anal,** or **cloacal, gland,** located anterolaterad the cloacal opening. Dorsal to the cloacal gland are two muscles, the fibers of which are longitudinally arranged. The more medial muscle is the **ischiocaudalis.** It passes from the posterior part of the ischium to the tail. Laterad the ischiocaudalis is the **caudopuboischiotibialis.** This muscle originates on the fascia covering the puboischiotibialis muscle and inserts on the tail. Just above this muscle lies the **caudofemoralis** which passes from the femur to the tail. These three pairs of muscles are used in bending the tail in different directions.

Several additional muscles of the pelvic girdle are found toward the dorsal side of the body. The most anterior of these is the **puboischiofemoralis internus.** It originates from the dorsal side of the pelvic girdle near the acetabulum and inserts on the shaft of the femur. Immediately behind it, still on the dorsal side, is a slender **iliotibialis.** In back of this lies the **ilioextensorius.** These two muscles, which originate on the iliac region of the pelvic girdle, insert on the tibia. The last of the dorsal muscles is the **iliofibularis,** passing from the ilium to the fibula. A small triangular-shaped **iliofemoralis** arises from the base of the ilium and passes to the posterior border of the femur. On the ventral side of the above group of muscles is the **pubotibialis,** originating on the puboischiac plate and inserting on the proximal end of the tibia. The puboischiotibialis partly covers this muscle. Last comes the **ischioflexorius,** passing from the puboischiac plate to the fascia of the lower leg.

The muscles of the lower leg, like those of the forearm, consist of a dorsal **extensor digitorum communis** and a ventral **flexor digitorum communis.** Each is divided into separate smaller elements which pass to the digits.

COELOM

The **body cavity,** or **coelom,** in *Necturus* is divided into two separate compartments. The first, or **pericardial cavity,** containing the heart, is situated anteriorly. It is surrounded by a membranous **pericardium (parietal pericardium).** This is continuous with the **visceral pericardium,** or **epicardium,** which is closely applied to the surface of the heart itself.

The remaining viscera lie in that part of the coelom called the **pleuroperitoneal cavity.** A partition, the **septum transversum,** or **false diaphragm,** separates pericardial and pleuroperitoneal cavities. The large veins bringing blood to the heart from the abdominal viscera pass through the septum transversum. The outer wall of the pleuroperitoneal cavity is lined with **parietal peritoneum.** A **visceral peritoneal layer** is reflected over the surface of the organs in the pleuroperitoneal cavity (Fig. 16.8).

DIGESTIVE SYSTEM

Mouth. The mouth opening is bordered by heavy, soft **lips** which, although immovable, are capable of closing the mouth completely.

Two rows of **teeth** are present in the upper jaw. The first row is short, being confined to the premaxillary bones. The other is longer and situated on the vomers and palatopterygoids. The teeth on the lower jaw are located on the dentary and splenial bones. When the mouth is closed the single row of teeth on the lower jaw fits into the groove between the two rows on the upper jaw.

The **internal nares,** or **choanae,** lie lateral to the last teeth of the posterior row. They appear as small slits which are often difficult to find in preserved specimens because of the coagulated mucus which obscures them.

The **tongue** lies in the floor of the mouth. It is immovable in *Necturus* and supported by the hyoid cartilages.

Pharynx. The mouth cavity is continued posteriorly as the **pharynx.** The wall of the pharynx on each side opens to the exterior through two **gill slits,** one behind the other. The **visceral arches** are cartilaginous bars, covered with mucous membrane, between which the gill slits are located. Short, blunt projections on both sides of the visceral arches are **gill rakers.**

They are not so well developed nor do they function so efficiently as those of the dogfish but, nevertheless, aid in retaining food. No internal gills, homologous with those of fishes, are present in *Necturus*. The gills are entirely external and are modifications of the integument. A small longitudinal slit in the floor of the pharynx, about 1 in. posterior to the tip of the tongue, is the **glottis.** It leads to the lungs which are described below. The glottis is bordered by a pair of small, **lateral cartilages.**

Esophagus. The **esophagus** of *Necturus* is short and serves merely to connect the pharynx with the stomach. It lies dorsal to the pericardium and passes through the septum transversum.

Stomach. The **stomach** (Fig. 17.11) is an elongated sac lying on the left side of the body cavity. Its posterior end is marked by a constriction, the **pyloric sphincter.** The stomach is suspended from the dorsal body wall by a mesentery, the **mesogaster.**

Intestine. The first part of the **small intestine,** between the pylorus and the entrance of the bile duct, is the **duodenum.** It bends rather sharply to the right and then passes posteriorly. The coiled portion of the small intestine beyond the duodenum is the **ileum.** It terminates at the posterior end of the coelom in a short, expanded portion, the **large intestine,** which in turn joins the cloaca. The latter opens to the outside through the **cloacal aperture.** The small intestine is supported by the **mesentery proper,** which is continuous with the mesogaster. The portion of the dorsal mesentery suspending the large intestine is the **mesorectum.**

Liver. The **liver** of *Necturus* is a large organ filling up a good part of the pleuroperitoneal cavity. Its margins are notched at various points,

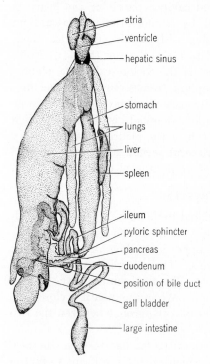

atria
ventricle
hepatic sinus
stomach
lungs
liver
spleen
ileum
pyloric sphincter
pancreas
duodenum
position of bile duct
gall bladder
large intestine

Fig. 17.11. Ventral view of digestive organs and lungs of *Necturus*.

giving it a lobulated appearance. A ventral mesentery, the **mesohepar,** or **falciform ligament** of the liver, attaches the ventral face of the organ to the midventral body wall. A **gastrohepatic ligament** passes from the anterior end of the stomach to the dorsal side of the liver. A small, thin, **gall bladder** is located on the dorsal aspect of the right side of the liver near its posterior end. The **bile duct,** or **ductus choledochus,** passes from the gall bladder to the duodenum. It is surrounded by pancreatic tissue.

Pancreas. Lying in the loop between the duodenum and stomach is the irregularly shaped, whitish **pancreas.** It is partially enclosed in the hepatoduodenal ligament which connects duodenum and liver. Several small ducts from the pancreas join the bile duct or enter separately into the duodenum.

RESPIRATORY SYSTEM

In addition to the external gills, previously referred to and the vascular integument, *Necturus* possesses a pair of **lungs** which may be used to some extent in respiration (Fig. 17.11). In this respect *Necturus* shows a decided advance over the dogfish.

On each side of the stomach in the anterior portion of the pleuroperitoneal cavity is an elongated, thin-walled, translucent lung. The lungs are *not* enclosed in separate portions of the coelom as in the case of mammals. Hence, the term pleuroperitoneal is an appropriate name for this portion of the body cavity. The lungs of *Necturus* are unusually long, simple, thin-walled sacs which may extend posteriorly even past the end of the liver.

The **glottis,** previously mentioned, in the midventral part of the pharynx, leads to a small **larynx.** At the base of the larynx is a short, narrow **trachea** from which the lungs arise directly without the intervention of bronchi.

The walls of the lung, although smooth, are highly vascular. The blood vessels, in times of emergency, supplement those of the gills and skin in taking up oxygen and getting rid of carbon dioxide. Blood going to the lungs under ordinary conditions has been oxygenated in the gills. It is probable that the lungs are effective only when the oxygen supply of the water in which the animal lives is depleted and the gills and skin are unable to obtain sufficient oxygen. Although *Necturus* is permanently aquatic, it comes to the surface at irregular intervals to replenish the air in the lungs. The passage of air from the outside to the lungs takes the following course: external nares, nasal passages, internal nares, mouth, pharynx, glottis, larynx, trachea, and lungs.

EXCRETORY SYSTEM

The **kidneys** of *Necturus* are of the **opisthonephric type.** They consist of a pair of brown, narrow, elongated organs which lie in the posterior part of the body cavity close to the dorsal body wall (Figs. 17.12 and 17.13). The anterior end is narrower than the posterior end. The kidneys of the female are shorter than those of the male. Each is entirely surrounded by visceral peritoneum, a condition not usually encountered in vertebrates. Along the lateral border of each opisthonephros lies the **archinephric duct.** It passes to the cloaca. The archinephric duct of the female is of a finer structure than that of the male, in which it serves to transport spermatozoa in addition to urinary wastes.

A large, saclike **urinary bladder** comes off the ventral wall of the cloaca. A ventral mesenterylike band, the **median ligament of the bladder,** passes

Fig. 17.12. Urogenital system of male *Necturus*, ventral view.

Fig. 17.13. Urogenital system of female *Necturus* during the nonbreeding season, ventral view. The left ovary has been removed to show the opisthonephros above.

from the urinary bladder to the ventral body wall. The archinephric ducts have no connection with the bladder. Urinary wastes pass from the opisthonephric kidneys and archinephric ducts to the cloaca and thence to the bladder, which serves as a temporary storage place. The bladder is evacuated from time to time.

REPRODUCTIVE SYSTEM

In the male *Necturus* the reproductive and excretory systems are intimately connected, but in the female this relationship does not exist.

The Male

The **testes** are a pair of elongated bodies, each attached to the middorsal body wall by a mesenterylike membrane, the **mesorchium.** The size of the testes varies during different seasons of the year. A few delicate tubules, the **efferent ductules,** pass from the testes through the mesorchium to the medial border of the kidney (Fig. 17.12). Here they form connections with certain anterior kidney tubules. Spermatozoa thus pass from the testes through the efferent ductules to kidney tubules. The tubules in turn join the convoluted archinephric duct which serves as a **ductus deferens** in transporting spermatozoa to the cloaca. The archinephric ducts open independently into the dorsolateral part of the cloaca anterior to the opening of the urinary bladder.

The Female

The **ovaries** of the female vary greatly in size and appearance during different seasons of the year. When filled with ripe eggs just prior to the breeding season, they occupy a considerable portion of the pleuroperitoneal cavity. Each ovary is an elongated structure suspended from the middorsal body wall by a membrane, the **mesovarium,** corresponding to the mesorchium of the male. A white, thick-walled, convoluted **oviduct,** or **Müllerian duct,** lies laterad each ovary (Fig. 17.13). Each oviduct is attached to the middorsal body wall by a mesenterylike membrane, the **mesotubarium.** The kidney lies within this two-layered membrane. The oviducts pass forward dorsal to the lung to the anterior end of the pleuroperitoneal cavity where each opens independently by means of a slitlike **ostium tubae** into the body cavity.

The posterior end of each oviduct is somewhat enlarged to form a **uterus.** The uteri open into the sides of the cloaca lateral to the opening of the urinary bladder.

When eggs are fully ripened, the follicles in which they lie rupture and the eggs pass directly into the pleuroperitoneal cavity. They are engulfed by the ostia and then pass in a rotary manner down the long, convoluted oviducts where they receive an albuminous coating. A few may be stored temporarily in the uteri from which they soon pass to the outside through the cloaca and cloacal aperture.

Fertilization of the eggs is internal. The method by which internal fertilization is accomplished in *Necturus* has been discussed previously.

ENDOCRINE SYSTEM

There are eight glandular structures in *Necturus*, some of which have been described, usually considered to belong to the endocrine system.

Gonads. The ovaries and testes, already mentioned, in addition to their function of producing gametes, secrete **sex hormones** which are of importance in controlling the development of secondary sex characters and in the development, maintenance, and function of the accessory sex organs. The exact cellular elements which secrete these hormones in amphibians are not clearly understood.

Pancreas. Besides secreting enzymes used in digestion, the pancreas serves as an endocrine organ. Certain groups of cells which may be identified in histological preparations of the pancreas secrete a hormone, **insulin,** into the blood stream. They are called the **islands of Langerhans.** Insulin plays an important part in the metabolism of carbohydrates and fats. The anatomical relations of the pancreas have been described above.

Thyroid gland. In *Necturus* the thyroid gland consists of a small mass of tissue located along the sides of the second basibranchial cartilage and partly covered by the branchiohyoid muscles.

Parathyroid glands. Small masses of cells derived embryonically from visceral pouches come to lie ventral and lateral to the aortic arches. Two or three such structures in *Necturus* are considered to be homologous with the **parathyroid glands** of higher forms. Not much investigation has been carried out on their functions in amphibians.

Adrenal glands. The adrenal glands of caudate amphibians are not discrete structures such as those of salientians and higher vertebrates. **Interrenal** (cortical) and **chromaffin** (medullary) components are more or less intermingled. Small isolated masses of tissue are present, usually in association with sympathetic ganglia. These are considered to be the homologues of the adrenal glands of higher forms. Gross observation of these masses in *Necturus* is difficult.

Pituitary gland. The various components of the pituitary gland of *Necturus* are not clearly evident upon gross dissection. The **pituitary gland** lies ventral to the diencephalon of the brain (Fig. 17.17*B*). Histological examination reveals it to be the usual three-lobed structure.

Thymus gland. Uncertainty exists as to whether the **thymus** should be included in the category of endocrine structures. Derived from the dorsolateral portions of the visceral pouches in amphibians, the thymus consists of small masses of tissue lying laterad the aortic arch region and dorsal to the so-called parathyroid elements.

Pineal body. Another structure often included among the endocrine organs is the **pineal body,** which extends dorsally from the roof of the diencephalic portion of the brain. Homologies with a third, median eye, found in rudimentary condition in several vertebrates, are suggestive in explaining the existence of this unusual structure of doubtful function.

CIRCULATORY SYSTEM

The circulatory system of *Necturus* consists of a three-chambered **heart** and numerous blood vessels. These include **arteries, arterioles, capillaries, venules,** and **veins.** In addition, **lymphatic vessels** and **glands,** as well as the **spleen,** make up parts of the circulatory system.

Heart

The **heart,** lying in the pericardial cavity, consists, as in other amphibians, of two thin-walled **atria** and a single muscular **ventricle** (Fig. 17.14). The atria lie anterior and dorsal to the ventricle. In *Necturus* the cavities

of the two atria are separated only by a thin, perforated **interatrial septum.**
Dorsal to the heart and attached to the septum transversum is a large
thin-walled **sinus venosus** which collects blood from all parts of the body
except the lungs. It opens into the right atrium through the **sinuatrial
aperture** which is guarded by a **sinua-
trial valve.** Two large **common cardinal veins,** or **ducts of Cuvier,** join the
sinus venosus. They are located dorsal
to the pericardial cavity, and one enters
each side of the sinus venosus. A pair
of large **hepatic sinuses** joins the posterior part of the sinus venosus dorsal to
the ventricle (Figs. 17.14 and 17.17).
The hepatic sinuses come from the liver
and pass through the septum transversum. A pair of **pulmonary veins** from
the lungs comes together to form a common vessel which courses dorsal to the
hepatic veins and enters the left atrium.
The two atria have a common opening
into the ventricle. This is guarded by
an **atrioventricular valve.** A single

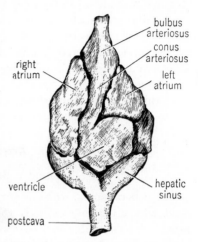

FIG. 17.14. Ventral view of heart of
Necturus.

vessel, the **conus arteriosus,** leaves the ventricle, and from it blood is
distributed to the gills, and hence to all parts of the body. At the point
where the conus leaves the ventricle there is a row of pocketlike **semilunar valves.** Although most amphibians have a longitudinal septum in
the conus arteriosus, dividing its cavity into two separate channels, such a
septum is lacking in *Necturus.* Just anterior to the conus is an expanded
bulbus arteriosus which actually represents the proximal part of the
ventral aorta. Anterior to the bulbus the **ventral aorta** branches, as
described in the following section, distributing blood to the gills.

    The heart of *Necturus,* even though it is not a very good example of a
three-chambered heart, shows an important advance over that observed
in the shark. A **double circulation** of blood passes through it. Oxygenated
blood coming from the lungs via the gills enters the left atrium. Blood
entering the right atrium from the sinus venosus is mixed. It consists of
unoxygenated blood coming from most parts of the body and some oxygenated blood from the skin and lining of the mouth. The system of vessels coming from the lungs to the heart, and those leading from the heart
to the lungs, is referred to as the **pulmonary circulation.** That which is
distributed to the body in general and then returned to the heart via the
sinus venosus is called the **systemic circulation.** The pulmonary circulation of *Necturus* is atypical since the blood in the pulmonary arteries,
under normal conditions, has already been oxygenated in the gills (page

525). This indicates that the lungs of *Necturus* normally function but little as respiratory organs and are probably used only in times of emergency. Although many amphibians have developed a rather complicated system of valves and partitions which ostensibly serve to keep the two blood streams in the heart fairly separate, the heart of *Necturus*, with its perforated interatrial septum, and lacking a longitudinal septum in the conus, cannot be very effective in this respect. This is really of little importance because under ordinary circumstances blood is sent to the gills for aeration after leaving the heart. It is possible, however, for blood to bypass the gills (page 524).

At this point it is important to note that the three-chambered condition of the heart first appears in the true lungfishes of the superorder Dipnoi.

Arterial System

Afferent Branchial Arteries

The ventral aorta, which is very short, divides almost immediately into right and left trunks (Fig. 17.15). Each of these in turn gives off two branches. The anterior branch on each side passes to the first gill. The posterior branch passes laterally for a short distance and then splits into anterior and posterior branches which pass to the second and third gills, respectively. The three vessels going to the gills are the **afferent branchial arteries.**

The first afferent branchial artery gives off a small **external carotid artery** at the base of the gill. It passes medially and then turns forward to supply the floor of the pharynx and mouth. The external carotid artery actually has connections with the first **efferent branchial artery.** However, it also forms small connections with the first afferent branchial artery as noted. Within each gill the afferent branchial artery sends up a branch, the **afferent branchial loop,** which gives off numerous small capillary vessels to the gill filaments. Blood in these vessels is collected by other small vessels which unite to form another vessel, the **efferent branchial loop,** which returns blood to the efferent branchial artery. A short vessel at the base of each gill connects each afferent branchial artery with its respective efferent branchial artery. This is actually part of the original aortic arch which serves as a **gill bypass.** Unlike the condition in fishes, therefore, the aortic arches are continuous and are not distinctly separated into afferent and efferent portions by a capillary network. Blood may course directly through them or may go through the branchial loops (Fig. 17.15).

Efferent Branchial Arteries

Blood is collected from the gill region by three **efferent branchial arteries** corresponding to the three gills. Each vessel parallels a correspond-·

ing afferent branchial artery with which, as already noted, it forms a
direct connection, the **gill bypass,** as well as an indirect connection by way
of the branchial loop with its afferent and efferent branches. The second
and third efferent branchial arteries join each other to form a single vessel

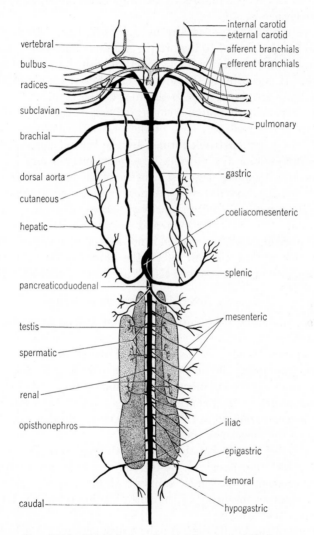

FIG. 17.15. Ventral view of arterial system of *Necturus.*

which is then joined by the first efferent branchial artery. The combination of the three vessels on each side, as just described, results in the formation of a large **radix aortae.** The two radices pass medially and posteriorly
and then join to form the **dorsal aorta.** This vessel lies under the vertebral

column and passes to the posterior part of the body where it is continued into the tail as the **caudal artery.**

There is some disagreement among comparative anatomists as to which aortic arches are represented in *Necturus.* The work of Figge (page 524) indicates that in this perennibranchiate amphibian arches **3, 4,** and **5** are the ones which persist.

A small **vertebral artery** comes from each radix lateral to the vertebral column and passes forward to the brain. Another short vessel, the **carotid duct,** springs from the radix near its junction with the first efferent branchial artery. It is continued forward as the **internal carotid artery** which courses medially and anteriorly to the roof of the mouth. The external carotid artery, previously noted, is connected only indirectly to the carotid duct via the gill bypass and base of the first afferent branchial artery. Just before the common trunk formed by the second and third efferent branchial arteries joins the radix, a large **pulmonary artery** is given off. It passes posteriorly along the dorsal surface of the lung. Since the blood in the pulmonary artery has, for the most part, been oxygenated in the gill region, the lungs are of use primarily as accessory or emergency organs of respiration. The vascular skin and gills normally secure adequate amounts of oxygen, but when oxygen is not available in sufficient quantity the animal, by gulping air, can inflate the lung and thus secure enough oxygen through its pulmonary vessels to carry on its metabolic processes.

Dorsal Aorta and Its Branches

As the aorta courses posteriorly it gives off numerous paired and unpaired branches.

Paired vessels. A short distance beyond the point where the radices join to form the aorta, the latter gives off a pair of **subclavian arteries.** Each of these sends off a **cutaneous artery** which is distributed to the skin. The subclavian artery then continues out the arm as the **brachial artery.**

Parietal arteries come from the aorta at segmental intervals. They are distributed to the muscles of the body wall.

Genital arteries come from the aorta in the region of the gonads. In the male, in which they pass to the testes, they are called **spermatic arteries.** The **genital arteries** of the female supply both ovaries and oviducts.

Renal arteries are branches of the aorta coming off at the level of the kidneys which they supply.

At the level of the hindlimbs is a pair of **iliac arteries.** Each iliac gives off an anterior **epigastric artery** to the body wall and a **hypogastric artery** to cloaca and bladder. It continues into the hindlimb as the **femoral artery.** A small pair of **cloacal arteries,** supplying part of the cloacal region, comes off the dorsal aorta at the level of the cloaca.

Unpaired vessels. Not very far posterior to the point where the subclavian arteries arise, a large unpaired **gastric artery** comes off the aorta.

In addition to supplying the stomach with dorsal and ventral branches, it is distributed to a portion of the spleen.

Some distance caudally a **coeliacomesenteric artery** arises from the aorta. It is distributed to the duodenal region of the small intestine and to the pancreas, liver, and posterior end of the spleen.

Several unpaired **mesenteric arteries** come from the aorta at intervals posterior to the coeliacomesenteric. They supply the remainder of the intestine.

Venous System

Common cardinal veins and their tributaries. As was previously noted, a **common cardinal vein** enters the sinus venosus on each side from the dorsal part of the pericardial cavity. Each is joined posteriorly (Fig. 17.16) by a large **hepatic sinus** close to its opening into the sinus venosus. Laterad the pericardial cavity the common cardinal receives several vessels. These consist of (1) a **jugular vein** formed by external and internal tributaries from the head region, (2) a small **lingual vein** from the tongue, (3) a **subclavian vein** formed by the junction of the **brachial** vein from the arm and the **cutaneous vein** from the skin, (4) a **lateral vein** from the muscles of the body wall, (5) a **postcardinal vein** draining the kidneys, dorsal body wall, and some adjacent structures.

Renal portal system of veins. A single median **caudal vein** drains blood from the tail. When it reaches the body wall it divides in two, each branch passing along the lateral border of the kidney where it is called the **renal portal vein.** The renal portal sends numerous **afferent renal veins** into the kidney and receives small **parietal vessels** from the body wall. At the anterior end of the kidney the renal portal is continued as the **postcardinal vein** which, as described above, passes anteriorly to join the common cardinal vein. Near the posterior end of the kidney each renal portal gives off an **iliac vein** which is then joined by a **femoral vein** coming from the hindlimb. The common vessel thus formed is the **pelvic vein.** The two pelvic veins soon unite to form a single **ventral abdominal vein** which, after receiving some small **vesicular branches** from the bladder, and parietal veins from the body wall, forms connections with the hepatic portal vein.

Posterior vena cava. A rather large vein, the **posterior vena cava,** lies between the kidneys along the dorsal side of the body cavity. The vessel gradually becomes larger as it courses anteriorly, receiving **efferent renal veins** from the kidneys and **genital veins** from the gonads. Anterior to the kidneys the postcava forms connections with the **postcardinal veins.** At a point a short distance posterior to this junction, the main part of the postcava passes ventrally and penetrates the dorsal aspect of the liver. It receives several **hepatic veins** from the liver. One of these is a comparatively large vessel coming from the ventral aspect of the liver. It joins the postcava near the point where it emerges from the anterior end of the liver. The postcava passes forward to the septum transversum and then divides into the two **hepatic sinuses** which join the common cardinal before they enter the sinus venosus.

Hepatic portal system of veins. The hepatic portal vein drains the

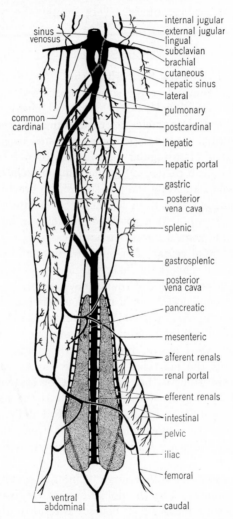

FIG. 17.16. Ventral view of venous system of *Necturus*.

digestive tract and spleen. It breaks up into capillaries in the substance of the liver. The vein is formed by the confluence of several tributaries. A large **mesenteric vein** originating in the large intestine courses forward along the intestinal wall. It is joined en route by a large number of small

intestinal veins. At the level of the pancreas it is joined by a large **gastrosplenic vein** draining stomach and spleen. The hepatic portal vein is formed by a joining together of the mesenteric, pancreatic, and gastrosplenic branches. It passes into the liver along the dorsal aspect of that organ.

The **ventral abdominal vein,** described in connection with the renal portal system, courses in the mesohepar and then sends branches to the liver. At the level of the hepatoduodenal omentum this vein forms a direct connection with the hepatic portal vein, thus effecting a connection between the two portal systems. The ventral abdominal vein of *Necturus* is homologous with the lateral veins of the shark.

Lymphatic System

The lymphatic system of *Necturus* does not lend itself to gross dissection. In caudate amphibians, in general, it consists of irregular vessels with thin walls. Two main portions are recognized. The first parallels the aorta and joins the two subclavian veins. The other courses beneath the skin and opens into the cutaneous and postcardinal veins.

Spleen

The **spleen** of *Necturus* is a dark, thin, elongated structure which lies to the left of the middle portion of the stomach. Like the digestive tract, it is drained by the hepatic portal vein.

NERVOUS SYSTEM

Since, in *Necturus*, the brain and spinal cord are surrounded by a bony protective covering, exposure of these structures for study is somewhat more difficult than in the shark with its cartilaginous skeleton. Exposure of the brain may be accomplished by slicing away thin layers of bone with a sharp scalpel and by chipping off small bits of the remainder.

Central Nervous System

Brain

Two distinctly separated membranes surround the brain. The first of these, the **dura mater,** lies just inside the skull from which it is separated by an **epidural space.** The second membrane, or **pia-arachnoid,** is a delicate vascular structure closely united with the brain. A **subdural space** filled with **cerebrospinal fluid** separates the dura from the pia-arachnoid.

The **brain** of *Necturus* (Fig. 17.17) is small, but its various components can be clearly observed, nevertheless. The **cerebral hemispheres (telencephalon)** are elongated and separated from each other by a longitudinal fissure. An **olfactory nerve** joins the anterior end of each cerebral hemisphere. **Olfactory lobes** are not distinct structures in the mud puppy, being imperceptibly united with the cerebral hemispheres. The **diencephalon** lies immediately posterior to the cerebral hemispheres. Its membranous roof forms a **tela choroidea.**

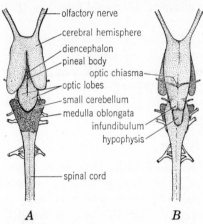

olfactory nerve
cerebral hemisphere
diencephalon
pineal body
optic chiasma
optic lobes
small cerebellum
medulla oblongata
infundibulum
hypophysis
spinal cord

A   *B*

Fig. 17.17. *A*, dorsal, and, *B*, ventral views of brain of *Necturus*.

Projecting upward from the roof of the diencephalon is a small, flat **pineal body.** The **optic lobes** forming the dorsal part of the **mesencephalon** lie posterior to the diencephalon. They are not very distinctly marked off from the latter. A small, transversely arranged **cerebellum** lies between the optic lobes and the **medulla oblongata (myelencephalon).** The cerebellum is poorly developed in *Necturus* in correlation with its sluggish habits. The medulla tapers posteriorly where it becomes continuous with the **spinal cord.** A **tela choroidea** roofs over the medulla oblongata.

On the ventral surface of the diencephalon is located the **optic chiasma,** formed by the crossing of the **optic nerves.** Most of the remainder of the **hypothalamus** is composed of an **infundibulum** which projects posteriorly and to which the **pituitary gland (hypophysis)** is attached. An inconspicuous **saccus vasculosus** is present on the dorsal aspect of the infundibulum.

As in the dogfish, the cavities of the brain consist of **lateral,** or **first** and **second, ventricles** in the cerebral hemispheres which, through **interventricular foramina,** join the **third ventricle** in the diencephalon. This is connected by a narrow **cerebral aqueduct** to the **fourth ventricle** in the medulla oblongata.

SPINAL CORD

The posterior end of the medulla oblongata is continuous with the **spinal cord.** The transition between the two is imperceptible. The spinal cord, which lies within the neural canal, continues to the tip of the tail. It is uniform in diameter except for a very slight enlargement in the sacral region. Posterior to this point it gradually tapers down to a fine thread, the **filum terminale.** A shallow longitudinal groove, the **dorsal fissure,** or **dorsal longitudinal sulcus,** is present along the middorsal line of the spinal cord. On the ventral side is a prominent **longitudinal ventral fissure.**

Peripheral Nervous.System

CRANIAL NERVES

Eleven cranial nerves are present in *Necturus*. They are small and are dissected with difficulty.

Terminal nerve (0). A small **terminal nerve** parallels the olfactory
nerve and enters the forebrain at the ventral border of the cerebral hemisphere on each side. It passes to the ventrolateral portion of the diencephalon.

Olfactory nerve (I). The olfactory nerves are prominent bands which
pass from the nasal mucosa to the anterior end of the cerebral hemisphere on each side. As previously noted, the olfactory lobes of the brain
are merged with the cerebral hemispheres.

Optic nerve (II). The optic nerves are small in *Necturus* in correlation
with the poorly developed eyes. They pass from the eyes to the ventral
surface of the diencephalon where their fibers cross, forming a typical
optic chiasma.

Oculomotor nerve (III). The third cranial nerves are very slender and
apt to escape observation. They arise from the posterior part of the
mesencephalon, passing to the superior rectus, inferior rectus, internal
rectus, and inferior oblique eye muscles.

Trochlear nerve (IV). The exceedingly minute trochlear nerves arise
from the dorsal part of the brain between mesencephalon and metencephalon. They innervate the superior oblique eye muscles.

Trigeminal nerve (V). The trigeminal nerve is the largest of the
cranial nerves. It comes from the anterior lateral border of the medulla
oblongata and passes forward in an oblique direction. Near its origin is
the **Gasserian,** or **semilunar, ganglion.** Beyond the ganglion the nerve
divides into three main trunks: **ophthalmic, maxillary,** and **mandibular.**
The ophthalmic branch passes straight forward. The maxillary courses
along the edge of the upper jaw. The mandibular passes to the angle of
the mouth and then continues along the lower jaw. Ophthalmic and
maxillary branches are sensory, but the mandibular contains both sensory
and motor fibers.

Abducens nerve (VI). The sixth cranial nerve, like the fourth, is very
fine and slender. It can be seen only with the aid of a dissecting microscope. The nerve arises rather far back on the ventral side of the medulla
oblongata and passes to the external rectus and retractor bulbi muscles.

Facial and auditory nerves (VII and VIII). The seventh and eighth
cranial nerves arise by a common trunk from the lateral border of the
myelencephalon just posterior to the origin of the trigeminal. A branch
of the facial joins the trigeminal at the Gasserian ganglion. Some of its
fibers run together with the ophthalmic branch of nerve V, forming the
superficial ophthalmic component of the facial nerve. Others, forming
the **buccal** branch of the facial nerve, parallel the fibers of the maxillary
branch of the trigeminal. These branches of the facial are composed only
of sensory fibers which innervate the lateral-line organs of the head.

From the common trunk formed by the facial and auditory nerves, an
anterior **hyomandibular branch,** composed of both sensory and motor
fibers, is distributed to the hyomandibular region.

The auditory nerve proper is short and passes to the structures composing the inner ear.

Glossopharyngeal and vagus nerves (IX and X). The last two cranial nerves have a common origin from the medulla oblongata, arising by three distinct roots. The most anterior of these is the glossopharyngeal. The roots enter a common ganglion and then branch. The glossopharyngeal nerve passes laterally and then branches to the pharynx, tongue, and muscles of the gill region. It is a mixed nerve. The vagus gives off a **lateral branch** to the lateral-line canal and sends other branches to the gills and viscera.

A **hypobranchial nerve** supplying the hypobranchial muscles is present in *Necturus*. It arises posterior to the vagus, but its exact components are somewhat uncertain. Apparently it contains fibers from the first and second spinal nerves.

Spinal Nerves

The metamerically arranged **spinal nerves** are paired structures arising from the spinal cord by two **roots, dorsal** and **ventral**. The two roots join at the **intervertebral foramen** to emerge from the vertebral column as a spinal nerve. Just *outside* the intervertebral foramen is a swelling, the **spinal ganglion.** From it arise **dorsal** and **ventral rami.** A short distance beyond the ganglion the ventral ramus gives off a branch, the **visceral ramus, or ramus communicans,** which passes to a **sympathetic ganglion.**

In amphibians the dorsal roots of the spinal nerves carry some visceral efferent motor fibers as well as the usual somatic sensory and visceral sensory fibers. The ventral roots also carry visceral efferent fibers in addition to somatic motor elements.

In the regions of the limbs the ventral rami of certain spinal nerves form **plexuses** by sending intercommunicating branches to one another. In the region of the forelimbs the third, fourth, and fifth spinal nerves are involved, forming a **brachial plexus** on each side. The nerves then pass from the plexus to the forelimb. At the level of the hindlimb is the **lumbosacral plexus.** Three or four spinal nerves enter into this plexus. The nerves which emerge pass to the hindlimb.

Peripheral Autonomic Nervous System

The peripheral autonomic nervous system of *Necturus* is difficult to study. The **parasympathetic portion** apparently consists of fibers carried by the third, seventh, ninth, and tenth cranial nerves. Possibly the sacral spinal nerves may also be involved. The **sympathetic components** consist of two slender **sympathetic trunks** running the length of the body on either side of the dorsal aorta from head to tail. They bear metamerically arranged **sympathetic ganglia** with which the visceral rami of the spinal nerves form connections. Certain large nerve plexuses are located along the main arteries leaving the aorta. Arrangement of preganglionic and postganglionic fibers undoubtedly follows the pattern observed in higher forms.

SENSE ORGANS

The small size of *Necturus* precludes a detailed study of its sense organs. The following points, nevertheless, should be noted.

Lateral-line Organs

Necturus, in accord with its permanently aquatic mode of life, retains its **lateral-line organs** in the adult. They are similar in arrangement to those of fishes, consisting of a **lateral-line canal proper** on either side of the body and of various canals in the head region. Branches of the facial (VII), glossopharyngeal (IX), and vagus (X) nerves innervate these organs.

Olfactory Organs

Lining the olfactory passage from external to internal nares are numerous folds which comprise the **olfactory epithelium.** Fibers of the olfactory nerve pass from the olfactory epithelium to the cerebral hemispheres **(olfactory lobes),** as previously noted. It should be recalled that in *Necturus* the nasal passages serve the dual purposes of olfaction and respiration.

Eyes

The **eyes** of *Necturus* are poorly developed and probably of little use other than in discerning the direction of light. The red rod cells in the retina of *Necturus* are the largest known. There are no movable eyelids. The **cornea** is fused to the skin, and the eye is capable of little movement despite the presence of the usual eye muscles. The **lens** is large in proportion to the other structures. Otherwise the various parts of the eye are similar to those of other vertebrates and require no separate description here.

Ears

In *Necturus* only the **inner ears** are present. They consist of a **membranous labyrinth** surrounded by a **bony labyrinth.** There is no tympanic cavity, as in salientian amphibians. The membranous labyrinth lies embedded within the **otic capsule,** from which it may be removed without too much difficulty after decalcification. It is composed of three **semicircular ducts:** anterior, posterior, and horizontal. Each has an enlargement, the **ampulla,** at its lower end and a saclike **vestibular region** with which the semicircular ducts communicate. The vestibule is composed of an upper chamber, the **utriculus,** which lies over a lower chamber, the **sacculus,** from which it is indistinctly separated. The sacculus contains an **otolith** composed of crystalline granules. The ears of *Necturus* serve primarily as organs of equilibration.

CHAPTER 18

THE CAT (*Felis domestica*)

The domestic cat is familiar to most civilized peoples. The common cat of today is descended from a cross between the European wildcat and the Egyptian race of the African wildcat. Manx cats, for which the Isle of Man in the Irish Sea is famous, are tailless, high-rumped forms. Ideally the tail is represented only by a tuft of hair. In this case the condition seems to have originated as a genetic mutation, the exact mechanism of hereditary transmission being at present unknown. Tailless cats, found in many parts of Russia, are believed to have originated in the Orient. The royal Siamese cats, with their blue eyes, black or chocolate-brown head and feet, and light-tan or cream-colored bodies, are domesticated descendants of the African jungle cat.

The average length of the domestic cat is about 2½ ft., the tail making up about one-third of this. Sexual dimorphism is exhibited primarily in size, full-grown males being larger than the females.

Cats have assimilated themselves well with our civilization, yet seem to have retained many of their feral instincts. Those which have reverted to nature are destructive and seek birds, mammals, and even fish as their prey. They can apparently see well in dim light. Cats stalk their prey stealthily, catch them by surprise, and kill them with their sharply pointed teeth. The olfactory sense is poorly developed.

Cats are prolific animals having from 3 to 12 young at a time. The kittens are born in a helpless condition with their eyelids fused together. The eyelids do not separate until the ninth day after birth. The body is covered with fur at birth. The mother cares for the young, but the male parent is lacking in parental instincts. The life span of the average cat is approximately 10 years.

Cats are of economic value as destroyers of insect pests. Their fur is of poor quality and known as **genet.**

EXTERNAL FEATURES

The external form of the cat is so familiar that a detailed description need not be given. The body is made up of four main regions: **head, neck, trunk,** and **tail.** The **eyes** have movable upper and lower **eyelids** as well as a **nictitating membrane.** This lies beneath the other eyelids and passes from the inner angle of the eye out over the surface of the eyeball. During life it is transparent. The **external ear** consists of a prominent **pinna** and an opening at its base which leads into the skull. This passage is the **external auditory meatus.**

The body is covered with **skin,** which is continuous with the mucous membranes lining the mouth, anus, and urogenital orifices. It varies in thickness in different parts of the body, being thickest in the ventral part of the neck region and on the pads of the feet. The skin is composed of an inner **dermis,** or **corium,** and an outer **epidermis.** The dermis is rather loosely bound to underlying structures by fibrous connective tissue. On the head and distal ends of the limbs, however, the skin is more firmly attached. **Hair,** a derivative of the epidermis, covers the entire body except the end of the nose and the foot pads. Special tactile hairs, the **vibrissae,** are to be found on either side of the nose, on the cheeks, and over the eyes. The **claws,** at the terminal ends of the digits, are also epidermal derivatives. Those of the cat family are *retractile,* being folded back into bony sheaths when not extended. There are five on the forefeet and four on the hind feet, in keeping with the number of digits. **Friction pads,** or **tori,** number seven on the forefeet and five on the hind feet.

The **anus** lies ventral to the base of the tail in the midline. In females the **urogenital opening** lies immediately anterior to the anus which it rather closely resembles. The opening is bordered by the **outer lips,** or **labia majora,** the entire structure being referred to as the **vulva.** In females there are five pairs of **nipples** through which the ducts of the **mammary glands** open to the outside. They are located in two longitudinal rows on the ventral side of the body on either side of the midline.

In males, the **scrotum,** a saclike structure containing the testes, is located a short distance anterior to the anus. Immediately in front of this is a slight elevation consisting of the **prepuce,** or **foreskin.** The **penis,** or male copulatory organ, is retracted under normal circumstances and, therefore, is not visible externally. When protruded it passes through the opening in the center of the prepuce, which actually is not the true urogenital opening.

In both sexes the region in which both anus and urogenital organs lie is called the **perineum.**

SKELETAL SYSTEM

The skeleton of the cat is completely bony except for the sternal ends of the ribs, which are cartilaginous and known as costal cartilages. Cartilage is also present at the articular surfaces of bones and in a few other places, as in the external ear.

The skeleton is divided into axial and appendicular portions. The axial skeleton consists of the skull, vertebral column, ribs, and sternum. The appendicular skeleton is composed of the limbs and limb girdles.

Axial Skeleton

Skull

The **skull** (Figs. 18.1 and 18.2) consists of three main parts: (1) the **cranium,** or bony case which surrounds and protects the brain, (2) the **sense capsules,** which enclose the organs of special sense, and (3) the **visceral skeleton,** forming the jaws and hyoid apparatus and contributing to the formation of the larynx. Cranium, sensory capsules, and the part of the visceral skeleton forming the upper jaw are rigidly united. Several large spaces, at least partially surrounded by bone, are to be observed in the skull of the cat. The eye socket, or **orbit,** is prominent when viewed from the dorsal side. A gap usually occurs in the bones surrounding the posterior end of the orbit. Through this, the orbit is in communication with another large space, the **temporal fossa,** into which a projection, the **coronoid process** of the lower jaw, extends. A long, bony **zygomatic arch** lies ventral and lateral to both orbit and temporal fossa. A rather large opening at the posterior end of the skull is the **foramen magnum.** It lies completely within the **occipital bone.** A prominent transverse ridge above the foramen magnum is the **lambdoidal ridge.** Extending anteriorly from its central portion is a longitudinal ridge, the **sagittal crest.** Lambdoidal ridge and sagittal crest are absent in kittens but become more and more prominent with age. The external opening of the ear, the **external auditory meatus,** lies at the posterior end of the zygomatic arch. Ventral to this is a prominent swelling, the **tympanic bulla.** The **external,** or **anterior, nares** (nostrils) are located at the anterior end of the skull. On the roof of the mouth are the **choanae,** or posterior openings of the nasal passages. Other small openings to be observed on the skull are **foramina** for the passage of cranial nerves and blood vessels.

The **occipital bone,** as previously mentioned, surrounds the foramen magnum and forms most of the posterior face of the skull. In kittens this bone is composed of four separate elements, which in adults become inseparably fused. These are a single **basioccipital,** two **exoccipitals,** and one **supraoccipital.** The exoccipital portions bear the **occipital condyles,** rounded structures for articulation with the **atlas,** or first vertebra. The inner surface of the occipital bone has a roughened appearance, the depressions of which correspond to the convolutions of the cerebellar portion of the brain. The basioccipital extends anteriorly on the ventral side of the skull to meet the basal portion of the **sphenoid bone.** A small foramen perforates the occipital bone at the ventral anterior border of each occipital condyle. It is called the **hypoglossal canal,** since the hypoglossal cranial nerve (XII) passes through it. Inside the foramen magnum and dorsal to each condyle is a small **condyloid canal.** A vein from the transverse sinus inside the skull passes through the condyloid canal.

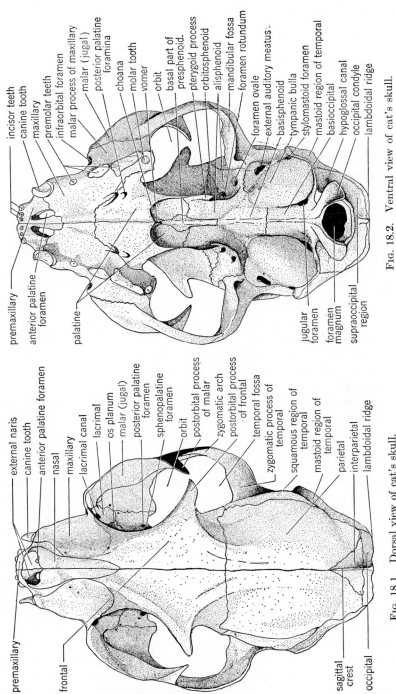

incisor teeth
canine tooth
maxillary
premolar teeth
infraorbital foramen
malar process of maxillary
malar (jugal)
posterior palatine foramina
choana
molar tooth
vomer
orbit
basal part of presphenoid.
pterygoid process
orbitosphenoid
alisphenoid
mandibular fossa
foramen rotundum
foramen ovale
external auditory meatus.
basisphenoid
tympanic bulla
stylomastoid foramen
mastoid region of temporal
basioccipital
hypoglossal canal
occipital condyle
lambdoidal ridge

premaxillary
anterior palatine foramen
palatine

jugular foramen
foramen magnum
supraoccipital region

FIG. 18.2.   Ventral view of cat's skull.

external naris
canine tooth
anterior palatine foramen
nasal
maxillary
lacrimal canal
lacrimal
os planum
malar (jugal)
posterior palatine foramen
sphenopalatine foramen
orbit
postorbital process of malar
zygomatic arch
postorbital process of frontal
temporal fossa
zygomatic process of temporal
squamous region of temporal
mastoid region of temporal
parietal
interparietal
lambdoidal ridge

premaxillary
frontal

sagittal crest
occipital

FIG. 18.1.   Dorsal view of cat's skull.

The large **parietal bones** lie anterior to the occipital on the dorsal surface. A prominent suture marks their point of union in the middorsal line. Each parietal extends rather far down on each side. On the inner surface is a prominent shelf, the **tentorium,** which in life lies between the cerebral and cerebellar portions of the brain. The tentorium really represents an ossification of the **dura mater** (page 582), which becomes secondarily united to the parietal bones. Each parietal articulates with the sphenoid bone by means of the tentorium. This is not obvious on casual examination.

A small, wedgelike, triangular **interparietal bone** lies between the occipital and posterior parts of the parietals. This bone is prominent in kittens but sooner or later fuses with the parietals.

Anterior to the parietals lie the paired **frontal bones** which form the remainder of the roof of the cranium as well as a large portion of the medial wall of each orbit. A **postorbital process** of the frontal on each side extends laterally and then ventrally toward a similar process projecting upward from the zygomatic arch. In some cats the two processes actually articulate with each other. Each frontal bone contains a cavity, the **frontal sinus.** This is in communication with the nasal passage.

A pair of **nasal bones** extends forward from the frontals to the external nares. A thin **nasoturbinate bone** passes inward from each nasal.

Paired **premaxillary bones** form the remainder of the boundary of the external nares. They also compose the anterior end of the upper jaw. Each bears three small **incisor teeth** set in sockets.

The **maxillaries** are large paired bones which form the rest of the jaw on each side as well as a large portion of the roof of the mouth, or **palate.** Each maxillary bears a single large **canine tooth,** three **premolars,** and a very small posterior **molar.** A large dorsal projection of the maxillary forms most of the lateral wall of the nasal passage. From this a thin **maxilloturbinate** extends into the nasal passage. The maxillaries articulate dorsally with nasals and frontals. A projection just above the premolar teeth is called the **malar process** of the maxillary, since it articulates with the **malar (jugal) bone.** A large **infraorbital foramen** pierces this portion of the maxillary bone. It serves for the passage of the infraorbital branch of the superior maxillary branch of the trigeminal (V) cranial nerve and for the infraorbital artery, which is part of the internal maxillary branch of the external carotid artery. On the ventral surface of the skull the two maxillaries join each other medially. Two large **anterior palatine foramina,** bounded by premaxillaries and maxillaries, lie on either side of the midline. Through these pass the nasal arteries and the nasopalatine branch of the maxillary portion of the trigeminal nerve.

The malar, or jugal, bones form the anterior part of the zygomatic arch. Each articulates with the malar process of the maxillary and is directed posteriorly. It sends a **postorbital process** dorsally toward the postorbital process of the frontal, with which it occasionally unites. The posterior extension of the malar is overlapped by a similar projection of the **temporal bone,** which forms the remainder of the zygomatic arch.

A small **lacrimal bone,** of irregular shape, forms part of the anterior medial wall of the orbit. It lies between maxillary and frontal. At its anterior border is the opening of the **lacrimal canal,** which communicates with the nasal cavity.

Another small bone, the **os planum,** which is really part of the **ethmoid,** also forms part of the medial wall of the orbit between lacrimal and frontal.

The **temporal bone** on each side is a complex of four regions which become secondarily united. It forms most of the lateral wall of the cranium posterior to the orbit. The **squamous region** of the temporal is a thin portion which articulates dorsally with the parietal. From it a **zygomatic process** extends anteriorly to meet the similarly named process of the malar. At the base of this process on the ventral side is a depression, the **mandibular fossa,** with which the lower jaw articulates. Only in mammals does the lower jaw articulate in this manner. The **tympanic region** of the temporal consists of the **auditory,** or **tympanic, bulla,** previously mentioned. The cavity of the **middle ear** and the three ear bones, **malleus, incus,** and **stapes,** lie within the bulla. At its junction with the basioccipital lies the **jugular foramen.** It serves for the passage of the ninth, tenth, and eleventh cranial nerves and the inferior cerebral vein. The **mastoid region** is a heavy, thick portion posterior to the external auditory meatus, lying between squamous and tympanic regions. It bears a small **stylomastoid foramen** through which part of the seventh cranial nerve passes. The **petrous** (stony) **region** cannot be seen from the external surface. It is of dense structure and on the side of the bone toward the cranial cavity. The delicate **inner ear** is enclosed by the petrous region of the temporal bone. A fairly large opening, the **internal auditory meatus,** is to be seen on the medial side of the petrous region. Just within the bone the opening divides into dorsal and ventral portions. The dorsal part is the **facial canal,** through which the seventh cranial nerve passes. The main part of this nerve emerges through the stylomastoid foramen. The lower canal is for the passage of the eighth, or auditory, nerve.

Paired **palatine bones** are included among several other bones on the ventral side of the skull. They lie immediately posterior to the maxillaries, meeting in the midline to complete the **hard palate.** Their posterior borders form the margins of the choanae. A lateral, vertical projection of each palatine contributes to the medial walls of the orbit. Two foramina are located in each vertical plate. These are a small **posterior palatine foramen** and a larger, more dorsal **sphenopalatine foramen.** The former carries the greater palatine branch of the maxillary portion of the trigeminal nerve, which then emerges from the skull through two small foramina on that part of the palatine forming a portion of the roof of the mouth. The descending palatine artery also passes through this foramen. The sphenopalatine foramen carries the sphenopalatine nerve of the maxillary branch of the trigeminal, the sphenopalatine artery, and the posterior nasal nerve.

The **vomer** is a slender unpaired bone with a troughlike depression along its dorsal aspect. It lies in the floor of the nasal cavity, articulating anteriorly with the palatines and maxillaries, posteriorly with the presphenoid, and dorsally with the ethmoid. The vomer forms part of the **nasal septum.**

The unpaired **ethmoid,** which cannot be seen externally, is a complex structure consisting of three parts. Its posterior end is termed the **cribriform plate** because of the numerous **olfactory foramina** which it contains for passage of fibers of the olfactory nerve. The cribriform plate separates the nasal and cranial cavities. A thin median vertical plate of bone, the **lamina perpendicularis** of the ethmoid, extends anteriorly from the cribriform plate. It contributes to the nasal septum. Folded, scroll-like **ethmoturbinates** extend from the cribriform plate into the nasal cavity.

Immediately in back of the vomer and separating the posterior portions of the two palatine bones is the **basal portion** of the **presphenoid.** It is partially overlapped by the vomer, palatines, and wings of the sphenoid (Fig. 18.2). On either side of the basal portion extends a wing of the presphenoid called the **orbitosphenoid.** These complete the medial walls of the orbits. Each orbitosphenoid bears an **optic foramen** which accommodates the optic nerve and ophthalmic artery.

The **sphenoid bone,** like the presphenoid, is composed of a basal portion, the **basisphenoid,** and two wings, the **alisphenoids.** The basisphenoid lies between the presphenoid and the basioccipital. Its *dorsal* face bears a depression, the **sella turcica,** in which the pituitary body lies. A slight bony projection forming the posterior border of the sella turcica is the **dorsum sellae.** The alisphenoids are thin projections which form articulations with the palatines, orbitosphenoids, frontals, parietals, and temporals. A small, curved **pterygoid process** projects forward from each wing. The alisphenoids partially overlap the basal portion of the presphenoid. Two foramina lie in each alisphenoid. These are an anterior **foramen rotundum** and a posterior **foramen ovale.** Both carry branches of the fifth cranial nerve. Another foramen, the **orbital fissure,** is formed at the junction of the orbitosphenoids and alisphenoids. Through it pass oculomotor, trochlear, and abducens nerves, going to the eye muscles. Part of the trigeminal nerve, a vein, and a branch of the internal maxillary artery also pass through the orbital fissure. Anterior to the tympanic bulla and bounded by it and the alisphenoid is a **canal for the passage of the Eustachian tube.**

The lower jaw, or **mandible** (Fig. 18.3), consists of two halves united firmly at their anterior ends by the **mandibular symphysis.** Each bone bears several teeth along its alveolar surface. There are three small

incisors, one large **canine,** two **premolars,** and one **molar.** A space, the **diastema,** separates the canine from the first premolar. A large depression, the **masseteric fossa,** on the lateral surface of the mandible marks the place of insertion of the masseter muscle. At the posterior ventral angle

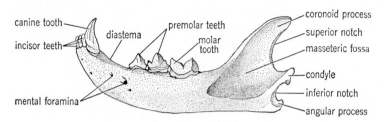

canine tooth
incisor teeth
diastema
premolar teeth
molar tooth
mental foramina
coronoid process
superior notch
masseteric fossa
condyle
inferior notch
angular process

FIG 18.3.   Lateral view of mandible of cat.

of the bone is an **angular process,** above which is an **inferior notch.** A **condyle** for articulation with the mandibular fossa of the temporal bone is dorsal to the inferior notch. Above the condyle is the **superior notch** lying along the posterior border of the large **coronoid process** which projects into the temporal fossa. On the medial face of the mandible near its posterior end is a large **mandibular foramen** through which the inferior alveolar nerve, and blood vessels, enter the lower jaw. They pass through the **mandibular canal** inside the bone, giving off branches to the teeth, and finally emerge on the lateral anterior face of the mandible as mental vessels and nerves, through one or more **mental foramina** near the base of the canine tooth.

The table on page 770 summarizes briefly the names of the various foramina of the cat's skull, their location, and the structures which pass through them.

The hyoid apparatus of the cat (Fig. 18.4) is derived from the second and third arches of the visceral skeleton. It serves to support the tongue and structures of the larynx. It consists on each side of a chain of bones extending from the tympanic bulla to the **thyroid cartilage** of the larynx. Named in order, these bones

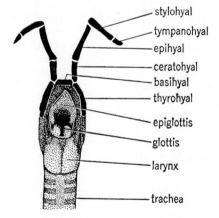

stylohyal
tympanohyal
epihyal
ceratohyal
basihyal
thyrohyal
epiglottis
glottis
larynx
trachea

FIG. 18.4.   Hyoid bones of cat shown in relation to larynx and trachea, dorsal view.

are **tympanohyal, stylohyal, epihyal, ceratohyal,** and **thyrohyal.** A crossbar, the **basihyal,** connects the two sides at the junction of ceratohyals and thyrohyals. The four bones between the tympanic bulla and the basihyal constitute the **anterior cornua.** The thyrohyals make up the

Foramina of the Skull of the Cat

Name	Location	Structures passing through:
Olfactory	Cribriform plate of ethmoid	Fibers of olfactory nerve
Optic	Orbitosphenoid	Optic nerve and ophthalmic artery
Orbital fissure	Junction of orbitosphenoid and alisphenoid	Oculomotor, trochlear, abducens, ophthalmic branch of V, internal maxillary artery, vein from sinus cavernosus
Infraorbital	Malar process of maxillary	Infraorbital branch of maxillary of V, infraorbital artery
Anterior palatine	Between premaxillary and maxillary	Nasopalatine branch of V and nasal artery
Posterior palatine	Palatine	Greater palatine branch of V, descending palatine artery
Sphenopalatine	Vertical plate of palatine	Sphenopalatine branch of V, posterior nasal nerve, sphenopalatine artery
Rotundum	Alisphenoid	Maxillary branch of trigeminal
Ovale	Alisphenoid	Mandibular branch of trigeminal, a small branch of the internal maxillary artery
Mandibular	Inner face of mandible	Inferior alveolar nerve (V) and vessels
Mental	Lateral anterior face of mandible	Mental vessels and nerves (V)
Facial canal	Petrous region of temporal	Facial nerve (VII)
Stylomastoid	Mastoid region of temporal	Facial nerve (VII)
Internal auditory meatus	Petrous region of temporal	Auditory nerve (VIII)
Jugular	Junction of temporal and basioccipital	Glossopharyngeal (IX), vagus (X), spinal accessory (XI), inferior cerebral vein
Hypoglossal	Occipital	Hypoglossal nerve (XII)
Condyloid canal	Occipital	Small vein
Magnum	Occipital	Spinal cord

posterior cornua. The former correspond to the lesser cornua of the human hyoid, and the latter to the greater cornua.

Vertebral Column

The notochord, or precursor of the vertebral column, is present in the cat only during the early part of embryonic life. It is completely replaced by the bony centra of the vertebrae. The vertebral column is divided into five regions.   There are **7 cervical, 13 thoracic, 7 lumbar, 3 sacral,** and from **4** to **26 caudal vertebrae.**   Those in each region, although having several features in common, nevertheless possess certain distinguishing characteristics.

The following features are common to all the vertebrae with the exception of the first, or atlas, and most of those of the tail.   Each consists of a **body,** or **centrum,** a solid rounded portion which lies ventrad the spinal cord.   The centra of adjacent vertebrae articulate with each other by means of cartilaginous **intervertebral discs** interposed between them.   A thin bony plate, the **epiphysis,** is present at either end of the centrum. In kittens the epiphyses are easily separated from the remainder of the centrum, but in adults they are firmly united with it.   Above the centrum and on either side a **neural process** extends dorsally.   The two

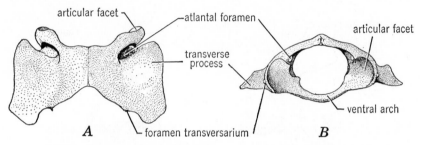

Fig. 18.5.   Atlas vertebra of cat: *A,* dorsal view; *B,* anterior view.

neural processes unite, forming a **neural arch** that encloses the spinal cord. A **neural spine,** or **spinous process,** projects dorsally from the top of the neural arch.   **Transverse processes** are lateral projections from the centrum and sides of the neural arch.   At the caudal border of each neural process is an **intervertebral notch** lying just above the centrum.   A smaller notch of similar nature is present at the cranial border of each neural process.   When two vertebrae are articulated, the two notches form an **intervertebral foramen** for the exit of a spinal nerve.   On the cranial border of each neural process is a projection, the **cranial articular process,** or **prezygapophysis.**   A smooth **articular facet** is located on its *dorsal* surface.   On the caudal border at the base of the neural spine is a similar **caudal articular process,** or **postzygapophysis,** with an articular facet on its *ventral* surface.   The prezygapophyses of one vertebra articulate with the postzygapophyses of the vertebra immediately in front of it by means of their articular facets.

Cervical vertebrae.   The first two of the seven cervical vertebrae differ so markedly from the others that they are best described separately.

The **atlas,** or first cervical vertebra (Fig. 18.5), differs from all others in that it lacks a spinous process and a centrum.   The centrum has been appropriated by the second cervical vertebra, as noted below.   In place of the centrum there is a narrow **ventral arch,** at the caudal end of which is a slight median projection, the **tuberculum anterius.** The transverse processes are in the form of large winglike masses which extend laterally for some distance. A **foramen transversarium,** through which the vertebral artery and vein pass, is located at the base of each transverse process. The cranial border of the atlas is marked by a pair of deep depressions, the **articular facets,** which receive the occipital condyles of the skull. Dorsal to them are located the **atlantal foramina,** through which the vertebral vessels are continued. At the caudal border of the bone are smaller articular processes, or depressions, for articulation with the second vertebra, the axis.

The **axis,** or **epistropheus** (Fig. 18.6), bears a marked projection, the **dens,** or **odontoid process,** at the anterior end of its centrum. This is

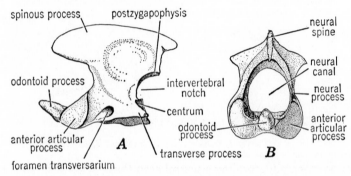

Fig. 18.6. Axis vertebra of cat: *A,* lateral view; *B,* anterior view.

really the centrum of the atlas which has formed a secondary union with the axis. On either side of the base of the odontoid process is a rounded **anterior articular process** for articulation with the atlas. A pair of small **transverse processes** extends ventrally from the centrum and base of the neural process. Each is pierced by a foramen transversarium. The neural spine is long and flattened and unusually prominent. The caudal end of the axis bears postzygapophyses with their characteristic ventral articular facets.

The remaining five cervical vertebrae are rather similar to one another. The spinous processes become progressively longer in passing posteriorly. The distinguishing feature of the cervical vertebrae is the presence of foramina transversaria (Fig. 18.7), which are lacking only in the seventh, or last. The transverse processes arise by two roots, one from the neural process and one from the centrum. The foramen transversarium lies between the two on each side. Distally the transverse process divides into two projections, a dorsal **transverse process proper** and a ventral **costal process** that represents the remains of a cervical rib.

Thoracic vertebrae.   The distinctive features of the thoracic vertebrae (Fig. 18.8) are those associated with rib articulation, for only these vertebrae bear ribs.   Each transverse process, which is a lateral projection from the neural arch, has a smooth **tubercular facet** on the ventral side near the tip for articulation with the tubercle of the rib.   All except the first, eleventh, twelfth, and thirteenth bear **cranial** and **caudal costal demifacets.** These are small, smooth areas at the dorsolateral angles of the cranial and caudal borders of the centrum.   When in position, the caudal costal demifacet of one vertebra and the cranial costal demifacet of the next posterior vertebra together form a depression, or **costal facet,** for reception of the capitulum of a rib.   Each rib, therefore, articulates with two vertebrae. The first thoracic vertebra bears an entire facet at its anterior end and a demifacet at its caudal end.   Each of the eleventh, twelfth, and thirteenth thoracic vertebrae bears an entire facet on each side of the centrum.   These three vertebrae lack tubercular facets.   The neural spines of the anterior thoracic vertebrae are long and slope posteriorly, but, beginning with number 10, they become perceptibly shorter and change their direction so as to point anteriorly.

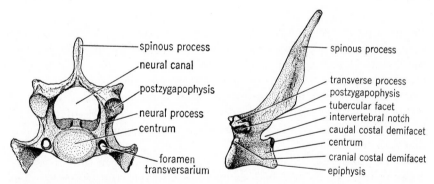

FIG. 18.7.   Typical cervical vertebra of cat, posterior view.

FIG. 18.8.   Thoracic vertebra of cat, lateral view.

Lumbar vertebrae.   The seven lumbar vertebrae are longer than those in the thoracic region.   Their spinous processes project anteriorly (Fig. 18.9).   The transverse processes, arising from the centra, are prominent and project in a ventrocranial direction.   Smaller **accessory transverse processes,** coming from the neural arch above the intervertebral notch, are prominent.   They are frequently lacking on the sixth and seventh lumbar vertebrae.   The prezygapophyses bear articular facets on their medial surfaces and rather prominent **mammillary processes** on their dorsolateral surfaces.

Sacrum.   Although the sacrum (Fig. 18.10) is considered to be a single bone, it is obviously formed by a union of three separate vertebrae.   Two pairs of **sacral foramina** are present on both dorsal and ventral sides.

These serve for the passage of the dorsal and ventral rami of the sacral spinal nerves. Three short spinous processes are present, lateral to which are two pairs of tubercles representing the points of union or fusion of prezygapophyses and postzygapophyses. The lateral surface of the ante-

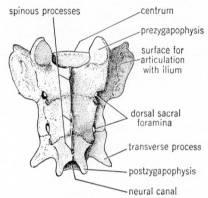

Fig. 18.9. Lumbar vertebra of cat, lateral view.

Fig. 18.10. Sacrum of cat, dorsal view.

rior portion of the sacrum on each side consists of a large roughened expanse, the **lateral mass,** which bears the surface for articulation with the ilium. It undoubtedly represents modified and expanded transverse processes to which sacral ribs have become indistinguishably fused. A pair of freely projecting transverse processes is present toward the caudal end of the bone. A pair of prezygapophyses serves for articulation with the seventh lumbar vertebra, and a pair of postzygapophyses for articulation with the first caudal vertebra.

Caudal vertebrae. The number of caudal vertebrae in the cat usually varies from 21 to 23, although as many as 26 have been observed. The caudal vertebrae decrease gradually in size from the sacrum to the tip of the tail. Only the first eight or nine caudal vertebrae are composed of the typical parts. Posterior to this they consist of little more than centra. On the eighth or ninth vertebra the neural canal is represented by a slight dorsal groovelike depression. Beginning with the third caudal vertebra a pair of rounded **hemal processes** is present on the ventral side. Small **chevron bones** articulate with these to form a **hemal arch** enclosing a **hemal canal.** These structures gradually diminish in size to finally disappear near the tip of the tail. Chevron bones are usually missing in prepared skeletons.

Ribs (Fig. 10.41)

A typical rib, such as the fifth or sixth, consists first of a **head,** or **capitulum,** the end of which articulates with the centra of two adjacent vertebrae be means of their costal demifacets. Close to the capitulum is the **tuber-**

culum (tubercle), which articulates with the tubercular facet on the ventral side of the transverse process. The portion between capitulum and tubercle is referred to as the **neck.** Distal to the tubercle is the long portion, or **shaft,** of the rib. The region where the shaft makes an abrupt turn, or bend, is the **angle.** The rib is bony. Its distal end is connected to the sternum by an intervening **costal cartilage.** There are 13 pairs of ribs in the cat. Only the first nine are considered to be **true ribs,** since they are the only ones to connect directly with the sternum. The remaining four are **false ribs,** of which the first three articulate with other ribs, the last ending freely and being called a **floating rib.** The length of the ribs of the cat increases from the first to the ninth. After the tenth they again become smaller. A decrease in thickness occurs from the fifth to the thirteenth. Not all the ribs are alike in structure. The first is flattened and has no perceptible angle. The last three lack tubercles.

STERNUM

The **breastbone** (Fig. 18.11) is composed of eight separate elements called **sternebrae.** The most anterior sternebra is the **presternum,** or **manubrium.** The costal cartilages of the first pair of ribs articulate with it near the central portion. The next six sternebrae, in their aggregate, make up the **mesosternum,** or **gladiolus.** The last piece is the **metasternum,** or **xiphoid process,** to the end of which is attached a flattened **xiphoid cartilage.** The second costal cartilage articulates at the junction of manubrium and gladiolus. The next five are attached at points of union of sternebrae. The eighth and ninth ribs join the seventh sternebra.

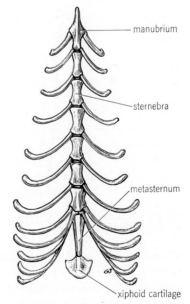

FIG. 18.11. Sternum of cat showing relation to costal cartilages. (*Drawn by G. Schwenk.*)

Appendicular Skeleton

PECTORAL GIRDLE

The **shoulder girdle** is composed of only two bones, **scapula** and **clavicle.** A third element, the coracoid, present in lower tetrapods but only in monotremes among mammals, is represented by the small **coracoid process** of the scapula.

The scapula, or shoulder blade (Fig. 18.12), is a large, flat bone, its shorter, more curved border being anterior. At its ventral end is a depression, the **glenoid fossa,** for articulation with the humerus. The coracoid process, mentioned above, is a medial projection at the anterior end of the glenoid fossa. A prominent keel, the **spine,** runs along the outer border of the scapula. It divides the surface into two large fossae, an anterior **supraspinous fossa** and a posterior **infraspinous fossa.** A projection at the end of the spine near the glenoid fossa is the **acromion.** Dorsal to this an angular process of the spine, the **metacromion,** projects caudad. The large, shallow depression on the medial side of the scapula is the **subscapular fossa.**

The clavicle of the cat is poorly developed. It consists of a short, slender rod of bone with no articulations. It is merely embedded in muscle tissue. In some mammals, as in man, the clavicle is a well-developed bone extending from scapula to sternum.

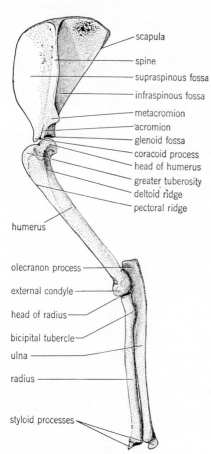

Fig. 18.12. Lateral view of left pectoral girdle and limb bones of cat.

FORELIMB

The **upper arm** (Fig. 18.12) contains a single bone, the **humerus.** A rounded **head** on the medial side of the proximal end articulates with the glenoid fossa. The **greater tuberosity** is a prominent ridge extending forward from the lateral border of the head. A smaller ridge, the **lesser tuberosity,** projects anteromedially from the head. Between the tuberosities is a deep **bicipital groove** which receives the tendon of the biceps muscle. Two ridges extend distally from the greater tuberosity. The more anterior of the two is the **pectoral ridge.** The **deltoid ridge** starts at the posterior end of the greater tuberosity. Not quite halfway down the shaft of the humerus it meets the pectoral ridge. The distal end of the humerus is marked by two projections, the external and internal **condyles.** A large **supracondyloid foramen,** through which the brachial artery and median nerve of the arm pass, is situated just above the inner condyle. The smooth area between the condyles is the surface for articulation with radius and ulna. On the caudal side of the bone between the two condyles is a deep depression, the **olecranon fossa,** into which a projection of the olecranon process of the ulna fits.

Two bones, **radius** and **ulna,** are located in the forearm. The ulna is the larger of the two. The prominent notch at the proximal end, for articulation with the humerus, is the **greater sigmoid cavity.** The part of the bone proximad this cavity is the **olecranon process,** or elbow. Just distad the greater sigmoid cavity is a smaller depression arranged in a transverse position. This is the **lesser sigmoid cavity** with which the head of the radius articulates. A projection mediad the lesser sigmoid cavity and distad the greater sigmoid cavity is the **coronoid process.** A **styloid process** projects from the distal end of the ulna. The radius articulates by means of its head with the humerus and with the lesser sigmoid cavity of the ulna. Just distad the head is a **bicipital tubercle** for insertion of the tendon of the biceps muscle. The distal end of the radius is larger than the head and, like the ulna, bears a **styloid process.**

The **carpus,** or **wrist,** of the cat (Fig. 18.13) is composed of seven bones arranged in two rows. The three bones making up the proximal row are the **scapholunar,** a large bone with which the radius articulates; the **cuneiform,** with which the ulna articulates; and the **pisiform,** somewhat smaller than the scapholunar and articulating with the styloid process of the ulna. In man the scapholunar is represented by two bones, the navicular and lunate. The cuneiform is referred to as the triangular. The pisiform called by the same name in both. The distal row of carpal bones consists of four separate elements named in order, from medial to lateral sides, the **trapezium, trapezoid, magnum,** and **unciform.** In man these bones are called, respectively, the greater multangular, lesser multangular, capitate, and hamate. Several **sesamoid bones,** representing ossified areas in tendons, are present in addition to the bones mentioned.

The **metacarpus,** or **hand,** is composed of five long **metacarpal bones.**

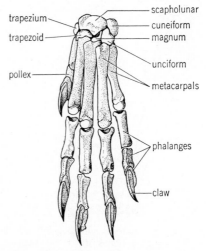

FIG. 18.13. Bones of left forefoot of cat as seen from above.

They are numbered from 1 to 5 beginning on the medial side.

The cat has five **digits,** or **fingers,** on the forefeet. Each except the first consists of three **phalanges.** The first, or most medial, digit, known as the **thumb,** or **pollex,** contains only two phalanges. The terminal phalanx in each case bears a depression, from the center of which projects a narrow bony plate. This gives support to the retractile claw. The second finger is known as the **index,** the third as the **medius,** the fourth as the **annularis,** and the fifth as the **minimus.**

Pelvic Girdle

The girdle supporting the hindlimb is composed of two halves, the **innominate bones** (Fig. 18.14), joined together ventrally to form a **symphysis.** Near the center on the lateral side of each innominate bone is a depression, the **acetabulum,** which receives the head of the femur. The acetabulum marks the point of union of the three components of the innominate bone, namely, the **ilium, ischium,** and **pubis.** Although easily recognizable as separate entities in kittens, these bones are rigidly fused together in adults. A fourth component, consisting of a small **acetabular,** or **cotyloid, bone** helps to form the acetabulum. It is wedged in between the others at their point of union. The ilium is the long portion of the innominate bone anterior to the acetabulum. It is joined to the vertebral column at the sacrum. The ischium lies posterodorsal to the acetabulum. It joins the symphysis ventrally. The pubis is the ventromedial projection. A large opening in each innominate bone between ischium and pubis is the **obturator foramen.**

Fig. 18.14. Lateral view of left pelvic girdle and limb bones of cat.

Hindlimb

The **femur,** or thigh bone, is the single large bone in the upper leg (Fig. 18.14). A large, rounded **head** articulates with the acetabulum. Lateral to the head is a constricted **neck,** anterolaterad of which is a prominent projection, the **greater trochanter.** A depression, the **digital,** or **trochanteric, fossa,** lies between the head and the great trochanter on the posterior side of the bone. On the posteromedial side, a short distance below the head, is a small tubercle, the **lesser trochanter.** At the distal end of the shaft of the femur are lateral and medial **condyles** for articulation with the tibia. An **intercondyloid fossa** lies between them. In front of this is located the **patella,** or **kneecap,** a pear-shaped sesamoid bone within the tendon of the quadriceps femoris muscle. Three additional small sesamoid bones are usually found in the patellar region.

The **lower leg,** or **crus** (Fig. 18.14), is made up of two bones: a large, stout **tibia** and a very slender **fibula.** The tibia of the cat is the longest bone in the body. At its proximal end are lateral and medial **tuberosities,** each with an articular facet for contact with the condyles of the femur. The anterior face of the proximal end of the shaft of the tibia is in the form of a narrow ridge, or **crest.** The distal end of the bone is longer on the medial side, the projection being spoken of as the **medial malleolus.** On the lateral side of the distal end is a facet for articulation with the end of the fibula. The fibula is situated along the lateral border of the tibia. Both ends of the fibula are expanded and form articulations with the tibia. A projection at the distal end is the **lateral malleolus.** It bears a facet at the point where it joins the tibia and another for articulation with the astragalus.

The **tarsus,** or **ankle,** of the cat (Fig. 18.15), like the carpus, is composed of seven bones arranged in two rows. A prominent heel bone, or **calcaneum,** is the longest of all the tarsal bones. Between it and the tibia is the **astragalus,** or **talus,** with which both tibia and fibula articulate. Distad the astragalus is the **scaphoid,** or **navicular.** In human anatomy calcaneum, astragalus, and scaphoid are called calcaneus, talus, and navicular, respectively. The distal row of four tarsal bones consists of a **cuboid,** at the end of the calcaneum, and **lateral, intermediate,** and **medial cuneiforms,** proceeding in order medially from the cuboid. In man these are referred to as the cuboid and third, second, and first cuneiform bones. The scaphoid lies between the astragalus and the three cuneiform bones. The cuboid forms articulations with the fourth and fifth metatarsals, the lateral cuneiform with the third, the intermediate with the second, and the medial cuneiform with the very small, rudimentary first metatarsal. In the cat the **big toe,** or **hallux,** is absent. Each of the four

calcaneum
astragalus (talus)
scaphoid
intermediate cuneiform
cuboid
lateral cuneiform
medial cuneiform
rudimentary 1st metatarsal
5th metatarsal
phalanges
claw

Fig. 18.15. Bones of left hind foot of cat as seen from above.

remaining digits is composed of three **phalanges,** the terminal one of which bears the claw. Sesamoid bones are found near the joints in the hind feet.

Joints

Two general types of joints are recognized: (1) **synarthroses, or immovable joints,** (2) **diarthroses, or movable joints.**

Among synarthroses in the cat are the **sutures** located between the various bones of the skull. The type of union exemplified by the roots of teeth fitting into sockets in the mandible, premaxillary, and maxillary bones is referred to as a **gomphosis.** Another type of synarthrosis is called a **schindylesis.** The articulation of the lamina perpendicularis of the ethmoid bone with the dorsal groove of the vomer is an example of a schindylesis.

In the diarthrosis, or type of joint permitting freedom of motion, the end of each bone is covered with cartilage. Between adjacent bones is a fluid-filled **synovial capsule,** composed of an outer, dense **fibrous layer** and an inner, very thin **synovial membrane** which is reflected over the cartilage at the end of the bone. About this complex are several ligaments which bind the bones together. Several types of diarthroses are recognized. The **ball-and-socket joint, or enarthrosis,** is exemplified by such joints as are found at the shoulder and hip. The **hinge joint, or ginglymus,** is found at the elbow and knee. **Gliding joints, or arthrodia,** occur in the ankle and wrist. The **pivotal joint, or rotatorium,** is illustrated by the point of articulation of atlas and axis. In some diarthroses, **articular discs, or menisci,** may at least partially separate the joint cavity into two parts. Such are the **semilunar cartilages** in the knee joint, which add to its complexity.

MUSCULAR SYSTEM

The muscles of the body are of two types: involuntary and voluntary. **Involuntary, or smooth, muscles,** which are under control of the autonomic nervous system, occur in the form of continuous sheets. They are found in the walls of various parts of the alimentary canal, blood vessels, ureters, reproductive ducts, bronchial tubes, etc. The **cardiac muscle** of the heart is an involuntary muscle of a special type. Involuntary muscles do not lend themselves well to dissection. Special histological preparations are usually required for their study. We shall therefore disregard them in our consideration of the muscular system of the cat.

Voluntary muscles are responsible for all ordinary movements of the various parts of the body. Since there are over 500 such muscles in the cat, it is not feasible to consider all of them in detail in a volume such as this. The student who is interested in a more comprehensive study of the musculature of the cat is referred to the latest edition of J. Reighard and

H. S. Jennings, "The Anatomy of the Cat," Henry Holt and Company, Inc.

Voluntary muscles are innervated by branches of cranial and spinal nerves. They exist as separate masses which are easily isolated from one another in properly preserved specimens. The muscles of freshly killed animals are studied with much more difficulty. Each muscle is surrounded by a sheet of connective tissue known as **fascia.** Fasciae also bind together groups of muscles. Dissection of muscles consists largely of tearing the fasciae between the separate elements so as to detach them.

Each end of a voluntary muscle is attached to some other structure. The structures to which they are attached are usually bones, but in some cases they join ligaments or tendons of other muscles. One end is generally attached to a part which is less movable than that to which the other end is joined. The former point of attachment is referred to as the **origin;** the latter as the **insertion.** Muscles may have one or more points of origin or insertion. Contraction of the muscle causes movement. The muscle must, therefore, pass over a joint in order to be effective in producing motion.

Muscles may have their origin or insertion in fasciae, but most frequently the attachment is accomplished by means of a **tendon,** a glistening, white cord of regularly arranged fibrous connective tissue. The term **aponeurosis** is applied to a broad, flat tendon. Ossifications sometimes take place within tendons to form the sesamoid bones referred to in connection with the skeletal system. The patella, or kneecap, is a good example of a sesamoid bone. Some muscles form ringlike bands around openings or cavities which are thus closed by muscular contraction. They are called **sphincter muscles.** Those sphincters closing the pylorus and anal opening are examples. Some muscles are attached to **raphes.** The term raphe is used to designate a furrow, or line, which marks the fusion of the two halves of certain symmetrical parts. The midventral line in the abdominal region is marked by a raphe, the **linea alba,** which separates the ventral muscles of the two sides of the body. Other raphes are present in the ventral thoracic region and along the middorsal line.

Voluntary muscles are arranged, in most cases, in opposing groups or sets of two, one set acting in just the opposite manner from that of the other. The terms used to distinguish the main types of opposing sets of muscles are explained on pages 466 and 467.

The skin of the cat and its underlying fat must, of course, be removed in order to expose the muscles underneath. Loose superficial fascia serves to connect the integument with the muscles. It is in this fascia that adipose, or fatty, tissue is usually deposited. A strong, tough fascia directly covering the surface of the muscles is called the deep fascia.

Since a few muscles insert on the skin, caution must be exercised so as not to destroy them. The mammary glands of female cats, particularly those which are lactating when killed, may obscure much of the ventral musculature. The mammary glands are integumentary derivatives.

Cutaneous Muscles

Cutaneus maximus, or panniculus carnosus. This dermal muscle consists of a thin layer of fibers on the undersurface of the skin over chest, shoulder, thoracic, and abdominal regions.

Origin. Linea alba, outer surface of latissimus dorsi (page 788), muscles of the arm in the ventral axillary region.

Insertion. Dermis of the skin.

Action. To move or shake the skin.

Platysma. A thin layer of muscle fibers, the platysma, covers the sides of the neck and lower part of the face. It is divided into several parts which are separated with difficulty.

Origin. Fascia of middorsal line, side of neck near lower anterior border of scapula.

Insertion. Skin of face, neck, ears, eyelids, lips.

Action. Moves skin of neck and face.

Muscles of the Abdomen (Fig. 18.16)

External oblique. On either side of the linea alba, in the abdominal region, lies the superficial, external oblique muscle. It forms a broad, flat sheet, the fibers of which pass in an anterodorsal direction.

Origin. Fascia in dorsolumbar region, last 9 or 10 ribs.

Insertion. Midventral raphe of thoracic region, linea alba, cranial border of pubis.

Action. Constricts the abdominal region.

Internal oblique. Immediately beneath the external oblique lies a thin muscular sheet, the internal oblique muscle. Its fibers are arranged almost at right angles to those of the external oblique.

Origin. From the same dorsolumbar fascia where part of the external oblique originates; from the crest of the ilium.

Insertion. Linea alba by an aponeurosis.

Action. Compresses abdominal region.

Transverse abdominal. Another thin muscular sheet lies beneath the internal oblique. The fibers of this muscle course in a transverse direction over the entire abdominal region.

Origin. From costal cartilages of the false and floating ribs, transverse processes of lumbar vertebrae, ventral border of ilium.

Insertion. Linea alba by a thin aponeurosis.

Action. Constricts abdominal region.

Rectus abdominis. Consisting of two longitudinally directed halves separated by the linea alba, the rectus abdominis extends from the costal cartilage of the first rib to the pubis. This muscle lies within a sheath formed by the aponeuroses of the two oblique and the transverse abdominal muscles.

Origin. Pubis.

Insertion. Costal cartilage of first and second ribs, anterior end of sternum.

Action. Compresses abdominal region; draws ribs and sternum caudad.

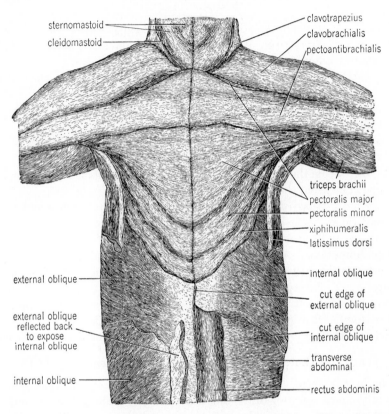

FIG. 18.16. Muscles of abdomen and chest of cat, ventral view. (*Drawn by Joanne Moore.*)

Muscles of the Chest (Fig. 18.16)

The thoracic muscles are arranged in superficial and deep layers. The superficial muscles are primarily associated with movements of the forelimb and pectoral girdle. On the ventral side lie the chest muscles, usually referred to as the **pectoralis group**. The four pairs of muscles of which this group is composed are not always easy to distinguish.

Pectoantibrachialis. The most superficial muscle in the pectoralis group is the pectoantibrachialis.

Origin. Manubrium of the sternum.

Insertion. Proximal part of ulna.

Action. Pulls arm toward chest.

Pectoralis major.   The pectoralis major, which lies immediately above and caudad the pectoantibrachialis, is composed of superficial and deep portions.

Origin.   SUPERFICIAL PORTION.   Midventral thoracic raphe in region of manubrium.

Insertion.   SUPERFICIAL PORTION.   Pectoral ridge of humerus.

Origin.   DEEP PORTION.   Cephalic half of sternum and midventral raphe immediately anterior to the sternum.

Insertion.   DEEP PORTION.   Humerus along a line parallel to the deltoid ridge and continued on to lower pectoral ridge.

Action.   PECTORALIS MAJOR.   Draws arm inward and turns foot in a forward direction.

Pectoralis minor.   The pectoralis minor lies immediately in back of the pectoralis major, from which it is rather indistinctly separated.

Origin.   From the six sternebrae making up the gladiolus of the sternum, in some cases from the xiphoid process as well.

Insertion.   Humerus, along ventral border of bicipital groove and along pectoral ridge.

Action.   Pulls arm and shoulder toward chest.

Xiphihumeralis.   A narrow muscle, the xiphihumeralis, is situated just posterior to the pectoralis minor of which it is sometimes considered to be a part.

Origin.   Midventral raphe in region of xiphoid process of sternum.

Insertion.   On ventral border of bicipital groove of humerus.

Action.   Aids pectoralis minor in pulling arm and shoulder toward chest.

Ventral and Lateral Muscles of the Neck and Head (Fig. 18.17)

The large external jugular vein is easily observed on the ventrolateral side of the neck anterior to the muscles of the pectoralis group.   It takes a rather superficial course.   Lymph glands and the submaxillary salivary gland are also prominent in this region.   They should be removed on one side so as to expose the underlying superficial muscles of the neck region for study.

Sternomastoid.   Immediately craniad the pectoantibrachialis and dorsal to the external jugular vein lies the sternomastoid muscle.

Origin.   Midventral raphe of thorax and manubrium of sternum.

Insertion.   Lambdoidal ridge, mastoid region of temporal bone.

Action.   Turns head; the two sides act together in pulling the head toward the neck.

Clavotrapezius.   Dorsolaterad the sternomastoid and pectoantibrachialis are two muscles which appear to be continuous.   The more anterior of the two is the clavotrapezius.   It is a wide muscle covering most of the lateral portion of the neck.   The clavotrapezius is the most anterior of the three components of the trapezius muscle (page 787).

Origin.   Lambdoidal ridge, middorsal raphe over axis vertebra.

Insertion.   Clavicle, raphe between clavotrapezius and clavobrachialis.

Action.   Pulls scapula forward and upward.

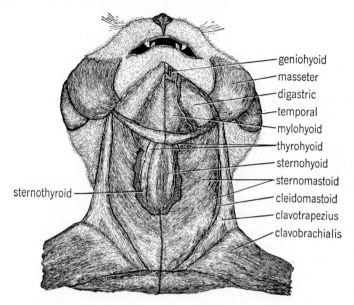

FIG. 18.17.   Ventral and lateral muscles of neck and head region of cat, ventral view. (*Drawn by Joanne Moore.*)

Clavobrachialis.   The posterior continuation of the clavotrapezius mentioned above is the clavobrachialis.

Origin.   Clavicle, raphe between clavotrapezius and clavobrachialis.

Insertion.   On brachialis muscle (page 794) a short distance before the latter inserts on the medial side of the ulna near the greater sigmoid cavity.

Action.   Flexes the forearm.

Cleidomastoid.   When viewed from the ventral side, the cleidomastoid muscle is obscured by the sternomastoid and clavotrapezius, since it lies just above them. The latter muscles must be separated in order to observe the cleidomastoid.

Origin.   Mastoid region of temporal bone.

Insertion.   Clavicle, raphe laterad the clavicle.

Action.   Depends upon whether clavicle or head is in a fixed position. (1) Turns head, pulls head toward neck; (2) pulls clavicle forward.

Sternohyoid.   Dorsal to the sternomastoid and coursing longitudinally on either side of the midventral line is the sternohyoid muscle. It is best to remove the sternomastoid in order to get a clear picture of the sternohyoid.

Origin.   Anterior border of first costal cartilage.

Insertion.   Basihyal bone.

Action. Depends upon whether hyoid or rib is in fixed position. (1) Pulls ribs and sternum forward and raises them; (2) draws hyoid posteriorly.

Sternothyroid. A small muscle with longitudinally directed fibers lies dorsal to the sternohyoid on each side of the trachea. The latter muscle should be removed in order to expose the sternothyroid to view.

Origin. Costal cartilage of first rib.

Insertion. Thyroid cartilage of larynx.

Action. Draws larynx posteriorly.

Thyrohyoid. A short narrow muscle, the thyrohyoid, is located on either side of the larynx anterior to the sternothyroid.

Origin. Thyroid cartilage of larynx.

Insertion. Thyrohyal bone.

Action. Elevates larynx.

Temporal. The temporal muscle can best be seen in a dorsolateral view of the head. It is a large muscle behind the eye and above the external ear.

Origin. Borders of the temporal fossa.

Insertion. Both inner and outer surfaces of the coronoid process of mandible.

Action. Closes mouth by elevating lower jaw.

Masseter. At the angle of each jaw, posteroventrad the eye and below the temporal muscle, is the large, thick masseter muscle. It lies anterior to the submaxillary and parotid salivary glands. The masseter is the chief muscle used in mastication.

Origin. Zygomatic arch.

Insertion. Masseteric fossa and surrounding area of mandible.

Action. Closes mouth by elevating lower jaw.

Digastric. Just medial to the masseter on the ventral surface of the lower jaw is the digastric muscle.

Origin. Occipital bone a short distance laterad the condyle; mastoid region of temporal.

Insertion. Ventral side of mandible.

Action. Opens mouth by depressing lower jaw.

Mylohyoid. The thin, superficial muscle, lying between the digastric and midventral raphe on each side, is the mylohyoid. Its fibers course in a transverse direction.

Origin. Posteromedial surface of mandible.

Insertion. Midventral raphe which extends from hyoid bone to symphysis of mandible.

Action. Pulls hyoid forward; elevates floor of mouth.

Geniohyoid. The geniohyoid muscle can be located by cutting the mylohyoids at their insertion and drawing back the cut edges. This will expose the geniohyoids.

Origin. Symphysis of mandible.

Insertion.   Basihyal bone.

Action.   Pulls hyoid apparatus forward.

Other Muscles of the Head

Several small muscles which we shall not consider are present in the deeper portions of the head and throat region. They are concerned primarily with movements of the tongue, pharynx, and hyoid apparatus and in the elevation of the lower jaw. Twenty or more superficial muscles have been identified on the head of the cat. They are the muscles of facial expression which are believed to be derived from specialized differentiation of various fibers of the platysma muscle (page 782). The separate elements are most difficult to identify.

Superficial Muscles of Dorsal Shoulder and Neck Regions (Fig. 18.18)

Turning now to the dorsal and lateral side of the animal, several large superficial muscles can be observed in the shoulder and neck regions. The

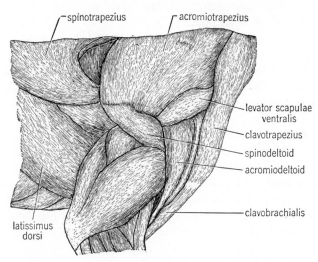

FIG. 18.18.   Superficial muscles of right dorsal shoulder and neck region of cat, lateral view.   (*Drawn by Joanne Moore.*)

most anterior muscle mass to be observed is the **trapezius.** This muscle is actually composed of three parts, the most anterior of which, the clavo-trapezius, has already been described.

Acromiotrapezius.   The acromiotrapezius, which is sometimes referred to as the **superior trapezius,** is a wide muscle which lies just posterior to the clavotrapezius.

Origin.   Middorsal raphe from neural spine of axis vertebra to spinous processes of the first few thoracic vertebrae.

Insertion.   On spine and metacromion of scapula.

Action. Pulls scapula upward; the two muscles aid in holding the scapulae together.

Spinotrapezius. The most posterior of the three trapezius muscles is the spinotrapezius. It is a flat triangular muscle with a broad origin.

Origin. Tips of the neural spines of most of the thoracic vertebrae.

Insertion. Fascia of supraspinatus and infraspinatus muscles (to be considered later).

Action. Pulls scapula backward and upward.

Levator scapulae ventralis. On the lateral side of the anterior shoulder region the rather small levator scapulae ventralis can be observed lying between the clavotrapezius and acromiotrapezius muscles.

Origin. Transverse process of atlas vertebra, basioccipital bone near tympanic bulla.

Insertion. Ventral border of metacromion.

Action. Pulls scapula forward.

Acromiodeltoid. The acromiodeltoid is a flat muscle which lies ventrad the levator scapulae and posterior to the clavobrachialis.

Origin. Acromion of scapula.

Insertion. Fascia of spinodeltoid muscle which in turn inserts on the deltoid ridge of the humerus.

Action. Flexes humerus and rotates it in an outward direction.

Spinodeltoid. The spinodeltoid lies over the head of the humerus. It is ventrad the acromiotrapezius and between that muscle and the acromiodeltoid.

Origin. Lower portion of spine of scapula.

Insertion. Deltoid ridge of humerus.

Action. Flexes humerus and rotates it in an outward direction.

Latissimus dorsi. The most prominent of the superficial muscles of the shoulder region as well as the last is the latissimus dorsi. It may be readily identified as a large, flat muscle lying posterior to the trapezius muscles.

Origin. Neural spines of vertebrae from the fifth thoracic to the sixth lumbar.

Insertion. Medial surface of shaft of humerus near proximal end.

Action. Pulls arm backward and upward.

Deeper Muscles of Shoulder and Posterior Neck Regions
(Figs. 18.19 and 18.20)

We shall not consider some of the small, deeper muscles of the neck which lie just ventral to the cervical vertebrae. In order to observe the deeper muscles of the shoulder and posterior neck region, it is best to cut across the three trapezius muscles as well as the levator scapulae ventralis, acromiodeltoid, and spinodeltoid. The underlying muscles, together with the borders of the scapula, will then be exposed.

Rhomboideus. The thick rhomboideus lies beneath the acromiotrapezius and spinotrapezius muscles. It connects the neural spines of the vertebrae in this region with the vertebral border of the scapula. The most anterior, lateral portion of the rhomboideus may appear as a separate muscle, to which the name **rhomboideus capitis** is sometimes applied.

Origin. Neural spines of the first four thoracic vertebrae and the interspinous ligaments in back of these spines.

Insertion. Vertebral border of scapula and its adjacent surfaces.

Action. Pulls scapula upward toward the vertebral column; the rhomboideus capitis portion helps to rotate the scapula by pulling it forward.

Splenius. Craniad the rhomboideus and under the trapezii is a large sheet of muscle which covers the dorsal and lateral sides of the neck. This is the splenius.

Origin. Middorsal line and adjacent fasciae.

Insertion. Lambdoidal ridge of occipital bone.

Action. The two acting together raise the head; each acting independently turns the head sideways.

Supraspinatus. The supraspinatus, which lies under the acromiotrapezius, covers most of the anterior, or supraspinous, fossa of the scapula.

FIG. 18.19. Muscles of right forelimb of cat, lateral view. (*Drawn by Joanne Moore.*)

Origin. Surface of supraspinous fossa of scapula.

Insertion. Greater tuberosity of humerus and the capsule covering the shoulder joint.

Action. Extends humerus.

Infraspinatus. The infraspinatus is a smaller muscle than the supraspinatus. As its name implies, it occupies the greater part of the infraspinous fossa of the scapula. It is somewhat posterior in relation to the spinotrapezius muscle and largely covered by the latissimus dorsi. The lower portion of the infraspinatus is covered by the spinodeltoid.

Origin. Surface of infraspinous fossa of scapula.

Insertion. Ventral portion of greater tuberosity of humerus.

Action. Rotates the humerus.

Teres major. Covering the caudal border of the scapula is the teres major. It lies directly behind the infraspinatus.

Origin. Caudal border of vertebral portion of scapula and neighboring fasciae.

Insertion. With the tendon of the latissimus dorsi on the medial surface of the shaft of the humerus near its proximal end.

Action. Lowers and rotates humerus.

Teres minor. The teres minor is a small muscle lying ventrad the in-

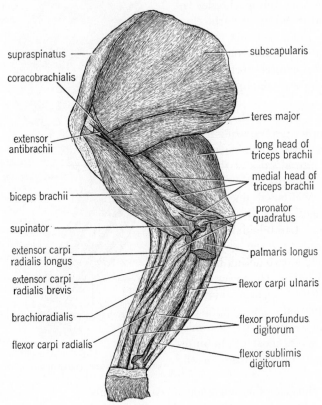

FIG. 18.20. Muscles of right forelimb of cat, medial view. (*Drawn by Joanne Moore.*)

fraspinatus and teres major. Its fibers run in a slightly different direction from those of these other muscles.

Origin. Portion of caudal border of scapula near glenoid fossa.

Insertion. Greater tuberosity of humerus.

Action. Rotates the humerus.

Subscapularis. The large, triangular muscle on the under or medial surface of the scapula is the subscapularis.

Origin. Almost the entire surface of the subscapular fossa.

Insertion. Lesser tuberosity of humerus.

Action. Draws humerus toward median line, thus serving as an adductor of the arm.

Serratus anterior. The serratus anterior lies underneath the scapula, between it and the body wall. This muscle is situated directly caudad the levator scapulae, with which it appears to be closely associated. Some authors refer to the levator scapulae as the anterior portion of the serratus anterior.

Origin. By several slips from the most anterior nine or ten ribs. The levator scapulae portion comes from the transverse processes of the last five cervical vertebrae.

Insertion. A small area on the medial surface of the scapula near its vertebral border.

Action. Pulls scapula toward wall of thorax in an anterior, ventral direction.

Muscles of the Thoracic Wall (Fig. 18.21)

A few muscles, not yet mentioned, are to be found in the thoracic wall. They are entirely dissociated from the limb and limb girdle.

Serratus posterior. Underneath the serratus anterior and continuing posteriorly is a thin muscular sheet, the serratus posterior. It covers the surface of the ribs in the upper part of thorax and neck.

Origin. Middorsal raphe from axis to lumbar region.

Insertion. Outer surfaces of ribs.

Action. Pulls ribs forward.

Scalenus. The scalenus lies on the ventrolateral side of neck and thorax. It is divided into several parts which are sometimes considered to be separate muscles.

Origin. From the ribs.

Insertion. Transverse processes of all the cervical vertebrae.

Action. Pulls ribs forward or bends neck, depending upon which structures are in a fixed position.

External intercostals. The external intercostal muscles lie in the outer part of the spaces between adjacent ribs. They are not present, however, between the costal cartilages of the first seven or eight ribs.

Origin. Ribs.

Insertion. Ribs.

Action. Pull ribs forward so as to raise them.

Internal intercostals. The small internal intercostal muscles lie directly beneath the external intercostals, from which they are separated with difficulty. The muscle fibers course in a direction almost at right angles to those of the external intercostals.

Origin. Ribs.

Insertion. Ribs.

Action. Pull ribs backward to lower them.

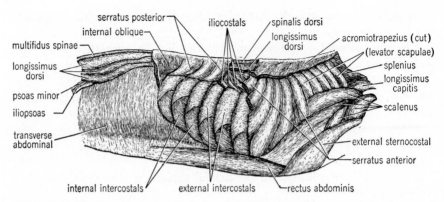

FIG. 18.21. Muscles of right thoracic and abdominal walls of cat, lateral view. (*Drawn by Joanne Moore.*)

External sternocostal. The thin external sternocostal covers over part of the anterior end of the rectus abdominis.

Origin. Sternum between third and sixth ribs.

Insertion. First rib.

Action. Pulls sternum forward.

Internal sternocostal. The internal sternocostal is often referred to as the transverse thoracic muscle. It is really a continuation of the transverse abdominal muscle into the thoracic region and lies on the inner surface of the wall of the thorax.

Origin. Dorsolateral part of sternum from third to eighth ribs.

Insertion. Costal cartilages near their junction with ribs.

Action. Moves ribs.

Muscles of the Back (Fig. 18.21)

Several muscles of the back, derived from the embryonic epaxial musculature, remain to be considered. Separation of the muscles into distinct masses is by no means so clear-cut as in the case of those which have already been discussed. We shall take up only a few of the more prominent muscles of the back.

Longissimus dorsi. The longissimus dorsi lies beneath the heavy fascia covering the lumbar region. It fills up most of the space between the neural spines and transverse processes of the caudal, sacral, lumbar, thoracic, and cervical vertebrae up to the atlas. The muscle appears to be divided into several parts.

Origin. Caudal, sacral, lumbar, thoracic, and cervical vertebrae; ilium.

Insertion. Parts of vertebrae all along vertebral column.

Action. Extends vertebral column.

Multifidus spinae. The multifidus spinae consists of large numbers of muscle fibers which pass from the transverse processes of one vertebra to the neural spine of another located some distance anterior to it. Anteriorly the multifidus spinae forms a long, single muscle which is sometimes considered separately as the **semispinalis cervicis.**

Origin. Transverse processes of vertebrae.

Insertion. Neural spines.

Action. Extends back or bends it, depending upon the particular elements involved.

Iliocostal. Ventrolaterad the longissimus dorsi in the thoracic region lies the iliocostal muscle. It covers part of the dorsal aspect of the ribs and is composed of several separate bundles.

Origin. Ribs.

Insertion. Third or fourth rib craniad that from which it originates.

Action. Draws ribs toward each other.

Spinalis dorsi. Under the dorsal attachment of the serratus posterior lies the spinalis dorsi. It is mediad the anterior end of the longissimus dorsi.

Origin. Tips of neural spines of posterior thoracic vertebrae.

Insertion. Neural spines of anterior thoracic and most cervical vertebrae.

Action. Extends vertebral column.

Iliopsoas. The iliopsoas, which lies ventral to the vertebral column, is described in connection with the muscles of the hind leg (page 801).

Psoas minor. Also located ventral to the vertebral column is the psoas minor which extends from the ilium to the more posterior thoracic vertebrae.

Origin. Centra of last one or two thoracic vertebrae and anterior lumbar vertebrae.

Insertion. Ilium anterior to acetabulum.

Action. Flexes lumbar region of back.

Quadratus lumborum. The flat quadratus lumborum lies ventral to the vertebral column in the lumbar region.

Origin. Last rib and posterior thoracic vertebrae.

Insertion. Transverse processes of lumbar vertebrae.

Action. Bends vertebral column laterally.

Many other muscles of epaxial origin, which we shall not take up in detail, are to be found in the back. They include the small **interspinal** and **intertransversarial muscles** which connect various parts of adjacent vertebrae. Portions of the longissimus dorsi in the neck region are often considered to be separate muscles. Extensor muscles in the tail are really caudal continuations of the multifidus spinae or longissimus dorsi muscles. Several flexor and abductor muscles are also present in the tail.

Muscles of the Arm (Figs. 18.19 and 18.20)

Muscles of the Upper Arm, or Brachium

Triceps brachii. The largest and most conspicuous of the muscles of the upper arm of the cat is the triceps brachii. It is composed of three main parts, or heads, all of which insert by means of a common tendon. The long head is located along the posterior part of the upper arm, the lateral head being directly anterior to it on the lateral surface. The medial head lies under the other two and may, therefore, be observed only by spreading apart the long and lateral heads.

Origin. (1) Lateral head, proximal end of humerus on deltoid ridge, (2) long head, scapula along border of glenoid fossa, (3) medial head, proximal part of dorsal side of humerus.

Insertion. Olecranon process of ulna.

Action. Extends the forearm.

Biceps brachii. The biceps brachii is a thick muscle lying along the anterior portion of the upper arm. In man this muscle has two heads (hence the name), but in the cat there is only one.

Origin. By a tendon from the glenoid fossa of the scapula.

Insertion. Bicipital tubercle of radius.

Action. Flexes the forearm; aids in supination of forearm.

Coracobrachialis. A short muscle on the medial surface of the upper arm, the coracobrachialis covers the joint between humerus and scapula.

Origin. Coracoid process of scapula.

Insertion. Proximal end of humerus on medial surface.

Action. Adducts the humerus.

Extensor antibrachii. The extensor antibrachii, or **epitrochlearis,** is a flat muscle on the inner surface of the upper arm. It partially covers the long head of the triceps.

Origin. Lateral ventral surface of latissimus dorsi.

Insertion. Olecranon process of ulna.

Action. Extends lower arm.

Brachialis. Anterior to the lateral head of the triceps, a rather small muscle, the brachialis, passes along the anterior lateral surface of the upper arm.

Origin. Lateral surface of distal shaft of humerus.

Insertion. Ulna just below the greater sigmoid cavity.

Action. Flexes the forearm.

Anconeus. A small, short muscle, the anconeus, is found in the region of the elbow joint on the lateral side of the arm.

Origin. Dorsal side of distal end of humerus.

Insertion. Lateral side of proximal end of ulna.

Action. May cause a slight rotation of ulna.

Muscles of the Lower Arm, or Antebrachium

(Figs. 18.19 and 18.20)

The muscles of the lower arm are chiefly concerned with movements of the hand and digits and with rotary movements required to place the lower arm in prone or supine positions, as the case may be.

Extensor muscles. The extensor muscles of the forearm consist of several long, narrow muscles more or less parallel to each other on the lateral or outer surface of the arm.

Extensor carpi radialis longus. The extensor carpi radialis longus is a long, thin muscle on the lateral side of the lower arm. It is the second muscle from the front of the arm, the first being the brachioradialis (page 796). It crosses over to the radial or thumb side of the arm.

Origin. A short distance above the lateral condyle of the humerus.

Insertion. By a long, thin tendon on the base of the second metacarpal.

Action. Extends the hand.

Extensor carpi radialis brevis. A very slender muscle, the extensor carpi radialis brevis, runs parallel and next to the extensor carpi radialis longus.

Origin. Above the lateral condyle of the humerus.

Insertion. Base of third metacarpal.

Action. Extends the hand.

Extensor digitorum communis. *Origin.* Above lateral condyle of humerus.

Insertion. The tendon of the muscle divides into four parts which insert on the dorsal surfaces of the phalanges of the second, third, fourth, and fifth digits, respectively.

Action. Extends the four digits on which it inserts.

Extensor digitorum lateralis. *Origin.* Above lateral condyle of humerus.

Insertion. The tendon of the muscle divides into three parts which insert on the dorsal surfaces of the phalanges of the third, fourth, and fifth digits.

Action. Extends digits 3, 4, and 5.

Extensor carpi ulnaris. *Origin.* Lateral condyle of humerus, above greater sigmoid cavity of ulna.

Insertion. Base of fifth metacarpal.

Action. Extends fifth digit and ulnar side of wrist.

Extensor indicis proprius. *Origin.* Ulna, distal to greater sigmoid cavity.

Insertion. The long, narrow tendon of the muscle divides into two or three parts which insert on the phalanges of digits 1, 2, and sometimes 3.

Action. Extends first two or three digits.

Extensor brevis pollicis. *Origin.* Shafts of ulna and radius.

Insertion. Base of first metacarpal.

Action. Extends and abducts the thumb, or pollex.

Flexor muscles. The flexor muscles of the forearm have a similar appearance to the extensors but are located on the medial, or inner, surface of the arm.

Flexor carpi radialis. *Origin.* Above medial condyle of humerus.

Insertion. Bases of second and third metacarpals.

Action. Flexes the hand.

Palmaris longus. *Origin.* Medial condyle of humerus.

Insertion. The tendon of the muscle divides into four or five parts which pass to the three-lobed pad on the palm of the hand to be inserted on the first phalanges of the digits.

Action. Flexes the digits.

Flexor carpi ulnaris. *Origin.* Medial condyle of humerus, lateral surface of olecranon process of ulna.

Insertion. Pisiform carpal bone.

Action. Flexes wrist.

Flexor profundus digitorum. *Origin.* Five heads: three from medial condyle of humerus, one from medial surface of shaft of ulna, one from shaft of radius.

Insertion. The tendon divides into five parts, each inserted on the terminal phalanx of a digit.

Action. Flexes the digits.

Flexor sublimis digitorum. *Origin.* From palmaris longus and flexor profundus digitorum.

Insertion. By four tendons passing to the second phalanx of the second, third, fourth, and fifth digits, respectively.

Action. Flexes digits 2, 3, 4, and 5.

Supinator muscles. Two muscles are used primarily to turn the lower arm and hand in a supine position.

Brachioradialis. The brachioradialis is a long, flat muscle lying along the lower lateral border of the upper arm and the anterolateral border of the forearm in front of the extensor carpi radialis longus.

Origin. Shaft of humerus.

Insertion. Styloid process of radius.

Action. Supinates the hand.

Supinator. *Origin.* Ligaments between humerus and proximal end of radius.

Insertion. By spirally arranged fibers on the proximal two-fifths of the shaft of the radius.

Action. Supinates the hand.

Pronator muscles. Only one pronator muscle, the pronator quadratus, is present in the forearm of the cat.

Pronator quadratus. *Origin.* Distal end of ulna.

Insertion. Distal end of radius.

Action. Pronates the lower arm and hand.

Muscles of the Hand

Several small muscles, which we shall not consider here, are responsible for the detailed and independent movement of the separate digits.

Muscles of the Leg (Figs. 18.22 to 18.25)

Muscles of the Upper Leg, or Thigh, and of the Hip

Biceps femoris.   The largest muscle on the lateral side of the thigh is the
biceps femoris.   It covers the caudal two-thirds of this portion of the leg.
Origin.   Posterior end of ischium.
Insertion.   Patella and proximal third of tibia.
Action.   Abducts thigh; flexes shank.

Tenuissimus.   A very slender muscle, the tenuissimus, lies just beneath
the biceps femoris and is closely adherent to it.   This muscle is sometimes
altogether lacking.

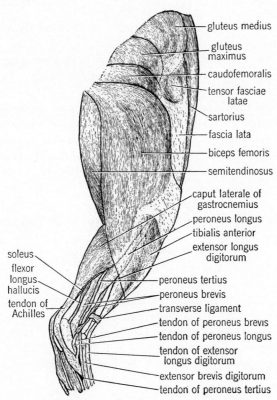

Fig. 18.22.   Superficial muscles of right hind leg of cat, lateral view.   (*Drawn by Joanne
Moore.*)

Origin.   Transverse process of second caudal vertebra.
Insertion.   Fascia of biceps femoris to tibia.
Action.   Very slight aid to biceps femoris.

Caudofemoralis.   The caudofemoralis lies just anterior the proximal end
of the biceps femoris and is largely covered by it.   Just distad the great
trochanter the muscle passes into a very narrow tendon.

Origin. Transverse processes of second and third caudal vertebrae.

Insertion. By a thin tendon on lateral side of patella.

Action. Abducts thigh; aids in extending the shank.

Gluteus maximus. A short muscle, the gluteus maximus, lies craniad the caudofemoralis which partly overlaps it.

Origin. Transverse processes of last sacral and first caudal vertebrae.

Insertion. Great trochanter of femur.

Action. Abducts the thigh.

Tensor fasciae latae. The tensor fasciae latae is a rather large muscle on the proximal cephalic face of the upper leg. It is difficult to separate the caudal border of the tensor fasciae latae from the cranial border of the gluteus medius.

Origin. Ventral border of ilium; fascia of the underlying muscle, the gluteus medius.

Insertion. On the fascia lata, a wide, heavy, glistening white fascia which covers most of the cephalic portion of the thigh. The fascia lata inserts on the patella.

Action. Pulls upon the fascia lata to help extend the shank.

Gluteus medius. Under the tensor fasciae latae and almost entirely covered by it is a short, thick, sturdy muscle, the gluteus medius.

Origin. Dorsal half of lateral surface of ilium, superficial fasciae, transverse processes of last sacral and first caudal vertebrae.

Insertion. Greater trochanter of femur.

Action. Abducts the thigh.

Gluteus minimus. Beneath the central part of the gluteus medius lies the small gluteus minimus.

Origin. Ventral portion of lateral side of ilium.

Insertion. Greater trochanter of femur.

Action. Rotates the thigh.

Pyriformis. The pyriformis lies underneath parts of both the gluteus medius and gluteus maximus, insertions of which may be cut in order to expose it. It lies directly over the proximal end of the large sciatic nerve of the upper leg.

Origin. Transverse processes of the last two sacral and first caudal vertebrae.

Insertion. Greater trochanter of femur.

Action. Abducts the thigh.

Gemellus superior. The gemellus superior is located directly beneath the pyriformis but is wider than the latter. Its cranial border is closely united with the caudal border of the gluteus minimus.

Origin. Dorsal border of innominate bone in region of posterior ilium and anterior ischium.

Insertion. Greater trochanter of femur.

Action. Abducts thigh and rotates it to some extent.

Capsularis. A short, flat muscle, the capsularis, lies under the gluteus minimus and gemellus superior.

Origin. Ilium in front of the acetabulum.

Insertion. Femur, just distad the greater trochanter.

Action. Rotates the thigh.

Obturator internus. Just caudad the gemellus superior lies the obturator internus.

Origin. Inner surface of ischium near the symphysis.

Insertion. The muscle passes over the dorsal border of the ischium to insert in the digital fossa.

Action. Abducts the thigh.

Gemellus inferior. The gemellus inferior is a flat, triangular muscle entirely covered by the obturator internus. The latter muscle must be cut in order to expose it. The gemellus inferior lies adjacent to the gemellus superior.

Origin. Dorsal part of lateral surface of ischium.

Insertion. On the tendon of the obturator internus and thence to the trochanteric fossa.

Action. Abducts the thigh.

Quadratus femoris. The most caudal of the series of fan-shaped muscles which have just been described is the quadratus femoris. It lies posterior to the obturator internus and gemellus inferior.

Origin. Posterior end of ischium.

Insertion. Both greater and lesser trochanters of femur.

Action. Extends and rotates the thigh.

Sartorius. From a lateral view, the sartorius appears as a thin band extending all along the cephalic border of the thigh. From a medial view, however, it is seen to be a broad, flat muscle covering almost half of the medial surface of the thigh.

Origin. Ventral border of ilium.

Insertion. Patella, proximal part of tibia, fasciae over knee joint.

Action. Adducts and rotates the thigh; extends tibia.

Gracilis. The remainder of the medial surface of the thigh is covered by the gracilis, another broad, thin muscle like the sartorius. These two muscles diverge near the proximal part of the thigh leaving between them a large, triangular area known as *Scarpa's triangle*. The large femoral artery and vein and the saphenous nerve are close to the surface in Scarpa's triangle.

Origin. Caudal two-thirds of the puboischial symphysis.

Insertion. By a thin aponeurosis on the medial surface of the tibia. It is continuous with the fasciae of the lower leg.

Action. Adducts the leg and pulls it backward.

Semitendinosus. The caudal border of the thigh is formed by a long muscle, the semitendinosus.

Origin.   Posterior end of ischium.

Insertion.   Proximal part of tibia on medial side.

Action.   Flexes the shank.

Semimembranosus.   A thick muscle, the semimembranosus, usually separable into two large masses, lies in front of the semitendinosus and under the gracilis.

gemellus superior

gluteus maximus (reflected)

pyriformis

sciatic nerve

obturator internus

caudofemoralis (cut)

biceps femoris

quadratus femoris

semitendinosus

semimembranosus

gluteus medius (reflected)

sartorius

tensor fasciae latae

gluteus minimus

tenuissimus

vastus lateralis

adductor femoris

biceps femoris

sciatic nerve

tenuissimus

Fig. 18.23.   Deeper muscles of right hind leg of cat, lateral view.   (*Drawn by Joanne Moore.*)

Origin.   Posterior end of ischium.

Insertion.   Distal end of femur and proximal end of tibia.

Action.   Extends the thigh.

Adductor femoris.   The adductor femoris is a large muscle in front of the semimembranosus, lying between the latter muscle and the femur.   It is also covered by the gracilis.

Origin.   Ventrolateral border of pubis and ischium, and from tendon of gracilis.

Insertion.   Shaft of femur.

Action.   Extends the thigh.

Adductor longus. The adductor longus is a relatively small muscle overlapping the upper margin of the adductor femoris and running parallel to it.

Origin. Anterior medial part of pubis.

Insertion. Middle portion of shaft of femur.

Action. Adducts the thigh.

iliopsoas
pectineus
rectus femoris
adductor longus
vastus medialis
adductor femoris
gracilis
sartorius
patella
semitendinosus
caput mediale of gastrocnemius
popliteus
flexor longus digitorum
tibia
plantaris
flexor longus hallucis
tibialis anterior
soleus
transverse ligament
tibialis posterior
medial malleolus
calcaneum
combined tendons of flexor longus digitorum and flexor longus hallucis
flexor brevis digitorum
tendon of extensor longus digitorum
metatarsal

FIG. 18.24. Superficial muscles of right hind leg of cat, medial view. (*Drawn by Joanne Moore.*)

Pectineus. The fibers of the small pectineus muscle run parallel to those of the adductor longus along its upper border. The two muscles are frequently united.

Origin. Anterior border of pubis.

Insertion. Proximal portion of shaft of femur.

Action. Adducts the thigh.

Iliopsoas. The iliopsoas has been referred to in connection with the muscles of the back. Only its terminal portion can be observed in a dissection of the leg. The capsularis, previously mentioned, lies anterior to the iliopsoas under the gluteus minimus.

Origin. Ventral border of ilium, from centra and transverse processes of the lumbar and last thoracic vertebrae.

Insertion. Lesser trochanter of femur.

Action. Flexes the thigh and rotates it.

Obturator externus. Underneath the adductor femoris lies a flat, triangular muscle, the obturator externus, which is not visible unless most of the thigh muscles are removed.

Origin. Inner border of obturator foramen on pubis and ischium.

Insertion. Trochanteric fossa of femur.

Action. Rotates the thigh.

Quadriceps femoris. The only remaining muscle mass of the upper leg which remains to be considered is the large quadriceps femoris. It occupies the entire front of the thigh. Its lateral surface is covered by the fascia lata. The quadriceps femoris is actually made up of four components with a common insertion on the patella and, by means of the patellar ligament, on the proximal end of the tibia.

Origin. VASTUS LATERALIS. This portion of the quadriceps femoris forms the entire lateral face of the muscle mass. It originates from the greater trochanter and the shaft of the femur.

RECTUS FEMORIS. A long, round muscle, visible only from a medial view, the rectus femoris lies next to the vastus lateralis and is partially covered by it. The muscle originates from the ilium just in front of the acetabulum.

VASTUS MEDIALIS. The vastus medialis lies entirely on the medial side of the leg next to the rectus femoris. It arises from along the shaft of the femur.

VASTUS INTERMEDIUS. Since the vastus intermedius is entirely covered by the other three parts of the quadriceps femoris, it is not visible unless they are cut or removed. It is usually of a darker color than the other parts and originates from almost the entire length of the shaft of the femur.

Insertion. Patella, by means of the patellar ligament on proximal end of tibia.

Action. Extends the shank.

MUSCLES OF THE LOWER LEG (SHANK OR CRUS) AND FOOT
(Figs. 18.22 to 18.25)

Gastrocnemius. The fleshy back part of the lower leg is commonly referred to as the calf. Toward the heel it narrows down into the heavy **tendon of Achilles.** The gastrocnemius muscle forms most of the muscle mass making up the calf. It arises from medial and lateral heads with a common insertion.

Origin. CAPUT LATERALE. The lateral head of the gastrocnemius originates from four points: (1) a tendon from the lateral side of the patella, (2) a tendon from the sesamoid bone laterad the patella, (3) superficial fasciae of the shank, (4) an aponeurosis which covers the plantaris.

CAPUT MEDIALE. The medial head of the gastrocnemius originates from the distal end of the femur and from a sesamoid bone mediad the patella.

Insertion. By means of the tendon of Achilles on the proximal end of the calcaneum.

Action. Extends the foot.

Plantaris. Between the two heads of the gastrocnemius lies the plantaris. Only a small portion of its proximal end is visible before dissection. It is rather difficult to separate from the caput laterale.

Origin. Lateral edge of patella, sesamoid bone laterad the patella.

Insertion. The inserting tendon of the plantaris forms the core of the tendon of Achilles. It passes to the ventral side of the calcaneum to form the origin of the flexor brevis digitorum (page 805).

Action. Extends the foot.

Soleus. The fourth muscle forming the calf is the soleus.

Origin. Proximal part of fibula.

Insertion. Tendon of Achilles.

Action. Extends the foot.

Popliteus. The popliteus is a short muscle which runs obliquely under the knee joint.

Origin. Lateral side of distal end of femur.

Insertion. Medial side of proximal end of tibia.

Action. Rotates the leg so as to turn the toes inward to a slight extent.

Flexor longus digitorum. On the medial side of the shank just in back of the tibia is a long, slender muscle, the flexor longus digitorum. Its proximal portion is partially covered by the popliteus.

Origin. Head of fibula and proximal end of tibia.

Insertion. Joins the tendon of the flexor longus hallucis to form a wide tendon which divides into four parts, one for each toe. Each of the four tendons inserts on the base of the terminal phalanx of the digit.

Action. Flexes toes; may aid in extending foot.

Flexor longus hallucis. Directly lateral in position to the flexor longus digitorum, which partly covers its medial surface, is the flexor longus hallucis. It is a larger muscle than the flexor longus digitorum.

Origin. Head and shaft of fibula; shaft of tibia; fasciae.

Insertion. Its tendon joins that of the flexor longus digitorum as noted above.

Action. Flexes toes; may aid in extending foot.

Quadratus plantae. A very small muscle, the quadratus plantae, is located on the ventral side of the foot. It is closely related to the combined tendon of the flexor longus digitorum and flexor longus hallucis on which it inserts.

Origin. Lateral surface of calcaneum and cuboid.

Insertion.   Tendon of flexor longus digitorum and flexor longus hallucis.

Action.   Keeps the above tendon in position.

Tibialis posterior.   Under the flexor longus digitorum and between it and the flexor longus hallucis is a slender muscle, the tibialis posterior, with a long, narrow tendon.

sartorius (cut)

vastus lateralis

vastus intermedius

vastus medialis

rectus femoris

sartorius

rectus femoris (cut)

gluteus medius

iliopsoas

pectineus

adductor longus

gracilis (cut)

gracilis

adductor femoris

semimembranosus

semitendinosus

Fig. 18.25.   Deeper muscles of right hind leg of cat, medial view.   (*Drawn by Joanne Moore.*)

Origin.   Head of fibula, proximal end of tibia near its head, adjacent aponeuroses.

Insertion.   Scaphoid and medial cuneiform bones of tarsus.

Action.   Helps to extend the foot.

Tibialis anterior.   The anterolateral side of the tibia is covered by the fleshy tibialis anterior.   As its tendon passes over the ankle, it goes beneath a transverse ligament.

Origin.   Proximal end of shaft of tibia, head and shaft of fibula.

Insertion.   First metatarsal.

Action.   Flexes the foot.

Extensor longus digitorum. The extensor longus digitorum is closely related to the tibialis anterior which covers its proximal end.

Origin. Lateral surface of distal end of femur.

Insertion. Its tendon passes under the transverse ligament and then divides into four parts. Each inserts on the first and second phalanges of its respective digit.

Action. Extends the toes; may aid in flexing foot.

Peroneus longus. Three peroneus muscles are all that remain on the lateral aspect of the lower leg. The largest and outermost of these is the peroneus longus.

Origin. Proximal half of shaft of fibula.

Insertion. Proximal ends of all the metatarsals.

Action. Flexes the foot.

Peroneus tertius. The peroneus tertius is the most slender muscle of the leg. It lies directly under the peroneus longus.

Origin. Lateral surface of shaft of fibula.

Insertion. Lateral side of fifth toe between first and second phalanges.

Action. Helps flex foot; extends and abducts the fifth toe.

Peroneus brevis. The peroneus brevis is a thick muscle surrounding most of the distal end of the fibula and lying under the other two peroneus muscles. It lies directly next to the flexor longus hallucis.

Origin. Distal half of shaft of fibula.

Insertion. Base of fifth metatarsal on lateral side.

Action. Extends the foot.

Extensor brevis digitorum. Confined entirely to the foot, the extensor brevis digitorum lies beneath the tendon of the extensor longus digitorum.

Origin. From transverse ligament noted above; proximal ends of third, fourth, and fifth metatarsals.

Insertion. By three tendons which go to the spaces between the toes. Each tendon then splits into two parts which insert on the digits on either side of the interspace.

Action. Extends the toes.

Flexor brevis digitorum. The flexor brevis digitorum is located on the bottom, or plantar surface, of the foot.

Origin. The muscle is really a continuation of the tendon of the plantaris muscle; it also has attachments to the scaphoid and medial cuneiform.

Insertion. By four tendons, each passing finally to the base of the second phalanx of a toe.

Action. Flexes toes.

Other Muscles of the Foot

Several small muscles, the description of which will be omitted, are to be found in the foot and ankle. They are concerned, for the most part, with detailed movements of the separate digits and phalanges.

COELOM AND COELOMIC VISCERA

The **body cavity,** or **coelom,** of the cat is divided into four separate compartments in which the viscera, or internal organs, lie. The **diaphragm** divides the coelom into anterior **thoracic** and posterior **abdominal regions.** It is composed largely of a dome-shaped sheet of muscle originating from the hypaxial region of certain cervical myotomes. It comes from the lower ribs, vertebrae, and sternum and inserts on a **central,** or **semilunar, tendon.** Part of it is homologous with the septum transversum of lower vertebrates. The **thoracic cavity** contains, among other structures, the lungs, the heart, and the great vessels which enter and leave the heart. It, in turn, is divided into three cavities, two of which, the **pleural cavities,** enclose the lungs; the other is the **pericardial cavity** containing the heart.

A sheet of serous membrane lines the coelom. A distinction is made between the serous membrane lining the body wall and that which is reflected over the viscera. They are called the **parietal** and **visceral layers,** respectively. The parietal serous membrane of the pleural cavities is the **parietal pleura;** the visceral portion, reflected over the lungs, is the **visceral pleura.** The medial walls of the two pleurae are in contact. Ventrally this forms a vertical partition, the **mediastinal septum,** which separates the two pleural cavities from one another. The two components of the mediastinal septum spread apart dorsally to form a large **mediastinal space.** All the thoracic viscera except the lungs lie in the mediastinal space. They include the heart, aorta, venae cavae, azygos vein, esophagus, trachea, bronchi, thymus gland, and various nerves.

Strictly speaking, the heart does not lie in the mediastinal space, since it is surrounded by a sac, the **pericardium.** It is actually the pericardium which lies in the mediastinal space. The pericardium is comparable to the parietal layer of serous membrane in other parts of the coelom. Closely applied to the surface of the heart is the visceral pericardium, or **epicardium.**

The parietal layer of serous membrane lining the abdominal, or peritoneal, cavity is called the **parietal peritoneum;** that reflected over the viscera is the **visceral peritoneum.** The viscera are thus actually outside the body cavity. Mesenteries, ligaments, and omenta are double layers of peritoneum which support the abdominal viscera. The term **mesentery** refers to the double layer of peritoneum which suspends the various parts of the alimentary canal from the dorsal body wall. **Ligaments** suspend organs other than those of the alimentary canal from the body wall. **Omenta** connect organs with other organs. The blood vessels which supply the abdominal viscera course between the two layers of mesenteries, ligaments, and omenta in order to reach their destination.

Among the mesenteries supporting the alimentary canal are the **mesentery proper,** suspending the small intestine, and the **mesocolon** and **mesorectum,** supporting the large intestine. The **dorsal mesogastrium,** or peritoneal fold which passes to the dorsal border or greater curvature of the stomach, takes a rather indirect course. During development the stomach undergoes a change from its original position, so that the greater curvature swings downward and to the left. In doing so, the dorsal mesogastrium necessarily is pulled along. It later becomes much elongated and forms a double fold which may extend posteriorly as far as the pelvis. This fold, which comes to lie between the viscera and ventral body wall, is called the **great omentum.** It really consists of four sheets of serous membrane. The two layers of the descending part of the great omentum enclose the left half of the pancreas and the spleen. The portion of the great omentum between stomach and spleen is spoken of as the **gastrosplenic omentum.** The great omentum is usually a site for deposition of adipose tissue. Fat may accumulate here in considerable quantity.

Between the two folds of the great omentum is a portion of the peritoneal cavity called the **omental bursa,** or **lesser peritoneal cavity.** This is in communication with the rest of the peritoneal cavity through an opening, the **foramen of Winslow,** or **epiploic foramen,** which lies adjacent to the bile duct near the posterior end of the liver on the right side.

The **lesser omentum** is a smaller sheet which connects the liver with the duodenum and the lesser curvature of the stomach. It is sometimes referred to as the **gastrohepatic omentum** or **duodenohepatic omentum,** depending upon the region concerned.

The liver is supported by several ligaments. A **falciform ligament** is attached to the ventral part of the diaphragm and ventral abdominal wall. A fibrous cord running from the umbilicus to the undersurface of the liver is the **round ligament,** or **ligamentum teres.** It represents the remnant of the left umbilical vein. The peritoneum is reflected over the ligamentum teres, which passes to the liver within the free margin of the falciform ligament. A single **coronary ligament** and two lateral **triangular ligaments,** from the dorsal and dorsolateral portions of the diaphragm, respectively, also support the liver.

At the posterior end of the body cavity the visceral peritoneum covers the urinary bladder. Along the midventral line it is a connection between the linea alba and bladder forming the **suspensory ligament** of the bladder.

The peritoneal cavity in males is entirely closed to the outside. In females, however, an external connection exists via the Fallopian tubes, uterus, and vagina.

CIRCULATORY SYSTEM

Many variations are encountered in the arrangement of blood vessels, particularly in regard to their points of origin. This is especially true of the veins. The differences may be traced back to deviations which take place during embryonic development. So many variations are to be found that it is difficult to give an accurate description of them. In the following account, therefore, only the most usual arrangement is stressed. In identifying a blood vessel it is best to observe its course and distribution rather than its point of origin. Any marked differences from the description given here should be carefully noted.

The Heart and Its Vessels

External Features

The heart of the cat lies in the pericardial cavity which is enclosed by the pericardial sac, previously noted. This in turn lies in the mediastinal space ventromediad the lungs. The heart of the mammal is more compact than the hearts previously studied. Its cranial end is called the **base;** the caudal end, the **apex.** The apical region projects slightly toward the left side. It is in contact with the diaphragm.

The mammalian heart is a four-chambered structure composed of two **atria (auricles)** and two **ventricles.** No sinus venosus is present. During development it becomes incorporated in the wall of the right atrium. The ventricles form the greater part of the heart and make up the posterior portion. The division between right and left ventricles is marked externally by a slight groove which extends from the left of the base to the right of the apex. The wall of the left ventricle is considerably thicker than that of the right.

The atria may be identified by their darker color and thinner walls. An external groove, the **sulcus coronarius,** marks the point of junction of atria and ventricles. From each atrium projects a pouchlike **auricula,** * or **auricular appendage,** with irregular edges.

Two main vessels leave the ventricular region. The most ventral is the **pulmonary trunk,** or **aorta,** arising from the right ventricle. The portion of the right ventricle leading to the pulmonary aorta is frequently referred to as the **conus arteriosus.** The pulmonary aorta divides into right and left pulmonary arteries which supply the right and left lungs, respectively. Dorsal to the pulmonary aorta and coming from the left ventricle is the **systemic aorta,** often referred to simply as *the aorta.* Two large veins enter the right atrium. The one entering on the posterior face is the **posterior vena cava,** or **postcaval vein,** often called the **inferior vena cava.** The vessel entering the anterior face is the **anterior vena cava,** or **precaval vein,** often referred to as the **superior vena cava.** Several **pulmonary veins** enter the left atrium.

A complex of vessels may be observed on the surface of the heart itself. These are the **coronary arteries** and **veins** which supply and drain the muscle of the heart itself.

* Some confusion exists in the terminology applied to this portion of the heart. The word atrium applies to the chamber under discussion, whereas the term auricle is applied to the auricular appendage alone. Many authors, however, use the term auricle to include both atrium and auricular appendage.

Internal Features

The wall of the heart is made up of three layers. Covering the surface is a thin layer of cells, the **epicardium.** It corresponds to the visceral layer of peritoneum and pleura, covering the abdominal viscera and lungs, respectively. Next comes the muscular layer, or **myocardium.** The membrane lining the cavity of the heart is the **endocardium.**

The separation of the heart into chambers is not very clearly indicated when the organ is viewed externally. It is separated into right and left halves by a dorsoventral partition. Each half in turn consists of an anterior atrium and a posterior ventricle, separated by valves. The **tricuspid valve** lies between the right atrium and ventricle; the **bicuspid valve** guards the opening between the two chambers on the left side.

The inferior and superior venae cavae bring blood to the right atrium from the posterior and anterior parts of the body, respectively. The blood then passes into the right ventricle. From here it goes to the conus arteriosus and pulmonary aorta. This divides into right and left branches going to the lungs. The tricuspid valve prevents the blood in the right ventricle from being regurgitated into the right atrium. After the blood has been oxygenated in the lungs, it again returns to the heart. This time it passes through the pulmonary veins which enter the left atrium. It then goes past the bicuspid valve into the left ventricle. The systemic aorta carries blood away from the left ventricle. Branches of the systemic aorta distribute blood to all parts of the body. **Semilunar valves** at the base of both the pulmonary and systemic aortae prevent blood in these vessels from returning to the ventricles.

A complex of vessels can be observed on the surface of the heart itself. These are the **coronary arteries** and **veins.** The coronary arteries arise from the systemic aorta just craniad the semilunar valves. They supply the walls of the heart itself with blood. The coronary veins collect this blood from the walls of the heart and empty it into the right atrium through a common opening, the **coronary sinus.** Three vessels, therefore, bring blood to the right atrium.

Atria. The atria are relatively thin walled sacs at the basal end of the heart. Each consists of two parts: a **principal cavity,** and an **auricula,** or **auricular appendage.** The latter is a pouchlike projection with irregular edges. It overlaps the roots of the pulmonary and systematic aortae. Parallel muscular ridges, the **musculi pectinati,** line the internal surface of the auricular appendages, but the walls of the principal chambers are smooth. The **interatrial septum** which separates the two atria bears an oval depression, the **fossa ovalis.** It marks the location of the **foramen ovale,** an opening between the two atria normally present only before birth.

The right atrium is larger than the left, but its walls are thinner. The superior vena cava opens into the anterior dorsal part. There is no valve at the opening.   The inferior vena cava enters the posterior dorsal side. Its opening is partially guarded by a small **Eustachian valve.**   The coronary sinus, guarded by the **valve of Thebesius,** opens into the atrium between the opening of the inferior vena cava and the atrioventricular aperture.

The left atrium receives the pulmonary veins which enter in three groups, as already described.

Ventricles.   The walls of the ventricles are much thicker than those of the atria, in correlation with the muscular force required to propel the blood to points at some distance from the heart.   The walls of the left ventricle are two or three times as thick as those of the right.   The internal surfaces of the ventricles are marked by numerous irregular muscular columns, the **trabeculae carneae,** or **columnae carneae.**   They are fewer in number in the region of the interventricular septum and are not present in the wall of the conus arteriosus.

The tricuspid valve between the right atrium and right ventricle consists of three thin, semicircular membranous flaps the bases of which are attached to the walls of the heart.   One is dorsal, another ventral, and the third is on the interventricular septum.   Several thin but tough nonelastic bands, the **chordae tendineae,** connect the free edge and ventricular surface of each flap to the walls of the ventricle.   The chordae tendineae of the dorsal and ventral flaps unite near the ventricular wall, where they are attached to muscular columns, the **papillary muscles.**   The chordae tendineae restrict the movement of the tricuspid valve, thus preventing regurgitation of blood into the atrium when the ventricle contracts.

The bicuspid valve between the left atrium and left ventricle consists of two flaps.   The base of one is attached to the interventricular septum; the other to the lateral wall.   Chordae tendineae serve to attach their free edges to the ventricular wall.   Trabeculae carneae are less numerous in the left ventricle than in the right.

Venous System (Fig. 18.26)

The venous system is composed of five main groups of veins.   They include (1) the veins of the heart, (2) the superior vena cava and its tributaries, (3) the inferior vena cava and its branches, (4) the hepatic portal system of veins, (5) the pulmonary veins.

Veins of the Heart

Numerous small veins which drain blood from the wall of the heart itself join together to form two main trunks, the right and left **coronary veins.**   These in turn unite to enter the **coronary sinus** which opens into the right atrium, its opening being guarded by the **valve of Thebesius.** In addition, several small **cardiac veins** open independently into the right atrium.   A few may even enter the ventricles.

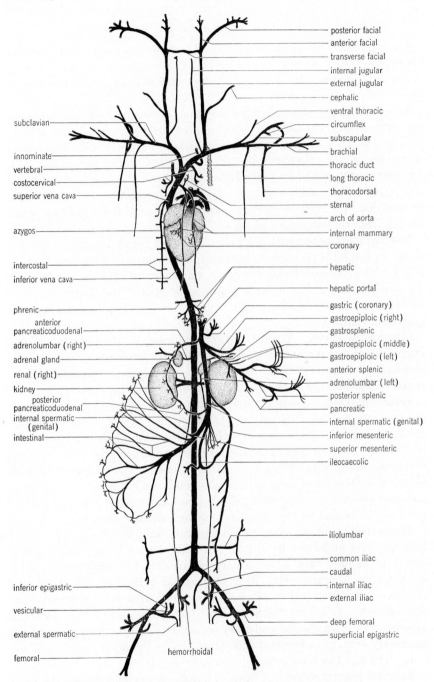

posterior facial
anterior facial
transverse facial
internal jugular
external jugular
cephalic
ventral thoracic
circumflex
subscapular
brachial
thoracic duct
long thoracic
thoracodorsal
sternal
arch of aorta
internal mammary
coronary
hepatic
hepatic portal
gastric (coronary)
gastroepiploic (right)
gastrosplenic
gastroepiploic (middle)
gastroepiploic (left)
anterior splenic
adrenolumbar (left)
posterior splenic
pancreatic
internal spermatic (genital)
inferior mesenteric
superior mesenteric
ileocaecolic
iliolumbar
common iliac
caudal
internal iliac
external iliac
deep femoral
superficial epigastric

subclavian
innominate
vertebral
costocervical
superior vena cava
azygos
intercostal
inferior vena cava
phrenic
anterior
pancreaticoduodenal
adrenolumbar (right)
adrenal gland
renal (right)
kidney
posterior
pancreaticoduodenal
internal spermatic
(genital)
intestinal
inferior epigastric
vesicular
external spermatic
femoral
hemorrhoidal

FIG. 18.26.   Diagram of venous system of cat, ventral view.

Superior Vena Cava and Its Branches

The superior vena cava, previously identified, is a large vessel through which blood from the head, neck, forelimbs, and thoracic region is returned to the right atrium. It enters the anterior dorsolateral part of that chamber.

Azygos vein. A short distance anterior to the point of junction with the right atrium, the superior vena cava receives on its right side a large branch, the azygos vein, which has already been observed. This vessel drains the dorsal thoracic wall and dorsal part of the abdominal wall. The **intercostal veins** have already been identified. A few of the anterior intercostal veins usually enter the azygos by means of a common trunk. In addition, the azygos receives small **esophageal** and **bronchial veins** coming from the esophagus and bronchi, respectively.

Internal mammary veins. A pair of internal mammary veins, running along the lateral borders of the sternum, unites anteriorly to form a single vessel. The common trunk receives a small **sternal vein** and then enters the medial ventral side of the superior vena cava. The continuations of the internal mammary veins on the ventral abdominal wall are the **superior epigastric veins.**

Innominate veins. A short distance anterior to the entrance of the azygos and internal mammary veins, the superior vena cava is formed by a fusion of two large vessels, the right and left innominate, or **brachiocephalic, veins.** The branches of these vessels on the two sides are alike.

Vertebral veins. A large vertebral vein enters each innominate a short distance craniad their junction. Occasionally one or both vertebrals enter the superior vena cava directly. The vertebrals bring blood from the brain. They pass through the foramina transversaria of the cervical vertebrae, along with the corresponding arteries. The **costocervical vein** usually joins the vertebral near the innominate vein but may, in some cases, join the innominate vein directly. Beyond the vertebral vein each innominate is formed by the confluence of three main vessels.

Subclavian veins. A large subclavian vein on each side receives blood from the arm and shoulder region. Outside the body wall this vessel is called the **axillary vein.** The axillary receives the following vessels: (1) a small **ventral thoracic vein,** (2) a **subscapular vein** from the muscles of the dorsal shoulder region, (3) a **thoracodorsal vein** from the latissimus dorsi muscle, (4) a **long thoracic vein** which passes under the pectoralis muscles after it leaves the mammary region, where it is called the **external mammary vein,** (5) a **brachial vein** which drains the deeper portion of the arm. The last has numerous tributaries.

External jugular veins. A large external jugular vein drains the head and face on each side. The tributaries of the two external jugulars are much alike except that the left is joined at its base by the **thoracic duct**

which is part of the lymphatic system (page 547). Not far from its junction with the innominate, the external jugular receives the **transverse scapular vein,** which is a continuation of the **cephalic vein** returning blood from the superficial portion of the arm. Anteriorly the external jugular is formed by the junction of **anterior** and **posterior facial veins**, which in turn are formed by a large number of tributaries from all parts of the head and face. Certain vessels from the **sinus cavernosus** on the ventral side of the brain emerge through the orbital fissure to join the posterior facial. The anterior facial veins of the two sides are connected by a rather large **transverse facial vein.**

Internal jugular veins. The internal jugular vein is frequently quite small in diameter. It joins the external jugular at a point which varies greatly in different individuals. The internal jugular receives an **inferior cerebral vein,** which emerges from the cranial cavity through the jugular foramen.

Inferior Vena Cava and Its Branches

The inferior vena cava, or postcava, which drains blood from the posterior part of the body, passes through the caudate lobe of the liver and penetrates the diaphragm before entering the posterior part of the right atrium.

Phrenic veins. As the postcava passes through the diaphragm, it receives small phrenic veins which drain that structure.

Hepatic veins. Numerous small branched hepatic veins join the portion of the postcava which passes through the liver. These vessels collect the blood brought to the liver by the hepatic portal vein and hepatic artery and return it to the systemic circulation.

Other vessels. Posterior to the liver the postcava takes a rather straight course along the dorsomedial part of the abdominal cavity. In an occasional individual it may split into two separate vessels which run parallel to each other. An **adrenolumbar vein** on the right side, draining the dorsal body wall and adrenal gland, joins the postcava craniad the kidney. The corresponding vessel on the left side usually enters the renal vein on that side instead of making a direct connection with the postcava. The renal veins from the kidneys are large but short vessels. It is not uncommon to find two renal veins coming from a single kidney. Caudad the renal veins are the **genital veins** from the gonads: **ovarian vein** in the female, **internal spermatic** in the male. The right genital vein usually enters the postcava directly, whereas that on the left side most frequently joins the left renal vein. Occasionally the condition is just opposite to that described. A few small **lumbar veins** enter the dorsal side of the postcava. These drain the dorsal body wall. A pair of **iliolumbar veins** joins the postcava about midway between the kidneys and the pelvic girdle. Farther back, the postcava receives the large, paired **common**

iliacs and a small, median **caudal,** or **sacral, vein** from the tail. The latter often enters one of the common iliac veins. The common iliac is formed by the junction of a large **external iliac** and a smaller **internal iliac.** Two vessels come together to form the external iliac. These are a **deep femoral vein** from the median side of the leg and a **femoral vein proper** which forms the main continuation of the external iliac. The external iliac, deep femoral, or femoral proper also receive several small vessels, the arrangement of which varies considerably in different specimens. These include (1) a **vesicular vein** from the urinary bladder, (2) an **external spermatic vein** from the testes, (3) an **inferior epigastric vein,** which passes along the inside of the abdominal wall and which extends anteriorly to anastomose with the **superior epigastric vein,** a continuation of the **internal mammary,** (4) a **superficial epigastric vein,** which extends forward to anastomose with the **external mammary vein.** The internal iliac is formed by the junction of several vessels from the gluteal region and a **hemorrhoidal vein** coming from the rectum and bladder.

HEPATIC PORTAL VEIN

The large and important hepatic portal system of veins drains the organs of the digestive system that are situated in the abdominal cavity. In addition, it drains the spleen, a structure which is considered to belong to the circulatory system. The portal vein proper lies dorsal to the bile duct. Upon entering the liver, it breaks into branches supplying the various liver lobes. These divide and redivide within the liver, ultimately terminating in capillaries (sinusoids). The portal vein is formed by the confluence of several vessels.

Anterior pancreaticoduodenal vein. In the region of the pylorus the hepatic portal vein is joined by the anterior pancreaticoduodenal vein which drains the anterior part of the duodenum and that portion of the pancreas adjacent to it.

Coronary vein of stomach. From the lesser curvature of the stomach a coronary vein **(gastric vein)** emerges which may join the portal near the anterior pancreaticoduodenal. Frequently, however, it joins the gastrosplenic vein instead.

Gastrosplenic vein. A large gastrosplenic vein is another vessel which joins the portal. It receives small **pancreatic veins** from the lobe of the pancreas adjacent to the stomach, one or two **middle gastroepiploic veins** from the stomach and great omentum, a large **posterior splenic branch** from the caudal end of the spleen, and an **anterior splenic** from the cranial portion of the spleen. The latter receives several **left gastroepiploic veins** from the stomach and great omentum.

Right gastroepiploic. The pyloric region, greater curvature of the stomach, and part of the greater omenum are drained by the right gastroepiploic vein which joins the portal near the point where the coronary and gastrosplenic veins enter.

Superior mesenteric vein. The largest tributary of the hepatic portal is the superior mesenteric vein. It is formed by a large number of radiating branches from the small intestine and part of the large intestine. These unite into a common vessel.

Posterior pancreaticoduodenal. From the posterior end of the duodenum and the adjacent region of the pancreas, a posterior pancreaticoduodenal vein arises, which joins the superior mesenteric. Branches of posterior and anterior pancreaticoduodenal veins anastomose with one another. In tracing these vessels be careful not to confuse them with the pancreatic ducts which ramify through the pancreatic tissue.

Inferior mesenteric vein. A rather large vessel, the inferior mesenteric vein, courses along the large intestine. Anteriorly it joins the superior mesenteric.

PULMONARY VEINS

Three groups of **pulmonary veins** enter the left atrium. Each group is composed of two or three vessels which enter into a slightly expanded portion of the atrium. Right, left, and dorsal expansions are present. The right one receives blood from the anterior and middle lobes of the right lung; the left expansion is joined by vessels from the anterior and middle lobes of the left lung. Blood from the caudal lobes of the two sides enters the dorsal expansion.

Arterial System (Fig. 18.27)

SYSTEMIC AORTA

The **systemic aorta,** which leads from the left ventricle, distributes blood to the entire body. A short distance from its point of origin it bends sharply to the left and then turns in a posterodorsal direction, swinging over to the left side of the midline underneath the vertebral column. It passes through the diaphragm and continues to the posterior end of the abdominal cavity. The bend is referred to as the **arch of the aorta;** the portion between the arch and the diaphragm is called the **thoracic aorta;** the remainder, posterior to the diaphragm, is the **abdominal aorta.** Numerous branches come off the aorta along its course. Slight variations from the following description are frequently encountered.

BRANCHES OF THE THORACIC AORTA

Coronary arteries. Two **coronary arteries,** right and left, arise from the aorta near its base, just craniad the semilunar valves (Fig. 12.13). These

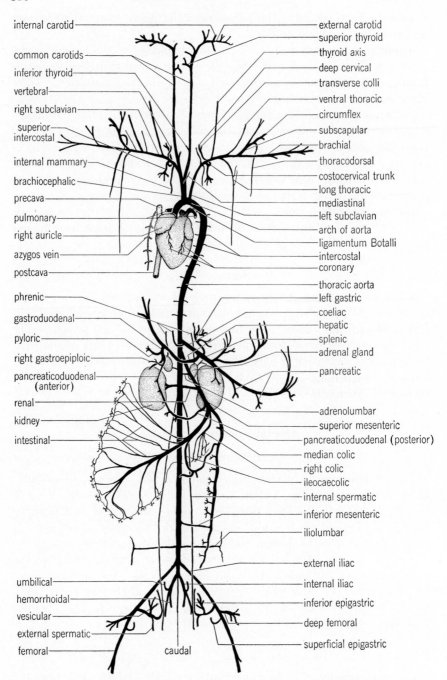

internal carotid

common carotids

inferior thyroid

vertebral

right subclavian

superior intercostal

internal mammary

brachiocephalic

precava

pulmonary

right auricle

azygos vein

postcava

phrenic

gastroduodenal

pyloric

right gastroepiploic

pancreaticoduodenal (anterior)

renal

kidney

intestinal

umbilical

hemorrhoidal

vesicular

external spermatic

femoral

caudal

external carotid

superior thyroid

thyroid axis

deep cervical

transverse colli

ventral thoracic

circumflex

subscapular

brachial

thoracodorsal

costocervical trunk

long thoracic

mediastinal

left subclavian

arch of aorta

ligamentum Botalli

intercostal

coronary

thoracic aorta

left gastric

coeliac

hepatic

splenic

adrenal gland

pancreatic

adrenolumbar

superior mesenteric

pancreaticoduodenal (posterior)

median colic

right colic

ileocaecolic

internal spermatic

inferior mesenteric

iliolumbar

external iliac

internal iliac

inferior epigastric

deep femoral

superficial epigastric

FIG. 18.27. Diagram of arterial system of cat, ventral view.

vessels, as previously mentioned, supply blood to the wall of the heart itself.

Brachiocephalic artery. The next vessel coming off the aorta is a large artery which passes craniad from the arch. This is the **brachiocephalic,** or **innominate, artery.** It gives off a small **mediastinal artery** to the mediastinum and then branches into two **common carotid arteries.** A small **inferior thyroid artery** is frequently found coming off each common carotid artery. It courses craniad along the trachea up to the thyroid gland (page 833), giving off small branches to the esophagus and trachea.

From the base of the right common carotid a large **right subclavian artery** is given off. This vessel passes to the arm. Before it goes through the body wall, it gives off several branches.

An **internal mammary artery** passes posteriorly from the subclavian, coursing along the lateral border of the sternum. Branches are distributed to the ventral side of the thorax, pericardium, mediastinum, and diaphragm. Posteriorly the internal mammary is continued as the **superior epigastric artery** in the ventral abdominal wall, supplying the rectus abdominis and other ventral muscles of the abdomen.

Close to the internal mammary and opposite the first rib, a **vertebral artery** arises from the right subclavian. It turns dorsad and craniad and enters the foramen transversarium of the sixth cervical vertebra. The vertebral continues forward through the foramina transversaria of the anterior cervical vertebrae. When it reaches the atlas, it passes through the atlantal foramen into the neural canal under the spinal cord. At the level of the foramen magnum the vertebral artery joins its fellow from the left side to form the **basilar artery.** The basilar continues craniad along the midventral line of the brain as far as the pituitary body, where it divides into two. These branches anastomose with branches of the internal carotid arteries to form the **circle of Willis,** which encircles the optic chiasma (Fig. 18.32*B*) and the pituitary body. Branches of the vertebral artery pass through the intervertebral foramina to the muscles of the neck. Other branches are distributed to the ventral surface of the spinal cord.

The **costocervical trunk** comes off the subclavian near the internal mammary and vertebral arteries. It quickly divides into two branches. The smaller branch is the **superior intercostal artery.** It passes caudad and is distributed to the most anterior intercostal muscles. The other branch of the costocervical trunk soon divides into lateral and dorsal branches. The lateral branch, or **transverse colli,** goes to the serratus anterior, levator scapulae, and rhomboideus muscles. The **dorsal,** or **deep, cervical branch** passes to the deep muscles of the neck.

The **thyrocervical trunk,** or **thyroid axis,** is another branch of the subclavian. It passes directly anteriorly, giving off numerous branches to various muscles of the shoulder.

The continuation of the subclavian outside the body wall is referred to as the **axillary artery.** Several branches arise from the axillary. These include a small **ventral thoracic artery** going to the pectoralis muscles; a **long thoracic artery,** which passes posteriorly on the abdominal wall as the **external mammary artery;** a **subscapular artery,** which gives off a number of branches distributed to the muscles of the scapular region. A main branch of the subscapular, called the **thoracodorsal artery,** supplies the latissimus dorsi and teres major muscles. Another branch, the **circumflex,** extends dorsally beside the head of the humerus.

The continuation of the axillary beyond the subscapular is called the **brachial artery.** It passes into the arm where it gives off many branches. It is the brachial artery that passes through the supracondyloid foramen of the humerus.

After giving off the right subclavian artery, the right common carotid continues forward. At the level of the larynx a small **superior thyroid artery** branches off, supplying the thyroid gland, larynx, and sternohyoid muscles. Other branches of the common carotid are distributed to the dorsal neck muscles and those of the occipital region. The common carotid then divides into two branches, the **internal** and **external carotid arteries.**

The internal carotid is a small vessel which passes forward to the anterior end of the tympanic bulla, where, in company with the Eustachian tube, it enters the bulla. A small foramen lacerum in the cranial part of the petrous region of the temporal bone provides passage for the internal carotid artery into the cranial cavity, where it helps supply the brain. Branches of the internal carotids, together with those from the basilar artery, form the circle of Willis, as mentioned above.

The external carotid passes anteriorly along the side of the face, where numerous branches are distributed to the tongue, larynx, and facial muscles. Branches of the **internal maxillary branch of the external carotid** enter the skull through the orbital fissure and foramen ovale. These are distributed to the dura mater and brain.

The left common carotid artery, unlike that on the right side, does not serve as the point of origin of the subclavian artery on that side. Otherwise the branches on the two sides correspond.

Left subclavian artery. The left subclavian artery arises independently from the aorta on the arch a short distance beyond the point of origin of the brachiocephalic artery. Its branches correspond to those of the right subclavian.

Intercostal arteries. From the arch of the aorta to the diaphragm, the thoracic aorta gives off paired **intercostal arteries** from its dorsal side. These vessels are distributed to all except the first two intercostal spaces, which, it will be recalled, are supplied by the superior intercostal arteries. Branches of the intercostal arteries pass to the muscles between the ribs, to the deep muscles of the back, and via the intervertebral foramina to the spinal cord, its membranes, and the vertebrae.

Bronchial arteries.   A pair of **bronchial arteries,** arising directly from the aorta or from the fourth pair of intercostal arteries, passes to the lungs along the bronchi.   These vessels supply the tissues of the lungs themselves with blood.

Esophageal arteries.   Small **esophageal branches** of the thoracic aorta pass directly to the esophagus which is in very close proximity to the aorta.

BRANCHES OF THE ABDOMINAL AORTA

Three kinds of vessels arise from the abdominal aorta: (1) paired parietal vessels pass to the body wall; (2) visceral branches supply the visceral organs, three of these being unpaired; (3) paired terminal branches supply the hindlimbs.

Parietal Vessels

Adrenolumbar arteries.   A pair of adrenolumbar arteries arises from the aorta 3 or 4 cm. from the diaphragm.   Each passes to the dorsal body wall, giving off a small branch to the adrenal gland en route.

Phrenic arteries.   The arteries which supply the diaphragm show considerable variation in origin, but their size is not of any great magnitude. They may arise independently from the aorta or else as branches of the adrenolumbar arteries to supply the diaphragm.   Sometimes a phrenic branch arises from the unpaired coelic artery.

Iliolumbar arteries.   A rather prominent pair of iliolumbar arteries arises from the abdominal aorta near its caudal end.   Each divides into cranial and caudal branches which supply adjacent muscles.

Lumbar arteries.   Paired lumbar arteries, corresponding to the intercostal arteries of the thoracic aorta, arise from the abdominal aorta and pass directly between the centra of the lumbar vertebrae and adjacent muscles to the dorsal body musculature in this region.   Branches enter the neural canal through the intervertebral foramina.

Visceral Vessels

Paired Arteries

Adrenolumbar arteries.   Although the adrenolumbars were included among the parietal vessels, they might just as well be included among the visceral vessels, since they supply the adrenal glands in addition to the dorsal body wall.

Renal arteries.   The large renal arteries arise from the aorta just caudad the adrenolumbars.   Each usually divides just before entering the kidney.

Genital arteries.   The genital arteries in the male are called the **internal spermatics**; in the female they are known as the **ovarian arteries.**

The internal spermatics are small in diameter, come off the aorta posterior to the renals, and pass posteriorly to the inguinal region, running parallel to the ductus deferens and to the corresponding vein to the testis and epididymis.

The ovarian artery is shorter but of greater diameter than the internal spermatic. It passes laterally to the ovary and ovarian end of the uterus.

Unpaired Arteries

Coeliac artery. The most anterior of the three unpaired visceral vessels is the coeliac artery. It arises from the ventral side of the abdominal aorta a short distance from the diaphragm and divides into **hepatic, left gastric,** and **splenic branches.** The **phrenic artery,** as noted above, may come off the proximal part of the coeliac.

The hepatic artery passes anteriorly to the liver and gall bladder, in company with the hepatic portal vein and bile duct. Just before the artery enters the liver a **gastroduodenal branch** is given off. This in turn divides into **pyloric, anterior pancreaticoduodenal,** and **right gastroepiploic branches.** The pyloric branch passes to the pylorus and continues along the lesser curvature of the stomach, where it breaks up into numerous vessels. The anterior pancreaticoduodenal supplies the duodenum and duodenal portion of the pancreas. The right gastroepiploic artery is distributed to the greater curvature of the stomach and part of the great omentum.

The left gastric branch of the coeliac goes to the lesser curvature of the stomach, where it anastomoses with the pyloric artery.

The splenic artery is the largest branch of the coeliac. It passes to the spleen, giving off branches to the pancreas, greater omentum, and stomach.

Superior mesenteric artery. The large superior mesenteric artery arises from the aorta a short distance caudad the coeliac. It is the vessel which supplies the greater part of the intestine. The **posterior pancreaticoduodenal** is a branch of the superior mesenteric, supplying the caudal end of the duodenum and the adjacent pancreatic tissue. Watch carefully for the pancreatic ducts so as not to destroy them. An **ileocaecolic branch** passes to the region of the ileocaecolic valve. A large **median colic branch** goes to the transverse and descending colon to anastomose with the inferior mesenteric artery. Another branch, the **right colic,** carries blood to the ascending colon and first part of the transverse colon. The main part of the superior mesenteric artery is represented by a large number of radiating branches which are distributed to all parts of the small intestine.

Inferior mesenteric artery. Posterior to the genital arteries the inferior mesenteric artery comes off the aorta. When it reaches the large intestine, it divides into anterior and posterior branches. The **anterior branch** goes forward to anastomose with the median colic branch of the superior mesenteric. The **posterior branch** supplies the rest of the colon and rectum.

Terminal Vessels

External iliac arteries. The external iliac arteries are large branches from the aorta near the anterior end of the pelvic girdle. Just before each vessel leaves the abdominal cavity, it gives off a **deep femoral branch** and three smaller branches: (1) a **vesicular artery** to the bladder, (2) an **external spermatic artery** (in the male), which passes along the spermatic cord to the testis, (3) an **inferior epigastric artery,** which passes ventral to the rectus abdominis muscle and courses anteriorly to anastomose with the **superior epigastric,** which is a continuation of the **internal mammary artery.** The deep femoral artery is distributed to the deep muscles of the thigh. Just external to the body wall a small **superficial epigastric** is given off. It passes anteriorly to anastomose with the **external mammary artery.**

After the external iliac emerges from the body cavity, it is called the **femoral artery.** At Scarpa's triangle (page 799) it lies close to the medial surface of the thigh. Numerous branches of the femoral artery are distributed to the remainder of the leg and foot.

Internal iliac arteries. The internal iliac, or **hypogastric, arteries** arise from the aorta a short distance caudad the point of origin of the external iliacs. Almost immediately each gives off an **umbilical artery** which passes to the bladder, where **vesicular branches** are distributed to both bladder and urethra. Farther on, the internal iliac sends branches to the pelvic wall, gluteal muscles, rectum, and reproductive organs.

Pulmonary Arteries

A short distance after leaving the conus arteriosus, the pulmonary aorta divides into **right** and **left pulmonary arteries.** The **ligamentum Botalli,** or **ligamentum arteriosum,** connects the systemic and pulmonary aortae at a point just proximad the division. This is the remnant of a shunt between the two vessels which functioned during embryonic and fetal life. Branches of the pulmonary arteries pass to the various lobes of the lung. The cranial lobe of the right lung is said to be *eparterial,* since it lies dorsal to the point where the right pulmonary artery enters the lung. All the other lobes are *hyparterial,* lying ventrad the pulmonary artery.

Lymphatic System

The lymphatic system is that part of the circulatory system which is concerned with collecting lymph from all parts of the body and carrying it to the external jugular veins. The system originates in a fine meshwork of delicate vessels called **lymph capillaries** which drain lymph from the tissue spaces. The small lymphatic vessels in the villi of the small intestine are known as **lacteals.** Small vessels unite to form larger vessels, which in turn join to form still larger vessels. Gradually the vessels increase in size, ultimately forming **lymphatic ducts.** Two lymphatic ducts drain the anterior portion of the body, and a single **thoracic duct** drains lymph from the posterior region.

Lymph, which is a colorless fluid, flows slowly through the lymphatic vessels, finally entering the venous system via the external jugular veins near their junction with the subclavians. Valves are present in the larger lymphatic vessels. This gives them a moniliform, or beaded, appearance. **Lymph glands,** or **lymph nodes,** interrupt the passage of the larger lymphatic vessels at various points. They serve as filters through which the lymph slowly passes. **Lymphocytes** are contributed to the lymph by the lymph nodes. Other structures considered to belong to the lymphatic system include the **thymus gland, spleen, tonsils,** and **bone marrow.** No special pumping organ is present in the cat to propel the lymph. Movements of the muscles in various parts of the body are largely responsible for the passage of lymph along the lymphatic vessels.

Since detailed features of the lymphatic system are difficult to observe in ordinary dissections, only a few of the more obvious structures will be treated here.

Superficial and deep lymphatic vessels of the head, neck, and forelimb of the cat, interrupted by lymph glands, finally unite on each side to form a single vessel. That on the left usually joins the thoracic duct, which drains lymph from the posterior regions, the two having a common opening into the left external jugular vein. On the right side the lymphatic duct enters the external jugular vein directly.

The largest vessel of the lymphatic system is the thoracic duct (Fig. 18.26). It is most clearly observed in the dorsal part of the body cavity along the left side of the vertebral column anterior to the kidneys. In the region of the kidneys it is somewhat enlarged to form the **cisterna chyli.** All the lymph from the thoracic and abdominal viscera, hind legs, pelvic wall, abdominal wall, and most of the thoracic wall ultimately enters the thoracic duct. Many lymph glands are present in these areas. In the mesentery of the small intestine the lymph glands are united into one large mass often referred to as the **pancreas aselli.** This is the largest lymph gland in the body.

Spleen

The spleen is generally considered to be a lymphatic organ. Small areas of lymphoidal tissue called **Malpighian corpuscles** are scattered throughout the spleen. They manufacture lymphocytes. In addition, the spleen serves for the storage of blood and plays a part in the final destruction of blood cells. It is a large, curved, flattened organ of a dark-red color. It lies close to the greater curvature of the stomach on the left side of the body. The spleen is actually enclosed within the descending limb of the greater omentum. It is the only structure not belonging to the digestive system that is drained by the hepatic portal vein.

DIGESTIVE SYSTEM

The digestive system of the cat consists of the **alimentary canal** and its associated organs. The alimentary canal is divided into several regions. Listing them in order from anterior to posterior ends, they are mouth, pharynx, esophagus, stomach, small intestine (duodenum, jejunum, ileum), and large intestine (colon, rectum, anal canal). The associated structures include the salivary glands, liver, pancreas, and their ducts.

Mouth. The **oral cavity,** or **mouth,** is the region between the lips and pharynx. It is divided into two parts: a **vestibule,** which is the portion between the lips and the teeth, and an **oral cavity proper,** which makes up the remainder. The portion of the vestibule bounded by the cheeks is referred to as the **buccal cavity.**

The **lips** are folds of skin covered with hair on the outside and with mucous membrane on the inner surface. Each is fastened to the jaw in the median line by a fold of tissue, the **labial frenum.**

The cat has five pairs of salivary glands, the ducts of which open into the mouth. The largest of these is the **parotid gland.** It lies just antero-ventrad the external auditory meatus and covers part of the masseter muscle. The duct of the parotid gland is called **Stensen's duct.** It courses over the surface of the masseter muscle in fascia to a point near the angle of the mouth, where it passes through the cheek to open on the inside opposite the last premolar tooth of the upper jaw. The second largest of the salivary glands is the **submaxillary.** It lies ventrad the parotid gland in back of the angular process of the lower jaw. Its duct, which is known as **Wharton's duct,** passes under the masseter, mylohyoid, and digastric muscles parallel to the mandible to open on a papilla located just in back of the incisor teeth. The **sublingual gland** is small. Its base is closely applied to the anterior border of the submaxillary gland. Its duct, the **sublingual duct,** runs parallel to Wharton's duct and opens on the same papilla. A very small **molar gland** is also present in the cat. It lies ventrad Stensen's duct near the angle of the mouth. The gland has several ducts, not easily seen, which penetrate the cheek to open on its inner surface. The last of the salivary glands is the **infraorbital,** or **zygomatic, gland.** It lies in the floor of the orbit near the lateral side. From the ventral portion of the gland a duct leads to the roof of the mouth caudad the small molar tooth.

The **tongue,** which normally occupies the floor of the mouth, is a mobile, fleshy organ, the surface of which is covered with small projections, or **papillae,** of four different types. **Conical,** or **filiform, papillae** are horny projections pointing caudad. They are concentrated in the middle portion of the free part of the tongue. No taste buds are associated with the filiform papillae. **Fungiform papillae** are small mushroom-shaped structures scattered over the surface of the tongue, most of them lying posterior to the main mass of filiform papillae. The fungiform papillae bear taste buds. **Vallate,** or **circumvallate, papillae** are few in number. They are arranged in two oblique rows of two or three each. The two rows meet in the form of a V, the apex of the V pointing caudad. The small depression at the apex is the **foramen caecum.** It represents the point of origin of the thyroid gland during embryonic development. Each circumvallate papilla is surrounded by a trenchlike depression along both sides of which taste buds are located. **Foliate,** or **flat, papillae** are numerous in the region of the root of the tongue and along the sides near the base (Fig. 5.6). Taste buds are present on the borders of the foliate papillae. A thin vertical fold of mucous membrane, the **frenum linguae,** attaches the anterior ventral part of the tongue to the floor of the mouth.

The **teeth** of the cat were studied in connection with the skull. They are **thecodont** (set in sockets), **heterodont** (of various shapes), **diphyodont** (only two sets, temporary and permanent), and **secodont** (cheek teeth adapted for cutting). The number of teeth on the two jaws differs. On each half of the lower jaw, or mandible, beginning at the anterior end, are three small, poorly developed **incisors;** one large, strong, pointed **canine;** two well-developed **premolars;** and a single large posterior **molar.** Molars are distinguished from premolars chiefly by the fact that they have no predecessors in the temporary set of teeth. A large gap, or space, between the canine and first premolar is called the **diastema.** The teeth of the upper jaw, on each side, consist of three small incisors attached to the premaxillary bone; a single large canine; three premolars; and a single very small molar at the posterior end, all set in sockets in the maxillary bone. There is no diastema in the upper jaw.

The **roof of the mouth** is composed of an anterior **hard palate** and a posterior **soft palate.** The hard palate is supported by premaxillary, maxillary, and palatine bones. Its mucous membrane is thrown into a number of prominent transverse ridges, or **rugae.** The soft palate has no bony support. At its ventral end on either side is a small swelling, the **palatine tonsil,** partially embedded in a shallow pocket.

Pharynx. The pharyngeal region, which lies in back of the soft palate, is common to both the digestive and respiratory systems. Its upper portion is called the **nasopharynx.** During the act of swallowing, the soft palate is pushed against the roof of the pharynx, temporarily blocking the opening between the nasopharynx and pharynx. The nasopharynx communicates anteriorly with the nasal passages through the **choanae,** or **internal nares.** At about the center of the nasopharynx is a pair of dorsolateral slits. These are the openings of the **Eustachian tubes.** It may be necessary to cut through the soft palate before these can be discerned.

The **glottis** is located on the floor of the pharynx. It is a longitudinal slit which marks the opening leading to the larynx, trachea, bronchi, and lungs. A flaplike projection, the **epiglottis,** previously observed, lies craniad the glottis, which it guards. Posteriorly the pharynx narrows down to join the esophagus.

Esophagus. The narrow tube of uniform diameter, connecting pharynx and stomach, is the esophagus. It passes through the thoracic cavity, its ventral surface being closely applied to the trachea. It finally penetrates the diaphragm to join the cardiac end of the stomach.

Stomach. The shape of the stomach (Fig. 18.28) is somewhat like that of a pear, with its broad end to the left. This is the **cardiac end** to which the esophagus is attached. The narrow end, which lies to the right, is the **pyloric end** of the stomach. It joins the duodenum, or first part of the small intestine. At the junction of the two is a thick sphincter muscle, the **pyloric valve.** The convex, longer outer border of the stomach is the **greater curvature.** It is here that the greater omentum is attached. The smaller, concave side of the stomach is the **lesser curvature.**

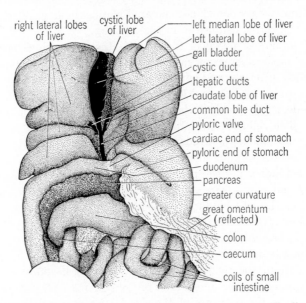

FIG. 18.28. Ventral view of a portion of abdominal viscera of cat. The liver and great omentum have been deflected to expose the structures covered by them.

Small intestine. The small intestine begins at the pyloric valve and terminates at its junction with the large intestine. It is very much coiled, and its length is 2½ to 3 times the length of the entire cat. The division of the small intestine into duodenum, jejunum, and ileum is not too clearcut. The **duodenum,** or first part of the small intestine, is from 12 to 15 cm. long. It bends rather sharply at the pylorus and runs backward for a short distance on the right side. Farther on it forms another sharp bend, this time to the left and craniad. Still farther on it joins the **jejunum,** the next bend generally being considered its termination. The beginning and end of the jejunum cannot be determined with exactitude. It is about 25 cm. long. The **ileum** is the longest part of the small intestine, making up about two-thirds of it. At its junction with the large intestine another valvelike sphincter is to be found. This is the **ileocolic,** or **ileocaecolic, valve** (Fig. 5.25).

Large intestine. The first part of the large intestine is the **colon.** It begins on the right side of the body where the ileum joins it. Posterior to the point of union the colon forms a small pouch, the **caecum.** The tip of the caecum ends in a slight projection which is, to a mild degree, comparable to the vermiform appendix of man. The regions of the colon are named according to their position. **Ascending, transverse,** and **descending portions** are recognized. The **rectum** is the terminal part of the large intestine. It begins where the colon reaches the median line and terminates at the **anus,** which is surrounded by sphincter muscles. On either side of the anus is a scent gland, the **anal gland,** the duct of which opens into the anus a short distance from the outside.

Liver. The largest gland of the body is the liver, which occupies the anterior part of the abdominal cavity. It lies against the diaphragm. The liver is divided into right and left lobes, each of which is subdivided. Each half bears a small **median** and a large **lateral lobe.** The median lobe on the right side is often called the **cystic lobe,** since the gall bladder lies against it. The right lateral lobe is deeply cleft. A small projection of the right lateral lobe is the **caudate lobe.** It lies in the omental bursa and partially closes the foramen of Winslow.

The **gall bladder** is a green pear-shaped organ situated on the right side of the body and partly surrounded by the cystic lobe of the liver. The narrow end of the gall bladder opens into a **cystic duct.** This is joined about 2 or 3 cm. from the gall bladder by two **hepatic ducts,** one from each side of the liver. Additional hepatic ducts are frequently encountered. The **common bile duct,** or **ductus choledochus,** empties into the duodenum about 3 cm. from the pyloric sphincter. Just before entering the duodenum, it is joined by the dorsal duct of the pancreas. A dilatation of the common duct at the entrance of the duodenum is called the **ampulla of Vater.** Its opening is regulated by a sphincter muscle, the **sphincter of Oddi.**

Pancreas. The second largest gland in the body is the pancreas. It is a flattened, irregular, elongated structure, sharply bent in the center to form two lobes. One lobe lies within the curve of the duodenum. The other is located within the descending portion of the greater omentum, opposite the greater curvature of the stomach and close to the spleen. The pancreas basically has two ducts: a **ventral duct (of Wirsung)** and a

dorsal duct (of Santorini). The duct of Wirsung is the chief duct of the gland. It receives branches from both lobes of the pancreas and joins the bile duct just before the latter opens into the duodenum. The duct of Santorini in the cat is usually found with difficulty or is missing entirely. It is by far the smaller of the two, its opening into the duodenum being located about 2 cm. beyond the ampulla of Vater. In order to locate these ducts, gently tease away the pancreatic tissue with a probe. They may be readily identified unless they were destroyed when the circulatory system in this region was studied.

It should be recalled that the pancreas is both an exocrine and an endocrine gland. The endocrine activity is brought about by the hormone **insulin,** secreted by the cells of the **islands of Langerhans.** Special histological preparations are necessary to demonstrate their presence.

RESPIRATORY SYSTEM

The structures making up the respiratory system include the nasal passages, nasopharynx, pharynx, glottis, larynx, trachea, bronchi, and lungs.

Nasal passages, nasopharynx, pharynx, and glottis. The external nares lead to the nasal passages. These are situated above the hard palate and are surrounded by the anterior bones of the face (page 426). Turbinate projections of nasal, maxillary, and ethmoid bones fill the greater portion of the nasal passages with their scroll-like folds. A septum, supported by the lamina perpendicularis of the ethmoid bone, separates the two sides. Mucous membrane covers all parts of the nasal passages. These passages open into the nasopharynx through the internal nares, or choanae. Nasopharynx, pharynx, and glottis have been discussed in connection with the digestive system.

Larynx. The first part of the respiratory tube leading from glottis to lungs is the **larynx,** or **voice box** (Fig. 18.29). It is supported by cartilages derived chiefly from the visceral skeleton. In addition to the cartilage supporting the epiglottis, a pair of **arytenoid cartilages** and unpaired **thyroid** and **cricoid cartilages** are the skeletal structures involved. The thyrohyal bones of the hyoid apparatus are attached to the thyroid cartilage. The single basihyal is fastened to the cranial end of the ventral border of the larynx (Fig. 18.4).

On either side of the base of the epiglottis is a fold of mucous membrane. These make up the **false vocal cords.** A short distance behind the false vocal cords is another pair of membranous folds, the **true vocal cords.** The space in front of them is called the **vestibule.** The cavity of the larynx extends from the glottis to the first cartilaginous ring of the trachea.

Trachea. The long tube extending posteriorly from the larynx is the **trachea.** Immediately above it lies the esophagus. The walls of the trachea are supported by about 45 incomplete cartilaginous rings which are open on the dorsal side. The gap, which is filled with connective tissue and muscle, forms a place for the reception of the ventral surface of the esophagus. The trachea divides at its caudal end to form two **bronchi** which almost immediately enter the lungs, where they divide and redivide.

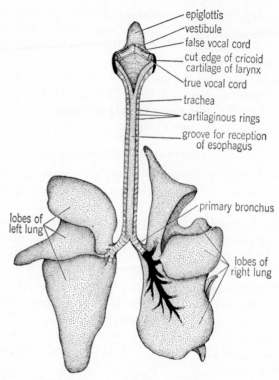

FIG. 18.29. Dorsal view of respiratory organs of cat. The larynx has been split open to show the vocal cords.

The bronchi, like the trachea, are supported by cartilaginous rings which prevent their walls from collapsing. The terminal branches of the bronchi are termed **bronchioles.** They lead into small sacs, the **infundibula,** which are lined with **alveoli.**

Lungs. The lungs are divided into several lobes. In the cat there are three lobes on the left and four on the right. As previously noted, the lungs are invested by the visceral pleura. The pleural cavities of the two sides are not confluent but are separated dorsally by the mediastinal space and ventrally by the mediastinal septum.

EXCRETORY SYSTEM

The structures making up the excretory system of the cat are paired kidneys and ureters and an unpaired urinary bladder and urethra. In the male, as will be pointed out, there is a close relationship between the excretory and reproductive systems. This is less marked in the case of the female.

Kidneys. The cat possesses the **metanephric type** of kidney. The kidneys are located along the dorsal part of the abdomen on either side of the vertebral column in the region of the fourth lumbar vertebra. The right one is usually slightly more anterior in position than the left. The peritoneum does not surround the kidneys as it does the other abdominal viscera but covers only the ventral side. The kidneys are therefore said to be **retroperitoneal.**

Each kidney (Fig. 18.30) is bean-shaped with a notch, the **hilum,** along its median border. It is at the hilum that the renal vessels enter or leave the kidney and the **ureter** emerges on its way to the bladder. The latter appears as a thin, whitish thread. A loose, fibrous **capsule** surrounds the kidney. Beneath the capsule is a dark layer of tissue, the **cortex,** surrounding a lighter-colored central **medulla.** A cavity, the **pelvis,** adjacent to the hilum, empties into the ureter. A projection of the medulla extends into the pelvis in the form of a cone-shaped **papilla.** Excretory products from the kidney pass into the pelvis and thence to the ureter.

Ureters. The duct of the kidney on each side is called the ureter. It is a slender tube which begins at the pelvis and passes posteriorly to the level of the caudal end of the bladder, where it turns in a ventrocraniad direction to enter the dorsal side of that organ near its narrow neck. The ureters are invested by a fold of peritoneum in which considerable fat may be deposited.

Urinary bladder. The pear-shaped **urinary bladder** is a large sac in the ventral posterior part of the abdominal cavity. It lies just craniad the pubic symphysis below the rectum. Visceral peritoneum is reflected over it. A fibromuscular cord of tissue, the **middle umbilical ligament,** connects the apex of the bladder with the umbilicus on the inner body wall. It represents the remnant of the embryonic **urachus,** or **allantoic stalk.** A peritoneal fold, the **suspensory ligament,** joins the bladder to the linea alba. In addition, the bladder is supported dorsally by a pair of **lateral**

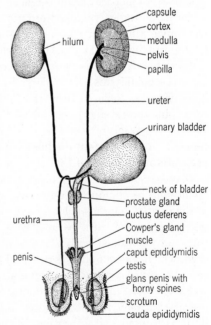

FIG. 18.30.   Male urogenital system of cat, ventral view (semidiagrammatic).

ligaments. The caudal portion of the bladder into which the ureters open is the **neck.** It joins a narrow tube, the **urethra,** the course of which differs, depending upon the sex. In the male it passes through the penis to open near the tip on the ventral side; in the female it joins the vagina to form the urogenital sinus, which in turn opens to the outside.

REPRODUCTIVE SYSTEM

The male (Fig. 18.30). The **primary reproductive organs** of the male are the **testes.** In addition to producing spermatozoa, the testes are endocrine glands. The hormone **testosterone,** produced by the **cells of Leydig,** or **interstitial cells** of the testes, controls the development and function of the **accessory sex organs** as well as the **secondary sex characters.**

Scrotum. The testes are located in an external pouch, the **scrotum,** which is covered with skin. The scrotum is divided by a septum into two halves, each of which contains a testis. A diverticulum of the abdominal cavity, lined with peritoneum, extends into each half of the scrotum. It does not completely surround the testis.

Testes. The peritoneum is reflected over part of the surface of the testes to form the **tunica vaginalis propria.** Beneath this is a tough membrane, the **tunica albuginea,** which invests the testis closely. Each testis measures approximately 1½ cm. in length and 1 cm. in thickness.

Epididymis. On the dorsal surface of each testis lies a flattened structure, the **epididymis.** Its enlarged cranial end is the **caput epididymidis.** This narrows down to form the body, or **corpus epididymidis,** which in turn joins the expanded caudal portion, or **cauda epididymidis.** Actually the entire structure consists of a long, coiled tube, very compactly arranged. A few **efferent ductules** connect the caput epididymidis with the **seminiferous tubules** of the testis in which spermatozoa are produced.

Ductus deferens. The coiled tube just mentioned leaves the cauda epididymis as the **ductus deferens,** which courses craniad. The first part of the ductus deferens is highly convoluted but then gradually straightens out. It runs forward, parallel with the spermatic artery and vein. All three are contained within a mesenterylike fold of tissue, the **spermatic cord,** which also contains nerves and lymphatic vessels. After penetrating the abdominal wall at the **inguinal ring,** the ductus deferens leaves the spermatic cord and turns medially and craniad the neck of the bladder, passing between the bladder and ureter. After looping over the ureter, it turns caudad and approaches its fellow from the other side. The two ducts enter the *dorsal* side of the urethra at a point about 2 or 3 cm. from the bladder.

Prostate gland. An enlargement on the urethra at the point where the two deferent ducts enter marks the location of the **prostate gland.** It is composed of many small tubules which pour their secretion into the urethra. The prostatic secretion serves as a vehicle for transport of spermatozoa to the outside. In many mammals a prominent seminal vesicle comes off the ductus deferens near its junction with the urethra. The cat lacks seminal vesicles.

Urethra. The **urethra** is made up of three portions. The first, or **prostatic urethra,** is the region surrounded by the prostate gland. Next comes the **membranous urethra,** which extends to the base of the penis. The last, or **spongy portion,** passes along the underside of the penis. The walls of this portion are composed of erectile tissue forming the **corpus spongiosum** of the penis. The opening of the urethra at the ventral side of the tip of the penis is called the **meatus.**

Penis. The cylindrical **penis** projects caudad. When relaxed, it measures about 3 cm. in length. It is covered with skin which forms a sheath, the **prepuce,** over its free end. The end of the penis, or **glans,** is covered with **horny spines.** On its underside the glans is connected to the prepuce by a fold of tissue, the **frenum** of the prepuce.

Cowper's glands. At the base of the penis a pair of **Cowper's glands** is to be found. Each opens by means of a duct into the urethra.

The Female (Fig. 18.31). The reproductive organs of the female consist of a pair of ovaries and oviducts, or tubes, which transport ova and in which the young develop.

Ovaries. The gonads of the female lie in the dorsolateral part of the body cavity just caudad the kidneys. They are narrow, oval bodies measuring about 1 cm. in length. Each ovary lies in a shallow pocket in a fold of peritoneum, the **broad ligament,** which in this region suspends the ovary from the body wall. The part of the broad ligament attached to the ovary is referred to as the **mesovarium.** In addition to producing egg cells, or ova, the ovaries have an endocrine function. Small, light-colored vesicles projecting from the surface of

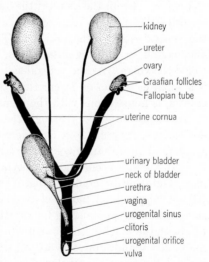

FIG. 18.31. Female urogenital system of cat, ventral view (semidiagrammatic).

the ovaries are **Graafian follicles,** each of which contains a microscopic ovum. The ovarian hormone **estradiol** is believed to be secreted by the cells of the Graafian follicle. Other dark, solid elevations, called **corpora lutea,** may also be present on the surface of the ovaries. A second ovarian hormone, **progesterone,** is secreted by the cells of the corpora lutea.

Fallopian tubes. From each ovary a narrow, twisted **Fallopian tube** extends in a caudal direction. At its ovarian end the Fallopian tube widens out into a funnel-shaped structure which receives ova after their discharge from the ovary. The opening into the Fallopian tube is called the **ostium tubae.** Each tube curves around the ovary and then extends a short distance caudad where it joins the uterus.

Uterus. The **uterus** of the cat is of the **bipartite type.** It consists of two expanded **cornua,** or **horns,** which are united caudally to form the **body** of the uterus. The body, which is approximately 4 cm. long, lies between the bladder and the rectum, its caudal end being located near the anterior border of the pubic symphysis. At this point the uterus joins the vagina. The caudal end of the uterus projects into the vagina for a short distance, this portion being referred to as the **cervix** of the uterus. A small opening in the cervix, the **os uteri,** connects the cavities of uterus and vagina. Ovaries, Fallopian tubes, and uterus are supported by a fold of peritoneum, the broad ligament, referred to above. A **round ligament** on each side also aids in supporting the uterus. It is connected to the broad ligament and extends from about the middle of the uterine horn to the posterior body wall at a point which corresponds to the inguinal ring of the male.

Vagina. From the os uteri the **vagina** passes caudally to a point about opposite the posterior end of the ischial symphysis, where it is joined on the ventral side by the urethra. The terminal tube common to urethra and vagina is the **urogenital sinus,** or **vestibule.** Its external portion is called the **vulva.** At the ventral side of the urogenital sinus near its orifice- is a small elevation no larger than the head of a pin. This structure, the **clitoris,** is homologous with the penis of the male.

Mammary glands. Although the **mammary glands** are integumentary derivatives, they are best considered in connection with the reproductive system. They are undeveloped or rudimentary in the male. In the female their size varies according to whether the animal is pregnant or not pregnant, lactating or nonlactating. The mammary tissue, in the form of a pair of longitudinal bands of tissue, lies beneath the skin on the ventral side of the body, extending forward from the posterior end of the abdomen to about the level of the fourth rib. The ducts of the various parts of the mammary glands converge at five distinct places on either side. Here are located the elevated **nipples** through which the mammary ducts open to the outside.

ENDOCRINE SYSTEM

Some of the glands making up the endocrine system have already been discussed (pancreas, testes, ovaries) and require no further treatment here. Others include the thyroid, parathyroids, adrenals, and pituitary gland. The thymus gland and pineal body, although no longer classified as endocrine glands by most authorities, are also mentioned.

Thyroid gland.   On either side of the trachea just caudad the larynx is a dark-colored, glandular structure.   These are the **lateral lobes** of the thyroid gland.   The two lobes are connected across the ventral side of the trachea by a narrow strip, the **isthmus,** composed of the same kind of tissue. The isthmus may be so thin as to escape ordinary notice.   The hormone of the thyroid gland **thyroxin** is important in controlling the metabolic activity of the body.

Parathyroid glands.   The parathyroid glands of the cat, usually four in number, are exceedingly minute structures embedded, at least partially, in thyroid tissue.   They are not noticeable in an ordinary dissection. **Parathormone,** the hormone of the parathyroid glands, is important in regulating the calcium and phosphorus metabolism of the body.   The parathyroid glands are essential for life.

Adrenal glands.   The adrenal glands are often referred to as the **suprarenal bodies.**   They are two oval-shaped, solid structures, scarcely 1 cm. long, lying a short distance craniad the kidneys on the dorsal side of the abdominal cavity near the median line.   Each is composed of an outer layer, the **cortex,** and an inner **medulla.**   Although so closely related anatomically, the two portions are functionally independent.   The hormones secreted by the cortex are concerned with maintaining the sodium level of the blood and regulating blood volume and have some relation to the carbohydrate metabolism of the body.   **Adrenalin** or **epinephrine,** the secretion of the medulla, is effective in raising the blood pressure.

Pituitary body.   A small glandular structure, the pituitary body, is attached to the ventral part of the brain in the region of the diencephalon. It lies in the sella turcica on the cranial side of the basisphenoid bone.   The pituitary body is made up of **anterior, intermediate,** and **posterior lobes,** each of which secretes one or more hormones.

Thymus gland.   The thymus gland is large in young animals but degenerates after puberty, so that in adults only vestiges remain.   It lies in the mediastinal space between the sternum and lungs and extends forward from the heart into the neck region.   The thymus is a flattened, irregular-shaped, glandular structure which is often incompletely divided into lobes. It seems to have some relation to sexual development, but there is considerable doubt as to whether the thymus is an endocrine gland.   Most evidence points to its being part of the lymphatic system.

Pineal body.   Lying on the dorsal surface of the brain, the small **pineal body,** or **epiphysis,** is practically hidden by surrounding parts.   It is located between the anterior, or cranial, corpora quadrigemina (page 836). Although the pineal body is considered by some authorities to be part of the endocrine system, the present consensus regards it merely as an interesting vestigial structure related to the median pineal eye found in certain of the lower vertebrates.

NERVOUS SYSTEM

As in the case of other vertebrates, the nervous system of the cat is made up of three main divisions: the central, peripheral, and peripheral autonomic nervous systems. The three parts are intricately interconnected functionally and structurally.

Central Nervous System

The spinal cord and brain belong to the **central nervous system.** They are well protected by surrounding bony structures; vertebrae enclose and protect the spinal cord; the cranial portion of the skull surrounds and protects the brain.

Spinal cord (myelon). The spinal cord is continuous with the brain at the foramen magnum in the occipital bone. It lies wholly within the neural canal of the vertebral column. The cord is a long, tubular structure, slightly flattened in a dorsoventral direction. The cavity within the spinal cord, the **central canal,** is very small in diameter. In the sacral region, the cord narrows down to terminate in a slender **filum terminale** in the tail region. Two swellings, or enlargements, are to be observed in the spinal cord of the cat and other mammals: an anterior, **cervical enlargement** and a posterior, **lumbar enlargement.** These mark the sites of origin of the nerves passing to the arms and legs, respectively.

Several external longitudinal grooves, or fissures, are to be observed on the spinal cord. These include a **posterior median sulcus** along the mid-dorsal line and an **anterior median fissure** along the midventral line. **Anterior and posterior lateral sulci** along the sides are less prominent. Spinal nerves, belonging to the peripheral nervous system, form metamerically arranged connections with the spinal cord.

Meninges of the cord. Surrounding the spinal cord are several membranes which, in their aggregate, are spoken of as **meninges.**

PIA MATER. Closely investing the cord is a delicate membrane, the pia mater. It closely follows the configurations of the cord and is well supplied with blood vessels.

ARACHNOID MEMBRANE. Surrounding the pia mater is the very delicate **arachnoid membrane.** It does not dip into the fissures and sulci as does the pia mater. The arachnoid is separated from the pia by a **subarachnoid space** which is filled with **cerebrospinal fluid.**

DURA MATER SPINALIS. A loose sheath, the **dura mater spinalis,** or **spinal dura,** lies outside the arachnoid membrane, separated from the latter by a **subdural space** containing cerebrospinal fluid. An **epidural space** outside the dura mater separates this membrane from the periosteum lining the neural canal of the vertebral column.

Brain (Fig. 18.32*A* and *B*). The brain, lying wholly within the cranial cavity, is continuous at the foramen magnum with the spinal cord. Like the latter, it is essentially a tubular structure. The cavities, or **ventricles,** within the brain are enlarged and subdivided. They are continuous posteriorly with the central canal of the cord. The mammalian brain differs from the brains of lower forms chiefly in the great development of the cerebral hemispheres.

Medulla oblongata (myelencephalon). The most posterior part of the brain is the **medulla oblongata.** It appears as an expanded continuation of the anterior end of the spinal cord. The place where the anterior pair of spinal nerves connects with the central nervous system is arbitrarily chosen as the point of demarcation between brain and spinal cord. The anterior part of the medulla is overhung by another portion of the brain, the cerebellum. The expanded cavity within the medulla oblongata is called the **fourth ventricle.** Its roof is composed of a thin membrane fused to the pia mater, which, in this region, is very vascular. The two together are known as the **tela choroidea.** Tufts of this vascular tissue, extending into the fourth ventricle, form the **posterior choroid plexus.** Cranial nerves V to XII arise from the medulla oblongata.

Metencephalon. The medulla oblongata together with the metencephalon make up the hindbrain, or rhombencephalon. The dorsal part of the metencephalon, the **cerebellum,** lies above and overhangs the anterior part of the medulla oblongata. The surface of the cerebellum is thrown into numerous folds **(gyri)** and depressions **(sulci).** The entire mass is subdivided into a central portion, the **vermis,** and two lateral areas, the **hemispheres.**

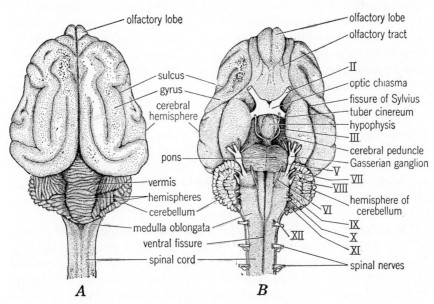

Fig. 18.32. Brain of cat from *A*, dorsal, and, *B*, ventral aspects.

The ventral portion of the metencephalon is called the **pons.** It consists of a mass of transversely arranged fibers on either side of the median line. The pons lies just anterior to the medulla oblongata.

Cerebral hemispheres (telencephalon). The two symmetrical **cerebral hemispheres** make up the greater portion of the brain of the cat. The hemispheres lie on either side just anterior to the cerebellum. Like the latter structure, their surfaces are thrown into elevated gyri separated by sulci. At about the middle of the lateral surface of each hemisphere is a short, deep fissure called the **lateral fissure, or fissure of Sylvius.** It serves as a landmark in dividing the hemisphere into **frontal** and **temporal lobes.** The cavities within the cerebral hemispheres are the **lateral,** or **first and second, ventricles.** If the two hemispheres are gently separated, a broad, white mass will be observed to connect them ventrally. This is the **corpus callosum,** which consists of masses of nerve fibers connecting the two cerebral hemispheres.

Olfactory lobes (rhinencephalon). At the anterior end of each cerebral hemisphere is a small projection, the **olfactory lobe,** which appears to be an extension of the hemisphere. The olfactory cranial nerve (I) forms connections with the olfactory lobe on each side.

Midbrain (mesencephalon). The **midbrain** is not visible from a dorsal view of the brain, being concealed by the cerebral hemispheres and cerebellum. From a ventral view, two **cerebral peduncles,** small areas just anterior to the pons, are all of the midbrain that is visible. If the covering structures are removed, the roof of the midbrain is seen to consist of two pairs of rounded elevations, the **corpora quadrigemina,** or **colliculi.** A small epiphysis, or pineal body, lies between the two anterior (superior) colliculi. This structure is actually a derivative of the diencephalon (page 574). The cavity of the midbrain is a narrow canal called the **cerebral aqueduct,** or **aqueduct of Sylvius.** This canal connects the third ventricle of the diencephalon with the fourth ventricle in the medulla oblongata.

'Tween brain (diencephalon). The portion of the brain between the cerebral hemispheres and the midbrain is the **'tween brain.** Like the midbrain, the **diencephalon** is covered over by the cerebral hemispheres, so that it is not visible from the dorsal side unless the latter structures are removed. Telencephalon and diencephalon together make up the **prosencephalon,** or **forebrain.** The olfactory lobes, or rhinencephalon, are considered to be part of the telencephalon.

The anterior end of the diencephalon, the **lamina terminalis,** lies in the median line in the deep fissure between the two cerebral hemispheres. This is considered to be the primitive cranial end of the brain. The roof of the diencephalon is very thin and fused to the pia mater. The cavity in this portion of the brain is referred to as the **third ventricle.** Vascular folds of the roof form the **anterior choroid plexus.** Similar folds also extend into the lateral ventricles. The **pineal body** is a dorsal projection of the caudal end of the roof of the diencephalon.

The lateral walls of the diencephalon are called the **thalami.** They are integrating and relay centers for nerve tracts which connect the cerebral hemispheres with the more posterior parts of the brain. Several important nuclei of gray matter are located in the thalami.

The ventral portion of the diencephalon, which is the only part visible externally, is called the **hypothalamus.** At its anterior end is located the **optic chiasma,** where fibers of the optic nerve cross. Posterior to the

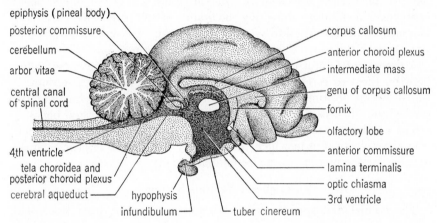

Fig. 18.33. Diagram of sagittal section of brain of cat. (*After Reighard and Jennings, "Anatomy of the Cat," Henry Holt and Company, Inc. By permission.*)

chiasma is an area, the **tuber cinereum,** which is attached ventrally by a narrow stalk to the **infundibulum.** A portion of the latter forms part of the **pituitary body.** The pituitary body, it will be recalled, lies in the sella turcica, a depression in the cranial aspect of the basisphenoid bone. A diverticulum of the third ventricle extends into the infundibular stalk.

Sagittal section of the brain (Fig. 18.33). A sagittal section of the brain exposes a few more important structures not visible otherwise. A complexly branched, central mass of white matter in the cerebellum, called the **arbor vitae,** is conspicuous. The continuity of the third ventricle, cerebral aqueduct, fourth ventricle, and central canal of the spinal cord is best observed in a sagittal section. The relation of anterior and posterior choroid plexuses to the third and fourth ventricles is also more clearly brought out in such a section. The **corpus callosum,** through which fibers pass between the two cerebral hemispheres, appears as a broad band of white matter above the diencephalon. A similar band, the **fornix,** is located ventrad the corpus callosum. Two transverse bands of white fibers, the **anterior** and **posterior commissures,** connect the two sides of the diencephalon. The anterior commissure lies at the ventral end of the fornix;

the posterior one is located at the base of the pineal body. The two halves of the diencephalon meet across the middle of the third ventricle, forming an **intermediate mass** which shows prominently in a sagittal section.

Meninges of the brain. The brain, like the spinal cord, is surrounded by meningeal membranes which are three in number.

PIA MATER AND ARACHNOID. The pia mater and arachnoid membrane surrounding the brain bear the same relation to the brain as the similarly named structures bear to the cord.

DURA MATER CRANIALIS (CRANIAL DURA). The cranial dura mater, unlike the spinal dura, serves as the internal periosteum of the cranial bones as well as a membrane protecting the brain. It will be recalled that these two membranes are separate over the spinal cord. The cranial dura is continuous with the spinal dura at the foramen magnum.

A prominent fold of the dura, the **falx cerebri,** extends into the fissure between the two cerebral hemispheres. Another fold, the **tentorium,** is transverse in position, lying between the cerebral hemispheres and the cerebellum. It is ossified in the cat and attached to the parietal bones.

The **diaphragma sellae** is the portion of the cranial dura which roofs over the sella turcica in which the pituitary body lies. It bears a small opening for the passage of the infundibular stalk.

Peripheral Nervous System

The cranial and spinal nerves, arising, respectively, from brain and spinal cord make up the peripheral nervous system.

Cranial nerves. Twelve cranial nerves are present in the cat in addition to the terminal nerve (0). (Fig. 18.32*B*).

Olfactory nerve (I). The purely sensory olfactory nerve for the sense of smell consists of a large number of branches which pass from the mucous membrane of the nose through the olfactory foramina in the cribriform plate of the ethmoid bone to form connections with the olfactory lobe. The cell bodies of the olfactory nerve are derived from the olfactory epithelium.

Optic nerve (II). The fibers of the purely sensory optic nerve arise in the retina of the eye. The nerve leaves the eyeball and passes through the optic foramen in the orbitosphenoid bone to the ventral side of the diencephalon, where the nerves from the two sides form the optic chiasma. The fibers of the optic nerves after leaving the chiasma form two **optic tracts** which terminate in the midbrain.

Oculomotor nerve (III). The third cranial nerve is a motor nerve which arises from the cerebral peduncle on the ventral side of the midbrain. It passes through the orbital fissure and sends branches to four of the six eye muscles: the superior, inferior, and internal rectus and the inferior oblique. Small branches also pass to the retractor oculi, levator palpebrae of the upper eyelid, and the ciliary apparatus of the eyeball itself.

Trochlear nerve (IV). The small, purely motor trochlear nerve comes from the dorsolateral portion of the posterior end of the midbrain. It passes through the orbital fissure on its way to the superior oblique eye muscle.

Trigeminal nerve (V). The fifth cranial nerve is a large structure with a wide distribution. It bears both sensory and motor fibers which arise from two roots from the posterior, lateral border of the pons. The dorsal root bears a large **Gasserian, or semilunar, ganglion** which gives off three branches: **ophthalmic, maxillary,** and **mandibular.**

OPHTHALMIC BRANCH. After leaving the Gasserian ganglion, the ophthalmic branch of the fifth nerve emerges from the cranial cavity through the orbital fissure in company with the third, fourth, and sixth cranial nerves. It gives off numerous branches to the skin of the upper eyelid, skin, and mucous membrane of the nose and to the eyeball.

MAXILLARY BRANCH. The maxillary branch of the trigeminal leaves the cranium through the foramen rotundum in the alisphenoid bone. It is a sensory branch which sends fibers to the palate, upper lip, teeth of upper jaw, forehead, and cheek.

MANDIBULAR BRANCH. The mandibular branch contains both sensory and motor fibers. It passes through the foramen ovale in the alisphenoid bone. Some of its fibers join those of the facial nerve. The mandibular branch is distributed to the skin of the ear, skin and muscles of the temporal region, chewing muscles, tongue, teeth of lower jaw, lower lip, mucosa and muscles of lower jaw, pharynx, submaxillary, and sublingual salivary glands.

Abducens nerve (VI). The sixth cranial nerve arises from the medulla oblongata, passes through the orbital fissure to the external (lateral) rectus muscle and to the nictitating membrane. It is a small motor nerve.

Facial nerve (VII). The seventh cranial nerve also has its origin in the medulla oblongata near the posterior border of the pons. From the brain it passes through the internal auditory meatus and facial canal. An enlargement in the facial canal is the **geniculate ganglion** of the facial nerve. The main part of the nerve emerges through the stylomastoid foramen of the temporal bone. Three branches are given off by the facial nerve within the facial canal. One goes to the small stapedius muscle. Another, the chorda tympani, passes across the tympanic cavity to emerge through a small opening between the tympanic bulla and the squamous region of the temporal bone. It receives fibers from the taste buds in the anterior part of the tongue and sends motor branches to the submaxillary and sublingual glands. A third branch, the superficial petrosal, joins a similarly named branch of the fifth nerve. The main part of the seventh nerve, after leaving the stylomastoid foramen, is widely distributed over the surface of the face and to the muscles of facial expression.

Auditory nerve (VIII). The purely sensory auditory nerve, which bears an acoustic ganglion, arises from the medulla oblongata near the floor of the fourth ventricle. It passes into the internal auditory meatus, where it divides into cochlear and vestibular branches which supply the auditory and equilibratory portions of the inner ear, respectively.

Glossopharyngeal nerve (IX). The ninth nerve also arises from the medulla along its lateral border. It is a mixed nerve which bears two ganglia. The first, or **superior, ganglion** is smaller than the second. The nerve emerges through the jugular foramen. The second, or **petrosal, ganglion** of the glossopharyngeal nerve lies just outside the jugular foramen. The nerve supplies the pharyngeal mucosa and muscles as well as the taste buds of the posterior portion of the tongue.

Vagus nerve (X). The vagus, or pneumogastric, nerve is of great importance in controlling such vital functions as respiration, heartbeat, and digestion. It is a mixed nerve arising by numerous roots from the ventrolateral part of the medulla. Like the ninth nerve, it bears two ganglia. The proximal one is called the **jugular**; the other, the **ganglion nodosum.** The latter lies just outside the jugular foramen through which the nerve emerges. The vagus is distributed to the external ear and to the muscles of the pharynx, larynx, esophagus, lungs, heart, and most of the visceral organs in the abdominal cavity.

Spinal accessory nerve (XI). The eleventh cranial nerve is rather small. It is a motor nerve and lacks a ganglion. It arises over a considerable distance along the side of the medulla oblongata by a number of roots, leaving the jugular foramen in company with the ninth and tenth cranial nerves to supply certain muscles of the neck and shoulder.

Hypoglossal nerve (XII). The twelfth, or last, cranial nerve comes from the ventral side of the medulla and emerges from the cranial cavity through the hypoglossal canal. It is a motor nerve going to the muscles of the tongue and neck region.

Spinal nerves. The spinal nerves are paired, metameric structures. In the cat there are usually 38 or 39 pairs. Of this number **8** are **cervical, 13 thoracic, 7 lumbar, 3 sacral,** and **7** or **8 caudal.** The number corresponds to the number of vertebrae in each region, with the following exceptions. The first cervical nerve emerges through the atlantal foramen of the atlas vertebra. The last cervical passes through the intervertebral foramen between the seventh cervical and first thoracic vertebrae. The other spinal nerves take their names from the vertebra which lies just anterior to the point of exit. Since the posterior caudal vertebrae consist of little more than centra and the spinal cord extends only a short distance into the tail, no spinal nerves are associated with them.

Each spinal nerve arises from the cord by two roots: dorsal and ventral. The **dorsal,** or **sensory, roots** bear ganglia. The cell bodies of the **ventral,** or **motor, roots** are located within the cord. Dorsal and ventral roots unite within the neural canal to form the spinal nerves, which emerge through the intervertebral foramina. Except in the case of the first two spinal nerves, the dorsal root ganglia are located *within* the neural canal or in the intervertebral foramina. The ganglia of the first two nerves are situated *outside* the vertebral column and lie embedded among muscles in the vicinity of the intervertebral foramina.

Only the more anterior spinal nerves leave the vertebral column at a point directly opposite their place of origin. Others course in a postero-lateral direction within the neural canal before emerging. This arrangement becomes more and more accentuated toward the posterior end, where the nerves run parallel to the cord for some distance before they pass through their respective intervertebral foramina. The region where the last sacral and the caudal spinal nerves run parallel to the filum terminale has a brushlike appearance and is referred to as the **cauda equina** (horse's tail).

After a spinal nerve leaves the vertebral column, it characteristically divides into two branches, the **dorsal** and **ventral rami,** each of which bears both sensory and motor fibers. The dorsal ramus is small and is distributed to the skin and muscles of the back. Just past its origin the ventral ramus gives off a visceral ramus **(white ramus, ramus communicans).** The ventral ramus then continues in a ventral direction to supply the skin and muscles of the ventral side of the body. In the pectoral and pelvic regions the ventral rami are also distributed to the limbs. It will be recalled that in these regions the spinal cord is of greater diameter than elsewhere and forms the cervical and lumbar enlargements. The visceral rami are short. They pass in a ventromedial direction to join the **sympathetic ganglia** of the peripheral autonomic nervous system. Visceral rami carry both sensory and motor fibers, the latter often being referred to as **preganglionic fibers.**

In the regions of the limbs the ventral rami of several spinal nerves give off branches which anastomose with one another in such a manner as to produce a complex **plexus** of nerves, which then continue into the limb. In the region of the forelimb, cervical nerves 5, 6, 7, and 8 and the first thoracic nerve are concerned in the formation of the **brachial plexus** (Fig. 13.14). A **phrenic nerve,** which supplies the diaphragm, is formed from branches of the fifth and sixth cervical nerves. It accompanies the vagus nerve on its way to the diaphragm. The **lumbosacral plexus** is composed of intercommunicating branches of lumbar nerves 4, 5, 6, and 7 and the three sacral spinal nerves.

Peripheral Autonomic Nervous System

The portion of the nervous system which controls all involuntary functions of the body is the peripheral autonomic nervous system. It is composed of two divisions which bring about opposite effects.

Not a great deal of the structure of the autonomic system can be learned from gross dissection. Histological and physiological studies, however, have brought to light many of the intricate interrelations between the autonomic, peripheral, and central nervous systems. These will be omitted from the following description.

Sympathetic nervous system. The sympathetic system is sometimes referred to as the **thoracolumbar outflow.** This is because preganglionic nerve fibers pass through the visceral rami of the thoracic and first four lumbar spinal nerves to connect with outlying ganglia of the sympathetic system. These ganglia consist of those in the sympathetic trunks and others which lie among the viscera.

The **sympathetic trunk** is a long nerve cord extending the length of the body cavity on each side under the centra of the vertebrae. Each trunk continues forward in close association with the vagus nerve, common carotid artery, and internal jugular vein, terminating just posterior to the tympanic bulla. Here it is enlarged and forms the **superior cervical ganglion.** The sympathetic trunk consists of a chain of ganglia united by nerve cords. The visceral rami of the thoracic and first four lumbar spinal nerves join these ganglia. Other collateral ganglia, lying along the abdominal aorta and its main branches, are the **coeliac, superior mesenteric,** and **inferior mesenteric ganglia.** Some preganglionic fibers of the thoracolumbar outflow continue through the chain ganglia of the sympathetic trunk to terminate in the collateral ganglia. **Postganglionic fibers** from the various sympathetic ganglia are distributed to all parts of the body. They are gray in color, since their fibers lack myelin sheaths. So-called **gray visceral rami,** which parallel the white visceral rami, are composed of postganglionic fibers which follow the spinal nerves, ultimately to be distributed to the skin. All spinal nerves possess gray rami.

Parasympathetic nervous system. The anatomical relations of the nerves making up the parasympathetic system are, for the most part, not so distinctly marked as are those of the sympathetic system. The parasympathetic system is also referred to as the **craniosacral outflow,** since preganglionic fibers of certain cranial and sacral nerves are chiefly involved. Fibers in the **oculomotor, facial, glossopharyngeal,** and **vagus nerves** form connections with ganglia which lie close to or within the walls of the structures which they supply. From these ganglia short postganglionic fibers pass to the actual tissues which this portion of the nervous system affects. In the cat the **visceral rami of the second and third sacral nerves** carry preganglionic fibers which pass directly to ganglia in the pelvic viscera from which short postganglionic fibers pass in turn to the tissues.

SENSE ORGANS

Basically the organs of special sense are specialized endings of sensory nerves. They have been so modified in each case that the nerve cells with which they are supplied are normally capable of receiving only one kind of stimulus.

Cutaneous sense organs. The integument is richly supplied with nerve endings which do not lend themselves to gross dissection and will not be discussed here. Stimuli for **touch, pressure, warmth, cold,** and **pain** are received by these widely distributed nerve endings.

Olfactory sense. The cells in the moist **olfactory mucous membrane,** or **Schneiderian membrane,** in the nasal passages carry impulses set up by olfactory stimuli via the olfactory nerve to the olfactory lobe of the brain. Substances must be in solution before they can stimulate the olfactory receptors.

Sense of taste. **Taste buds** associated with the papillae of the tongue as well as those on the soft palate and region about the epiglottis are special structures for reception of gustatory stimuli. Sensory branches of the seventh and ninth cranial nerves are responsible for conveying impulses from the taste buds to the brain. As in the case of the sense of smell, substances must be in solution before they can stimulate the gustatory nerve endings.

Sense of sight. The eye of the cat is well protected by the incomplete bony orbit in which it lies.

Accessory structures. The external surface of the eye is guarded by the upper and lower **eyelids,** which are extensions of the integument. Beginning at its border, each eyelid is lined by a thin layer of mucous membrane, the **conjunctiva,** which is also reflected over the exposed surface of the eyeball. A sphincter muscle, the **orbicularis oculi,** located on the margins of the eyelids is used in closing the eye. Another muscle, the **levator palpebrae,** arising near the optic foramen is inserted on the border of the upper eyelid. It serves to raise the upper lid.

The angle at either end of the slit, or **palpebral fissure,** between the eyelids is called the **canthus.** At the medial, or nasal, canthus are two small openings, the **lacrimal puncta,** which enter small canals. These unite to form the **nasolacrimal duct** which passes through the **lacrimal canal** bounded by lacrimal and maxillary bones, to enter the nasal passage. A prominent fold, the **nictitating membrane,** is present at the inner canthus. This is well developed in the cat in which it may cover the entire surface of the eye when expanded. A cartilage supports the nictitating membrane. On its undersurface is the **Harderian gland.** An **infraorbital salivary gland** lies on the floor of the orbit.

The **lacrimal gland** lies on the surface of the eyeball in the dorsolateral region. Its ducts open on the undersurface of the upper lid.

The usual six muscles controlling movements of the eyeball are present in the cat. They include the four **rectus muscles: superior,** inserted on the dorsal side; **inferior,** on the ventral side; **internal,** on the medial side; **external,** on the lateral aspect. The four rectus muscles originate from the bone surrounding the optic foramen in the orbitosphenoid portion of the sphenoid bone. The **superior oblique** muscle arises from the cranial border of the optic foramen and passes forward and dorsally to form a narrow tendon. This in turn passes through a pulleylike ring of connective tissue, then expands and turns caudolaterad to insert on the eyeball beneath the superior rectus. The **inferior oblique** comes from the maxillary bone near its junction with the lacrimal and crosses over the ventral side of the eyeball to insert between the external and inferior rectus muscles. Another muscle, the **retractor oculi,** arises near the optic foramen and is inserted on the eyeball near the equatorial region by means of four separate heads. The four parts alternate with the four rectus muscles.

Eyeball. The eyeball of the cat is approximately spherical in shape. Its outer coat is called the **fibrous tunic.** This, in turn, is composed of an anterior, exposed, transparent portion, the **cornea,** and a larger, opaque, posterior section, the **sclerotic coat (sclera).** The large optic nerve leaves the eyeball, piercing the sclerotic coat near its center. Beneath the sclerotic coat is the black, vascular **choroid coat.** The choroid does not line the inner surface of the cornea but at the junction of cornea and sclera becomes thickened to form the **ciliary ring.** It is then continued as the outer portion of the disclike **iris** which projects into the eyeball, forming a curtainlike structure some distance behind the cornea. An opening, the **pupil,** is present in the center of the iris. The pupil varies in shape, depending upon the amount of light striking the iris. It is circular when dilated in poor light, but forms a vertical slit when contracted in strong light. Action of muscles in the iris is responsible for changes in the shape of the pupil. Part of the choroid is lined with a layer, the **tapetum lucidum,** which contains light-reflecting crystals. These are responsible for the metallic luster with which the eyes of the cat "shine" at night.

The inner coat of the eye is the sensitive **retina** containing **rod** and **cone cells,** which are the actual light receptors. At the ciliary ring the retina appears to form a free border, the **ora serrata.** Actually, however, it is continued onto the iris as a very thin layer, the **iridial portion of the retina.** The point where the optic nerve leaves the retina is called the **blind spot,** since rods and cones are lacking there. In the direct line of the optical axis a small **area centralis** is present in the retina. This marks the area of most acute vision.

The **crystalline lens** of the eye lies directly behind the iris. It is elastic and compressible during life. A thin **capsule** surrounds the lens. To this are attached numerous radiating fibers of the **suspensory ligament** which, in turn, are attached to the **ciliary body. Ciliary muscles** which, at their other ends, are anchored to the ciliary ring, insert on the ciliary body.

The lens and ciliary apparatus divide the cavity of the eyeball into two parts. The cavity between the lens and the cornea is in turn partially separated by the iris into **anterior** and **posterior chambers,** which are continuous only through the pupil. These chambers are filled with a watery fluid, the **aqueous humor.** The large cavity behind the lens and ciliary apparatus is the **chamber of the vitreous humor.** It is bordered by the retina. The chamber contains a transparent, jellylike substance, the **vitreous humor.**

Senses of hearing and equilibrium. The auditory organ of the cat is made up of three main parts: the external, middle, and internal ears. The internal ear is the actual organ of hearing and equilibration, the other structures all serving to transmit sound waves to the sensory receptors.

External ear. The **pinna** is the visible portion of the external ear. It is covered with skin, is supported by cartilage, and can be moved in various directions by muscles. Within the external ear are several prominent **ridges.** A deep depression, the **concha,** leads to the **external auditory meatus.** This terminates at the **tympanic membrane** stretched across the opening of the tympanic bulla.

Middle ear. The cavity within the tympanic bulla is called the **middle ear,** or **tympanic cavity.** A bony plate partially separates the cavity into lateral and medial chambers. The lateral chamber contains a chain of three small bones, the **auditory ossicles.** These are the **malleus, incus,** and **stapes.** The malleus is attached to the tympanic membrane on one side and to the incus on the other. The incus in turn articulates with the stapes. The base of the stapes serves as a plug, completely filling a small opening in the petrous region of the temporal bone, the **fenestra ovalis.** The ossicles are held in position by small muscles and ligaments. The tympanic cavity connects with the pharynx by means of the **Eustachian tube.**

Internal ear. The **membranous labyrinth,** which serves both as an organ of equilibrium and an organ of hearing, lies wholly within the dense petrous region of the temporal bone. Since it does not lend itself to gross dissection, the inner ear is studied with difficulty. For further information the reader is urged to consult textbooks on physiology and histology, in which details of structure are described.

SUMMARY

CHAPTER 19

CHARACTERISTICS AND ADVANCES

PHYLUM CHORDATA

Unique features. A notochord; a hollow dorsal nerve tube; gill slits connecting to the pharynx, or traces of them, present some time during life.

Other features. Bilateral symmetry; cephalization; metamerism; true body cavity, or coelom; ventral-anterior direction of blood flow from heart.

Group A. Acrania

No brain or cranium.

SUBPHYLUM I. HEMICHORDATA

Marine, burrowing forms, body wormlike and unsegmented with proboscis, collar, and trunk; numerous gill slits connecting pharynx with outside; a stiffened, forward extension of the gut into the proboscis probably *not* homologous with notochord; dorsal and ventral nerve strands, the dorsal one being larger and having a tubular structure only in the collar region; presence of giant nerve cells in anterior region suggests the beginning of a brain; dioecious; tornaria larva of certain forms closely resembling larval echinoderms. EXAMPLE: *Dolichoglossus (Saccoglossus kowalevskii).*

SUBPHYLUM II. TUNICATA

Marine; some free-swimming forms, but others becoming sessile after a free-swimming larval period; excurrent and incurrent siphons; pharynx large with numerous gill slits; notochord only in larva and then confined to tail region; nervous system of adult reduced to a small ganglion; hermaphroditic; endostyle in midventral part of pharynx perhaps forerunner of thyroid gland of higher forms; adneural gland around nerve ganglion possibly homologous with pituitary gland of higher forms; covering of body, or tunic, composed of tunicin (cellulose); heart showing reversal of beat; mantle cavity present. EXAMPLES: Ascidians; *Molgula manhattensis, Botryllus, Doliolum, Salpa.*

SUBPHYLUM III. CEPHALOCHORDATA

Marine; free-swimming; notochord well developed and extending entire length of body; no well-defined head; nerve cord slightly enlarged at anterior end, forming a cerebral vesicle; pharyngeal gill slits connecting indirectly with outside through an atrium and atriopore; metamerism very clearly indicated; dioecious; gonads arranged metamerically; hepatic caecum off ventral side of digestive tract homologous with the liver of higher forms; heart a ventral pulsating tube, sometimes said to be one-chambered; hepatic portal vein; metapleural folds suggest possible origin of paired appendages of vertebrates (doubtful); epidermis one cell layer thick; integumentary glands all of unicellular type; spinal nerves metameric, but those of one side alternate with those of the other; dorsal and ventral nerve roots not united; endostyle lying along midventral line of pharynx; no reproductive ducts. EXAMPLE: Amphioxus; *Branchiostoma*.

Group B. Craniata (Vertebrata)

Anterior end of dorsal nerve cord enlarged to form a brain; protective and supporting endoskeleton; a cranium surrounding the brain, and a segmented spinal column composed of vertebrae enclosing the spinal cord; sense organs in head.

SUBPHYLUM IV. AGNATHA

Absence of jaws; absence of paired appendages, even in embryo; a single median nostril representing a fusion of two; aquatic habitat; poorly developed cranium.

Class I. Ostracodermi. Fossil forms only; heavy bony dermal plates in skin; some with endoskeleton of a sort; some with lateral body lobes posterior to head region, from which pectoral appendages of higher forms may have evolved. EXAMPLES: *Pterichthys, Birkenia.*

Class II. Cyclostomata. Living forms; body rounded, but tail laterally compressed; round suctorial mouth; median fins supported by cartilaginous fin rays; no scales in skin; skin soft with numerous unicellular mucous glands present; 6 to 14 pairs of gill pouches; poikilothermous; poorly developed brain not completely surrounded by cranium; vertebrae also poorly developed; protocercal tail; tongue specialized for rasping; epidermal horny teeth; persistent notochord; skeleton entirely cartilaginous; two-chambered heart; lateral-line system, but no true lateral line; no genital ducts; primitive in many respects, highly specialized in others. EXAMPLES: Lampreys and hagfishes.

ORDER I. PETROMYZONTIA. Inhabiting rivers, lakes, and the sea; dioecious; ventral suctorial funnel at anterior end; seven pairs of gill pouches, each opening separately to the outside; ammocoetes larvae undergo metamorphosis; pharynx a blind pouch guarded by a velum; pancreas essentially lacking; opisthonephric kidney; dorsal and ventral roots of spinal nerves not united; eyes primitive but well developed; only two semicircular ducts (the vertical ones) present in inner ear; nasal sac gives off nasopharyngeal pouch which ends blindly. EXAMPLES: Lampreys; *Petromyzon marinus, Entosphenus tridentatus.*

ORDER II. MYXINOIDEA. All marine; hermaphroditic; mouth nearly terminal and surrounded by four tentacles; no buccal funnel; few teeth; parasitic habit; 6 pairs of gill pouches with a single opening to the exterior on each side; an asymmetrical esophageo-cutaneous duct on left side; 6 to 14 pairs of gill pouches in *Bdellostoma:* holonephros in embryo, pronephros opisthonephros in adult; eyes degenerate and functionless; one semicircular duct in inner ear with an ampulla at either end; nasopharyngeal pouch connects with nasal sac in front and with pharynx behind; no metamorphosis. EXAMPLES: Hagfishes; *Myxine glutinosa, Myxine limosa, Bdellostoma.*

SUBPHYLUM V. GNATHOSTOMATA

Paired pectoral and pelvic appendages; true upper and lower jaws; paired nostrils; well-developed endoskeleton; closed cranium.

Superclass I. Pisces. Aquatic; in most cases respire throughout life chiefly by means of gills connected with pharyngeal gill slits; paired appendages are fins; median fins also present; dermal scales of various types in skin; unicellular and multicellular mucous glands abundant in skin; dioecious; poikilothermous; opisthonephric kidneys (persistent pronephros in a few); two-chambered heart [a few (lungfishes) have a three-chambered heart]; 10 pairs of cranial nerves in addition to the terminal nerve (0); genital ducts.

Class I. Placodermi. Fossil forms only; most primitive of fishes; primitive jaws and paired fins; bony armor of dermal plates in skin; some with lunglike pharyngeal diverticula. EXAMPLE: *Bothriolepis.*

Class II. Chondrichthyes. Marine with few exceptions; cartilaginous skeleton; placoid scales; ventral, subterminal mouth; heterocercal tail; pelvic fins of male modified to form claspers used in copulation; no swim bladder; spiral valve in small intestine; lower jaw skeleton composed of Meckel's cartilage, upper jaw of palatopterygoquadrate bar; oviparous, ovoviviparous, and viviparous forms; eggs large with abundant yolk; meroblastic cleavage; variable number of aortic arches. EXAMPLE: Cartilaginous fishes.

ORDER I. SELACHII (ELASMOBRANCHII). Five to seven pairs of gill slits opening separately to the outside; a pair of spiracles, representing the first pair of gill slits, usually opening on top of head; hyostylic method of jaw attachment; persistent notochord partially replaced by cartilaginous vertebrae; cloaca. EXAMPLES: Sharks, dogfish, skates, and rays (the elasmobranch fishes).

SUBORDER I. SQUALI. Pectoral fins distinctly marked off from cylindrical body; gill slits lateral in position; tail used in locomotion. EXAMPLES: Sharks and dogfish; *Squalus acanthias, Sphyrna zygaena, Mustelus canis.*

SUBORDER II. BATOIDEA. Dorsoventrally flattened bodies; pectoral fins not sharply marked off from body; demarcation between body and tail distinct; gill slits ventral in position; spiracle large and well developed;

undulatory movements of pectoral fins used in locomotion. EXAMPLES: Skates (oviparous) and rays (ovoviviparous); *Pristis pectinatus, Torpedo, Raja, Manta.*

ORDER II. HOLOCEPHALI. Persistent notochord; poorly developed vertebrae; operculum; autostylic method of jaw attachment; open lateral-line canals; no spiracle; no cloaca. EXAMPLES: Chimaeras; *Chimaera monstrosa, Hydrolagus colliei.*

Class III. Osteichthyes. Skeleton bony at least to some degree; scales usually present of ctenoid, cycloid, or ganoid types; terminal mouth; operculum; swim bladder usually present; tail usually homocercal but sometimes heterocercal or diphycercal; Meckel's cartilage invested by bone; dermatocranium roofs over most of chondrocranium; four pairs of aortic arches; oviparous, ovoviviparous, and viviparous forms; no cloaca. EXAMPLE: Bony fishes.

Subclass I. Paleopterygii. Fin rays of dorsal and anal fins exceeding in number the supporting skeletal elements; clavicles present; nostrils not connecting with mouth cavity; spiracle; spiral valve in small intestine. EXAMPLE: So-called "ancient fishes."

ORDER I. CLADISTIA. Physostomous swim bladder, ventral, smooth-walled, bilobed, and used as a lung; amphicoelous vertebrae; single pair of external gills in larval stage; well-developed bony skeleton; autostylic method of jaw attachment; paleoniscoid ganoid scales; diphycercal tail. EXAMPLES: The fringe-finned ganoids; *Polypterus bichir, Calamoichthys.*

ORDER II. CHONDROSTEI. Skeleton mostly cartilaginous; little bone present; persistent notochord; scales practically lacking or in form of keeled bony ganoid plates arranged in five longitudinal rows; no teeth; hyostylic method of jaw attachment; heterocercal tail. EXAMPLES: Spoon-bills, *Polyodon, Psephurus;* sturgeons, *Acipenser.*

Subclass II. Neopterygii. Occipital region of skull bony; homocercal tail (diphycercal in a few); number of fin rays in dorsal and anal fins corresponding to those of supporting skeletal elements; nostrils do not connect with mouth cavity (except *Astrocopus*); swim bladders often physoclistous and highly specialized; no clavicles; scales usually ctenoid or cycloid (lepisosteoid ganoid scales in *Lepisosteus*); no spiracles; amphicoelous vertebrae; hyostylic and modified hyostylic method of jaw attachment. EXAMPLES: *Amia, Lepisosteus,* and *teleosts.*

Subclass III. Choanichthyes. Nasal passages connecting with mouth cavity; clavicles present. EXAMPLES: Lobe-fins and lungfishes.

SUPERORDER I. CROSSOPTERYGII. Fins borne on fleshy, lobelike, scaly stalks; skeleton of pectoral and pelvic fins with single point of attachment to girdles; premaxillary and maxillary bones present. EXAMPLES: The lobe-finned fishes.

ORDER I. RHIPIDISTIA. Fossil forms only; of importance in evolution of tetrapod limb. EXAMPLE: *Eusthenopteron.*

ORDER II. COELACANTHINI. Head short and deep; hollow spinal column extending far forward into head; ancient fishes, until recently known only by fossil remains; first dorsal fin in living forms is fan-shaped, rest are lobate; hypophyseal duct connects pituitary gland with mouth cavity; brain small and of simple construction; internal nares lacking in living species. EXAMPLE: *Latimeria chalumnae*.

SUPERORDER II. DIPNOI. Swim bladders basically bilobed and physostomous with ventral connection to esophagus and used as lungs; internal as well as external nares in all; pulmonary circulation; three-chambered heart with double type of circulation; larval forms with external gills; sound production; diphycercal tail; cranium mostly cartilaginous; autostylic method of jaw attachment; spiral valve in intestine; premaxillary and maxillary bones lacking. EXAMPLES: The true lungfishes; *Protopterus*, *Lepidosiren*, and *Neoceratodus*.

Superclass II. Tetrapoda. Paired appendages are limbs which are typically pentadactyl; cornified epidermis; lungs; skeleton bony for the most part; sternum usually present; number of skull bones reduced; reduction in visceral skeleton.

Class I. Amphibia. Transition from aquatic to terrestrial life clearly indicated in this group; eggs laid in water or in moist situations and covered with gelatinous envelopes; metamorphosis; larvae with integumentary gills; respiration in adults (with few exceptions) by means of lungs and smooth, moist, vascular integument; buccopharyngeal respiration; poikilothermous; multicellular mucous and poison glands in skin; five pairs of pharyngeal pouches in embryo; lungs simple in structure, appearing at time of metamorphosis; opisthonephric kidneys; cloaca; reduction in number of bones in skull; skull flattened; two occipital condyles; three-chambered heart; pentadactyl limbs usually modified; no nails or claws; 10 pairs of cranial nerves in addition to terminal nerve (0). EXAMPLES: Caecilians, salamanders, newts, frogs, and toads.

Subclass I. Stegocephalia. Head covered almost solidly with bony dermal plates; fossil forms with more skull bones than modern amphibians and many with ventral armor of overlapping bony dermal plates (a few forms with dorsal bony plates in addition). EXAMPLES: Fossil forms; living caecilians.

ORDERS I–III. Fossil forms; labyrinthodonts, lepospondyls, and phyllospondyls, varying primarily in structure of vertebral column.

ORDER IV. APODA (GYMNOPHIONA). Snakelike bodies; no limbs or limb girdles; very short tail; anus almost at posterior end of body and ventral; fishlike dermal scales embedded in skin; no gills or gill slits in adult; extremely small eyes embedded in skin; no eyelids; internal fertilization; male with protrusible copulatory organ; intestine not differentiated into large and small regions; compact skull. EXAMPLES: Caecilians; *Ichthyophis glutinosus*, *Typhlonectes*.

Subclass II.   Caudata (Urodela).   Body divided into head, trunk, and persistent tail regions; two pairs of weak limbs in most species; larvae closely resembling parents; internal fertilization (except *Cryptobranchus*); oviparous (except black salamander); larvae with true teeth in both upper and lower jaws; no middle ear; parietal muscles distinctly segmented; sternum poorly developed and primitive; lateral line lost at metamorphosis except in perennibranchiates.   Examples: Newts and salamanders; *Necturus maculosus, Triturus viridescens, Proteus.*

Subclass III.   Salientia (Anura).   Absence of tail in adult; head and trunk fused; large, wide mouth; two pairs of well-developed limbs, the hind-limbs being fitted for leaping and swimming; toes webbed; tympanic membrane flush with head; middle ear present for first time; true sound-producing organs; amplexus and external fertilization, therefore oviparous; larvae do not resemble parents; larvae with horny jaws in lieu of teeth; nine vertebrae plus urostyle; movable eyelids; lacrimal glands; well-developed sternum and limb girdles.   Examples: Frogs and toads; *Rana pipiens, Bufo americanus.*

Class II.   Reptilia.   Many fossil forms. Living species with following characteristics: internal fertilization; oviparous and ovoviviparous forms; large-yolked eggs laid on land; three embryonic membranes, amnion, chorion, and allantois, appearing for the first time; poikilothermous; skin dry with dead corneal layer well developed; epidermal scales, some with bony plates underlying them; skin almost devoid of glands; limbs typically pentadactyl, terminating in claws (not in snakes or limbless lizards); respiration entirely by means of lungs except for cloacal respiration in aquatic chelonians; no metamorphosis; at least a partial separation of nasal and oral cavities; five pairs of pharyngeal pouches in embryo; vertebral column divided into cervical, thoracic, lumbar, sacral, and caudal regions (except snakes and limbless lizards); metanephric kidneys; one occipital condyle; three-chambered heart (except in crocodiles and alligators in which it is four-chambered); no lateral-line system; 12 pairs of cranial nerves in addition to terminal nerve (0).

Order I.   Chelonia.   Living forms represent a very old group which has persisted with little change for 175,000,000 years. Short wide bodies; no teeth, each jaw being covered by a horny scale; shell composed of plastron and carapace covering body and made of bone covered with large epidermal scales; poikilobaric respiration; single penis in male; oviparous; lumbar region of vertebral column lacking; thoracic vertebrae and ribs fused to carapace; solidity of skull bones well marked; limbs pentadactyl except in marine forms; terrestrial, fresh-water, and marine species; anus a longitudinal slit.   Examples: Turtles, tortoises, and terrapins; *Chelydra serpentina, Chrysemys picta.*

Order II.   Rhynchocephalia.   Well-developed parietal eye; no copulatory organs in male; anal opening a transverse slit; diapsid condition in regard to temporal fossae; amphicoelous vertebrae; lizardlike body form with scaly skin; gastralia; only one living species. Example: *Sphenodon punctatum.*

Order III. Squamata. Skin covered with horny epidermal scales; anal opening a transverse slit; paired eversible hemipenes in male as copulatory organs; large palatal vacuities in roof of mouth; quadrate bone forms a movable union with squamosal; vertebrae usually procoelous; gastralia lacking. Examples: Lizards and snakes.

Suborder I. Sauria (Lactertilia). Visible external earpits; tympanic membrane not at surface of head; movable eyelids and nictitating membrane; urinary bladder usually present; tail readily detachable; metachrosis well exemplified in most; usually two pairs of pentadactyl limbs terminating in claws; two halves of lower jaw firmly united and size of mouth opening restricted; well-developed protrusible tongue; air sacs in some; some with a well-developed parietal eye; oviparous and ovoviviparous forms. Examples: Lizards, geckos, glass snakes, and skinks; *Heloderma horridum, Chameleon vulgaris.*

Suborder II. Serpentes (Ophidia). No limbs, but a few have vestiges of limb girdles; no sternum; no external ear openings or tympanic membranes; middle ear lacking; eyelids immovably fused and transparent; loose ligamentous attachment of jaws; ventral scales used in locomotion; left lung smaller than right and often absent altogether; hemipenes as copulatory organs; vertebral column divided into precaudal and caudal portions; tongue long, forked, protractile; no urinary bladder. Examples: Snakes; *Crotalus viridis, Naja tripudians.*

Order IV. Crocodilia (Loricata). Tail laterally compressed; two pairs of short legs; five toes on forefeet and four on hind feet; toes webbed; tympanic membrane exposed but protected by a fold of skin; teeth set in sockets in jawbones; oviparous; anal opening a longitudinal slit; single penis in male; four-chambered heart; first appearance of true cerebral cortex; adapted for amphibious life; diapsid condition in regard to temporal fossae; gastralia; dorsal and ventral scales reinforced with bony plates; tongue not protrusible; no urinary bladder. Examples: *Alligator mississippiensis, Crocodylus americanus.*

Class III. Aves. Feathers; legs and feet covered by horny skin or scales of reptilian type; light, hollow bones; loss of right ovary and oviduct except in certain birds of prey; very well developed eyes; nictitating membrane; forelimbs modified to wings; homoiothermous; sexual dimorphism often highly developed; oviparous; large size of eggs; meroblastic cleavage; skin almost devoid of glands; one occipital condyle; four-chambered heart; claws at ends of digits of hindlimbs; at least partial separation of nasal and oral cavities; four pairs of pharyngeal pouches in embryo; syrinx for sound production; air sacs from lungs; metanephric kidneys; fertilization internal; copulation by cloacal apposition except in a few forms with a single penis;

rigidity of spinal column with posterior thoracic, lumbar, sacral, and proximal caudal regions firmly united; right aortic arch 4 persisting, left one disappearing; toes reduced to four or less; intratarsal joints in legs; flexible neck; no urinary bladder; 12 pairs of cranial nerves; absence of terminal nerve (0). EXAMPLE: Birds.

Subclass I. Archaeornithes. Fossil forms only; long, jointed tail with 18 to 20 separate caudal vertebrae; gastralia; three clawed digits on wings; thecodont method of tooth attachment; poorly developed sternum. EXAMPLES: *Archaeopteryx.*

Subclass II. Neornithes. Thirteen or fewer compressed caudal vertebrae; metacarpal and distal carpal bones fused; no free, clawed digits on wings (except young hoatzin); well-developed sternum; uncinate processes on ribs.

SUPERORDER I. ODONTOGNATHAE. Fossil forms only; teeth present in jaws and set in grooves or shallow sockets. EXAMPLES: *Hesperornis*, a flightless, swimming bird; *Ichthyornis*, a flying, toothed form.

SUPERORDER II. PALEOGNATHAE (RATITAE). Flightless; wings poorly developed or rudimentary; no keel on sternum except in the tinamous; distal caudal vertebrae free; toothless; horny beaks, or bills. EXAMPLES: Walking or running birds; ostrich, rhea, kiwi, cassowary.

SUPERORDER III. NEOGNATHAE. Keeled (carinate) sternum; wings well developed; five or six free caudal vertebrae terminating in a pygostyle; no teeth; horny beaks, or bills. EXAMPLES: Most modern birds; penguins use wings for swimming, not for flight.

Class IV. Mammalia. Hair present but sometimes scanty; homoiothermous; mammary glands; sweat glands and oil glands in skin with few exceptions; pentadactyl limbs often modified; claws, nails, or hoofs at ends of digits; movable lips and tongues in most forms; highly developed cerebral cortex; four-chambered heart; palate partially separates nasal and oral cavities; four pairs of pharyngeal pouches in embryo; metanephric kidneys; urinary bladder; single penis for copulation; seven cervical vertebrae (four exceptions); two occipital condyles; increased cranial capacity of skull; reduction in number of skull bones; long movable tail usually present; 12 pairs of cranial nerves in addition to terminal nerve (0); pinna usually present; lungs for respiration; diaphragm; nonnucleated red corpuscles except in embryo; left aortic arch 4 persisting, right one disappearing; blood platelets instead of spindle cells; testes located in scrotum in most cases; three auditory ossicles; dentition thecodont and usually heterodont.

Subclass I. Prototheria

ORDER I. MONOTREMATA. Oviparous; eggs incubated outside body; cloaca present; no nipples or teats; oviducts distinct, undifferentiated, and opening separately into cloaca; temperature-regulating mechanism not highly integrated; rather poorly developed brain; separate coracoid and precoracoid bones; epipubic bones; males with intra-abdominal testes; no pinna; penis used only for sperm transport; monophyodont. EXAMPLES: Egg-laying mammals; *Ornithorhynchus anatinus, Echidna.*

Subclass II. Theria. Mammary glands with nipples or teats; no cloaca (except pika); viviparous; eggs practically microscopic in size; testes usually in scrotum; penis for passage of both urine and spermatozoa; oviducts differentiated into Fallopian tubes, uterus, and vagina; pinna usually present; coracoid represented by a process on scapula. EXAMPLES: Marsupials and placental mammals.

Infraclass I. Metatheria

ORDER I. MARSUPIALIA. Young born in immature condition, further development usually in marsupium; usually no placental attachment; epipubic bones usually present; paired uteri and vaginae; a third vaginal canal often present; mammary glands provided with nipples; no cloaca; testes in scrotum; brain having corpus callosum for first time. Most species confined to Australia and surrounding islands. EXAMPLES: Marsupials; opossum, *Didelphis virginiana;* kangaroo, *Macropus.*

Infraclass II. Eutheria. Developing young nourished by means of an allantoic placenta; no marsupial pouch or epipubic bones; single vagina. EXAMPLES: The placental mammals.

Living eutherian, or placental, mammals are grouped in the following orders:

ORDER I. INSECTIVORA. Small size; elongated snouts; prism-shaped molar teeth; pentadactyl; insectivorous diet usually. EXAMPLES: Moles, shrews, hedgehogs.

ORDER II. DERMOPTERA. Patagium; webbed feet; nocturnal; arboreal; herbivorous. EXAMPLE: *Galeopithecus,* the flying lemur.

ORDER III. CHIROPTERA. Pentadactyl forelimbs modified to form wings used in flight; keeled sternum; nocturnal; diet primarily insectivorous and herbivorous. EXAMPLE: Bats.

ORDER IV. PRIMATES. Well-developed nervous system, particularly the cerebral portion; long pentadactyl limbs; eyes directed forward and completely encircled by bony orbits; thumb and big toe usually opposable; plantigrade foot posture; usually only one young at a birth. EXAMPLES: Lemurs, tarsiers, monkeys, apes, and man.

SUBORDER I. LEMUROIDEA. Long tails not prehensile; second digit of hind foot bearing claw, other digits bearing nails; thumb and hallux well developed; arboreal; crepuscular or nocturnal. EXAMPLE: Lemurs.

SUBORDER II. TARSIODEA. Elongated heel bone; small size; large protruding eyes and ears; second and third digits of hind foot bearing claws, nails on others; tails not prehensile; arboreal, nocturnal. EXAMPLE: Tarsiers.

SUBORDER III. ANTHROPOIDEA. Flattened or slightly rounded nails usually on all digits; arboreal or terrestrial; diurnal; tendency to upright posture; specialization of nervous system with highly developed, convoluted cerebral hemispheres. EXAMPLES: Monkeys, apes, and man.

Superfamily I. Ceboidea (Platyrhinii). Nostrils far apart and outwardly directed; tail may be prehensile; cheek pouches lacking. EXAMPLE: New World monkeys.

Family I. Hapalidae. Tail not prehensile; claws on all digits except large toe, which bears a nail; small size. EXAMPLE: Marmosets.

Family II. Cebidae. Long prehensile tails in some. EXAMPLES: Spider monkeys, howling monkeys, capuchins.

Superfamily II. Cercopithecoidea (Catarrhini).

Family I. Cercopithecidae. Narrow septum between nostrils; nostrils directed downward; tails never prehensile; most have cheek pouches; ischial callosities often highly colored. EXAMPLES: Old World monkeys, macaques, baboons, mandrills.

Superfamily III. Hominoidea. Lack tail and cheek pouches; narrow septum between nostrils; nostrils directed downward. EXAMPLES: Apes and man.

Family I. Pongidae. Manlike, anthropoid apes; tendency to walk upright. EXAMPLES: Gorilla, orangutan, gibbon, chimpanzee.

Family II. Hominidae. Great development of cerebral portion of brain; upright posture; generalized condition of skeleton. EXAMPLE: Man, *Homo sapiens.*

ORDER V. EDENTATA. Adults lacking teeth or having only poorly developed molar teeth. EXAMPLES: South American anteater, sloths, armadillos.

ORDER VI. PHOLIDOTA. Body covered with large, overlapping, horny scales with a few hairs interspersed; teeth lacking. EXAMPLE: Scaly anteater, *Manis.*

ORDER VII. RODENTIA. Two incisor teeth on both upper and lower jaws, used for gnawing, grow throughout life; canine teeth lacking; diastema between incisors and premolars; foot posture plantigrade or approximately so; claws. EXAMPLES: Rats, mice, squirrels, beavers, gophers, capybara.

ORDER VIII. LAGOMORPHA. Four incisor teeth in upper jaw, one pair behind the other, grow continuously; canine teeth lacking; tails short and stubby. Pikas are the only members of the subclass Theria to have a cloaca in the adult. EXAMPLES: Rabbits, hares, pikas.

ORDER IX. CARNIVORA. Three pairs of small incisor teeth in both jaws; canine teeth well developed; flesh-eating mammals; poorly developed clavicles, sometimes absent; mobility of limbs; bipartite uterus; zonary type of placenta.

SUBORDER I. FISSIPEDIA. Toes separated. EXAMPLES: Cats, dogs, weasels, martens.

SUBORDER II. PINNIPEDIA. Aquatic carnivores; toes webbed; appendages in form of flippers; males larger than females; short tail. EXAMPLES: Seals, walrus, sea lions.

ORDER X. CETACEA. Pectoral appendages webbed to form flippers;

no claws; pelvic appendages lacking; tail (flukes) flattened dorsoventrally and notched; males with intra-abdominal testes; nasal openings on top of head; homodont dentition in toothed forms. EXAMPLES: Whales, dolphins, porpoises.

ORDER XI. TUBULIDENTATA. Thick-set body; large, pointed ears; long snout; thick skin; scanty hair covering; few permanent teeth; those present lacking enamel; no incisors or canines; very long claws; plantigrade foot posture. EXAMPLE: Aardvark.

ORDER XII. PROBOSCIDEA. Great size; massive legs; nose and upper lip form proboscis, or trunk, with nostrils at tip; upper incisor teeth are tusks; thick skin with scant hairy coat; males with intra-abdominal testes. EXAMPLE: Elephants.

ORDER XIII. HYRACOIDEA. Somewhat resemble guinea pigs in size and shape; more closely related to ungulates; small ears; short tail; persistent growth of upper incisor teeth; four toes on forefeet; three toes on hind feet; second toe on hind feet bearing claw, the rest being hooflike nails; males with intra-abdominal testes; canine teeth lacking. EXAMPLE: Conies.

ORDER XIV. SIRENIA. Herbivorous, aquatic forms; heavy dense bones; forelimbs in the form of flippers; hindlimbs lacking; tail bearing horizontally arranged flukes which are not notched; no external ears; skin sparsely haired; males with intra-abdominal testes. EXAMPLES: Manatees and dugongs.

ORDER XV. PERISSODACTYLA. Odd-toed, hoofed forms; unguligrade foot posture; axis of leg passes through middle toe; herbivorous; gall bladder lacking. EXAMPLES: Horses, donkeys, zebras, tapirs.

ORDER XVI. ARTIODACTYLA. Even-toed, hoofed forms; unguligrade foot posture; axis of leg passing between third and fourth toes; herbivorous; true horns or antlers only in this group; incisors and canines of upper jaw usually absent (except in pigs). EXAMPLES: Cattle, pigs, hippopotami, camels, deer.

INDEX

Numbers in **boldface** type indicate pages on which a term appears in an illustration. Words in italics refer to the scientific names of animals. Structures coming under the following categories are not listed separately but are to be found under Arteries, Bones, Cartilages, Muscles, Nerves, and Veins.

A

Aardvark, 46, 49, 286, 650, 856
Abdominal pores, 263, 272, 273, 694
Abdominal respiration, 230
Aberrant ductules, 308
Abomasum, **169**
Acanthodian sharks, 439, **440**
Accessory sex organs, 263, 334, 341, 342, 344, 345, 348, 830
Accommodation, 596, 624, 632, 640
Acetabulum, **387, 390,** 443, 445, **778**
Acetylcholine, 85, 603, 609
Acid-secreting cells, 171
Acidosis, 339, 340
Acinous glands, 101
Acipenser (*see* Sturgeon)
Acoelous vertebrae, **385, 388,** 392
Acoustic ganglion, 598
Acousticolateralis area, 570
Acousticolateralis system, 592–593, 598, 678
Acrania, 11, 48, 846
Acrochordal bar, **395**
Acrodont dentition, **156**–158, 702
Acromegaly, 356, 372
Acromion, 776
ACTH (adrenocorticotropic hormone), 336, 357
ACTH-hypophysiotropic hormone, 357, 575
Adam's apple, 219
Adaptive radiations, **20,** 21, 185
Addison's disease, 334, 336
Adenohypophysis, 353, 358
Adenoids, 236, 547
Adipose tissue, 73, **74,** 89, **91,** 109
Adiposogenital dystrophy, 609
Adneural gland, **13,** 14, 358, 503
Adrenal cortex, 65, 109, 330, 332, **333,** 335, 336, 346, 357, 833
Adrenal gland, 62, 65, 97, 330–337, 606, 709, 833
Adrenal medulla, 62, 330, 332, **333,** 334, 606, 833
Adrenalin (*see* Epinephrine)
Adrenergic fibers, 603
Adrenocorticoids, 335, 336, 357, 363

Adrenocorticotropic hormone (ACTH), 336, 357
Adrenosterone, 334, 335
Aerobic respiration, 187
Afferent nerve fibers, 566, 583
Aftershaft, **123**–125
Age of Reptiles, 28, 29
Age involution, 235
Aglomerular kidneys, 247, 258
Aglossa, 149, 413
Agnatha, 17, 48, 847
Air bladder (*see* Swim bladder)
Air capillaries, 224
Air sacs, 224, 225, 297
Albinos, 94, 628
Albula, 510
Alecithal eggs, 50, 52
Algesireceptors, 621, 673, 675
Alimentary canal (*see* Digestive tract)
Alkaline reserve, 340
Allantoic circulation, 541
Allantoic ducts, **226**
Allantoic placenta, 362
Allantoic stalk, 829
Allantois, 27, 64, 73, 231, 254, 531
Alligator, characteristics, 32, 33, 852
classification, 28, 32, 49
glands, oral, 148
oviducal, 278
heart, 514
oviducts, 278
scales, 117
skin, 120
sound production, 218
vertebrae, 389
Alloxan, 339
Alpaca, 657
Alveolar ducts, **226**
Alveolar glands, 101
Alveolar sacs, 223, 226
Alveolus, lung, 223, **226, 828**
mammary gland, 109
swim bladder, **213**
teeth, 160
Alytes obstetricans, 277
Ambystoma jeffersonianum, **448**
opacum, **27,** 342
texanum, **190, 320, 322,** 342
tigrinum, 206, 525
Ameiurus, 535
Ameloblasts, 155

Amia, 22, 48, 113, 173, 202, **209,** 210, 247, 384, **400,** 407, 849
Amino acids, 177, 183, 497
Ammocoetes, 18, 265, 684
endostyle, 321
eyes, 640, 691
gall bladder, 180
hermaphroditism, 315
metamorphosis, 18
olfactory sac, 663
pericardial cavity, 509
respiratory system, 197
Amniocardiac vesicle, **507**
Amnion, 27
Amniota, definition, 27
Amorphous ground substance, 70–72, 368
Amphibians, aortic arches, 205, 522–525
archinephric duct, 242, 248
bladder, urinary, 174, 178, 249, 250
carotid body, 237
caudate (*see* Caudates)
cerebellum, 570
cerebral hemispheres, 577
characteristics, 25, 26, 850
chromatophores, 72, 94, 97, 354
classification, 25–27, 49
cloaca, 144, 174, 249
copulatory organs, 310
cranial nerves, 569
dermal musculature, 490
ear, 236, 655, 657, 660
eggs, 25, 50, 51
esophagus, 164
evolutionary origin, 23
eyes, 643–646
fertilization, 276
gastralia, 430
gills, 204, 205
girdles and limbs, 447–450
glands, adrenal, 331
Harderian, 639
integumentary, 99, 103
intermaxillary, 147
internasal, 147
lacrimal, 639
lingual, 147
mouth, 147
mucous, 101
oral, 147

857